TRANSLATIONS
OF
MATHEMATICAL
MONOGRAPHS

VOLUME 17

EXPANSIONS IN EIGENFUNCTIONS OF SELFADJOINT OPERATORS

BY Iurii Makarovich

JU. M. BEREZANSKIĬ

american mathematical society
providence, rhode island
1968

РАЗЛОЖЕНИЕ ПО СОБСТВЕННЫМ ФУНКЦИЯМ САМОСОПРЯЖЕННЫХ ОПЕРАТОРОВ

Ю. М. БЕРЕЗАНСКИЙ

Академия Наук
Украинской ССР
Институт Математики

Издательство „Наукова Думка"
Киев — 1965

Translated from the Russian by
R. Bolstein, J. M. Danskin, J. Rovnyak, L. Shulman

Library of Congress Card No. 67-22347

Printed in the United States of America

PREFACE

The subject of this book is the application of the general theory of selfadjoint operators to spectral problems for differential and difference equations. Developments in this field have been very rapid in recent years and now those mathematicians who are inclined to make categorical judgements may say (and in fact do say) that the subject has been brought to completion, a judgement in which there is some truth. Nevertheless, there are no books in existence in which the relevant questions are discussed in any complete way. More precisely, the spectral theory of selfadjoint ordinary differential and difference equations in the spaces L_2 and l_2 are discussed, from the point of view of the theory of operators, in the books of M. A. Naĭmark [2] and N. I. Ahiezer [2] and also in the recently published second volume of the book by Dunford and Schwartz [2]. On the other hand, the analogous questions for partial differential equations are dealt with in only one chapter of the book of Gel'fand and Šilov [3], in one chapter of the book by Dunford and Schwartz, and in certain sections of the book by K. Maurin, "Hilbert space methods", which is soon to be published in a Russian translation. The author of the present book has tried to fill this gap.

It is impossible to present the spectral theory of partial differential equations, either in form or in substance, without introducing the present-day theory of boundary problems (preferably by the methods of functional analysis). Unfortunately, the author was not able to refer to any books of this sort, since they did not exist, and it was necessary for him to develop a number of questions himself in the theory of boundary problems. Now the situation has changed; the book of Hörmander on general equations [4] has appeared, and in the USSR the book of Ladyženskaja and Ural'ceva on elliptic equations of second order will soon appear, and also the general survey of Agranovič in "Uspehi Matematičeskih Nauk" on general elliptic equations.[1)] However, it is to be hoped that the

---

1) Translator's note. These works are: 1) O. A. Ladyženskaja and N. N. Ural'ceva, *Linear and quasilinear elliptic differential equations*, "Nauka", Moscow, 1964; English transl., Scripta Technica, New York (to appear); 2) M. S. Agranovič, *Elliptic singular integro-differential operators*, Uspehi Mat. Nauk 20 (1965), no. 5, 3–120 = Russian Math. Surveys 20 (1965), nos. 5/6, 1–121.

sections of the present book dealing with boundary problems will be useful for mathematicians interested only in boundary problems, all the more because these sections are written independently of the discussion of spectral questions. In general, the title of the present book should perhaps have read not only "Expansion in eigenfunctions of selfadjoint operators" but also "Boundary problems", since the latter occupy one-third of its pages.

Let us give a brief outline of the contents of the book.

The discussion is based on generalized functions of *finite* order, since it is precisely such generalized functions that are suitable in a theory of boundary problems and in questions in which it is not necessary to consider differential operators as acting continuously in one and the same space. The theory of these generalized functions is presented in the first chapter.

The smaller second chapter takes up the general framework and concepts of the theory of boundary problems, whereas the third chapter presents a rather detailed discussion of elliptic equations. In the third chapter our chief attention is turned to questions of the smoothness of generalized solutions of elliptic equations both in the interior of the domain and also up to and including its boundary. It is precisely these facts that are necessary for the construction of expansions in eigenfunctions. The fourth chapter is only slightly related to spectral theory; it contains some "nonelliptic" examples in the framework of the second chapter.

The fifth chapter is concerned with the general theory of expansions in eigenvectors (generalized and ordinary). Here we discuss their construction by means of generalized functions of finite order, and only touch on the question how these constructions enable us to set up the framework for expansions by introducing linear topological spaces, and this framework itself is left without detailed investigation. The latter fact is explained not only by the personal interests of the author, but also by the general character of the book and by the indispensability of these constructions for setting up expansions in eigenfunctions of differential operators considered together with their boundary conditions. In the sixth chapter we discuss expansions in eigenfunctions of selfadjoint partial differential operators in the space L_2, dealing particularly with elliptic operators. For these latter operators we prove the existence of expansions up to and including the boundary of the domain. The case of ordinary differential operators is not discussed in detail, the situation for them being described only briefly in the last section of the chapter. The seventh chapter deals with the spectral theory of selfadjoint difference operators in the space l_2. The first section contains the classical theory of Jacobian matrices, and against this background we then construct the theory of expansions for equations with operator coefficients and partial differences. In the eighth and last chapter we construct the theory of selfadjoint operators (differential and difference) acting in a space with a scalar product generated by a positive-definite kernel. The foundations for this theory were laid in the work of M. G. Kreĭn on integral representations for positive-definite functions by means of the eigenfunctions of ordinary differential operators. In the present chapter this work is presented from various points of view.

Let us emphasize that several of the topics traditional in spectral theory are not considered here; for example, localization of the spectrum, asymptotic behavior of the spectral function and so forth.

Prerequisite for reading the book is a knowledge of the basic theory of operators in Hilbert space, as it is to be found e. g. in the book of N. I. Ahiezer and I. M. Glazman [1], and with the elements of the theory of partial differential equations. It would also be useful to be acquainted with the first few sections of the book of I. M. Gel'fand and G. E. Šilov [1]. In order to make the present book easier to read the author has sometimes not discussed the most general constructions, or else he has introduced them step by step, particularly if they are somewhat cumbersome. But in other cases the general constructions are introduced first, and then particular examples are discussed.

The parts of the book in small print[1)] may be omitted in first reading. The detailed table of contents will serve for the better orientation of the reader. The formulas are numbered independently in each chapter. With few exceptions, the

---

1) Translator's note. For technical reasons we cannot use small type in this edition. The passages appearing in small type in the original are the following: Chapter I, §1. 5 and the statement and proof of Theorems 3. 2 and 3. 6; Chapter II, §§2. 4, 3. 1, 3. 8, and the statement and proof of Theorem 1. 1; Chapter III, §2. 2, the proofs of Theorems 3. 3 and 4. 3, and the whole of §6; and Chapter IV in its entirety. None of Chapter V is in small type; small type is used in Chapter VI for §§1. 6 and 3. 4, for the statement and proof of Theorems 2. 4 and 2. 7, for the ends of §§2. 9 (from equation (2. 72) on), 3. 2 (from Lemma 3. 2), 4. 4 (from equation (4. 42)), and for the passage from equation (2. 86) through Theorem 2. 10. Also Chapter VII, §1. 9 and the proof of Theorem 2. 6; Chapter VIII, §§1. 4, 3. 8 and 3. 9, the statement of Theorem 2. 8, the ends of §§3. 2 (from Theorem 3. 3 on), 4. 4 (from the end of the proof of Theorem 4. 6) and 5. 1 (from the end of Theorem 5. 1), and the whole of §6. There are also small-type passages of a paragraph or two here and there that we have not bothered to list.

references are assembled in the "Notes on the Literature" at the end of the book. Here it should be emphasized that the greatest influence on the contents of the book (as well as on the work of the author in general) has been exercised by S. L. Sobolev, S. G. Kreĭn (Chapters I–IV, the "boundary" part) and M. G. Kreĭn, I. M. Gel′fand and A. Ja. Povzner (Chapters V–VIII, the "spectral" part).

M. G. Kreĭn and S. G. Kreĭn have examined the individual chapters and given valuable advice. In the preparation of the manuscript I have received assistence from my colleagues and students. Thus §§5–6 of Chapter III were written in collaboration with Ja. A. Roĭtberg, §§1.5 and 1.6 of Chapter IV with L. P. Nižnik, and §§5.1–5.3 of Chapter VII with N. N. Čaus. Individual sections of the book were examined by G. I. Kac, V. I. Gorbačuk, M. L. Gorbačuk and Ju. B. Oročko, who made some corrections. The entire book was read through and edited from a mathematical point of view by E. G. Šeftel′.

To all these mathematicians I express my profound gratitude.

September 1964 *Ju. M. Berezanskiĭ*

TABLE OF CONTENTS

INTRODUCTION

The purpose of this introduction is to describe the range of ideas on which the book is based and, in addition, to give a precise definition of the terminology in cases where usage has varied. It is assumed here that the reader is more familiar with the fundamentals of functional analysis than with differential equations. Therefore, the corresponding questions on functional analysis and the theory of functions are only recalled or indicated, whereas the questions connected with differential equations (the theory of Sobolev spaces, for instance) are treated in more detail. Throughout the book references are given either to the Introduction if the corresponding question is dealt with there in sufficient detail, or to other books.

§1. TOPOLOGICAL NOTIONS

In what follows we will employ the usual notation of set theory: $\in$, $\bar{\in}$, $\subseteq$, $\subset$, $\cup, \cap, \setminus, \times$. In addition, we will write $A \subseteq B$ if each $x \in A$ is contained in B, and $A \subset B$ if $A \subseteq B$ and if B has an element which is not an element of A ("A is properly contained in B").

We will sometimes denote by $\{x_1, x_2, \cdots\}$, $\{x_j\}$, $j = 1, 2, \cdots$ or $\{x_\alpha, \alpha \in A\}$, the set consisting of the elements $x_1, x_2, \cdots$ or x_α, $\alpha \in A$. The empty set is denoted by 0.

By a topological space we mean a set Q with a system Σ of subsets $U, V, \cdots$ ("basic neighborhoods"), where every $U \in \Sigma$ is called a neighborhood of an arbitrary point $X \in U$ and the following axioms are required: 1) if $x, y \in Q$ and $x \neq y$, then there is always a neighborhood of the point x which does not contain y ("separation axiom"); 2) if $x \in Q$ and U, V are two neighborhoods of x, then there is always a third neighborhood $W \subseteq U \cap V$ of x.

If $A \subseteq Q$, the closure of A is the set of all $x \in Q$ with the property that every neighborhood of x contains at least one point of A. We will always denote this set by $\overline{A}$. The same notation will be used to denote the set of conjugate vectors $\overline{A}$ of a set of vectors A (see §3 below). The meaning of $\overline{A}$ is usually clear from context.

A set $F \subseteq Q$ for which $\overline{F} = F$ is said to be closed. If $O \subseteq Q$ and $Q \setminus O$ is closed, then O is open. It is clear that every neighborhood is open. If $A \subseteq Q$ is such that $\overline{A} = Q$, then A is said to be everywhere dense in Q. The points of

$\bar{A}\setminus A$ are called limit points of A.

The basic neighborhoods Σ define a topology on the abstract set Q. Obviously, two different bases Σ' and Σ'' may sometimes define the same topology on Q. This means that for any $A \subseteq Q$, the closures of A relative to Σ' and to Σ'' are identical. There is a well-known criterion for Σ' and Σ'' to define the same topology on Q. We omit this criterion and mention only the following fact. Suppose Q is a topological space with a basis Σ. If we extend the notion of a neighborhood of the point x to include any open set of Q which contains x, it is easy to see that this extended neighborhood system defines the original topology on Q. By a neighborhood of a set $A \subseteq Q$ we will mean any open set in Q which contains A.

If R is any set of a topological space Q with basis Σ, then R itself may be converted into a topological space by taking the sets $U \cap R$, $U \subseteq \Sigma$ as a basis for R. The topology so introduced is called the relative topology on R; this is the topology induced on R by Q. It is easy to verify that $A \subseteq R$ is open (closed) in the relative topology if and only if $A = B \cap R$ where B is open (closed) in Q.

Let Q' and Q'' be two topological spaces. If $x'' = f(x')$ is a given function where x' is an arbitrary element of Q' and x'' ranges over some set $\mathfrak{R}(f) \subseteq Q''$, then a transformation of all of Q' into Q'' is said to take place. The operator f: $Q' \to Q''$ is also called a transformation acting on all of Q' and taking values in its range $\mathfrak{R}(f) \subseteq Q''$. If $\mathfrak{R}(f) = Q''$, then the transformation is said to be onto Q''. If the function $x'' = f(x')$ is defined only on the set $\mathfrak{D}(f)$ in Q', then the transformation is said to have domain $\mathfrak{D}(f)$. If $x'' = f(x')$ is defined in a one to one fashion from $\mathfrak{D}(f)$ onto all of $\mathfrak{R}(f)$, then an inverse f^{-1} exists which takes x'' into x'; $\mathfrak{D}(f^{-1}) = \mathfrak{R}(f)$, $\mathfrak{R}(f^{-1}) = \mathfrak{D}(f)$. We will also use the notation $f(\cdot)$ with the "unwritten variable x'."

The notion of continuity of the transformation f, from Q' to Q'', at the point $x_0' \in Q'$ is well known. If the transformation is continuous at each point $x_0' \in \mathfrak{D}(f) \subseteq Q'$, then f is said to be continuous on its domain $\mathfrak{D}(f)$ (on Q' when $\mathfrak{D}(f) = Q'$). If f takes Q' onto Q'' in a one to one fashion, where f and f^{-1} are each continuous, then f is called a homeomorphism between Q' and Q''.

For f, Q' and Q'' as above the notation $x' \to x'' = f(x')$, f: $Q' \to Q''$ or f: $\mathfrak{D}(f) \to \mathfrak{R}(f)$ is also used.

Let Q' and Q'' again be two topological spaces. A topological inclusion $Q' \subseteq Q''$ is said to occur if $Q' \subseteq Q''$ when these are considered as sets and if for every $A \subseteq Q'$, the closure of A constructed relative to the topology of Q' is contained in the closure of A constructed relative to the topology of Q''.

Let $Q' \subseteq Q''$ (here the inclusion may be nontopological). The inclusion operator O is that operator which assigns to each x' in Q' the same element x' of Q''. Obviously, the topological inclusion $Q' \subseteq Q''$, is equivalent to the continuity of O.

In what follows, we will consider only topological spaces for which there is a countable basis of neighborhoods. For these the topology may be given with the help of convergence of sequences: with the usual notion of $\lim_{n\to\infty} x_n = x (x, x_n \in Q)$ it turns out that $x \in \bar{A}$ if and only if there is a sequence $x_n \in A$ such that $x = \lim x_n$.

We recall some properties of metric spaces. Let Q be some set provided with a function $\rho(x, y)$ $(x, y \in Q)$ on $Q \times Q$, satisfying the following:

1) $\rho(x, y) \geq 0$ $(x, y \in Q)$, $\rho(x, y) = 0$ if and only if $x = y$;

2) $\rho(x, y) = \rho(y, x)$ $(x, y \in Q)$;

3) $\rho(x, y) \leq \rho(x, z) + \rho(z, y)$ $(x, y, z \in Q)$.

The set Q with such a function $\rho(x, y)$ (the "distance" between x and y), is called a metric space. The open ball $U_r(a)$, in this space, with center at the point a and radius $r > 0$ is the set of all $x \in Q$ for which $\rho(x, a) < r$. If $\rho(x, a) = r$ then this point, by definition, belongs to the corresponding sphere $K_r(a)$. The closure of the ball $U_r(a)$ is defined to be $U_r(a) \cup K_r(a)$ (this will be seen to be the natural definition). A subset of Q is called bounded if it is contained in some ball. A complex function on Q is called locally bounded if it is bounded on every ball.

A metric space may be converted into a topological space by using the aggregate of all possible spheres for a system of basic neighborhoods; it is easy to see that requirements 1) and 2) in the definition of a topological space are satisfied. Also, it is clear that a metric space has a countable basis if and only if there is a countable dense set for the space. If such a set exists for a topological space or a metric space, the space is called separable. From now on we will consider separable metric spaces only. Finally we note that $x = \lim_{n\to\infty} x_n$ is equivalent to the statement that $\rho(x_n, x) \to 0$ as $n \to \infty$.

A simple construction shows that the separation axiom may be stated in a stronger form in a metric space: if F_1 and F_2 are two closed and disjoint subsets of Q it is always possible to find disjoint neighborhoods of these sets, i.e., two disjoint open sets U_1, U_2 such that $F_1 \subset U_1$ and $F_2 \subset U_2$. A topological space with this property is called normal. If the above condition is satisfied whenever F_1 consists of a single point $(F_1 = \{x\})$, then the topological space is called regular. If the condition is known to be satisfied when $F_1 = \{x\}$ and $F_2 = \{y\}$ $(x \neq y)$, then the space is called Hausdorff. A regular topological space with a countable basis is known to be metrizable i.e., a metric may be introduced so that the topology induced by this metric is the same as the original topology.

Let Q be a metric space; a sequence $x_1, x_2, \cdots \in Q$ is called fundamental if $\rho(x_n, x_m) \to 0$ as $n, m \to \infty$. The space Q is called complete if every fundamental sequence converges to some point in the space. By the usual diagonalization procedure every metric space may be completed, i.e., there is a complete metric space $\tilde{Q}$ such that Q is everywhere dense in $\tilde{Q}$ and the metric of $\tilde{Q}$ agrees with that of Q on Q. In what follows, unless otherwise stated, by a metric space we will always mean a complete metric space.

The distance between the sets $A, B \subseteq Q$ is defined to be the number

$$\varrho(A, B) = \inf_{x \in A,\, y \in B} \varrho(x, y).$$

Let Q be a general topological space (in the sense of the definition on page 1). A set $F \subseteq Q$ is called compact if a finite subcovering of F may be chosen from any open covering of F, i.e., from each system of neighborhoods. $\{U_\alpha, \alpha \in A\}$ such that $\bigcup_{\alpha \in A} U_\alpha \supset F$, a finite system may be chosen having the same property. If $\bar{F}$ is compact then F is called precompact. It is easy to verify that a compact subset of a Hausdorff space is always closed.

Suppose Q itself is compact and Hausdorff. Then every closed subset F of Q will be compact and consequently F will be regular. So if Q is, in addition, assumed to have a countable basis, then Q is necessarily a metric space. Since we have stipulated that all spaces considered have a countable basis, in what follows a compact space will always be understood to be a metric space.

Let Q be a complete separable metric space. Such a space is called locally compact if every closed ball in Q is compact. A locally compact space Q may always be imbedded in a compact one, "by adjoining the point at ∞," i.e., by introducing the formal point ∞ and considering the set $Q \cup \infty$ in which the neighborhoods of $x \neq \infty$ are those of Q, and the neighborhoods of ∞ are the sets of the form $Q \setminus F$ where F is compact. Finally we note that in a metric space, compactness of a set F is equivalent to the statement that from every sequence $x_1, x_2, \cdots$ in F a convergent subsequence may be chosen with a limit in F. Precompactness of F then means that this limit point need not belong to F.

We proceed to the consideration of the real, n-dimensional Euclidean spaces E_n, consisting of points $x = (x_1, \cdots, x_n)$ $(n = 1, 2, \cdots)$. By a region $G \subseteq E_n$ we will mean an open set in E_n. Bounded and unbounded regions are considered. The set $\Gamma = \overline{G}\setminus G$ is called the boundary of the region G. We will only consider regions with "nice" boundaries. We will say that the boundary Γ is in the class C^m $(m = 0, 1, \cdots)$ (or is m times continuously differentiable) if for each point $x_0 \in \Gamma$, there is a sphere $U_\epsilon(x_0)$ so small that the set $\Gamma \cap U_\epsilon(x_0)$ may be given by an equation of the form $x_j = f(x_1, \cdots, x_{j-1}, x_{j+1}, \cdots, x_n)$, where $1 \leq j \leq n$ and $f(\cdot)$ is an m times continuously differentiable function of the point $(x_1, \cdots, x_{j-1}, x_{j+1}, \cdots, x_n)$ $(C_0 = C)$. General surfaces of class C^m are defined analogously. Also clear are the analogous definitions with $m = \infty$.

Let G be an arbitrary region with boundary Γ of class C. A piece γ of the boundary Γ (or a piece γ on Γ) is the set $\gamma \subseteq \Gamma$ which is open in the relative topology on Γ induced by the topology on E_n. We will say that the boundary Γ is piecewise m times continuously differentiable if Γ is equal to the closure of $\bigcup_j \Gamma_j$ where each Γ_j is a piece of Γ with an associated surface of class C^m. In addition $\bigcup_j \Gamma_j$ consists of only a finite or countable number of terms, where in the the countable case every ball in E_n has a nonempty intersection with at most a finite number of the Γ_j.

To simplify formulations in the entire book, we will not make any particular effort to minimize the smoothness required of the boundary of a given region. In this connection we make the following definition: we will say that a region G has a piecewise smooth boundary y if it has an m times piecewise continuously differentiable boundary for some $m = 1, 2, \cdots$ the exact value of which is left to the reader. Aside from this we also exclude "cusped" and other bad vertices, i.e., along with the indicated definition of m times continuous differentiability of the boundary, we will make the following requirement. If Γ_j and Γ_k are two adjacent pieces of Γ and if $\nu(x)$ and $\nu(y)$ are unit vectors corresponding to the points $x \in \Gamma_j$, $y \in \Gamma_k$ which are normal to these respective pieces, then it must not be the case that the directed vectors $\nu(x)$ and $\nu(y)$ tend to coincide for x near y.

In addition, the terms "sufficiently smooth boundary Γ" (i.e., Γ of class C^m for sufficiently large m), "sufficiently smooth surface," "piecewise smooth surface," "sufficiently smooth piece of Γ," "piece of a surface, " and "piecewise smooth surface," will be used. When speaking of a piece γ of the boundary Γ, we will always assume that the boundary of this piece (relative to Γ) is piecewise smooth (to pass to the relative topology on Γ, apply the usual topology of

E_{n-1} after "flattening" Γ locally by means of sufficiently smooth homeomorphisms on the neighborhoods of Γ_j). We also note that the normal vector to a sufficiently smooth surface S at the point $x \in S$ will always be denoted $\nu(x)$. If S is a piece of the boundary of a region G, then $\nu(x)$ will always denote the exterior normal. Finally, we will always write $G \cup \Gamma$ in place of $\overline{G}$. If the set $A \subset G$ is such that $\rho(A, \Gamma) > 0$, we will say that A lies strictly inside G. If A is compact and $A \subseteq G$, then, of course, A lies strictly inside G.

§2. INTEGRATION

Aside from the ordinary integration on an n-dimensional space or on a sufficiently smooth piece of a surface, we will often encounter integrals with respect to abstract measures. We recall the relevant definitions.

We consider an abstract set Q which for convenience will now be called a space. A family of sets $\mathfrak{R}$ of Q is called a ring if $A \setminus B \in R$ and $A \cup B \in R$ whenever $A, B \in R$. Since $A \cap B = (A \cup B) \setminus [((A \cup B) \setminus A) \cup ((A \cup B) \setminus B)]$, therefore $A \cap B$ also belongs to $\mathfrak{R}$. A ring $\mathfrak{R}$ is said to be closed, or is called a σ-ring, if $\bigcup_{j=1}^{\infty} A_j \in \mathfrak{R}$ whenever $A_1, A_2, \cdots \in \mathfrak{R}$. It is easy to show that $\bigcap_{j=1}^{\infty} A_j$ also belongs to $\mathfrak{R}$ in this case.

Let Q be a given space, and $\mathfrak{R}$ be a ring of subsets of Q. A function $\mu(\Delta)$ $(\Delta \in \mathfrak{R})$ is called a measure if $0 \leq \mu(\Delta) \leq \infty$ $(\Delta \in \mathfrak{R})$, if $\mu(0) = 0$ (0 denotes the empty set) and if the following complete additivity condition is satisfied: if $\Delta_1, \Delta_2, \cdots$ are in $\mathfrak{R}$ and are pairwise disjoint and if $\bigcup_{j=1}^{\infty} \Delta_j \in \mathfrak{R}$, then $\mu(\bigcup_{j=1}^{\infty} \Delta_j) = \sum_{j=1}^{\infty} \mu(\Delta_j)$. Moreover, we will always assume that μ is locally finite (or locally bounded), i.e. there exists a sequence of sets $Q_1, Q_2, \cdots \in \mathfrak{R}$ such that $Q_1 \subseteq Q_2 \subseteq \cdots$, $Q = \bigcup_{j=1}^{\infty} Q_j$ and $\mu(Q_j) < \infty$ $(j = 1, 2, \cdots)$. The measure μ is said to be finite if $Q \in \mathfrak{R}$ and $\mu(Q) < \infty$.

If $\mathfrak{R}$ is a given σ-ring and μ is a measure on the sets of $\mathfrak{R}$, then the notions of measurable function, integral, summability etc., may be introduced in the usual way, with the Lebesgue measurable sets replaced by those of $\mathfrak{R}$. We will denote the integrals in the usual way:

$$\int_A f(x)\, d\mu(x), \qquad \int_A f d\mu \quad (A \in \mathfrak{R}).$$

We recall that a set $A \in \mathfrak{R}$ is said to be of full measure whenever $Q \in \mathfrak{R}$ and $\mu(Q \setminus A) = 0$. In order to construct an integration theory relative to a measure μ on a nonclosed ring $\mathfrak{R}$, the measure must be extended to some σ-ring. Namely, a closed ring $\widetilde{\mathfrak{R}} \supset \mathfrak{R}$ of sets of Q must be constructed and a measure $\widetilde{\mu}$ on $\widetilde{\mathfrak{R}}$ such that $\tilde{\mu}(\Delta) = \mu(\Delta)$ whenever $\Delta \in \Re$. The procedure for constructing $\tilde{\Re}$ is well known: this ring may be taken to be the collection of all sets of Q which are measurable relative to the measure μ and the measure $\tilde{\mu}$ may be taken to be the exterior measure defined by μ on these sets (this turns out to be additive on $\tilde{\Re}$). We agree in what follows to consider only locally finite measures, i.e., measures μ on a ring $\Re$ such that $Q_1, Q_2, \cdots$ exist as above.

We recall the notion of a generalized measure. If μ_1 and μ_2 are given measures on $\Re$ and if the set function $\omega(\Delta) = \mu_1(\Delta) - \mu_2(\Delta)$ is considered for $\Delta \in \Re$ such that $\omega(\Delta)$ makes sense, then $\omega(\Delta)$ is called a generalized measure. Its variation on the set Δ is defined to be the number

$$\operatorname*{Var}_{\Delta} \omega = \sup \sum_{j=1}^{n} |\omega(\Delta_j)|, \tag{1}$$

where the sup is taken over all finite disjoint unions $\Delta_j \in \Re$ such that $\bigcup_{j=1}^{n} \Delta_j \subseteq \Delta$. It is possible to show that $\nu(\Delta) = \mathrm{Var}_\Delta \omega$, after the natural extension to all of $\Re$ $(\nu(\Delta) = \lim_{j\to\infty} \nu(\Delta \cap Q_j)$ $\Delta \in \Re)$, is an ordinary locally finite real valued measure such that $\nu(\Delta) = \mathrm{Var}_\Delta \omega \leq \mu_1(\Delta) + \mu_2(\Delta)$ $(\Delta \in \Re)$. If ω_1 and ω_2 are two generalized real-valued measures, then $\omega(\Delta) = \omega_1(\Delta) + i\omega_2(\Delta)$ is a generalized (complex valued) measure. The variation of $\omega(\Delta)$ is introduced analogously to (1).

The Radon-Nikodym theorem plays an important role in what follows. We review its formulation here.

Let ω be a generalized measure and μ an ordinary one on a closed ring $\Re$. The measure ω is said to be absolutely continuous with respect to μ if $\omega(\Delta) = 0$ whenever $\mu(\Delta) = 0$ $(\Delta \in \Re)$.

The Radon-Nikodym theorem asserts the following.

For ω to be absolutely continuous with respect to μ, it is necessary and sufficient that there exist some function $\Omega(x)$ defined on Q and summable on each Q_j $(j = 1, 2, \cdots)$ such that

$$\omega(\Delta) = \int_{\Delta} \Omega(x)\, d\mu(x) \qquad (\Delta \in \Re). \tag{2}$$

The function $\Omega(x)$ is defined uniquely by ω and μ except for sets of μ-measure zero. In addition, we have

$$\operatorname*{Var}_{\Delta} \omega = \int_{\Delta} |\Omega(x)|\, d\mu(x) \qquad (\Delta \in \Re).$$

If μ' and μ'' are given measures on the spaces Q' and Q'', the well-known definition of the product measure $\mu'\mu''$ on $Q' \times Q''$ is given by first defining $\mu'\mu''$ on the rectangles $E' \times E''$: $\mu'\mu''(E' \times E'') = \mu'(E')\mu''(E'')$ $(E' \subseteq Q', E'' \subseteq Q'')$. Along with the notation $\mu'\mu''$ we will also make use of the notation $d\mu' d\mu''$.

So far we have not assumed that Q is a topological space. If we now make this assumption, the problem arises of finding a σ-ring $\mathfrak{R}$ so that every continuous function on Q is measurable. It is easy to verify that for this to be the case, $\mathfrak{R}$ must be the closed ring of all the Borel sets on Q, i.e., the σ-ring generated by the open and closed sets of Q. Frequently, when speaking of a measure defined on the sets of a topological space we only consider it to be given on the Borel sets, and we are not interested in its extension to all of the measurable sets. We will often consider Borel measurable functions, i.e., those which are measurable with respect to the ring of Borel sets. When the meaning is clear from context, the term measurable is often used in place of Borel measurable.

In what follows, we will only consider measures given on the Borel sets of a metric space Q where the role of the Q_j is played by a set of balls of the form $U_j(x_0)$ with centers $j = 1, 2, \cdots$.

For measures on the space E_n, some more detailed results may be obtained. We note only the following. There exists a sequence of partitions of E_n into half closed rectangles of the form $[a_1, b_1) \times \cdots \times [a_n, b_n)$, $(-\infty < a_j < b_j < \infty;\ j = 1, \cdots, n)$, the diameters of which tend to zero, such that the formula

$$\Omega(x) = \lim_{\Delta_\nu \to x} \frac{\omega(\Delta_\nu)}{\mu(\Delta_\nu)}. \tag{3}$$

holds for μ-almost all x (i.e., for all x except possibly some set of μ-measure zero). Here Δ_ν is a sequence of rectangles taken from the above partitions which tend to the point $x \in \Delta_\nu$; the measures μ and ω are given on the bounded Borel sets.

Finally we recall that any nondecreasing function of the variable $x \in E_1$ induces a locally finite measure on the bounded Borel sets of E_1. Namely, for the half closed interval $[a, b)$, $(-\infty < a < b < \infty)$, set $\mu_f([a, b)) = f(b) - f(a)$ and thereupon extend this measure to all of the measurable sets. Conversely, it is clear that any locally finite measure μ which is defined on the bounded Borel sets of the line may be obtained by such a function $f(x)$: set $f(x) = \mu([0, x))$ for $x > 0$, $f(x) = -\mu([x, 0))$ for $x < 0$ and $f(0) = 0$. If $f(x)$ $(x \in E_1)$ is bounded, then μ_f is defined on every Borel set $\Delta \subseteq E_1$ and is finite. Conversely every finite μ corresponds to a bounded $f(x)$.

Similarly, a one-to-one correspondence may be established between generalized measures defined on the bounded Borel sets and functions $f(x)$ $(x \in E_1)$ which are locally of bounded variation.

Below we will not distinguish the nondecreasing function on the real line from the measure which it induces. We will denote such a function by $\mu(x)$ and the corresponding measure by $\mu(\Delta)$, μ, $d\mu(x)$, $d\mu$ or sometimes simply by dx. The same convention and notation will hold for functions of bounded variation. In what follows (unless the contrary is indicated), when speaking of measures on the real line, an interval will always mean a half closed interval of the form $[a, b)$ $(-\infty < a < b < \infty)$. We will also sometimes use intervals of the form $[a, \infty)$ or $(-\infty, b]$.

§3. NORMED LINEAR SPACES AND HILBERT SPACES

As we have already mentioned, the book freely assumes a familiarity with the basic principles of functional analysis for these spaces. Since these principles must be well known by the reader, we will not review them but will limit ourselves only to some definitions and notation.

By a normed linear (Banach) space B, we will always mean a complete complex normed linear space (unless otherwise stated). By a subspace of B we will mean a closed linear subset. We will consider continuous linear and antilinear functionals on B. An antilinear functional $l(f)$ satisfies the equation $l(\lambda f + \mu g) = \bar{\lambda} l(f) + \bar{\mu} l(g)$ where λ and μ are scalars and $f, g \in B$. The word "continuous" will often be dropped. The dual space of B, consists of all the continuous linear functionals on B and is denoted B'. The identical notation will be used for the dual space of antilinear functionals; the meaning will be clear from context. Every continuous linear operator A from the Banach space B_1 to the Banach space B_2 defines an adjoint operator A^*, which takes B_2 into B_1, by the equation $(A^* l)(f) = l(Af)$ $(f \in B_1,\ l \in B_2')$. The characteristics of A^* induced by those of A are well known. Since $\| A^* \| = \| A \|$, continuity of one implies the continuity of the other, etc.

The identity operator will be denoted by E and the inverse of A, by A^{-1}. In addition, we will say that an operator A (continuous or not) on B has an inverse A^{-1} if the range of A is all of B and the operator A^{-1} is continuous on all of B and such that $A^{-1}Ax = x$ for every x in the domain of A. A consequence is then that $AA^{-1}y = y$ $(y \in B)$.

Let us agree on some further notation. The norm in the space B will usually be written with the corresponding subscript: $\|\cdot\|_B$. The subscript is omitted when this does not lead to an ambiguity. Subscripts are usually not written for the norm of operators. We assume, unless stated to the contrary, that a continuous or bounded operator is defined on the whole space. The domain and range of an operator A are always denoted by $\mathfrak{D}(A)$ and $\mathfrak{R}(A)$ respectively (cf. p. 2). If an operator C is an extension of the operator A, we write: $C \supseteq A$ or $A \subseteq C$ (i.e. $\mathfrak{D}(C) \supseteq \mathfrak{D}(A)$ and $Cf = Af$ for $f \in \mathfrak{D}(A)$). If an operator A acts on a function or sequence according to the variable x, then it is denoted by A_x.

The closure of an operator A is usually denoted by $\bar{A}$; if $\bar{A} = A$, then A is said to be closed. If an operator A acts from the space B_1 to the space B_2 and has domain $\mathfrak{D}(A)$, then by the closure $\bar{A}$ we mean the extension of the operator A, defined in the following way: $f \in \mathfrak{D}(\bar{A})$ if and only if there is a sequence $f_n \in \mathfrak{D}(A)$ such that $f_n \rightarrow f$ (in B_1) and Af_n is fundamental in B_2. Let $g = \lim Af_n$; then $\bar{A} = g$. In order for this definition to make sense, it is necessary to require that the limit element g does not depend on the choice of sequence f_n which approximates f. In other words, it is necessary that the following condition hold: if a sequence $h_n \in \mathfrak{D}(A)$ is such that $h_n \rightarrow 0$ in B_1 and $Ah_n \rightarrow u$ in B_2, then $u = 0$. Operators which have this property are called operators which admit a closure. Clearly, $\mathfrak{D}(\bar{A})$ can be obtained from $\mathfrak{D}(A)$ by completing the latter space with respect to the new norm: $\|f\| = \|f\|_{B_1} + \|Af\|_{B_2}$ $(f \in \mathfrak{D}(A))$.

A particular case of the operation of closure is the so-called closure by continuity. Suppose that an operator A acts continuously from B_1 to B_2, where it is defined on some domain $\mathfrak{D}(A)$. Then the procedure of closure is simpler; it suffices to require only that $f_n \rightarrow f$, since it follows automatically from the continuity of A that Af_n is then fundamental. Clearly A admits a closure and $\bar{A}$ is a continuous operator from B_1 to B_2 with domain $\mathfrak{D}(\bar{A}) = \overline{\mathfrak{D}(A)}$.

We turn to the consideration of a Hilbert space H. By such a space we always mean (unless stated to the contrary) a complete complex Hilbert space (an incomplete space is called unitary). We will encounter only separable H. The scalar product and norm in H are denoted $(\cdot, \cdot)_H$ and $\|\cdot\|_H$; the subscripts are omitted when this will not lead to confusion. It will quite often be necessary to consider a so-called quasi-Hilbert space, i.e. a linear space F in which there is introduced a quasi-scalar product, i.e. a bilinear form $(f, g)_F$ $(f, g \in F)$, which has all the properties of a scalar product except that the equality $(f, f)_F = 0$ can occur for nonzero vectors f. To convert F into a Hilbert space, as is well known, one proceeds as follows: the set of all $f \in F$ for which $(f, f)_F = 0$ forms a linear manifold G, since the Cauchy-Bunjakovskiĭ inequality

$$|(f, g)_F|^2 \leqslant (f, f)_F\ (g, g)_F\ (f, g \in F);$$

holds for a quasi-scalar product; one must consider the quotient space F/G consisting of cosets with respect to G, introduce a scalar product with respect to $(\cdot, \cdot)_F$ for these classes and then take the completion. As a result we obtain a Hilbert space.

An orthogonal decomposition of H into a sum of subspaces $H_1, H_2, \cdots$ is denoted $H = H_1 \oplus H_2 \oplus \cdots = \oplus \sum_j H_j$, and a direct decomposition of H into the sum of H_1 and H_2 is denoted $H = H_1 \dot{+} H_2$. We will sometimes use, along with orthogonal projection operators (orthogonal projectors), skew projection operators: if $H = H_1 \dot{+} H_2$, then $f = f_1 + f_2$ ($f \in H$, $f_1 \in H_1$, $f_2 \in H_2$), and an operator which takes f into f_1 is a skew projection on H_1.

Of course, all that was mentioned about operators in a general normed linear space carries over to operators in Hilbert space. We make some additional remarks. Thus, in the consideration of adjoints to bounded operators, one must take into account that $H' = H$. Further, as is well known, the adjoint operator A^* is defined even for unbounded A acting in H, with an everywhere dense domain: one must consider all those $g \in H$ for which there is a $g^* \in H$ such that

$$(Af, g) = (f, g^*) \quad (f \in \mathfrak{D}(A)).$$

These g make up $\mathfrak{D}(A^*)$ and in this connection we set $A^* g = g^*$. If A admits a closure, then there exists $A^{**} = (A^*)^* = \bar{A}$. Selfadjoint operators, i.e. operators A in H such that $A^* = A$, play an essential role in the book. For these operators, the spectral theorem occurs in the form

$$Af = \int_{-\infty}^{\infty} \lambda dE_\lambda f \quad (f \in \mathfrak{D}(A)), \qquad f = \int_{-\infty}^{\infty} dE_\lambda f \quad (f \in H). \tag{4}$$

where E_λ is the resolution of the identity corresponding to A. In the simplest case of a discrete spectrum $\lambda_1, \lambda_2, \cdots, E_\lambda = \sum_{\lambda_j < \lambda} P_{\lambda_j}$ where P_{λ_j} is the orthogonal projection onto the eigensubspace, corresponding to the eigenvalue λ_j. In the general case E_λ $(-\infty < \lambda < \infty)$ denotes a certain family of orthogonal projections, increasing from 0 to E as λ varies from $-\infty$ to ∞, and having well-known properties.

An operator A in H is called Hermitian if $(Af, g) = (f, Ag)$ for any $f, g \in \mathfrak{D}(A)$. It is clear that each selfadjoint operator is Hermitian, but the converse is not true. The question whether a given Hermitian operator A is selfadjoint is connected with the nature of the deficiency numbers. Recall that the deficiency number of a Hermitian operator A, corresponding to the upper half-plane, is the dimension of the orthogonal complement N_z of the linear manifold $\Re(A - zE)$ (Im $z > 0$; if A is also closed, then $\Re(A - zE)$ is closed, i.e. a subspace). This dimension is independent of z, Im $z > 0$. The deficiency number corresponding to the lower half-plane is defined similarly: one must consider z, Im $z < 0$. As is known, an operator A is selfadjoint if and only if both its deficiency numbers are zero. A Hermitian operator admits a selfadjoint extension in H if and only if its deficiency numbers are equal. Equations (4) hold for each of these extensions. If one of the deficiency numbers is zero, then the operator does not even admit Hermitian extensions in H and is called maximal. In any case A can be extended nevertheless to a selfadjoint operator, if we go outside of H to a larger space $\widetilde{H}$. Let $\widetilde{E}_\lambda$ be a resolution of the identity in $\widetilde{H}$, corresponding to an extension of A, and let P be the orthogonal projector, which projects $\widetilde{H}$ onto H. Then the family of operators $E_\lambda = P\widetilde{E}_\lambda P$ $(-\infty < \lambda < \infty)$ in H is called a generalized resolution of the identity. We note that instead of an ordinary or generalized resolution of the identity E_λ we will often speak of the operator measure $E(\Delta)$, corresponding to E_λ (Δ is an arbitrary Borel set on the axis). In the simplest case $\Delta = [a, b)$, $E(\Delta) = E([a, b)) = E_b - E_a$.

We do not mention here the remaining facts connected with the construction of a resolution of the identity and generalized resolution of the identity for a Hermitian operator A, with the construction and description of all of the selfadjoint extensions etc., although all of these facts are necessary for the understanding of Chapters V–VIII. The reader not acquainted with this theory must turn to the appropriate sources. We also do not call to mind definitions and properties of other classes of operators in H, which are encountered later (isometric, unitary, and normal). Let us make a few further remarks.

The orthogonal complement N_z to $\Re(A - zE)$, where A is a Hermitian operator, is called the deficiency subspace corresponding to the number z (Im $z \neq 0$). It can be characterized differently as the eigensubspace of the operator A^* corresponding to the eigenvalue $\bar{z}$. As was already pointed out, the question whether the deficiency numbers of A are equal, i.e. whether the dimensions of N_z and $N_{\bar{z}}$ coincide or not, plays an important part. In this connection, the following construction is useful. We say that an involution is introduced in H if for each $f \in H$ a vector $\bar{f} \in H$ is defined (the conjugate of the vector f), where the operator

$f \to \bar{f}$ has the following properties:

$$\overline{(\lambda f+\mu g)} = \bar{\lambda}\bar{f}+\bar{\mu}\bar{g},\ \bar{\bar{f}} = f,\ \overline{(f, g)} = (\bar{f}, \bar{g})\ (f, g \in H).$$

An operator A is called real with respect to the involution $f \to \bar{f}$ if the domain $\mathfrak{D}(A)$ is invariant under it and $A\bar{f} = \overline{Af}$ $(f \in \mathfrak{D}(A))$. It is not difficult to prove that if a Hermitian operator A is real with respect to some involution, then it has equal deficiency numbers.

Finally, let us agree to say that an operator A in H is positive, if

$$(Af, f) \geqslant \varepsilon (f, f)\ (\varepsilon > 0,\ f \in H)$$

and $\Re(A) = H$. In this case A^{-1} exists. If it is only known that $(Af, f) \geq 0$ $(f \in H)$, then A is said to be nonnegative and we write $A \geq 0$.

In conclusion, we note that occasionally we will use some information concerning linear topological spaces. Appropriate references to the literature will be given to speed up the presentation.

§4. CLASSES OF FUNCTIONS. FUNCTIONAL SPACES

We introduce a series of definitions, which will be needed later on.

Recall that E_n denotes n-dimensional real Euclidean space. For the scalar product and length of a vector (norm) in E_n the notations $\langle \cdot, \cdot \rangle$ and $|\cdot|$ will be used everywhere except in Chapter VIII. Complex n-dimensional space, i.e. the space of vectors $x = (x_1, \cdots, x_n)$, where $x_1, \cdots, x_n$ are complex numbers, is denoted by C_n. As before $\langle \cdot, \cdot \rangle$ and $|\cdot|$ denote the scalar product and norm in C_n:

$$\langle x, y \rangle = \sum_{j=1}^{n} x_j \bar{y}_j,\ |x| = \sqrt{\langle x, x \rangle}\quad (x, y \in C_n).$$

We introduce our notation for derivatives. For a sufficiently smooth function $u(x)$ $(x \in E_n)$ we set

$$(D^\alpha u)(x) = (D_1^{\alpha_1} \ldots D_n^{\alpha_n} u)(x), \qquad D_j = \frac{\partial}{\partial x_j} \qquad (j = 1, \ldots, n), \tag{5}$$

where $\alpha = (\alpha_1, \cdots, \alpha_n)$ is a vector with nonnegative integral coordinates. The order of the derivative D^α is denoted $|\alpha| = \alpha_1 + \cdots + \alpha_n$. Sometimes it is more convenient to use, instead of the derivatives (5), the derivatives

$$(\partial^\alpha u)(x) = (\partial_1^{\alpha_1} \ldots \partial_n^{\alpha_n} u)(x),\quad \partial_j = \frac{1}{i} D_j\ (j = 1, \ldots, n;\ \alpha = (\alpha_1, \ldots, \alpha_n)). \tag{6}$$

For differentiation in the direction of a unit vector e we use the usual notation $\partial / \partial e$.

Let $G \subseteq E_n$ be a region (bounded or not) having a piecewise-smooth boundary Γ. We denote by $C^l(G)$ $(l = 0, 1, \cdots)$ the set of all complex-valued functions $u(x)$ $(x \in G)$, which have l continuous derivatives in G; similarly $C^\infty(G)$ denotes the set of all infinitely differentiable functions in G. Clearly, $C^l(G)$ $(l = 0, 1, \cdots, \infty)$ is a linear class. The index $l = 0$ is usually omitted.

We denote by $C^l(G \cup \Gamma)$ $(l = 0, 1, \cdots, \infty)$ the set of functions $u(x)$ $(x \in G \cup \Gamma)$, l times continuously differentiable up to the boundary Γ, i.e. in $G \cup \Gamma$. In other words, $C^l(G \cup \Gamma)$ coincides on $G \cup \Gamma$ with the functions of the class $C^l(E_n)$. The class $C^l(G \cup \Gamma)$ for $l < \infty$ and G bounded is a complete normed space, if the norm in it is introduced in the usual way:

$$\| u \|_{C^l(G)} = \max_{\substack{x \in G \cup \Gamma, \\ |\alpha| \leq l}} | (D^\alpha u)(x) |.$$

It is easy to show that the class $C^\infty(G \cup \Gamma)$ is dense in such a space $C^l(G \cup \Gamma)$: $C^l(G \cup \Gamma) = \overline{C^\infty(G \cup \Gamma)}$.

We note certain other classes of functions, which are parts of the class $C^l(G)$. If γ is a piece on Γ, then $C^l(G \cup \gamma)$ denotes the set of functions $u(x)$ $(x \in G \cup \gamma)$, l times continuously differentiable in G up to the piece γ, i.e. in $G \cup \gamma$.

Consider a function $u(x)$ which vanishes in some "strip near the boundary Γ" (i.e. which vanishes for $\rho(x, \Gamma) < \epsilon$, where $\epsilon > 0$ is sufficiently small) and, if G is unbounded, in some neighborhood of ∞ (i.e. for $|x| \geq R$, where $R > 0$ is sufficiently large). Such functions are called finite with respect to G and ∞. The set of all finite functions with respect to G and ∞ in $C^l(G)$ $(l = 0, 1, \cdots, \infty)$ is denoted $C_0^l(G)$ (ϵ and R depend on $u \in C_0^l(G)$). Addition of the subscript "0" has a similar meaning in notations of other classes of functions on G. We also use the term "function finite at ∞." Such a function is a function $u(x)$, $x \in G$ (G is unbounded), which vanishes for $|x| \geq R$, where $R > 0$ is sufficiently large. This fact, for functions in $C^l(G)$ which are finite at ∞, we will still express thus: u belongs to $C^l(G) \cap C_0(E_n)$.

Similar but less rigorous "intersections" and also inclusions of the type $C(E_n) \subset C(G)$ will sometimes be used later on. Their meaning will be explained or will follow from the context.

Let Q be a locally compact separable space, and let $d\mu(x)$ be a measure defined on the Borel sets of Q. The Hilbert space $L_2(Q, d\mu(x))$ of complex-valued functions which are square summable with respect to $d\mu(x)$ is constructed in the usual way:

$$\|f\|^2_{L_2(Q,d\mu(x))}=\int_Q |f(x)|^2\,d\mu(x). \qquad (f,g)_{L_2(Q,d\mu(x))}=\int_G f(x)\overline{g(x)}\,d\mu(x).$$

We say that a Borel measurable function $f(x)$ $(x \in Q)$ is locally square summable, if the integral $\int_{U_r(a)} |f(x)|^2 d\mu(x)$ extended over any sphere $U_r(a) \subset Q$ exists.

In the case when Q coincides with a region $G \subseteq E_n$ and $d\mu(x)$ with ordinary Lebesgue measure, the space $L_2(Q, d\mu(x))$ is $L_2(G)$. If $\mu(\Delta) = \int_\Delta m(x)\,dx$, where dx is Lebesgue measure, then the space is $L_2(G, m(x)\,dx)$ ("the space with weight $m(x)$").

We say that a function $f(x)$ $(x \in G)$ is square summable inside G (or belongs to L_2 inside G), if it is square summable in each bounded region lying strictly in the interior of G. In other words, this is the previous definition of local square summability in connection with the space $Q = G$. The class of all functions $f(x)$ of the form described is denoted $L_{2,\mathrm{loc}}(G)$.

Let γ be a piece on Γ. Consider all possible bounded subregions $G' \subseteq G$, whose boundaries meet Γ only in the strict interior of γ. If $f(x) \in L_2(G')$ $(x \in G')$ for any G', then we say that $f(x)$ belongs to L_2 inside G up to γ. The class of such functions is denoted $L_{2,\mathrm{loc}}(G, \gamma)$.

All that was just mentioned concerning square summability may be repeated for pth power summable functions $(p \geq 1)$. In this connection, of course, such functions form a complete normed space $L_p(Q, d\mu(x))$ with respect to the norm

$$\|f\|_{L_p(Q,d\mu(x))} = \left(\int_Q |f(x)|^p d\mu(x)\right)^{\frac{1}{p}}$$

The notation

$$L_p(G),\ L_{p,\mathrm{loc}}(G),\ L_{p,\mathrm{loc}}(G,\gamma).$$

is clear.

Special cases of the Hilbert space $L_2(Q, d\mu(x))$ are the spaces of sequences $l_2([0, \infty), m_j)$, where $m_j > 0$ $(j = 0, 1, \cdots)$ is a given weight sequence. The elements of the space $l_2([0, \infty), m_j)$ are sequences $(f_0, f_1, \cdots)$ of complex numbers, where

$$\|f\|^2_{l_2([0,\infty),m_j)} = \sum_{j=0}^{\infty} |f_j|^2 m_j, \qquad (f,g)_{l_2([0,\infty),m_j)} = \sum_{j=0}^{\infty} f_j \bar{g}_j m_j.$$

If $m_j = 1$ $(j = 0, 1, \cdots)$, then the space under consideration becomes $l_2([0, \infty))$.

Analogous spaces are introduced for the case when j runs through other infinite discrete sets. Notation of the type $l_p([0, \infty), m_j)$ is also clear.

We point out that the notation $\kappa_A(x)$ is always used for the characteristic function of the set A. By the support of a function $f(x)$ $(x \in Q)$ we mean the set of all x such that $f(x) \neq 0$. For an arbitrary topological space Q the set of all continuous complex-valued functions on Q is denoted, naturally, by $C(Q)$.

§5. THE CONCEPT OF SOBOLEV SPACE

We introduce the Sobolev spaces, which are used systematically in almost all the later chapters. Let G be a bounded region in n-dimensional space E_n with a once piecewise-continuously differentiable boundary Γ.[1] We consider the functions $u \in C^l(G \cup \Gamma)$ $(l = 0, 1, \cdots)$ with the norm

$$\| u \|_{W_p^l(G)} = \sum_{|\alpha| \leqslant l} \| D^\alpha u \|_{L_p(G)} \qquad (p > 1). \tag{7}$$

The completion of $C^l(G \cup \Gamma)$ with respect to this norm is called the Sobolev space $W_p^l(G)$. Since

$$\| u \|_{L_p(G)} \leqslant \| u \|_{W_p^l(G)} \quad (u \in C^l(G \cup \Gamma)),$$

the functions in this completion belong, in any case, to the space $L_p(G)$. Later on we will see that for $l > 0$ the functions of $W_p^l(G)$ have additional smoothness properties. For $l = 0$, it is clear that $W_p^l(G) = W_p^0(G) = L_p(G)$.

Instead of (7), it is often convenient to introduce the norm in $W_p^l(G)$ in the following way:

$$\| u \|_{W_p^l(G)} = \Big(\sum_{|\alpha| \leqslant l} \| D^\alpha u \|_{L_p(G)}^p \Big)^{\frac{1}{p}} = \Big(\sum_{|\alpha| \leqslant l} \int_G | (D^\alpha u)(x) |^p \, dx \Big)^{\frac{1}{p}}. \tag{8}$$

Of course, the expressions in (7) and (8) are different and these norms, by virtue of the inequality

$$N^{p-1} (a_1 + \ldots + a_N) \leqslant (a_1^p + \ldots + a_N^p)^{\frac{1}{p}} \leqslant a_1 + \ldots + a_N \quad (a_1, \ldots, a_N \geqslant 0),$$

are only equivalent. However we retain the same notation $\| \cdot \|_{W_p^l(G)}$ for both norms (7) and (8). Moreover, the norms (7) and (8) are equivalent to the norm

$$\| u \|_{W_p^l(G)} = \Big(\| u \|_{L_p(G)}^p + \sum_{|\alpha| = l} \| D^\alpha u \|_{L_p(G)}^p \Big)^{\frac{1}{p}} \tag{9}$$

(we clarify this later; see §7). The same notation for the equivalent norms (7)–

1) For simplicity, we will not weaken this restriction.

(9) in what follows will not lead to confusion.

Thus $W_p^l(G)$ $(l = 0, 1, \cdots, p > 1)$ is a complete normed linear space. We will almost exclusively be concerned with the spaces $W_2^l(G)$ $(l = 0, 1, \cdots)$, which are Hilbert spaces. The scalar product in $W_2^l(G)$ can be introduced in one of two equivalent ways:

$$(u, v)_{W_2^l(G)} = \sum_{|\alpha| \leqslant l} (D^\alpha u, D^\alpha v)_{L_2(G)} = \sum_{|\alpha| \leqslant l} \int_G (D^\alpha u)(x)(D^\alpha v)(x) dx. \tag{10}$$

$$(u, v)_{W_2^l(G)} = (u, v)_{L_2(G)} + \sum_{|\alpha| = l} (D^\alpha u, D^\alpha v)_{L_2(G)}$$

$$= \int_G u(x)\overline{v(x)} dx + \sum_{|\alpha| = l} \int_G (D^\alpha u)(x)\overline{(D^\alpha v)(x)}\, dx. \tag{11}$$

We will usually use the notations $(\cdot, \cdot)_l$ and $\| \cdot \|_l$ $(l = 0, 1, \cdots)$, for the scalar product and norm in $W_2^l(G)$.

Finally, we note that the inequality

$$\| u \|_{W_p^l(G)} \leqslant C \| u \|_{C^l(G \cup \Gamma)} \quad (C > 0;\ u \in C^l(G \cup \Gamma)),$$

holds, from which, in particular, it follows that $C^\infty(G \cup \Gamma)$ is dense in $W_p^l(G)$ $(l = 0, 1, \cdots; p > 1)$.

§6. THE CONCEPT OF IMBEDDING THEOREMS

The application of the Sobolev spaces $W_p^l(G)$ to the theory of boundary value problems and to related questions depends on the remarkable fact that functions in these spaces, unlike $L_2(G)$, have meaning, for l sufficiently large, on manifolds of dimension smaller than n, and, moreover, $W_2^l(G)$ (unlike $C^l(G \cup \Gamma)$) is a Hilbert space. We now present the basic results relevant here, first clarifying the nature of the situation arising from the simplest example.

Let $n = 1$ and let G be a finite interval (a, b). If we fix $x \in (a, b)$, then for any $\xi \in (a, b)$ we have

$$u(x) = u(\xi) - \int_x^\xi u'(t)\, dt \quad (u \in C^1([a, b])). \tag{12}$$

Integrating this expression with respect to ξ from x to b, we obtain

$$(b - x)\, u(x) = \int_x^b u(\xi)\, d\xi - \int_x^b \left(\int_x^\xi u'(t)\, dt \right) d\xi = \int_x^b u(\xi)\, d\xi$$

$$+ \int_x^b (t - b)\, u'(t)\, dt. \tag{13}$$

Similarly, integrating (12) with respect to ξ from a to x, adding the result to (13) and dividing by $b - a$, we find that

$$u(x) = \frac{1}{b-a}\int_a^b u(\xi)\,d\xi + \frac{1}{b-a}\int_a^b B(x,\xi)\,u'(\xi)\,d\xi \quad (x \in (a,b)), \tag{14}$$

where $B(x, \xi)$ is a certain bounded kernel, constructed as the sum of two kernels of the type

$$B_1(x,\xi) = \varkappa_{(x,b)}(\xi)\,(\xi - b).$$

From (14) we conclude by means of Hölder's inequality that

$$\| u \|_{C([a,b])} \leqslant C \| u \|_{W_p^1((a,b))} \quad (u \in C^1([a,\ b])). \tag{15}$$

Thus, if a sequence $u_n(x)$ is fundamental in the metric of $W_p^1((a,\ b))$, then it is fundamental in the metric of $C([a,\ b])$ and hence the limit function belongs to $C([a,\ b])$. In other words, we have the inclusion: $W_p^1((a,\ b)) \subset C([a,\ b])$.

A similar situation occurs in the case of n dimensions, but now, in the representation of the type (14), the kernel $B(x,\ \xi)$ has a singularity as $|x - \xi| \to 0$ and instead of (15), it is necessary to write a weaker inequality, often with $\|\cdot\|_{C([a,\ b])}$ replaced by norms of the type $\|\cdot\|_{L_q(D)}$, where $D \subseteq G$ is a manifold of the same or different dimension. This leads to the following results, which are known as the imbedding theorems.

Consider the space $W_p^l(G)$ $(l = 0, 1, \cdots;\ p > 1)$, *where* $G \subset E_n$ *is a bounded region with a once piecewise-continuously differentiable boundary* Γ. *Then*

1) *Assume that* $k = 0, 1, \cdots$ *is such that*

$$0 \leqslant k < l - \frac{n}{p}. \tag{16}$$

Then $W_p^l(G) \subset C^k(G \cup \Gamma)$, *and moreover the imbedding operator* O *of the space* $W_p^l(G)$ *into the space* $C^k(G \cup \Gamma)$ *is continuous (i.e. the operator which relates each* $u \in W_p^l(G)$ *to this same* u *considered as an element of* $C^k(G \cup \Gamma)$, *is continuous).*

2) *Suppose that the reverse inequality to* (16) *holds:*

$$k \geqslant l - \frac{n}{p}. \tag{17}$$

Let $m = 0, 1, \cdots$ *and let* q *real be such that*

$$m > n - (l-k)\,p,\quad 1 < q < \frac{mp}{n-(l-k)\,p}; \tag{18}$$

let $D \subseteq G \cup \Gamma$ *be any* l *times continuously differentiable manifold of dimension* m. *Then for each* $u \in W_p^l(G)$, *the derivative* $(D^\alpha u)(x) \in L_q(D)$ $(x \in D)$, *where* $|\alpha| \leq k$, *and moreover we have "continuity of the imbedding operator":*

$$\| D^\alpha u \|_{L_q(D)} \leqslant C \| u \|_{W_p^l(G)} \quad (C > 0; \quad u \in W_p^l(G)).$$

Under shrinkage of the manifold D, *the element* $D^\alpha u$ *depends continuously on the magnitude of this shrinkage; this can be expressed as*

$$\| (D^\alpha u)(\cdot + \delta) - (D^\alpha u)(\cdot) \|_{L_q(D)} \to 0 \quad \text{for} \quad \delta \to 0 \quad (|\alpha| \leqslant k).$$

Furthermore, it is shown that in 1) *and* 2), *the operator is not only continuous, but also completely continuous. In case* 2), *one must understand by this the property that from a bounded sequence in* $W_p^l(G)$ *of functions* $u_n \in W_p^l(G)$ *one can extract a subsequence* u_{n_ν} *such that* $(D^\alpha u_{n_\nu})(x)$ $(x \in D)$ *converges in the space* $L_q(D)$ *for any* α, $|\alpha| \leq k$.

We point out that one might introduce the Sobolev space $W_q^k(D)$ of functions, defined on the manifold D (for this it is necessary to "rectify" D by means of substitution of variables). Then from 2) follows, in particular, the "inclusion" $W_p^l(G) \subset W_q^k(D)$, and the continuity, even complete continuity, of the imbedding operator O of $W_p^l(G)$ in $W_q^k(D)$.

We clarify the complete continuity of the imbedding operator for the example of the space $W_p^1((a, b))$ considered. Here one must establish complete continuity of the imbedding operator $W_p^1((a, b)) \longrightarrow C([a, b])$ or, in other words, show that the set of functions $u \in W_p^1((a, b))$ such that $\| u \|_{W_p^1((a,b))} \leqslant 1$ is precompact in $C([a, b])$. Because of Arzelà's Theorem, one must prove that this set is bounded in $C([a, b])$ and equicontinuous. Boundedness follows from inequality (15), and equicontinuity from (12): for x', $x'' \in [a, b]$ we have

$$|u(x') - u(x'')| = \left| \int_{x'}^{x''} u'(t)\, dt \right| \leqslant |x' - x''|^{\frac{1}{p'}} \left(\int_{x'}^{x''} |u'(t)|^p dt \right)^{\frac{1}{p}}$$

$$\leqslant |x' - x''|^{\frac{1}{p'}} \| u \|_{W_p^1((a,b))} \leqslant |x' - x''|^{\frac{1}{p'}} \quad \left(\frac{1}{p} + \frac{1}{p'} = 1 \right)$$

We emphasize that from the imbedding theorems it follows that the smoothness of a function $u(x) \in W_p^l(G)$ increases with increasing l, p and decreasing n. Further, for each $u \in W_p^l(G)$ for $l > 0$ there exists a value $(D^\alpha u)(x)$ with $|\alpha| \leq l - 1$ for x varying on a surface S of dimension $n - 1$, lying in $G \cup \Gamma$. Moreover, the corresponding norms of $(D^\alpha u)(x)$, regarded as functions on S, are bounded by the norm $\| u \|_{W_p^l(G)}$.

§7. SOME INEQUALITIES RELATING THE SOBOLEV NORM AND THE SPACE $\overset{0}{W}{}^l_p(G)$

As a first case we introduce the Ehrling-Nirenberg inequality. It connects the norms of the spaces $W^k_p(G)$, $W^l_p(G)$ and $W^s_p(G)$ where $0 \leq k \leq l < s$ and is expressed as follows. *For arbitrary* $\epsilon > 0$ *there exists a* $k(\epsilon) > 0$ *such that*

$$\| u \|_{W^l_p(G)} \leqslant \varepsilon \| u \|_{W^s_p(G)} + K(\varepsilon) \| u \|_{W^k_p(G)} \quad (u \in W^s_p(G)).^{1)} \tag{19}$$

We will state this inequality explicitly for the case $W^0_2((a, b)) = L_2((a, b))$, $W^1_2((a, b))$ and $W^2_2((a, b))$. We fix $\delta_0 > 0$ and extend $u(x)$ to $[a, b + \delta_0]$ so that $u \in C^2([a, b + \delta_0])$ and

$$\int_b^{b+\delta_0} |(D^\alpha u)(x)|^2 dx \leqslant \int_a^b |(D^\alpha u)(x)|^2 dx \quad (\alpha = 0, 1, 2). \tag{20}$$

In relation (12) we replace $u(x)$ by $u'(x)$:

$$u'(x) = u'(\xi) - \int_x^\xi u''(t)\, dt \quad (x, \xi \in (a, b)).$$

Integrating this equation with respect to ξ between the limits x and $x + \delta$ for some $\delta < \delta_0$, we obtain

$$\delta u'(x) = u(x+\delta) - u(x) - \int_x^{x+\delta} \left(\int_x^\xi u''(t)\, dt \right) d\xi = u(x+\delta) - u(x)$$

$$- \int_x^{x+\delta} (x + \delta - t)\, u''(t)\, dt. \tag{21}$$

We further have

$$\left| \int_x^{x+\delta} (x + \delta - t)\, u''(t)\, dt \right| \leqslant \left(\int_x^{x+\delta} (x + \delta - t)^2\, dt \right)^{\frac{1}{2}} \| u'' \|_{L_2((a, b+\delta_0))}$$

$$\leqslant \frac{\delta^{\frac{3}{2}}}{\sqrt{3}} \| u \|_{W^2_2((a,b))} \quad (x \in (a, b)). \tag{22}$$

We now estimate the norm $\| \cdot \|_{L_2((a,b))}$ of the function $u'(x)$ by using (21), (22) and (20):

---

1) We will often use an equivalent form of this inequality in which the norm $\| u \|$ is replaced by its square $\| u \|^2$.

$$\delta\|u'\|_{L_2((a,b))}\leqslant\|u(\cdot+\delta)\|_{L_2((a,b))}+\|u\|_{L_2((a,b))}+C_1\delta^{\frac{3}{2}}\|u\|_{W_2^2((a,b))}$$

$$\leqslant C_2\|u\|_{L_2((a,b))}+C_1\delta^{\frac{3}{2}}\|u\|_{W_2^2((a,b))}.$$

Dividing by δ we obtain the inequality

$$\|u'\|_{L_2((a,b))}\leqslant C_1\delta^{\frac{1}{2}}\|u\|_{W_2^2((a,b))}+\frac{C_2}{\delta}\|u\|_{L_2((a,b))},$$

from which (19) follows for the special case being considered.

We note that the preceding argument is clear for the equivalent norms in (7) and (9): we may estimate $\|D^\alpha u\|_{L_p(G)}$ for $0<|\alpha|<l$ by similar norms with $\alpha=0$ and $|\alpha|=l$.

We introduce the space $\overset{0}{W}{}^l_p(G)$ $(l=0,1,\cdots,p>1)$. It is the closure of the linear space $C_0^\infty(G)\subset W^l_p(G)$ in the metric of $W^l_p(G)$. It is clear that instead of $C_0^\infty(G)$ it is possible to form the closure of the union of all functions of $W^l_p(G)$ which are finite relative to G (they are denoted $W^l_{p,0}(G)$). It turns out that $\overset{0}{W}{}^l_p(G)$ for $l=1,2,\cdots$ coincides with the *collection of all functions* $u(x)\in W^l_p(G)$ *for which* $(D^\alpha u)(x)=0$ $(x\in\Gamma)$ *if* $|\alpha|\leq l-1$ (*we assume that* Γ *is* l *times piecewise continuously differentiable*). That each function $u(x)\in\overset{0}{W}{}^l_p(G)$ has this property follows from the imbedding theorem: for $u_n(x)\in C_0^\infty(G)$ it is obvious. By the imbedding theorem one may write an inequality of the type

$$\|D^\alpha u_n\|_\Gamma\leqslant C\|u_n\|_{W^l_p(G)},$$

where $|\alpha|<l-1$ and $\|\cdot\|_\Gamma$ is as in the imbedding theorem. If $u_n\to u$ in $W^l_p(G)$ then this inequality implies that $D^\alpha u_n\to D^\alpha u$. Therefore $(D^\alpha u)(x)=0$ $(x\in\Gamma)$ for $|\alpha|\leq l-1$. We will omit the proof of the converse.

The following inequality will be useful.

Let G *be a bounded region with a piecewise continuously differentiable boundary* Γ, *and let* d *be its diameter. Then the estimate*

$$\|u\|_{W^k_p(G)}\leqslant d^{l-k}\|u\|_{W^l_p(G)}\quad(u\in\overset{\circ}{W}{}^l_p(G)).\tag{23}$$

is valid for $0\leq k<l$.

Clearly it is sufficient to establish the inequality for the particular case

$$\|u\|_{L_p(G)}\leqslant d\|u\|_{W^1_p(G)}\quad(u\in\overset{\circ}{W}{}^1_p(G)).$$

The last estimate follows from a simple inequality which we will illustrate in the one-dimensional case.

Let $u \in \overset{0}{W}{}^1_p((a, b))$. Then $u(a) = 0$ and it is possible to write

$$u(x) = \int_a^x u'(t)\,dt \quad (x \in (a, b)). \tag{24}$$

Using the Hölder inequality we obtain that

$$\|u\|^p_{L_p((a,b))} = \int_a^b |u(x)|^p dx = \int_a^b \left| \int_a^x u'(t)\,dt \right|^p dx$$

$$\leqslant \int_a^b (x-a)^{p-1} \left(\int_a^x |u'(t)|^p dt \right) dx \leqslant \int_a^b (x-a)^{p-1} dx \cdot \int_a^b |u'(t)|^p dt$$

$$\leqslant d^p \|u\|^p_{W^1_p((a,b))},$$

as required.

One consequence of inequality (23) is that in place of (7)–(9) the norm on $\overset{0}{W}{}^l_p(G)$ may be given by

$$\|u\|_{W^l_p(G)} = \left(\sum_{|\alpha|=l} \|D^\alpha u\|^p_{L_p(G)} \right)^{\frac{1}{p}} \quad (u \in \overset{\circ}{W}{}^l_p(G)). \tag{25}$$

It follows from these arguments that the relations (23) and (25) are valid not only for functions $u \in W^l_p(G)$ which, with all of their derivatives up to order $l-1$, vanish on Γ, but also for functions for which these derivatives vanish, for example, only in neighborhoods (on Γ) of points of the boundary which may be connected with any point of G by a straight line contained in G.

§8. THE NOTION OF A GENERALIZED FUNCTION

At this point we recall the notion of a generalized function introduced by S. L Sobolev and L. Schwartz. Let $G \subseteq E_n$ be a (possibly unbounded) region with a piecewise smooth boundary Γ. We consider the collection of all functions of $C_0^\infty(G)$ which are finite with respect to G and ∞ and introduce on them the norm defined by the convergence: $u_n \to u$ if each of the u_n have a common compact support in G and for any α, $(D^\alpha u_n)(x) \to (D^\alpha u)(x)$ uniformly in x. This linear topological space will be denoted $D(G)$. An antilinear functional $l(u) = (l, u)$ which is continuous with respect to this convergence is called a generalized function.[1] The set of all generalized functions is denoted by $D'(G)$.

As example of a generalized function is an ordinary locally summable function $l(x)$ $(x \in G)$; $l(u)$ is given by the formula

$$l(u) = \int_G l(x)\,\overline{u(x)}\,dx \qquad (u \in C_0^\infty(G)).$$

We now illustrate some examples of generalized functions which are not ordinary functions. If $\xi \in G$ is fixed, we may put $l(u) = \overline{u(\xi)}$, $l(u) = \overline{(D_j u)(\xi)}$ $(u \in D(G))$. The first of these generalized functions is called the δ-function concentrated at the point ξ.

Any equation which involves generalized functions must be regarded as a functional equation: if $l_1, l_2 \in D'(G)$, then $l_1 = l_2$ if and only if $l_1(u) = l_2(u)$ $(u \in D(G))$.

We now consider the differentiation operation on generalized functions. It will be convenient to consider a more general operation, namely that of taking a differential expression of a generalized function. For this purpose we consider a general linear differential expression of order $r \geq 1$:

$$(Lu)(x) = (L(x, D)\,u)(x) = \sum_{|\alpha| \leq r} a_\alpha(x)\,(D^\alpha u)(x), \tag{26}$$

where the coefficients $a_\alpha(x) \in C^\infty(G)$. The (formal) adjoint expression L^+ is the expression

$$(L^+ v)(x) = \sum_{|\alpha| \leq r} (-1)^{|\alpha|} (D^\alpha (\overline{a_\alpha} v))(x)$$

(it may, of course, be written in the form of (26)). The expression L^+ is related to L by the equation $\int_G Lu \cdot \bar{v}dx = \int_G u\overline{L^+ v}dx$ where $u, v \in C^\infty(G)$, and one of them is finite with respect to G and ∞. Conversely the last equation uniquely defines L^+.

If l is a generalized function, then by Ll we will mean the generalized function defined by $(Ll)(u) = l(L^+ u)$ $u \in D(G) = C_0^\infty(G)$). It is clear that if l is an ordinary function in $C^r(G)$ then

$$(Ll)(u) = l(L^+ u) = \int_G l(x)\,\overline{(L^+ u)(x)}\,dx = \int_G (Ll)(x)\,\overline{u(x)}dx$$

$$(u \in C_0^\infty(G)),$$

---

1) Sometimes we will consider linear functionals also; here, however, we will always mean the original definition.

i.e. Ll is the ordinary function obtained by applying L to $l(x)$.

A consequence of the above is that in the theory of generalized functions an arbitrary locally summable function may be differentiated an infinite number of times. The following fact is also well known: every element $l \in D'(G)$ with compact support contained inside G may be represented in the form $l = \sum_{|\alpha| \leq p} D^\alpha f_\alpha$, where f_α is a function in $C(G)$ and p is some number.

Moreover, any l concentrated on $F \subseteq G(\overline{F} = F)$ may be considered to have the property that $l(u) = 0$ for any $u \in C_0^\infty(G)$ which vanishes in a neighborhood of F. Let $l \in D'(G)$ be given; the intersection of all F on which l is concentrated is called the support of l. In particular if $l = l(x) \in C(G)$ then its support is the closure of the set of all $x \in G$ such that $l(x) \neq 0$.

As is well known, one may construct a space of generalized functions by taking some other space Φ in place of $C_0^\infty = D(G)$. (This space of functions is called the space of basic functions.) In order to avoid confusion a generalized function of $D'(G)$ will be called generalized in the sense of L. Schwartz.

It is now relevant to recall the notion of a resolution of the identity as it applies to the theory of generalized functions.

Let $G \subseteq E_n$ be a region which may be covered by a countable collection of neighborhoods $U_1, U_2, \cdots \subseteq G$. In addition, we assume that every subregion of G which is strictly inside G has a nonempty intersection with only a finite number of the U_j. It is then well known that a system of functions $\chi_1(x), \chi_2(x), \cdots \in C^\infty(G)$ may be constructed with the following properties: a) $0 \leq \chi_j(x) \leq 1$ $(x \in G;\ j = 1, 2, \cdots)$; b) $\chi_j(x) = 0$ when $x \overline{\in} U_j$ $(j = 1, 2, \cdots)$; c) for each $x \in G$, $\sum_{j=1}^\infty \chi_j(x) = 1$. Such a system of functions is also called a resolution of the identity constructed from the covering $U_1, U_2, \cdots$. Sometimes we will speak of a resolution of the identity corresponding to an arbitrary (not necessarily countable) covering. By this we will mean the following: we will assume that the given covering has a countable subcovering with the above properties and then construct the resolution of the identity from this subcovering.

§9. THE NOTION OF A GENERALIZED DERIVATIVE IN THE SENSE OF S. L. SOBOLEV

Let $u \in L_{1,\mathrm{loc}}(G)$. u is said to have a generalized derivative D^α in the sense of S. L. Sobolev if there is a function $f \in L_{1,\mathrm{loc}}(G)$ such that $D^\alpha u = f$.

Here, $D^{\alpha}u$ is understood in the sense of a generalized function of L. Schwartz, and the equation $D^{\alpha}u = f$ is a functional equation. In other words the relations

$$(-1)^{|\alpha|}\int_G u\overline{D^{\alpha}v}dx = (D^{\alpha}u,\ v) = \int_G f\bar{v}dx \quad (v\in C_0^{\infty}(G)). \tag{27}$$

hold.

The difference therefore between this and a derivative in the sense of L. Schwartz is that here $D^{\alpha}u \in L_{1,\text{loc}}(G)$, and $u \in L_{1,\text{loc}}(G)$.

We will omit the verification of many of the "ordinary-like" properties of these Sobolev derivatives and mention only the following two which are due to the local nature of the definition.

First of all, if $f \in L_{1,\text{loc}}(G)$ is the Sobolev derivative $D^{\alpha}u$ ($u \in L_{1,\text{loc}}(G)$), then for $x \in G'$ (G', a fixed subregion of G), $f(x)$ will be the derivative of $u(x)$. Moreover, if G' and G'' are two intersecting regions, if $u \in L_{1,\text{loc}}(G' \cup G'')$ and if $D^{\alpha}u$ exists separately on G' and G'', then $(D^{\alpha}u)(x)$ is a single-valued function of $x \in G' \cap G''$ and the derivative $(D^{\alpha}u)(x)$ of u on $G' \cup G''$ is an element of $L_{1,\text{loc}}(G' \cup G'')$. This assertion is easily established by using resolutions of the identity.

In the case of a one-dimensional space ($u = 1$, $G = (a,\ b)$) the existence of the Sobolev derivative D^{α} of the function $u \in L_{1,\text{loc}}((a,\ b))$ means that $u \in C^{\alpha-1}((a,\ b))$ and its derivative of order $(\alpha - 1)$, $(D^{\alpha-1}u)(x)$ is absolutely continuous; the Sobolev derivative is equal to the derivative of this absolutely continuous function. We clarify this remark for the case $\alpha = 1$. It follows from (27) that

$$-\int_a^b u\,\bar{v}'dx = \int_a^b f\,\bar{v}dx \quad (v\in C_0^{\infty}((a,\ b))).$$

We set $g(x) = \int_a^x f(\xi)\,d\xi$ $(x\in (a,\ b))$. Then clearly $-\int_a^b g\,\bar{v}'dx = \int_a^b f\,\bar{v}dx$ $(v\in C_0^{\infty}((a,\ b)))$, and therefore

$$\int_a^b (u - g)\bar{v}'dx = 0 \quad (v\in C_0^{\infty}((a,\ b))).$$

So from a well-known lemma in the calculus of variations it follows that $u(x) - g(x) = C$ $(x\in (a,\ b))$ and consequently that $u(x) = C + \int_a^x f(\xi)\,d\xi$ $(x\in (a,\ b))$ as required.

In the multi-dimensional case, the existence of some Sobolev derivative D^α for $u(x) \in L_{1,\mathrm{loc}}(G)$ does not induce any kind of smoothness on $u(x)$. For example, if $u(x_1, x_2) = \phi(x_1) + \chi(x_2)$ where $\phi, \chi \in L_{1,\mathrm{loc}}((-\infty, \infty))$ are such that the Sobolev derivatives exist and satisfy $D_1 D_2 u = 0$. The function u, however, does not have to be smooth in any sense.

§10. AVERAGING OPERATORS

In §11 we will show that the functions of a Sobolev space may be characterized by means of Sobolev derivatives. Part of the apparatus for this will consist of averaging operators.

The simplest example of an averaging operator is the following: from $f(x) \in L_{1,\mathrm{loc}}((-\infty, \infty))$ we pass to the operator

$$(S_\varepsilon f)(x) = \frac{1}{2\varepsilon} \int_{x-\varepsilon}^{x+\varepsilon} f(\xi)\, d\xi \quad (\varepsilon > 0;\ x \in (-\infty, \infty)). \tag{28}$$

It is clear that (28) is a smoother function than $f(x)$. The smoothing may be strengthened by means of the following construction. We note that the integral in (28) may be rewritten in the form $\int_{-\infty}^{\infty} \omega_\epsilon(x-\xi) f(\xi)\, d\xi$, where $\omega_\epsilon(y) = (1/2\epsilon)\kappa_{(-\epsilon,\epsilon)}(y)$ $(y \in (-\infty, \infty))$; $\kappa_{(-\epsilon,\epsilon)}$ is the characteristic function of the interval $(-\epsilon, \epsilon)$. We introduce a function $\omega_\epsilon(y) \in C_0^\infty(E_n)$ $(\epsilon > 0)$, which has the following properties: a) $\omega_\epsilon(y) = 0$ for $|y| \geq \epsilon$; b) $\omega_\epsilon(y) \geq 0$ $(y \in E_n)$; c) $\int_{E_n} \omega_\epsilon(y)dy = 1$. We then construct the averaging operator S_ϵ, putting

$$(S_\varepsilon f)(x) = \int_{E_n} \omega_\varepsilon(x-\xi) f(\xi)\, d\xi = (\omega_\varepsilon * f)(x) \quad (f \in L_{1,\mathrm{loc}}(E_n);\ x \in E_n) \tag{29}$$

($\omega_\epsilon * f$ is called the convolution of ω_ϵ with f). In the case where $f(x)$ is defined for $x \in G \subseteq E_n$ and is in L_1 inside G up to the (piecewise smooth) boundary Γ, $(f \in L_{1,\mathrm{loc}}(G, \Gamma))$, then $S_\epsilon f$ is understood as before in (29) but first $f(x)$ must be extended to zero on all of E_n (the extension will be contained in $L_{1,\mathrm{loc}}(E_n)$). We will often consider $S_\epsilon f(x)$ only for $x \in G$. In this case $f \to S_\epsilon f$ represents a linear operator on a class of functions of $x \in G$.

We now indicate some fundamental properties of averaging operators in the case where G is bounded.

a) $(S_\epsilon f)(x) \in C^\infty(E_n)$. This follows immediately from definition (29).

b) If $f(x)$ is continuous at the fixed point $x_0 \in E_n$, then $\lim_{\epsilon \to 0} (S_\epsilon f)(x_0) = f(x_0)$. This follows from the relation

$$|(S_\varepsilon f)(x_0) - f(x_0)| = \left| \int_{E_n} \omega_\varepsilon (x_0 - \xi) f(\xi)\, d\xi - \int_{E_n} \omega_\varepsilon (x_0 - \xi) f(x_0)\, d\xi \right|$$

$$\leqslant \int_{E_n} \omega_\varepsilon (x_0 - \xi) | f(\xi) - f(x_0) |\, d\xi.$$

c) The operator S_ϵ is continuous on the space $L_p(G)$ $(p \geq 1)$.

d) If $f \in L_p(G)$ $(p \geq 1)$, then $\lim_{\epsilon \to 0} S_\epsilon f = f$ in the sense of convergence in the space $L_p(G)$. This holds for an arbitrary extension of $f(x)$ outside of G to a function of $L_{p,\mathrm{loc}}(E_n)$.

e) Let G' be a subregion of G, strictly inside G, with a piecewise smooth boundary. We assume that $f \in C^{|\alpha|}(G)$. Then the equation

$$(D^\alpha S_\varepsilon f)(x) = (S_\varepsilon D^\alpha f)(x) \quad (x \in G'),$$

is valid for $0 < \epsilon < \rho(G', \Gamma)$.

In fact, since $\omega_\epsilon(x - \xi) = 0$ for ξ in a strip near Γ with $x \in G'$, we find, integrating by parts, that

$$(D^\alpha S_\varepsilon f)(x) = D^\alpha_x \int_{E_n} \omega_\varepsilon (x - \xi) f(\xi)\, d\xi = \int_{E_n} D^\alpha_x \omega_\varepsilon (x - \xi) \cdot f(\xi)\, d\xi$$

$$= (-1)^{|\alpha|} \int_{E_n} D^\alpha_\xi \omega_\varepsilon (x - \xi) \cdot f(\xi)\, d\xi = \int_{E_n} \omega_\varepsilon (x - \xi) (D^\alpha f)(\xi) d\xi = (S_\varepsilon D^\alpha f)(x). \quad (30)$$

f) Assertion e) remains valid if instead of the inclusion $f \in C^{|\alpha|}(G)$, it is known that $D^\alpha f$ exists in the sense of S. L. Sobolev. For in this case equation (30) may be replaced by the equation

$$(-1)^{|\alpha|} \int_{E_n} D^\alpha_\xi \omega_\varepsilon (x - \xi) f(\xi)\, d\xi = \int_{E_n} \omega_\varepsilon (x - \xi) (D^\alpha f)(\xi)\, d\xi$$

which is based on (27) (we take $v(\xi) = \omega_\epsilon(x - \xi)$).

In conclusion of this section we note that an example of a possible choice of $\omega_\epsilon(y)$ is given by

$$\omega_\varepsilon (y) = \begin{cases} C_\varepsilon e^{\frac{|y|^2}{|y|^2 - \varepsilon^2}}, & |y| < \varepsilon, \\ 0, & |y| \geqslant \varepsilon, \end{cases}$$

where $C_\epsilon > 0$ is chosen such that $\int_{E_n} \omega_\varepsilon (y)\, dy = 1$.

§11. A SECOND DEFINITION OF A GENERALIZED DERIVATIVE IN THE SENSE OF S. L. SOBOLEV, AND A CHARACTERIZATION OF THE ELEMENTS OF A SOBOLEV SPACE

We show that these derivatives may be obtained by means of the closure of an ordinary differentiation operator if this closure is constructed in a suitably chosen space.

We introduce in $L_{1,\mathrm{loc}}(G)$ a new convergence: $u_n \to u$ if $\|u_n(x) - u(x)\|_{L_1(G')} \to 0$ on each bounded subregion of G lying strictly inside G. We define the operator A on $L_{1,\mathrm{loc}}(G)$ by $(Au)(x) = (D^\alpha u)(x)$ $(u \in \mathfrak{D}(A) = C^\infty(G))$. It is not difficult to see that this operator admits a closure. For if $u_n \to 0$ and $Au_n \to h$ in $L_{1,\mathrm{loc}}(G)$, then for any $v \in C_0^\infty(G)$,

$$\int_G h\bar{v}dx = \lim_{n\to\infty}\int_G Au_n\cdot\bar{v}dx = \lim_{n\to\infty}\int_G D^\alpha u_n\cdot\bar{v}dx$$

$$= (-1)^{|\alpha|}\lim_{n\to\infty}\int_G u_n\overline{D^\alpha v}dx = 0.$$

Since v is arbitrary it follows that $h = 0$ and consequently that A admits a closure $\bar{A}$.

The following assertion is valid: *a function $u \in L_{1,\mathrm{loc}}(G)$ has a generalized Sobolev derivative D^α if and only if $u \in D(\bar{A})$. Then $D^\alpha u = \bar{A}u$.*

For this let $u \in C^\infty(G)$ be such that $u_n \to u$ in $L_{1,\mathrm{loc}}(G)$ and $D^\alpha u_n \to \bar{A}u$. It follows that

$$(-1)^{|\alpha|}\int_G u_n\overline{D^\alpha v}dx = \int_G D^\alpha u_n\cdot\bar{v}dx$$

holds for any $v \in C_0^\infty(G)$. Passing to the limit as $n \to \infty$ in this expression we find that (27) is satisfied with $f = \bar{A}u$. Thus the Sobolev derivative $D^\alpha u = \bar{A}u$ exists for every $u \in \mathfrak{D}(\bar{A})$.

Conversely, suppose $u \in L_{1,\mathrm{loc}}(G)$ is such that the Sobolev derivative $D^\alpha u$ exists and is in $L_{1,\mathrm{loc}}(G)$. We show that $u \in \mathfrak{D}(\bar{A})$ and that $\bar{A}u = D^\alpha u$. For this purpose we construct a sequence of functions $u_n \in C^\infty(G)$ as follows. If $x \in G$ and such that $\rho(x, \Gamma) \geq 2/n$ we set $u_n(x) = (S_{1/n}u)(x)$, where S_ϵ is the smoothing operator constructed in §10. For the remaining $x \in G$, $u_n(x)$ is defined arbitrarily so that $u_n \in C^\infty(G)$. If G' is a bounded region strictly inside G, it follows from property d) above that $\|u_n - u\|_{L_1(G')} = \|S_{1/n}u - u\|_{L_1(G')} \to 0$. Consequently, $u_n \to u$ in $L_{1,\mathrm{loc}}(G)$. Moreover, by property f) if $x \in G$ and n is sufficiently large, we may write $(D^{\alpha}u_n)(x) = (D^{\alpha}S_{1/n}u)(x) = (S_{1/n}D^{\alpha}u)(x)$. On applying property d) again we find that

$$\| D^{\alpha}u_n - D^{\alpha}u \|_{L_1(G')} = \| S_{\frac{1}{n}} D^{\alpha}u - D^{\alpha}u \|_{L_1(G')} \to 0.$$

It is then clear that $u \in \mathfrak{D}(\bar{A})$ and $\bar{A}u = D^{\alpha}u$, the required conclusion.

Now, suppose G is bounded and consider the operator $(Bu)(x) = (D^{\alpha}u)(x)$, $u \in \mathfrak{D}(B) = C^{\infty}(G \cup \Gamma)$ on $L_1(G)$. Since convergence in $L_1(G)$ implies convergence in $L_{1,\mathrm{loc}}(G)$ then the closure $\bar{B}$ of B in $L_1(G)$ is, in particular, the closure of the operator A in $L_{1,\mathrm{loc}}(G)$. It therefore follows that the Sobolev derivative D^{α} exists for $u \in \mathfrak{D}(\bar{B})$ and in this case that $D^{\alpha}u = \bar{B}u$.

We may now give the following characterization of the elements of the space $W_p^l(G)$. *A function $u(x)$ $(x \in G)$ is an element of $W_p^l(G)$, $(l = 0, 1, \cdots)$ if and only if $u \in L_p(G)$, the Sobolev derivatives D^{α} exist for $|\alpha| \leq l$, and each such derivative $D^{\alpha}u \in L_p(G)$ (G is assumed to be bounded and to have an l times piecewise continuously differentiable boundary).*

That every $u \in W_p^l(G)$ has a derivative D^{α} for $|\alpha| \leq l$ such that $D^{\alpha}u \in L_p(G)$ is almost obvious. By the definition of the space $W_p^l(G)$ there is a sequence of functions $u_n \in C^{\infty}(G \cup \Gamma)$ which converges to u in the metric of $W_p^l(G)$. By the definition of this metric given in (8) it follows that $\|u_n - u\|_{L_p(G)} \to 0$ and $\|D^{\alpha}u_n - f\|_{L_p(G)} \to 0$. It is then clear that this relation holds in the norm of $L_1(G)$ which implies that $u \in \mathfrak{D}(\bar{B})$ and $\bar{B}u = f$. We then conclude from previous remarks that $D^{\alpha}u = f \in L_p(G)$ in the Sobolev sense.

Now let $u \in L_p(G)$ be such that the derivatives $D^{\alpha}u$, $|\alpha| \leq l$ exist in the Sobolev sense and $D^{\alpha}u \in L_p(G)$. As in the case where the ordinary derivative of such a function $u(x)$ exists, it is possible to extend to a larger region $\tilde{G}$ which contains G strictly, while preserving the properties of $u(x)$. We consider the sequence $u_n(x) = (S_{1/n}u)(x) \in C^{\infty}(G \cup \Gamma)$. Using properties e) and f) of the averaging operator, we conclude that

$$\| D^{\alpha}u_n - D^{\alpha}u \|_{L_p(G)} = \| D^{\alpha}S_{\frac{1}{n}}u - D^{\alpha}u \|_{L_p(G)} = \| S_{\frac{1}{n}} D^{\alpha}u - D^{\alpha}u \|_{L_p(G)} \to 0$$

for all α such that $|\alpha| \leq l$. It then follows that $\|u_n - u\|_{W_p^l(G)} \to 0$ which in turn implies that $u \in W_p^l(G)$. The assertion is proved.

In conclusion we make one remark about linear subspaces of $W_p^l(G)$. As in §7, it is easy to see that the set of all functions $u \in W_p^l(G)$ $(l \geq 1)$ satisfying

$$\sum_{|\alpha|<m_j} b_{j\alpha}(x)\,(D^\alpha u)(x) = 0 \qquad (x \in \Gamma;\ j = 1, \ldots, k) \tag{31}$$

($b_{j\alpha}(x) \in C(\Gamma)$; $m_j < l$; $j = 1, \cdots, k$), forms a closed subspace of $W_p^l(G)$. In fact, if $u_n \in W_p^l(G)$ satisfies (31) and $u_n \longrightarrow u$ in $W_p^l(G)$, then by the inclusion theorem, if $|\alpha| \leq l-1$, $D^\alpha u_n \longrightarrow D^\alpha u$ sufficiently well so that one may pass to the limit and obtain (31) for the limit function $u(x)$.

On the other hand the relations in (31) with $|\alpha| \geq l$ ($b_{j\alpha}(x) \neq 0$ when $x \in \Gamma$) characterize an, in general, dense subspace of smooth functions in $W_p^l(G)$. The reason for this is connected with the fact that the condition $u|_\Gamma = 0$ ($u \in C(G \cup \Gamma)$), defines a dense subspace of $L_p(G)$.

CHAPTER I

SPACES WITH NEGATIVE NORMS AND GENERALIZED FUNCTIONS

The construction of generalized functions is usually carried out in the following way: consider a linear topological space Φ of infinitely differentiable functions, called the space of basic functions. The adjoint space Φ' consists of the continuous linear functionals on Φ, and its elements are called generalized functions. Operations on generalized functions (such as differentiation) are defined by corresponding operations on the space of basic functions, which are well defined by the smoothness of the latter. However, for us it will be more convenient to use normed (in fact, Hilbert) spaces Φ of finitely differentiable functions; in this case the conjugate space Φ' will consist of the so-called generalized functions of finite order. The theory of such functions is formulated below in a convenient abstract form.

We outline a simple example of such a construction. Consider two Hilbert spaces: the usual space $L_2((a, b))$ and the Sobolev space $W_2^1((a, b))$, which is the completion of the continuously differentiable functions on $[a, b]$ with respect to the scalar product

$$(u, v)_1 = \int_a^b u\bar{v}dx + \int_a^b u'\bar{v}'dx.$$

Every continuous linear functional $l(u)$ on $W_2^1((a, b))$ may be represented in the form $l(u) = (u, h)_1$, where $h \in W_2^1((a, b))$, by Riesz's theorem. However, there is another representation, given in terms of the original metric of $L_2((a, b))$, which is very useful. Roughly speaking, it is given by $l(u) = \int_a^b u\bar{\eta}\,dx$, where η is some generalized function. The norm $\|\cdot\|_1$, which is constructed in terms of derivatives, is naturally called positive. It turns out that the generalized functions η form a Hilbert space, in which the scalar product is defined by an integral operation which is inverse to differentiation. Therefore the norm in this space is naturally called negative.

§1. GENERAL THEORY OF SPACES WITH NEGATIVE NORMS

1. **Positive and negative norms.** Let H_0 be a complete Hilbert space with scalar product $(\cdot,\cdot)_0$ and norm $\|\cdot\|_0$ Suppose that H_0 has a dense linear subspace H_+ which is a complete Hilbert space in another scalar product $(\cdot,\cdot)_+$; $\|\cdot\|_+$ is the norm in H_+. Suppose that

$$\|u\|_0 \leq \|u\|_+ \quad (u \in H_+); \tag{1.1}$$

H_+ is called a space with positive norm.

Sometimes in applications, instead of (1.1) we have $\|u\|_0 \leq C\|u\|_+$ $(C > 0)$. Such a space H_+ is called a space with positive norm as before, since the estimate (1.1) can be obtained by renorming H_+.

A vector $f \in H_0$ generates a conjugate linear functional l (i.e. $l(\lambda u) = \bar{\lambda} l(u)$) on H_+ as follows: $l(u) = l_f(u) = (f, u)_0$. This functional is continuous, since by (1.1)

$$|l_f(u)| = |(f, u)_0| \leqslant \|f\|_0 \|u\|_0 \leqslant \|f\|_0 \|u\|_+ (u \in H_+).$$

Its norm is estimated by

$$\|l_f\| = \sup_{u \in H_+} \frac{|(f, u)_0|}{\|u\|_+} \leqslant \|f\|_0 \quad (f \in H_0).$$

The completion of the space H_0 in the norm $\|f\|_- = \|l_f\|$ is called a space with negative norm. As a convenient preliminary, we introduce an alternate construction and definition of negative norm in a somewhat different way. In the following subsection we will establish the equivalence of these definitions.

Consider a bilinear form of $f \in H_0$ and $u \in H_+$: $B(f, u) = (f, u)_0$. Because of (1.1), this bilinear form is continuous for f and u in their respective spaces. Therefore it may be represented either by a scalar product in H_0 or by a scalar product in H_+:

$$(f, u)_0 = B(f, u) = (If, u)_+ \quad (f \in H_0, u \in H_+), \tag{1.2}$$

where I is a linear operator acting continuously from H_0 to H_+. Let O be the inclusion mapping of H_+ into H_0. Then (1.2) asserts that for any $f \in H_0$ and $u \in H_+$ $(f, Ou)_0 = (If, u)_+$, i.e. the operators O and I are adjoints. Since $\|O\| \leq 1$ (see (1.1)), $\|I\| \leq 1$.

We introduce a scalar product for $f, g \in H_0$ by setting

$$(f, g)_- = (If, g)_0 = (If, Ig)_+ \tag{1.3}$$

and form the completion. We obtain a Hilbert space H_- called a space with negative norm. The scalar product in H_- is denoted $(\cdot,\cdot)_-$ and the norm $\|\cdot\|_-$. Since $\|I\| \le 1$, $\|f\|_- \le \|f\|_0$ $(f \in H_0)$. In what follows, the elements of the space H_0, which is called a space with zero norm, will be denoted $f, g, \cdots$; the elements of H_+ and H_- will be denoted $u, v, \cdots$ and $\alpha, \beta, \cdots$ respectively. So

$$H_- \supseteq H_0 \supseteq H_+, \qquad \|u\|_- \leqslant \|u\|_0 \leqslant \|u\|_+ \ (u \in H_+). \tag{1.4}$$

If (1.4) holds, we will say that the Hilbert space H_0 is equipped with spaces H_+ and H_-.

According to (1.3), I maps a dense subspace in H_- (namely H_0) isometrically into a set in H_+. Extending this operator by continuity to all of H_-, we obtain an operator $\mathbf{I}$ which maps H_- into H_+. The range $\Re(\mathbf{I})$ of the operator $\mathbf{I}$ fills H_+; in fact, $\Re(\mathbf{I})$ is closed, and therefore if $\Re(\mathbf{I}) \neq H_+$, we can find $u \in H_+$ such that $0 = (\mathbf{I}f, u)_+ = (f, u)_0$ for all $f \in H_0$. But then $u = 0$. So $\mathbf{I}$ is an isometric operator which maps all of H_- onto all of H_+, i.e. $\mathfrak{D}(\mathbf{I}) = H_-$, $\Re(\mathbf{I}) = H_+$ and $(\alpha, \beta)_- = (\mathbf{I}\alpha, \mathbf{I}\beta)_+$ $(\alpha, \beta \in H_-)$.

We will show that there is a "scalar product" $(\alpha, u)_0$, defined for $\alpha \in H_-$ and $u \in H_+$, which coincides with the scalar product in H_0 for $\alpha \in H_0$ (we will also write $(u, \alpha)_0$ for $\overline{(\alpha, u)_0}$). The Cauchy-Bunjakowskiĭ inequality

$$|(\alpha, u)_0| \leqslant \|\alpha\|_- \|u\|_+ \quad (\alpha \in H_-, u \in H_+). \tag{1.5}$$

holds for this bilinear form.

In fact, if $f \in H_0$, then for any $u \in H_+$ we have

$$|(f, u)_0| = |(\mathbf{I}f, u)_+| \leqslant \|\mathbf{I}f\|_+ \|u\|_+ = \|f\|_- \|u\|_+; \tag{1.6}$$

we obtain (1.5) by passing to the limit here with $f \longrightarrow \alpha$ (in H_-).

By passing to the limit in (1.3) and (1.2), we easily obtain the equations

$$\begin{gathered}(\alpha, \beta)_- = (\alpha, \mathbf{I}\beta)_0 = (\mathbf{I}\alpha, \beta)_0 = (\mathbf{I}\alpha, \mathbf{I}\beta)_+, \\ (\alpha, u)_0 = (\mathbf{I}\alpha, u)_+ \quad (\alpha, \beta \in H_-, u \in H_+).\end{gathered} \tag{1.7}$$

2. **Generalized vectors.** We now call H_+ the space of basic vectors and consider the continuous conjugate linear functionals $l(u)$ on H_+. By virtue of (1.5), every $\alpha \in H_-$ induces a functional l_α by the formula $l_\alpha(u) = (\alpha, u)_0$ $(u \in H_+)$. Conversely, if l is a functional on H_+, then it has a representation $l(u) = (v_l, u)_+$, where v_l is some element of H_+. It follows from the second equation in (1.7) that $l(u) = (v_l, u)_+ = (\alpha_l, u)_0$, $\alpha_l = \mathbf{I}^{-1} v_l \in H_-$. Moreover, if $l = 0$, it is not difficult

to see that $\alpha_l = 0$. Thus the correspondence $l \longleftrightarrow \alpha$ between functionals on H_+ and vectors in H_- is one-to-one, and moreover $\|l\| = \|v_l\|_+ = \|\alpha\|_-$ (v_l is the element of H_+ corresponding to l). This proves the equivalence of the two definitions of spaces with negative norm, which was asserted in subsection 1.

The continuous functionals on the basic space H_+ are naturally called generalized vectors. Thus H_- is the space of generalized vectors. To clarify its isometric relation with H_+, we now write the functional $l(u)$ in the "original" scalar product $(\cdot,\cdot)_0$: $l(u) = (\alpha, u)_0$. The vectors in H_0 (H_+) will sometimes be called ordinary (smooth) vectors. Obviously, H_+ and H_0 are dense in H_-.

We illustrate the concepts introduced above by means of an example. Let G be a bounded region in n-dimensional space $(n \geq 1)$ with sufficiently smooth boundary Γ. Let $H_0 = L_2(G)$ and $H_+ = W_2^1(G)$, where $W_2^1(G)$ is the Sobolev space with scalar product

$$(u, v)_+ = \int_G u\bar{v}dx + \sum_{j=1}^n \int_G D_ju \cdot \overline{D_jv}dx \quad \left(D_j = \frac{\partial}{\partial x_j}\right).$$

Equation (1.2), which defines I, takes the form

$$\int_G f\bar{u}dx = \int_G h\bar{u}dx + \sum_{j=1}^n \int_G D_jh \cdot \overline{D_ju}dx \quad (u \in W_2^1(G),\ f \in L_2(G)),$$

where $h = If \in W_2^1(G)$. Since the set u, of functions $u \in W_2^2(G)$ which satisfy the condition $\partial u/\partial\nu|_\Gamma = 0$ ($\partial/\partial\nu$ is the exterior normal derivative), is dense in $W_2^1(G)$, to prove (1.8) it is sufficient to show that this relation holds for $u \in U$. If we suppose in (1.8) that $u \in U$ and integrate by parts, we obtain

$$\int_G f\bar{u}dx = \int_G h\overline{(-\Delta u + u)}dx. \tag{1.9}$$

We define on U an operator L in $L_2(G)$ by setting $\mathrm{L}u = -\Delta u + u$; then (1.9) asserts that $h \in \mathfrak{D}(\mathrm{L}^*)$ and $f = \mathrm{L}^*h$. It is known (see Chapter VI, §1.3) that the operator L is selfadjoint, and therefore $h \in U$ and $f = -\Delta h + h$; thus $If = h = \mathrm{L}^{-1}f$. The operator L^{-1} is an integral operator with a smooth kernel $R(x, y)$, which is the Green's function for the expression $-\Delta u + u$ with the boundary condition $\partial u/\partial\nu|_\Gamma = 0$. Therefore the elements of the space with negative norm are obtained as the completion of $L_2(G)$ with respect to the scalar product

$$(f, g)_- = \int\limits_G \int\limits_G R(x, y) f(y) \overline{g(x)} dx dy.$$

3. **Operators on generalized vectors.** Let H_0 be a space with zero norm, and let H_{+1} be a space with positive norm. Let H_{+2} be a linear subspace of H_{+1}, which is a space with positive norm with respect to H_{+1}. Clearly H_{+2} is a space with positive norm with respect to H_0. Let H_{-1} and H_{-2} be spaces with negative norm, constructed with respect to H_0 and corresponding to the basic spaces H_{+1} and H_{+2}; $(\cdot, \cdot)_k$ and $\| \cdot \|_k$ denote the scalar product and norm in H_k. Then

$$H_{-2} \supseteq H_{-1} \supseteq H_0 \supseteq H_{+1} \supseteq H_{+2}, \; \|u\|_{-2} \leqslant \|u\|_{-1} \leqslant \|u\|_0 \leqslant \|u\|_{+1} \leqslant \|u\|_{+2} \tag{1.10}$$

$$(u \in H_{+2}),$$

where each H_l is dense in each H_k for $k < l$. In fact, the part of the assertion concerning nonnegative indices is obvious. Let $\mathbf{I}_k$ be the operator $\mathbf{I}$ constructed for H_0 and H_k $(k > 0)$. For $f \in H_0$ we have

$$\|f\|_{-2}^2 = (\mathbf{I}_2 f, f)_0 \leqslant \|\mathbf{I}_2 f\|_{+1} \|f\|_{-1} \leqslant \|\mathbf{I}_2 f\|_{+2} \|f\|_{-1} = \|f\|_{-2} \|f\|_{-1}.$$

Hence $\|f\|_{-2} \leq \|f\|_{-1}$. Forming the closures of H_0 with respect to the corresponding norms, we obtain the inclusion $H_{-2} \supseteq H_{-1}$. The stated density relations are now obvious.

Consider a continuous linear operator A, which maps all of H_k into H_l $(k, l \geq 0)$.[1)] There exists an adjoint operator A^+ which maps all of H_{-l} continuously into H_{-k}, which is connected with A by the relation

$$(\alpha, Au)_0 = (A^+\alpha, u)_0 \quad (\alpha \in H_{-l}, u \in H_k). \tag{1.11}$$

In fact, let A^* be the usual adjoint of A in the sense of the theory of operators on Hilbert spaces (i.e. an operator acting from H_l to H_k and satisfying the equation $(Au, v)_l = (u, A^*v)_k$ $(u \in H_k, v \in H_l)$). For $\alpha \in H_{-l}$, $u \in H_k$ we have

$$(\alpha, Au)_0 = (\mathbf{I}_l \alpha, Au)_l = (A^* \mathbf{I}_l \alpha, u)_k = (\mathbf{I}_k^{-1} A^* \mathbf{I}_l \alpha, u)_0 = (A^+ \alpha, u)_0,$$

where

---

1) The restriction $k, l \geq 0$ is made only for definiteness. The arguments below are valid for all k and l. In particular, (1.12) remains valid if it is only assumed that $\mathbf{I}_m = \mathbf{I}_{-m}^{-1}$ for $m < 0$.

$$A^+ = \mathbf{I}_k^{-1} A^* \mathbf{I}_l. \tag{1.12}$$

Thus (1.11) and the connection between A^+ and A^* are established; from (1.12) we immediately see that $\|A^+\| = \|A^*\| = \|A\|$.

It should be kept in mind in what follows that if $H_0 = L_2(G)$ and if A is a pure differentiation, then A^+ need not be the same. We illustrate this with the example of the previous subsection. Let $H_{+1} = H_0 = L_2(G)$, $H_{+2} = W_2^1(G)$, $Au = \partial u/\partial \tau$, where τ is some unit vector; $\mathfrak{D}(A) = W_2^1(G)$, $\mathfrak{R}(A) \subseteq L_2(G)$. By (1.11), $(A^+\alpha, u)_0 = (\alpha, \partial u/\partial \tau)_0$, $\alpha \in L_2(G)$, $u \in W_2^1(G)$. In particular, if $\alpha = v \in W_2^1(G)$, then on integrating by parts we find (where $\nu(x)$ is the unit exterior normal)

$$(A^+v, u)_0 = \int_G v(x) \overline{\frac{\partial u(x)}{\partial \tau}}\, dx = -\int_G \frac{\partial v(x)}{\partial \tau} \overline{u(x)}\, dx$$

$$+ \int_\Gamma v(x)\overline{u(x)} \langle \nu(x), \tau\rangle\, dx$$

$$= \int_G \left(-\frac{\partial v(x)}{\partial \tau} + v(x) \langle \nu(x), \tau\rangle\, \delta_\Gamma(x)\right) \overline{u(x)}\, dx$$

$$(\langle a, b\rangle = a_1 b_1 + \ldots + a_n b_n),$$

here $\delta_\Gamma(x)$ is the δ-function, which is concentrated on the boundary Γ and defined by the relation $\int_G f(x)\delta_\Gamma(x)\, dx = \int_\Gamma f(x)\, dx$. It follows that

$$(A^+v)(x) = -\frac{\partial v(x)}{\partial \tau} + v(x) \langle \nu(x), \tau\rangle\, \delta_\Gamma(x) \text{ for } v \in W_2^1(G).$$

It is clear that the presence of the δ-function here is connected with the fact that in the transfer of A in (1.11), the functions do not satisfy boundary conditions.

4. Factorization of the operator $\mathbf{I}$. Recall that $\mathbf{I}$ maps H_- isometrically into H_+; we now show that this operator may be factored into two operators, the first of which maps H_- isometrically into H_0, and the second H_0 into H_+.

The operator I acts continuously from H_0 to H_+. Since $H_+ \subseteq H_0$, this operaator may be considered as acting in H_0. We introduce the notation $\hat{I} = OI$ for the latter operator. The operator $\hat{I}$ is obviously continuous, nonnegative, and invertible on $\mathfrak{R}(\hat{I})$. We will show that $\mathfrak{R}(\hat{I}) = \mathfrak{D}(\hat{I}^{-1})$ is dense in H_0: if $h \perp \mathfrak{R}(\hat{I})$, then $0 = (h, \hat{I}f)_0 = (Ih, If)_+ = (Ih, f)_0$ for any $f \in H_0$; therefore $Ih = 0$, and hence $h = 0$. It is clear that $\hat{I}^{-1}$ is selfadjoint and positive in H_0.

Theorem 1.1. *Consider the operator* $D = \sqrt{\hat{I}^{-1}}$ *in the space* H_0. *It is a* *positive selfadjoint operator for which* $\mathfrak{D}(D) = H_+$, $\mathfrak{R}(D) = H_0$. *This operator acts isometrically from* H_+ *to* H_0:

$$(u, v)_+ = (Du, Dv)_0 \quad (u, v \in H_+). \tag{1.13}$$

Consider D *as an operator acting from* H_0 *to* H_- *and form the closure by continuity; denote this operator by* $\mathbf{D}$. $\mathbf{D}$ *acts isometrically from all of* H_0 *to* H_-:

$$(f, g)_0 = (\mathbf{D}f, \mathbf{D}g)_- \quad (f, g \in H_0) \tag{1.14}$$

and moreover

$$\mathbf{I}^{-1} = \mathbf{D}D. \tag{1.15}$$

The relation

$$(f, Du)_0 = (\mathbf{D}f, u)_0 \quad (f \in H_0, u \in H_+) \tag{1.16}$$

holds, from which it appears that D *and* $\mathbf{D}$ *are adjoints of each other* ($\mathbf{D} = D^+$).

Proof. By definition $D = \int_0^\infty \sqrt{\lambda}\, dE_\lambda$, where E_λ is the resolution of the identity corresponding to $\hat{I}^{-1}$; $\mathfrak{D}(D)$ consists of all vectors $f \in H_0$ for which $\int_0^\infty \lambda d(E_\lambda f, f)_0 = (Df, Df)_0 < \infty$. It is clear that D is positive and selfadjoint. We will show that $H_+ \subseteq \mathfrak{D}(D)$. Suppose to begin with that $v \in \mathfrak{D}(\hat{I}^{-1}) = \mathfrak{R}(I)$; then

$$\int_0^\infty \lambda d(E_\lambda v, v)_0 = (\hat{I}^{-1} v, v)_0 = (v, v)_+. \tag{1.17}$$

But $\mathfrak{R}(I)$ is dense in H_+: if for some $w \in H_+$ and all $f \in H_0$ we have $(If, w)_+ = 0$, then by virtue of (1.2) it follows that $w = 0$. Since $\mathfrak{R}(I)$ is dense in H_+, for each $u \in H_+$ there is a sequence $v_n \in \mathfrak{R}(I)$ such that $v_n \longrightarrow u$ in H_+. On replacing v by v_n in (1.17) and passing to the limit as $n \longrightarrow \infty$, we find that $\int_0^\infty \lambda d(E_\lambda u, u)_0 = (u, u)_+ < \infty$. Thus $H_+ \subseteq \mathfrak{D}(D)$.

Conversely, suppose $f \in \mathfrak{D}(D)$. Then there exists a sequence $u_n \in \mathfrak{D}(\hat{I}^{-1}) \subseteq H_+$ such that $u_n \longrightarrow f$ in H_0 and $\int_0^\infty \lambda d(E_\lambda u_n, u_n)_0 \longrightarrow \int_0^\infty \lambda d(E_\lambda f, f)_0$ (for example, $u_n = E(\Delta_n)f$, where Δ_n is a sequence of intervals expanding to $(-\infty, \infty)$). By virtue of (1.17), written with $v = u_n$, we conclude that $(u_n, u_n)_+ \longrightarrow C < \infty$. It is then clear that $f \in H_+$. Thus $\mathfrak{D}(D) = H_+$. Finally $(Du, Dv)_0 = (\hat{I}^{-1}u, v)_0 = (u, v)_+$ for $u, v \in H_+ = \mathfrak{D}(D)$; i.e. (1.13) is established.

We now consider the operator $\mathbf{D}$. Since $\mathfrak{D}(D) = H_+$ is dense in H_0, and $\mathfrak{R}(D) = H_0$ is dense in H_-, and moreover $(Du, Dv)_- = (IDu, Dv)_0 = (u, v)_0$, it is possible to close the operator D to the operator $\mathbf{D}$, which then maps all of H_0 isometrically onto all of H_-. To prove (1.15) it is sufficient to show that $D^{-1}\mathbf{D}^{-1}\alpha = \mathbf{I}\alpha$ on a dense set in H_-. If $\alpha = f \in H_0$, then $D^{-1}\mathbf{D}^{-1}f = D^{-1}D^{-1}f = \hat{I}f$

and $\mathbf{I}f = If$; i.e. $D^{-1}\mathbf{D}^{-1}f = \mathbf{I}f\ (f \in H_0)$ and $\mathbf{I}^{-1} = \mathbf{D}D$. Further, by (1.7) we have

$$(f, Du)_0 = (\mathbf{D}f, \mathbf{D}Du)_- = (\mathbf{D}f, \mathbf{I}^{-1}u)_- = (\mathbf{D}f, u)_0$$
$$(f \in H_0,\ u \in H_+),$$

and so (1.16) also holds. The theorem follows.

Equation (1.15) gives a factorization of $\mathbf{I}^{-1}$. From this it follows that $\mathbf{I} = D^{-1}\mathbf{D}^{-1}$, or, if we introduce the operator $J = D^{-1}$,

$$\mathbf{I} = J\mathbf{J}. \tag{1.18}$$

Here $\mathbf{J}$ denotes $\mathbf{D}^{-1}$; this notation is appropriate since the operator $\mathbf{J}$ may be obtained from J (considered as an operator from H_- to H_0) by forming the closure by continuity. Thus (1.18) gives a factorization of $\mathbf{I}$ into isometric operators $\mathbf{J}$ and J, which are inverse to the operators $\mathbf{D}$ and D described in Theorem 1.1. If we replace f by $\mathbf{J}\alpha$ and u by Jf in (1.16), we obtain

$$(\mathbf{J}\alpha, f)_0 = (\alpha, Jf)_0\ (\alpha \in H_-, f \in H_0), \text{ i.e. } \mathbf{J} = J^+. \tag{1.19}$$

For the convenience of the reader, we list the basic properties of the isometric operators introduced in this subsection:

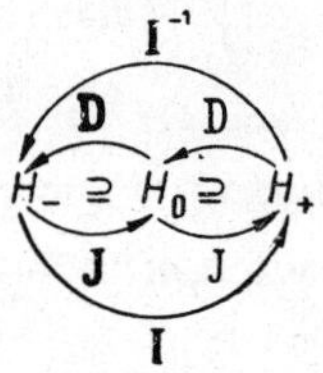

$$, \quad \mathbf{I} = J\mathbf{J},\ D = J^{-1},\ \mathbf{D} = \mathbf{J}^{-1}; \tag{1.20}$$

$$(\mathbf{I}\alpha, \mathbf{I}\beta)_+ = (\alpha, \beta)_-,\ (Jf, Jg)_+ = (f, g)_0,\ (\mathbf{J}\alpha, \mathbf{J}\beta)_0 = (\alpha, \beta)_-$$
$$= (\alpha, \mathbf{I}\beta)_0 = (\mathbf{I}\alpha, \beta)_0,\ (Du, Dv)_0 = (u, v)_+,\ (\mathbf{D}f, \mathbf{D}g)_- = (f, g)_0$$
$$(\alpha, \beta \in H_-;\ f, g \in H_0;\ u, v \in H_+);$$
$$\mathbf{J} = J^+, \mathbf{D} = D^+, \text{ i.e. } (\mathbf{J}\alpha, f)_0 = (\alpha, Jf)_0, (\mathbf{D}f, u)_0 = (f, Du)_0$$
$$(\alpha \in H_-, f \in H_0, u \in H_+).$$

5. **A theorem on the continuity of Hermitian operators.** In conclusion we establish an interesting property of Hermitian operators.

Theorem 1.2. *Let H_k and H_l be two spaces in the sequence* (1.10), $k \leq l$. *Let A be a continuous operator in the space H_l with norm $\|A\|_l$, and suppose that A is Hermitian symmetric in H_k, i.e.* $(Au, v)_k = (u, Av)_k$ $(u, v \in H_l)$. *Then A is continuous in the space H_k, and its norm here does not exceed $\|A\|_l$.*

Proof. Fix $u \in H_l$, $\|u\|_k = 1$, and let $s_n = (A^n u, A^n u)_k$ ($n = 0, 1, \cdots; s_0 = 1$). For any real λ we have the inequality

$$0 \leq (A^{n-1}u + \lambda A^{n+1}u, A^{n-1}u + \lambda A^{n+1}u)_k = s_{n-1} + 2\lambda s_n + \lambda^2 s_{n+1},$$

from which we conclude that $s_n^2 \leq s_{n-1}s_{n+1}$ ($n = 1, 2, \cdots$). Since all of the numbers s_n are nonnegative this implies

$$s_1 \leq \frac{s_2}{s_1} \leq \frac{s_3}{s_2} \leq \cdots.$$

Hence

$$s_n \geq s_1 s_{n-1} \geq s_1^2 s_{n-2} \geq \cdots \geq s_1^n,\ s_1 \leq \sqrt[n]{s_n} \quad (n = 1, 2, \cdots).$$

On the other hand

$$s_n = (A^n u, A^n u)_k \leq (A^n u, A^n u)_l \leq \|A^n\|_l^2 \|u\|_l^2 \leq \|A\|_l^{2n} \|u\|_l^2$$

and therefore

$$s_1 \leq \sqrt[n]{s_n} \leq \|A\|_l^2 \sqrt[n]{\|u\|_l^2} \quad (n = 1, 2, \cdots; \|u\|_l^2 \geq \|u\|_k^2 = 1).$$

Letting $n \to \infty$ in this inequality we obtain $(Au, Au)_k = s_1 \leq \|A\|_l^2$. Thus for any $u \in H_l$, $\|u\|_k = 1$, we have $\|Au\|_k \leq \|A\|_l$, and therefore $\|Au\|_k \leq \|A\|_l \|u\|_k$ ($u \in H_l$). Since H_l is dense in H_k, this inequality proves the theorem.

It is clear from the proof that the theorem remains valid when H_l is a Banach space, with respect to some norm $\|\cdot\|_l$, which is dense in H_k and such that $\|u\|_k \leq \|u\|_l$ ($u \in H_l$).

§2. TENSOR PRODUCTS AND GENERALIZED KERNELS

In this section we state the theory of generalized kernels in a general form.

1. Tensor products of Hilbert spaces. General concepts. Let H' and H'' be two complete Hilbert spaces, with elements denoted respectively by $f', g', \cdots$ and $f'', g'', \cdots$. We construct the tensor product of H' and H''. Consider the linear span L of formal products $f' \otimes f''$, where

$$\begin{gathered}(f' + g') \otimes f'' = f' \otimes f'' + g' \otimes f'', f' \otimes (f'' + g'') = f' \otimes f'' + f' \otimes g'', \\ (\lambda f') \otimes f'' = f' \otimes (\lambda f'') = \lambda (f' \otimes f'').\end{gathered} \tag{2.1}$$

We introduce a scalar product in L by setting

$$(f' \otimes f'', g' \otimes g'')_{H' \otimes H''} = (f', g')_{H'} (f'', g'')_{H''} \tag{2.2}$$

for elements of the form $f' \otimes f''$, and then we extend this in a bilinear way to other elements of L. The completion of L with respect to this scalar product is called the tensor product of H' and H'' and is denoted $H' \otimes H''$.

We give a more precise construction in the special case when H' and H'' are separable. Let $e'_1, e'_2, \cdots$ and $e''_1, e''_2, \cdots$ be orthonormal bases for the spaces H' and H'' respectively; $e'_j \otimes e''_k$ denotes a formal product. The tensor product $H' \otimes H''$ is now defined to be the linear space of all vectors of the form $F = \sum_{j,k=1}^{\infty} F_{jk} e'_j \otimes e''_k$, where the F_{jk} are complex numbers satisfying the condition $\sum_{j,k=1}^{\infty} |F_{jk}|^2 < \infty$. On defining a scalar product by the formula $(F, G) = \sum_{j,k=1}^{\infty} F_{jk} \overline{G_{jk}}$, we see that $H' \otimes H''$ becomes a complete Hilbert space, and $e'_j \otimes e''_k$ is an orthonormal basis for the space. Let $f' = \sum_{j=1}^{\infty} f'_j e'_j$, $f'' = \sum_{k=1}^{\infty} f''_k e''_k$ be expansions of vectors in H' and H'' with respect to the corresponding bases, and put $f' \otimes f'' = \sum_{j,k=1}^{\infty} f'_j f''_k e'_j \otimes e''_k$. Obviously, conditions (2.1) and (2.2) are satisfied with this definition. It is also clear that the linear combinations of elements of the form $f' \otimes f''$ are dense in $H' \otimes H''$. If

$$f'_n \longrightarrow f' \text{ (in } H') \text{ and } f''_m \longrightarrow f'' \text{ (in } H''),$$

then

$$f'_n \otimes f''_m \longrightarrow f' \otimes f''$$

in $H' \otimes H''$ as $m, n \longrightarrow \infty$ (i.e. the tensor product is continuous with respect to its factors). Finally, we note that another choice of the bases e'_j and e''_k gives rise to a tensor product which is isometric with $H' \otimes H''$.

It is possible to define the tensor product $L' \otimes L''$ of two linear subspaces $L' \subseteq H'$ and $L'' \subseteq H''$: this is the set of all linear combinations of products $f' \otimes f''$ ($f' \in L'$, $f'' \in L''$). It is clear that $L' \otimes L''$ is dense in $H' \otimes H''$, if L' is dense in H' and L'' is dense in H''. We emphasize that we do not form the closure of the stated linear combinations for the definition of $L' \otimes L''$. Thus, for example, $H' \otimes H''$ has a double meaning depending on how H' and H'' are considered. In what follows, the meaning of $\otimes$ will be explained, if it is not clear from context.

One of the simplest examples of a tensor product is as follows: $H' = L_2(G')$ where G' is a region in n'-dimensional space with points x', and $H'' = L_2(G'')$ similarly. By the formal product $f' \otimes f''$ we understand the ordinary product $f'(x') f''(x'')$ of these functions; this is a function of the point $(x', x'') \in G' \times G''$. The scalar product (2.2) coincides with the scalar product in $L_2(G' \times G'')$, and the closure of the linear combinations of functions $f'(x') f''(x'')$ ($f' \in L_2(G')$, $f'' \in L_2(G'')$) is obviously all of $L_2(G' \times G'')$. Thus $L_2(G') \otimes L_2(G'') = L_2(G' \times G'')$. Other examples of tensor products will be given in §3.

Let A' be a continuous linear operator from a Hilbert space H' to a Hilbert space G', and similarly for A'' from H'' to G''. We define the tensor product $A' \otimes A''$ of the operators A' and A'' as an operator which maps $H' \otimes H''$ into $G' \otimes G''$. We first set

$$(A' \otimes A'')\Big(\sum_j f'_j \otimes f''_j\Big) = \sum_j (A'f'_j) \otimes (A''f''_j). \tag{2.3}$$

on elements of the form $\Sigma_j f'_j \otimes f''_j$ ($f'_j \in H'$, $f''_j \in H''$; the sum is finite).

This definition does not depend on the choice of representation of the element $\Sigma_j f'_j \otimes f''_j \in H' \otimes H''$ *as a finite sum of products* $h' \otimes h''$ ($h' \in H'$, $h'' \in H''$), *and the operator so defined from* $H' \otimes H''$ *to* $G' \otimes G''$ *is continuous. It may therefore be extended by continuity to an operator* $A' \otimes A''$ *which maps all of* $H' \otimes H''$ *into* $G' \otimes G''$. *For this operator*

$$\|A' \otimes A''\| = \|A'\| \, \|A''\|. \tag{2.4}$$

A proof of this assertion is given only in the separable case. It is convenient to proceed in the following way: we first define $A' \otimes A''$ in a somewhat different way on all of $H' \otimes H''$ and show that it is continuous. We then show that this operator acts according to (2.3) on elements of the form $\Sigma_j f'_j \otimes f''_j$.

Let e'_j and e''_k ($j, k = 1, 2, \cdots$) be any orthonormal bases for H' and H'' respectively. We will interpret the elements of $H' \otimes H''$ as vectors $F = \Sigma_{j,k=1}^{\infty} F_{jk} e'_j \otimes e''_k$, and set

$$AF = \sum_{j,k=1}^{\infty} F_{jk} (A'e'_j) \otimes (A''e''_k). \tag{2.5}$$

We will show that this series is weakly convergent in $G' \otimes G''$, and the operator A acts continuously from $H' \otimes H''$ to $G' \otimes G''$. In fact, let l'_α and l''_β ($\alpha, \beta = 1, 2, \cdots$) be any orthonormal bases for G' and G'', so that $l'_\alpha \otimes l''_\beta$ is an orthonormal basis for $G' \otimes G''$, and consider $U = \Sigma_{\alpha,\beta=1}^{\infty} U_{\alpha\beta} l'_\alpha \otimes l''_\beta \in G' \otimes G''$. Let F_k be a vector in H' with coordinates F_{jk} with respect to the basis e'_j, and let U_α be a vector in G'' with coordinates $U_{\alpha\beta}$ with respect to the basis l''_β. Let A''^* be the operator adjoint of A'', i.e. $(A''f'', g'')_{G''} = (f'', A''^* g'')_{H''}$ ($f'' \in H''$, $g'' \in G''$). Let $\Sigma_{j,k}$ denote a finite summation, and assume that $F_{jk} = 0$ for indices not occurring in this summation. We then have

$$\left|\left(\sum_{j,k} F_{jk}(A'e'_j)\otimes(A''e''_k), U\right)_{G'\otimes G''}\right|^2 =$$

$$= \left|\sum_{j,k}\sum_{\alpha,\beta=1}^{\infty} F_{jk}\bar{U}_{\alpha\beta}(A'e'_j, l'_\alpha)_{G'}(A''e''_k, l''_\beta)_{G''}\right|^2$$

$$= \left|\sum_{j,k}\sum_{\alpha,\beta=1}^{\infty}(A'e'_j, l'_\alpha)_{G'} F_{jk}\overline{(A''^*l''_\beta, e''_k)_{H''}U_{\alpha\beta}}\right|^2$$

$$= \left|\sum_{k}\sum_{\alpha=1}^{\infty}(A'F_k, l'_\alpha)_{G'}\overline{(A''^*U_\alpha, e''_k)_{H''}}\right|^2$$

$$\leqslant \sum_{k}\sum_{\alpha=1}^{\infty}|(A'F_k, l'_\alpha)_{G'}|^2\cdot\sum_{k=1}^{\infty}\sum_{\alpha=1}^{\infty}|(A''^*U_\alpha, e''_k)_{H''}|^2 =$$

$$= \sum_{k}\|A'F_k\|^2_{G'}\cdot\sum_{\alpha=1}^{\infty}\|A''^*U_\alpha\|^2_{H''} \leqslant \|A'\|^2\|A''^*\|^2\sum_{k}\|F_k\|^2_{H'}\cdot\sum_{\alpha=1}^{\infty}\|U_\alpha\|^2_{G''}$$

$$= \|A'\|^2\|A''\|^2\sum_{j,k}|F_{jk}|^2\cdot\sum_{\alpha,\beta=1}^{\infty}|U_{\alpha\beta}|^2.$$

Since U is arbitrary here, it follows that the series (2.5) converges weakly in $G'\otimes G''$, and we have the estimate $\|AF\|_{G'\otimes G''} \leq \|A'\|\,\|A''\|\,\|F\|_{H'\otimes H''}$. Therefore A is a continuous mapping of $H'\otimes H''$ into $G'\otimes G''$, and

$$\|A\| \leq \|A'\|\,\|A''\|. \tag{2.6}$$

We now compute the action of A on $F = \Sigma_\gamma f'_\gamma \otimes f''_\gamma$. Let $f'_{\gamma,j}$ and $f''_{\gamma,k}$ be the coordinates with respect to the bases e'_j and e''_k. Then in accordance with (2.3) we obtain

$$AF = A\left(\sum_{j,k=1}^{\infty}\left(\sum_{\gamma} f'_{\gamma,j}f''_{\gamma,k}\right)e'_j\otimes e''_k\right)$$

$$= \sum_{j,k=1}^{\infty}\left(\sum_{\gamma} f'_{\gamma,j}f''_{\gamma,k}\right)(A'e'_j)\otimes(A''e''_k) = \sum_{\gamma}(A'f'_\gamma)\otimes(A''f''_\gamma) = (A'\otimes A'')F.$$

Thus our continuous and well defined operator A coincides with the operator $A'\otimes A''$ defined by (2.3). Therefore $A'\otimes A''$ is well defined and continuous. The relation (2.4) follows from (2.6) and the equation $\|(A'\otimes A'')(f'\otimes f'')\|_{G'\otimes G''} = \|A'f'\|_{G'}\,\|A''f''\|_{G''}$ follows from (2.3) and the definition of the norm in $H'\otimes H''$. Our assertion follows.

We note the following simple properties of tensor products:

$$\begin{aligned} (A' + B') \otimes A'' &= A' \otimes A'' + B' \otimes A'', \\ A' \otimes (A'' + B'') &= A' \otimes A'' + A' \otimes B'', \\ \lambda(A' \otimes A'') &= (\lambda A') \otimes A'' = A' \otimes (\lambda A''), \\ (C' \otimes C'')(A' \otimes A'') &= (C'A') \otimes (C''A''), \\ (A' \otimes A'')^* &= A'^* \otimes A''^*. \end{aligned} \tag{2.7}$$

These properties follow easily from (2.3). In particular, the fourth relation in (2.7) implies the commutativity of any two operators of the form $E' \otimes A''$ and $A' \otimes E''$ where E', E'' are the identity operators. Notice also that $(A' \otimes A'')^{-1} = A'^{-1} \otimes A''^{-1}$.

In what follows we will also use tensor products $A' \otimes A''$ of operators A' and A'' with domains $\mathfrak{D}(A')$ and $\mathfrak{D}(A'')$, at least one of which is not the full space. For $\mathfrak{D}(A' \otimes A'')$ we take the tensor product $\mathfrak{D}(A') \otimes \mathfrak{D}(A'')$ of the linear subspaces $\mathfrak{D}(A')$ and $\mathfrak{D}(A'')$ and define $A' \otimes A''$ by the formula (2.3), where $f'_j \in \mathfrak{D}(A')$, $f''_j \in \mathfrak{D}(A'')$. It follows from previous assertions that the definition is meaningful (note that in the case of continuous A' and A'' we pass to the extension by continuity).

2. **Tensor products of spaces with positive and negative norms.** Suppose that we have two sequences of spaces with positive, zero, and negative norms:

$$H'_- \supseteq H'_0 \supseteq H'_+, \quad H''_- \supseteq H''_0 \supseteq H''_+. \tag{2.8}$$

On taking the tensor products of these spaces we obtain

$$H'_- \otimes H''_- \supseteq H'_0 \otimes H''_0 \supseteq H'_+ \otimes H''_+.$$

The elements of these spaces will usually be denoted by $A, B, \cdots$; $F, G, \cdots$ and $U, V, \cdots$ respectively. Quantities related to the first sequence in (2.8) will be written with a prime, the second, with two primes.

It is clear that the inclusion operator O of the space $H'_+ \otimes H''_+$ in $H'_0 \otimes H''_0$ is equal to $O' \otimes O''$, and therefore $\|O\| = \|O'\| \, \|O''\| \le 1$ by the general equation (2.4). It follows that $\|U\|_{H'_0 \otimes H''_0} = \|OU\|_{H'_0 \otimes H''_0} \le \|U\|_{H'_+ \otimes H''_+}$. Since $H'_+ \otimes H''_+$ is dense in $H'_0 \otimes H''_0$, we can consider $H'_+ \otimes H''_+$ as a positive space with respect to $H'_0 \otimes H''_0$.

Theorem 2.1. *Let $\mathcal{H}_0 = H'_0 \otimes H''_0$ be considered as a space with zero norm and $\mathcal{H}_+ = H'_+ \otimes H''_+$ as a space with positive norm. Then $H'_- \otimes H''_-$ coincides with the corresponding negative space $\mathcal{H}_-$. The operators I, $\mathbf{I}$, D, $\mathbf{D}$, J, $\mathbf{J}$ are equal to* *the tensor products of the corresponding operators in the first and second sequences in* (2.8) (*for example*, $I = I' \otimes I''$).

Proof. First note that from the equation $O = O' \otimes O''$ and the general relation $(A' \otimes A'')^* = A'^* \otimes A''^*$, it follows that

$$I = I' \otimes I''. \tag{2.9}$$

To construct the space $\mathcal{H}_-$ we must form the closure of $H'_0 \otimes H''_0$ with respect to the scalar product $(F, G)_- = (IF, G)_{H'_0 \otimes H''_0}$; but since the elements of the form $\sum_j f'_j \otimes f''_j$ (finite sums) are dense in $H'_0 \otimes H''_0$, it is sufficient to form the closure of these elements. However, by (2.2)

$$\left(\sum_j f'_j \otimes f''_j, \sum_k g'_k \otimes g''_k\right)_- = \left(\sum_j (I'f'_j) \otimes (I''f''_j), \sum_k g'_k \otimes g''_k\right)_{H'_0 \otimes H''_0}$$

$$= \sum_{j,k} (I'f'_j, g'_k)_{H'_0} (I''f''_j, g''_k)_{H''_0} = \sum_{j,k} (f'_j, g'_k)_{H'_-} (f''_j, g''_k)_{H''_-} =$$

$$= \left(\sum_j f'_j \otimes f''_j, \sum_k g'_k \otimes g''_k\right)_{H'_- \otimes H''_-},$$

from which it follows that this closure coincides with the closure with respect to the norm in $H'_- \otimes H''_-$, which is, obviously, all of $H'_- \otimes H''_-$. Thus

$$\mathcal{H}_- = H'_- \otimes H''_-. \tag{2.10}$$

Further, from (2.10) it easily follows that $\mathbf{I} = \mathbf{I}' \otimes \mathbf{I}''$: because of (2.9),

$$\mathbf{I}\left(\sum_j f'_j \otimes f''_j\right) = \sum_j (\mathbf{I}'f'_j) \otimes (\mathbf{I}''f''_j) \quad (f'_j \in H'_0, f''_j \in H''_0) \tag{2.11}$$

(finite sum). Let $f'_{jn} \longrightarrow \alpha'_j \in H'_-$ for each j ($n \longrightarrow \infty$, convergence in H'_-), and similarly let $f''_{jn} \longrightarrow \alpha''_j \in H''_-$ in H''_-. On writing (2.11) for these sequences and passing to the limit, we find that the equation $\mathbf{I} = \mathbf{I}' \otimes \mathbf{I}''$ holds on elements of the form $\sum_j \alpha'_j \otimes \alpha''_j$, and hence everywhere. The passage to the limit may be performed because of the continuity of a tensor product with respect to its factors, the continuity of the operators $\mathbf{I}, \mathbf{I}', \mathbf{I}''$, and equation (2.10).

Consider the operator $\hat{I} = OI$. Because of $O = O' \otimes O''$, $(C' \otimes C'')(A' \otimes A'') = (C'A') \otimes (C''A'')$, and (2.9), we have $\hat{I} = \hat{I}' \otimes \hat{I}''$. From this we conclude that $J' \otimes J'' = \sqrt{\hat{I}'} \otimes \sqrt{\hat{I}''} = \sqrt{\hat{I}} = J$. On forming closures in the equation $J = J' \otimes J''$, we find that $\mathbf{J} = \mathbf{J}' \otimes \mathbf{J}''$ (as in the case of the operator $\mathbf{I}$). In exactly the same way for the equations involving the inverse operators, we obtain similar representations for D and **D**. The theorem follows.

Consider two sequences of spaces as in (1.10):

$$H'_{-2} \supset H'_{-1} \supset H'_0 \supset H'_{+1} \supset H'_{+2}, \quad H''_{-2} \supset H''_{-1} \supset H''_0 \supset H''_{+1} \supset H''_{+2}.$$

Let $\mathcal{H}_j = H'_j \otimes H''_j$ $(j = 0, \pm 1, \pm 2)$. This notation is appropriate: if $\mathcal{H}_0$ is considered as a space with zero norm, then $\mathcal{H}_{+1}$ and $\mathcal{H}_{+2}$ may be considered as spaces with positive norm, and moreover $\mathcal{H}_{+2}$ is dense in $\mathcal{H}_{+1}$. By the theorem just proved, the space with negative norm corresponding to $\mathcal{H}_{+1} = H'_{+1} \otimes H''_{+1}$ coincides with $H'_{-1} \otimes H''_{-1} = \mathcal{H}_{-1}$, and similarly for $\mathcal{H}_{+2}$. Thus the sequence

$$\mathcal{H}_{-2} \supset \mathcal{H}_{-1} \supset \mathcal{H}_0 \supset \mathcal{H}_{+1} \supset \mathcal{H}_{+2}$$

has all the properties of the sequence (1.10).

Consider an operator A which acts continuously from all of $\mathcal{H}_k$ to $\mathcal{H}_l$ $(k, l \geq 0)$; according to §1.3 there exists an adjoint operator A^+ which satisfies $(\mathbf{A}, AU)_0 = (A^+ \mathbf{A}, U)_0$ $(\mathbf{A} \in \mathcal{H}_{-l}, U \in \mathcal{H}_k)$. If A' and A'' act continuously from H'_k to H'_l and from H''_k to H''_l respectively $(k, l \geq 0)$, then the operator $A = A' \otimes A''$ is continuous as a mapping of $\mathcal{H}_k$ into $\mathcal{H}_l$. It is not difficult to show that

$$(A' \otimes A'')^+ = A'^+ \otimes A''^+. \tag{2.12}$$

3. **Generalized kernels.** As a preliminary, we recall some concepts concerning ordinary kernels. Let Q be any set. A complex valued function $K(x, y)$ of points $(x, y) \in Q \times Q$ is called a kernel. A kernel is called Hermitian if $K(x, y) = \overline{K(y, x)}$ $(x, y \in Q)$, and positive definite if for any finite set of points $x_1, \cdots$ $\cdots, x_N \in Q$ and any complex numbers $\xi_1, \cdots, \xi_N$

$$\sum_{j,k=1}^{N} K(x_j, x_k)\, \xi_k \bar{\xi}_j \geq 0.$$

The condition asserts that each of the matrices $\| K(x_j, x_k) \|_1^N$ is nonnegative. It follows that the kernel is Hermitian and satisfies the inequality $|K(x, y)|^2 \leq K(x, x)\, K(y, y)$ $(x, y \in Q)$.

Along with this "point" definition, it is possible to give an "integral" definition. Let Q be a locally compact separable space, and let dx be a measure, defined on the Borel sets in Q, which is finite on compact sets and positive on open sets. A function $K(x, y)$ of points $(x, y) \in Q \times Q$, which is locally summable with respect to the measure $dxdy$, is also called a kernel. It is called Hermitian if $B_K(u, v) = \overline{B_K(v, u)}$ for any $u, v \in C(Q)$ with compact support, where the bilinear form is given by

$$B_K(u, v) = \int_Q \int_Q K(x, y) u(y) \overline{v(x)}\, dxdy.$$

This is obviously equivalent to the equation $K(x, y) = \overline{K(y, x)}$ for almost all points $(x, y) \in Q \times Q$. If for all such u, $B_K(u, u) \geq 0$, then the kernel $K(x, y)$ is called positive definite. By the Cauchy-Bunjakovskiĭ inequality, $|B_K(u, v)|^2 \leq B_K(u, u) B_K(v, v)$, from which it follows that $|K(x, y)|^2 \leq K(x, x) K(y, y)$ for almost all $(x, y) \in Q \times Q$, if only the behavior of $K(x, y)$ near the diagonal $x = y$ is "sufficiently nice". It is not difficult to see that if the kernel $K(x, y)$ is continuous as a function of $(x, y) \in Q \times Q$, then the "point" and "integral" definitions of positive definiteness are equivalent.

We now consider generalizations of these concepts. We introduce the concept of a generalized kernel in a way similar to that used in L. Schwartz's theory of generalized functions. An arbitrary space H_+ with positive norm will play the role of the space of basic functions of one variable. We use an abstract concept of conjugation which describes the passage from a function $u(x)$ to $\overline{u(x)}$.

Thus, suppose that we have a sequence of spaces

$$H_- \supseteq H_0 \supseteq H_+. \tag{2.13}$$

Suppose that $f \longrightarrow \bar{f}$ is a conjugation in H_0. We will assume that H_+ is invariant under this conjugation and $(\bar{u}, \bar{v})_+ = \overline{(u, v)}_+$; in other words $u \longrightarrow \bar{u}$ is a conjugation in H_+. Because of this isometric property of the conjugation operator, we obtain a conjugation in H_-. Precisely, it is given by the relation

$$\alpha \longrightarrow \bar{\alpha} = \mathbf{I}^{-1}(\overline{\mathbf{I}\alpha}) \quad (\alpha \in H_-). \tag{2.14}$$

It is easily verified that (2.14) is a conjugation in H_-. It is essential that it coincide with the previous conjugation on H_0. In fact,

$$(I\bar{f}, u)_+ = (\bar{f}, u)_0 = \overline{(\bar{u}, f)_0} = \overline{(\bar{u}, If)_+} = (\overline{If}, u)_+$$
$$(f \in H_0,\, u \in H_+),$$

i.e. $I\bar{f} = \overline{If}$, and hence (2.14) coincides with the previous conjugation in H_0.

An operator A, which maps any one of the spaces in the sequence (2.13) into any other one, is called real if $\mathfrak{D}(A)$ is invariant under the conjugation and $A\bar{\alpha} = \overline{A\alpha}$ $(\alpha \in \mathfrak{D}(A))$. It follows from equation (2.14) that $\mathbf{I}$ is real. Since $\mathbf{I}$ is real, it is easily seen that D, $\mathbf{D}$, J, and $\mathbf{J}$ are real.

We proceed to the definition of a generalized kernel. Suppose that we have a sequence (2.13) of spaces with a conjugation. We construct the sequence

$$H_- \otimes H_- \supseteq H_0 \otimes H_0 \supseteq H_+ \otimes H_+.$$

According to Theorem 2.1, we may take $\mathcal{H}_0 = H_0 \otimes H_0$ as a zero space and $\mathcal{H}_+ = H_+ \otimes H_+$ and $\mathcal{H}_- = H_- \otimes H_-$ as positive and negative spaces. The elements K of $H_- \otimes H_-$ are called generalized kernels. If $K \in H_0 \otimes H_0$ or $K \in H_+ \otimes H_+$, then K will be called, correspondingly, a simple kernel or a smooth kernel.

For every generalized kernel K there is an analogue of the form $\int_Q \int_Q K(x, y)\, u(y)\, \overline{v(x)}\, dxdy$ for ordinary kernels; it is the bilinear form B_K:

$$B_K(u, v) = (K, v \otimes \bar{u})_0 \qquad (u, v \in H_+), \tag{2.15}$$

and it is continuous with respect to convergence of u and v in H_+ (continuity follows from $\|v \otimes \bar{u}\|_{H_+ \otimes H_+} = \|v\|_{H_+} \|u\|_{H_+}$). It is clear that the form B_K completely defines the kernel K; i.e. the function $(K, U)_0$ $(U \in H_+ \otimes H_+)$ is determined by the function $B_K(u, v)$ $(u, v \in H_+)$. However, it should be kept in mind that not every bilinear form on H_+ is given by (2.15) for some generalized kernel (see subsection 4).

A generalized kernel K is called Hermitian (positive definite) if the form $B_K(u, v)$ is Hermitian (positive definite). It is clear that every positive definite kernel is automatically Hermitian.

The theory of generalized kernels is a particular case of the theory in §1, and therefore the general results obtained there are valid for kernels. The verifications will not be repeated here. We only note the following important fact: let $K \in H_0 \otimes H_0$ be an ordinary kernel and let A' and A'' be two operators acting continuously from H_+ to H_0. Then from (2.12) it follows that there exists a generalized kernel $\Phi \in H_- \otimes H_-$ (namely $\Phi = (A'^+ \otimes A''^+) K$) such that

$$(K, (A' \otimes A'')\, U)_0 = (\Phi, U)_0 \qquad (U \in H_+ \otimes H_+). \tag{2.16}$$

When A' and A'' are real operators, the relation (2.16) is usually written in terms of bilinear forms. Namely, on setting $U = v \otimes \bar{u}$ we obtain an equation equivalent to (2.16):

$$(K, (A'v) \otimes \overline{(A''u)})_0 = (\Phi, v \otimes \bar{u})_0 \quad \text{or} \quad B_K(A''u, A'v) = B_\Phi(u, v) \quad (u, v \in H_+). \tag{2.17}$$

4. **A theorem on kernels.** We prove an abstract form of a theorem of L. Schwartz which asserts that every continuous bilinear form may be written in terms of a generalized kernel. We assume below that H_+, and hence H_0 and H_-,

are separable.

Recall that an operator C, acting from a separable Hilbert space H_1 to a Hilbert space H_2 is of Hilbert-Schmidt type if for some (and hence any) orthonormal basis $e_1, e_2, \cdots$ of the space H_1 the series $\sum_{j=1}^{\infty} \|Ce_j\|_{H_2}^2$ converges (see also Chapter V, §1.1). If H_1 is contained in H_2, we say that the inclusion is quasi-nuclear if the inclusion operator is of Hilbert-Schmidt type.

Theorem 2.2. *Let $H_- \supseteq H_0 \supseteq H_+$ be a sequence of spaces with a conjugation, and suppose that the inclusion $H_+ \longrightarrow H_0$ is quasi-nuclear. Then every continuous bilinear form $B(f, g)$ on the space H_0 may be written in terms of a generalized kernel $\Phi \in H_- \otimes H_-$:*

$$B(u, v) = (\Phi, v \otimes \bar{u})_0 \quad (u, v \in H_+). \tag{2.18}$$

This kernel is of the form $\Phi = (\mathbf{D} \otimes \mathbf{D}) K$, where K is an ordinary kernel; moreover, K will survive application of each of the operators $\mathbf{D} \otimes E$ and $E \otimes \mathbf{D}$: the kernels $(\mathbf{D} \otimes E)K$, $(E \otimes \mathbf{D}) K \in H_0 \otimes H_0$, that is, they are ordinary. Thus equation (2.18) may be written

$$B(u, v) = ((\mathbf{D} \otimes \mathbf{D}) K, v \otimes \bar{u})_0 = (K, (Dv) \otimes \overline{(Du)})_0$$
$$(u, v \in H_+), \tag{2.19}$$

$$B(u, g) = ((E \otimes \mathbf{D}) (\mathbf{D} \otimes E) K, g \otimes \bar{u})_0 = ((\mathbf{D} \otimes E) K, g \otimes \overline{(Du)})_0$$
$$(u \in H_+, g \in H_0), \tag{2.20}$$

$$B(f, v) = ((\mathbf{D} \otimes E) (E \otimes \mathbf{D}) K, v \otimes \bar{f})_0 = ((E \otimes \mathbf{D}) K, (Dv) \otimes \bar{f})_0$$
$$(f \in H_0, v \in H_+). \tag{2.21}$$

Conversely, if every continuous bilinear form $B(f, g)$ on H_0 may be written in either of the forms $B(u, g) = (K_1, g \otimes \overline{(Du)})_0$ $(u \in H_+, g \in H_0)$ or $B(f, v) = (K_2, (Dv) \otimes \bar{f})_0$ $(f \in H_0, v \in H_+)$, where $K_1, K_2 \in H_0 \otimes H_0$, then the inclusion $H_+ \longrightarrow H_0$ is quasi-nuclear.

The proof is based on the following simple fact.

Lemma 2.1. *Let H be a separable Hilbert space with conjugation, and let C be a bounded operator acting in H. The form $(Cf, g)_H$ may be written in the form $(K, g \otimes \bar{f})_{H \otimes H}$ $(f, g \in H)$ for some element K of $H \otimes H$ if and only if C is of Hilbert-Schmidt type.*

In fact, if $e_1, e_2, \cdots$ is an orthonormal basis for H, so is $\bar{e}_1, \bar{e}_2, \cdots$. The vectors $e_j \otimes \bar{e}_k$ form an orthonormal basis for $H \otimes H$, and therefore from the equation

$$(Cf, g)_H = (K, g \otimes \bar{f})_{H \otimes H} \qquad (f, g \in H)$$

we obtain

$$\sum_{j,k=1}^{\infty} |(Ce_k, e_j)_H|^2 = \sum_{j,k=1}^{\infty} |(K, e_j \otimes \bar{e}_k)_{H \otimes H}|^2 = \| K \|^2_{H \otimes H} < \infty$$

and so C is of Hilbert-Schmidt type. Conversely, suppose that C is of Hilbert-Schmidt type, i.e. $\sum_{j,k=1}^{\infty} |(Ce_k, e_j)_H|^2 < \infty$. Then we can take for K the element of $H \otimes H$ whose coordinates with respect to the basis $e_j \otimes \bar{e}_k$ are the numbers $(Ce_k, e_j)_H$; obviously, $(Cf, g)_H = (K, g \otimes \bar{f})_{H \otimes H}$ $(f, g \in H)$. The lemma follows.

We proceed to the proof of the theorem. First we note that *the inclusion* $H_+ \longrightarrow H_0$ *is quasi-nuclear if and only if* J, *considered as an operator in* H_0, *is an operator of Hilbert-Schmidt type (i.e.* $\hat{J} = OJ$ *is of Hilbert-Schmidt type).*

In fact, if the inclusion $H_+ \longrightarrow H_0$ is quasi-nuclear, and if $e_1, e_2, \cdots$ is an orthonormal basis for H_+, then $\sum_{j=1}^{\infty} \|e_j\|_0^2 < \infty$. In other words, $\sum_{j=1}^{\infty} \|\hat{J} l_j\|_0^2 = \sum_{j=1}^{\infty} \|e_j\|_0^2 < \infty$, where $l_j = De_j$ is an orthonormal basis for H_0; i.e. $\hat{J}$ is an operator of Hilbert-Schmidt type. The argument can be reversed and shows that $H_+ \longrightarrow H_0$ is quasi-nuclear if $\hat{J}$ is an operator of Hilbert-Schmidt type.

Now suppose that the inclusion $H_+ \longrightarrow H_0$ is quasi-nuclear. The form $B(f, g)$ may be written in the form $B(f, g) = (Af, g)_0$ $(f, g \in H_0)$, where A is a continuous operator in H_0. Let $C = \hat{J} A \hat{J}$. The operator C in H_0 is an operator of Hilbert-Schmidt type since, as is well known, the product of two bounded operators acting in some space is of Hilbert-Schmidt type if one of the original operators is of Hilbert-Schmidt type. Let $K \in H_0 \otimes H_0$ be the corresponding kernel in Lemma 2.1. Then for any $u, v \in H_+$ we obtain

$$B(u, v) = (Au, v)_0 = (A\hat{J}Du, \hat{J}Dv)_0 = (CDu, Dv)_0 = (K, (Dv) \otimes (\overline{Du}))_0$$

$$= (K, (Dv) \otimes (D\bar{u}))_0 = (K, (D \otimes D)(v \otimes \bar{u}))_0 = ((D \otimes D)^+ K, v \otimes \bar{u})_0$$

$$= ((D^+ \otimes D^+) K, v \otimes \bar{u})_0 = ((\mathbf{D} \otimes \mathbf{D}) K, v \otimes \bar{u})_0,$$

i.e. (2.19) is established.

We show that $(\mathbf{D} \otimes E) K \in H_0 \otimes H_0$. In fact, for $u, v \in H_+$ we have

$$((\mathbf{D} \otimes E) K, v \otimes \bar{u})_0 = (K, (D \otimes E)(v \otimes \bar{u}))_0 = (K, (Dv) \otimes \bar{u})_0,$$

$$= (\hat{J} A \hat{J} u, Dv)_0 = (A\hat{J}u, v)_0 = (K_1, v \otimes \bar{u})_0, \tag{2.22}$$

where $K_1 \in H_0 \otimes H_0$ is the kernel constructed in Lemma 2.1 for the Hilbert-Schmidt operator $A\hat{J}$ By the arbitrariness of u and v in (2.22), it follows that $(\mathbf{D} \otimes E)K = K_1 \in H_0 \otimes H_0$, and the assertion follows. The proof that $(E \otimes \mathbf{D})K \in H_0 \otimes H_0$ is similar.

We now prove the converse statement in the theorem. Suppose, for example, that for any form $B(f, g)$ the representation $B(u, g) = (K_1, g \otimes \overline{(Du)})_0$ is valid, $K_1 \in H_0 \otimes H_0$. Letting $B(f, g) = (f, g)_0$, we obtain

$$(\hat{J}f, g)_0 = B(\hat{J}f, g) = (K_1, g \otimes \overline{(DJf)})_0 = (K_1, g \otimes \bar{f})_0 \quad (f, g \in H_0).$$

It follows from Lemma 2.1 that $\hat{J}$ is a Hilbert-Schmidt operator; i.e. the inclusion $H_+ \longrightarrow H_0$ is quasi-nuclear. The theorem is completely proved.

The presence of a conjugation in the spaces in the chain $H_- \supseteq H_0 \supseteq H_+$ is required only for our particular method of construction of forms with respect to kernels (see (2.15)). Clearly, it is possible to prove a similar theorem without this condition. Theorem 2.2 is essentially a consequence of two simple facts: Lemma 2.1 and the fact that the product of two bounded operators, one of which is of Hilbert-Schmidt type, is of Hilbert-Schmidt type.

In conclusion, note that *the inclusion $H_+ \longrightarrow H_0$ is quasi-nuclear if and only if the inclusion $H_0 \longrightarrow H_-$ is quasi-nuclear.* This follows quickly from the fact that orthonormal bases for the spaces H_+ and H_0 map into one another under the operators D and J, and from the isometric natures of $\mathbf{D}$ and $\mathbf{J}$.

§3. EXAMPLES OF SYSTEMS OF GENERALIZED FUNCTIONS

1. **Sobolev spaces.** Let G be a bounded region in n-dimensional space E_n with piecewise smooth boundary Γ. Take for the zero space $L_2(G) = W_2^0(G)$, and for the positive space the Sobolev space $W_2^l(G)$ $(l = 1, 2, \cdots)$; the corresponding negative space, consisting of generalized functions, is denoted $W_2^{-l}(G)$. The scalar product and norm in the space $W_2^k(G)$ $(k = \cdots, -1, 0, 1, \cdots)$ are denoted by $(\cdot,\cdot)_k$ and $\|\cdot\|_k$ respectively. We obtain the following relations (see (1.10)):

$$\begin{gathered}\cdots \supseteq W_2^{-2}(G) \supseteq W_2^{-1}(G) \supseteq W_2^0(G) \supseteq W_2^1(G) \supseteq W_2^2(G) \supseteq \cdots, \\ \cdots \leqslant \|u\|_{-2} \leqslant \|u\|_{-1} \leqslant \|u\|_0 \leqslant \|u\|_1 \leqslant \|u\|_2 \leqslant \cdots,\end{gathered} \tag{3.1}$$

and moreover, each space $W_2^l(G)$ is dense in each $W_2^k(G)$ if $k < l$ $(k, l = \cdots, -1, 0, 1, \cdots)$. The operators I, $\mathbf{I}$, J, $\cdots$, constructed for the chain $W_2^{-l}(G) \supseteq W_2^0(G) \supseteq W_2^l(G)$, are written with an index l.

Using the methods in the example in §1.2, it is possible to show that each I_l is an integral operator whose kernel is the Green's function for a boundary value problem corresponding to some elliptic differential equation of order $2l$, obtained from the scalar product $(u, v)_l$ by shifting all derivatives to u. It is possible to study the properties of the spaces $W_2^{-l}(G)$ in this way, but this approach is awkward and will not be pursued here.

It follows from the Imbedding Theorem (see §6 of the Introduction) that for $l > n/2$, $W_2^l(G) \subset C(C = C(G \cup \Gamma)$, the space of continuous functions on $G \cup \Gamma)$ and the correspondence $u \longrightarrow u(\xi)$ $(u \in W_2^l(G),\ \xi \in G \cup \Gamma)$ is continuous; therefore $f(u) = u(\xi)$ is a functional on $W_2^l(G)$ and may be written in terms of $W_2^{-l}(G)$: there exists $\delta_\xi \in W_2^{-l}(G)$ such that

$$(u, \delta_\xi)_0 = \overline{(\delta_\xi, u)_0} = u(\xi) \qquad (u \in W_2^l(G), \xi \in G \cup \Gamma). \tag{3.2}$$

Thus for $l > n/2$, $W_2^{-l}(G)$ contains the generalized function δ_ξ concentrated at ξ. It satisfies (3.2).

Lemma 3.1. *δ_ξ is a continuous vector-valued function of $\xi \in G \cup \Gamma$ with values in $W_2^{-l}(G)$ $(l > n/2)$.*

Proof. Consider the inclusion operator O acting from the space $W_2^l(G)$ to C. As is known, O is completely continuous. We pass to the adjoint space. Since $W_2^l(G) \subset C$ and $\|u\|_C \leq A\|u\|_l$, it follows that $W_2^{-l}(G) \supset C'$ and $\|\alpha\|_{-l} \leq A\|\alpha\|_{C'}$. The operator O^*, adjoint to the inclusion operator, acts from C' to the space $W_2^{-l}(G)$, and it transforms each functional in C' into another such functional; moreover since O is completely continuous, O^* is completely continuous. Now suppose that $\xi_n \longrightarrow \xi$ $(\xi_n, \xi \in G \cup \Gamma)$ but $\delta_{\xi_n} \not\rightarrow \delta_\xi$ in $W_2^{-l}(G)$. Then there exists an $\epsilon_0 > 0$ and a subsequence $\delta_{\xi'_n}$ of the sequence δ_{ξ_n} such that

$$\|\delta_{\xi'_n} - \delta_\xi\|_{-l} \geqslant \varepsilon_0. \tag{3.3}$$

If δ_y is considered as a functional in C', then $\|\delta_y\|_{C'} = 1$. By virtue of the complete continuity of the operator O^*, the sequence $\delta_{\xi'_n}$ is precompact in $W_2^{-l}(G)$; choose a convergent subsequence $\delta_{\xi'_{nk}}$, $\delta_{\xi'_{nk}} \longrightarrow \alpha \in W_2^{-l}(G)$. If $u \in W_2^l(G)$, then $(\alpha, u)_0 = \lim(\delta_{\xi'_{nk}}, u)_0 = \lim \overline{u(\xi'_{nk})} = \overline{u(\xi)} = (\delta_\xi, u)_0$, i.e. $\alpha = \delta_\xi$, in contradiction to (3.3). The lemma follows.

Theorem 3.1. *If $l > n/2$, then the operator $\hat{I}_l$ is an integral operator with positive definite kernel $K(x, \xi)$ which is continuous with respect to*

$(x, \xi) \in (G \cup \Gamma) \times (G \cup \Gamma)$.

Proof. If $f \in L_2(G)$, then according to (1.7) we have

$$(\hat{I}_l f)(x) = (I_l f, \delta_x)_0 = (f, \mathrm{I}_l \delta_x)_0 = \int_G \overline{(\mathrm{I}_l \delta_x)(\xi)}\, f(\xi)\, d\xi.$$

Let $K(x, \xi) = (\mathrm{I}_l \delta_x)(\xi)$. Since by Lemma 3.1 δ_x depends continuously on x, and I_l acts continuously from $W_2^{-l}(G)$ to $W_2^l(G)$, $\mathrm{I}_l \delta_x$ is a continuous vector-valued function of $x \in G \cup \Gamma$ with values in $W_2^l(G)$. Similarly for $\mathrm{I}_l \delta_x$ as a function with values in C, since $\|u\|_l \geq (1/A)\, \|u\|_C$; this gives the required continuity of $K(x, \xi)$ with respect to (x, ξ). The positive definiteness of $K(x, \xi)$ follows from the fact that $\hat{I}_l$ is nonnegative. The theorem follows.

Corollary 1. *If $l > n/2$, the operator $\hat{I}_l$ has a finite trace (i.e. for some, and hence every, orthonormal basis $e_1, e_2, \cdots \in L_2(G)$,* tr. $(\hat{I}_l) = \Sigma_{j=1}^{\infty} (\hat{I}_l e_j, e_j)_0 < \infty$) (see also Chapter V, §1.1).

This follows from the theorem and the following general fact, which is obtained from Mercer's theorem: if K is an integral operator in $L_2(G)$ (G bounded), whose kernel $K(x, \xi)$ is positive definite and continuous with respect to $(x, \xi) \in (G \cup \Gamma) \times (G \cup \Gamma)$, then tr. $(K) < \infty$.

Corollary 2. *If $l > n/2$, then $\hat{J}_l$ is a Hilbert-Schmidt operator; i.e. the inclusion $W_2^l(G) \longrightarrow L_2(G)$ is quasi-nuclear.*

2. Generalized kernels. We construct the tensor products of the spaces $W_2^k(G)$ in the sequence (3.1)

$$\cdots \supseteq W_2^{-2}(G) \otimes W_2^{-2}(G) \supseteq W_2^{-1}(G) \otimes W_2^{-1}(G) \supseteq L_2(G \times G)$$
$$\supseteq W_2^1(G) \otimes W_2^1(G) \supseteq W_2^2(G) \otimes W_2^2(G) \supseteq \cdots; \tag{3.4}$$

and take into account the fact that $L_2(G) \otimes L_2(G) = L_2(G \times G)$ (the operation $\otimes_H$ is now the usual product of functions: $f(x) \otimes g(y) = f(x)\, g(y)$). Each space $W_2^{-l}(G) \otimes_H W_2^{-l}(G)$ is a negative space with respect to the positive space $W_2^l(G) \otimes W_2^l(G)$ and the zero space $L_2(G \times G)$ (Theorem 2.1). The elements of $W_2^l(G) \otimes W_2^l(G)$ are called smooth; the elements of $L_2(G \times G)$ are called ordinary; and the elements of $W_2^{-l}(G) \otimes W_2^{-l}(G)$ are called generalized kernels ($l = 1, 2, \cdots$). These elements are denoted respectively by $U(x, y), V(x, y), \cdots$; $K(x, y), H(x, y), \cdots$ and $\Phi, \Psi, \cdots$.

If $u(x) \in W_2^l(G)$, then we can apply differentiation $D^\alpha(|\alpha| \leq l)$ to $u(x)$, and

$D^\alpha u \in W_2^{l-|\alpha|}(G)$ where $D^\alpha = D_1^{\alpha_1} \cdots D_n^{\alpha_n}$, $D_j = \partial/\partial x_j$, $\alpha = (\alpha_1, \cdots, \alpha_n)$, $|\alpha| = \alpha_1 + \cdots + \alpha_n$. Therefore $D^\alpha \otimes D^\beta$ $(|\alpha|, |\beta| \le l)$ is defined on $W_2^l(G) \otimes W_2^l(G)$ and it maps this space into $W_2^{l-|\alpha|}(G) \otimes W_2^{l-|\beta|}(G)$. The operator $D^\alpha \otimes D^\beta$ can be written as a finite product of commutative operators which are of the form $D_j \otimes E$ or $E \otimes D_j$. This means that for $U(x, y) \in W_2^l(G) \otimes W_2^l(G)$, the derivatives $\partial^{|\alpha|+|\beta|} U/\partial x_1^{\alpha_1} \cdots \partial x_n^{\alpha_n} \partial y_1^{\beta_1} \cdots \partial y_n^{\beta_n}$ exist and are sufficiently smooth, and moreover differentiation can be performed in any other.

We clarify the connection between $W_2^k(G) \otimes W_2^k(G)$ and the Sobolev space $W_2^m(G \times G)$ constructed from the region $G \times G$.

Theorem 3.2. *The following inclusions and inequalities hold:*

$$W_2^{-2l}(G \times G) \supset W_2^{-l}(G) \otimes W_2^{-l}(G) \supset L_2(G \times G) \supset W_2^l(G) \otimes W_2^l(G) \supset W_2^{2l}(G \times G),$$

$$\frac{1}{C} \| U \|_{W_2^{-2l}(G \times G)} \le \| U \|_{W_2^l(G) \otimes W_2^l(G)} \le \| U \|_{L_2(G \times G)} \le \| U \|_{W_2^l(G) \otimes W_2^l(G)} \le$$
$$\le C \| U \|_{W_2^{2l}(G \times G)} \tag{3.5}$$
$$(U \in W_2^{2l}(G \times G); \quad l = 1, 2, \ldots; \quad C > 0);$$

moreover each space in the sequence (3.5) *is dense in each space to its left.*

Proof. We first prove the inequality on the right in (3.5). Suppose first that U has the form

$$U(x, y) = \sum_j u_j'(x) u_j''(y) \tag{3.6}$$

$(u_j', u_j'' \in W_2^{2l}(G)$; the sum is finite). Then

$$(U, U)_{W_2^{2l}(G \times G)} \ge (U, U)_{L_2(G \times G)} + \sum_{|\alpha| = l} (D_x^\alpha U, D_x^\alpha U)_{L_2(G \times G)}$$
$$+ \sum_{|\beta| = l} (D_y^\beta U, D_y^\beta U)_{L_2(G \times G)} + \sum_{|\alpha| = |\beta| = l} (D_x^\alpha D_y^\beta U, D_x^\alpha D_y^\beta U)_{L_2(G \times G)}$$
$$= \sum_{j, k} \{(u_j', u_k')_{L_2(G)} (u_j'', u_k'')_{L_2(G)} + (u_j'', u_k'')_{L_2(G)} \sum_{|\alpha| = l} (D^\alpha u_j', D^\alpha u_k')_{L_2(G)}$$
$$+ (u_j', u_k')_{L_2(G)} \sum_{|\beta| = l} (D^\beta u_j'', D^\beta u_k'')_{L_2(G)}$$
$$+ \sum_{|\alpha| = |\beta| = l} (D^\alpha u_j', D^\alpha u_k')_{L_2(G)} (D^\beta u_j'', D^\beta u_k'')_{L_2(G)}\} =$$
$$= \sum_{j, k} (u_j', u_k')_{W_2^l(G)} (u_j'', u_k'')_{W_2^l(G)} = (U, U)_{W_2^l(G) \otimes W_2^l(G)}.$$

Here we use the expression for the scalar product in W_2^l which contains only the zeroth and lth derivatives (see §5 of the Introduction, equation (9)); the constant C in (3.5) appears in this connection. Thus the inequality $\|U\|_{W_2^l(G)\otimes W_2^l(G)} \le C\|U\|_{W_2^{2l}(G\times G)}$ is valid for functions of the form (3.6). Now for any $U \in W_2^{2l}(G\times G)$, there exists a sequence U_ν of functions of the form (3.6) converging to U in the metric of $W_2^{2l}(G\times G)$. Since U_ν is fundamental in this metric, and since the inequality is known for functions of the form U_ν, U_ν is fundamental in the metric of $W_2^l(G)\otimes W_2^l(G)$, and it therefore has a limit in this space; we denote this limit by U. The desired inequality is obtained in the limit. We thus have the last inequality on the right in (3.5). The density of $W_2^{2l}(G\times G)$ in $W_2^l(G)\otimes W_2^l(G)$ follows from the fact that functions of the form (3.6) can be used to approximate any function in $W_2^l(G)\otimes W_2^l(G)$. The remaining assertions follow from the assertions of §1.3. The theorem follows.

Theorem 3.2 shows that generalized kernels in $W_2^{-l}(G)\otimes W_2^{-l}(G)$, i.e. functionals on $W_2^l(G)\otimes W_2^l(G)$, can be considered as functionals on the simpler space $W_2^{2l}(G\times G)$. This observation is sometimes useful.

In the spaces $W_2^l(G)$ $(l = 0, 1, \cdots)$ we have a natural conjugation, namely the passage from the function $u(x)$ to the complex conjugate function $\overline{u(x)}$. This conjugation satisfies the conditions stated in §2, and therefore it can be extended to the negative space $W_2^{-l}(G)$. It is clear that all the relations obtained previously for abstract kernels also hold for the generalized kernels considered here.

We now state Theorem 2.2 on kernels in a way which is more suitable to the present spaces.

Theorem 3.3. *If $l > n/2$ then for every continuous bilinear form $B(f, g)$ on the space $L_2(G)$ we can construct a kernel $K(x, y)$, which is continuous with respect to its arguments (i.e. $K(x, y) \in C((G \cup \Gamma)\times(G\cup\Gamma))$ and which will survive application of each of the operators $\mathbf{D}_l$ (i.e. $(\mathbf{D}_l\otimes E)K, (E\otimes \mathbf{D}_l)K \in L_2(G\times G)$), such that the following representations hold:*

$$B(u, v) = \int_G\int_G K(x, y)(D_l u)(y)\overline{(D_l v)(x)}\,dxdy$$

$$= \int_G\int_G ((\mathbf{D}_l \otimes E)K)(x, y)(D_l u)(y)\overline{v(x)}\,dxdy$$

$$= \int_G\int_G ((E\otimes \mathbf{D}_l)K)(x, y)\,u(y)\overline{(\mathbf{D}_l v)(x)}\,dxdy =$$

$$= ((\mathbf{D}_l\otimes\mathbf{D}_l)K, v(x)\overline{u(y)})_0 \quad (u, v \in W_2^l(G)) \tag{3.7}$$

(in the representation of $B(u, v)$ by means of the second (third) integral, $v(u)$ may be any element of $L_2(G)$).

This theorem follows immediately from Theorem 2.2 and Corollary 2 to Theorem 3.1; it is only necessary to show that $K(x, y)$ is continuous. As we saw in the proof of Theorem 2.2, $K(x, y)$ is the kernel of the operator $\hat{J}_l A \hat{J}_l$ in $L_2(G)$ where A is constructed with respect to $B(f, g)$. We compute this kernel directly. Since $\hat{J}_l A \hat{J}_l f \in W_2^l(G)$ for $f \in L_2(G)$,

$$(\hat{J}_l A \hat{J}_l f)(x) = (J_l A \hat{J}_l f, \delta_x)_0 = (A \hat{J}_l f, \mathbf{J}_l \delta_x)_0 = (\hat{J}_l f, A^* \mathbf{J}_l \delta_x)_0$$
$$= (f, \hat{J}_l A^* \mathbf{J}_l \delta_x)_0 = \int_G \overline{(J_l A^* \mathbf{J}_l \delta_x)(\xi)} f(\xi)\, d\xi,$$

and so $K(x, \xi) = \overline{(J_l A^* \mathrm{J}_l \delta_x)(\xi)}$. According to Lemma 3.1 $\delta_x (x \in G \cup \Gamma)$ is a continuous vector-function with values in $W_2^{-l}(G)$; therefore $J_l A^* \mathrm{J}_l \delta_x$ is a continuous vector-function with values in $W_2^l(G)$ (and a fortiori in $C(G \cup \Gamma)$. The continuity of K follows. This completes the proof of the theorem.

We give an elementary theorem on kernels, the proof of which does not depend on the theory of spaces with positive and negative norms developed above. It is essentially weaker than Theorem 3.3 since a representation of the type in (3.7) is obtained only for finite functions. However, part of the theorem is nevertheless useful.

We assume below that G is a region, which is perhaps unbounded (in particular, G may coincide with all of n-dimensional space E_n). Consider the characteristic function of a closed parallelepiped in E_n, determined by the coordinate hyperplanes and parallel hyperplanes passing through a point x. Let $\omega(x, \xi)$ $(\xi \in G)$ denote the product of this function with the characteristic function $\kappa(\xi)$ of the region G and $(-1)^n \operatorname{sign} x_1 \cdots \operatorname{sign} x_n$, where $x = (x_1, \cdots, x_n)$. Obviously $\omega(x, \cdot) \in L_2(G)$ is a continuous function of $x \in E_n$ with convergence in the metric of $L_2(G)$. Let

$$\mathrm{D} = D_1 \ldots D_n = \frac{\partial^n}{\partial x_1 \ldots \partial x_n}. \tag{3.8}$$

Theorem 3.4. *Let $B(f, g)$ be a continuous bilinear form on $L_2(G)$. Then for any $u, v \in C_0^n(G)$ we have the representation*

$$B(u, v) = \int_G \int_G K(x, y)(\mathrm{D}u)(y) \overline{(\mathrm{D}v)(x)}\, dx dy \tag{3.9}$$

where the kernel $K(x, y) = (C\omega(y, \cdot), \omega(x, \cdot))_0$ *is continuous for* $(x, y) \in E_n \times E_n$; *here* C *is the continuous operator in* $L_2(G)$ *corresponding to* $B(f, g)$:

$$(Cf, g)_0 = B(f, g) \ (f, g \in L_2(G)).$$

As usual $C_0^n(G)$ *denotes the set of functions in* $C^n(G)$ *which are finite with respect to* G *and* ∞.

Proof. We first establish the equation

$$\int_G (f, \omega(x, \cdot))_0 \overline{(\mathrm{D}u)(x)}\, dx = (f, u)_0 \ (f \in L_2(G),\ u \in C_0^n(G)). \tag{3.10}$$

Extending the functions f and u so as to be zero outside G and integrating by parts, we obtain

$$\int_G (f, \omega(x, \cdot))_0 \overline{(\mathrm{D}u)(x)}\, dx$$

$$= (-1)^n \int_{E_n} \left(\int_0^{x_1} \ldots \int_0^{x_n} f(\xi)\, \varkappa(\xi)\, d\xi_1 \ldots d\xi_n \ \overline{(\mathrm{D}u)(x)}\, dx \right.$$

$$= \int_{E_n} \mathrm{D}_x \left(\int_0^{x_1} \ldots \int_0^{x_n} f(\xi)\, \varkappa(\xi)\, d\xi_1 \ldots d\xi_n \right) \overline{u(x)}\, dx = (f, u)_0 .$$

We prove (3.9) using (3.10)

$$\int_G \int_G (C\omega(y, \cdot), \omega(x, \cdot))_0 (\mathrm{D}u)(y) \overline{(\mathrm{D}v)(x)}\, dx dy$$

$$= \int_G \left\{ \int_G (C\omega(y, \cdot), \omega(x, \cdot))_0 \overline{(\mathrm{D}v)(x)}\, dx \right\} (\mathrm{D}u)(y)\, dy$$

$$= \int_G (C\omega(y, \cdot), v)_0 (\mathrm{D}u)(y)\, dy = \overline{\int_G (v, C\omega(y, \cdot))_0 \overline{(\mathrm{D}u)(y)}\, dy}$$

$$= \overline{\int_G (C^*v, \omega(y, \cdot))_0 \overline{(\mathrm{D}u)(y)}\, dy} = \overline{(C^*v, u)_0} = \overline{(v, Cu)_0} = (Cu, v)_0 .$$

The continuity of the kernel $(C\omega(y, \cdot), \omega(x, \cdot))_0$ follows from the fact that $\omega(x, \cdot)$ depends continuously on x as a vector-function with values in $L_2(G)$. The theorem follows.

If the kernel $K(x, y)$ is sufficiently smooth, the operator D in (3.9) may be shifted by an integration by parts and we obtain the usual integral representation of the form $B(u, v) = (Cu, v)_0$:

$$B(u, v) = (Cu, v)_0 = \int_G \int_G (D_x D_y K)(x, y) u(y) \overline{v(x)} \, dx dy. \tag{3.11}$$

In general, the derivatives of $K(x, y)$ exist only in the generalized sense, and therefore the kernel which occurs in (3.11) must be taken in the generalized sense (the sense of L. Schwartz).

In this theorem, of course, instead of the differential expression $\mathbf{D}$ given by (3.8) we could take any differential expression of order r, having the property that the adjoint expression $\mathbf{D}^+$ admits a fundamental solution $e(x, \xi)$[1] for which $\omega(x, \xi) = e(x, \xi)\kappa(\xi)$ belongs to $L_2(G)$ as a function of ξ and is continuous as a function of $x \in E_n$ (but in this case u and v in (3.9) must be taken from $C_0^r(G)$). In fact, it is sufficient to establish (3.10) for $u \in C_0^r(G)$ and for smooth f. Using the specified fundamental solution, we obtain

$$\int_G (f, \omega(x, \cdot))_0 \overline{(Du)(x)} \, dx = \int_G D_x^+ \left(\int_G f(\xi) e(x, \xi) \, d\xi \right) \overline{u(x)} \, dx$$

$$= \int_G f(x) \overline{u(x)} \, dx = (f, u)_0 .$$

This establishes the identity (3.10). The relation (3.9) follows from (3.10) as before. It is clear, however, that by taking $\mathbf{D}$ other than in (3.8) we cannot remove the restriction that u and v in (3.9) are finite functions.

3. **Sobolev spaces in the case of an unbounded region.** Suppose that the region G is not bounded. For functions which are $l = 1, 2, \cdots$ times continuously differentiable up to the boundary Γ of G, and which vanish in a neighborhood of ∞, we introduce the scalar product

$$(u, v)_l = \sum_{|\alpha| \leq l} (D^\alpha u, D^\alpha v)_{L_2(G)}$$

and form the completion. As the result we obtain the Sobolev space $W_2^l(G)$. As in the case of bounded G, the spaces $W_2^l(G)$ $(l = 1, 2, \cdots)$ form a sequence of positive spaces. We can construct negative spaces $W_2^{-l}(G)$ with respect to the zero space $W_2^0(G) = L_2(G)$, and then the relations (3.1) hold.

If $l > n/2$, then the functions in $W_2^l(G)$ are continuous in $G \cup \Gamma$, and in every bounded part G' of the region G we can write

---

1) Concerning the concept of a fundamental solution, see Chapter III, §4.1.

$$|u(x)| \leq A_{G'} \|u\|_{W_2^l(G')} \leq A_{G'} \|u\|_l \quad (x \in G')$$

by virtue of the imbedding theorem. As G' increases in G, the constant $A_{G'}$, roughly speaking, grows large. Therefore, for any $x \in G$ we have an estimate

$$|u(x)| \leq A(x) \|u\|_l \quad (u \in W_2^l(G)), \tag{3.12}$$

where $A(x) \geq \delta > 0$ is some function which, roughly speaking, grows large as $x \longrightarrow \infty$, and which may be assumed to be continuous on $G \cup \Gamma$.

The form of this function depends essentially on the region G. We determine it now for the simple case of a conical region, i.e. a region G which contains, along with each point x, the entire half-line tx $(0 \leq t < \infty)$ (in particular, G may coincide with all of E_n). Let G_R be the intersection of G with the sphere $|x| < R$. For y in closure of G_1 we have the estimate $|u(y)| \leq C \|u\|_{W_2^l(G_1)}$ $(C = A_{G_1})$. On substituting the function $u(Rx)$ $(R \geq 1)$ for $u(x)$ in this inequality and then making the change of variable $\eta = R\xi$, we obtain

$$\begin{aligned} |u(Ry)|^2 &\leqslant C^2 \sum_{|\alpha| \leqslant l} R^{2|\alpha|} \int_{G_1} |(D^\alpha u)(R\xi)|^2 d\xi \\ &= C^2 \sum_{|\alpha| \leqslant l} R^{2|\alpha| - n} \int_{G_R} |(D^\alpha u)(\eta)|^2 d\eta \\ &\leqslant C^2 R^{2l-n} \sum_{|\alpha| \leqslant l} \int_{G_R} |(D^\alpha u)(\eta)|^2 d\eta \leqslant C^2 R^{2l-n} \|u\|_l^2 . \end{aligned} \tag{3.13}$$

Now suppose $x \in G$, $|x| \geq 1$, is arbitrary, and in (3.13) let $R = |x|$ and $y = x/|x|$; we find that $|u(x)| \leq C|x|^{l-n/2} \|u\|_l$. It follows that *if $l > n/2$ and G is conical, then*

$$|u(x)| \leqslant C(1 + |x|^{l - \frac{n}{2}}) \|u\|_l \quad (u \in W_2^l(G), \ x \in G). \tag{3.14}$$

Since the functions in $W_2^l(G)$ for $l > n/2$ are continuous, δ_ξ belongs to $W_2^{-l}(G)$ and operates on $W_2^l(G)$ by means of equation (3.2). Moreover, by (3.12),

$$\|\delta_\xi\|_{-l} \leq A(\xi) \quad (\xi \in G \cup \Gamma). \tag{3.15}$$

It is not difficult to see that δ_ξ *is continuous in the metric of $W_2^{-l}(G)$ as a function of $\xi \in G \cup \Gamma$*: suppose $R > |\xi|$ and, for $u(x) \in W_2^l(G)$, let $u_R(x)$ be the restriction of this function to G_R. We have

$$|(u, \delta_\xi)_0| = |u(\xi)| = |(u_R, \delta_\xi)_0| \leqslant \|\delta_\xi\|_{W_2^{-l}(G_R)} \|u_R\|_{W_2^l(G_R)}$$
$$\leqslant \|\delta_\xi\|_{W_2^{-l}(G_R)} \|u\|_l,$$

from which it follows that $\|\delta_\xi\|_{-l} \leq \|\delta_\xi\|_{W_2^{-l}(G_R)}$. Our assertion follows from this inequality and Lemma 3.1.

For an unbounded region G, the inclusion $W_2^l(G) \longrightarrow L_2(G)$ $(l > n/2)$ is not, in general, quasi-nuclear; this follows from the fact that, according to (3.15), $\|\delta_\xi\|_{-l}$ may become large as $\xi \longrightarrow \infty$. However, we now show that by introducing a positive space in a somewhat different way, we may obtain any degree of smallness for $\|\delta_\xi\|_-$ at ∞ and show that the corresponding inclusion is quasi-nuclear.

Let $q(x) \geq 1$ be a fixed function in $C^l(G \cup \Gamma)$. We define $W_2^{(l,q)}(G)$ as the closure of the functions in $W_2^l(G)$ $(l = 1, 2, \cdots)$, vanishing in a neighborhood of ∞, with respect to the scalar product $(u, v)_{(l,q)} = (uq, vq)_l$. We take $L_2(G)$ for the zero space as before; obviously, $\|u\|_0 \leq \|u\|_{(l,q)}$; the negative space will be denoted with the index $-(l, q)$. According to (3.12) $|u(x)q(x)| \leq A(x)\|uq\|_l = A(x)\|u\|_{(l,q)}$, and hence $|u(x)| \leq (A(x)/q(x))\|u\|_{(l,q)}$ $(u \in W_2^{(l,q)}(G),\ x \in G)$. This inequality shows that

$$\|\delta_\xi\|_{-(l,q)} \leqslant \frac{A(\xi)}{q(\xi)} \quad (\xi \in G \cup \Gamma). \tag{3.16}$$

It is also clear that δ_ξ *is continuous as a function of* $\xi \in G \cup \Gamma$ *with respect to the metric of* $W_2^{-(l,q)}(G)$.

Theorem 3.5. *Suppose* $l > n/2$. *If* $q(x)$ *satisfies*

$$\int_G \frac{A^2(x)}{q^2(x)}\, dx < \infty, \tag{3.17}$$

then the operator $\hat{J}$ *is a Hilbert-Schmidt operator, and therefore the inclusion* $W_2^{(l,q)}(G) \longrightarrow L_2(G)$ *is quasi-nuclear. The operator* $\hat{I}$ *has finite trace and a kernel which is continuous on* $(G \cup \Gamma) \times (G \cup \Gamma)$.

Proof. For $f \in L_2(G)$ we have

$$(Jf)(x) = (Jf, \delta_x)_0 = (f, \mathbf{J}\delta_x)_0 = \int_G \overline{(\mathbf{J}\delta_x)(\xi)}\, f(\xi)\, d\xi = \int_G K(x, \xi) f(\xi)\, d\xi,$$

where $K(x, \xi) = \overline{(\mathbf{J}\delta_x)(\xi)}$. Taking into account (3.16) and (3.17) we obtain

$$\int_G \int_G |K(x, \xi)|^2 dx\, d\xi = \int_G \left(\int_G |(\mathbf{J}\delta_x)(\xi)|^2 d\xi \right) dx =$$

$$= \int_G \|\delta_x\|^2_{-(l,q)} dx \leqslant \int_G \frac{A^2(x)}{q^2(x)} dx < \infty,$$

i.e. $\hat{J}$ is a Hilbert-Schmidt operator.[1] Since $\hat{I} = \hat{J}^2$, $\hat{I}$ has a finite trace. The continuity of its kernel is proved as in Theorem 3.1. The theorem follows.

In conclusion, note that *Theorem 3.3 on kernels is valid in the case of an unbounded region G, for any space* $W_2^{(l,q)}(G)$ *such that* $l > n/2$ *and* $q(x)$ *satisfies* (3.17). The formulation of the theorem and its proof are exactly the same as in the case of a bounded region. Theorem 3.4, as was already pointed out, is valid without the assumption that G is bounded.

4. A generalization of Sobolev spaces. Let G be a bounded region; take $L_2(G)$ as a zero space H_0 and let some closed subspace $W_2'^l(G)$ of $W_2^l(G)$ $(l \geq 1)$ be taken as a positive space; suppose that $W_2'^l(G)$ is dense in $L_2(G)$ (for example, we could use $\mathring{W}_2^l(G)$, the closure in $W_2^l(G)$ of all smooth finite functions). Let $W_2'^{-l}(G)$ denote the corresponding negative space. Since $W_2'^l(G) \subseteq W_2^l(G)$, $W_2'^{-l}(G) \supseteq W_2^{-l}(G)$: if $\alpha \in W_2^{-l}(G)$, then the expression $(\alpha, u)_0$ has meaning for $u \in W_2'^l(G)$ and defines a continuous functional on this space; therefore we may write $\alpha \in W_2'^{-l}(G)$. However, any other $\alpha' \in W_2^{-l}(G)$ such that $(\alpha - \alpha', u)_0 = 0$ for all $u \in W_2'^l(G)$ will induce a functional on $W_2'^l(G)$ which coincides with the functional induced by α; such α and α' belong to an equivalence class of elements. To be more precise, instead of the inclusion $\alpha \in W_2'^{-l}(G)$ it is necessary to write the inclusion of the corresponding class in $W_2'^{-l}(G)$. However, as is frequently done, we indicate the inclusion of a class by the inclusion of a representative element of the class (this is similar to writing "$f(x) \in L_2(G)$" instead of "the equivalence class of functions determined by $f(x)$ belongs to $L_2(G)$"). This convention is used below.

It is clear that

$$\|\alpha\|_{W_2'^{-l}(G)} \leqslant \|\alpha\|_{-l} \qquad (\alpha \in W_2^{-l}(G)).$$

Similar constructions can be made in the case of an unbounded region G. We take $L_2(G)$ for H_0; for H_+ we take a closed subspace $W_2'^{(l,q)}(G)$ $(q(x) \geq 1)$ of the space $W_2^{(l,q)}(G)$ which is dense in $L_2(G)$. If $W_2'^{-(l,q)}(G)$ is the corresponding

1) Recall that an integral operator K with kernel $K(x, \xi)$, acting in a Hilbert space $L_2(Q, d\mu(x))$, is a Hilbert-Schmidt operator if and only if $\int_Q\int_Q |K(x, \xi)|^2 d\mu(x) d\mu(\xi) < \infty$; this integral is equal to $|K|^2$ (see Chapter V, §1.1).

negative space, then $W'^{-(l,q)}_2(G) \supseteq W^{-(l,q)}_2(G)$, $\|\alpha\|_{W'^{-(l,q)}_2(G)} \leq \|\alpha\|_{-(l,q)}$ ($\alpha \in W^{-(l,q)}_2(G)$).

The majority of the constructions in subsections 1–3 can be extended to the sequence $H_- \supseteq H_0 \supseteq H_+$. We now point out a useful connection between norms of the type $\|\cdot\|_{W'^{-l}_2(G)}$ and $\|\cdot\|_{-l}$. The relation is conveniently developed in an abstract form.

Let $H_- \supseteq H_0 \supseteq H_+$ be a sequence as in (1.4), and let M_+ be a closed subspace of H_+ which is dense in H_0. Construct a negative space M_- with respect to the positive space M_+, and notice that $H_- \subseteq M_-$ in the above sense, and

$$H_- \supseteq H_0 \supseteq H_+ \supset M_+,$$
$$\|u\|_{M_-} \leqslant \|u\|_- \leqslant \|u\|_0 \leqslant \|u\|_+ = \|u\|_{M_+} \qquad (u \in M_+).$$

For $\alpha \in H_-$ we obtain the equation

$$\|\alpha\|_{M_-} = \inf_\beta \|\alpha+\beta\|_-, \tag{3.18}$$

where the inf is taken over the subspace N_- of the space H_- consisting of all $\beta \in H_-$ such that $(\beta, u)_0 = 0$, $u \in M_+$ (i.e. N_- is the orthogonal complement of M_+ with respect to $(\cdot,\cdot)_0$). This assertion is a paraphrase of a particular case of the following well-known general fact (see, for example, Bourbaki [2], Chapter 4, §1): suppose that the space B is a Banach space with adjoint space B', and let M be a subspace of B. Then the adjoint space M' is isometric with the factor space B'/N', where N' is the subspace of functionals in B' which are orthogonal to M.

In conclusion, we call attention to the general construction in Chapter VIII, §1.4, where, however, a negative space corresponding to $H_0 \supseteq H_+$ is introduced in the case that the scalar product $(\cdot,\cdot)_0$ in H_0 is degenerate (i.e. for some $u \neq 0$, $(u, u)_0 = 0$). This is connected with the previous constructions by the above discussion.

5. The space $\overset{\circ}{W}{}^l_2(G)$. We consider the spaces discussed in the previous subsection in detail. Thus suppose that $H_0 = L_2(G)$, $H_+ = \overset{\circ}{W}{}^l_2(G)$ ($l = 1, 2, \cdots$; G bounded). The corresponding negative space is denoted $\overset{\circ}{W}{}^{-l}_2(G)$. The spaces $\overset{\circ}{W}{}^k_2(G)$ are conveniently studied by means of Fourier transforms; in particular, this approach presents the possibility of making an extension to fractional k.

Let

$$\tilde{f}(\xi) = \frac{1}{\sqrt{(2\pi)^n}} \int_{E_n} f(x)\, e^{-i\langle \xi, x\rangle}\, dx$$

$$(\xi = (\xi_1, \ldots, \xi_n) \in E_n, \quad \langle \xi, x\rangle = \xi_1 x_1 + \ldots + \xi_n x_n)$$

denote the Fourier transform of the function $f(x)$ and let $\hat{f}\,(\xi)$ denote the inverse Fourier transform; $\hat{\tilde{f}} = f = \tilde{\hat{f}}$. If f is finite and sufficiently smooth, then on integrating by parts we find $\widetilde{(D^\alpha f)}\,(\xi) = i^{|\alpha|}\xi^\alpha \tilde{f}\,(\xi)$ $(\xi^\alpha = \xi_1^{\alpha_1} \cdots \xi_n^{\alpha_n})$. Therefore, by Parseval's formula, we find that the expression (9) of §5 of the Introduction for the scalar product in $W_2^l(G)$ is given by

$$(u, v)_l = (u, v)_0 + \sum_{|\alpha|=l} (D^\alpha u, D^\alpha v)_0 = \int_{E_n} \Big(1 + \sum_{|\alpha|=l} \xi^{2\alpha}\Big)\, \tilde{u}(\xi)\overline{\tilde{v}(\xi)}\, d\xi,$$

where $\tilde{w}(\xi)$ is the Fourier transform of the function $w \in W_2^l(G)$, which is extended so as to vanish outside of G. On the other hand,

$$C_1 |\xi|^{2l} \leqslant \sum_{|\alpha|=l} \xi^{2\alpha} \leqslant C_2 |\xi|^{2l} \qquad (C_1, C_2 > 0;\ \xi \in E_n). \tag{3.19}$$

In fact, the form $\phi(\xi) = \Sigma_{|\alpha|=l}\, \xi^{2\alpha}/|\xi|^{2l}$ is homogeneous of degree zero and continuous for $\xi \neq 0$. It is easy to show that every such form is bounded over all of E_n, and from this follows the inequality on the right in (3.19). The left inequality is established in an analogous way. From (3.19) and the expression for $(u, v)_l$ mentioned above, it follows that the metric of $\overset{\circ}{W}{}_2^l(G)$ may be described by means of the equivalent scalar product

$$(u, v)_k = \int_{E_n} (\varepsilon^{-2} + |\xi|^2)^k\, \tilde{u}(\xi)\, \overline{\tilde{v}(\xi)}\, d\xi, \tag{3.20}$$

where $k = l$ and $0 < \epsilon \leq \infty$ is an arbitrary fixed number (for different ϵ, the metrics defined by the scalar product (3.20) are equivalent; the value $\epsilon = \infty$ is admitted in connection with the possibility of using formula (25) on p. 22). Thus $\overset{\circ}{W}{}_2^l(G)$ may be considered as the set of Fourier transforms of functions in $C_0^\infty(G)$, completed with respect to the metric (3.20) with $k = l$. It is not difficult to see that since $u(v) = \int_{E_n} \tilde{u}(\xi)\, \overline{\tilde{v}(\xi)}\, d\xi$, $(u, v)_{-l}$ is given by the integral (3.20), with $k = -l$. Thus the integrals (3.20) give the scalar product for a series of spaces with positive ($k > 0$), zero ($k = 0$), and negative ($k < 0$) norms. All of these spaces are closures of $\widetilde{C_0^\infty(G)}$ in appropriate metrics (they may also be considered in the x-representation as suitable closures of $C_0^\infty(G)$). Above, k may be any real number; we keep the original notation $\overset{\circ}{W}{}_2^k(G)$ for these spaces.

Theorem 3.6. *Consider a fixed* $\phi(x) \in C_0(E_n)$, $\int_{E_n} \phi(x)\,dx \neq 0$, $0 < \epsilon_0 < \infty$. *Then the norm* $\|u\|_{-l}$ $(l > 0)$ *is topologically equivalent to the norm*

$$\|u\|_{-l}^2 = \int_0^{\varepsilon_0} \| u * \varphi_\varepsilon \|_{L_2(E_n)}^2 \varepsilon^{2l-1} d\varepsilon, \tag{3.21}$$

where $u * \phi_\epsilon$ *denotes the convolution of the function* u, *extended to be zero outside of* G, *and the function* $\phi_\epsilon(x) = \phi(x/\epsilon)/\epsilon^n$ $(x \in E_n)$.

Proof. Applying the Fourier transformation, we obtain the representation $\|u\|_{-l}^2 = \int_{E_n} |\tilde{u}(\xi)|^2 \left(\int_0^{\epsilon_0} |\tilde{\phi}_\epsilon(\xi)|^2 \epsilon^{2l-1} d\epsilon\right) d\xi$. Comparing this expression with (3.20), we see that it is sufficient to prove the estimate

$$C_1 (\varepsilon_0^{-2} + |\xi|^2)^{-l} \leqslant \int_0^{\varepsilon_0} |\tilde{\varphi}_\varepsilon(\xi)|^2 \varepsilon^{2l-1} d\varepsilon \leqslant C_2 (\varepsilon_0^{-2} + |\xi|^2)^{-l} \tag{3.22}$$
$$(C_1, C_2 > 0; \quad \xi \in E_n).$$

We prove the right inequality. Noting that $\tilde{\phi}_\epsilon(\xi) = \tilde{\phi}(\epsilon\xi)$, by the change of variable $\delta = \epsilon|\xi|$ we obtain

$$\int_0^{\varepsilon_0} |\tilde{\varphi}_\varepsilon(\xi)|^2 \varepsilon^{2l-1} d\varepsilon = \int_0^{\varepsilon_0} |\tilde{\varphi}(\varepsilon\xi)|^2 \varepsilon^{2l-1} d\varepsilon =$$

$$= \frac{1}{|\xi|^l} \int_0^{\varepsilon_0 |\xi|} \left| \tilde{\varphi}\left(\delta \frac{\xi}{|\xi|}\right) \right|^2 \delta^{2l-1} d\delta \leqslant \frac{1}{|\xi|^{2l}} \int_0^{\infty} \left| \tilde{\varphi}\left(\delta \frac{\xi}{|\xi|}\right) \right|^2 \delta^{2l-1} d\delta. \tag{3.23}$$

The integral $\int_0^\infty |\tilde{\phi}(\delta\eta)|^2 \delta^{2l-1}\, d\delta$ depends continuously on $\eta = \xi/|\xi|$, ranging over the unit sphere, and is therefore bounded (note that $\tilde{\phi}(\xi)$ decreases rapidly as $|\xi| \to \infty$, since $\phi \in C_0^\infty(G)$). Thus we obtain the estimate

$$\int_0^{\varepsilon_0} |\tilde{\varphi}_\varepsilon(\xi)|^2 \varepsilon^{2l-1} d\varepsilon \leqslant C_3 / |\xi|^{2l},$$

which gives the right inequality in (3.22). For the proof of the left inequality note that $\tilde{\phi}(0) = (2\pi)^{-n/2} \int_{E_n} \phi(x)dx \neq 0$, and therefore $\tilde{\phi}(\xi) \geq C_4 > 0$ where $|\xi| \leq R$ for some $R > 0$. Now using (3.23), we obtain for $|\xi| \geq R/\epsilon_0$

$$\int_0^{\varepsilon_0} |\tilde{\varphi}_\varepsilon(\xi)|^2 \varepsilon^{2l-1} d\varepsilon = \frac{1}{|\xi|^{2l}} \int_0^{\varepsilon_0|\xi|} \left|\tilde{\varphi}\left(\delta \frac{\xi}{|\xi|}\right)\right|^2 \delta^{2l-1} d\delta$$

$$\geqslant \frac{1}{|\xi|^{2l}} \int_0^R \left|\tilde{\varphi}\left(\delta \frac{\xi}{|\xi|}\right)\right|^2 \delta^{2l-1} d\delta \geqslant \frac{C_5}{|\xi|^{2l}} \qquad (3.24)$$

For $|\xi| \leq R/\epsilon_0$ and $\epsilon \in [0, \epsilon_0]$ $|\epsilon\xi| \leq R$; therefore $\int_0^{\epsilon_0} |\tilde{\phi}_\epsilon(\xi)|^2 \epsilon^{2l-1} d\epsilon = \int_0^{\epsilon_0} |\tilde{\phi}(\epsilon\xi)|^2 \epsilon^{2l-1} d\epsilon \geq C_4^2 \int_0^{\epsilon_0} \epsilon^{2l-1} d\epsilon > 0$. The left inequality in (3.22) hence follows from (3.24). The theorem follows.

The theorem just proved is essential, since it presents the possibility of substituting for the less transparent (in the x-representation) norm $\|\cdot\|_{-l}^{\cdot}$ $(l > 0)$ the norm $\|\cdot\|_{-l}$, which is simply expressed in terms of a zero norm. This permits an estimate for differential expressions with constant coefficients, taking place in the metric of $L_2(G)$, to extend to the metric of $\mathring{W}_2^{-l}(G)$. In passing to variable coefficients, we use the estimate

$$\int_0^{\varepsilon_0} \| a(u * \varphi_\varepsilon) - (au) * \varphi_\varepsilon \|^2_{L_2(E_n)} \varepsilon^{2l-1} d\varepsilon \leqslant C_1 \| u \|^2_{-l-1} (u \in C_0^\infty(G)), \qquad (3.25)$$

which we will not prove now. We remark that the constants in the estimates (3.22) and (3.25) may be chosen the same for all $l \in [\alpha, \beta]$ $(0 < \alpha < \beta < \infty)$.

6. Construction of equipment with respect to a prescribed operator. Let T be a closed operator in a Hilbert space H_0, having everywhere dense domain $\mathfrak{D}(T)$, and such that

$$\| Tu \|_0 \geq \| u \|_0 \quad (u \in \mathfrak{D}(T)). \qquad (3.26)$$

Obviously, $\mathfrak{D}(T)$ is a Hilbert space with respect to the scalar product

$$(u, v)_+ = (Tu, Tv)_0; \qquad (3.27)$$

and we can take this space as a positive space H_+ and then construct a corresponding negative space H_-.

Consider the operator D with respect to the sequence $H_- \supseteq H_0 \supseteq H_+$; equations (1.13) and (3.27) show that D and T are metrically equal (if T is, in addition, positive, then obviously $D = T$). On $\mathfrak{R}(T)$, T^{-1} exists and is continuous; it is metrically equal to $D^{-1} = \hat{I}$. Thus $\|f\|_- = \|D^{-1}f\|_0$ $(f \in H_0)$. From this and the assertion on p. 43, it follows that the inclusion $H_+ \longrightarrow H_0$ is quasi-nuclear if, and only if, T^{-1} is a Hilbert-Schmidt operator. Notice that in place of the control inequality (3.26) it is possible to use the estimate $\|Tu\|_0 \geq C\|u\|_0$ ($u \in \mathfrak{D}(T)$) with some $C > 0$, or what is equivalent, the equation $T^* x = f$ is solvable for any $f \in H_0$ and x depends continuously on f (see Chapter II, proof of Lemma 2.1).

We consider an example. Let G be a bounded region in n-dimensional space with piecewise smooth boundary Γ, and let $H_0 = L_2(G)$. For T we take the closure in $L_2(G)$ of the operator defined by $u \longrightarrow (\partial^n/\partial x_1 \cdots \partial x_n)\, u$ on finite functions. It is easy to show that the inequality (3.26) is satisfied. The inclusion $H_+ \longrightarrow H_0$ is quasi-nuclear; this follows from the fact that the operator T^{-1} is an integral operator and has the form

$$(T^{-1}f)(x) = \int_G K(x, \xi) f(\xi)\, d\xi, \tag{3.28}$$

$$K(x, \xi) = \varkappa_{(-\infty, x_1)}(\xi_1) \ldots \varkappa_{(-\infty, x_n)}(\xi_n) \qquad (f \in \Re(T)),$$

where $\kappa_{(a,b)}$ is the characteristic function of the interval (a, b). In the case of unbounded G, the present construction carries over, but the inclusion $H_+ \longrightarrow H_0$ is not quasi-nuclear for mes $G = \infty$. To obtain a quasi-nuclear inclusion, we can, for example, consider a positive scalar product of the form $(u, v)_+ = (T(qu), T(qv))_0$, where $q(x)$ is a function in $C^n(G \cup \Gamma)$ which grows sufficiently fast as $|x| \longrightarrow \infty$ (for more explicit details concerning constructions involving operators T, see §3, Chapter V).

7. **Construction of equipment with respect to a prescribed negative space.** We show that the sequence (1.4) can be constructed not only from a knowledge of H_0 and H_+, but also from a knowledge of H_0 and H_-.

Theorem 3.7. *Let H_0 be a complete Hilbert space which is contained as a dense subspace in a larger complete Hilbert space $H_- \supset H_0$, such that $\|f\|_- \leq \|f\|_0$ and the equation $\|f\|_- = 0$ implies $f = 0$ ($f \in H_0$).*

Then it is possible to construct a positive space $H_+ \subseteq H_0$ such that the corresponding negative space coincides with H_-.

Proof. Consider the bilinear form $B(f, g) = (f, g)_-$; it depends continuously on $f, g \in H_0$, and therefore admits a representation in the form $(f, g)_- = (Kf, g)_0$ ($f, g \in H_0$), where K is a continuous operator acting in H_0. Since $\|f\|_- \leq \|f\|_0$ and $(f, f)_- \geq 0$, the operator K satisfies $\|K\| \leq 1$ and $K \geq 0$. Its range $\Re(K)$ is dense in H_0: if $0 = (Kf, h)_0 = (f, h)_-$ for all $f \in H_0$, then $\|h\|_- = 0$ by virtue of the density of H_0 in H_-; i.e. $h = 0$. The inverse operator K^{-1} exists on $\Re(K)$:

if $Kf=0$, then $(f, g)_- = (Kf, g)_0 = 0$ for any $g \in H_0$; i.e. $f=0$.

Put $(u, v)_+ = (K^{-1}u, v)_0$ $(u, v \in \Re(K))$. Since $\|K\| \leq 1$, it follows from the spectral decomposition of K that $(K^{-1}u, u)_0 = \|u\|_+^2 \geq \|u\|_0^2$ $(u \in \Re(K))$. Hence H_+, the completion of $\Re(K)$ with respect to $(\cdot, \cdot)_+$, is a complete Hilbert space satisfying all the requirements for a positive space with respect to H_0. Now forming the operator I, we find immediately that

$$I = K, \tag{3.29}$$

where K is considered as an operator from H_0 to $\Re(K)$. The negative space, constructed with respect to $H_0 \supseteq H_+$, coincides with the closure of H_0 in the metric $(If, g)_0 = (Kf, g)_0 = (f, g)_-$; i.e. it coincides with H_-. The theorem follows.

It often happens that the hypotheses of the theorem are satisfied except that from $\|f\|_- = 0$, it does not follow that $f=0$ for $f \in H_0$. In this case, consider the linear set F in H_0 consisting of all f for which $\|f\|_- = 0$. Because of the inequality $\|f\|_- \leq \|f\|_0$, it is closed in H_0. Now, in the theorem, if H_0 is replaced by the orthogonal complement F_0 of F in H_0, then the hypotheses turn out to be satisfied and H_- may be considered as a negative space with respect to the zero space F_0.

Theorem 3.7 allows us to consider as negative spaces some important spaces constructed from positive definite kernels $K(x, y)$. For example, suppose that G is a bounded region in n-dimensional space with boundary Γ, and let $K \in C((G \cup \Gamma) \times (G \cup \Gamma))$. The space H_K is constructed as the closure of $L_2(G)$ with respect to the scalar product

$$(f, g) = \int_G \int_G K(x, y) f(y) \overline{g(x)}\, dx\, dy.$$

The space H_K can be considered as a negative space, and moreover, we can take $L_2(G)$ or some subspace as the zero space (for more details see Chapter VIII, §3.7).

§4. EQUIPMENT BY MEANS OF LINEAR TOPOLOGICAL SPACES

It is possible to construct a sequence of the type (1.5) where a linear topological space $\Phi \subseteq H_0$, Φ dense in H_0, plays the role of the space H_+ (the inclusion is topological).[1] Then $\Phi' \supseteq H_0' = H_0$ and we obtain

---

1) For the terminology used here, see, e.g., Kantorovič and Akilov [1], Chapter 11.

$$\Phi' \supseteq H_0 \supseteq \Phi. \tag{4.1}$$

We now outline how, for certain spaces Φ constructed with respect to Hilbert spaces, the results in §§1 and 2 essentially lead to assertions with respect to the sequence (4.1).

Let Φ be a sequential-Hilbert space, i.e. a complete locally convex linear topological space, the topology in which is given by a denumerable system of norms $\|\cdot\|_1 \leq \|\cdot\|_2 \leq \cdots$, each constructed with respect to a corresponding scalar product (spheres of the form $\|u\|_n < \epsilon_n$ serve as neighborhoods of the origin). The norms $\|\cdot\|_n$ are assumed to satisfy this condition: if a sequence of vectors in Φ is fundamental with respect to the norm $\|\cdot\|_{n+1}$ and converges to zero in the norm $\|\cdot\|_n$, then it converges to zero in the norm $\|\cdot\|_{n+1}$ $(n = 1, 2, \cdots)$. Let Φ_n denote the completion of Φ with respect to the norm $\|\cdot\|_n$; then $\Phi_1 \supseteq \Phi_2 \supseteq \cdots$, $\Phi = \bigcap_{n=1}^{\infty} \Phi_n$ and $\Phi' = \bigcup_{n=1}^{\infty} \Phi'_n$.

Instead of the concept of a quasi-nuclear inclusion $\Phi \longrightarrow H_0$, it is now convenient to introduce the concept of a nuclear space Φ.

A separable space Φ is called nuclear if for each n, there is an $m > n$ such that the inclusion $\Phi_m \longrightarrow \Phi_n$ is quasi-nuclear. *If $H_0 \supseteq \Phi$ and Φ is nuclear, then we can always find an n, depending on the nature of H_0, such that the inclusion $\Phi_n \longrightarrow H_0$ is quasi-nuclear.* This follows immediately from the definition of the topology in Φ, and depends more on the inclusion $H_0 \supseteq \Phi$ than on the topology of H_0. Thus, if we have equipment for H_0 of the type (4.1) with nuclear Φ, then we have equipment of the type (1.4) with $H_+ = \Phi_n$, and since the inclusion $H_+ \longrightarrow H_0$ is quasi-nuclear we can apply the theory in §§ 1 and 2.

Theorem 2.2 reduces now to the following theorem on kernels.

Let $B(u, v)$ be a continuous bilinear form, defined for u, v in a nuclear space Φ. We then have the representations (2.18)–(2.21) *with $H_0 = \Phi_n$ and $H_+ = \Phi_m$, where $m > n$ are sufficiently large.*

In fact, by the definition of the topology in Φ, the continuity of $B(u, v)$ on Φ implies its continuity on some Φ_n. Setting $H_0 = \Phi_n$ and choosing $m > n$ so large that the inclusion $\Phi_m = H_+ \longrightarrow \Phi_n = H_0$ is quasi-nuclear, we reduce the problem to Theorem 2.2.

Analogous results are obtained in a similar way in more general cases, when the sequentially-normed Φ is given by semi-norms or when Φ is a projective limit of Hilbert spaces or an inductive limit of nuclear spaces. In conclusion, we remark that an inclusion $H_+ \longrightarrow H_0$ of separable Hilbert spaces is called nuclear if the inclusion operator has finite trace. Since the product of two quasi-nuclear inclusions is nuclear, in the above definition of a nuclear space Φ we may equivalently substitute the condition that $\Phi_m \longrightarrow \Phi_n$ is nuclear.

CHAPTER II

BOUNDARY VALUE PROBLEMS. GENERAL CONCEPTS

Below we consider boundary value problems for linear partial differential equations, i.e. problems concerning the determination of a solution of the equation

$$Lu = f \tag{*}$$

(f is a given function) satisfying specific boundary conditions on the boundary of the region. In this chapter we present only formal schemes for the application of functional methods to the analysis of the problem (*); a series of important examples will be considered in Chapters III and IV. Generally, such applications appear in the following way. Consider an analogous problem for a system of equations, in a finite dimensional space, of the form

$$Au = f, \tag{**}$$

where A is some matrix. It is known from linear algebra that for such an equation (**) we have so-called normal solvability: the equation admits a solution for those and only those f which are orthogonal to the subspace of solutions of the homogeneous adjoint equation $A^*v = 0$. Thus the equation (**) is solvable for any f if the homogeneous adjoint equation has only the zero solution, i.e. if the uniqueness theorem holds for it. This provides a reason to expect that for the boundary value problem (*), we will have a certain solvability for any f, if for the homogeneous adjoint problem $L^+v = 0$ the uniqueness theorem holds for smooth solutions. This is in fact the case, but the solution obtained is in the generalized sense. It becomes "more classical" if instead of the uniqueness theorem we have a stronger fact, namely an "energy inequality", i.e. an inequality of the form $\|L^+v\|_1 \geq C\|v\|_2$ $(C > 0)$ for some norms $\|\cdot\|_1$ and $\|\cdot\|_2$ (such inequalities are also called coercive inequalities or a priori inequalities). Throughout the chapter we consider differential expressions in a bounded (unless otherwise stated) region G in n-dimensional space E_n, and assume that its boundary Γ is piecewise smooth.

§1. GENERAL INFORMATION CONCERNING DIFFERENTIAL EXPRESSIONS

1. Differential expressions and boundary conditions. Recall that we introduced the notation

$$D_j = \frac{\partial}{\partial x_j} (j = 1, \dots, n), \quad D^\alpha = D_1^{\alpha_1} \dots D_n^{\alpha_n}, \qquad \alpha = (\alpha_1, \dots, \alpha_n),$$
$$|\alpha| = \alpha_1 + \dots + \alpha_n \tag{1.1}$$

for partial derivatives. By means of (1.1), an arbitrary linear differential expression of order r can be written in the form

$$Lu = L(x, D)\, u = \sum_{|\alpha| \leqslant r} a_\alpha(x) D^\alpha u. \tag{1.2}$$

We assume that the complex-valued coefficients $a_\alpha(x)$ are sufficiently smooth: in all that follows, it will be assumed, unless otherwise stated, that $a_\alpha(x) \in C^{|\alpha|}(G \cup \Gamma)$; we will call these the usual smoothness conditions. (In some of the arguments these conditions can be weakened.) Sometimes we will consider expressions L whose coefficients are sufficiently smooth only in the interior of G, and also expressions in unbounded regions. By the adjoint to L, we mean the differential expression

$$L^+u = \sum_{|\alpha| \leqslant r} (-1)^{|\alpha|} D^\alpha (\overline{a_\alpha(x)}\, u) = \sum_{|\alpha| \leqslant r} b_\alpha(x) D^\alpha u. \tag{1.3}$$

If the coefficients of L satisfy the usual smoothness conditions, then the coefficients $b_\alpha(x)$ of the expression L^+ also satisfy these conditions. For functions $u, v \in W_2^r(G)$, one of which is finite, we obtain, on integrating by parts, the equation

$$W_2^r(\mathrm{bd})^{++} \supseteq W_2^r(\mathrm{bd}), \tag{1.4}$$

Here and in all of this chapter, $(\cdot, \cdot)_0$ denotes the scalar product in $L_2(G)$. Obviously, $L^{++} = L$. We will sometimes use the Lagrange adjoint expression $L^\oplus = (\overline{L})^+ = \overline{(L^+)}$, where the bar means that the coefficients of L are replaced by their complex conjugates. Instead of (1.4) we have

$$\int_G Lu \cdot v\, dx = \int_G uL^\oplus v\, dx.$$

We introduce the concept of boundary conditions. In order to include possibly more general conditions, we proceed in the following way. Consider the space $W_2^r(G)$ and the subspace $\overset{\circ}{W}{}_2^r(G)$ which is the closure of the set of all finite functions $W_{2,0}^r(G)$ of $W_2^r(G)$. Any subspace of $W_2^r(G)$ which contains $\overset{\circ}{W}{}_2^r(G)$ will be called a subspace of functions which satisfy specific boundary conditions (bd), and will be denoted $W_2^r(\mathrm{bd})$. Until the particular form of these equations on the boundary (for instance, $u|_\Gamma = 0$) concern us, we will distinguish the functions of $W_2^r(\mathrm{bd})$ from the functions of $W_2^r(G)$. We note that the extreme cases $W_2^r(\mathrm{bd}) = \overset{\circ}{W}{}_2^r(G)$ and $W_2^r(\mathrm{bd}) = W_2^r(G)$ are possible. In the latter case, we say that the boundary condition is removed. In general, if on a certain part Γ' of the boundary the conditions (bd) do not impose any restrictions on the function $u \in W_2^r(G)$, then we say that the conditions on Γ' are removed and we denote this by $u|_{\Gamma'} \sim$.

Let $W_2^r(\mathrm{bd})^+$ be the set of all functions $v \in W_2^r(G)$, for which equation (1.4) holds for any $u \in W_2^r(\mathrm{bd})$. Since convergence $v_n \to v$ in $W_2^r(G)$ implies convergence $L^+ v_n \to L^+ v$ in $L_2(G)$, the set $W_2^r(\mathrm{bd})^+$ is closed in $W_2^r(G)$; it is obviously linear and contains $\overset{\circ}{W}{}_2^r(G)$. Thus, $W_2^r(\mathrm{bd})^+$ is a subspace of $W_2^r(G)$ which contains $\overset{\circ}{W}{}_2^r(G)$, that is, it is a subspace of functions which satisfy certain boundary conditions $(\mathrm{bd})^+$ (this justifies its notation). The boundary conditions $(\mathrm{bd})^+$ will be called adjoint to (bd); since we associate (bd) with the expression L, we will, naturally, associate the conditions $(\mathrm{bd})^+$ with L^+.

If $W_2^r(\mathrm{bd})_1 \subseteq W_2^r(\mathrm{bd})_2$, then $W_2^r(\mathrm{bd})_1^+ \supseteq W_2^r(\mathrm{bd})_2^+$. Also

$$W_2^r(\mathrm{bd})^{++} \supseteq W_2^r(\mathrm{bd}), \tag{1.5}$$

and it is not difficult to give examples for which the inclusion in (1.5) is strict. Moreover, it is always true that $W_2^r(\mathrm{bd})^{+++} = W_2^r(\mathrm{bd})^+$. Indeed, from (1.5) it follows that $W_2^r(\mathrm{bd})^{+++} \subseteq W_2^r(\mathrm{bd})^+$. Applying (1.5) to the boundary condition $(\mathrm{bd})^+$, we obtain $W_2^r(\mathrm{bd})^{+++} \supseteq W_2^r(\mathrm{bd})^+$. Q.E.D. Thus if we pass from the boundary condition (bd) to its "closure" $(\mathrm{bd})^{++}$, we obtain the equation

$$W_2^r(\mathrm{bd})^{++} = W_2^r(\mathrm{bd}). \tag{1.6}$$

In what follows, we will only consider conditions (bd) for which (1.6) holds.

We now point out that an assignment of a certain subspace $W_2^r(\mathrm{bd})$ is in fact an assignment of specific relations between the normal derivatives on Γ of functions in $W_2^r(G)$. Indeed, according to the imbedding theorems (see §6 of the Introduction), functions in $W_2^r(G)$ have derivatives defined on Γ of orders up to $r - 1$.

So, the exterior normal derivatives $\partial^m u/\partial \nu^m$ are contained in $C(\Gamma)$ for $0 \le m < r - n/2$, and in $L_q(\Gamma)$ where $q < 2(n-1)/(n-2(r-m))$ for $r - n/2 < m \le r-1$. They are continuous (with respect to the norm of the spaces $C(\Gamma)$ and $L_q(\Gamma)$ respectively) as a function of $u \in W_2^r(G)$. The subspace $\mathring{W}_2^r(G)$ coincides with the set of functions in $W_2^r(G)$ for which all derivatives of orders up to $r-1$ inclusive vanish on Γ or what is the same thing, all derivatives $\partial^m u/\partial \nu^m$, $m = 0, 1, \cdots, r-1$, vanish. We denote by N the orthogonal complement of $\mathring{W}_2^r(G)$ in $W_2^r(G)$:

$$W_2^r(G) = \mathring{W}_2^r(G) \oplus N. \tag{1.7}$$

The subspace $W_2^r(\text{bd})$ can be decomposed, according to (1.7), into $\mathring{W}_2^r(G) \oplus N(\text{bd})$, where $N(\text{bd})$ is the component of N which completely determines $W_2^r(\text{bd})$. Moreover, each function in N, obviously, is uniquely determined by the collection of derivatives

$$u|_\Gamma, \quad \left.\frac{\partial u}{\partial \nu}\right|_\Gamma, \cdots, \left.\frac{\partial^{r-1} u}{\partial \nu^{r-1}}\right|_\Gamma. \tag{1.8}$$

Thus the subspace $N(\text{bd})$ of N, and hence each condition (bd), is determined by a relation between the derivatives (1.8). It is clear that one can not give an effective description of all boundary conditions in terms of the derivatives (1.8). However, it is easy now to write out examples: any relation between (1.8) which determines a linear manifold in $W_2^r(G)$ and which holds under passage to the limit in the metric of $W_2^r(G)$ through variable u in $W_2^r(G)$ is a certain boundary condition. For instance, it is possible to define $W_2^r(\text{bd})$ as the set of all functions $u \in W_2^r(G)$ which satisfy the equations $(B_1(x, D)u)(x) = 0, \cdots, (B_p(x, D)u)(x) = 0$ $(x \in \Gamma)$, where $B_j(x, D)$ is a certain linear differential expression of order $m_j < r$, with sufficiently smooth coefficients, defined on Γ.

We will say that on a certain part Γ_0 of the boundary Γ, (bd) has a specific form, for example, $B_j(x, D)u|_{\Gamma_0} = 0$ $(j = 1, \cdots, p)$, if the behavior of the functions in $W_2^r(\text{bd})$ on Γ_0 is completely described by these restrictions, and therefore each function $u \in W_2^r(G)$, $D^\alpha u|_{\overline{\Gamma \setminus \Gamma_0}} = 0$ $(|\alpha| \le r-1)$, which satisfies them, is contained in $W_2^r(\text{bd})$.

2. **The case of differential expressions of second order.** We consider such expressions in more detail. It is convenient to write (1.2) in the form

$$Lu = L(x, D)\,u = \sum_{j,k=1}^{n} b_{jk}(x)\, D_j D_k u + \sum_{j=1}^{n} b_j(x)\, D_j u + b(x)\, u \tag{1.9}$$

$$(b_{jk}(x) = b_{kj}(x);\quad j,\ k = 1, \ldots, n)$$

with the usual assumptions of smoothness of the complex-valued coefficients. We let $B(x) = \|b_{jk}(x)\|_1^n$.

The concept of characteristic of the expression L plays an essential part in boundary value problems. Let S be some smooth piece of surface, and $a = (a_1, \cdots, a_n)$ be a fixed point on it. Introduce a new orthonormal system of coordinates $(\xi_1, \cdots, \xi_n)$, putting its origin at the point a and directing the ξ_1 axis along the normal to S. Let $O = \|o_{jk}\|_1^n$ be the orthogonal matrix which effects the passage to the new system. Obviously,

$$\xi_j = \sum_{p=1}^{n} (x_p - a_p)\, o_{jp}, \quad D_j u = \sum_{p=1}^{n} \frac{\partial u}{\partial \xi_p}\, o_{pj}, \quad D_j D_k u = \sum_{p,q=1}^{n} \frac{\partial^2 u}{\partial \xi_p \partial \xi_q}\, o_{pj}\, o_{qk}. \tag{1.10}$$

If we substutute these expressions in (1.9), we find that the matrix $\widetilde{B}(x) = \|\widetilde{b}_{pq}(x)\|_1^n$ of coefficients of the second derivatives $\partial^2 u/\partial \xi_p \partial \xi_q$ in our expression has the form

$$\widetilde{b}_{pq}(x) = \sum_{j,k=1}^{n} b_{jk}(x)\, o_{pj} o_{qk}, \quad \text{i.e.} \quad \widetilde{B}(x) = OB(x)\,O'. \tag{1.11}$$

The coefficient of $\partial^2 u/\partial \xi_1^2$ is $\widetilde{b}_{11} = \Sigma_{j,k=1}^n b_{jk}\, o_{1j}\, o_{1k}$; the unit vector $(o_{11}, \cdots, o_{1n})$ is directed along the normal to S at the point a. Hence clearly if we denote by $\nu(x)$ the unit vector of the normal (in either direction) to the surface S we obtain the formula

$$\langle B(x)\,\nu(x), \nu(x) \rangle = \sum_{j,k=1}^{n} b_{jk}(x)\, \nu_j(x)\, \nu_k(x) \quad (x \in S). \tag{1.12}$$

We introduce near S a curvilinear system of coordinates $(\phi_1, \cdots, \phi_n)$ so that the coordinate curve ϕ_1 is orthogonal to S, and the curves $\phi_2, \cdots, \phi_n$ lie in S. If the form (1.12) is everywhere different from zero on S, then these coordinates can be chosen so that Lu assumes the form $\partial^2 u/\partial \phi_1^2 + Mu$, where M contains differentiation with respect to ϕ_1 of order not higher than one. In other words, if the form (1.12) is different from zero on S, then the differential equation $Lu = f$

can be resolved into an equation with the higher derivative in the direction of the normal to S. It is well known that then one can apply the method of Cauchy-Kowalewski to the Cauchy problem for the equation $Lu = f$ with given data on the surface S (if the coefficients and surface are analytic) and easily obtain the solution of this problem.

We say that S forms a piece of characteristic, if for all $x \in S$, $\langle B(x)\nu(x), \nu(x)\rangle = 0$. We say that S is of weak characteristic, if $\langle B(x)\nu(x), \nu(z)\rangle = 0$ on S but $B(x)\nu(x) \neq 0$ for almost all $x \in S$ (in the sense of Lebesgue measure on the surface), and of strong characteristic, if $B(x)\nu(x) = 0$ $(x \in S)$. It is clear that the Cauchy problem with data just mentioned is, in general, unsolvable on characteristics. In this connection, characteristics play a critical role in the theory of boundary value problems.

Suppose that on the boundary Γ of the region G, X_w is a piece of weak characteristic and X_s is a piece of strong characteristic. Let $X = X_w \cup X_s$. Allow the form (1.12) to have zeros on $\Gamma \setminus X$, but assume that the surface measure of the set on which it vanishes is zero. There exists almost everywhere on $\Gamma \setminus X_s$ a conormal unit vector defined by the equation

$$\mu(x) = \frac{B(x)\nu(x)}{|B(x)\nu(x)|}, \tag{1.13}$$

where $\nu(x)$ is the unit vector in the direction of the normal.

By the derivative with respect to the conormal we understand the derivatives at the points of $\Gamma \setminus X_s$ calculated along the unit vector $\mu_1(x)$, that is,

$$\frac{\partial u}{\partial \mu} = \sum_{i=1}^{n} \mu_i(x) D_i u = \frac{1}{|B(x)\nu(x)|} \sum_{i,k=1}^{n} b_{ik}(x) D_i u \cdot \nu_k(x). \tag{1.14}$$

If for $x \in \Gamma \setminus X_s$, $\langle B(x)\nu(x), \nu(x)\rangle = 0$, then $\mu(x) \perp \nu(x)$, i.e., the derivative with respect to the conormal is tangential. This situation holds everywhere on X_w, so therefore $\partial/\partial\mu$ exists on X_w for functions defined only on this part of the boundary. This permits us to introduce the differential expression

$$\mathfrak{M}u = |B(x)\nu(x)| \frac{\partial u}{\partial \mu} = \sum_{i,k=1}^{n} b_{ik}(x) D_i u \cdot \nu_k(x) \tag{1.15}$$

defined for such functions. By $\mathfrak{M}^+$ we mean the adjoint expression, that is, the expression for which $\int_{X_s} \mathfrak{M}u \cdot \bar{v}\,dx = \int_{X_s} u\overline{\mathfrak{M}^+ v}\,dx$ for any smooth u and v, one of which vanishes in a strip near the boundary of the region X_w on the surface Γ.

We now introduce Green's formula for the expression (1.9). For sufficiently smooth u and v, the following equations are easily obtained by integration by parts:

$$\int_G Lu \cdot \bar{v}dx = -\int_G \sum_{j,k=1}^n b_{jk} D_j u \cdot D_k \bar{v} dx + \int_G \sum_{j=1}^n \left(b_j - \sum_{k=1}^n D_k b_{jk} \right) D_j u \cdot \bar{v} dx + \int_G bu\bar{v}dx + \int_\Gamma \sum_{j,k=1}^n b_{jk} D_j u \cdot \bar{v} \nu_k dx,$$

$$\int_G \{Lu \cdot \bar{v} - u\overline{L^+ v}\}\, dx = \int_\Gamma \left\{ \sum_{j,k=1}^n b_{jk} D_j u \cdot \nu_k \bar{v} - u \sum_{j,k=1}^n b_{jk} D_j \bar{v} \cdot \nu_k \right\} dx + \int_\Gamma \sum_{j=1}^n \left(b_j - \sum_{k=1}^n D_k b_{jk} \right) \nu_j u\bar{v} dx.$$

If we introduce the notation

$$\beta(x) = \sum_{j=1}^n \left(b_j(x) - \sum_{k=1}^n D_k b_{jk}(x) \right) \nu_j(x) \quad (x \in \Gamma) \tag{1.16}$$

and use the conormal derivative, we can rewrite these as

$$(Lu, v)_0 = -\int_G \sum_{j,k=1}^n b_{jk} D_j u \cdot D_k \bar{v} dx + \int_G \sum_{j=1}^n \left(b_j - \sum_{k=1}^n D_k b_{jk} \right) D_j u \cdot \bar{v} dx + \int_G bu\bar{v}dx + \int_{\Gamma \setminus X_s} |B\nu| \frac{\partial u}{\partial \mu} \bar{v} dx, \tag{1.17}$$

$$(Lu, v)_0 - (u, L^+v)_0 = \int_{\Gamma\setminus X_s} |B\nu| \left\{\frac{\partial u}{\partial \mu}\bar{v} - u\frac{\partial \bar{v}}{\partial \mu}\right\} dx + \int_{\Gamma} \beta u \bar{v} dx. \tag{1.18}$$

Equations (1.17) and (1.18) are valid in all cases for $u, v \in C^2(G \cup \Gamma)$. If we approximate functions in $W_2^l(G)$, by such functions and use the imbedding theorems, it is easy to see that (1.17) is valid for $u \in W_2^2(G)$, $v \in W_2^1(G)$, and (1.18) for $u, v \in W_2^2(G)$.

By means of (1.18), it is easy to find the adjoint boundary conditions. The following theorem holds.

Theorem 1.1. *Let Γ be decomposed into disjoint pieces $\Gamma_\sim$, Γ_0, Γ_{00}, Γ_{000} (some of which may be empty; $\Gamma = \Gamma_\sim \cup \Gamma_0 \cup \Gamma_{00} \cup \Gamma_{000}$), where $\Gamma_{00} \cup \Gamma_{000} \subseteq \Gamma\setminus X_s$, and $\Gamma_\sim \cap X_s$ lie in a smooth piece of the boundary and is at a positive distance from $\Gamma_{00} \cup X_w$. The adjoint conditions to the conditions*

$$u|_{\Gamma_\sim}\sim, \quad u|_{\Gamma_0} = 0, \quad \left.\frac{\partial u}{\partial \mu}\right|_{\Gamma_{00}} = 0, \quad u|_{\Gamma_{000}} = \left.\frac{\partial u}{\partial \mu}\right|_{\Gamma_{000}} = 0 \tag{1.19}$$

are the conditions

$$v|_{\Gamma_\sim\setminus X} = \left.\frac{\partial v}{\partial \mu}\right|_{\Gamma_\sim\setminus X} = 0, \quad \mathfrak{M}^+v - \overline{\mathfrak{M}}v + \bar{\beta}v|_{\Gamma_\sim\cap X_w} = 0, \quad \bar{\beta}v|_{\Gamma_\sim\cap X_s} = 0,$$
$$v|_{\Gamma_0\setminus X} = 0, \quad -\overline{\mathfrak{M}}v + \bar{\beta}v|_{\Gamma_{00}} = 0, \quad v|_{(\Gamma_0\cap X)\cup\Gamma_{000}}\sim. \tag{1.20}$$

The proof of the theorem is elementary, but rather bulky. We show first that if $v \in W_2^2(G)$ is such that $(Lu, v)_0 = (u, L^+v)_0$ for all $u \in W_2^2(\text{bd})$, then v satisfies the conditions (1.20). By (1.18) and (1.19)

$$0 = \int_{\Gamma\setminus X_s} |B\nu| \left\{\frac{\partial u}{\partial \mu}\bar{v} - u\frac{\partial \bar{v}}{\partial \mu}\right\} dx + \int_{\Gamma} \beta u\bar{v} dx = \int_{\Gamma_\sim\setminus X_s} |B\nu| \frac{\partial u}{\partial \mu}\bar{v} dx$$
$$+ \int_{\Gamma_\sim\setminus X_s} \left\{-|B\nu|\frac{\partial \bar{v}}{\partial \mu} + \beta\bar{v}\right\} u dx + \int_{\Gamma_\sim\cap X_s} \beta u\bar{v} dx + \int_{\Gamma_0\setminus X_s} |B\nu| \frac{\partial u}{\partial \mu}\bar{v} dx$$
$$+ \int_{\Gamma_{00}} \left\{-|B\nu|\frac{\partial \bar{v}}{\partial \mu} + \beta\bar{v}\right\} u dx. \tag{1.21}$$

We take for u in (1.21) a function in $W_2^2(\text{bd})$, which, in addition, vanishes in some neighborhood (in G) of the set $(\Gamma\setminus(\Gamma_\sim X_s)$ and on $\Gamma_\sim\setminus X_s$. We use the following general fact: if on some piece $S \subseteq \Gamma\setminus X_s$, $u(x) = 0$, then $\operatorname{grad} u =$

$(\partial u/\partial \nu)\,\nu(x)$ and therefore

$$|B\nu|\frac{\partial u}{\partial \mu}=\sum_{j,k=1}^{n} b_{jk}D_j u\cdot \nu_k=\langle B\nu, \operatorname{grad} u\rangle=\langle B\nu, \nu\rangle\frac{\partial u}{\partial \nu} \tag{1.22}$$

With regard to (1.22), equation (1.21) for the choice of u under consideration becomes $\int_{\Gamma_\sim\setminus X_s}\langle B\nu, \nu\rangle(\partial u/\partial \nu)\bar v\,dx=0$. Since the normal derivative $\partial u/\partial \nu$ of functions $u\in \mathring{W}_2^2(G)$ which vanish on $\Gamma_\sim\setminus X_s$, can assume sufficiently arbitrary values, it follows from the latter equation that $\langle B\nu, \nu\rangle\,\bar v=0$ on $\Gamma_\sim\setminus X_s$ and (since $\langle B\nu, \nu\rangle\neq 0$ on $\Gamma\setminus X$) $v=0$ on $\Gamma_\sim\setminus X$.

Taking this property into account, we obtain from (1.21), for functions $u\in W_2^2(\mathrm{bd})$, which vanish in a neighborhood of the set $\Gamma\setminus(\Gamma_\sim\setminus X)$, but are arbitrary elsewhere, the equation $\int_{\Gamma_\sim\setminus X}|B\nu|\,u(\partial\bar v/\partial\mu)\,dx=0$. Hence it follows that $\partial v/\partial\bar\mu|_{\Gamma_\sim\setminus X}=0$. Thus the first of the relations (1.20) is established.

We now choose $u\in W_2^2(\mathrm{bd})$ in (1.21) to vanish in a neighborhood of the set $\Gamma\setminus(\Gamma_\sim\setminus X_s)$. Taking into account the equation just obtained for v, we find

$$0=\int_{\Gamma_\sim\cap X_w}|B\nu|\frac{\partial u}{\partial\mu}\bar v\,dx+\int_{\Gamma_\sim\cap X_w}\left\{-|B\nu|\frac{\partial\bar v}{\partial\mu}+\beta\bar v\right\}u\,dx;$$

$$0=\int_{\Gamma_\sim\cap X_w}\{\mathfrak{M}u\cdot\bar v-u\overline{\mathfrak{M}v}+\beta u\bar v\}\,dx=\int_{\Gamma_\sim\cap X_w}u\,\overline{\{\mathfrak{M}^{+}v-\overline{\mathfrak{M}}v+\bar\beta v\}}\,dx. \tag{1.23}$$

The latter equation is obtained from the previous by means of integration by parts over $\Gamma_\sim\cap X_w$ and is valid with the additional assumption that u vanish in a neighborhood of the boundary (on Γ) of the region $\Gamma_\sim\cap X_w$. In view of the arbitrariness of u in (1.23), the second of the relations (1.20) follows.

We take $u\in W_2^2(\mathrm{bd})$ in (1.21) equal to zero in a neighborhood of the set $\Gamma\setminus(\Gamma_\sim\cap X_s)$. Because of the arbitrariness of u on $\Gamma_\sim\cap X_s$, it is necessary that $\bar\beta v|_{\Gamma_\sim\cap X_s}=0$.

Now let $u\in W_2^2(\mathrm{bd})$ vanish in a neighborhood of the set $\Gamma\setminus(\Gamma_0\setminus X_s)$. Since $u=0$ on $\Gamma_0\setminus X_s$, from (1.21) and (1.22), we obtain

$$\int_{\Gamma_0\setminus X_s}\langle B\nu,\nu\rangle\frac{\partial u}{\partial\nu}\bar v\,dx=0.$$

Since the derivative here can assume sufficiently arbitrary values, we can therefore conclude that $v = 0$ on $\Gamma_0 \setminus X$.

Finally, we take $u \in W_2^2(\mathrm{bd})$ in (1.21) equal to zero in a neighborhood of the set $\Gamma \setminus \Gamma_{00}$. Since u can assume sufficiently arbitrary values on Γ_{00}, from this relation we obtain the fifth of the equations (1.20).

For the completion of the proof of the theorem it remains to be shown that if $u, v \in W_2^2(G)$ satisfy the conditions (1.19) and (1.20) respectively, then $(Lu, v)_0 = (u, L^+ v)_0$. Writing Green's formula (1.18), and using (1.19), (1.20), and (1.22), we obtain

$$(Lu, v)_0 - (u, L^+v)_0 = \int_{\Gamma \setminus X_s} |B\nu| \left\{ \frac{\partial u}{\partial \mu} \bar{v} - u \frac{\partial \bar{v}}{\partial \mu} \right\} dx + \int_{\Gamma} \beta u \bar{v} dx$$

$$= \int_{\Gamma_\sim \setminus X} \left\{ |B\nu| \left(\frac{\partial u}{\partial \mu} \bar{v} - u \frac{\partial \bar{v}}{\partial \mu} \right) + \beta u \bar{v} \right\} dx + \int_{\Gamma_\sim \cap X_w} \{ \mathfrak{M} u \cdot \bar{v} - u \overline{\mathfrak{M} v} + \beta u \bar{v} \} \, dx$$

$$+ \int_{\Gamma_\sim \cap X_s} \beta u \bar{v} dx + \int_{\Gamma_0 \setminus X_s} \langle B\nu, \nu \rangle \frac{\partial u}{\partial \nu} \bar{v} dx + \int_{\Gamma_{00}} \overline{\{ -\overline{\mathfrak{M}} v + \bar{\beta} v \}} \, u dx$$

$$= \int_{\Gamma_\sim \cap X_w} \{ \mathfrak{M} u \cdot \bar{v} - u \overline{\mathfrak{M} v + \beta u \bar{v}} \} \, dx. \tag{1.24}$$

For the differential expression $\mathfrak{M}$ and arbitrary, sufficiently smooth u, v, we can rewrite Green's formula

$$\int_{\Gamma_\sim \cap X_w} \mathfrak{M} u \cdot \bar{v} dx = \int_{\Gamma_\sim \cap X_w} u \overline{\mathfrak{M}^+ v} dx + \int_{\gamma} \mathfrak{R} [u, v] \, dx, \tag{1.25}$$

where γ is the boundary of $\Gamma_\sim \cap X_w$, and $\mathfrak{R}[u, v]$ is a certain boundary expression, which is a bilinear form of u and v ($\mathfrak{M}$ is of first order, and therefore derivatives do not enter in $\mathfrak{R}$). For the u and v previously considered, the integral over γ in (1.25) is equal to zero. In fact, denote by γ_1 the part of the boundary γ which borders on $\Gamma \setminus \Gamma_\sim$, and by γ_2 the part which lies interior to $\Gamma_\sim$. By virtue of the first of the equations (1.20) and the hypothesis that $\Gamma_\sim \cap X_w$ is at a positive distance from X_s, γ_2 borders the region in which $v = 0$. Similarly, γ_1 borders the region in which $u = 0$ (in view of the second and fourth equations of (1.19) and the assumption that $\rho((\Gamma_\sim \cap X_w), \Gamma_{00}) > 0$). It follows from the imbedding theorems that $v|_{\gamma_2}, u|_{\gamma_1} = 0$; but then $\mathfrak{R}[u, v]|_\gamma = 0$. Q.E.D. It now follows from (1.24) and (1.25), and the second of the equations (1.20), that $(Lu, v)_0 - (u, L^+ v)_0 = 0$. The theorem is proved.

§2. THE EXISTENCE OF SOLUTIONS OF THE BOUNDARY VALUE PROBLEM IN THE SPACE $L_2(G)$

We will connect with the differential expression (1.2) a certain operator equation in the space $L_2(G)$. The solutions of this equation will be interpreted as solutions of the corresponding boundary value problems. The consideration of $L_2(G)$ as the fundamental space is the most simple case; in fact, similar questions will be studied in other spaces.

1. **Minimal and maximal operators.** Consider the expression (1.2) of order r with the usual smoothness conditions on the coefficients and define an operator Λ' in $L_2(G)$ with an everywhere dense domain by setting $\Lambda' u = Lu$, $\mathfrak{D}(\Lambda') = C_0^\infty(G)$. This operator admits a closure: let $u_n \in C_0^\infty(G)$, $u_n \to 0$ and $Lu_n \to h \in L_2(G)$; then for any $v \in C^\infty(G \cup \Gamma)$, $(h, v)_0 = \lim (Lu_n, v)_0 = \lim (u_n, L^+ v)_0 = 0$. Thus $h = 0$, which is what was required. Let $\Lambda = \Lambda''$; this operator is called the minimal operator induced by the expression L. Clearly, $\overset{\circ}{W}{}_2^r(G) \subseteq \mathfrak{D}(\Lambda)$ and for $u \in \overset{\circ}{W}{}_2^r(G)$, $\Lambda u = Lu$.

Construct the minimal operator Λ^+ with respect to the formally adjoint expression L^+ and let $Л = (\Lambda^+)^*$. The operator $Л$ is called the maximal operator induced by L.

It is not difficult to see that the operator A defined by $u \to Lu \, (u \in W_2^r(G))$ is, generally speaking, a part of $Л$: $A \subseteq Л$. In fact, for $u \in W_2^r(G)$ and $v \in C_0^\infty$ we have

$$(Au, v)_0 = (Lu, v)_0 = (u, L^+ v)_0 = (u, (\Lambda^+)' v)_0,$$

and hence $A \subseteq ((\Lambda^+)')^* = (\Lambda^+)^* = Л$. The inclusion $A \subseteq Л$ accounts for the term "maximal": the operator $Л$ is in any case defined on smooth functions which do not satisfy any boundary conditions and its action on such functions coincides with the action of the expression L. In certain cases we will show that $Л = \overline{A}$ (see subsection 5).

From what has been said above, we have

$$\Lambda \subseteq Л. \tag{2.1}$$

2. **Classical formulation of the boundary value problem and the existence of solvable extensions.** The equation $Lu = f$ and the boundary condition (bd) defined by the subspace $W_2^r(\text{bd})$ naturally combine to form the boundary value problem

$$Lu = f, \quad u \in (\text{bd}). \tag{2.2}$$

With this point of view, for example, the mixed problem for the wave equation $\Delta u - \partial^2 u/\partial t^2 = f(x, t)$ $(x \in G, t \in (0, T))$ can also be regarded as a boundary value problem. Thus, in case u is fixed on the boundary of G, the boundary conditions have the form $u = \partial u/\partial t = 0$ on the lower base of the cylinder $G \times (0, T)$, $u \sim$ on its upper base, and $u = 0$ on its lateral surface. The problem of finding an arbitrary solution of the equation $Lu = f$ is also a boundary value problem: the boundary condition is now $u|_\Gamma \sim$.

The ideal solution of the problem (2.2) might be considered as the determination of a function $u \in W_2^r(\text{bd})$, which satisfies the equation (2.2). Such a solution will be called smooth. However, for arbitrary L, such a solution exists only in exceptional cases, and therefore the concept of other generalized solutions must be introduced.

One of the most simple generalizations is the following. Suppose that it is possible to put an operator L between Λ and $Л$ in (2.1), such that L^{-1} is defined and continuous on all of $L_2(G)$:

$$\Lambda \subset \mathrm{L} \subset Л. \tag{2.3}$$

Then one can take as a boundary value problem for the equation $Lu = f$, the equation

$$\mathrm{L}u = f \in L_2(G), \tag{2.4}$$

and as its solution $- u = \mathrm{L}^{-1} f$. The membership of u in $\mathfrak{D}(\mathrm{L})$ is naturally interpreted as the superposition of a certain boundary condition on the generalized solutions of the equation $Lu = f$, which is of course not of the form (bd). Clearly, if a classical solution of the problem (2.2) exists for all $f \in L_2(G)$, and if it depends continuously on f, then it is generalized in this sense.

The operator L is called a solvable extension of the operator Λ. We have

Theorem 2.1. *For there to exist a solvable extension for L, i.e. an operator* L *which satisfies* (2.3) *and has a continuous inverse defined on all of $L_2(G)$, it is necessary and sufficient that*

$$\| Lu \|_0 \geqslant C \| u \|_0, \quad \| L^+ v \|_0 \geqslant C \| v \|_0 \ (C > 0;\ u, v \in C_0^\infty(G)). \tag{2.5}$$

Before proving the theorem, we will make some general constructions. Let A and B be operators on a Hilbert space H. We say that B is a right inverse of A, if $\mathfrak{D}(B) = H$, $\mathfrak{R}(B) \subseteq \mathfrak{D}(A)$, and $ABf = f (f \in H)$.

Lemma 2.1. *Let A be a closed, densely defined operator in H. In order that there exist a bounded operator B which is a right inverse of A, it is neces-*

sary and sufficient that

$$\|A^*v\| \geqslant C\|v\| \quad (C>0;\ v\in \mathfrak{D}(A^*)). \tag{2.6}$$

Proof. If B exists, then the equation

$$Au = f \tag{2.7}$$

is solvable for any $f \in H$. We show that this fact implies the inequality (2.6). In fact, if we denote by u_f some solution of equation (2.7), then for any $v \in \mathfrak{D}(A^*)$ we have $(f, v) = (Au_f, v) = (u_f, A^*v)$, whence $|(f, v)| = |(u_f, A^*v)| \le \|u_f\| \cdot \|A^*v\|$. Thus, for any $f \in H$ $|(f, v/\|A^*v\|)| \le \|u_f\| = C_f$. By a well-known theorem in the theory of Hilbert space, the set of vectors $v/\|A^*v\|$ $(v \in \mathfrak{D}(A^*))$ is bounded, and hence (2.6) follows.

We establish the sufficiency. By the theorem of Neiman AA^* is selfadjoint and nonnegative. In view of (2.6) $(AA^*w, w) = (A^*w, A^*w) \ge C^2\|w\|^2 (w \in \mathfrak{D}(AA^*) \subseteq \mathfrak{D}(A^*))$; therefore there exists a bounded inverse $(AA^*)^{-1}$ defined on all of H. If we put $Bf = A^*(AA^*)^{-1}f$, then since $\mathfrak{R}(AA^*)^{-1} = \mathfrak{D}(AA^*) \subseteq \mathfrak{D}(A^*)$, this operator makes sense for any $f \in H$. It is closed, since A^* is closed, and $(AA^*)^{-1}$ is bounded. Consequently, B is bounded. Moreover, it is clear that $AB = E$. The lemma is proved.

Corollary. $\mathfrak{R}(A) = H$, *if and only if inequality* (2.6) *holds*.

Indeed, the necessity follows from the proof of the necessity of the lemma, and the sufficiency follows from the lemma itself.

We denote by N the null subspace of the operator A, i.e., the subspace of those $u \in H$ for which $Au = 0$. If $N \neq 0$, then the continuous operator B given in Lemma 2.1 is not unique; for instance, it can be replaced by $b + C$, where C is any continuous operator which maps all of H into N. Clearly, by altering C we obtain all the continuous operators which are right inverses of A.

Proof of the theorem. Assume that (2.5) holds. We will prove the existence of L. Apply Lemma 2.1 with $H = L_2(G)$ and $A = \Pi$. Then $A^* = \Pi^*(\Lambda^+)^{**} = \Lambda^+$. From the second inequality in (2.5) we find by means of passage to the limit, that $\|\Lambda^+v\|_0 \ge C\|v\|_0$ $(v \in \mathfrak{D}(\Lambda^+))$, i.e. (2.6) holds, and therefore the conditions of the lemma are satisfied. Let B be a right inverse of Π and P be the orthogonal projection operator onto $\mathfrak{R}(\Lambda) \subseteq L_2(G)$. For any $f \in L_2(G)$ we define a continuous operator

$$Tf = \Lambda^{-1}Pf + B(E-P)f; \tag{2.8}$$

(note that Λ^{-1} exists and is continuous on $\mathfrak{R}(\Lambda)$; this follows from the inequality $\|\Lambda u\|_0 \geq C\|u\|_0$ $(u \in \mathfrak{D}(\Lambda))$, which in turn follows from the first estimate in (2.5)). Let $\mathfrak{D}(\mathrm{L}) = \mathfrak{R}(T)$. Obviously, $\mathfrak{D}(\Lambda) \subseteq \mathfrak{D}(\mathrm{L}) \subseteq \mathfrak{D}(\mathcal{J\!I})$ and $\mathcal{J\!I}(Tf) = Pf + (E - P)f = f$ $(f \in L_2(G))$. Hence the restriction of $\mathcal{J\!I}$ to $\mathfrak{D}(\mathrm{L})$ can be taken as L.

We establish the necessity of the inequalities (2.5). By the continuity of L^{-1}, $\|Lu\|_0 = \|\mathrm{L}u\|_0 \geq C\|u\|_0$ $(u \in C_0^\infty(G) \subset \mathfrak{D}(\mathrm{L}))$. The second estimate also holds: since $\mathfrak{R}(\mathrm{L}) = L_2(G)$, then, a fortiori, $\mathfrak{R}(\mathcal{J\!I}) = L_2(G)$. The required inequality $\|\Lambda^+ v\|_0 = \|\mathcal{J\!I}^* v\|_0 \geq C\|v\|_0$ $(v \in \mathfrak{D}(\Lambda^+) \supset C_0^\infty(G))$ follows from the corollary to Lemma 2.1. This proves the theorem.

Thus the presence of the inequalities (2.5) guarantees the existence of certain "boundary conditions" – i.e. certain $\mathfrak{D}(\mathrm{L})$ – for which the extended boundary value problem for the equation $Lu = f$ is solvable.

3. **Almost correct boundary conditions.** From the previous discussion it is evident that the boundary conditions which determine a solvable extension of the operator Λ are actually not connected with boundary conditions of the type (bd). We will nevertheless try to establish similar connections.

Consider an expression L of the form (1.2) and some subspace $W_2^r(\mathrm{bd})$, defining (bd). The correspondence $u \to Lu$ $(u \in W_2^r(\mathrm{bd}))$ defines an operator in $L_2(G)$, which we denote by $\Lambda'(\mathrm{bd})$. Since $\Lambda'(\mathrm{bd}) \subseteq \mathcal{J\!I}$, and since $\mathcal{J\!I}$ is closed, $\Lambda'(\mathrm{bd})$ admits a closure $\Lambda(\mathrm{bd})$. This latter operator will be called the strong operator of the problem (2.2). Moreover, we set $\mathcal{J\!I}(\mathrm{bd}) = (\Lambda^+(\mathrm{bd})^+)^*$, where $\Lambda^+(\mathrm{bd})^+$ denotes the strong operator of the adjoint problem

$$L^+ v = f, \quad v \in (\mathrm{bd})^+. \tag{2.9}$$

The operator $\mathcal{J\!I}(\mathrm{bd})$ will be called the weak operator of the problem (2.2). It is clear that Λ and $\mathcal{J\!I}$ are special cases of the operators $\Lambda(\mathrm{bd})$ and $\mathcal{J\!I}(\mathrm{bd})$ respectively.

It is not difficult to see that the inclusions

$$\Lambda \subseteq \Lambda(\mathrm{bd}) \subseteq \mathcal{J\!I}(\mathrm{bd}) \subseteq \mathcal{J\!I}. \tag{2.10}$$

always hold. In fact, it is obvious that $\Lambda \subseteq \Lambda(\mathrm{bd})$. Similarly $\Lambda^+ \subseteq \Lambda^+(\mathrm{bd})^+$, whence $\mathcal{J\!I} = (\Lambda^+)^* \supseteq (\Lambda^+(\mathrm{bd})^+)^* = \mathcal{J\!I}(\mathrm{bd})$. It remains to prove the middle inclusion. For $u \in W_2^r(\mathrm{bd}) \subseteq \mathfrak{D}(\Lambda(\mathrm{bd}))$ and any $v \in W_2^r(\mathrm{bd})^+ = \mathfrak{D}(\Lambda^{+'}(\mathrm{bd})^+)$ we have

$$(\Lambda(\mathrm{bd})u, v)_0 = (Lu, v)_0 = (u, L^+ v)_0 = (u, \Lambda^{+'}(\mathrm{bd})^+ v)_0,$$

whence $\Lambda(\mathrm{bd}) \subseteq (\Lambda^{+'}(\mathrm{bd})^{+})^{*} = (\Lambda^{+}(\mathrm{bd})^{+})^{*} = \text{Л}(\mathrm{bd})$. This proves the assertion.

We now clarify in which cases the operator L of subsection 2 can be chosen between $\Lambda(\mathrm{bd})$ and $\text{Л}(\mathrm{bd})$.

Theorem 2.2. *In order that for given* L *and* (bd) *there exist a solvable extension* L *such that*

$$\Lambda(\mathrm{bd}) \subseteq \mathrm{L} \subseteq \text{Л}(\mathrm{bd}) \tag{2.11}$$

it is necessary and sufficient that the two energy inequalities

$$\| Lu \|_0 \geqslant C \| u \|_0, \ \| L^+ v \|_0 \geqslant C \| v \|_0 \ (C > 0; \\ u \in W_2^r(\mathrm{bd}),\ v \in W_2^r(\mathrm{bd})^+). \tag{2.12}$$

hold.

The proof of this theorem is obtained with the help of Lemma 2.1 in a manner similar to the proof of the previous theorem. Namely, set $H = L_2(G)$ and $A = \text{Л}(\mathrm{bd})$. Then $A^* = (\text{Л}(\mathrm{bd}))^* = (\Lambda^+(\mathrm{bd})^+)^{**} = \Lambda^+(\mathrm{bd})^+$, and therefore (2.6) follows from the second estimate in (2.12). The inequality $\|\Lambda(\mathrm{bd})\, u\|_0 \geq C\|u\|_0$ $(u \in \mathfrak{D}(\Lambda(\mathrm{bd})))$ follows from the first estimate, guaranteeing the existence and continuity on $\Re(\Lambda(\mathrm{bd}))$ of the operator $(\Lambda(\mathrm{bd}))^{-1}$. The subsequent construction is also as in the previous proof. This proves the theorem.

We associate with the boundary value problem (2.2), where $f \in L_2(G)$, four types of solutions.

1. A smooth solution is a function $u \in W_2^r(\mathrm{bd})$ which satisfies the equation $Lu = f$. Sometimes we will call it more precisely an r-smooth solution.

2. A strong solution is a function $u \in \mathfrak{D}(\Lambda(\mathrm{bd}))$, which satisfies the equation $\Lambda(\mathrm{bd})\, u = f$.

3. A semistrong solution is a function $u \in \mathfrak{D}(L)$, which satisfies the equation $\mathrm{L}u = f$, where L is a solvable operator such that $\Lambda(\mathrm{bd}) \subseteq \mathrm{L} \subseteq \text{Л}(\mathrm{bd})$.

4. A weak solution is a function $u \in \mathfrak{D}(\text{Л}(\mathrm{bd}))$, which satisfies the equation $\text{Л}(\mathrm{bd})\, u = f$.

Each of these solutions is a solution of the subsequent type, but not conversely. We will clarify when one or the other type of solution exists.

For the existence of a weak solution for any $f \in L_2(G)$ *it is necessary and sufficient that the second of the inequalities* (2.12) *hold.* In fact, this inequality is equivalent to the estimate $\|\Lambda^+(\mathrm{bd})^+ v\|_0 \geq C\|v\|_0$ $(v \in \mathfrak{D}(\Lambda^+(\mathrm{bd})^+))$, which (since $\Lambda^+(\mathrm{bd})^+ = (\text{Л}(\mathrm{bd}))^*$) implies, because of the corollary to Lemma 2.1, the solvability of the equation $Л\,(\text{bd})\,u = f$ for any $f \in L_2(G)$.

We note that a weak solution can be defined in the equivalent form: $u \in L_2(G)$ is a weak solution of the problem (2.2) if

$$(u, L^+v)_0 = (f, v)_0 \quad (v \in W_2^r(\text{bd})\text{*}). \tag{2.13}$$

The second inequality of (2.12) implies the existence of a weak solution for any $f \in L_2(G)$; however this solution is not uniquely determined by f, and hence even more so it does not depend continuously on f. Moreover, the first inequality of (2.12) implies that a strong solution depends continuously on f when it exists, but it does not imply that a strong solution exists for arbitrary $f \in L_2(G)$. Suppose that both inequalities of (2.12) hold; such (bd) will be called almost correct with respect to L. This is a necessary and sufficient condition for the existence of a semistrong solution for arbitrary $f \in L_2(G)$ (see Theorem 2.2): on the other hand, in this case a weak solution exists for any $f \in L_2(G)$ and the strong solution, when it exists, depends continuously on f.

A semistrong solution is, of course, not uniquely determined by (bd), it depends still on the choice of $\mathfrak{D}(L)$, lying between $\mathfrak{D}(\Lambda(\text{bd}))$ and $\mathfrak{D}(Л(\text{bd}))$: $\mathfrak{D}(\Lambda(\text{bd})) \subseteq \mathfrak{D}(L) \subseteq \mathfrak{D}(Д(\text{bd}))$. Since a fortiori, $W_2^r(\text{bd}) \subseteq \mathfrak{D}(L) \mathfrak{D} Л(\text{bd}))$, then the domain $\mathfrak{D}(L)$ is determined by the vectors of the quotient-space $\mathfrak{D}(Л(\text{bd}))/W_2^r(\text{bd})$ (here $\mathfrak{D}(Л(\text{bd}))$ and $W_2^r(\text{bd})$ are considered as linear spaces without a topology). A class of this quotient-space is a translation of $W_2^r(\text{bd})$ by a vector $f \in \mathfrak{D}(Л(\text{bd})) \setminus W_2^r(\text{bd})$. However, any such vector is not sufficiently smooth. More precisely,

$$\mathfrak{D}(Л(\text{bd})) \cap W_2^r(G) = W_2^r(\text{bd}) \tag{2.14}$$

In fact, one need only show that if $u \in \mathfrak{D}(Л(\text{bd})) \cap W_2^r(G)$, then $u \in W_2^r(\text{bd})$. If $v \in C_0^\infty(G)$, then

$$(Lu, v)_0 = (u, L^+v)_0 = (u, \Lambda^+(\text{bd})^+v)_0 = ((\Lambda^+(\text{bd})^+)^* u, v)_0$$
$$= (Л(\text{bd})\,u, v)_0.$$

Because of the arbitrariness of v, it follows that $Lu = Л(\text{bd})\,u$. Now let $v \in W_2^r(\text{bd})^+$. Then $(Lu, v)_0 = (Л(\text{bd})u, v)_0 = (u, \Lambda^+(\text{bd})^+v)_0 = (u, L^+v)_0$. By the arbitrariness of v, this equation implies that $u \in W_2^r(\text{bd})^{++} = W_2^r(\text{bd})$. Q.E.D. This establishes the relation (2.14).

The relation (2.14) shows, on the one hand, that $\mathfrak{D}(L)$ consists of translations of $W_2^r(\text{bd})$ by insufficiently smooth functions and is therefore difficult to describe, and on the other hand, that *weak solutions preserve the original boundary conditions, i.e. if such a solution is a function in* $W_2^r(G)$, *then it necessarily satisfies* (bd); *that is, it belongs to* $W_2^r(\mathrm{bd})$.

Finally, we discuss the question when a strong solution exists for arbitrary $f \in L_2(G)$ and depends continuously on f. The latter has already been disposed of. For the existence of u for any f it is sufficient that $L[W_2^r(\mathrm{bd})]$ be dense in $L_2(G)$, i.e. that if $(Lu, v)_0 = 0$ for all $u \in W_2^r(\mathrm{bd})$ and a $v \in L_2(G)$, then $v = 0$. Comparing this with the definition (2.13), we conclude that *a strong solution exists for any* $f \in L_2(G)$ *and depends continuously on* f *if and only if the first estimate of* (2.12) *holds and any weak solution* v *of the homogeneous adjoint problem* $(\Pi(\mathrm{bd})^+ v = 0)$ *is zero.* If $\Lambda'(\mathrm{bd})$ is closed, then a strong solution will be smooth.

Thus the problem of determining boundary conditions for given L, for which a general solution exists for all $f \in L_2(G)$ and depends continuously on f, is handled in the following way: in any case, the validity of the energy estimates (2.5) for finite functions is necessary. If they hold, then the existence of a solvable operator L, i.e. of certain generalized boundary conditions, is guaranteed by Theorem 2.1. If (bd) can be chosen, so that instead of (2.5) the estimates (2.12) hold, i.e. to be almost correct conditions, then it is further possible to make a special choice of L between $\Lambda(\mathrm{bd})$ and $\Pi(\mathrm{bd})$ and therefore functions of $\mathfrak{D}(\mathrm{L})$ satisfy (bd) in the weak sense, i.e. belong to $\mathfrak{D}(\Pi(\mathrm{bd}))$. If it can be proven that the weak solutions of the homogeneous adjoint problem are zero, then we can take $\mathrm{L} = \Lambda(\mathrm{bd})$. In this case the boundary conditions (bd) are naturally called correct.

4. **The case when L^{-1} is completely continuous.** We now determine the cases in which there exists a choice of an operator L, satisfying (2.3) or (2.11), such that L^{-1} exists and is completely continuous.

Theorem 2.3. *For the existence of an operator* L *which satisfies* (2.3) *such that* L^{-1} *exists and is completely continuous, it is necessary and sufficient that the energy inequalities* (2.5) *hold and that the operators* Λ^{-1} *and* $(\Lambda^+)^{-1}$ *are completely continuous.*

Similarly, in the case when (2.3) *is replaced by* (2.11), *the required conditions are that* (2.12) *hold and that the operators* $(\Lambda(\mathrm{bd}))^{-1}$ *and* $(\Lambda^+(\mathrm{bd})^+)^{-1}$ *be completely continuous.*

We give a proof only in the case of the inclusions (2.3). By (2.8), L can be chosen so that $\mathrm{L}^{-1} = \Lambda^{-1}P + B(E - P)$, and hence the complete continuity of L^{-1}

will follow if we can establish complete continuity of B. By the proof of Lemma 2.1, it follows that $B = A^*(AA^*)^{-1} = A^*(\sqrt{AA^*})^{-1}(\sqrt{AA^*})^{-1}$, where $A = Л$. Since it is known that the operator $A^*(\sqrt{AA^*})^{-1}$ is isometric, the complete continuity of B will follow from the complete continuity of $(\sqrt{AA^*})^{-1}$. Since $A^* = \Lambda^+$, then for $v \in \mathfrak{D}(\Lambda^+)$

$$\|\sqrt{AA^*}v\|_0 = \|A^*v\|_0 = \|\Lambda^+ v\|_0,$$

and therefore the complete continuity of $(\sqrt{AA^*})^{-1}$ follows from the complete continuity of $(\Lambda^+)^{-1}$, which we assumed.

Conversely, suppose that there exists an L which satisfies (2.3) such that L^{-1} is completely continuous. It follows from the inclusion $\Lambda \subseteq L$ that Λ^{-1} is completely continuous. Moreover, since $(L^{-1})^* = (L^*)^{-1}$ is completely continuous, where $L^* \supseteq \Lambda^+$, $(\Lambda^+)^{-1}$ is completely continuous. The theorem is proved.

5. **Another definition of maximal operator.** In accordance with the discussion in subsection 1, under maximal operators, it is natural to consider another definition of a maximal operator. Namely, if we consider an expression L of the form (1.2), the closure of the operator in $L_2(G)$ defined by $u \to Lu$ $(u \in W_2^r(G)$ might be called a maximal operator. In general, this definition differs from that of subsection 1; however, in a number of important cases they coincide (see pp. 182, 273). For the proof of these coincidences later on, we will need the following lemma.

Lemma 2.2 *Suppose that the coefficients of L can be extended to all of E_n in such a way as to preserve their smoothness. Consider $u \in L_2(G)$ and extend it to a function $\hat{u}$ by defining $\hat{u}$ to be zero outside of G; assume that $\hat{u}$ is such that $L^+\hat{u} \in L_2(E_n)$ in the sense of the generalized functions of L. Schwartz, i.e. there is an $h \in L_2(E_n)$ for which*

$$(\hat{u}, Lv)_{L_2(E_n)} = (h, v)_{L_2(E_n)} \quad (v \in C_0^\infty(E_n)). \tag{2.15}$$

If all such $\hat{u}$ belong to the domain of the minimal operator Λ^+, constructed with respect to L^+ on G, then the maximal operator $Л$, constructed with respect to L on G, coincides with the closure of the operator A: $v \to Lv$, $v \in \mathfrak{D}(A) = C^\infty(G \cup \Gamma)$.

Proof. The inclusion $\bar{A} \subseteq Л$ is obvious, so we need only show that $\bar{A} \supseteq Л$ or equivalently, that $A^* \subseteq Л^* = \Lambda^+$. Let $u_0 \in \mathfrak{D}(A^*)$ and choose $f \in L_2(G)$ such that

$$(u_0, Lw)_{L_2(G)} = (f, w)_{L_2(G)} \quad (w \in C^\infty(G \cup \Gamma)).$$

Denote by $\hat{u}_0$ and $\hat{f}$ the extensions of u_0 and f to all of E_n by setting them equal to zero outside of E_n. Then it follows from the last equation that $(\hat{u}_0, Lv)_{L_2(E_n)} = (\hat{f}, v)_{L_2(E_n)}$ for any $v \in C_0^\infty(E_n)$, by the hypothesis that $u_0 \in \mathfrak{D}(\Lambda^+)$. Thus $A^* \subseteq \bar{\Lambda}^+$. The lemma is proved.

§3. GENERALIZED SOLUTIONS OF BOUNDARY VALUE PROBLEMS

In the preceding section we introduced a generalization of the concept of a solution of the problem (2.2), where f and u were functions in $L_2(G)$. Now we consider a similar generalization in which f and u are functions from spaces of the form $W_2^l(G)$ $(l = \cdots, -1, 0, 1, \cdots)$. For simplicity of presentation, we confine ourselves to the most characteristic and important spaces. It is easy to see that many of the definitions and facts cited below are valid in the case of more general positive and negative spaces. This remark is important, since in the consideration of nonelliptic operators the various energy inequalities can often only be established in metrics other than the Sobolev metrics, and therefore modifications of the presentation below are absolutely necessary.

The concepts of a generalized solution given below is essential for spectral theory.

We shall begin with similar questions, connected with the realization of the general ideas mentioned at the beginning of this chapter.

1. **Conditional solvability.** We introduce a generalization of the concept of solvability of the problem (2.2) for which the Fredholm alternative is valid (i.e. normal solvability is valid) and the adjoint problem is easily investigated. For $f \in W_2^{-r}(G)$ we will say that the problem (2.2) is conditionally solvable if there exists a sequence $u_n \in W_2^r(\mathrm{bd})$ such that $Lu_n \to f$ in $W_2^{-r}(G)$. The sequence u_n here may not converge to anything.

Theorem 3.1. *A necessary and sufficient condition for the conditional solvability of the problem* (2.2) *with* $f \in W_2^{-r}(G)$ *is that* $(f, v)_0 = 0$ *for all solutions* v *of the equation* $L^+ v = 0$ *belonging to* $W_2^r(\mathrm{bd})^+$.

Proof. Conditional solvability of the problem is equivalent to the membership of f in the closure in $W_2^{-r}(G)$ of the linear space of functions $L[W_2^r(\mathrm{bd})]$.

Therefore the theorem is equivalent to the decomposition

$$W_2^{-r}(G) = \overline{L[W_2^r(\mathrm{bd})]} \oplus \mathbf{I}_r^{-1} Z, \tag{3.1}$$

where the bar indicates closure, Z is the set of all solutions in $W_2^r(\mathrm{bd})^+$ of the equation $L^+v = 0$, and the operator $\mathbf{I}_r$ is defined in Chapter I, §3.1 (here it is necessary to use the fact that $(f, \mathbf{I}_r^{-1}v)_{-r} = (f, v)_0$).

So we prove (3.1). Let $\alpha \perp \overline{L[W_2^r(\mathrm{bd})]}$, i.e.

$$0 = (Lu, \alpha)_{-r} = (Lu, \mathbf{I}_r \alpha)_0 \quad (u \in W_2^r(\mathrm{bd})). \tag{3.2}$$

Letting $u \in C_0^\infty(G)$ and setting $v = \mathbf{I}_r\alpha \in W_2^r(G)$, we find that $(u, L^+v)_0 = 0$. Since $C_0^\infty(G)$ is dense in $L_2(G)$, it follows that $L^+v = 0$. Also from (3.2) it follows that $(Lu, v)_0 = (u, L^+v)_0$ for any $u \in W_2^r(\mathrm{bd})$, i.e. $v \in W_2^r(\mathrm{bd})^+$. Thus $v \in Z$ and $\alpha \in \mathbf{I}_r^{-1}Z$.

Conversely, each $\mathbf{I}_r^{-1}v$ $(v \in Z)$ is orthogonal in $W_2^{-1}(G)$ to $\overline{L[W_2^r(\mathrm{bd})]}$: for $u \in W_2^r(\mathrm{bd})$ we have $(Lu, \mathbf{I}_r^{-1}v)_{-r} = (Lu, v)_0 = (u, L^+v)_0 = 0$. The decomposition (3.1) follows and the theorem is proved.

This theorem implies that the problem (2.2) is conditionally solvable for any $f \in W_2^{-r}(G)$ if and only if there is no nonzero solution of the equation $L^+v = 0$ which belongs to $W_2^r(\mathrm{bd})^+$, i.e. the uniqueness of smooth solutions is valid for the adjoint problem.

2. **Some remarks on generalized functions.** We say that $\alpha \in W_2^{-k}(G)$ $(k \geq 0)$ is concentrated on the set A contained in G, if $(\alpha, u)_0 = 0$ for each $u \in W_2^k(G)$ which vanishes in some neighborhood of A. By this definition the δ-function δ_ξ is in fact concentrated at the point $\xi \in G$. Denote by $W_{2,0}^{-k}(G)$ the linear set of all generalized functions which are concentrated on sets contained in the interior of G. This set is dense in $W_2^{-k}(G)$, since it contains $C_0^\infty(G)$, which is dense in $L_2(G)$ with respect to the $L_2(G)$ metric.

We denote by $\widetilde{W}_2^{-k}(G) \subseteq W_2^{-k}(G)$ the linear span of $W_{2,0}^{-k}(G)$ and $L_2(G)$; later on the functions of $\widetilde{W}_2^{-k}(G)$ will be used for the functions f on the right side of (2.2).

Lemma 3.1. *If $\alpha \in \widetilde{W}_2^{-k}(G)$ is such that $(\alpha, u)_0 = 0$ for all $u \in \mathring{W}_2^k(G)$ (or even $u \in C_0^\infty(G)$), then $\alpha = 0$. In other words, the functionals in $\widetilde{W}_2^{-k}(G) \subseteq W_2^{-k}(G)$ are uniquely determined by their values on $C_0^\infty(G)$.*

For the proof, it is sufficient to consider the case of the equation $(\alpha, u)_0 = 0$ for all $u \in \mathring{W}_2^k(G)$; the case $u \in C_0^\infty(G)$ is reduced to the former by passage to the limit. We have $\alpha = \beta + f$, where $\beta \in W_{2,0}^{-k}(G)$, $f \in L_2(G)$; let B be the set on which β is concentrated. We construct the following partition of unity (see p. 24): $\chi_1(x)$ and $\chi_2(x)$ are nonnegative functions from $C^\infty(E_n)$, $\chi_1(\chi_2)$ vanishes in some neighborhood of the boundary Γ (of the set B), and $\chi_1(x) + \chi_2(x) = 1$ $(x \in E_n)$. Below we only consider these functions on G. For any $u \in \overset{\circ}{W}{}_2^k(G)$, $\chi_2 u \in \overset{\circ}{W}{}_2^k(G)$ and vanishes in a neighborhood of B; hence $0 = (\alpha, \chi_2 u)_0 = (f, \chi_2 u)_0 = \int_G f(x)\chi_2(x)\overline{u(x)}\,dx$; it follows that $f\chi_2 = 0$ in $L_2(G)$. Now let $u \in W_2^k(G)$ be arbitrary. Since $\chi_1 u \in \overset{\circ}{W}{}_2^k(G)$, then $(\alpha, \chi_1 u)_0 = 0$; since $\chi_2 u$ vanishes in a neighborhood of B, then $(\beta, \chi_2 u)_0 = 0$. In conclusion we have $(\alpha, u)_0 = (\alpha, (\chi_1 + \chi_2)u)_0 = (\alpha, \chi_1 u)_0 + (\alpha, \chi_2 u)_0 = \int_G f\chi_2 \bar{u}\,dx = 0$ $(u \in W_2^k(G))$, i.e. $\alpha = 0$. This proves the lemma.

Let $W_2'^k(G)$ be some subspace of the space $W_2^k(G)$ which contains $C_0^\infty(G)$, and construct the negative space $W_2'^{-k}(G)$ (see Chapter I, §3.4). If we assume that A acts continuously from all of $W_2'^k(G)$ into $W_2^l(G)$ $(l = \cdots, -1, 0, 1, \cdots)$, then as in Chapter I, §1.3 there exists an operator A^+ which takes $W_2^{-l}(G)$ continuously into $W_2'^{-l}(G)$ and is such that

$$(\alpha, Au)_0 = (A^+\alpha, u)_0 \qquad (\alpha \in W_2^{-l}(G),\ u \in W_2'^k(G)). \tag{3.3}$$

It will be useful to us to form adjoint operators $\tilde{A}^+$ to A so that $\tilde{A}^+ W_2^{-l}(G)$ is contained in $W_2^{-k}(G)$, and not in the larger space $W_2'^{-k}(G)$. One cannot simply take the restriction of A^+ to those α, for which $A^+\alpha \in W_2^{-k}(G)$, since such $A^+\alpha$ are not uniquely determined from (3.3). However, if A^+ is restricted to α for which $A^+\alpha \in \tilde{W}_2^{-k}(G) \subseteq W_2^{-k}(G)$, then our aim will be achieved (Lemma 3.1). This restriction will be denoted by $\tilde{A}^+$.

By $\tilde{A}^+$ is understood an operator (in general, not continuous) from $W_2^{-l}(G)$ to $W_2^{-k}(G)$, the domain of which consists of functions $\alpha \in W_2^{-l}(G)$ for which there exists a $\beta \in \tilde{W}_2^{-k}(G)$ such that $(\alpha, Au)_0 = (\beta, u)_0$ for all $u \in W_2'^k(G)$; in this connection we set $\tilde{A}^+\alpha = \beta$. We have

$$(\alpha, Au)_0 = (\tilde{A}^+\alpha, u)_0 \quad (u \in W_2'^k(G),\ \alpha \in \mathfrak{D}(\tilde{A}^+)). \tag{3.4}$$

If $l = 0$, we consider the operator A as acting in the space $L_2(G) = W_2^0(G)$ with dense domain $W_2'^k(G)$. It is clear that then the adjoint (in $L_2(G)$) operator is the restriction of the operator $\tilde{A}^+$ (namely, one must take $\beta \in L_2(G)$).

3. **Generalized solutions.** We will extend the concept of the strong and weak operators $\Lambda(\mathrm{bd})$ and $\Pi(\mathrm{bd})$ of the problem (2.2). Let $s > -r$ and assume that

coefficients of the expression L are such that $a_\alpha(x) \in C^{|\alpha|+\max(0,s)}(G \cup \Gamma)$, and (bd) is such that $W_2^r(\text{bd}) \cap W_2^{r+s}(G)$ is dense in $W_2^r(\text{bd})$, and $W_2^r(\text{bd})^+ \cap W_2^{r+s}(G)$ is dense in $W_2^r(\text{bd})^+$.[1]

We define the s-strong operator $\Lambda_s(\text{bd})$ of the problem (2.2) as the operator which maps $W_2^r(\text{bd}) \cap W_2^{r+s}(G)$ (equipped with the topology of the space $W_2^{\max(r,r+s)}(G)$) continuously into $W_2^s(G)$ defined by: $\Lambda_s(\text{bd})\,u = Lu(u \in W_2^r(\text{bd}) \cap W_2^{r+s}(G))$.

Acting from $W_2^{-s}(G)$ into $W_2^{-\max(r,r+s)}(G)$, we have the operator

$$\mathcal{J}\!\mathcal{I}_s(\text{bd}) = \widetilde{(\Lambda_s^+(\text{bd})^+)^+} \;(\mathfrak{D}(\mathcal{J}\!\mathcal{I}_s(\text{bd})) \subseteq W_2^{-s}(G),$$
$$\mathfrak{R}(\mathcal{J}\!\mathcal{I}_s(\text{bd})) \subseteq \widetilde{W}_2^{-\max(r,r+s)}(G)), \tag{3.5}$$

where $\Lambda_s^+(\text{bd})^+$ is the s-strong operator of the adjoint problem (2.9). It will be called the s-weak operator of the problem (2.2).

In the case $s = 0$, $\Lambda_0(\text{bd})$ coincides with the operator $\Lambda'(\text{bd})$, considered as acting from $W_2^r(\text{bd})$ into $L_2(G) = W_2^0(G)$. The operator $\mathcal{J}\!\mathcal{I}_0(\text{bd})$ is some extension of $\mathcal{J}\!\mathcal{I}(\text{bd})$ (see the end of subsection 2).

We continue the list of solutions of the problem (2.2) begun in §2.3.

5) An $(r+s)$-smooth solution $(s \geq 0)$ is a function $u \in W_2^r(\text{bd}) \cap W_2^{r+s}(G)$ which satisfies the equation $Lu = f$, or, equivalently, the equation $\Lambda_s(\text{bd})\,u = f$ (it is clear that we must assume $f \in W_2^s(G)$). In case $s = 0$, this definition coincides with 1).

6) An s-generalized solution $(-s < r)$ is a function $u \in \mathfrak{D}(\mathcal{J}\!\mathcal{I}_s(\text{bd})) \subseteq W_2^{-s}(G)$ which satisfies the equation $\mathcal{J}\!\mathcal{I}_s(\text{bd})\,u = f$. Here $f \in \widetilde{W}_2^{-\max(r,r+s)}(G)$. For $s = 0$ and $f \in L_2(G)$ it coincides with 4).[2]

---

1) It is easy to construct an example of (bd) for which $W_2^r(\text{bd}) \cap W_2^{r+s}(G)$ for large $s > 0$ is not dense in $W_2^r(\text{bd})$. Let $r = 2$, and $W_2^r(\text{bd})$ consist of those $u \in W_2^2(G)$ for which $\partial u/\partial \nu - \sigma(x)\,u|_\Gamma = 0$. Here $\sigma(x)$ is continuous, but not a sufficiently smooth function. The set $W_2^2(\text{bd}) \cap W_2^{2+s}(\text{bd})$ for large s consists of functions u for which $\partial u/\partial \nu|_\Gamma$ and $u|_\Gamma$ can be arbitrarily smooth (by the imbedding theorem) and which satisfy the equation $\partial u/\partial \nu|_\Gamma = \sigma(x)\,u|_\Gamma$. Because of the nonsmoothness of σ, this equation can hold only when $u|_\Gamma = \partial u/\partial \nu|_\Gamma = 0$. Thus, $W_2^2(\text{bd}) \cap W_2^{2+s}(G) = \overset{\circ}{W}{}_2^2(G) \cap W_2^{2+s}(G)$ and is not dense in $W_2^2(\text{bd})$.

In all that follows, it is assumed, unless otherwise stated, that the smooth functions of $W_2^r(\text{bd})$, $W_2^r(\text{bd})^+$ are dense in these spaces.

2) Actually, we will usually not say what type of generalized solution is being considered, provided this is clear from the context.

The definition of an s-generalized solution can be stated, obviously, as follows: let $f \in \widetilde{W}_2^{-\max(r,r+s)}(G)$; then $u \in W_2^{-s}(G)$ is called such a solution if

$$(u, L^+ v)_0 = (f, v)_0 \ (v \in W_2^r(\mathrm{bd})^+ \cap W_2^{r+s}(G)). \tag{3.6}$$

It is clear that for $r > -s \geq 0$ and $f \in L_2(G)$, an s-generalized solution is also a weak solution. An attempt to define an s-generalized solution for $-s \geq r$, as is not difficult to understand, leads to the concept of an s-smooth solution (see in connection with Theorem 3.2). We must remark that an s-generalized solution may, of course, turn out to be a smoother function than the function from $W_2^{-s}(G)$.

It may seem strange that in the construction of generalized solutions we take f from $\widetilde{W}_2^{-\max(r,r+s)}(G)$ and not from all of $W_2^{-\max(r,r+s)}(G)$ or what amounts to the same thing, that in the definition (3.5) of the operator $\Pi_s(\mathrm{bd})$, we must choose a wave and not make use of definition (3.3). This is because of the following fact.

Suppose that we have some generalization of the concept of a solution of the boundary value problem (2.2) for which the generalized functions of some space $H_- \supseteq W_2^r(G)$ serve as the solutions. We will say that the boundary conditions are preserved by this generalization if, whenever a generalized solution is a function in $W_2^r(G)$, it also belongs to $W_2^r(\mathrm{bd})$. Clearly, these are the only reasonable generalizations. The following theorem, a special case of which has already been established in §2.3 is valid.

Theorem 3.2. *By construction of the s-generalized solutions of the problem* (2.2), *the boundary conditions are preserved. Moreover, if* $f \in W_2^{-\max(r,r+s)}(G)$ *in the definition* (3.6), *then the boundary conditions are not preserved.*

Proof. Let $u \in \mathfrak{D}(\Pi_s(\mathrm{bd})) \cap W_2^r(G)$. On taking $v \in C_0^\infty(G) \subset W_2^r(\mathrm{bd})^+ \cap W_2^{r+s}(G)$ in (3.6), we obtain $(f, v)_0 = (u, L^+ v)_0 = (Lu, v)_0$, i.e. $(f - Lu, v)_0 = 0$. Since $f \in \widetilde{W}_2^{-\max(r,r+s)}(G)$, and $Lu \in L_2(G)$, $f = Lu \in \widetilde{W}_2^{-\max(r,r+s)}(G)$ and from the latter equation and Lemma 3.1, it follows that $f = Lu$. Now (3.6) gives $(u, L^+ v)_0 = (f, v)_0 = (Lu, v)_0$, $v \in W_2^r(\mathrm{bd})^+ \cap W_2^{r+s}(G)$. Since the latter set is assumed to be dense in $W_2^r(\mathrm{bd})^+$, after passage to the limit we obtain $(u, L^+ w)_0 = (Lu, w)_0$, $w \in W_2^r(\mathrm{bd})^+$. This equation means that $u \in W_2^r(\mathrm{bd})^{++} = W_2^r(\mathrm{bd})$, as asserted.

We establish the second assertion of the theorem. Let $u \in W_2^r(G) \setminus W_2^r(\mathrm{bd})$ be fixed. The expression $l(v) = (u, L^+ v)_0$ is obviously a continuous conjugate-linear functional on $W_2^{\max(r,r+s)}(G)$ and can therefore be expressed in the form

$(u, L^+v)_0 = (f, v)_0$ $(v \in W_2^{\max(r,r+s)}(G))$, where f is some vector in $W_2^{-\max(r,r+s)}(G)$. If we consider $v \in W_2^r(\mathrm{bd})^+ \cap W_2^{r+s}(G)$ in this equation, we find that u satisfies (3.6), it belongs to $W_2^r(G)$, and it does not belong to $W_2^r(\mathrm{bd})$, i.e. the boundary conditions are not preserved. The theorem is proved.

Nevertheless, it is sometime convenient to consider u, satisfying (3.6) for $f \in W_2^{-\max(r,r+s)}(G)$. Such u can, as before, be regarded as a generalized solution of the problem (2.2), but the possibility of not preserving the boundary conditions must be kept in mind. Another approach to the preservation of boundary conditions under passage to generalized solutions is possible: one must introduce a negative space with respect to (bd) (see Theorem 3.6 and 6.12 of Chapter III, concerning elliptic equations, in connection with this). The scheme is not presented in the general case.

4. **The existence of generalized solutions.** We prove a simple theorem of the type of Theorems 2.1 and 2.2. It is assumed in what follows that the coefficients of L are sufficiently smooth.

Theorem 3.3. *Fix $k, l = \cdots, -1, 0, 1, \cdots$, with $l \le \max(r, r+k)$. For each $f \in W_2^{-l}(G)$ there is a $u \in W_2^{-k}(G)$ such that*

$$(u, L^+ v)_0 = (f, v)_0 \qquad (v \in W_2^r(\mathrm{bd})^+ \cap W_2^{r+k}(G)). \tag{3.8}$$

if and only if the inequalities

$$\| L^+ v \|_k \geqslant C \| v \|_l \quad (C > 0; \quad v \in W_2^r(\mathrm{bd})^+ \cap W_2^{r+k}(G)) \tag{3.7}$$

hold.

In particular, from (3.7) it follows that there exists a $-k$-generalized solution $(-k < r)$ of the problem (2.2) for any $f \in \widetilde{W}_2^{-l}(G)$ of a $-k$-smooth solution for $-k \ge r$.

Proof. We show that (3.8) follows from (3.7). Fix $f \in W_2^{-l}(G)$ and consider the expression $(f, v)_0$, where $v \in W_2^r(\mathrm{bd})^+ \cap W_2^{r+k}(G)$. By (3.7) it actually depends not on v, but on L^+v, and therefore we may assume that $(f, v)_0 = l(L^+v)$, where l is an additive and homogeneous functional on the linear set $L^+[W_2^r(\mathrm{bd})^+ \cap W_2^{r+k}(G)]$.

Furthermore, we have

$$| l(L^+ v) | = | (f, v)_0 | \leqslant \| f \|_{-l} \| v \|_l \leqslant \frac{1}{C} \| f \|_{-l} \| L^+ v \|_k,$$

i.e. $l(w)$ is a continuous functional on $L^+[W_2^r(\mathrm{bd})^+ \cap W_2^{r+k}(G)]$, considered as a subspace of $W_2^k(G)$. Continuing this functional by virtue of the Hahn-Banach theorem to all of $W_2^k(G)$, we find a vector $u \in W_2^{-k}(G)$ such that $(f, v)_0 = l(L^+ v) = (u, L^+ v)_0$ $(v \in W_2^r(\mathrm{bd})^+ \cap W_2^{r+k}(G))$, and this is what was required.

Conversely, assume that for any $f \in W_2^{-l}(G)$ there exists a $u = u_f \in W_2^{-k}(G)$ such that (3.8) holds. From this equation we obtain

$$|(f, v)_0| = |(u_f, L^+ v)_0| \leqslant \| u_f \|_{-k} \| L^+ v \|_k = C_f \| L^+ v \|_k.$$

In other words, for any $f \in W_2^{-l}(G)$

$$\left| \left(\mathrm{I}_l f, \frac{v}{\| L^+ v \|_k} \right)_l \right| \leqslant C_f \ (v \in W_2^r(\mathrm{bd})^+ \cap W_2^{r+k}(G)) \tag{3.9}$$

(for $l < 0$ here $\mathrm{I}_l = \mathrm{I}_{-l}^{-1}$; $\mathrm{I}_0 = E$). As f varies, the vector $\mathrm{I}_l f$ runs through all of the Hilbert space $W_2^l(G)$, and therefore it follows from (3.9) that the norms $\| v / \| L^+ v \|_k \|_l$ are uniformly bounded, i.e. the inequality (3.7) holds. The theorem is proved.

It is clear that the theorem can be extended to norms in other spaces congruent to $W_2^l(G)$. We remark only that the inequality $\| L^+ v \|_0 \geq C \| v \|_+ (C > 0;\ v \in W_2^r(\mathrm{bd}))$, where $\| \cdot \|_+$ is the norm in a positive space $H_+ \supseteq W_2^r(\mathrm{bd})^+$ implies that for any $f \in H_-$ there exists a $u \in L_2(G)$ such that $(u, L^+ v)_0 = (f, v)_0$ $(v \in W_2^r(\mathrm{bd})^+)$ (in this connection $H_0 = L_2(G)$).

5. **Local behavior of generalized functions and local satisfaction of the equation and boundary conditions.** We introduce simple but essential concepts which will be used repeatedly later on. The region G with boundary Γ and the subregions G_j considered below may be unbounded. Let $G_1, G_2 \subseteq G$, $G_3 \subseteq G_1 \cap G_2$. We will say that functions (generalized or not) $\alpha \in W_2^{k_1}(G_1)$, $\beta \in W_2^{k_2}(G_2)$ $(k_1, k_2 = \cdots, -1, 0, +1, \cdots)$ coincide inside G_3 if for any $u \in C_0^\infty(G_3)$, extended by zero to G_1 and G_2, $(\alpha, u)_0 = (\beta, u)_0$. Suppose now that G_3 and G have a common piece of boundary, and let γ be a piece of it. We say that α and β coincide inside G_3 up to γ, if $(\alpha, u)_0 = (\beta, u)_0$ for any $u \in C^\infty(G \cup \Gamma)$ which vanishes in neighborhoods of the set $(G \setminus G_3) \cup (\Gamma \setminus \gamma)$ and infinity. These definitions contain, in particular, the concepts of two generalized or ordinary functions coinciding inside G_3 and inside G_3 up to γ.

Let $\alpha \in W_2^k(G)$. We will say that α belongs to W_2^l inside G with $l \geq k$, if for each bounded subregion G' of G lying strictly interior to G, there exists a

$\beta_{G'} \in W_2^l(G)$ such that $\alpha = \beta_{G'}$ inside G' (here $k, l = \cdots, -1, 0, +1, \cdots$). We will denote this by: $\alpha \in W_{2,\mathrm{loc}}^l(G)$.

Lemma 3.2. *Let $\alpha \in W_2^k(G)$, and suppose that for each $x \in G$ there is a neiborhood U_x of x and a $\beta_x \in W_2^l(U_x)$ such that α and β_x coincide inside U_x. Then $\alpha \in W_{2,\mathrm{loc}}^l(G)$.*

Proof. We restrict ourselves to the case $k, l < 0$. Let $\chi_1(x), \chi_2(x), \cdots$ be a partition of unity, constructed with respect to U_ξ $(\xi \in G)$, G' some bounded subregion of G lying strictly interior to G, and N be such that $\Sigma_{j=1}^N \chi_j(x)$ is equal to one on G'. Define a generalized function $\beta_{G'} \in W_2^l(G)$ by the equation $(\beta_{G'}, u)_0 = \Sigma_{j=1}^N (\beta_{x_j}, \chi_j(x)u(x))_0$, where $u \in W_2^{-l}(G)$ is a smooth function; clearly, such a definition makes sense. Since $(\alpha, \chi_j u)_0 = (\beta_{x_j}, \chi_j u)_0$ for $u \in C_0^\infty(G')$, then for these u we have $(\alpha, u)_0 = (\alpha, \Sigma_{j=1}^N \chi_j u)_0 = \Sigma_{j=1}^N (\alpha, \chi_j u)_0 = (\beta_{G'}, u)_0$, i.e. α coincides with $\beta_{G'} \in W_2^l(G)$ inside G'. By the arbitrariness of G', α belongs to W_2^l inside G. This proves the lemma.

Similarly, we can introduce a more general definition of belonging to W_2^l inside G up to a piece of the boundary $\gamma \subseteq \Gamma$. We will say that $\alpha \in W_2^k$ belongs thus to $W_2^l (l \geq k)$, if for each bounded subregion $G' \subseteq G$ whose boundary is contained in $G \cup \gamma$ there exists a $\beta_{G'} \in W_2^l(G)$ such that $\alpha = \beta_{G'}$ inside G' up to the common part of the boundary of G' with G $(k, l = \cdots, -1, 0, 1, \cdots)$ (see Figure 1). We denote this by $\alpha \in W_{2,\mathrm{loc}}^l(G, \gamma)$.

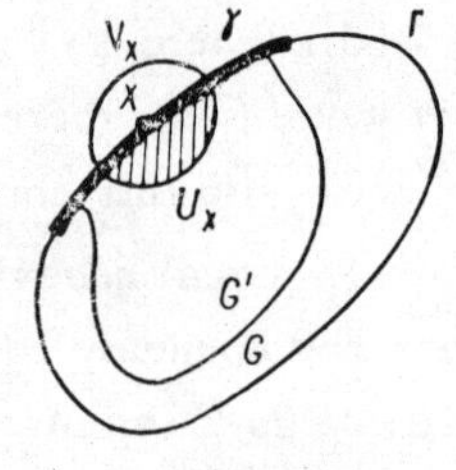

Figure 1

In other words, $\alpha \in W_2^k(G)$ belongs to $W_{2,\mathrm{loc}}^l(G, \gamma)$ $(l \geq k,\ 0 \subseteq \gamma \subseteq \Gamma)$, if for each subregion $G' \subseteq G$ of the form stated, there is a $\beta_{G'} \in W_2^l(G)$ such that $(\alpha, u)_0 = (\beta_{G'}, u)_0$ for all $u \in C^\infty(G \cup \Gamma)$ which in addition vanishes in a neighborhood of $G \setminus G'$. In particular, for $l = 0, 1, \cdots$, the notation $u \in W_{2,\mathrm{loc}}^l(G, \gamma)$ means that for each $G' \subseteq G$ of the form stated, $u \in W_2^l(G')$. For $l = 0$ this definition agrees with the definition in the Introduction (§4).

A variant of Lemma 3.2 holds for functions belonging inside G up to $\gamma \subseteq \Gamma$; it is only necessary to take the points x from $G \cup \gamma$, and moreover, if $x \in \gamma$, then by U_x is meant the intersection of a neighborhood V_x in E_n with G, and it is required that α coincide with $\beta_x \in W_2^l(U_x)$ up to $\gamma \cap V_x$. If $x \in G$, U_x is as before. The proof of this variant of Lemma 3.2 is almost identical with the original.

Finally, we note that in the definitions of belonging to W_2^l we can consider $\alpha \in W_2^k(G_0)$, where $G_0 \supset G$. All the assertions above are valid for any of the spaces $W_2^{\pm(k,q)}(G)$.

We turn to the definition of locally satisfying the equation $Lu = f$ and the boundary condition (bd); we will assume for simplicity that G is bounded. In what follows, it is assumed that the coefficients of L are sufficiently smooth and that $W_2^r(\text{bd})^+ \cap W_2^{r+s}(G)$ is dense in $W_2^r(\text{bd})^+$ for specified $s \geq 0$.

Let $G_1 \subseteq G$; $k, l = \cdots, -1, 0, 1, \cdots$. We say that $\alpha \in W_2^k(G_1)$ satisfies the equation $Lu = f \in W_2^l(G_1)$ (or is, generally speaking, a generalized solution) inside G_1, if for any $v \in C_0^\infty(G_1)$, extended by zero to G, the equation

$$(\alpha, L^+ v)_0 = (f, v)_0 \tag{3.10}$$

holds.

Let $\gamma \subseteq \Gamma$ be a piece of the common part of the boundary G_1 and G; $f \in W_2^{-\max(r, r+s)}(G_1)$ ($s > -r$). The function $\alpha \in W_2^{-s}(G_1)$ satisfies $Lu = f$ inside G_1 up to γ, where the boundary condition (bd) is prescribed, if (3.10) holds for all $v \in W_2^r(\text{bd})^+ \cap W_2^{r+s}(G)$ which vanish in a neighborhood of the set $(G \setminus G_1) \cup (\Gamma \setminus \gamma)$.

It is clear that these definitions agree with the definition (3.6) of a generalized solution. See Chapter III §5.8 concerning (bd) for unbounded G.

6. **Differential expressions with quadratic form bounded from below.** Such an expression L of the form (1.2) is one for which there exists a number $m \in [0, [r/2]]$ and a boundary condition (bd) such that

$$|(Lu, u)_0| \geqslant C \| u \|_m^2 \qquad (C > 0;\ u \in W_2^r(\text{bd})). \tag{3.11}$$

The inequality (3.11) will be trivially satisfied if $(Lu, u)_0 \geq C\|u\|_m^2$ or $\operatorname{Re}(Lu, u)_0 \geq C\|u\|_m^2$; such expressions L are called respectively positive or having positive Hermitian part.

From (3.11) we easily obtain the energy inequality $C\|u\|_m^2 \leq |(Lu, u)_0| \leq \|Lu\|_{-m}\|u\|_m$, and hence

$$\| Lu \|_{-m} \geqslant C \| u \|_m \qquad (C > 0;\ u \in W_2^r(\text{bd})). \tag{3.12}$$

Applying Theorem 3.3 we obtain that for any $f \in W_2^{-m}(G)$ there is a $u \in W_2^m(G)$ such that

$$(u, Lv)_0 = (f, v)_0 \qquad (v \in W_2^r\,(\mathrm{bd})). \tag{3.13}$$

In particular, for the expressions under consideration the adjoint boundary value problem (2.9) with $f \in \widetilde{W}_2^{-m}(G)$ always has an m-generalized solution.

Theorem 3.4. *Assume that the expression L has order $r = 2m$ with quadratic form bounded from below, i.e.* (3.11) *holds. In addition, assume that* a) *the boundary conditions* (bd) *and* $(\mathrm{bd})^+$ *are "close": this means that the closures of* $W_2^r(\mathrm{bd})$ *and* $W_2^r(\mathrm{bd})^+$ *in the space* $W_2^m(G)$ *coincide; we denote this common closure by* $W_2'^{\,m}(G)$; b) *the estimate*

$$|(Lu, v)_0| \leqslant C_1 \|u\|_m \|v\|_m \qquad (u \in W_2^r(\mathrm{bd}),\ v \in W_2^r(\mathrm{bd})^+) \tag{3.14}$$

holds.

Consider the m-strong operator $\Lambda_{-m}(\mathrm{bd})$ *(defined by* $\Lambda_{-m}(\mathrm{bd})u = Lu(u \in W_2^r(\mathrm{bd}))$*) as an operator from* $W_2'^{\,m}(G)$ *into* $W_2'^{\,-m}(G)$*, and take its closure. Denote the resulting closure by* $\Lambda(\mathrm{bd})$*. It will be established that this closure exists and is a homeomorphism between all of* $W_2'^{\,m}(G)$ *and all of* $W_2'^{\,-m}(G)$*. For any* $f \in W_2'^{\,-m}(G)$

$$((\Lambda(\mathrm{bd}))^{-1} f, L^+ v)_0 = (f, v)_0 \qquad (v \in W_2^r(\mathrm{bd})^+). \tag{3.15}$$

In particular, for $f \in \widetilde{W}_2^{-m}(G) \subseteq W_2^{-m}(G) \subseteq W_2'^{\,-m}(G)$ *the function* $u = (\Lambda(\mathrm{bd}))^{-1} f \in W_2'^{\,m}(G) \subseteq W_2^m(G)$ *is an m-generalized solution of the problem* (2.2)*, which depends continuously on f:* $\|u\|_m \le C_2 \|f\|_{W_2'^{\,-m}(G)} \le C_2 \|f\|_{-m}$.

Proof. The bilinear form $B(u, v) = (Lu, v)_0$ is continuous in the variables $u \in W_2^r(\mathrm{bd})$, $v \in W_2^r(\mathrm{bd})^+$ in the metric of $W_2^m(G)$ (see (3.14)). Hence it can be extended by continuity to a bilinear form of $u, v \in W_2'^{\,m}(G)$. It follows that the representation $(Lu, v)_0 = (Ku, v)_m$ $(u \in W_2^r(\mathrm{bd}),\ v \in W_2^r(\mathrm{bd})^+)$ holds, where K is a continuous operator which acts in $W_2'^{\,m}(G)$.

We show that K has a bounded inverse K^{-1}, defined on all of $W_2'^{\,m}(G)$. First of all

$$\|Ku\|_m \geqslant C\|u\|_m \qquad (C > 0;\ u \in W_2'^{\,m}(G)). \tag{3.16}$$

It is sufficient to check this inequality for $u \in W_2^r(\mathrm{bd})$; for these u it follows from the estimate (see (3.11): $\|Ku\|_m \|u\|_m \ge |(Ku, u)_m| \ge C\|u\|_m^2$. To prove that K^{-1} exists, it remains to show that $\Re(K) = W_2'^{\,m}(G)$. It follows from (3.16) that $\Re(K)$ is closed in $W_2'^{\,m}(G)$. On the other hand, it follows from (3.11) that $|(Ku, u)_m| \ge C\|u\|_m^2$ $(u \in W_2'^{\,m}(G))$, which shows that $\Re(K)$ is dense in $W_2'^{\,m}(G)$.

Thus $\Re(K) = W_2'^m(G)$.

Furthermore, we have $(Ku, v)_m = (Lu, v)_0 = (\mathbf{I}\,Lu, v)_m (u \in W_2^r(\mathrm{bd}), v \in W_2^r(\mathrm{bd})^+)$, where $\mathbf{I}$ is constructed for the sequence $W_2'^{-m}(G) \supseteq L_2(G) \supseteq W_2'^m(G)$. Hence, since $W_2^r(\mathrm{bd})^+$ is dense in $W_2'^m(G)$,

$$Ku = \mathbf{I}\,Lu \qquad (u \in W_2^r(\mathrm{bd})). \tag{3.17}$$

Thus, $\Lambda_{-m}(\mathrm{bd})$ is the restriction to $W_2^r(\mathrm{bd})$ of the operator $\mathbf{I}^{-1}K$, which is, obviously, a homeomorphism between $W_2'^m(G)$ and $W_2'^{-m}(G)$. Since $W_2^r(\mathrm{bd})$ is dense in $W_2'^m(G)$, then, if we extend $\Lambda_{-m}(\mathrm{bd})$ by continuity, we obtain the required closure $\mathbf{I}^{-1}K = \Lambda(\mathrm{bd})$. It remains to establish the relation (3.15). It is sufficient to prove it for a dense set of functions f in $W_2'^{-m}(G)$, in particular for $L[W_2^r(\mathrm{bd})]$. We have for $f = Lu = \Lambda(\mathrm{bd})u$ $(u \in W_2^r(\mathrm{bd}))$ $((\Lambda(\mathrm{bd}))^{-1}f, L^+v)_0 = (u, L^+v)_0 = (Lu, v)_0 = (f, v)_0$ $(v \in W_2^r(\mathrm{bd})^+)$, which is as required. This proves the theorem.

Note that by a) the conditions (3.11) and (3.14) are equivalent to the conditions

$$|(v, L^+v)_0| \geqslant C\,\|v\|_m^2,\ |(u, L^+v)_0| \leqslant C_1\,\|u\|_m\,\|v\|_m$$
$$(u \in W_2^r(\mathrm{bd}), v \in W_2^r(\mathrm{bd})^+). \tag{3.18}$$

Indeed, suppose that (3.11), (3.14), and a) hold; we establish the estimates (3.18). The second of these is obvious. For the proof of the first we construct a sequence $u_\nu \in W_2^r(\mathrm{bd})$ such that $u_\nu \to v$ in $W_2^m(G)$. We get

$$(v, L^+v)_0 = \lim_{\nu\to\infty}(u_\nu, L^+v)_0 = \lim_{\nu\to\infty}(Lu_\nu, v)_0$$
$$= \lim_{\nu\to\infty}(Ku_\nu, v)_m = (Kv, v)_m. \tag{3.19}$$

As was already noted, it follows from (3.11) that $|(Ku, u)_m| \geq C\|u\|_m^2$ $(u \in W_2'^m(G))$. The first inequality in (3.18) follows from this and (3.19). In exactly the same way, it can be shown that (3.18) and a) imply (3.11) and (3.14). Thus, *in the conditions of Theorem* 3.4 *the estimates* (3.18) *can be substituted for the estimates* (3.11) *and* (3.14).

In summary, it can be said that in Theorem 3.4 another concept of generalized solutions of the problem (2.2) with $f \in W_2'^{-m}(G)$ is introduced. Namely, by its solution we mean

$$u = (\Lambda(\mathrm{bd}))^{-1} f \in W_2'^m(G). \tag{3.20}$$

We can give an equivalent definition. *A function* $u \in W_2^m(G)$ *is a generalized solution in this sense of the problem under consideration, if* $u \in W_2'^m(G)$ *and if it is an m-generalized solution of the problem* (*i.e.* $(u, L^+v)_0 = (f, v)_0$, $v \in W_2^r(\mathrm{bd})^+$).

For the proof, the only fact that is needed is that a function u which is a solution of (2.2) in the sense of the second definition satisfies (3.20). Let $u_\nu \in W_2^r(\mathrm{bd})$, $u_\nu \to u$ in $W_2^m(G)$. Then in our notation, for any $v \in W_2^r(\mathrm{bd})^+$ we have

$$(\mathbf{I}f, v)_m = (f, v)_0 = (u, L^+v)_0 = \lim_{\nu\to\infty}(u_\nu, L^+v)_0 = \lim_{\nu\to\infty}(Lu_\nu, v)_0$$
$$= \lim_{\nu\to\infty}(Ku_\nu, v)_m = (Ku, v)_m.$$

Thus, $\mathbf{I}f = Ku$, whence $u = K^{-1}\mathbf{I}f = (\Lambda(\mathrm{bd}))^{-1}f$, as required.

As has been already mentioned, the concept of a generalized solution for arbitrary $f \in W_2^{-m}(G)$ (and the more so for $f \in W_2'^{-m}(G)$) has an incorrectness in that the boundary conditions may not be preserved (although this is not always the case—see Chapter III, §2.1). If we take $f \in \widetilde{W}_2^{-m}(G)$, the conditions will be preserved. We note also that the inclusion $u \in W_2'^m(G)$ often follows just from the fact that u is an m-generalized solution, which allows us to regard u as a generalized solution in the above sense.

7. **Eigenvalue problems.** Consider the differential expression $L - \lambda E$, where λ is a complex parameter. We will investigate the generalized solvability of the problem

$$Lu - \lambda u = f, \quad u \in (\mathrm{bd}). \tag{3.21}$$

A precise formulation of the problem depends on the form of the operator equation which replaces the problem (3.21). We will use the operator and the concept of generalized solution introduced in Theorem 3.4.

We will assume that for some λ_0 the expression $L - \lambda_0 E$ has a quadratic form which is bounded below or, more precisely, that inequality (3.11) and conditions a) and b) of Theorem 3.4 hold for it. We can assume without loss of generality that $\lambda_0 = 0$. We denote by A the restriction of $\Lambda(\mathrm{bd})$ to those $u \in W_2'^m(G) \subseteq W_2^m(G)$ for which $\Lambda(\mathrm{bd})u \in L_2(G)$; A is considered as an operator in $L_2(G)$. In particular, $W_2^r(\mathrm{bd}) \subseteq \mathfrak{D}(A)$, and therefore $\mathfrak{D}(A)$ is dense in $L_2(G)$.

Lemma 3.3. *The operator* A^* *adjoint to* A *in the sense of* $L_2(G)$ *is constructed in just the same way as* A *is, but with respect to* L^+ *and* $(\mathrm{bd})^+$ (*its construction is possible because of the equivalence of the conditions* (3.11), (3.14), *and* a) *with the conditions* (3.18) *and* a), *which hold for* L^+ *and* $(\mathrm{bd})^+$ *since they* *hold for* L *and* (bd)).

Proof. Together with $\Lambda(\mathrm{bd})$, we consider the operator $\Lambda^+(\mathrm{bd})^+$, constructed with respect to L^+ and $(\mathrm{bd})^+$; both these operators are continuous mappings from $W_2'^m(G)$ into $W_2'^{-m}(G)$. To establish the equation

$$(\Lambda(\mathrm{bd})\,u,\, v)_0 = (u,\, \Lambda^+(\mathrm{bd})^+v)_0 \quad (u, v \in W_2'^m(G)), \tag{3.22}$$

it is sufficient to prove it for $u \in W_2^r(\mathrm{bd})$ and $v \in W_2^r(\mathrm{bd})^+$, but here we obviously have $(Lu, v)_0 = (u, L^+v)_0$. By setting $\Lambda(\mathrm{bd})u = \alpha$, $\Lambda^+(\mathrm{bd})^+v = \beta$, we obtain from (3.22) $(\alpha, (\Lambda^+(\mathrm{bd})^+)^{-1}\beta)_0 = ((\Lambda(\mathrm{bd}))^{-1}\alpha, \beta)_0$ $(\alpha, \beta \in W_2'^{-m}(G))$. Having taken $\alpha, \beta \in L_2(G)$, we find $(\alpha, B^{-1}\beta)_0 = (A^{-1}\alpha, \beta)_0$, where B is constructed with respect to L^+ and $(\mathrm{bd})^+$ in the same way as A was constructed from L and (bd). Thus $B^{-1} = (A^{-1})^* = (A^*)^{-1}$, whence $B = A^*$. This proves the lemma.

It is easy to see that the operator A^{-1} is completely continuous. In fact $A^{-1} = O_2(\Lambda(\mathrm{bd}))^{-1}O_1$, where O_1 is the inclusion mapping of $L_2(G)$ in $W_2'^{-m}(G)$ and O_2 is the inclusion mapping of $W_2'^m(G)$ in $L_2(G)$. In view of the imbedding theorems (Introduction §6) the operators O_1 and O_2 are completely continuous, and this implies complete continuity of A^{-1}. Thus, the pair of equations $(E - \lambda A^{-1})u' = f'$, $(E - \lambda A^{-1*})v' = g'$ in $L_2(G)$ are Fredholm. But then the pair

$$(A - \lambda E)\,u = f, \quad (A^* - \lambda E)\,v = g. \tag{3.23}$$

is Fredholm.

Because of Lemma 3.3, the Fredholm property of the pair (3.23) can be interpreted as normal solvability for the generalized solutions of the problem (3.21). By the same token, we obtain

Theorem 3.5. *Assume that there exists a value* λ_0 *of the parameter* λ *such that the expression* $L - \lambda_0 E$ *has order* $2m$ *and the boundary conditions* (bd) *satisfy the relations* (3.22), (3.14) *and* a) (*or* (3.18) *and* a)). *For those solutions which are generalized in the sense that they are m-generalized and belong to* $W_2'^m(G)$, *the problem* (3.21) *with* $f \in L_2(G)$ *is Fredholm. Explicitly, this means that the problem*

$$Lu - \lambda u = 0, \quad u \in (\mathrm{bd}) \tag{3.24}$$

has nonzero generalized solutions (eigenfunctions) for only a countable number of values of the parameter $\lambda = \lambda_k$ $(k = 1, 2, \cdots;\ |\lambda_k| \to \infty)$*—its eigenvalues. The* *subspace of generalized solutions corresponding to* λ_k *is finite dimensional, and the eigenvalues for the adjoint problem*

$$L^{+}v - \lambda v = 0, \quad v \in (\mathrm{bd})^{+} \tag{3.25}$$

are precisely the numbers $\bar{\lambda}_k$ $(k = 1, 2, \cdots)$; *the eigenmanifolds for* (3.24) *and* (3.25) *corresponding to* λ_k *and* $\bar{\lambda}_k$ *have the same dimension. The problem* (3.21) *is solvable for those, and only those* $f \in L_2(G)$ *which are orthogonal to the eigenmanifold of the problem* (3.25) *corresponding to* $\bar{\lambda}$.

8. Generalizations. The constructions in the previous two subsections have a general character and can easily be formulated in abstract form. Such formulation is useful in the study of boundary value problems for nonelliptic expressions.

Theorem 3.6. *Consider the chain* $H_- \supseteq H_0 \supseteq H_+$. *Let* B *be an operator with domain* $\mathfrak{D}(B) \subseteq H_+$, *operating in the space* H_0 *and satisfying the inequalities*

$$|(Bu, u)_0| \geq C_1 \|u\|_+, \quad |(Bu, v)_0| \leq C_2 \|u\|_+ \|v\|_+ \tag{3.26}$$

$$(C_1, C_2 > 0;\ u, v \in \mathfrak{D}(B)).$$

Assume that $\mathfrak{D}(B)$ *(in general, not dense in* H_+*) is dense in* H_0. *Let* $H'_+ \subseteq H_+$ *be the closure of* $\mathfrak{D}(B)$ *in* H_+, *and let* H'_- *be the negative space corresponding to* H'_+ *and* H_0. *Then the closure of the operator* B, *considered as an operator from* H'_+ *to* H'_-, *is a homeomorphism between these spaces.*

Proof. Consider the bilinear form $B(u, v) = (Bu, v)_0$ $(u, v \in \mathfrak{D}(B))$, which is continuous in the variables u, v in the metric of H_+. Extend it by continuity to a continuous form of $u, v \in H'_+$; hence it follows that the representation $(Bu, v)_0 = (Ku, v)_+$ $(u, v \in \mathfrak{D}(B))$ holds, where K is some continuous operator in H'_+. In the same way as in the proof of Theorem 3.4 it is shown that K has a bounded inverse K^{-1}, defined on all of H'_+. If we consider the operator $\mathbf{I}$ for the chain $H'_- \supseteq H_0 \supseteq H'_+$, we can write $(Ku, v)_+ = (Bu, v)_0 = (\mathbf{I}Bu, v)_+$ $(u, v \in \mathfrak{D}(B))$, whence $Ku = \mathbf{I}Bu$ $(u \in \mathfrak{D}(B))$. Therefore, B is the restriction to $\mathfrak{D}(B)$ of the operator $\mathbf{I}^{-1}K$, which is a homeomorphism between H'_+ and H'_-. Hence the theorem follows.

Denote the closure of B above by $\mathbf{B}$. The closure by continuity of the bilinear form $(Bu, v)_0$ $(u, v \in \mathfrak{D}(B))$ gives rise to the bilinear form $(\mathbf{B}u, v)_0$ $(u, v \in H'_+)$. Obviously, each conjugate-linear continuous functional $l(v)$ on H'_+ admits the representation

$$l(v) = (\mathbf{B}u_0, v)_0 \quad (v \in H'_+) \tag{3.27}$$

with some $u_0 \in H'_+$. In particular, if $H_+ = H_0 = H_-$ and $\mathfrak{D}(B) = H_0$, this representation assumes the form $l(g) = (Bf_0, g)_0$ $(g \in H_0)$, where $f_0 \in H_0$.

The formulation of Theorem 3.6 is somewhat different from Theorem 3.4 in that now no analogue of L^+ appears. For completeness of the identification, we introduce the operator B^+, equal to the restriction to H_+ of the operator B^* – the ordinary adjoint in H_0 of B if the latter is regarded as acting in H_0. Assume that $\mathfrak{D}(B^+)$ is dense in H_0 and that its closure in H_+ coincides with the analogous closure of $\mathfrak{D}(B)$ (i.e. with H'_+). Then (3.26) is equivalent to similar conditions for B^+, and also to conditions in which the second estimate has the form $|(Bu, v)_0| \leq C_2\|u\|_+\|v\|_+$ $(u \in \mathfrak{D}(B),\ v \in \mathfrak{D}(B^+))$. Now all the other results of subsections 6 and 7 are easily formulated and proved.

CHAPTER III

BOUNDARY VALUE PROBLEMS AND SMOOTH GENERALIZED SOLUTIONS FOR ELLIPTIC EQUATIONS. GREEN'S FUNCTION

In this chapter we first investigate boundary value problems for elliptic equations, and then consider an important set of problems, connected with the theorem on when each generalized solution of an elliptic equation is sufficiently smooth. In the fifth section we study Green's function for an elliptic equation. The argument is given for equations of high order only in the case of null boundary conditions: for equations of second order other conditions are considered as well; moreover, for the most part we study only strongly elliptic equations. In the sixth and last section we formulate (largely without complete proofs) the general case. The region G, if the contrary is not stated, is assumed bounded, and its boundary Γ is assumed piecewise smooth.

§1. LOWER ESTIMATES FOR QUADRATIC FORMS ON FINITE FUNCTIONS

1. **Definitions.** A differential expression

$$Lu = L(x, D)\, u = \sum_{|\alpha| \leq r} a_\alpha(x) D^\alpha u \tag{1.1}$$

with, in general, complex coefficients $a_\alpha(x)$ having the usual smoothness properties, is called elliptic at the point x if for every real vector $\xi = (\xi_1, \cdots, \xi_n) \neq 0$ the r-linear form

$$L_c(x, \xi) = \sum_{|\alpha| \leq r} a_\alpha(x)\, \xi^\alpha, \quad \xi^\alpha = \xi_1^{\alpha_1} \ldots \xi_n^{\alpha_n} \tag{1.2}$$

is different from zero. Since the leading coefficients of $L^+(x, D)$ are equal to $(-1)^r \overline{a_\alpha(x)}$, the expressions $L(x, D)$ and $L^+(x, D)$ are simultaneously elliptic or not. Below we consider expressions $L = L(x, D)$ which are elliptic in $G \cup \Gamma$, i.e. elliptic at every point $x \in G \cup \Gamma$.

It is not difficult to see that *if the leading coefficients* $a_\alpha(x)$ (*i.e. the coefficients for* $|\alpha| = r$) *are real, then necessarily the order* r *is even* ($r = 2m$) *and one of these two estimates holds for the form* (1.2):

$$\sum_{|\alpha|=2m} a_\alpha(x)\xi^\alpha \geqslant \varepsilon|\xi|^{2m} \quad \text{or} \quad \leqslant -\varepsilon|\xi|^{2m} \quad (\varepsilon > 0;\ x \in G \cup \Gamma;\ \xi \in E_n) \tag{1.3}$$

(*G is assumed connected*).

In fact, the function $L_c(x, \xi)$ is continuous with respect to $(x, \xi) \in (G \cup \Gamma) \times K$ (K denotes the sphere $|\xi| = 1$) and therefore on this set it is either strictly positive or strictly negative. If the order r is odd, then replacing ξ by $-\xi$ we obtain $L_c(x, -\xi) = -L_c(x, \xi)$, which contradicts the fact that $L_c(x, \xi)$ has a fixed sign. Thus $r = 2m$. Suppose, for example, $L_c(x, \xi) \geq \epsilon > 0$ ($(x, \xi) \in (G \cup \Gamma) \times K$). If ξ is any vector, then $\xi/|\xi| \in K$, and we have by homogeneity $\epsilon \leq L_c(x, \xi/|\xi|) = L_c(x, \xi)/|\xi|^{2m}$, i.e. we obtain (1.3). The assertion follows.

Let Re L denote the real part of L, where L is the differential expression whose coefficients are the real parts of the corresponding $a_\alpha(x)$. We often consider expressions L for which Re L has the same order as L and is elliptic. This is a subclass of the class of elliptic expressions, since for such L, $\operatorname{Re}\{L_c(x, \xi)\} = \sum_{|\alpha|=r} \operatorname{Re} a_\alpha(x)\xi^\alpha \neq 0$ and therefore we already have $L_c(x, \xi) \neq 0$: the order of L is even: $r = 2m$. The form Re $L_c = (\operatorname{Re} L)_c$ satisfies one of the estimates (1.3); in what follows we usually assume that in the case that m is even the first estimate is satisfied, in the odd case — the second. Expressions in the indicated subclass are called strongly elliptic.

For $n \geq 3$, *the general elliptic expression also has even order* $r = 2m$.

The proof of this fact is postponed until p. 130 (see Lemma 3.2). We remark that for $n = 2$, the evenness of r does not follow, since $Lu = D_1 u + iD_2 u$ is elliptic and has first order.

2. Lower estimates of quadratic forms. We prove the following theorem, on which is based the application to elliptic equations of the general schemes in subsections 6–7, §3, Chapter II.

Theorem 1.1. *For a strongly elliptic differential expression* L *of order* $2m$,

$$\operatorname{Re}(Lu, u)_0 \geqslant C\|u\|_m^2 \quad (C > 0;\ u \in \mathring{W}_2^m(G) \cap W_2^{2m}(G)), \tag{1.4}$$

provided that the diameter of the region G *is sufficiently small. On the other hand, for any fixed region* G *there exists a constant* $k \geq 0$ *so large that*

$$\operatorname{Re}(Lu+ku,\ u)_0 \geqslant C\,\|u\|_m^2 \quad (C>0;\ u\in \mathring{W}_2^m(G)\cap W_2^{2m}(G)). \tag{1.5}$$

Conversely, if for an expression L of order 2m and for some region G the inequality (1.4) *holds for* $u \in C_0^\infty(G)$, *then L is strongly elliptic in* $G\cup\Gamma$.

The proof of the first part of the theorem is based on the following lemma.

Lemma 1.1. *Suppose that the coefficients* b_α *are constant and* $Mu = \sum_{|\alpha|=2m} b_\alpha D^\alpha u$ *is strongly elliptic. Then*

$$\operatorname{Re}(Mu,\ u)_0 \geqslant C\,\|u\|_m^2 \quad (u\in C_0^\infty(G)). \tag{1.6}$$

Proof. Consider the Fourier transform of a function f:

$$\tilde{f}(\xi) = \frac{1}{\sqrt{(2\pi)^n}} \int_{E_n} f(x)\, e^{-i\langle \xi, x\rangle}\, dx \quad (\xi = (\xi_1, \ldots, \xi_n)\in E_n). \tag{1.7}$$

On integrating by parts in (1.7) for a finite, sufficiently smooth f, we obtain

$$\widetilde{(D^\alpha f)}(\xi) = i^{|\alpha|}\xi^\alpha \tilde{f}(\xi). \tag{1.8}$$

To prove (1.6) we proceed in the following way. For $u \in C_0^\infty(G)$, continued to be zero outside of G, we find from (1.8)

$$\widetilde{(Mu)}(\xi) = (-1)^m\Big(\sum_{|\alpha|=2m} b_\alpha \xi^\alpha\Big)\tilde{u}(\xi). \tag{1.9}$$

By (1.3), written for Re M,

$$(-1)^m \sum_{|\alpha|=2m} \operatorname{Re} b_\alpha \xi^\alpha \geqslant \varepsilon\Big(\sum_{j=1}^n \xi_j^2\Big)^m \geqslant \varepsilon \sum_{|\alpha|=m} (\xi^\alpha)^2 \quad (\xi\in E_n). \tag{1.10}$$

Now by Parseval's equation, (1.9), and (1.10), we obtain

$$\operatorname{Re}(Mu,\ u)_0 = \operatorname{Re}\int_{E_n} \widetilde{(Mu)}(\xi)\,\overline{\tilde{u}(\xi)}\, d\xi = (-1)^m \operatorname{Re}\int_{E_n}\Big(\sum_{|\alpha|=2m} b_\alpha\xi^\alpha\Big)|\tilde{u}(\xi)|^2\, d\xi$$

$$= (-1)^m \int_{E_n}\Big(\sum_{|\alpha|=2m} \operatorname{Re} b_\alpha\xi^\alpha\Big)|\tilde{u}(\xi)|^2 d\xi \geqslant \varepsilon\int_{E_n}\Big(\sum_{|\alpha|=m}(\xi^\alpha)^2\Big)|\tilde{u}(\xi)|^2\, d\xi$$

$$= \varepsilon\sum_{|\alpha|=m}\int_{E_n} |\xi^\alpha\tilde{u}(\xi)|^2\, d\xi = \varepsilon\sum_{|\alpha|=m}\int_{E_n} |\widetilde{(D^\alpha u)}(\xi)|^2\, d\xi = \varepsilon\sum_{|\alpha|=m}\|D^\alpha u\|_0^2.$$

The last sum is $\geq C_1\|u\|_m^2$ for finite functions (see p. 22). Thus we have arrived at (1.16). The lemma follows.

We prove the first part of the theorem. We first establish the inequality (1.4) for $u \in C_0^\infty(G)$. For $x_0 \in E_n$, we will consider a region G having sufficiently small diameter and containing the point $L_c(x_0, D)\, u = \sum_{|\alpha|=2m} a_\alpha(x_0) D^\alpha u$. We fix a region G_0 containing x_0. By Lemma 1.1

$$\operatorname{Re}(L_c(x_0, D)\,u,\, u)_{L_2(G_0)} \geqslant C \| u \|^2_{W_2^m(G_0)} \quad (u \in C_0^\infty(G_0)). \tag{1.11}$$

Suppose $u \in C_0^\infty(G)$, $G \subseteq G_0$: below we shift various derivatives by integration by parts to the second factor; the process is carried out until, for each function u appearing inside the scalar product sign, differentiation appears $\leq m$ times. We obtain

$$(L(x, D)\,u,\, u)_0 - (L_c(x_0, D)\,u,\, u)_0 = \Big(\sum_{|\alpha|=2m} [a_\alpha(x) - a_\alpha(x_0)]\, D^\alpha u,\, u \Big)_0$$

$$+ \sum_{|\alpha|<2m} (a_\alpha(x)\, D^\alpha u,\, u)_0 = \sum_{|\alpha|,\, |\beta| \leqslant m} (b_{\alpha\beta}(x)\, D^\alpha u,\, D^\beta u)_0,$$

where the $b_{\alpha\beta}(x)$ are certain derivatives of order not greater than m of the differences $a_\alpha(x) - a_\alpha(x_0)$ ($|\alpha| = 2m$) or the coefficients $a_\alpha(x)$ ($|\alpha| < 2m$). In the last sum, the terms are of two types: the form $([a_\alpha(x) - a_\alpha(x_0)]\, D^\alpha u, D^\beta u)_0$, with $|\alpha| = |\beta| = m$, and the form $(b_{\alpha\beta}(x)\, D^\alpha u, D^\beta u)_0$, where at least one of the numbers $|\alpha|$, $|\beta|$ is less than m. For the choice of a sufficiently small region G, each of the first terms can be majorized by the expression $\epsilon \| u \|_m^2$ for preassigned $\epsilon > 0$. The second terms can be majorized by expressions $C_1 \| u \|_{|\alpha|} \| u \|_{|\beta|}$, each of which can be made smaller than $dC_1 \| u \|_m^2$ by means of the estimate $\| u \|_{W_2^k(G)} \leq d^{l-k} \| u \|_{W_2^l(G)}$ $(0 \leq k < l;\ u \in \mathring{W}_2^l(G))$, where d is the diameter of G (see p. 21). It is clear from this that by choosing $G \subseteq G_0$ of sufficiently small diameter, we can obtain the inequality

$$|(L(x, D)\,u,\, u)_0 - (L_c(x_0, D)\,u,\, u)_0| \leqslant \varepsilon \| u \|_m^2. \tag{1.12}$$

If $u \in C_0^\infty(G)$, we extend it by zero to obtain a function in $C_0^\infty(G_0)$. Then (1.11) gives the inequality $\operatorname{Re}(L(x_0, D)\, u, u)_0 \geq C \| u \|_m^2$ where C does not depend on G. Taking into account this estimate and (1.12), we obtain

$$\operatorname{Re}(L(x, D)\,u,\, u)_0 = \operatorname{Re}(L_c(x_0, D)\,u,\, u)_0 + \operatorname{Re}[(L(x, D)\,u,\, u)_0$$

$$- (L_c(x_0, D)\,u,\, u)_0] \geqslant (C - \varepsilon) \| u \|_m^2.$$

Thus for $\epsilon > 0$ sufficiently small, we arrive at (1.4).

Now suppose $u \in \mathring{W}_2^m(G) \cap W_2^{2m}(G)$. Since all derivatives of $u(x)$ up to the order $m - 1$ inclusive vanish on Γ, on integrating by parts we obtain

$$(L(x,\ D)u,\ u)_0 = \sum_{|\alpha|,|\beta|\leqslant m} (f_{\alpha\beta}(x) D^\alpha u,\ D^\beta u)_0, \tag{1.13}$$

where the $f_{\alpha\beta}$ are certain coefficients, continuous in all cases on $G \cup \Gamma$. Construct $u_\nu \in C_0^\infty(G)$, $u_\nu \to u$ in $W_2^m(G)$; by (1.13), $(L(x,\ D)\, u_\nu, u_\nu)_0 \to (L(x,\ D)\, u,\ u)_0$. The estimate (1.4) holds for u_ν, and so it holds for u.

We proceed to the proof of (1.5). It is clear from the proof of (1.4) that it is sufficient to establish (1.5) for $u \in C_0^\infty(G)$. Extend the coefficients of L across the boundary of G so as to preserve smoothness and the ellipticity of Re L. By the part of the theorem already proved, for each $x \in G \cup \Gamma$ there exists a neighborhood (in E_n) U_x such that $\operatorname{Re}(Lu,\ u)_0 \geq C_x \| u \|_m^2$ $(C_x > 0)$ for $u \in C_0^\infty(U_x)$. For each $x \in G \cup \Gamma$ choose a neighborhood V_x, strictly contained in U_x, and choose a finite cover $V_{x_1}, \cdots, V_{x_N}$ of such neighborhoods V_x for $G \cup \Gamma$. We find that there exists a constant $C > 0$ such that

$$\operatorname{Re}(Lu,\ u)_0 \geqslant C \| u \|_m^2 \quad (u \in C_0^\infty(U_{x_j});\ j = 1,\ \ldots,\ N). \tag{1.14}$$

Construct a decomposition of unity, corresponding to the covering of $G \cup \Gamma$, by means of the neighborhoods V_{x_j}; i.e. construct N nonnegative functions $\chi_j(x) \in C_0^\infty(E_n)$, each of which vanishes outside of V_{x_j}, such that $\sum_{j=1}^N \chi_j(x) = 1$ $(x \in G)$. If $u \in C_0^\infty(G)$, then $\sqrt{\chi_j(x)}\, u(x) \in C_0^\infty(U_{x_j})$ and by (1.14) we may write $\operatorname{Re}(L[\sqrt{\chi_j} u],\ \sqrt{\chi_j} u)_0 \geq C \| \sqrt{\chi} u \|_m^2$ $(j = 1, \cdots, N)$. Summing these inequalities, we find

$$\| u \|_m^2 = \left\| \sum_{j=1}^N \chi_j u \right\|_m^2 \leqslant \left(\sum_{j=1}^N \| \chi_j u \|_m \right)^2 \leqslant N \sum_{j=1}^N \| \chi_j u \|_m^2$$

$$\leqslant C_1 N \sum_{j=1}^N \| \sqrt{\chi_j} u \|_m^2 \leqslant C_2 \sum_{j=1}^N \operatorname{Re}(L[\sqrt{\chi_j} u],\ \sqrt{\chi_j} u)_0. \tag{1.15}$$

Obviously $L[\sqrt{\chi_j} u] = \sqrt{\chi_j} Lu + \sum_{|\alpha| \leqslant 2m-1} b_{j\alpha}(x) D^\alpha u$, where the $b_{j\alpha}$ are any sufficiently smooth coefficients. Therefore the right part of (1.15) can be rewritten in the form

$$\sum_{j=1}^{N} \operatorname{Re}(L[\sqrt{\chi_j}u], \sqrt{\chi_j}u)_0 = \sum_{j=1}^{N} \operatorname{Re}(\sqrt{\chi_j}Lu, \sqrt{\chi_j}u)_0$$

$$+\sum_{j=1}^{N} \sum_{|\alpha| \leqslant 2m-1} \operatorname{Re}(b_{j\alpha}(x) D^{\alpha}u, \sqrt{\chi_j}u)_0 = \operatorname{Re}(Lu, u)_0$$

$$+\sum_{j=1}^{N} \sum_{|\beta| \leqslant m, |\gamma| \leqslant m-1} \operatorname{Re}(f_{j\beta\gamma}(x) D^{\beta}u, g_{j\beta\gamma}(x) D^{\gamma}u)_0, \tag{1.16}$$

where $f_{j\beta\gamma}$ and $g_{j\beta\gamma}$ are certain coefficients, continuous in $G \cup \Gamma$, obtained by shifting derivatives in (1.16) from the first factor to the second.

For the following estimates, the Ehrling-Nirenberg inequality is used (see Introduction, §7): if $0 \le k < l < s$, then for any $\epsilon > 0$, it is possible to find a $K(\epsilon) > 0$ such that $\| u \|_l^2 \le \epsilon \| u \|_s^2 + K(\epsilon) \| u \|_k^2$ for any smooth u. If $\delta > 0$, then by means of the inequality $ab \le \frac{1}{2}(a^2 + b^2)$ we obtain

$$\left| \sum_{j=1}^{N} \sum_{|\beta| \leqslant m, |\gamma| \leqslant m-1} \operatorname{Re}(f_{j\beta\gamma}(x) D^{\beta}u, g_{j\beta\gamma}(x) D^{\gamma}u)_0 \right|$$

$$\leqslant C_3 \| u_m \| \| u \|_{m-1} \leqslant \frac{C_3^2\delta^2}{2} \| u \|_m^2 + \frac{1}{2\delta^2} \| u \|_{m-1}^2 \leqslant \left(\frac{C_3^2\delta^2}{2} + \frac{\varepsilon}{2\delta^2} \right) \| u \|_m^2$$

$$+ \frac{K(\varepsilon)}{2\delta^2} \| u \|_0^2. \tag{1.17}$$

From (1.15)–(1.17) follows:

$$\frac{1}{C_2} \| u \|_m^2 \leqslant \operatorname{Re}(Lu, u)_0 + \left(\frac{C_3^2\delta^2}{2} + \frac{\varepsilon}{2\delta^2} \right) \| u \|_m^2 + \frac{K(\varepsilon)}{2\delta^2} \| u \|_0^2. \tag{1.18}$$

Choose first $\delta > 0$, and then $\epsilon > 0$ so small that $C_3^2 \delta^2/2 + \epsilon/2\delta^2$ is less than $1/C_2$, and in (1.18) transfer the term involving $\| u \|_m^2$ from the right side to the left. This gives us the required estimate (1.5).

We proceed to the proof of the last part of the theorem. We prove a lemma, converse to Lemma 1.1.

Lemma 1.2. *Let $Mu = \Sigma_{|\alpha|=2m} b_\alpha D^\alpha u$ be an expression of order 2m with constant coefficients, and having the property that for functions $u \in C_0^\infty(U)$, where $U = G$ is some sphere with center at the origin, the inequality (1.6) holds. Then* Re M *is elliptic, and moreover the constant $\epsilon > 0$ in (1.3) depends on C in (1.6) and does not depend on b_α.*

Proof. From the inequality (1.6) we obtain the estimate

$$\operatorname{Re}(Mu,\ u)_0 \geqslant C \sum_{|\alpha|=m} (D^\alpha u,\ D^\alpha u)_0 \quad (u \in C_0^\infty(U)). \tag{1.19}$$

We show that the same constant C can be used for any $v \in C_0^\infty(E_m)$. In fact, for $t > 0$ sufficiently large, $u(x) = v(tx) \in C_0^\infty(U)$ and therefore it satisfies (1.19). Since $(D^\alpha u)(x) = t^{|\alpha|}(D^\alpha v)(tx)$, by a change of variable we obtain

$$\operatorname{Re}(Mv,\ v)_{L_2(E_n)} = t^n \operatorname{Re} \int_{E_n} \sum_{|\alpha|=2m} b_\alpha (D^\alpha v)(tx)\,\overline{v(tx)}\,dx$$

$$= t^{n-2m} \operatorname{Re} \int_{E_n} \sum_{|\alpha|=2m} b_\alpha (D^\alpha u)(x)\,\overline{u(x)}\,dx \geqslant C t^{n-2m} \sum_{|\alpha|=m} \int_{E_n} |(D^\alpha u)(x)|^2\,dx$$

$$= C \sum_{|\alpha|=m} (D^\alpha v,\ D^\alpha v)_{L_2(E_n)} \tag{1.20}$$

as desired.

Now consider the Fourier transform $\tilde{v}(\xi)$ of $v(x)$. If we use (1.8) and Parseval's equality, we can rewrite (1.20) in the form

$$\int_{E_n} \left[(-1)^m \sum_{|\alpha|=2m} \operatorname{Re} b_\alpha \xi^\alpha\right] |\tilde{v}(\xi)|^2 d\xi \geqslant C \int_{E_n} \sum_{|\alpha|=m} (\xi^\alpha)^2 |\tilde{v}(\xi)|^2\,d\xi,$$

or, setting $P(\xi) = (-1)^m \sum_{|\alpha|=2m} \operatorname{Re} b_\alpha \xi^\alpha - C \sum_{|\alpha|=m} (\xi^\alpha)^2$, in the form

$$\int_{E_n} P(\xi)\,|\tilde{v}(\xi)|^2\,d\xi \geqslant 0. \tag{1.21}$$

To prove the lemma, it is sufficient to show that if (1.21) holds for the Fourier transform $\tilde{v}(\xi)$ of any $v \in C_0^\infty(E_n)$, then $P(\xi) \geq 0$ $(\xi \in E_n)$. However, from analysis it is known that for any $\xi_0 \in E_n$ there exists a sequence $v_\nu(x)$ of smooth finite functions, for which $|\tilde{v}_\nu(\xi)|^2$ forms a δ-sequence concentrated at ξ_0. Substituting $\tilde{v}_\nu$ instead of $\tilde{v}$ in (1.21) and passing to the limit, we obtain $P(\xi_0) \geq 0$. The lemma follows.

We complete the proof of the theorem. We fix a point $x_0 \in G$ and establish the ellipticity of $\operatorname{Re} L_c(x_0,\ D)$. Then

$$\operatorname{Re}(L_c(x_0,\ D)\,u,\ u)_0 = \operatorname{Re}(L(x,\ D)\,u,\ u)_0 - \operatorname{Re}[(L(x,\ D)\,u,\ u)_0 - (L_c(x_0,\ D)\,u,\ u)_0]. \tag{1.22}$$

Consider functions $u \in C_0^\infty(G)$ which vanish outside of a small sphere U with center x_0. If the radius of the sphere is sufficiently small, the estimate

(1.12) holds for small $\epsilon > 0$. Hence from (1.22) and (1.4) we obtain the inequality $\operatorname{Re}(L_c(x_0, D)u, u)_0 \geq \tfrac{1}{2}C\,\|u\|_m^2$ $(u \in C_0^\infty(U))$. If we use Lemma 1.2, we can conclude that $\operatorname{Re} L_c(x_0, D)$ is elliptic. Moreover, in the corresponding inequalities (1.3), $\epsilon > 0$ depends only on C in (1.4) and not on the point $x_0 \in G$. Therefore in these inequalities we may pass to the limit with x_0 tending to the boundary of the region G. Hence we obtain the inequalities in all of $G \cup \Gamma$. Thus $\operatorname{Re} L$ is elliptic in $G \cup \Gamma$. The theorem follows.

In conclusion, we remark that upper estimates of the form $(Lu, v)_0$ are trivial: from a representation similar to (1.13) it follows that for any L of order $2m$

$$|(Lu, v)_0| \leq C_1\,\|u\|_m\,\|v\|_m \qquad (u \in \mathring{W}_2^m(G) \cap W_2^{2m}(G),\ v \in \mathring{W}_2^m(G)). \tag{1.23}$$

3. Lower estimates of quadratic forms, constructed in Sobolev spaces. Let L' and L'' be differential expressions with corresponding orders r' and r'' and with sufficiently smooth coefficients $a'_\alpha(x)$ and $a''_\alpha(x)$. First apply L'' and then L': $L'L''u$. We obtain a differential expression $L'L''$ of order $r' + r''$; its leading part is, obviously,

$$\sum_{|\alpha|=r',\ |\beta|=r''} a'_\alpha(x)\, a''_\beta(x)\, D^{\alpha+\beta}u,$$

and therefore the corresponding multilinear form is given by

$$(L'L'')_c(x, \xi) = \sum_{|\alpha|=r',\ |\beta|=r''} a'_\alpha(x)\, a''_\beta(x)\, \xi^{\alpha+\beta}$$

$$= \Bigl(\sum_{|\alpha|=r'} a'_\alpha(x)\,\xi^\alpha\Bigr)\Bigl(\sum_{|\beta|=r''} a''_\beta(x)\,\xi^\beta\Bigr) = (L'_c)(x, \xi)\,(L''_c)(x, \xi). \tag{1.24}$$

Lemma 1.3. *The differential expression of order* $2s$

$$\Omega u = (-1)^s \sum_{|\alpha|=s} D^\alpha D^\alpha u \qquad (s > 0) \tag{1.25}$$

is elliptic. The three expressions L, ΩL, *and* $L^+\Omega L$ *are simultaneously elliptic or not. A similar situation holds for the pairs* $\operatorname{Re} L$, $\operatorname{Re}(\Omega L)$ *and* L, $\operatorname{Re}(L^+\Omega L)$.

Proof. The form corresponding to (1.25) is given by $\Omega(\xi) = (-1)^s \sum_{|\alpha|=s} (\xi^\alpha)^2$. Therefore if $\Omega(\xi) = 0$, then $\xi^\alpha = 0$ for all α $(|\alpha| = s)$, from which it follows that $\xi = 0$. Thus Ω is elliptic. The second assertion of the lemma follows from the fact that the forms for L, ΩL, and $L^+\Omega L$, according to (1.24), are given by $\sum_{|\alpha|=r} a_\alpha \xi^\alpha$, $\Omega(\xi)\,(\sum_{|\alpha|=r} a_\alpha \xi^\alpha)$, $(-1)^r \Omega(\xi)\,|\sum_{|\alpha|=r} a_\alpha \xi^\alpha|^2$. For the following, let ω_β denote the coefficient of D^β in the expression (1.25). The forms corresponding to $\operatorname{Re} L$ and $\operatorname{Re}(\Omega L)$ are equal to

$$\sum_{|\alpha|=r} \operatorname{Re} a_\alpha \xi^\alpha, \quad \sum_{|\alpha|=r,\ |\beta|=2s} \operatorname{Re}(a_\alpha \omega_\beta)\, \xi^{\alpha+\beta} = \Omega(\xi) \left(\sum_{|\alpha|=r} \operatorname{Re} a_\alpha \xi^\alpha \right).$$

It therefore follows that Re L and Re (ΩL) are simultaneously elliptic or not.

Finally, put $a_\alpha = b_\alpha + ic_\alpha$, where $b_\alpha = \operatorname{Re} a_\alpha$, $c_\alpha = \operatorname{Im} a_\alpha$. Then $\operatorname{Re}(\bar{a}_\alpha a_\gamma) = b_\alpha b_\gamma + c_\alpha c_\gamma$ and therefore the form corresponding to Re $(L^+\Omega L)$ is given by

$$(-1)^r \sum_{\substack{|\alpha|=|\gamma|=r,\\ |\beta|=2s}} \operatorname{Re}(\bar{a}_\alpha \omega_\beta a_\gamma)\, \xi^{\alpha+\beta+\gamma} = (-1)^r \Omega(\xi) \sum_{|\alpha|=|\gamma|=r} \operatorname{Re}(\bar{a}_\alpha a_\gamma)\, \xi^{+\gamma}$$

$$= (-1)^r \Omega(\xi) \left\{ \left(\sum_{|\alpha|=r} b_\alpha \xi^\alpha \right)^2 + \left(\sum_{|\alpha|=r} c_\alpha \xi^\alpha \right)^2 \right\} = (-1)^r \Omega(\xi) \left| \sum_{|\alpha|=r} a_\alpha \xi^\alpha \right|^2.$$

From this equation it follows that L and Re $(L^+\Omega L)$ are simultaneously elliptic or not. The lemma follows.

It is now easy to generalize the results in Theorem 1.1 to the case of quadratic forms in the space $W_2^s(G)$.

Theorem 1.2. *Let $s \geq 0$ be fixed, and consider an expression L of order $2m$ for which $a_\alpha(x) \in C^{\max(|\alpha|, s)}(G \cup \Gamma)$. Then the assertions in Theorem 1.1 remain valid if in this theorem the scalar product $(\cdot, \cdot)_0$ and norm $\|\cdot\|_m$ are replaced by $(\cdot, \cdot)_s$ and $\|\cdot\|_{m+s}$, and the space $\mathring{W}_2^m(G) \cap W_2^{2m}(G)$ by $\mathring{W}_2^{m+s}(G) \cap W_2^{2m+s}(G)$.*

Proof. We establish a generalization of the estimate (1.4):

$$\operatorname{Re}(Lu, u)_s \geqslant C \| u \|^2_{m+s} \qquad (C > 0;\ u \in \mathring{W}_2^{m+s}(G) \cap W_2^{2m+s}(G)). \quad (1.26)$$

As before, it is sufficient to prove this for $u \in C_0^\infty(G)$. It is also possible to assume that the coefficients of L are as smooth as desired, since then in the obtained inequality we can pass to the limit to the original coefficients. By the finiteness of u we have

$$\operatorname{Re}(Lu, u)_s = \operatorname{Re} \sum_{|\alpha|=s} (D^\alpha Lu, D^\alpha u)_0 = (-1)^s \operatorname{Re} \sum_{|\alpha|=s} (D^\alpha D^\alpha Lu, u)_0$$
$$= \operatorname{Re}(\Omega Lu, u)_0. \quad (1.27)$$

By Lemma 1.3 the expression Re (ΩL) of order $2(m+s)$ is elliptic; applying the estimate (1.4) we find $\operatorname{Re}(\Omega Lu, u)_0 \geq C \| u \|^2_{m+s}$. Hence (1.26) follows from (1.27).

The inequality

$$\operatorname{Re}(Lu + ku, u)_s \geqslant C \| u \|^2_{m+s} \quad (C > 0;\ u \in \mathring{W}_2^{m+s}(G) \cap W_2^{2m+s}(G))$$

(even stronger, with $\operatorname{Re}(Lu + ku, u)_s$ replaced by $\operatorname{Re}(Lu, u)_s + k(u, u)_0$) is similarly deduced from (1.5). Conversely, suppose now that (1.26) is satisfied for $u \in C_0^\infty(G)$. Since $\operatorname{Re}(Lu, u)_s = \operatorname{Re}(\Omega Lu, u)_0$, it follows from the last part of Theorem 1.1 that $\operatorname{Re}(\Omega L)$, and hence $\operatorname{Re} L$, are elliptic in $G \cup \Gamma$. The theorem follows.

It is easy to deduce the energy inequality for finite functions from this theorem.

Corollary. *Let L be elliptic of order r and with $a_\alpha \in C^{\max(|\alpha|, s)}(G \cup \Gamma)$. If G has sufficiently small diameter, then*

$$\| Lu \|_s \geqslant C \| u \|_{r+s} \quad (C > 0;\ u \in C_0^\infty(G)). \tag{1.28}$$

For fixed G and sufficiently large $k \geq 0$,

$$\| Lu \|_s^2 + k \| u \|_0^2 \geqslant C_1 \| u \|_{r+s}^2, \quad \| Lu + ku \|_s \geqslant C_2 \| u \|_{r+s}$$
$$(C_1,\ C_2 > 0;\ u \in C_0^\infty(G)) \tag{1.29}$$

(for the validity of the second inequality, it is necessary to assume that L is strongly elliptic). Conversely, if for L and some $s \geq 0$ the estimate (1.28) *holds, then L is elliptic in $G \cup \Gamma$.*

We establish (1.28). As in Theorem 1.2, we may assume that the coefficients of L are sufficiently smooth. For $u \in C_0^\infty(G)$, we have

$$\| Lu \|_s^2 = \sum_{|\alpha|=s} (D^\alpha Lu,\ D^\alpha Lu)_0 = (-1)^s \sum_{|\alpha|=s} (L^+ D^\alpha D^\alpha Lu,\ u)_0$$
$$= (L^+ \Omega Lu,\ u)_0. \tag{1.30}$$

Since $\operatorname{Re}(L^+ \Omega L)$ is elliptic (Lemma 1.3) with order $2(r+s)$, we may apply (1.4) to $L^+ \Omega L$ to obtain $(L^+ \Omega Lu, u)_0 \geq C \| u \|_{r+s}^2$, which coupled with (1.30) gives (1.28). The remaining assertions, except for the second inequality in (1.29), are proved similarly.

We deduce this inequality. Let $k = k_1 + k_2$ $(k_1, k_2 \geq 0)$, and choose k_1 so large that $\operatorname{Re}(M_{k_1} u, u)_s \geq C \| u \|_{m+s}^2 \geq 0$ $(u \in C_0^\infty(G))$, where $M_{k_1} = L + k_1 E$ (see Theorem 1.2). Now

$$\| Lu + ku \|_s^2 = (M_{k_1} u + k_2 u,\ M_{k_1} u + k_2 u)_s = \| M_{k_1} u \|_s^2$$
$$+ k_2 2\operatorname{Re}(M_{k_1} u,\ u)_s + k_2^2 \| u \|_s^2 \geqslant \| M_{k_1} u \|_s^2 + k_2^2 \| u \|_s^2.$$

Choosing k_2 sufficiently large and using the first inequality in (1.29), we obtain the second. The corollary is established.

§ 2. BOUNDARY VALUE PROBLEMS FOR STRONGLY ELLIPTIC EQUATIONS. GENERALIZED SOLUTIONS

In this section we consider solutions which are m times differentiable, where $2m$ is the order of the equation.

1. **The case of equations of order $2m$ and null boundary conditions.** Let L be a strongly elliptic expression of order $2m$. We will assume that the coefficients of L are sufficiently positive for us to have the estimate $\operatorname{Re}(Lu, u)_0 \geq C\| u \|_m^2$ $(C>0;\ u \in \overset{\circ}{W}{}_2^m(G) \cap W_2^{2m}(G))$ (see Theorem 1.1). This estimate shows that the Hermitian part of the expression L is positive (see Chapter II, §3.6), and moreover the corresponding boundary conditions have the form

$$W_2^{2m}(\mathrm{bd}) = \overset{\circ}{W}{}_2^m(G) \cap W_2^{2m}(G),$$

i.e. u and all of its derivatives of order $\leq m-1$ vanish on Γ.

In this subsection these conditions are denoted by (bd) and are called null conditions.[1] It is not difficult to show that $(\mathrm{bd})^+ = (\mathrm{bd})$ (for $m = 1$ this follows from Theorem 1.1, Chapter II, the proof in the general case being similar). Since for $u \in W_2^{2m}(\mathrm{bd}) = W_2^{2m}(\mathrm{bd})^+$, $(Lu, u)_0 = (u, L^+u)_0$, the Hermitian part L^+ is positive, and therefore from (3.12) of Chapter II we obtain the estimate

$$\| L^+ v \|_{-m} \geqslant C \| v \|_m \quad (C > 0;\ v \in W_2^{2m}(\mathrm{bd})^+). \tag{2.1}$$

It follows (see Theorem 3.3, Chapter II) that the problem

$$Lu = f,\ D^\alpha u|_\Gamma = 0 \quad (|\alpha| \leqslant m-1) \tag{2.2}$$

has an m-generalized solution $u \in W_2^m(G)$ for any $f \in \widetilde{W}_2^{-m}(G)$.

Moreover, in this case it is easy to verify that conditions a) and b) of Theorem 3.4, Chapter II, are satisfied: condition a) is trivial, since $(\mathrm{bd})^+ = (\mathrm{bd})$; the estimate (3.14) follows from (1.23).

The subspace $W'^m_2(G)$ is equal to the closure of the set $\overset{\circ}{W}{}_2^m(G) \cap W_2^{2m}(G)$ in the metric of $W_2^m(G)$, i.e. $W'^m_2(G) = \overset{\circ}{W}{}_2^m(G)$. Therefore $W'^m_2(G) \cap W_2^{2m}(G) = W_2^{2m}(\mathrm{bd})$, i.e. the passage from $\overset{\circ}{W}{}_2^m(G) \cap W_2^{2m}(G) = \mathfrak{D}(\Lambda_{-m}(\mathrm{bd}))$ to $W'^m_2(G)$ preserves boundary conditions. This shows that the generalized solutions for the problem

1) They are also called Dirichlet conditions.

(2.2) are correct even in the case $f \in W'^{-m}_2(G) = \overset{\circ}{W}{}^{-m}_2(G)$ [1] (see Theorem 3.2, Chapter II). We thus have this theorem.

Theorem 2.1. *Let L be a strongly elliptic expression of order $2m$. Consider the boundary value problem (2.2). For sufficiently positive coefficients (or for the diameter of G sufficiently small), it has a generalized solution (in the sense of the definition on p. 98) $u \in \overset{\circ}{W}{}^m_2(G)$ for any $f \in \overset{\circ}{W}{}^{-m}_2(G)$. Furthermore, the operator $\Lambda_{-m}(\mathrm{bd})$, considered as an operator from $\overset{\circ}{W}{}^m_2(G)$ to $\overset{\circ}{W}{}^{-m}_2(G)$, after closure is a homeomorphism $\Lambda(\mathrm{bd})$ between $\overset{\circ}{W}{}^m_2(G)$ and $\overset{\circ}{W}{}^{-m}_2(G)$. The generalized solutions are determined by the formula*

$$u = (\Lambda(\mathrm{bd}))^{-1} f \in \overset{\circ}{W}{}^m_2(G) \quad (f \in \overset{\circ}{W}{}^{-m}_2(G)); \tag{2.3}$$

and they depend uniquely and continuously on f.

We will consider below differential expressions of the second order; for these it is convenient to write, along with the notation (1.2) and (1.9) of Chapter II,

$$Lu = L(x, D)u = \sum_{i,k=1}^{n} D_i(b_{ik}(x) D_k u) + \sum_{j=1}^{n} p_j(x) D_j u + b(x)u,$$

$$B = B(x) = \| b_{jk}(x) \|_1^n. \tag{2.4}$$

Comparing this expression with (1.9), we find

$$p_j(x) = b_j(x) - \sum_{k=1}^{n} (D_k b_{jk})(x) \quad (j = 1, \dots, n), \quad \beta(x) = \sum_{j=1}^{n} p_j(x) \nu_j(x), \tag{2.5}$$

where β is the function (1.16), Chapter II, which occurs in Green's formula. For the passage in (2.4) to the adjoint expression $L^+ u$, we must take complex conjugates of all coefficients, replace p_j by $-p_j$, and b by $b - \Sigma_{j=1}^n D_j p_j$ (or, in other words, $p_j D_j u$ by $-D_j(p_j u)$). The notation (2.4) is used because of the simplicity of this procedure.

In this subsection we will indicate some details which originate from the consideration of strongly elliptic expressions in the form (2.4). We integrate by parts one time in the expression $(u, L^+ v)_0$; we find that for a generalized solution to the problem with the condition $u|_\Gamma = 0$, we can take a function $u \in \overset{\circ}{W}{}^1_2(G)$ for which

---

1) Recall that $\overset{\circ}{W}{}^{-l}_2(G)$ denotes the negative space constructed with respect to $H_+ = \overset{\circ}{W}{}^l_2(G)$ and $H_0 = L_2(G)$ $(l = 1, 2, \cdots)$ (see Chapter I, §3.5).

$$\int_G \left\{ - \sum_{j,k=1}^n b_{jk} D_j u \cdot D_k \bar{v} + \sum_{j=1}^n p_j D_j u \cdot \bar{v} + bu\bar{v} \right\} dx = (f, v)$$

$$(f \in \mathring{W}_2^{-1}(G), \ v \in \mathring{W}_2^1(G)). \tag{2.6}$$

In the case of equations with real p_j, it is easy to give conditions which guarantee that the Hermitian part of L is positive. In fact, it follows from the symmetry of the matrix $B = \| b_{jk} \|_1^n$ that for a complex vector $\zeta = (\zeta_1, \cdots, \zeta_n)$, $\mathrm{Re} \langle B\zeta, \zeta \rangle = \langle \tfrac{1}{2}(B + B^*)\zeta, \zeta \rangle = \langle (\mathrm{Re}\, B)\zeta, \zeta \rangle$, where $\mathrm{Re}\, B = \| \mathrm{Re}\, b_{jk} \|_1^n$. Now from (1.17), Chapter II, by the ellipticity of Re L and the second estimate in (1.3), for any $u \in \mathring{W}_2^1(G) \cap W_2^2(G)$ we obtain

$$\mathrm{Re}(Lu, u)_0 = -\int_G \sum_{j,k=1}^n \mathrm{Re}\, b_{jk} \cdot D_j u \cdot D_k \bar{u}\, dx + \frac{1}{2} \int_G \sum_{j=1}^n p_j D_j |u|^2 dx$$

$$+ \int_G \mathrm{Re}\, b \cdot |u|^2 dx \geqslant \varepsilon \int_G \sum_{j=1}^n |D_j u|^2 dx + \int_G \left(\mathrm{Re}\, b - \frac{1}{2} \sum_{j=1}^n D_j p_j \right) |u|^2 dx. \tag{2.7}$$

It follows that we will have the estimate $\mathrm{Re}(Lu, u)_0 \geq C \| u \|_1^2$ $(C > 0)$ in the case that

$$\mathrm{Re}\, b(x) - \frac{1}{2} \sum_{j=1}^n (D_j p_j)(x) \geqslant 0 \qquad (x \in G \cup \Gamma). \tag{2.8}$$

In conclusion, we remark that for the problem (2.2), each m-generalized solution is now considered in the sense that $(u, L^+ v)_0 = (f, v)_0$ for some $u \in W_2^m(G)$, $f \in \mathring{W}_2^{-m}(G)$ and all $v \in \mathring{W}_2^m(G) \cap W_2^{2m}(G)$, and necessarily $u \in \mathring{W}_2^m(G) = W'^m_2(G)$. We restrict proof to $m = 1$. If we use Green's formula (1.17), Chapter II, we find

$$(f, v)_0 = (u, L^+ v)_0 = -\int_G \sum_{j,k=1}^n b_{jk} D_j u \cdot D_k \bar{v}\, dx - \int_G u \sum_{j=1}^n p_j D_j \bar{v}\, dx$$

$$+ \int_G \left(b - \sum_{j=1}^n D_j p_j \right) u\bar{v}\, dx + \int_\Gamma |B\nu| u \frac{\partial \bar{v}}{\partial \mu} dx.$$

Hence $\left| \int_\Gamma |B\nu| u \frac{\partial \bar{v}}{\partial \mu} dx \right| \leqslant C_1 \| u \|_1 \| v \|_1 + \| f \|_{\mathring{W}_2^{-1}(G)} \| v \|_1 \leqslant C_2 \| v \|_1.$

Moreover, among the functions $v \in \mathring{W}_2^1(G) \cap W_2^2(G)$ satisfying $\| v \|_1 \leq 1$, we can find a function with arbitrarily large derivative $\partial v/\partial\mu|_\Gamma$. For this, $|\int_\Gamma(|B\nu|\, u\partial\bar{v}/\partial\mu)\, dx| \leq C_2$, which can hold only when $u|_\Gamma = 0$, i.e. $u \in \mathring{W}_2^1(G)$. The assertion follows.

2. **Boundary value problems of the third type for equations of second order.** Consider a differential expression (2.4) with boundary condition.

$$|B(x)\nu(x)|\frac{\partial u}{\partial\mu} + Tu + Qu = 0 \qquad (x \in \Gamma). \tag{2.9}$$

Here $\partial/\partial\mu$ is a differentiation with respect to the co-normal; T, defined on functions given on Γ, is a linear differential expression of the first order consisting of a linear combination of tangent (i.e. directed along Γ) derivatives with real coefficients in $C^1(\Gamma)$; Q is a bounded linear operator in $L_2(G)$. If $T = Q = 0$, we obtain boundary conditions of the second kind; if $T = 0$ and Q is an operator which is defined by multiplication by a bounded function $\sigma(x)$, we have the third kind; if $T \neq 0$, with Q and $\sigma(x)$ as before, we have a problem with fiber bundle. In the case $T \neq 0$ we will require that the boundary Γ is of class C^2.

Thus $W_2^2(\text{bd})$ consists of all functions in $W_2^2(G)$ satisfying equation (2.9). We suppose in addition that T and Q are such that the functions $u \in W_2^2(\text{bd})$, considered only on Γ, form a dense set in $L_2(\Gamma)$.[1] Similarly, let $W_2^2(\text{bd})^+$ denote the collection of all functions $v \in W_2^2(G)$ satisfying the relation

$$|B(x)\nu(x)|\frac{\partial v}{\partial\bar{\mu}} + T^+v + Q^*v - \overline{\beta(x)}\, v = 0 \; (x \in \Gamma). \tag{2.10}$$

We also assume that the functions $v \in W_2^2(\text{bd})^+$, considered on Γ, form a dense set in $L_2(\Gamma)$.

The linear sets $W_2^2(\text{bd})$ and $W_2^2(\text{bd})^+$ are closed in $W_2^2(G)$. Thus, if a sequence $u_\nu \in W_2^2(G)$ satisfies (2.9) and converges in $W_2^2(G)$ to u, then by virtue of the imbedding theorem the values of $u_\nu|_\Gamma$ also converge to $u|_\Gamma$, so we can pass to the limit in (2.9) to see that u satisfies this condition. We show that $W_2^2(\text{bd})$ and $W_2^2(\text{bd})^+$ are mutually adjoint conditions. In fact, suppose $v \in W_2^2(G)$

---

1) This is far from being always the case. Example: $n = 3$, $L = -\Delta$. The boundary conditions are $\partial u/\partial\nu + Qu = 0$ (*), where Q is a continuous operator in $L_2(\Gamma)$ defined by the equation $(Qu)(x) = q(x)\int_\Gamma u(x)\, dx$, where $q(x)$ is a fixed function belonging to $L_2(\Gamma)$ but not in $L_3(\Gamma)$. If $u \in W_2^2(G)$ satisfies (*), then $\partial u/\partial\nu = Cq(x)$ does not belong to $L_3(\Gamma)$ for $C \neq 0$, in contradiction to the imbedding theorem. Thus $C = 0$, i.e. $\int_\Gamma u(x)\, dx = 0$. In other words, 1 is orthogonal to all $u|_\Gamma$; i.e. these are not dense in $L_2(\Gamma)$.

is such that for all $u \in W_2^2(\mathrm{bd})$ $(Lu, v)_0 = (u, L^+v)_0$. It follows from (1.18), Chapter II, and (2.9) that

$$0 = \int_\Gamma |B\nu| \left\{ \frac{\partial u}{\partial \mu} \bar{v} - u \frac{\partial \bar{v}}{\partial \mu} \right\} dx + \int_\Gamma \beta u \bar{v}\, dx = \int_\Gamma \Big\{ - u |B\nu| \frac{\partial \bar{v}}{\partial \mu}$$

$$+ \beta u \bar{v} - Tu \cdot \bar{v} - Qu \cdot \bar{v} \Big\} dx = \int_\Gamma u \overline{\left(- |B\nu| \frac{\partial v}{\partial \mu} - T^+ v - Q^* v + \bar{\beta} v \right)} dx. \quad (2.11)$$

Here we shifted T from u to v; the boundary terms do not appear since Γ is closed. Since we assume that the $u|_\Gamma$ are dense in $L_2(\Gamma)$, it follows from (2.11) that v satisfies (2.10), i.e. $v \in W_2^2(\mathrm{bd})^+$. Similarly, it can be shown that $W_2^2(\mathrm{bd})^{++} = W_2^2(\mathrm{bd})$.

Suppose that L is strongly elliptic and all $p_j(x)$ are real. We will show that it is possible to give additional restrictions on the coefficients of L and the boundary condition to guarantee that the Hermitian part of L^+ is positive on $W_2^2(\mathrm{bd})^+$. If $v \in W_2^2(\mathrm{bd})^+$, it follows from (1.17), Chapter II, and (2.10), similarly to (2.7), that

$$\mathrm{Re}\,(L^+ v, v)_0 = - \int_G \sum_{j,k=1}^n \mathrm{Re}\, b_{jk} \cdot D_j v \cdot D_k \bar{v}\, dx + \int_G \left(\mathrm{Re}\, b - \frac{1}{2} \sum_{j=1}^n D_j p_j \right) |v|^2\, dx$$

$$+ \mathrm{Re} \int_\Gamma \left(|B\nu| \frac{\partial v}{\partial \mu} - \frac{1}{2} \beta v \right) \bar{v}\, dx = \int_G \ldots dx + \mathrm{Re} \int_\Gamma \left(- T^+ v - Q^* v + \frac{1}{2} \beta v \right) \bar{v}\, dx$$

$$= \int_G \ldots dx + \mathrm{Re} \int_\Gamma \left(- Tv - Qv + \frac{1}{2} \beta v \right) \bar{v}\, dx. \quad (2.12)$$

The differential expression T may be written in the form $Tu = \sum_{j=1}^{n-1} \gamma_j(s) \partial u / \partial s_j$ $(s \in \Gamma)$, where $(s_1, \cdots, s_{n-1})$ are coordinates on the surface Γ; the coefficients $\gamma_j(s) \in C^1(\Gamma)$ are real. Integrating by parts and taking into account the fact that Γ is a closed surface, we obtain

$$\mathrm{Re} \int_\Gamma Tv \cdot \bar{v}\, dx = \mathrm{Re} \int_\Gamma \left(\sum_{j=1}^{n-1} \gamma_j \frac{\partial v}{\partial s_j} \right) \bar{v}\, ds = \frac{1}{2} \int_\Gamma \sum_{j=1}^{n-1} \gamma_j \frac{\partial}{\partial s_j} |v|^2\, ds$$

$$= - \frac{1}{2} \int_\Gamma \sum_{j=1}^{n-1} \frac{\partial \gamma_j}{\partial s_j} |v|^2\, ds. \quad (2.13)$$

Let $Q = Q_1 + iQ_2$ be the decomposition of Q into Hermitian components. Taking into account (2.13), we obtain from (2.12)

$$\operatorname{Re}(L^+v, v)_0 = -\int_G \sum_{j,k=1}^n \operatorname{Re} b_{jk}\cdot D_jv\cdot D_k\bar{v}\,dx + \int_G \left(\operatorname{Re} b - \frac{1}{2}\sum_{j=1}^n D_jp_j\right)|v|^2\,dx;$$

$$+\int_\Gamma \left(\frac{1}{2}\sum_{j=1}^{n-1}\frac{\partial\gamma_j}{\partial s_j} + \frac{1}{2}\beta\right)|v|^2\,ds - \int_\Gamma Q_1v\cdot\bar{v}\,ds \tag{2.14}$$

Thus, for example, if we have the conditions

$$\operatorname{Re} b(x) - \frac{1}{2}\sum_{j=1}^n (D_jp_j)(x) \geqslant 0 \qquad (x \in G \cup \Gamma).$$

$$\int_\Gamma \left(\frac{1}{2}\sum_{j=1}^{n-1}\frac{\partial\gamma_j}{\partial s_j} + \frac{1}{2}\beta\right)|v|^2\,ds - \int_\Gamma Q_1v\cdot\bar{v}\,ds \geqslant 0 \quad (v \in L_2(\Gamma)), \tag{2.15}$$

where the first inequality is strict for at least one point,[1] then by (2.14) and (1.3) we can conclude that the Hermitian part of L^+ is positive: $\operatorname{Re}(L^+v, v)_0 \geq C\|v\|_1^2$ $(C > 0;\ v \in W_2^2(\mathrm{bd})^+)$. This shows that the energy inequality holds for L^+ and $(\mathrm{bd})^+$, and therefore *the problem* $Lu = f$, $u \in (\mathrm{bd})$, *has a 1-generalized solution* $u \in W_2^1(G)$ *for any* $f \in \tilde{W}_2^{-1}(G)$.

From (1.17), Chapter II, by means of an integration by parts, it follows from (2.10) that for any $u \in W_2^1(G)$ and $v \in W_2^2(\mathrm{bd})^+$

$$(u, L^+v)_0 = \int_G \left\{-\sum_{j,k=1}^n b_{jk}D_ju\cdot D_k\bar{v} + \sum_{j=1}^n p_jD_ju\cdot\bar{v} + bu\bar{v}\right\}dx$$

$$+\int_\Gamma u\overline{\left(|B\nu|\frac{\partial v}{\partial\mu} - \beta v\right)}dx = \int_G \{\ldots\}\,dx - \int_\Gamma u\overline{T^+v}\,dx - \int_\Gamma Qu\cdot\bar{v}\,dx. \tag{2.16}$$

This permits us to write the condition that $u \in W_2^1(G)$ is a 1-generalized solution in the form

1) Without this stipulation, it only follows from (2.14) that we have a lower estimate for the form by means of $\sum_{j=1}^n \int_G |D_jv|^2\,dx$, and for $v|_\Gamma$ arbitrary this is not equivalent to $\|v\|_1^2$. When the strict inequality holds, the form can be estimated by $\sum_{j=1}^n \int_G |D_jv|^2\,dx + \epsilon\int_{G_1} |v|^2\,dx$ $(\epsilon > 0)$ where G_1 is some subregion of G. This expression is equivalent to $\|v\|_1^2$.

$$\int_G \left\{-\sum_{j,k=1}^n b_{jk}D_ju\cdot D_k\bar{v}+\sum_{j=1}^n p_jD_ju\cdot\bar{v}+bu\bar{v}\right\}dx$$

$$-\int_\Gamma u\overline{T^+v}\,dx-\int_\Gamma Qu\cdot\bar{v}\,dx=(f,\,v)_0\qquad(v\in W_2^2\,(\mathrm{bd})^+). \tag{2.17}$$

We show that conditions a) and b) of Theorem 3.4 are now satisfied. We establish b) in the form (3.18), Chapter II. The first of the required inequalities is already established; the second follows from the estimate

$$|(u,\,L^+v)_0|\leqslant C\,\|u\|_1\,\|v\|_1\qquad(u\in W_2^1\,(G),\ v\in W_2^2\,(\mathrm{bd})^+). \tag{2.18}$$

We prove (2.18) by using the expression (2.16) for the form $(u,\ L^+v)_0$. To prove (2.18), it is sufficient to establish it for each of the three integrals in the right side of (2.16). This is obvious for the first integral; the third is estimated by $C_1\|u\|_{L_2(\Gamma)}\|v\|_{L_2(\Gamma)}$ and (2.18) for it follows from the imbedding theorem. We estimate the second integral.

We proceed in the following way. Consider n-dimensional vectors $\tau^{jk}(x)$ $(j\neq k)$, all of whose coordinates are equal to zero except for the jth, which is equal to $\nu_k(x)$, and the kth, which is equal to $-\nu_j(x)$ $(j,\ k=1,\cdots,\ n;\ x\in\Gamma)$. Since $\langle\nu,\ \tau^{jk}\rangle=0$, $\tau^{jk}(x)$ lies in the tangent hyperplane to Γ at the point x: it is easy to see that these form a complete system of vectors (linearly dependent). Therefore the given tangent differential expression T^+ may be represented (in various ways) in the form of a linear combination of derivatives with respect to the directions $\tau^{jk}(x)$ with real coefficients in $C^1(\Gamma)$:

$$T^+v=\sum_{j\neq k}\omega_{jk}(x)\frac{\partial v}{\partial\tau^{jk}}=\sum_{j\neq k}\omega_{jk}(x)\left(\nu_k(x)\frac{\partial v}{\partial x_j}-\nu_j(x)\frac{\partial v}{\partial x_k}\right).$$

We extend $\omega_{jk}(x)$ in an arbitrary way to G, so as to obtain a real function in $C^1(G\cup\Gamma)$. By integration by parts we obtain

$$\int_\Gamma u\overline{T^+v}\,dx=\int_\Gamma\sum_{j\neq k}u\omega_{jk}\left\{\nu_k\frac{\partial\bar{v}}{\partial x_j}-\nu_j\frac{\partial\bar{v}}{\partial x_k}\right\}dx=\int_G\sum_{j\neq k}\{D_k(u\omega_{jk}D_j\bar{v})$$

$$-D_j(u\omega_{jk}D_k\bar{v})\}\,dx=\int_G\left\{\sum_{j\neq k}\omega_{jk}(D_ku\cdot D_j\bar{v}-D_ju\cdot D_k\bar{v})\right.$$

$$\left.+\sum_{j\neq k}u\,(D_k\omega_{jk}\cdot D_j\bar{v}-D_j\omega_{jk}\cdot D_k\bar{v})\right\}dx.$$

The required estimate follows from this equation. Thus (2.18), and hence condition b), are satisfied.

The closures $W'^1_2(G)$ of the sets $W^2_2(\mathrm{bd})$ and $W^2_2(\mathrm{bd})^+$ in the metric of $W^1_2(G)$ coincide with all of $W^1_2(G)$, since conditions (2.9) and (2.10) relate a function and its first derivatives (see p. 30). Thus, condition a) is also satisfied, and therefore Theorem 3.4 of Chapter II, holds for the problem under consideration.

Finally, we remark that since now $W'^1_2(G) = W^1_2(G)$, *every 1-generalized solution of the problem under consideration is in fact generalized in the sense of* p. 98. We can state the following result.

Theorem 2.2. *Let L be a strongly elliptic expression in the form (2.4) with real $p_j(x)$. Consider the boundary value problem $Lu = f$ with boundary conditions (2.9). If the inequalities (2.15) are satisfied, then this problem has a 1-generalized solution $u \in W^1_2(G)$ for any $f \in \widetilde{W}^{-1}_2(G)$, and moreover $\| u \|_1 \leq C \| f \|_{-1}$ $(f \in \widetilde{W}^{-1}_2(G))$. The property that $u \in W^1_2(G)$ is a 1-generalized solution can be expressed in the following manner: for any $v \in W^2_2(G)$ satisfying (2.10), the identity (2.17) holds.*

Since now $W'^1_2(G) = W^1_2(G)$, $W'^1_2(G) \cap W^2_2(G) = W^1_2(G)$, and the passage to $W'^1_2(G)$ does not preserve boundary conditions. Therefore the condition $F \in \widetilde{W}^{-1}_2(G)$ is essential for a correct concept of generalized solution.

3. **Eigenvalue problems.** Let L be a strongly elliptic expression of order $2m$, considered with null boundary conditions. By the last assertion of §1.1 for a proper choice of the parameter λ_0, the expression $L - \lambda_0 E$ satisfies the conditions of Theorem 3.5, Chapter II, and therefore the corresponding problem is of Fredholm type.

We also consider expressions and boundary conditions as in subsection 2, but without the assumptions in (2.15). We show that if Γ is of class C^1 and $k \geq 0$ is sufficiently large, then we have the inequality $\mathrm{Re}((L + kE)^+ v, v)_0 \geq C \| v \|^2_1$ $(C > 0;\ v \in W^2_2(\mathrm{bd})^+)$, and this permits application of Theorem 3.5, Chapter II. In fact, let $k = k_1 + k_2$ $(k_1, k_2 \geq 0)$ and first choose k_1 so large that $k_1 + \mathrm{Re}\, b(x) - \frac{1}{2} \sum_{j=1}^n (D_j p_j)(x) \geq 0$ $(x \in G)$. From (2.14) we obtain

$$\mathrm{Re}((L+kE)^+ v, v)_0 \geqslant \varepsilon \int_G \sum_{j=1}^n |D_j v|^2 dx + k_2 \int_G |v|^2 dx$$

$$+ \int_\Gamma \left(\frac{1}{2} \sum_{j=1}^{n-1} \frac{\partial \gamma_j}{\partial s_j} - \frac{1}{2} \beta \right) |v|^2 ds - \int_\Gamma Q_1 v \cdot \bar{v}\, ds \geqslant \varepsilon \int_G \sum_{j=1}^n |D_j v|^2 dx +$$

$$+ k_2 \int\limits_G |v|^2 dx - C_1 \int\limits_\Gamma |v|^2 ds = \varepsilon \| v \|_1^2 + (k_2 - \varepsilon) \| v \|_0^2$$

$$- C_1 \int\limits_\Gamma |v|^2 ds \qquad (C_1 > 0;\ v \in W_2^2(\mathrm{bd})^+). \tag{2.19}$$

Here we make use of the estimate $\int (\cdots) |v|^2 ds + \int_\Gamma Q_1 v \cdot \bar{v}\, ds \le C_1 \int_\Gamma |v|^2 ds$. We leave to the reader the verification that for differentiable Γ, $\int_\Gamma |u|^2 ds \le C \| u \|_0 \ \| u \|_1$ $(u \in W_2^1(G))$. If we apply this inequality and the inequality $ab \le \frac{1}{2}(a^2 + b^2)$, we obtain $C_1 \int_\Gamma |v|^2 ds \le \epsilon/2 \ \| v \|_1^2 + C_1^2 C^2/2\epsilon \ \| v \|_0^2$ $(v \in W_2^2(\mathrm{bd})^+)$. On choosing $k_2 \ge 0$ large, we see from (2.19) that $\mathrm{Re}\,((L + kE)^+ v, v)_0 \ge \epsilon/2 \ \| v \|_1^2$, as required. Thus Theorem 3.5 of Chapter II applies, as in the case with null boundary conditions. We have arrived at the following result.

Theorem 2.3. *Consider an expression L and boundary conditions as in subsection 1, but without the assumption concerning sufficiently positive coefficients, or an expression and boundary conditions as in subsection 2, with Γ of class C^1 and without the assumption that (2.15) is satisfied. Then the boundary value problem $Lu - \lambda u = f \in L_2(G)$ $(u \in (\mathrm{bd}))$ is of Fredholm type, i.e. the conclusions of Theorem 3.5, Chapter II, hold.*

§3. BOUNDARY VALUE PROBLEMS FOR ELLIPTIC EQUATIONS. SMOOTH SOLUTIONS

In this section, unlike the previous ones, we find solutions which are differentiable a number of times equal to the order of the equation.

1. **The energy inequalities for functions satisfying null boundary conditions.** The energy inequalities (1.28) and (1.29) (for $s = 0$) cannot be applied to determine solutions of the boundary value problem, since they are satisfied for a too restricted class of functions, namely the finite functions, and therefore by Theorem 3.3, Chapter II, they give only the existence of generalized solutions with removed boundary conditions. We now extend this class.

Theorem 3.1. *Suppose that $n \ge 3$, L is an elliptic expression of order $r = 2m$, and $s \ge 0$ is some integer. Suppose that the coefficients $a_\alpha(x) \in C^{\max(|\alpha|, s)}(G \cup \Gamma)$, and the boundary Γ is of class C^{2m+s}. Then for sufficiently large $k \ge 0$,*

$$\| Lu \|_s^2 + k \| u \|_0^2 \geqslant C \| u \|_{2m+s}^2 \quad (C > 0;\ u \in \mathring{W}_2^m(G) \cap W_2^{2m+s}(G)). \tag{3.1}$$

If $n = 2$ the theorem remains valid for elliptic expressions $L(x, D)$ which satisfy the following additional condition, called the condition of regular ellipticity. We will assume that the order of $L(x, D)$ is even: $r = 2m$. If $x \in \Gamma$, we consider the form $L_c(x, \xi) = L_c(x, \tau + t\nu(x))$, where $\xi = \tau + t\nu(x)$ is the decomposition of the vector $\xi \in E_n$ into the component $\tau \in E_{n-1}$, parallel to the tangent hyperplane to Γ at the point x, and the component $t\nu(x)$, where $\nu(x)$ is the exterior normal, $-\infty < t < \infty$. We construct the equation of algebraic degree $2m$ with complex ζ: $L_c(x, \tau + \zeta\nu(x)) = 0$; it is required that for each $x \in \Gamma$ and $\tau \in E_{n-1}$, $\tau \neq 0$, this equation has exactly m roots interior to the upper half-plane and m roots interior to the lower half-plane (for counting roots we take into account their multiplicity). In the case $n \geq 3$ this condition is automatically satisfied by ellipticity, and for $n = 2$ it is guaranteed by strong ellipticity (see Lemma 3.2 and its corollary).

We remark further that the smoothness hypothesis stated in the theorem is excessive, as will be seen from the proof; we may assume that $a_\alpha(x) \in C^s(G \cup \Gamma)$ ($|\alpha| = 2m$) and $a_\alpha(x)$ has s bounded derivatives for $|\alpha| < 2m$. Similar relaxations of smoothness conditions on coefficients will not be written out in what follows; we only use expressions for which automatically $a_\alpha(x) \in C^{|\alpha|}(G \cup \Gamma)$ (see Chapter II, §1.1).

We proceed to the proof. It is similar to the proof of Theorem 1.1 and is based on the estimate (1.28) and the following lemma, which will be proved somewhat later.

Lemma 3.1. *In a region G, lying on one side of some plane and containing a piece S of its boundary,*[1] *consider the expression $Mu = \sum_{|\alpha|=2m} b_\alpha D^\alpha u$ with constant coefficients satisfying the conditions of Theorem 3.1. Then for the class $W_2^{2m+s}(G; (\mathrm{bd})_S, 0)$ of functions $u \in W_2^{2m+s}(G)$ such that $D^\alpha u|_S = 0$ ($|\alpha| \leq m-1$) and vanishing in a neighborhood of $\Gamma \setminus S$ the inequality*

$$\| Mu \|_s \geqslant C \| u \|_{2m+s} \qquad (C > 0) \tag{3.2}$$

holds.

The proof of the theorem is carried out in several steps.

---

1) We assume that G is a general region with boundary of class C^{2m+s}; we could even restrict attention to the case where G is a hemisphere. Similar remarks can be made with respect to Lemmas 3.4, 3.5, and 3.7.

1. Suppose $x_0 \in E_n$; consider a region G as in the lemma, and suppose that the point x_0 lies on the plane piece of the boundary (see Figure 2). If the diameter of G is sufficiently small, then for the expression $L(x, D)$ considered in the theorem we have

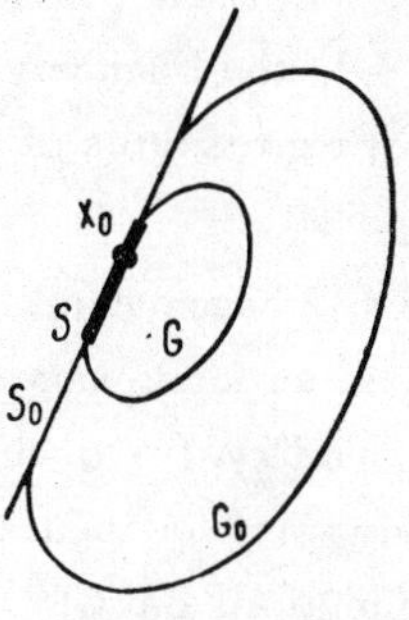

Figure 2

$$\|L(x, D)u\|_s \geqslant C_1\|u\|_{2m+s}$$
$$(C_1>0;\ u\in W_2^{2m+s}(G;\ (\mathrm{bd})_S,\ 0)). \tag{3.3}$$

In fact, we can apply Lemma 3.1 to the expression $M = L_c(x_0, D)$ for some region G_0 ($G \subset G_0$; see Figure 2). We obtain

$$\|L_c(x_0, D)u\|_{W_2^s(G_0)} \geqslant C\|u\|_{W_2^{2m+s}(G_0)}\ (C>0;\ u\in W_2^{2m+s}(G_0;\ (\mathrm{bd})_{S_0},\ 0)). \tag{3.4}$$

Furthermore, for functions $u \in W_2^{2m+s}(G_0)$ vanishing in a neighborhood of $G_0 \setminus G$, we have

$$\|L(x, D)u - L_c(x_0, D)u\|_{W_2^s(G_0)} \leqslant \left\|\sum_{|\alpha|=2m}[a_\alpha(x) - a_\alpha(x_0)]D^\alpha u\right\|_{W_2^s(G_0)}$$
$$+\left\|\sum_{|\alpha|<2m} a_\alpha(x)D^\alpha u\right\|_{W_2^s(G_0)} \leqslant \sum_{|\alpha|=2m,\ |\beta|=s}\left\|[a_\alpha(x) - a_\alpha(x_0)]D^{\alpha+\beta}u\right\|_{L_2(G)}$$
$$+\sum_{|\gamma|<2m+s}\|b_\gamma(x)D^\gamma u\|_{L_2(G)} \tag{3.5}$$

Here the b_ν are certain coefficients, part of which coincide with derivatives of order $1, \cdots, s$ of the differences $a_\alpha(x) - a_\alpha(x_0)$, and part with derivatives of order $\leq s$ of $a_\alpha(x)$; these coefficients are bounded in G_0. By choosing G sufficiently small, each of the first terms on the right in (3.5), obviously, can be majorized by the expression $\frac{1}{2}\epsilon\, \|u\|_{W_2^{2m+s}(G_0)}$ for any preassigned $\epsilon > 0$. The terms of the second type are majorized by

$$C_2\|u\|_{W_2^{2m+s-1}(G)} \leqslant dC_2\|u\|_{W_2^{2m+s}(G)} = dC_2\|u\|_{W_2^{2m+s}(G_0)},$$

where d is the diameter of G (see pp. 21–22). Choosing d sufficiently small, we obtain

$$\|L(x, D)u - L_c(x_0, D)u\|_{W_2^s(G_0)} \leqslant \varepsilon\|u\|_{W_2^{2m+s}(G_0)}.$$

Hence (3.3) follows from (3.4).

2. Consider a region G, the boundary of which contains a piece S of class C^{2m+s}. If the diameter of G is sufficiently small, then the estimate (3.3) holds

for functions $u \in W_2^{2m+s}(G)$ such that $D^\alpha u|_S = 0$ ($|\alpha| \leq m-1$) and vanishing in a neighborhood of $\Gamma \setminus S$. This assertion follows immediately from the previous one by mapping the given region onto a region as in Lemma 3.1, the boundary of which contains a plane piece. We clarify this by examples of expressions of second order (i.e. $m = 1$).

Let $x' = \phi(x)$ be a $2+s$ times continuously differentiable homeomorphism in E_n, transforming $G \cup \Gamma$ into a region $G' \cup \Gamma'$ of the desired form; moreover suppose S is mapped into the plane piece S' lying on the boundary Γ' of the region G'. Let $x = \phi^{-1}(x')$ be the inverse mapping. The mapping ϕ induces an operator T_ϕ, transforming functions $u'(x')$ on G' into functions on G: $(T_\phi u')(x) = u'(\phi(x))$. It is clear that T_ϕ is a homeomorphism between $W_2^l(G')$ and $W_2^l(G)$ for $0 \leq l \leq 2+s$. If we define $W_2^{2+s}(G; (\mathrm{bd})_S, 0)$ similarly to the previously introduced class of functions on G, then T_ϕ is a homeomorphism between $W_2^{2+s}(G'; (\mathrm{bd})_{S'}, 0)$ and $W_2^{2+s}(G; (\mathrm{bd})_S, 0)$. Given an expression L of the second order, we construct an expression L' on G' by setting $(L'u')(x') = T_\phi^{-1} L T_\phi u'$ on smooth functions $u'(x')$. In particular, the derivatives $\partial/\partial x_j, \partial^2/\partial x_j \partial x_k$ pass into

$$\frac{\partial}{\partial x_j} u'(\varphi(x)) = \sum_{p=1}^{n} \frac{\partial u'}{\partial x'_p} \frac{\partial x'_p}{\partial x_j},$$

$$\frac{\partial^2}{\partial x_j \partial x_k} u'(\varphi(x)) = \sum_{p,q=1}^{n} \frac{\partial^2 u'}{\partial x'_p \partial x'_q} \frac{\partial x'_p}{\partial x_j} \frac{\partial x'_q}{\partial x_k} + \sum_{p=1}^{n} \frac{\partial u'}{\partial x'_p} \frac{\partial^2 x'_p}{\partial x_j \partial x_k}$$

$$(x = \varphi^{-1}(x')). \tag{3.6}$$

Thus for the leading coefficients $b'_{pq}(x')$ of L' we have

$$b'_{pq}(x') = \sum_{j,k=1}^{n} b_{jk}(x) \frac{\partial x'_p}{\partial x_j} \frac{\partial x'_q}{\partial x_k}, \qquad x = \varphi^{-1}(x'). \tag{3.7}$$

Since the matrix $\| \partial x'_s / \partial x_t \|_1^n$ is nonsingular, L and L' are simultaneously elliptic or not; since L is elliptic by hypothesis, so is L'. It is also clear that the coefficients of L' are sufficiently smooth. If the diameter of G is sufficiently small, so is the diameter of G'; all this is used to permit application of the result in step 1 to L' and $W_2^{2+s}(G'; (\mathrm{bd})_{S'}, 0)$. The required inequality is now easily obtained:

$$\| Lu \|_{W_2^s(G)} = \| T_\varphi L' [T_\varphi^{-1} u] \|_{W_2^s(G)} \geqslant C_2 \| L' [T_\varphi^{-1} u] \|_{W_2^s(G')}$$

$$\geqslant C_2 C_1 \| T_\varphi^{-1} u \|_{W_2^{2+s}(G')} \geqslant C_2 C_1 C_3 \| u \|_{W_2^{2+s}(G)}$$

$$(u \in W_2^{2+s}(G; (\mathrm{bd})s, 0), \; T_\varphi^{-1} u \in W_2^{2+s}(G'; (\mathrm{bd})s', 0)).$$

3. We proceed to estimates over all of G. For every $x \in G$ there exists a neighborhood U_x interior to G such that

$$\| Lu \|_s \geqslant C_x \| u \|_{2m+s} \quad (C_x > 0;\ u \in \dot{W}_{2,0}^{2m+s}(U_x)); \tag{3.8}$$

this follows from the corollary to Theorem 1.2. By step 2, for any $x \in \Gamma$ there also exists a neighborhood U_x (in E_n) such that the inequality (3.8) is satisfied for functions in $W_2^{2m+s}(U_x \cap G)$ vanishing along with their derivatives of order $\leq m-1$ on $\Gamma \cap U_x$ and in a neighborhood of the remaining part of the boundary of $U_x \cup G$.

We select a finite cover of $G \cup \Gamma$ consisting of neighborhoods V_x, strictly interior to the corresponding U_x; denote these neighborhoods by $V_{x_1}, \cdots, V_{x_N}$. Construct a decomposition of unity, consisting of functions $\chi_1(x), \cdots, \chi_n(x)$ $(x \in E_n)$, each of which vanishes outside of the corresponding V_{x_j}. We have $\sum_{j=1}^N \chi_j(x) = 1$ in a neighborhood of $G \cup \Gamma$. If $u \in \mathring{W}_2^m(G) \cap W_2^{2m+s}(G)$, then $\chi_j(x)\, u(x)$ vanishes in a neighborhood of part of the boundary of the region $U_{x_j} \cap G$, different from Γ, and it satisfies null boundary conditions on Γ. We therefore have the estimate (3.8)

$$\| L[\chi_j u] \|_s \geqslant C \| \chi_j u \|_{2m+s} \quad (u \in \mathring{W}_2^m(G) \cap W_2^{2m+s}(G);\ j = 1, \ldots, N).$$

From this we obtain

$$\| u \|_{2m+s}^2 = \left\| \sum_{j=1}^N \chi_j u \right\|_{2m+s}^2 \leqslant C_1 \sum_{j=1}^N \| \chi_j u \|_{2m+s}^2 \leqslant C_2 \sum_{j=1}^N \| L[\chi_j u] \|_s^2$$

$$= C_2 \sum_{j=1}^N \sum_{|\alpha| \leqslant s} \int_G | D^\alpha L[\chi_j u] |^2 dx \leqslant C_2 \sum_{j=1}^N \sum_{|\alpha| \leqslant s} \int_G | \chi_j |^2 | D^\alpha Lu |^2 dx$$

$$+ \sum_{|\gamma| < 2m+s} \int_G | b_\gamma(x) D^\gamma u |^2 dx \leqslant NC_2 \sum_{|\alpha| \leqslant s} \int_G | D^\alpha Lu |^2 dx + C_3 \| u \|_{2m+s-1}^2$$

$$\leqslant C_4 (\| Lu \|_s^2 + \| u \|_{2m+s-1}^2) \quad (u \in \mathring{W}_2^m(G) \cap W^{2m+s}(G)). \tag{3.9}$$

4. Let G be a fixed region. By the Ehrling-Nirenberg inequality, for any $\epsilon > 0$ we can find a $K(\epsilon) > 0$ such that

$$\| u \|^2_{2m+s-1} \leqslant \varepsilon \| u \|^2_{2m+s} + K(\varepsilon) \| u \|^2_0.$$

This and (3.9) yield the required estimate (3.1).

To complete the proof of the theorem we must prove Lemma 3.1. Without loss of generality, we may assume that the equation of the plane in question in the lemma is $x_n = 0$, and that G lies in the half-plane $x_n > 0$. We could proceed in a more direct and general way, and obtain the estimate (3.2) as a consequence of a representation of the solutions of the equation $Mu = f$, with definite boundary conditions, in the form of a singular integral $u(x) = \int_{\xi_n > 0} G(x, \xi) f(\xi) d\xi$; then estimating the integral, $\| u \|_{2m+s} \leq C_1 \| f \|_s = C_1 \| Lu \|_s$. However, we do not dwell on this approach, since its execution requires subtle estimates. Instead we consider two other methods. The inequality (3.2) will first be proved for $s = 0$, and then with the help of a general device we deduce the estimate for all $s > 0$ from this special case.

5. First method: namely, the method of integration by parts, suitable for elliptic expressions M of the second order with real coefficients. Below we use the notation $Mu = \sum_{j,k=1}^n b_{jk} D_j D_k u$. For the proof of the lemma we proceed as follows. On integrating by parts for functions $u \in W_2^3(G; (\mathrm{bd})_S, 0)$, we obtain[1)]

$$\begin{aligned}
\| Mu \|_0^2 &= \int_G Mu \cdot \overline{Mu}\, dx = \int_G \sum_{j,k,p,q=1}^n b_{jk} \bar{b}_{pq} D_j D_k u \cdot D_p D_q \bar{u}\, dx \\
&= -\int_G \sum_{j,k,p,q=1}^n b_{jk} \bar{b}_{pq} D_k u \cdot D_j D_p D_q \bar{u}\, dx \\
&\quad + \int_S \sum_{j,k,p,q=1}^n b_{jk} \bar{b}_{pq} D_k u \cdot D_p D_q \bar{u} \cdot \nu_j\, dx \\
&= \int_G \sum_{j,k,p,q=1}^n b_{jk} \bar{b}_{pq} D_k D_p u \cdot D_j D_q \bar{u}\, dx \\
&\quad + \int_S \sum_{j,k,p,q=1}^n b_{jk} \bar{b}_{pq} D_k u \cdot (D_p D_q \bar{u} \cdot \nu_j - D_j D_q \bar{u} \cdot \nu_p)\, dx.
\end{aligned} \tag{3.10}$$

Consider the last integral. Because of the location of G, the unit exterior

1) Later we will need relations (3.10) and (3.11) for complex coefficients, and so for these, a choice of real coefficients is not assumed.

normal on S is equal to $(0, \cdots, 0, -1)$, and therefore this integral assumes the form

$$-\int_S \left(\sum_{k,p,q=1}^n b_{nk}\bar{b}_{pq} D_k u \cdot D_p D_q \bar{u} - \sum_{j,k,q=1}^n b_{jk}\bar{b}_{nq} D_k u \cdot D_j D_q \bar{u} \right) dx. \tag{3.11}$$

But $u(x) = 0$ for $x \in S$, and therefore $D_j u = 0 \, (j \neq n)$ and $D_j D_k u = 0$ if both $j \neq n$, $k \neq n$. Substituting these values for the derivatives in (3.11) and assuming that b_{st} is real $(s, t = 1, \cdots, n)$, we find that the integral is equal to zero. Thus equation (3.10), after passing to the limit from functions of the class $W_2^3(G; (\mathrm{bd})_S, 0)$ to functions of the class $W_2^2(G; (\mathrm{bd})_S, 0)$, assumes the form

$$\| Mu \|_0^2 = \int_G \sum_{j,k,p,q=1}^n b_{jk} b_{pq} D_k D_p u \cdot D_j D_q \bar{u} \, dx \quad (u \in W_2^2(G; (\mathrm{bd})_S, 0)). \tag{3.12}$$

Since we assume that M is elliptic and has real coefficients, it follows from (1.3) that the matrix $\| -b_{jk} \|_1^n = \| t_{jk} \|_1^n = T$ is strictly positive definite. It is well known that then the tensor product $T \otimes T$ is strictly positive definite. The matrix $T \otimes T$ has elements $\tau_{(\mu, \nu)(\sigma, \rho)}$ of the form $t_{\mu\sigma} t_{\nu\rho}$, and acts on vectors ζ with coordinates $\zeta_{(\sigma, \rho)}$: the condition that it is positive definite can be written

$$\langle (T \otimes T) \zeta, \zeta \rangle = \sum_{\mu,\nu,\sigma,\rho=1}^n t_{\mu\sigma} t_{\nu\rho} \zeta_{(\sigma,\rho)} \bar{\zeta}_{(\mu,\nu)} \geqslant \delta \sum_{\mu,\nu=1}^n | \zeta_{(\mu,\nu)} |^2 \quad (\delta > 0). \tag{3.13}$$

Letting $\zeta_{(\mu, \nu)} = (D_\mu D_\nu \bar{u})(x)$, by the symmetry of b_{jk} and (3.13) we obtain

$$\sum_{j,k,p,q=1}^n b_{jk} b_{pq} D_k D_p u \cdot D_j D_q \bar{u} = \sum_{j,k,p,q=1}^n t_{kj} t_{pq} \zeta_{(j,q)} \bar{\zeta}_{(k,p)} \geqslant \delta \sum_{j,k=1}^n | D_j D_k u |^2. \tag{3.14}$$

Integrating (3.14) over G and using (3.12), we obtain

$$\| Mu \|_0^2 = \int_G \sum_{j,k,p,q=1}^n b_{jk} b_{pq} D_k D_p u \cdot D_j D_q \bar{u} \, dx \geqslant \delta \int_G \sum_{j,k=1}^n | D_j D_k u |^2 dx$$

$$\geqslant C \| u \|_2^2 \quad (u \in W_2^2 (G; (\mathrm{bd})_S, 0))$$

i.e. we arrive at the inequality (3.2) for $s = 0$. So this particular case of the inequality is proved.

6. Second method: the method of Fourier transforms. We prove Lemma 3.1 in the general case, using a method different from 5. The argument now is more tedious. It is convenient to denote a point in E_n by (x, y), where $x = (x_1, \cdots, x_{n-1})$, $y = x_n$; thus G lies in the half-plane $y > 0$ and the equation of

S is $y=0$. Since we repeatedly operate with Fourier transforms, it is convenient to write the operator M of order $r=2m$ in the form

$$Mu = \sum_{|\tau|+\nu=2m} b_{\tau\nu}\partial^{\tau}\partial_n^{\nu}u;\ \partial^{\tau} = \partial_1^{\tau_1}\dots\partial_{n-1}^{\tau_{n-1}},\ \partial = \frac{1}{i}D_i,\ \tau=(\tau_1,\dots,\tau_{n-1});$$

$$\partial_n = \frac{1}{i}\frac{\partial}{\partial y}. \tag{3.15}$$

For the proof of the lemma, we let $C^k(G\cup\Gamma;0)$ denote the class of functions in $C^k(G\cup\Gamma)$ which vanish in a neighborhood of $\Gamma\setminus S$; $C^k(G\cup\Gamma;(\mathrm{bd})_S,0)$ $(k\geq m-1)$ will denote the subclass of $C^k(G\cup\Gamma;0)$ consisting of functions u for which $D^{\alpha}u|_S=0$ $(|\alpha|\leq m-1)$. Functions defined in G, when necessary, will be assumed to be extended to E_n so as to vanish outside of G. In terms of the coordinates (x,y), the Fourier transform (1.7) becomes

$$\tilde{f}(\xi,\eta) = \frac{1}{\sqrt{(2\pi)^n}}\int_{E_n} f(x,y)\,e^{-i\langle\xi,x\rangle-i\eta y}\,dxdy$$

$$(\xi=(\xi_1,\dots,\xi_{n-1})\in E_{n-1},\ \eta\in E_1).$$

We also introduce the "tangential" Fourier transform

$$\hat{f}(\xi) = \frac{i}{\sqrt{(2\pi)^n}}\int_{E_{n-1}} f(x)\,e^{-i\langle\xi,x\rangle}\,dx \qquad (\xi=(\xi_1,\dots,\xi_{n-1})\in E_{n-1}).$$

If $u\in C^0(G\cup\Gamma;0)$, then in everything that follows $\hat{u}(\xi)$ denotes $\widehat{u(x,0)}$. By integration by parts, we easily obtain the equations (cf. (1.8)):

$$\widetilde{(\partial^{\tau}u)}(\xi,\eta) = \xi^{\tau}\tilde{u}(\xi,\eta),\quad \widetilde{(\partial_n u)}(\xi,\eta) = \eta\tilde{u}(\xi,\eta)+\hat{u}(\xi).$$

$$\widetilde{(\partial_n^{\nu}u)}(\xi,\eta) = \eta^{\nu}\tilde{u}(\xi,\eta)+\sum_{s=0}^{\nu-1}\eta^{\nu-s-1}\widehat{(\partial_n^s u)}(\xi), \tag{3.16}$$

where $u(x,y)$ is a sufficiently smooth function in $C^0(G\cup\Gamma;0)$.

If we use this formula and (3.15), we find for $u\in C^{2m}(G\cup\Gamma;0)$:

$$\widetilde{(Mu)}(\xi,\eta) = M(\xi,\eta)\tilde{u}(\xi,\eta)+P_u(\xi,\eta);$$

$$M(\xi,\eta) = \sum_{|\tau|+\nu=2m} b_{\tau\nu}\xi^{\tau}\eta^{\nu},\quad P_u(\xi,\eta)$$

$$= \sum_{\nu=1}^{2m}\sum_{s=0}^{\nu-1}\sum_{|\tau|=2m-\nu} b_{\tau\nu}\xi^{\tau}\eta^{\nu-s-1}\widehat{(\partial_n^s u)}(\xi). \tag{3.17}$$

For what follows we assume that $u\in C^{2m}(G\cup\Gamma;(\mathrm{bd})_S,0)\subset C^{2m}(G\cup\Gamma;0)$;

then $(\partial_n^s u)(x, 0) = 0$ for all $s \leq m-1$, and therefore the Fourier transform $\widehat{\partial_n^s u}$ of this function also vanishes. Thus,

$$P_u(\xi, \eta) = \sum_{\nu=m+1}^{2m} \sum_{s=m}^{\nu-1} \sum_{|\tau|=2m-\nu} b_{\tau\nu}\xi^\tau \eta^{\nu-s-1}\widehat{(\partial_n^s u)}(\xi) \quad (u \in C^{2m}(G \cup \Gamma; (\mathrm{bd})_S, 0). \tag{3.18}$$

Let $Nu = \sum_{|\tau|+\nu=2m} c_{\tau\nu}\partial^\tau \partial_n^\nu u$ be some other expression of order $r = 2m$, with constant coefficients, not necessarily elliptic. Similarly to (3.17) and (3.18), we may write for it

$$\widetilde{(Nu)}(\xi, \eta) = N(\xi, \eta)\tilde{u}(\xi, \eta) + Q_u(\xi, \eta);$$

$$N(\xi, \eta) = \sum_{|\tau|+\nu=2m} c_{\tau\nu}\xi^\tau \eta^\nu, \quad Q_u(\xi, \eta) = \sum_{\nu=m+1}^{2m} \sum_{s=m}^{\nu-1} \sum_{|\tau|=2m-\nu} c_{\tau\nu}\xi^\tau \eta^{\nu-s-1}\widehat{(\partial_n^s u)}(\xi)$$

$$(u \in C^{2m}(G \cup \Gamma; (\mathrm{bd})_S, 0)) \tag{3.19}$$

On functions $u \in C^{2m}(G \cup \Gamma; (\mathrm{bd})_S, 0)$, the expression $\sqrt{\sum_{|\alpha|=2m}\|D^\alpha u\|_0^2}$ is equivalent to $\|u\|_{2m}$, and therefore to prove (3.2) (with $s = 0$) it is sufficient to show that for any N of order $2m$

$$\|Nu\|_0 \leqslant C\|Mu\|_0 \quad (C > 0;\ u \in C^{2m}(G \cup \Gamma; (\mathrm{bd})_S, 0)). \tag{3.20}$$

It is not difficult to show (see Lemma 3.2 below) that the ellipticity of M implies $|N(\xi, \eta)| \leq C|M(\xi, \eta)|$ $((\xi, \eta) \in E_n)$, and therefore if the expressions $P_u(\xi, \eta)$ and $Q_u(\xi, \eta)$ in (3.17) and (3.19) did not appear, then the estimate (3.20) would follow from this by Parseval's equality (cf. Lemma 1.1 and its proof). In the general case, it would be sufficient to establish the inequality $|\widetilde{(Nu)}(\xi, \eta)|^2 \leq C^2|\widetilde{(Mu)}(\xi, \eta)|^2$ $((\xi, \eta) \in E_n)$; however, it is easy to see that for fixed ξ, η, we do not have this because of the arbitrariness of the numbers $\tilde{u}(\xi, \eta)$, $\widehat{(\partial_\nu^m u)}(\xi)$, $\ldots$, $\widehat{(\partial_\nu^{2m-1} u)}(\xi)$ $(u \in C^{2m}(G \cup \Gamma; (\mathrm{bd})_S, 0))$. At the same time, it turns out that

$$\int_{-\infty}^{\infty} |\widetilde{(Nu)}(\xi, \eta)|^2 d\eta \leqslant C^2 \int_{-\infty}^{\infty} |\widetilde{(Mu)}(\xi, \eta)|^2 d\eta \quad (\xi \in E_{n-1},\ u \in C^{2m}(G \cup \Gamma; (\mathrm{bd})_S, 0)). \tag{3.21}$$

Integrating this with respect to $\xi \in E_{n-1}$ and using Parseval's equality, we obtain (3.20); i.e. the lemma follows. Thus we need only establish (3.21). We first obtain two lemmas.

Lemma 3.2. *Let M and N be expressions, defined as above, of some order r which is not now assumed to be even; M elliptic. Then*

$$|N(\xi, \eta)| \leqslant C|M(\xi, \eta)| \quad (C > 0;\ (\xi, \eta) \in E_n). \tag{3.22}$$

If $n \geq 3$, then the order of M is necessarily even: $r = 2m$. For any fixed $\xi \neq 0$ ($\xi \in E_{n-1}$) the equation in ζ, $M(\xi, \zeta) = 0$, has m roots in the upper half-plane and m roots in the lower half-plane.

If M is strongly elliptic, then the second part of the lemma is true for $n = 2$.

Proof. Consider the function $\phi(\xi, \eta) = N(\xi, \eta)/M(\xi, \eta)$ $((\xi, \eta) \in E_n, (\xi, \eta) \neq 0)$. It is homogeneous of degree zero and continuous except at 0; it is clear that this property implies boundedness, i.e. the inequality (3.22).

For $n \geq 3$, we discuss the location of the roots of the equation $M(\xi, \zeta) = 0$. As ξ varies over an arc not containing 0, the number of roots ζ, lying in the upper (lower) half-plane, does not change — for otherwise there is a $\xi_0 \neq 0$ such that the equation $M(\xi_0, \zeta) = 0$ has a real root, and this contradicts the ellipticity of M. Since the vectors ξ and $-\xi$ can be joined to each other by an arc not passing through 0 $(n - 1 \geq 2)$, the number of roots of the equations $M(\xi, \zeta) = 0$ and $M(-\xi, \zeta) = 0$ lying in the upper half-plane coincide. But since $M(-\xi, \zeta) = (-1)^r \times M(\xi, -\zeta)$, $M(-\xi, \zeta) = 0$ has as many roots in the upper half-plane as $M(\xi, \zeta) = 0$ has in the lower. Thus $M(\xi, \zeta) = 0$ has the same number m of roots in the upper and lower half-planes. It also follows that $r = 2m$.

The proof of the last assertion in the lemma is left to the reader.

Corollary. *For $n \geq 3$, an elliptic expression $L(x, D)$ is regularly elliptic, and in particular it has even order (for a fixed point x on Γ, it is necessary to set $M = L(x, D)$ and transfer the origin of the coordinates to x and direct the y-axis along $\nu(x)$).*

Lemma 3.3. *Consider forms $P_u(\xi, \eta)$ and $Q_u(\xi, \eta)$ given by*

$$P_u(\xi, \eta) = \sum_{\nu=m+1}^{2m} \sum_{s=m}^{\nu-1} \sum_{|\tau|=2m-\nu} b_{\tau\nu} \xi^\tau \eta^{\nu-s-1} |\xi|^{s+1} w_{u,s}(\xi),\quad w_{u,s}(\xi) = \frac{\widehat{(\partial_n^s u)}(\xi)}{|\xi|^{s+1}}; \tag{3.23}$$

with $Q_u(\xi, \eta)$ defined in the same way with $b_{\tau\nu}$ replaced by $c_{\tau\nu}$. Suppose that

$$\int_{-\infty}^{\infty} |\widetilde{(Mu)}(\xi, \eta)|^2 \, d\eta \geq \int_{-\infty}^{\infty} \Big| M(\xi, \eta) \tilde{u}(\xi, \eta) + \sum_{s=m}^{2m-1} v_s(\xi, \eta) w_{u,s}(\xi) \Big|^2 d\eta$$

$$+ \sum_{j,k=m}^{2m-1} H_{jk}(\xi) w_{u,k}(\xi) \overline{w_{u,j}(\xi)} \quad (\xi \in E_{n-1},\ \xi \neq 0), \tag{3.24}$$

for each $u \in C^{2m}(G \cup \Gamma; (\mathrm{bd})_S, 0)$, where $v_s(\xi, \eta)$ is a function, continuous for

$\xi \neq 0$ and homogeneous of degree $2m$ for $(\xi, \eta) \in E_n$, and $H_{jk}(\xi)$ $(\xi \in E_{n-1}, \xi \neq 0)$ is continuous and homogeneous of degree $4m+1$, and moreover for each $\xi \neq 0$ the matrix $\| H_{jk}(\xi) \|_m^{2m-1}$ is strictly positive definite. Then the estimate (3.20) *holds.*

Proof. As was already explained, it is sufficient to establish the inequality (3.21). We set $J_\alpha(\xi, \eta) = |M(\xi, \eta)|^2 - \alpha |N(\xi, \eta)|^2$, where α is some real number which will be chosen later. Taking (3.24) and (3.19) into account, it is easy to obtain for fixed $\xi \neq 0$

$$\int_{-\infty}^{\infty} \{ |\widetilde{(Mu)}(\xi, \eta)|^2 - \alpha |\widetilde{(Nu)}(\xi, \eta)|^2 \} d\eta \geqslant \sum_{j,k=m}^{2m-1} H_{jk} w_{u,k} \overline{w_{u,j}}$$

$$+ \int_{-\infty}^{\infty} \{ \| M | \tilde{u} + \Sigma |^2 - \alpha | N\tilde{u} + Q_u |^2 \} d\eta = \sum_{j,k=m}^{2m-1} H_{jk} w_{u,k} \overline{w_{u,j}}$$

$$+ \int_{-\infty}^{\infty} \{ J_\alpha |\tilde{u}|^2 + 2\mathrm{Re}[(|M| \overline{\Sigma} - \alpha N \overline{Q}_u)\tilde{u}] + |\Sigma|^2 - \alpha |Q_u|^2 \} d\eta$$

$$= \sum_{j,k=m}^{2m-1} H_{jk} w_{u,k} \overline{w_{u,j}} + \int_{-\infty}^{\infty} J_\alpha \left| \tilde{u} + J_\alpha^{-1} \left(|M| \Sigma - \alpha \overline{N} Q_u \right) \right|^2 d\eta$$

$$- \alpha \int_{-\infty}^{\infty} J_\alpha^{-1} \| M | Q_u - N \Sigma |^2 d\eta \qquad (u \in C^{2m}(G \cup \Gamma; (\mathrm{bd})_S, 0)). \qquad (3.25)$$

We show that the last two integrals actually exist for $\alpha \in (-\infty, \epsilon]$, where ϵ is so small that $|N(\xi, \eta)|^2 \leq |M(\xi, \eta)|^2 / 3\epsilon$ $((\xi, \eta) \in E_n)$. For $\alpha \leq 0$, they obviously converge by the convergence of the integral in the left part of (3.25). For $\alpha \in (0, \epsilon)$ we may write $|N(\xi, \eta)|^2 \leq |M(\xi, \eta)|^2 / 3\alpha$ $((\xi, \eta) \in E_n)$, and hence $J_\alpha = |M|^2 - \alpha |N|^2 \geq \frac{1}{2}(|M|^2 + \alpha |N|^2) = \frac{1}{2} J_{-\alpha}$. Therefore,

$$\int_{-\infty}^{\infty} J_\alpha^{-1} \| M | Q_u - N \Sigma |^2 d\eta \leqslant 2 \int_{-\infty}^{\infty} J_{-\alpha}^{-1} \| M | Q_u - N \Sigma |^2 d\eta < \infty,$$

i.e. the last integral in (3.25) converges. As before, since the integral on the left side of (3.25) converges, the next to the last integral converges. Thus, the validity of the conversion in (3.25) is established.

From (3.25) we obtain

$$\int_{-\infty}^{\infty} \{|\widetilde{(Mu)}(\xi, \eta)|^2 - \alpha\,|\widetilde{(Nu)}(\xi, \eta)|^2\} d\eta \geqslant \sum_{j,k=m}^{2m-1} H_{jk}(\xi)\, w_{u,k}(\xi)\, \overline{w_{u,j}(\xi)}$$

$$- \alpha \int_{-\infty}^{\infty} \frac{\left| M(\xi, \eta)\, |\, Q_u(\xi, \eta) - N(\xi, \eta) \sum_{s=m}^{2m-1} v_s(\xi, \eta)\, w_{u,s}(\xi) \right|^2}{|M(\xi, \eta)|^2 - \alpha\, |N(\xi, \eta)|^2}\, d\eta$$

$$(0 \leqslant \alpha \leqslant \varepsilon). \qquad (3.26)$$

By (3.23) $Q_u(\xi, \eta)$, like $\Sigma_{s=m}^{2m-1} v_s(\xi, \eta)\, w_{u,s}(\xi)$, is a linear combination of $W_{u,m}(\xi), \cdots, W_{u,2m-1}(\xi)$ with coefficients which are functions of the point (ξ, η) homogeneous of degree $2m$. Therefore, squaring the numerator in the last integral in (3.26), we bring this integral into the form of a positive definite form $\Sigma_{j,k=m}^{2m-1} L_{jk}(\xi, \alpha)\, w_{u,k}(\xi)\, w_{u,j}(\xi)$, where $L_{jk}(\xi, \alpha)$ is continuous with respect to $(\xi, \alpha) \in E_{n-1} \times [0, \epsilon]$, $\xi \neq 0$, and homogeneous with respect to ξ of degree $4m+1$ (the degree of homogeneity is raised from $4m$ to $4m+1$ by integration with respect to η).[1)]

Consider the function of the $n+m-1$-dimensional vector $(\xi, \omega) = (\xi_1, \cdots, \xi_{n-1}, \omega_m, \cdots, \omega_{2m-1}) \in E_{n-1} \times C_m$, $\xi \neq 0$, and $\alpha \in [0, \epsilon]$

$$\varphi(\xi, \omega, \alpha) = \frac{\sum_{j,k=m}^{2m-1} L_{jk}(\xi, \alpha)\, \omega_k \overline{\omega_j}}{\sum_{j,k=m}^{2m-1} H_{jk}(\xi)\, \omega_k \overline{\omega_j}}. \qquad (3.27)$$

Since the denominator vanishes only for $\omega = 0$ and the numerator is continuous for $\xi \neq 0$, $\phi(\xi, \omega, \alpha)$ is continuous with respect to $(\xi, \omega, \alpha) \in ((E_{n-1} \times C_m) \setminus (\{\xi = 0\} \cup \{\omega = 0\})) \times [0, \epsilon]$. Moreover, ϕ has the homogeneity property

$$\varphi(\lambda\xi, \omega, \alpha) = \varphi(\xi, \mu\omega, \alpha) = \varphi(\xi, \omega, \alpha).$$

Hence we easily conclude that $\phi(\xi, \omega, \alpha)$ is uniformly bounded with respect to all variables (a simple fact of a similar type was used in the proof of the previous

---

1) It is easy to see that if $H(\xi, \eta)$ is homogeneous of degree t with respect to (ξ, η), then the function $F(\xi) = \int_{-\infty}^{\infty} H(\xi, \eta)\, d\eta$ (if the integral exists) is homogeneous of degree $t+1$ with respect to ξ.

lemma). Thus from (3.27) it follows that for some $\delta > 0$

$$\sum_{j,k=m}^{2m-1} H_{jk}(\xi)\,\omega_k\overline{\omega_j} \geqslant \delta \sum_{j,k=m}^{2m-1} L_{jk}(\xi,\ \alpha)\,\omega_k\overline{\omega_j}\ (\xi \in E_{n-1},\ \omega \in C_m,\ \alpha \in [0,\ \varepsilon]).$$

In particular, setting $\omega_j = w_{u,j}(\xi)$ $(j = m, \cdots, 2m-1)$, we obtain the estimate

$$\sum_{j,k=m}^{2m-1} H_{jk}(\xi)\, w_{u,k}(\xi)\,\overline{w_{u,j}(\xi)} \geqslant \delta \int_{-\infty}^{\infty} \ldots d\eta\ (\xi \in E_{n-1}).$$

We choose α in (3.26) so small that $\alpha \leq \delta$, and then the right side of (3.26) becomes nonnegative and we arrive at (3.21). The lemma follows.

We proceed to the proof of Lemma 3.1; according to Lemma 3.3, it is sufficient to establish the inequality (3.24). Suppose $u \in C^{2m}(G \cup \Gamma;\ (\mathrm{bd})_S,\ 0)$, $\epsilon > 0$; set

$$l_{u,j}(\xi) = \varepsilon\,|\,\xi\,|^{2m-j} \int_{-\infty}^{\infty} \frac{\eta^j \overline{P_u(\xi,\ \eta)}}{M(\xi,\ \eta)}\, d\eta$$

$$(j = 0,\ \ldots,\ m-1;\ \xi \in E_{n-1},\ \xi \neq 0) \tag{3.28}$$

(the integral exists, since the numerator is equal to $O(|\eta|^{2m-2})$ as $|\eta| \to \infty$, and the denominator grows like $|\eta|^{2m}$). Taking into account that $\widetilde{\partial_n^j u} = \eta^j \tilde{u}\ (j = 0, \cdots, m-1)$ (see (3.16), $\widehat{\partial_n^s u} = 0$ for $s = 0, \cdots, m-1$), with the help of (3.17) we obtain

$$|\widetilde{(Mu)}(\xi,\ \eta)|^2 - 2\mathrm{Re} \sum_{j=0}^{m-1} l_{u,j}(\xi)\,|\,\xi\,|^{2m-j-1}\, \widetilde{\partial_n^j u} = |\,M\tilde{u} + P_u\,|^2$$

$$- 2\mathrm{Re} \sum_{j=0}^{m-1} l_{u,j}\,|\,\xi\,|^{2m-j-1}\eta^j \tilde{u} = \Big|\,M\tilde{u} + P_u - \frac{1}{M}\sum_{j=0}^{m-1} \overline{l_{u,j}}\,|\,\xi\,|^{2m-j-1}\eta^j\Big|^2$$

$$+ 2\mathrm{Re} \sum_{j=0}^{m-1} l_{u,j}\,|\,\xi\,|^{2m-j-1}\, \frac{\eta^j P_u}{M} - \left|\frac{1}{M}\sum_{j=0}^{m-1} l_{u,j}\,|\,\xi\,|^{2m-j-1}\eta^j\right|^2. \tag{3.29}$$

Integrate the identity (3.29) with respect to $\eta \in (-\infty,\ \infty)$. Since

$i\int_{-\infty}^{\infty}\widetilde{\partial_n^j u}\,d\eta=\pi\widehat{\partial_n^j u}=0 \quad (j=0,\ldots,m-1)$,[1] we find

$$\int_{-\infty}^{\infty}|\widetilde{Mu}|^2\,d\eta=\int_{-\infty}^{\infty}\Big|M\tilde{u}+\sum_{s=m}^{2m-1}v_s(\xi,\eta)\,w_{u,s}(\xi)\Big|^2 d\eta+\frac{2}{\varepsilon|\xi|}\sum_{j=0}^{m-1}|l_{u,j}|^2$$
$$-\int_{-\infty}^{\infty}\left|\frac{1}{M}\sum_{j=0}^{m-1}l_{u,j}\,|\xi|^{2m-j-1}\eta^j\right|^2 d\eta. \tag{3.30}$$

Here $v_s(\xi,\eta)$ is a function which is obtained by substitution of the expression (3.23); it is important to notice that it is continuous (for $\xi\neq 0$) and homogeneous of degree $2m$. The integrals in the right side of (3.30) exist: this follows from the convergence of the last integral, in which the integrand is equal to $O(1/|\eta|^{2m+2})$.

Consider the function of the $n+m-1$-dimensional vector $(\xi,\lambda)=(\xi_1,\ldots,\xi_{n-1},\lambda_0,\ldots,\lambda_{m-1})\in E_{n-1}\times C_m$

$$\varphi(\xi,\lambda)=\frac{\displaystyle\int_{-\infty}^{\infty}\left|\frac{1}{M(\xi,\eta)}\sum_{j=0}^{m-1}\lambda_j|\xi|^{2m-j-1}\eta^j\right|^2 d\eta}{\displaystyle\frac{2}{|\xi|}\sum_{j=0}^{m-1}|\lambda_j|^2} \tag{3.31}$$

It is continuous with respect to $(\xi,\lambda)\in(E_{n-1}\times C_m)\setminus(\{\xi=0\}\cup\{\lambda=0\})$ and homogeneous of degree zero with respect to each of the variables; therefore it is

---

1) We have the general identity

$$i\int_{-\infty}^{\infty}\tilde{u}(\xi,\eta)\,d\eta=\pi\hat{u}(\xi)\ (u\in C^1(G\cup\Gamma;\,0)).$$

In fact, if $v(y)$ is piecewise differentiable and summable over $(-\infty,\infty)$, then by the formula for the inverse Fourier transform we can write

$$v(z+0)+v(z-0)=\frac{1}{\pi}\int_{-\infty}^{\infty}e^{i\eta z}\int_{-\infty}^{\infty}e^{-i\eta y}v(y)\,dy\,d\eta\ (-\infty<z<\infty).$$

Setting $z=0$ here and

$$v(y)=\frac{1}{\sqrt{(2\pi)^n}}\int_G e^{-i\langle\xi,x\rangle}u(x,y)\,dx$$

and observing that $iv(+0)=\hat{u}$, $v(-0)=0$, we obtain the desired relation.

bounded. We therefore obtain an estimate of the numerator in (3.31) in terms of the denominator; this permits us to choose ϵ in (3.30) so small that the difference of the last two expressions is estimated below by $(\partial/|\xi|)\,\Sigma_{j=0}^{m-1}|l_{u,j}|^2$ for some $\delta>0$. Expressing $l_{u,j}(\xi)$ as a linear combination of $w_{u,s}(\xi)$, from (3.30) we obtain

$$\int_{-\infty}^{\infty}|\widetilde{Mu}|^2 d\eta \geqslant \int_{-\infty}^{\infty}\Big|\widetilde{Mu}+\sum_{s=m}^{2m-1}v_s(\xi,\eta)\,w_{u,s}(\xi)\Big|^2 d\eta + \sum_{j,k=m}^{2m-1}H_{jk}(\xi)\,w_{u,j}(\xi)\overline{w_{u,k}(\xi)}. \tag{3.32}$$

$$\sum_{j,k=m}^{2m-1}H_{jk}(\xi)\,w_{u,k}(\xi)\overline{w_{u,j}(\xi)}=\frac{\delta}{|\xi|}\sum_{j=0}^{m-1}|l_{u,j}(\xi)|^2 \quad (\xi\in E_{n-1},\ \xi\neq 0). \tag{3.33}$$

By (3.28), the coefficients $H_{jk}(\xi)$ are continuous for $\xi\neq 0$ and homogeneous of degree $4m+1$. It is also clear that the matrix $\|H_{jk}(\xi)\|_m^{2m-1}$ is positive definite. If it is strictly positive definite, then (3.32) asserts that the hypotheses of Lemma 3.3 are satisfied, and therefore Lemma 3.1 follows.

Thus, suppose that for some fixed $\xi_0\neq 0$ there exists a vector $(\omega_m,\cdots,\omega_{2m-1})$ such that $\Sigma_{j,k=m}^{2m=1}H_{jk}(\xi_0)\,\omega_k\overline{\omega_j}=0$; we must show that $\omega_m=\cdots=\omega_{2m-1}=0$. Choose $u\in C^{2m}(G\cup\Gamma;(\mathrm{bd})_S,0)$ such that $w_{u,j}(\xi_0)=\omega_j$ $(j=m,\cdots,2m-1)$; it follows from (3.33) and (3.28) that

$$\int_{-\infty}^{\infty}\frac{\eta^j P_u(\xi_0,\eta)}{M(\xi_0,\eta)}\,d\eta=0 \quad (j=0,\ldots,m-1). \tag{3.34}$$

By Lemma 3.2, $M(\xi_0,\eta)$ can be represented as the product of two polynomials of degree m: $M(\xi_0,\eta)=P_+(\eta)\,P_-(\eta)$, where P_+ (P_-) is constructed from the roots of the equation $M(\xi_0,\zeta)=0$ in the upper (lower) half-plane. On cancelling common factors we can write $P_u/M=P_u^*/P_+^*P_-^*$, where the polynomials $P_+^*(\eta)$ and $P_-^*(\eta)$ are relatively prime to $P_u^*(\xi_0,\eta)$. Since $P_u(\xi_0,\eta)$ has degree $m-1$, and $P_+(\eta)$ and $P_-(\eta)$ degree m, P_+^* and P_-^* are not constants. It now follows from (3.34) that for any polynomial $Q(\eta)$ of degree $<m$,

$$\int_{-\infty}^{\infty}\frac{Q(\eta)\,P_u^*(\xi_0,\eta)}{P_+^*(\eta)\,P_-^*(\eta)}\,d\eta=0.$$

In particular, we can take $Q(\eta) = P^*_+(\eta)(\eta - \alpha)^{-1}$, where α is a zero of $P^*_+(\eta)$. Using the integral with this choice, we find

$$0 = \int_{-\infty}^{\infty} \frac{Q(\eta) P^*_u(\xi_0, \eta)}{P^*_+(\eta) P^*_-(\eta)} d\eta = \int_{-\infty}^{\infty} \frac{P^*_u(\xi_0, \eta)}{(\eta - \alpha) P^*_-(\eta)} d\eta = 2\pi i \frac{P^*_u(\xi_0, \alpha)}{P^*_-(\alpha)},$$

i.e. $P^*_u(\xi_0, \alpha) = 0$. Since α is not a zero of $P^*_u(\xi_0, \eta)$, the last equation can hold only if $P^*_u(\xi_0, \eta) \equiv 0$, i.e. if $P_u(\xi_0, \eta) \equiv 0$.

We show that this implies the relation $w_{u,m}(\xi_0) = \cdots = w_{u,2m-1}(\xi_0) = 0$. In fact, we can write (3.23) in the form

$$P_u(\xi, \eta) = \sum_{j=0}^{m-1} \left(\sum_{\nu=j+m+1}^{2m} \sum_{|\tau|=2m-\nu} b_{\tau\nu} \xi^\tau |\xi|^{\nu-j} w_{u,\nu-j-1}(\xi) \right) \eta^j.$$

Since $P_u(\xi_0, \eta) \equiv 0$, it follows that

$$\sum_{\nu=j+m+1}^{2m} \sum_{|\tau|=2m-\nu} b_{\tau\nu} \xi_0^\tau |\xi_0|^{\nu-j} w_{u,\nu-j-1}(\xi_0) = 0 \ (j = 0, \ldots, m-1). \quad (3.35)$$

On setting $j = m - 1$ here, we obtain $b_{0,2m} |\xi_0|^{m+1} w_{u,m}(\xi_0) = 0$, and hence $w_{u,m}(\xi_0) = 0$ since $b_{0,2m} \neq 0$. Using this equation and setting $j = m - 2$ in (3.35), we obtain $w_{u,m+1}(\xi_0) = 0$, etc. Thus $(\omega_m, \cdots, \omega_{2m-1}) = (w_{u,m}(\xi_0), \cdots$ $\cdots, w_{u,2m-1}(\xi_0)) = 0$ as required.

Lemma 3.1 follows for $s = 0$.

7. We prove Lemma 3.1 for $s > 0$. We establish this general fact: *the estimate* (3.2) *for any* $s > 0$ *follows from the same estimate for* $s = 0$. As we have already seen, it is sufficient to prove this for functions $u \in C^{2m+s}(G \cup \Gamma; (\mathrm{bd})_S, 0)$. Suppose $u \in C^{2m+1}(G \cup \Gamma; (\mathrm{bd})_S, 0)$ and set

$$u^h_k(x) = h^{-1}(u(x_1, \cdots, x_{k-1}, x_k + h, x_{k+1}, \cdots, x_n) - u(x_1, \cdots, x_n))$$

$(k = 1, \cdots, n-1)$; we assume that the origin of the coordinates is located at x_0 and that x_n is in a direction orthogonal to S. It is clear that $u^h_k \in C^{2m+1}(G \cup \Gamma; (\mathrm{bd})_S, 0)$ for $|h|$ sufficiently small, and therefore the inequality (3.2) with $s = 0$ holds for u^h_k: $\| Mu^h_k \|_0 \geq C \| u^h_k \|_{2m}$. Since M has constant coefficients, $Mu^h_k = (Mu)^h_k$ and $\| (Mu)^h_k \|_0 \geq C \| u^h_k \|_{2m}$. Passing to the limit here with $h \to 0$, we obtain

$$\| Mu \|_1 \geqslant \| D_k Mu \|_0 \geqslant C \| D_k u \|_{2m} \quad (k = 1, \ldots, n-1). \tag{3.36}$$

We establish a similar estimate for D_n. To this end we write

$$b_{(0,\ldots,0,2m)} D_n^{2m} u = Mu - \sum_{|\tau|+\nu=2m,\ \nu<2m} b_{(\tau,\nu)} D^\tau D_n^\nu u;$$

it follows from the ellipticity of M that $b_{(0,\cdots,0,2m)} \neq 0$. Differentiating this identity with respect to x_n, we find that

$$b_{(0,\ldots,0,2m)} D_n^{2m+1} u = D_n Mu - \sum_{|\tau|+\nu=2m,\ \nu<2m} b_{(\tau,\nu)} D^\tau D_n D_n^\nu u.$$

Hence

$$C_1 \| D_n^{2m+1} u \|_0 \leqslant \| D_n Mu \|_0 + C_2 \sum_{|\tau|+\nu=2m,\ \nu<2m} \| D^\tau D_n^{\nu+1} u \|_0$$

$$(C_1 = | b_{(0,\ldots,0,2m)} |). \tag{3.37}$$

Since each expression $D^\tau D_n^{\nu+1} u$ contains a maximum of $2m$ derivatives with respect to x_n, $\| D^\tau D_n^{\nu+1} u \|_0 \leq \| D_k u \|_{2m}$ for some $k = 0, \cdots, n-1$ depending on (τ, ν). Thus from (3.37) and (3.36) we can conclude that

$$C_1 \| D_n^{2m+1} u \|_0 \leqslant \| D_n Mu \|_0 + C_3 \sum_{k=0}^{n-1} \| D_k u \|_{2m} \leqslant \| D_n Mu \|_0$$

$$+ \frac{C_3}{C} \sum_{k=0}^{n-1} \| D_k Mu \|_0 \leqslant C_4 \| Mu \|_1.$$

From this and (3.36) we find that $\| Mu \|_1 \geq C_5 \sum_{k=0}^n \| D_k u \|_{2m} \geq C_6 \| u \|_{2m+1}$. Thus

$$\| Mu \|_1 \geqslant C_6 \| u \|_{2m+1} \quad (u \in C^{2m+1}(G \cup \Gamma;\ (\mathrm{bd})_S,\ 0)). \tag{3.38}$$

Repeating this argument with the estimates (3.2) ($s = 0$) and (3.38) interchanged, we arrive at (3.2) with $s = 2$, etc. Thus Lemma 3.1, and hence Theorem 3.1, are completely proved.

In conclusion, note that we have obtained the inequality (3.1) with the term $k \| u \|_0^2$. In subsection 4, we will obtain, from (3.1), for strongly elliptic expressions, the energy inequality in the usual form, without this term. For the case of general expressions see §6.

2. **Extension of the energy inequalities to the case of negative norms.** We obtain an important addition to the results of subsection 1. We use the same

notation as in that subsection.

Theorem 3.2. *Let* L *be a regularly elliptic expression of order* $2m$; $s = -m, \cdots, 0$. *Suppose that the coefficients* $a_\alpha(x) \in C^{\max(|\alpha|,|s|)}(G \cup \Gamma)$ *and that the boundary* Γ *is of class* $C^{2m+|s|}$. *Then if* $k \geq 0$ *is sufficiently large, we have the estimate*

$$\| Lu \|^2_{\mathring{W}_2^s(G)} + k \| u \|_0^2 \geqslant C \| u \|^2_{2m+s} \tag{3.39}$$

$$(C > 0;\ u \in \mathring{W}_2^m(G) \cap W_2^{2m}(G)).$$

(*Here* $\mathring{W}_2^s(G)$ *is the negative space constructed with respect to the positive space* $\mathring{W}_2^{|s|}(G)$ *and the zero space* $L_2(G)$.)

The proof is carried out along the lines of the proof of Theorem 3.1. Below we set $\sigma = -s$ ($\sigma = 0, \cdots, m$). We first state two lemmas, which will be proved later.

Lemma 3.4. *Let* $Mu = \sum_{|\alpha|=2m} b_\alpha D^\alpha u$ *be an expression with constant coefficients satisfying the hypotheses of Theorem* 3.2. *Then*

$$\| Mu \|_{\mathring{W}_2^{-\sigma}(G)} \geqslant C \| u \|_{2m-\sigma}\ (C > 0;\ u \in W_{2,0}^{2m}(G);\ \sigma = 0, \ldots, m). \tag{3.40}$$

Lemma 3.5. *In a region* G *as in Lemma* 3.1, *consider an expression* $Mu = \sum_{|\alpha|=2m} b_\alpha D^\alpha u$ *with constant coefficients satisfying the hypotheses of Theorem* 3.2. *Then*

$$\| Mu \|_{\mathring{W}_2^{-\sigma}(G)} \geqslant C \| u \|_{2m-\sigma}\ (C > 0;\ u \in W_2^{2m}(G;(\mathrm{bd})_S,\ 0);\ \sigma = 0, \ldots, m). \tag{3.41}$$

We show that the theorem follows from these lemmas by a pasting-together procedure similar to that outlined at the beginning of the previous proof. We first formulate three obvious assertions concerning the spaces $\mathring{W}_2^{-l}(G)$ ($l = 0, 1, \cdots$).[1)]

a) Suppose that $a(x) \in \underline{C^l(G \cup \Gamma)}$ and let A be the operator multiplication by $\bar{a}$ in $\mathring{W}_2^l(G)$: $(Au)(x) = \overline{a(x)}\ u(x)$ $(u \in \mathring{W}_2^l(G))$. Its norm is $\| A \| = \max_{x \in G\cup\Gamma,\ |\alpha| \leqslant l} |(D^\alpha a)(x)|$. The adjoint operator A^+, acting in $\mathring{W}_2^{-l}(G)$, is called the operator multiplication of generalized functions in $\mathring{W}_2^{-l}(G)$ by $a(x)$. Thus, in particular,

$$\| af \|_{\mathring{W}_2^{-l}(G)} \leqslant \max_{x \in G\cup\Gamma,\ |\alpha| \leqslant l} |(D^\alpha a)(x)| \cdot \| f \|_{\mathring{W}_2^{-l}(G)} (f \in L_2(G),\ a \in C^l(G \cup \Gamma)). \tag{3.42}$$

---

1) The first two facts hold for the spaces $W_2^{-l}(G)$; they are also easily paraphrased for general spaces $W_2'^{-l}(G)$.

b) Suppose that Γ is of class C^l. Let $x' = \phi(x)$ be an l-times continuously differentiable homeomorphism, mapping G into G'; then $(T_\phi u')(x) = u'(\phi(x))$ is a homeomorphism between $\overset{\circ}{W}{}_2^l(G)$ and $\overset{\circ}{W}{}_2^l(G')$. The adjoint operator T_ϕ^+ is a homeomorphism between $\overset{\circ}{W}{}_2^{-l}(G)$ and $\overset{\circ}{W}{}_2^{-l}(G')$, which coincides on $f \in L_2(G)$ with the operator $f(x) \to f(\phi^{-1}(x'))\,|dx/dx'|$, where $|dx/dx'|$ is the modulus of the Jacobian.

c) Let $G_1 \subseteq G_2$, $f \in L_2(G_2)$. Then

$$\|f\|_{\overset{\circ}{W}{}_2^{-l}(G_1)} \leqslant \|f\|_{\overset{\circ}{W}{}_2^{-l}(G_2)} \tag{3.43}$$

(this follows from the inequality $|(f, u)_{L_2(G_1)}| = |(f, u)_{L_2(G_2)}| \leqslant \|f\|_{\overset{\circ}{W}{}_2^{-l}(G_2)} \|u\|_{\overset{\circ}{W}{}_2^{l}(G_2)} = \|f\|_{\overset{\circ}{W}{}_2^{-l}(G_2)} \|u\|_{\overset{\circ}{W}{}_2^{l}(G_1)}$, which holds for $u \in C_0^\infty(G_1)$, extended by zero to G_2).

Lemma 3.6. *For any differential expression N of order r whose coefficients have the usual smoothness properties we have the estimate*

$$\|Nu\|_{\overset{\circ}{W}{}_2^{-l}(G)} \leqslant C\|u\|_{r-l} \quad (l = 0, \ldots, r;\ u \in W_2^r(G)). \tag{3.44}$$

Proof. Let $v \in C_0^\infty(G)$, $u \in W_2^l(G)$. Shifting l derivatives from u onto v, we obtain $(Nu, v)_0 = \sum_{|\alpha| \leq r-1, |\beta| \leq l} (c_{\alpha\beta}(x) D^\alpha u D^\beta v)_0$, for some coefficients $c_{\alpha\beta}$. Hence $|(Nu, v)_0| \leq C\|u\|_{r-l}\|v\|_{\overset{\circ}{l}}$. Passing to the limit, we conclude that the last inequality holds even for $v \in \overset{\circ}{W}{}_2^l(G)$; but then from this we obtain (3.44). The lemma follows.

We proceed to the proof of the theorem.

1°. Consider a point x_0 and regions G, G_0 as in Figure 2. By (3.41), applied to $M = L_c(x_0, D)$, we can write

$$\|L_c(x_0, D)u\|_{\overset{\circ}{W}{}_2^{-\sigma}(G_0)} \geqslant C_1\|u\|_{W_2^{2m-\sigma}(G_0)} \quad (C_1 > 0;\ u \in W_m^{2m}(G_0; (\mathrm{bd})_{S_0}, 0)). \tag{3.45}$$

For functions $u \in W_2^{2m}(G)$ vanishing in a neighborhood of the set $G_0 \backslash G$, we obtain by (3.43) and (3.44)

$$\|L(x, D)u\|_{\overset{\circ}{W}{}_2^{-\sigma}(G)} - \|L_c(x_0, D)u\|_{\overset{\circ}{W}{}_2^{-\sigma}(G_0)} \leqslant \|L(x, D)u\|_{\overset{\circ}{W}{}_2^{-\sigma}(G_0)}$$

$$- \|L_c(x_0, D)u\|_{\overset{\circ}{W}{}_2^{-\sigma}(G_0)} \leqslant \|L(x, D)u - L_c(x_0, D)u\|_{\overset{\circ}{W}{}_2^{-\sigma}(G_0)}$$

$$\leqslant \Big\|\sum_{|\alpha|=2m} [a_\alpha(x) - a_\alpha(x_0)]\, D^\alpha u\Big\|_{\overset{\circ}{W}{}_2^{-\sigma}(G_0)} + \Big\|\sum_{|\alpha| \leqslant 2m-1} a_\alpha(x) D^\alpha u\Big\|_{\overset{\circ}{W}{}_2^{-\sigma}(G_0)}$$

$$\leqslant \Big\|\sum_{|\alpha'|=\sigma, |\alpha''|=2m-\sigma} D^{\alpha'}([a_{(\alpha',\alpha'')}(x) - a_{(\alpha',\alpha'')}(x_0)]\, D^{\alpha''}u)\Big\|_{\overset{\circ}{W}{}_2^{-\sigma}(G_0)} +$$

$$+\Big\|\sum_{|\alpha|\leqslant 2m-1} c_\alpha(x)D^\alpha u\Big\|_{\mathring{W}_2^{-\sigma}(G_0)}+\Big\|\sum_{|\alpha|\leqslant 2m-1} a_\alpha(x)D^\alpha u\Big\|_{\mathring{W}_2^{-\sigma}(G_0)}$$

$$\leqslant \sum_{|\alpha'|=\sigma,\,|\alpha''|=2m-\sigma} \|[a_{(\alpha',\alpha'')}(x)-a_{(\alpha',\alpha'')}(x_0)]D^{\alpha''}u\|_{L_2(G)}+C_2\|u\|_{W_2^{2m-\sigma-1}(G)}. \tag{3.46}$$

It should be explained that here we have shifted the coefficients $[a_\alpha(x)-a_\alpha(x_0)]$ in the expression $\Sigma_{|\alpha|=2m}[a_\alpha(x)-a_\alpha(x_0)]\,D^\alpha u$ using σ derivatives, and this gives rise to the term $\Sigma_{|\alpha|\leq 2m-1}\,c_\alpha(x)\,D^\alpha u$. Taking into account the continuity of $a_{(\alpha',\alpha'')}(x)$ at the point x_0, the estimate $\|u\|_{W_2^{2m-\sigma-1}(G)}\leqslant d\|u\|_{W_2^{2m-\sigma}(G)}=d\|u\|_{W_2^{2m-\sigma}(G_0)}$ (d is the diameter of G), and the estimates (3.45), (3.46), we find that for sufficiently small d,

$$\|L(x,D)u\|_{\mathring{W}_2^{-\sigma}(G)}\geqslant C_3\|u\|_{2m-\sigma}\,(C_3>0;\ u\in W_2^{2m}(G;(\mathrm{bd})_S,0)). \tag{3.47}$$

In a similar manner using Lemma 3.4 we obtain an estimate of the type (3.47) on compact subsets of a small region G; now in (3.47) $u\in W_{2,0}^{2m}(G)$.

2′. The second step in the proof, derivation of an estimate of the type (3.47) near a curvilinear piece S of the boundary, is carried out by means of a change of variable similar to that used in the proof of Theorem 3.1. For this it is necessary to use assertion b) above with the choice of a homeomorphism $x'=\phi(x)$, which flattens the piece S, such that $dx/dx'=1$. Such a choice is possible if only G is a region whose boundary intersects every line parallel to the normal at x_0 in at most two points (see Figure 3); a region G of this form is sufficiently general to prove the theorem. Place the origin of the coordinates at the point x_0, and direct the axis Ox_n along the normal to Γ at this point. A homeomorphism of the region G onto the region G', as indicated in the diagram, is given by the formulas $x_i'=x_1,\cdots,x_{n-1}'=x_{n-1},\ x_n'=\phi_n(x_1,\cdots,x_n)$, where for fixed $x_1,\cdots,x_{n-1}$, $\phi_n(x_1,\cdots,x_n)$ maps a segment of the type $[a,b]$ into the segment $[a',b']$. That is, in a neighborhood of the point x_0, $x_1'=\phi_n(x_1,\cdots,x_n)=x_n-f(x_1,\cdots,x_{n-1})$ where $x_n=f(x_1,\cdots,x_{n-1})$ is the equation of S in the vicinity of x_0. Obviously $dx/dx'=1$ in G.

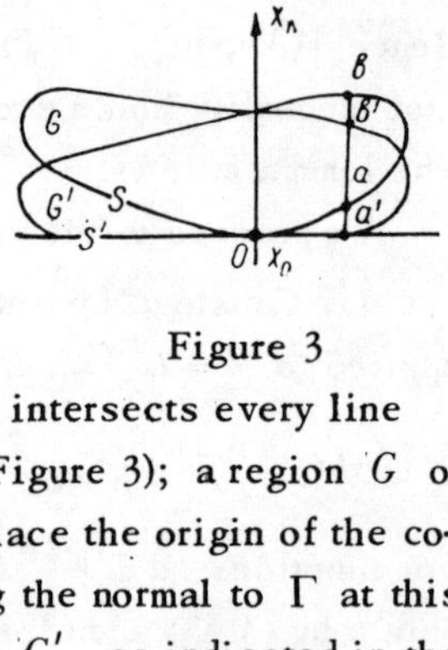

Figure 3

3′. Our derivation of an inequality similar to (3.9) is carried out using a decomposition of unity. Let this decomposition $1=\Sigma_{j=1}^N\chi_j(x)$ be chosen as in step 3 of the proof of Theorem 3.1. We will then have the estimate

$$\| L[\chi_j u] \|_{\mathring{W}_2^{-\sigma}(G)} \geqslant C \| \chi_j u \|_{2m-\sigma} \qquad (u \in \mathring{W}_2^m (G) \cap W_2^{2m} (G);\ j = 1, \ldots, N).$$

From this and (3.42) and (3.44) we obtain

$$\| u \|_{2m-\sigma}^2 = \left\| \sum_{j=1}^N \chi_j u \right\|_{2m-\sigma}^2 \leqslant C_1 \sum_{j=1}^N \| \chi_j u \|_{2m-\sigma}^2 \leqslant C_2 \sum_{j=1}^N \| L[\chi_j u] \|_{\mathring{W}_2^{-\sigma}(G)}^2$$

$$\leqslant C_3 \sum_{j=1}^N \| \chi_j L[u] \|_{\mathring{W}_2^{-\sigma}(G)}^2 + C_3 \sum_{j=1}^N \left\| \sum_{|\alpha| \leqslant 2m-1} c_{j\alpha}(x) D^\alpha u \right\|_{\mathring{W}_2^{-\sigma}(G)}^2$$

$$\leqslant C_4 \left(\| Lu \|_{\mathring{W}_2^{-\sigma}(G)}^2 + \| u \|_{2m-\sigma-1}^2 \right) \qquad (u \in \mathring{W}_2^m (G) \cap W_2^{2m} (G)). \quad (3.48)$$

4′. Since $2m - \sigma - 1 \geq 0$ in the norm $\| \cdot \|_{2m-\sigma-1}$, we can apply the Ehrling-Nirenberg inequality $\| u \|_{2m-\sigma-1}^2 \leq \epsilon \| u \|_{2m-\sigma}^2 + K(\epsilon) \| u \|_0^2$, which along with (3.48) implies (3.39).

6′. To complete the proof of the theorem, it remains to show that Lemmas 3.4 and 3.5 hold. First recall (see p. 62) that for $f \in L_2(G)$, $\| f \|_{\mathring{W}_2^{-\sigma}(G)}$ can be written in terms of the Fourier transform $\widetilde{f}(\xi)$:

$$\| f \|_{\mathring{W}_2^{-\sigma}(G)}^2 = \int_{E_n} \frac{| \widetilde{f}(\xi) |^2}{\Delta^2(\xi)} d\xi, \qquad \Delta(\xi) = \sqrt{\sum_{|\alpha| = \sigma} \xi^{2\alpha}},$$

$$\widetilde{f}(\xi) = \frac{1}{\sqrt{(2\pi)^n}} \int_G f(x) e^{-i\langle \xi, x \rangle} dx. \qquad (3.49)$$

Lemma 3.4 is established by elementary means: it is sufficient to prove (3.40) for finite functions $u \in C_0^{2m}(G)$; by (1.9), for these we have

$$\| Mu \|_{\mathring{W}_2^{-\sigma}(G)}^2 = \int_{E_n} |\widetilde{Mu}|^2 \Delta^{-2}(\xi)\, d\xi = \int_{E_n} |\widetilde{u}|^2 \left| \sum_{|\alpha| = 2m} b_\alpha \xi^\alpha \right|^2 \Delta^{-2}(\xi)\, d\xi.$$

Construct the function

$$\varphi(\xi) = \frac{\sum_{|\alpha| = 2m-\sigma} \xi^{2\alpha}}{\left| \sum_{|\alpha| = 2m} b_\alpha \xi^\alpha \right|^2 \Delta^{-2}(\xi)} \qquad (\xi \in E_n,\ \xi \neq 0).$$

It is continuous and homogeneous of degree zero, and therefore ϕ is bounded. Thus $|\Sigma_{|\alpha| = 2m} b_\alpha \xi^\alpha|^2 \Delta^{-2}(\xi)$ can be estimated below by the function

$C\,\Sigma_{|\alpha|=2m-\sigma}\xi^{2\alpha}$, and therefore by (1.8)

$$\|Mu\|^2_{\overset{\circ}{W}{}_2^{-\sigma}(G)} = \int_{E_n} |\tilde{u}|^2 \Big| \sum_{|\alpha|=2m} b_\alpha \xi^\alpha \Big|^2 \Delta^{-2}(\xi)\,d\xi \geqslant C \int_{E_n} |\tilde{u}|^2 \sum_{|\alpha|=2m-\sigma} \xi^{2\alpha}\,d\xi$$

$$= C \sum_{|\alpha|=2m-\sigma} \|D^\alpha u\|_0^2 \geqslant C_1 \|u\|^2_{2m-\sigma}.$$

The inequality (3.40) follows.

Lemma 3.5 is considerably more subtle; its proof is similar to the proof of Lemma 3.1 in the case $s = 0$ given above; we outline it. Below we use the same notation as in the earlier proof; in particular, M has the form (3.15); the function $\Delta(\xi)$ is now written $\Delta(\xi, \eta)$, where $\xi \in E_{n-1}$, $\eta \in E_1$. Let N be an arbitrary homogeneous differential expression of order $2m - \sigma$ with constant coefficients. For the proof of the inequality (3.41), it is sufficient to establish the estimate

$$\|Nu\|_0 \leqslant C \|Mu\|_{\overset{\circ}{W}{}_2^{-\sigma}(G)} \quad (C > 0;\ u \in C^{2m}(G \cup \Gamma;\ (\mathrm{bd})_S,\ 0)).$$

This estimate follows from the inequality

$$\int_{-\infty}^{\infty} |\widetilde{(Nu)}(\xi, \eta)|^2 d\eta \leqslant C^2 \int_{-\infty}^{\infty} |\widetilde{(Mu)}(\xi, \eta)|^2 \Delta^{-2}(\xi, \eta)\,d\eta$$

$$(\xi \in E_{n-1},\ u \in C^{2m}(G \cup \Gamma; (\mathrm{bd})_S,\ 0)) \tag{3.50}$$

–integrate (3.50) with respect to $\xi \in E_{n-1}$ and use the expression (3.49) for the norm $\|\cdot\|_{\overset{\circ}{W}{}_2^{-\sigma}(G)}$ and Parseval's equality. Thus we will prove (3.50).

We introduce the notation: $\widetilde{(Mu)}^*(\xi, \eta) = \widetilde{(Mu)}(\xi, \eta)\,\Delta^{-1}(\xi, \eta)$, $M^*(\xi, \eta) = M(\xi, \eta)\,\Delta^{-1}(\xi, \eta)$, $P^*_u(\xi, \eta) = P_u(\xi, \eta)\,\Delta^{-1}(\xi, \eta)$ $((\xi, \eta) \neq 0;\ u \in C^{2m}(G \cup \Gamma;\ (\mathrm{bd})_S,\ 0))$. From (3.17) it follows that

$$\widetilde{(Mu)}^*(\xi, \eta) = M^*(\xi, \eta)\,\tilde{u}(\xi, \eta) + P^*_u(\xi, \eta). \tag{3.51}$$

Let $Nu = \Sigma_{|\tau|+\nu=2m-\sigma}\, c_{\tau\nu}\partial^\tau \partial^\nu_n u$; similarly to (3.19) and (3.23) we find

$$\widetilde{(Nu)}(\xi, \eta) = N(\xi, \eta)\,\tilde{u}(\xi, \eta) + Q_u(\xi, \eta), \qquad N(\xi, \eta) = \sum_{|\tau|+\nu=2m-\sigma} c_{\tau\nu}\xi^\tau \eta^\nu,$$

$$Q_u(\xi, \eta) = \sum_{\nu=m+1}^{2m-\sigma} \sum_{s=m}^{\nu-1} \sum_{|\tau|=2m-\sigma-\nu} c_{\tau\nu}\xi^\tau \eta^{\nu-s-1} |\xi|^{s+1} w_{u,s}(\xi)$$

$$(u \in C^{2m}(G \cup \Gamma; (\mathrm{bd})_S,\ 0)) \tag{3.52}$$

(if $\sigma = m$, we assume $Q_u = 0$). Note that similarly to the estimate (3.22), we have $|N(\xi, \eta)| \le C|M^*(\xi, \eta)|$ ($(\xi, \eta) \in E_n$, $(\xi, \eta) \neq 0$). Furthermore, we have the following generalization of Lemma 3.3: *if for each* $u \in C^{2m}(G \cup \Gamma; (\mathrm{bd})_S, 0)$ *we have the inequality*

$$\int_{-\infty}^{\infty} |\widetilde{(Mu)}^*(\xi, \eta)|^2 d\eta \geqslant \int_{-\infty}^{\infty} \Big| |M^*(\xi, \eta)|^2 \tilde{u}(\xi, \eta) + \sum_{s=m}^{2m-1} v_s^*(\xi, \eta) w_{u,s}(\xi) \Big|^2 d\eta + \sum_{j,k=m}^{2m-1} H^*_{jk}(\xi) w_{u,k}(\xi) \overline{w_{u,j}(\xi)}$$

$$(\xi \in E_{n-1}, \ \xi \neq 0), \tag{3.53}$$

in which $v_s^*(\xi, \eta)$ *is continuous for* $\xi \neq 0$ *and homogeneous of degree* $2m - \sigma$ *as a function of* $(\xi, \eta) \in E_n$, $H^*_{jk}(\xi)$ $(\xi \in E_{n-1}, \xi \neq 0)$ *is continuous and homogeneous of degree* $4m - 2\sigma + 1$, *and moreover for each* $\xi \neq 0$ *the matrix* $\| H^*_{jk}(\xi) \|_m^{2m-1}$ *is strictly positive definite, then the estimate* (3.50) *holds.* The proof of this fact is hardly different from the proof of Lemma 3.3: it is necessary to use the representations (3.51) and (3.52) instead of (3.17) and (3.19), and observe that Q is now a linear form with respect to $w_{u,s}$ whose coefficients are continuous and homogeneous of degree $2m - \sigma$.

The proof of the inequality (3.53) is similar to the proof of (3.24); it is only necessary to set

$$l^*_{u,j}(\xi) = \varepsilon |\xi|^{2m-\sigma-j} \int_{-\infty}^{\infty} \frac{\eta^j \overline{P_u^*(\xi, \eta)}}{M^*(\xi, \eta)} d\eta = |\xi|^{-\sigma} l_{u,j}(\xi)$$

and transform not the expression (3.29), but

$$|\widetilde{(Mu)}^*(\xi, \eta)|^2 - 2 \operatorname{Re} \sum_{j=0}^{m-1} l^*_{u,j}(\xi) |\xi|^{2m-\sigma-j-1} \widetilde{\partial_n^j u}.$$

Lemma 3.5, and along with it Theorem 3.2, follow.

3. **The energy inequalities for other boundary conditions.** We generalize the results in the previous two subsections to a broad class of boundary conditions, corresponding to elliptic expressions considered in Theorems 3.1 and 3.2. This generalization is constructed according to the following scheme. Consider boundary conditions (bd), for which $W_2^{2m}(\mathrm{bd})$ consists of functions $u \in W_2^{2m}(G)$ satisfying equations $B_1(x, D)u = 0, \cdots, B_m(x, D)u = 0$, where the $B_j(x, D)$ are certain linear differential expressions of order $m_j < 2m$ defined on Γ (in the case

of null conditions, $B_1(x, D)\,u = u$, $B_2(x, D)\,u = \partial u/\partial\nu, \cdots, B_m(x, D)\,u = \partial^{m-1}u/\partial\nu^{m-1}$). With certain conditions on systems of boundary expressions B_j, we can generalize the inequality (3.1) as

$$\| L(x, D)\,u \|_s^2 + k\| u \|_0^2 + \sum_{j=1}^{m} \ll B_j(x, D)\,u \gg^2_{2m-m_j+s-\frac{1}{2}} \geqslant C\| u \|^2_{2m+s}$$

$$(C > 0;\ s = 0, 1, \ldots); \tag{3.54}$$

here $\ll\cdot\gg_k$ is some norm defined for functions given on Γ (the "boundary norm"). It is a remarkable fact that the relation (3.54) holds for any $u \in W_2^{2m}(G)$. If $u \in W_2^{2m}$(bd), i.e. $B_1 u = \cdots = B_m u = 0$, then (3.54) reduces to the usual form of the energy inequality. The proof of the estimate (3.54) is obtained by generalizing the arguments in the proof of Theorem 3.1. For this it is essential that it be established on functions which do not satisfy boundary conditions. For example, in the decomposition of unity $1 = \Sigma_{j=1}^{N}\chi_j$ we do not encounter the following difficulty: if $u \in W_2^{2m}$(bd), then $\chi_j u$ does not, in general, satisfy (bd) (see p. 146 below). As in the case of null boundary conditions, the inequality can also be generalized to negative $\|\cdot\|_s$.

The problem arises: what kind of boundary expressions $B_j(x, D)$ $(j = 1, \cdots, m)$ must we have in order to obtain an inequality (3.54) (in this case we say that $B_1, \cdots, B_m$ cover L). It turns out that the following localization principle holds: consider a fixed $x_0 \in \Gamma$ and the hyperplane $\tilde{\Gamma}$ to Γ at this point; let $\tilde{G}$ be the corresponding half-space lying on one side of $\tilde{\Gamma}$, and consider the expression $L(x_0, D)$ in this region, with the system of boundary expressions $B_1(x_0, D), \cdots$ $\cdots, B_m(x_0, D)$ on $\tilde{\Gamma}$; all coefficients here are constant. Suppose that the $B_j(x_0, D)$ are such that the inequality (3.54) holds, with x replaced by x_0, for functions $u \in C^\infty(\tilde{G})$ which vanish for large $|x|$. If this situation holds for each $x_0 \in \Gamma$, then the system $B_1(x, D), \cdots, B_m(x, D)$ covers $L(x, D)$.

The above mentioned scheme is awkward and will not be treated in detail now; however, the problems originating here will be treated more explicitly in §6. We now discuss the derivation of the ordinary energy inequalities (without boundary norms) for strongly elliptic expressions of the second order and boundary conditions of the type in the third boundary value problem. The proof is based on the method of integration by parts and is sufficiently brief. At the same time it should be pointed out that it does not serve as a model for general constructions.

Theorem 3.3. *Let L be a strongly elliptic expression of the second order.*

with the usual smoothness conditions on its coefficients; let the boundary Γ *be of class* C^2, *and suppose that the boundary condition* (bd) *is* $\partial u/\partial \mu + \sigma(x)\, u|_\Gamma = 0$, *where* $\sigma \in C^1(\Gamma)$. *Then it is possible to choose* $k \geq 0$ *so large that*

$$\| Lu \|_0^2 + k \| u \|_0^2 \geqslant C \| u \|_2^2 \qquad (C > 0,\ u \in W_2^2(\mathrm{bd})). \tag{3.55}$$

Proof. Suppose that we have proven

Lemma 3.7. *Consider an elliptic expression* $Mu = \Sigma_{j,k=1}^n b_{jk} D_j D_k u$ *with constant coefficients in a region* G *as in Lemma* 3.1. *Let* $W_2^2(G;\ (\mathrm{bd})_S,\ 0)$ *denote the class of functions in* $W_2^2(G)$ *satisfying* $\partial u/\partial \mu + \sigma(x)\, u = 0$ *on* $S (\sigma \in C^1(S))$ *and vanishing in a neighborhood of* $\Gamma \setminus S$. *Then*

$$\| Mu \|_0^2 + k \| u \|_0^2 \geqslant C \| u \|_2^2 \qquad (C > 0;\ u \in W_2^2(G;(\mathrm{bd})_S,\ 0)). \tag{3.56}$$

The theorem follows from this lemma in about the same way as Theorem 3.1 follows from Lemma 3.1. We give an outline of it.

1″. As before, we can obtain the estimate

$$\| L(x, D)\, u \|_0 \geqslant C \| u \|_2 \qquad (C > 0;\ u \in W_2^2(G;(\mathrm{bd})_S,\ 0)) \tag{3.57}$$

for a region G with sufficiently small diameter d. In fact, for functions $u' \in W_2^2(G;\ (\mathrm{bd})_S,\ 0)'$, where $W_2^2(G;\ (\mathrm{bd})_S,\ 0)'$ is constructed with respect to $L(x_0, D)$ instead of $L(x, D)$, the inequality (3.57) is proved exactly as before. Then we need only observe that every function in $W_2^2(G;\ (\mathrm{bd})_S,\ 0)$ can be approximated in the metric of $W_2^2(G)$ by functions in $W_2^2(G;\ (\mathrm{bd})_S,\ 0)'$ for $d \to 0$.

2″. The inequality (3.57) implies a similar inequality in the case when S is twice continuously differentiable, and not only when S is a plane piece of the boundary of a region G of small diameter.

In fact, let $x' = \phi(x)$ be a twice continuously differentiable homeomorphism in E_n which maps $G \cup \Gamma$ onto $G' \cup \Gamma'$ and S onto the plane piece S' of the boundary Γ'. The induced mapping $(T_\phi u')(x) = u'(\phi(x))$ is a homeomorphism between $W_2^2(G')$ and $W_2^2(G)$. It is not difficult to see that T_ϕ is a homeomorphism between $W_2^2(G';\ (\mathrm{bd})_S',\ 0)$ and $W_2^2(G;\ (\mathrm{bd})_S,\ 0)$, where $(\mathrm{bd})_S'$ is a boundary condition on S' of the form $\partial u/\partial \mu' + \sigma'(x')\, u = 0$ (μ' is the co-normal for L' on S', $\sigma' \in C^1(\Gamma')$ is some function). For the proof, we show first how the unit normal $\nu(x)$ to S can be expressed in terms of the unit normal $\nu'(x')$ to S'. Let $f'(x') = 0$ be the equation of the plane piece S'; then $f(x) = f'(\phi(x)) = 0$

is the equation for S; $f \in C^2$. Therefore

$$\nu_k(x) = \alpha(x)\frac{\partial f}{\partial x_k} = \alpha(x)\sum_{q=1}^{n}\frac{\partial f'}{\partial x'_q}\frac{\partial x'_q}{\partial x_k} = \beta(x')\sum_{q=1}^{n}\nu'_q(x')\frac{\partial x'_q}{\partial x_k} \qquad (x' = \varphi^{-1}(x)), \tag{3.58}$$

Where α and β are some positive factors in C^1 which appear from the normalization of vectors normal to the unit vector. We now relate derivatives with respect to the co-normals $\mu(x)$ for L and $\mu'(x')$ for L'. By the first of the equations in (3.6), (3.58), and (3.7), we obtain

$$\frac{\partial u}{\partial \mu} = \frac{1}{|B\nu|}\sum_{j,k=1}^{n} b_{jk}(x)\,\nu_k(x)\frac{\partial u}{\partial x_j} = \frac{\beta(x')}{|B\nu|}\sum_{p,q=1}^{n}\left(\sum_{j,k=1}^{n} b_{jk}(x)\frac{\partial x'_p}{\partial x_j}\frac{\partial x'_q}{\partial x_k}\right)\nu'_q(x')\frac{\partial u}{\partial x'_p}$$

$$= \frac{\beta(x')}{|B\nu|}\sum_{p,q=1}^{n} b'_{pq}(x')\,\nu'_q(x')\frac{\partial u}{\partial x'_p} = \gamma(x')\frac{\partial T_{\varphi}^{-1}u}{\partial \mu'}, \tag{3.59}$$

where $\gamma \in C^1(\Gamma')$ is a factor arising from normalization. It follows from (3.59) that if u satisfies the condition $\partial u/\partial\mu + \sigma(x)\,u\,|_S = 0$, then $T_{\phi}^{-1}u$ satisfies the condition $\partial T_{\phi}^{-1}/\partial\mu' + \sigma'(x')\,T_{\phi}^{-1}u|_{S'} = 0$. It is clear from this connection that T_{ϕ} is a homeomorphism between $W_2^2(G'; (\mathrm{bd})'_S, 0)$ and $W_2^2(G; (\mathrm{bd})_S, 0)$. The proof is now completed exactly as before.

3″.–4″. The passage to an estimate over all of G is similar to that in the previous proof and uses a decomposition of unity $1 = \Sigma_{j=1}^N \chi_j$; it is only necessary to construct χ_j near Γ so that from the inclusion $u \in W_2^2$ (bd) follows the inclusion $\chi_j u \in W_2^2$ (bd). For this it is sufficient to choose $\chi_j(x)$ by means of constants in neighborhoods of Γ in the direction of the co-normals $\mu(x)$ $(x \in \Gamma)$. It is easy to see that this construction is possible since by the ellipticity of L, the co-normals are nontangential.

5″. We prove Lemma 3.7; for this we somewhat modify our earlier arguments. The identity (3.10) survives, but the last term in it, i.e. the term (3.11), now reduces to zero. We transform it, integrating by parts over S, and take into account the boundary condition $-\sigma u = \partial u/\partial\mu = (1/|B\nu|)\,\Sigma_{j=1}^n b_{jn} D_j$,

$$I_M = -\int_S \left(\sum_{k,p,q=1}^{n} b_{nk}\bar{b}_{pq}D_k u\cdot D_p D_q \bar{u} - \sum_{j,k,q=1}^{n} b_{jk}\bar{b}_{nq}D_k u\cdot D_j D_q \bar{u}\right) dx =$$

$$= -\int_S \left(\sum_{\substack{k,p,q=1\\p\neq n}}^n b_{nk}\bar{b}_{pq} D_k u \cdot D_p D_q \bar{u} - \sum_{\substack{j,k,q=1\\j\neq n}}^n b_{jk}\bar{b}_{nq} D_k u \cdot D_j D_q \bar{u} \right) dx$$

$$= -2\,\mathrm{Re} \int_S \sum_{\substack{k,p,q=1\\p\neq n}}^n b_{nk}\bar{b}_{pq} D_k u \cdot D_p D_q \bar{u}\, dx$$

$$= 2\,|B\nu|\,\mathrm{Re} \int_S \sum_{\substack{p,q=1\\p\neq n}}^n \sigma u \bar{b}_{pq} D_p D_q \bar{u}\, dx = -2\,|B\nu|\,\mathrm{Re} \int_S \sum_{\substack{p,q=1\\p\neq n}}^n \bar{b}_{pq} D_p (\sigma u) \cdot D_q \bar{u}\, dx.$$

Extending σ smoothly into G, and taking into account the inequality $\int_S |u|^2\, dx \leq C \| u \|_0 \| u \|_1$ and the Ehrling-Nirenberg inequality, we further obtain

$$|I_M| \leqslant C_1 \sum_{\substack{p,q=1\\p\neq n}}^n \int_S |D_p(\sigma u) \cdot D_q \bar{u}|\, dx$$

$$\leqslant C_1 \sum_{\substack{p,q=1\\p\neq n}}^n \left(\int_S |D_p(\sigma u)|^2 dx \int_S |D_q \bar{u}|^2\, dx \right)^{\frac{1}{2}} \leqslant C_2 \| u \|_1 \| u \|_2$$

$$\leqslant \frac{C_2^2 \delta^2}{2} \| u \|_2^2 + \frac{1}{2\delta^2} \| u \|_1^2 \leqslant \left(\frac{C_2^2 \delta^2}{2} + \frac{\eta}{2\delta^2} \right) \| u \|_2^2 + \frac{K(\eta)}{2\delta^2} \| u \|_0^2.$$

Choose first $\delta > 0$, and then $\eta > 0$, sufficiently small; then for any $\epsilon > 0$ we obtain the inequality $|I_M| \leq \epsilon \| u \|_2^2 + K_1(\epsilon) \| u \|_0^2$. Thus

$$\| Mu \|_0^2 = \int_G \sum_{j,k,p,q=1}^n b_{jk}\bar{b}_{pq} D_k D_p \bar{u} \cdot D_j D_q \bar{u}\, dx + I_M,$$

$$|I_M| \leqslant \varepsilon \| u \|_2^2 + K_1(\varepsilon) \| u \|_0^2 \quad (K_1(\varepsilon) > 0,\ u \in \mathring{W}_2^2(G; (\mathrm{bd})_S, 0)). \tag{3.60}$$

Similar inequalities can be written for $\| \overline{M} u \|_0^2$, $\| (\mathrm{Re}\, M)\, u \|_0^2$ (the bar denotes passage to complex conjugates in the coefficients of M); for the corresponding terms $I_{\overline{M}}$, $I_{\mathrm{Re}\, M}$ we then have estimates of the type (3.60). Using these relations and the equation

$$\int_G \sum_{j,k,p,q=1}^n b_{jk}\bar{b}_{pq} D_k D_p u \cdot D_j D_q \bar{u}\, dx = \int_G \sum_{j,k,p,q=1}^n \bar{b}_{jk} b_{pq} D_k D_p u \cdot D_j D_q \bar{u}\, dx,$$

we may write

$$\| Mu \|_0^2 = \frac{1}{2} (\| Mu \|_0^2 + \| \overline{M}u \|_0^2) + \frac{1}{2} (I_M - I_{\overline{M}}) \geq \frac{1}{4} (\| Mu \|_0 + \| \overline{M}u \|_0)^2$$

$$+ \frac{1}{2} (I_M - I_{\overline{M}}) \geq \left\| \frac{1}{2} (M + \overline{M}) u \right\|_0^2 + \frac{1}{2} (I_M - I_{\overline{M}}) = \| (\mathrm{Re}\, M) u \|_0^2$$

$$+ \frac{1}{2} (I_M - I_{\overline{M}}) = \int_G \sum_{j,k,p,q=1}^{n} (\mathrm{Re}\, b_{jk}) (\mathrm{Re}\, b_{pq}) D_k D_p u \cdot D_j D_q \bar{u}\, dx$$

$$+ \frac{1}{2} (I_M - I_{\overline{M}}) + I_{\mathrm{Re}\, M}. \tag{3.61}$$

The integral in the right side is estimated below by $C \| u \|_2^2$, as before; the remaining terms in this side are estimated above by the expression $\epsilon \| u \|_2^2 + K_2(\epsilon) \| u \|_0^2$ $(K_2(\epsilon) > 0)$. Thus for $\epsilon > 0$ sufficiently small, $\| Mu \|_0^2 \geq (C - \epsilon) \| u \|_2^2 - K_2(\epsilon) \| u \|_0^2$, which proves (3.56). Lemma 3.7, and along with it Theorem 3.3, follow.

4. Existence of smooth solutions for strongly elliptic equations. Method of extension by a parameter. Theorems 3.1 and 3.3 present the possibility of proving the existence of solutions for boundary value problems having a degree of smoothness equal to the order of the equation. We now achieve this by a simpler device, called the method of extension by a parameter, in the case of strongly elliptic expressions and simple boundary conditions. The general method will be presented in §6.

From Theorems 3.1 and 3.3 follows:

Corollary 3.1. *Let L be a strongly elliptic expression of order $2m$ satisfying all the assumptions in Theorem 3.1 for $s = 0$. Then one can always choose $k \geq 0$ so large that*

$$\| Lu + ku \|_0 \geq C \| u \|_{2m} \qquad (C > 0;\ u \in \overset{\circ}{W}{}_2^m(G) \cap W_2^{2m}(G)). \tag{3.62}$$

Similarly, if for a strongly elliptic expression of the second order the hypotheses of Theorem 3.3 are satisfied and the coefficients $p_j(x)$ appearing in connection with (2.4) are real, then for a corresponding choice of $k \geq 0$ and $C > 0$ the estimate (3.62) holds for functions $u \in W_2^2(\mathrm{bd})$ where (bd) has the form $\partial u/\partial \mu + \sigma(x) u |_\Gamma = 0$ $(\sigma \in C^2(\Gamma))$.

In the inequality (3.62), the constants k and C do not depend on the concrete form of the coefficients $a_\alpha(x)$ of the expression L and the function $\sigma(x)$, but only on $\max_{x \in G \cup \Gamma, |\beta| \leq |\alpha|} | D^\beta a_\alpha(x) |$ $(0 \leq |\alpha| \leq r)$,[1] *the number $\epsilon > 0$ in the*

1) And even on the maximum of the modulus of fewer derivatives. See p. 122.

estimates (1.3), *and the maximum on* Γ *of the modulus of the function* $\sigma(x)$ *and its derivative.*

Proof. We establish the first assertion. Let $k = k_1 + k_2$ $(k_1, k_2 \geq 0)$ and choose k_1 so large that $\operatorname{Re}(M_{k_1}u, u)_0 \geq C_1 \| u \|_m^2 \geq 0$ $(u \in \overset{\circ}{W}{}_2^m(G) \cap W_2^{2m}(G))$, where $M_{k_1} = L + k_1 E$ (see Theorem 1.1). For these u,

$$\| Lu + ku \|_0^2 = (M_{k_1}u + k_2 u, M_{k_1}u + k_2 u)_0 = \| M_{k_1}u \|_0^2$$

$$+ k_2 2\operatorname{Re}(M_{k_1}u, u)_0 + k_2^2 \| u \|_0^2 \geqslant \| M_{k_1}u \|_0^2 + k_2^2 \| u \|_0^2. \tag{3.63}$$

Choosing k_2 so large that the right side of (3.63) is $\geq C_2 \| u \|_{2m}^2$ (see (3.1)), we arrive at (3.62).

To prove the second assertion, we need only repeat the previous calculation. We remark that the realization of the inequality $\operatorname{Re}(M_{k_1}u, u)_0 \geq C_1 \| u \|_1^2 \geq 0$ $(u \in W_2^2(\mathrm{bd}))$ for sufficiently large $k_1 \geq 0$ follows from the discussion in §2.3, where such an inequality is obtained for adjoint expressions and conditions.

The third assertion is easily established by analyzing the proofs of Theorems 3.1 and 3.3 and the two arguments above.

We see from the proofs that for larger k the inequality (3.62) remains valid.

Theorem 3.4. *Let* L *be a strongly elliptic expression of order* $2m$ *whose coefficients have the usual smoothness properties;* Γ *is assumed to be of class* C^{2m}. *Consider the boundary value problem with zero boundary conditions:*

$$Lu = f \in L_2(G), \qquad D^\alpha u|_\Gamma = 0 \qquad (|\alpha| \leqslant m - 1). \tag{3.64}$$

If the coefficients of the expression are sufficiently positive, this problem has a $2m$*-smooth solution for any* $f \in L_2(G)$; *i.e. there is a* $u \in \overset{\circ}{W}{}_2^m(G) \cap W_2^{2m}(G)$ *such that* $Lu = f$. *Furthermore, the transformation* $u \to Lu$ $(u \in W_2^{2m}(\mathrm{bd}) = \overset{\circ}{W}{}_2^m(G) \cap W_2^{2m}(G)$, $Lu \in L_2(G))$ (*i.e.* 0-*strong operator problems*) *is a homeomorphism between* $W_2^{2m}(\mathrm{bd})$ *and all of* $L_2(G)$.

Let L *be an expression of second order as above, having in addition real coefficients* $p_j(x)$ *in its representation* (2.4), *and consider the problem*

$$Lu = f \in L_2(G), \qquad \left. \frac{\partial u}{\partial \mu} + \sigma(x) u \right|_\Gamma = 0 \qquad (\sigma \in C^1(\Gamma)); \tag{3.65}$$

with Γ *of class* C^2. *The previous conclusions remain valid for the problem* (3.65).

As a preliminary we establish a general lemma.

Lemma 3.8. *Let E' and E'' be two complete Banach spaces; let A_0 and A_1 be continuous linear operators acting from E' to E'', and suppose that A_0 is a homeomorphism between E' and E''. Suppose that there exists a family B_t of continuous operators acting from E' to E'', depending continuously on $t \in [0, 1]$ (with respect to the operator norm), joining A_0 and A_1 (i.e. $B_0 = A_0$, $B_1 = A_1$), and such that*

$$\| B_t u \|_{E''} \geqslant \delta \| u \|_{E'} \qquad (u \in E') \tag{3.66}$$

where $\delta > 0$ does not depend on t. Then A_1 is a homeomorphism between E' and E''.

Proof. By the uniform continuity of B_t with respect to t, we can find an $\eta > 0$ such that $\| B_{t'} - B_{t''} \| < \delta$ when $| t' - t'' | < \eta$. We now show that if B_{t_0} is a homeomorphism between E' and E'', then so is B_t whenever $| t - t_0 | < \eta$. We have $B_t = B_{t_0} - (B_{t_0} - B_t)$, and hence $B_{t_0}^{-1} B_t = E - B_{t_0}^{-1}(B_{t_0} - B_t)$. By (3.66) the norm of the operator $B_{t_0}^{-1}$ is $\leq 1/\delta$, and therefore the norm of the operator $B_{t_0}^{-1}(B_{t_0} - B_t)$ acting in E' is $\leq \| B_{t_0}^{-1} \| \, \| B_{t_0} - B_t \| \leq (1/\delta) \cdot \delta = 1$. It follows that the operator $B_{t_0}^{-1} B_t$ in E' has a continuous inverse $(B_{t_0}^{-1} B_t)^{-1}$; but then $(B_{t_0}^{-1} B_t)^{-1} B_{t_0}^{-1}$ is a continuous inverse to B_t. The existence of B_t^{-1} means that B_t effects a homeomorphism.

It is obvious how to complete the proof of the lemma: arrange the points $t_0 = 0, t_1, \cdots, t_{N-1}, t_N = 1$ in $[0, 1]$ with a distance less than η between them. Since $B_{t_0} = A_0$ is a homeomorphism, then step-by-step $B_{t_1}, B_{t_2}, \cdots$ are homeomorphisms. As the result we find that $A_1 = B_{t_N}$ is a homeomorphism.

Proof of the theorem for the problem (3.64). We restrict attention to the case when G is the sphere $|x| < 1$ in n-dimensional space, since a mapping of G onto this sphere which is $2m$ times continuously differentiable will reduce the problem to this case (see step 2 of the proof of Theorem 3.1).[1] Let $E' = W_2^{2m}(\text{bd}) = \overset{\circ}{W}{}_2^m(G) \cap W_2^{2m}(G)$ (E' is topologized by the metric of $W_2^{2m}(G)$) and $E'' = L_2(G)$. Define a family of differential expressions by setting $L_t = tL + (1-t)(-\Delta)^m + kE$, where $t \in [0, 1]$, $k \geq 0$; L_t is strongly elliptic. The transformation $u \longrightarrow L_t u \; (u \in E')$ provides the operator B_t, which acts continuously

---

1) We can thus prove the theorem only for regions G which admit such a mapping. For the general case, it is necessary to use Theorem 4.6 below (the proof of the latter uses Theorem 3.4 only for regions G under consideration).

from E' to E'' and depends continuously on t. According to Corollary 3.1, k may be chosen so large that L_t satisfies (3.62), and moreover by the last assertion the choice may be made so that the inequality holds at the same time for all $t \in [0, 1]$. Since $L_1 = L + kE$, $L_0 = (-\Delta)^m + kE$, to prove the theorem (with the expression $L + kE$) it is sufficient to show that $u \longrightarrow ((-\Delta)^m + kE)\, u$ is a homeomorphism between $\overset{\circ}{W}{}_2^m(G) \cap W_2^{2m}(G)$ and $L_2(G)$. For this it remains only to show that $((-\Delta)^m + kE)\,(\overset{\circ}{W}{}_2^m(G) \cap W_2^{2m}(G))$ is dense in $L_2(G)$; this clearly follows from the well-known circumstance that for the sphere in the problem, $(-\Delta)^m u + ku = f$, $D^\alpha u\,|_\Gamma = 0$ $(|\alpha| \leq m-1)$ has a solution in $C^{2m}(G \cup \Gamma)$ for $f \in C^1(G \cup \Gamma)$. Thus the theorem follows for null boundary conditions.

We outline the proof in the case of the problem (3.65). As before, we reduce the problem to the region G consisting of the unit sphere $|x| < 1$, and introduce the differential expression $L_t = tL + (1-t)\,(-\Delta) + kE$; let $\mu_t(x)$ denote the corresponding unit co-normal ($\mu_0(x)$ is the unit normal). The situation is now complicated by the fact that the subspace $W_2^2(\text{bd})_t$ consists of the functions in $W_2^2(G)$ satisfying the condition $\partial u/\partial \mu_t + \sigma(x)\, u\,|_\Gamma = 0$, which varies with $t \in [0, 1]$, and therefore Lemma 3.8 cannot be applied directly. We show that it is possible to define a homeomorphism F_t of $W_2^2(G)$ with itself, mapping $W_2^2(\text{bd})_0$ into $W_2^2(\text{bd})_t$ and depending continuously on $t \in [0, 1]$ with respect to the operator norm. According to the discussion in step 2 of the proof of Theorem 3.1, a twice continuously differentiable homeomorphism $x' = \phi(x)$ of the sphere $|x| < 1$ onto itself induces a homeomorphism $(T_\phi u)(x) = u(\phi(x))$ of the space $W_2^2(G)$ onto itself. We choose $\phi = \phi_t$ in a special way, requiring that it leave every point on the sphere $\Gamma(|x| = 1)$ fixed, that it map each diameter intersecting the sphere at y, z into a curve directed along $\mu_t(y)$ and $\mu_t(z)$ respectively, and that near y, $|\phi_t(x) - \phi_t(y)| = |x - y|$ and similarly near t. Since $\mu_t(x)$ has a nontangential direction for each $x \in \Gamma$, such a construction is possible. It is also clear that $\phi_t(x)$ can always be extended to a band about Γ (where it can be defined by means of the vector $\mu_t(x)$) inside the sphere, such that the function defining this mapping depends continuously along with its first two derivatives on t. What is the same thing, in $W_2^2(G)$ the operator T_ϕ depends continuously in norm on $t \in [0, 1]$. We set $F_t = T_{\phi_t}^{-1}$; this operator has the required properties since if $\partial u/\partial \mu_0 + \sigma(x)\, u\,|_\Gamma = 0$, then on Γ, $\partial F_t u/\partial \mu_t = \partial u(x)/\partial \mu_0 = -\sigma(x)\, u(x) = -\sigma(x)\,(F_t u)(x)$.

Now let $E' = W_2^2(\text{bd})_0$, $E'' = L_2(G)$, and $B_t = L_t F_t u$ $(u \in E',\ B_t u \in E'')$. The operators act continuously from E' to E''. For $k \geq 0$ sufficiently large, we have

$\|(L_t + kE)v\|_0 \geq C\|v\|_2$ ($v \in W_2^2(\mathrm{bd})_t$; $k \geq 0$ and C may be chosen independent of t) by Corollary 3.1. By the invertibility of F_t, this gives the estimate (3.66). It is also easy to verify that B_t depends continuously in norm on $t \in [0, 1]$. The operator B_0 effects a homeomorphism between $W_2^2(\mathrm{bd})_0$ and $L_2(G)$, and so, according to Lemma 3.8, $B_1 = (L + kE)\,F_1$ is a similar homeomorphism. In other words, $u \longrightarrow (L + kE)\,u$ is a homeomorphism between $W_2^2(\mathrm{bd})$ and $L_2(G)$. The theorem follows.

5. **Eigenvalue problems.** We prove the following important companion to Theorem 2.3.

Theorem 3.5. *Let L be a strongly elliptic expression of order $2m$ whose coefficients have the usual smoothness properties; Γ piecewise smooth. Consider the problem*

$$Lu - \lambda u = f \in L_2(G), \qquad u \in (\mathrm{bd}), \tag{3.67}$$

where (bd) *has the form* a) $D^\alpha u|_\Gamma = 0$ ($|\alpha| \leq m - 1$) *or* b) $\partial u/\partial\mu + \sigma(x)\,u|_\Gamma = 0$ ($m = 1$; $\sigma \in C^1(\Gamma)$; *in this case we further require that the coefficients* $p_j(x)$ *in the representation* (2.4) *are real and* Γ *is of class* C^1). $W_2^{2m}(\mathrm{bd})$ *denotes the subspace corresponding to condition* a) *or* b). *Clearly, Theorem* 2.3 *applies to the problem* (3.67).

If Γ is of class C^{2m}, then the solutions and eigenfunctions in Theorem 2.3 *belong, not to $W_2^m(G)$, but to $W_2^{2m}(\mathrm{bd})$ or $W_2^{2m}(\mathrm{bd})^+$; i.e. they are smooth. If λ is not an eigenvalue for the problem* (3.67), *then the transformation $u \longrightarrow (L - \lambda E)\,u$ is a homeomorphism between $W_2^{2m}(\mathrm{bd})$ and $L_2(G)$.*

We first show that under the assumptions of the theorem we have

Lemma 3.9. *Consider the operator $\Lambda'(\mathrm{bd})$ in $L_2(G)$ defined by the equation $\Lambda'(\mathrm{bd})\,u = Lu$, $u \in \mathfrak{D}(\Lambda'(\mathrm{bd})) = W_2^{2m}(\mathrm{bd})$. Then $(\Lambda'(\mathrm{bd}))^*$ has the form $(\Lambda'(\mathrm{bd}))^*\,u = L^+u$, $u \in \mathfrak{D}((\Lambda'(\mathrm{bd}))^*) = W_2^{2m}(\mathrm{bd})^+$. In other words, the adjoint to the* 0-*strong operator problem $Lu = f$, $u \in (\mathrm{bd})$, considered as an operator in $L_2(G)$, is the* 0-*strong operator adjoint problem.*

Since $(C - zE)^* = C^* - \bar{z}E$, it is sufficient to prove the lemma for $L + kE$ with sufficiently large $k \geq 0$. We assume at once that the coefficient of u is sufficiently positive that $u \longrightarrow Lu$ ($v \longrightarrow L^+v$) is a homeomorphism between $W_2^{2m}(\mathrm{bd})$ and $L_2(G)$ ($W_2^{2m}(\mathrm{bd})^+$ and $L_2(G)$). If $v \in W_2^{2m}(\mathrm{bd})^+$, then $(\Lambda'(\mathrm{bd})\,u, v)_0 = (Lu, v)_0 = (u, L^+v)_0$ ($u \in \mathfrak{D}(\Lambda'(\mathrm{bd}))$), where $L^+v \in L_2(G)$; i.e. $W_2^{2m}(\mathrm{bd})^+ \subseteq \mathfrak{D}((\Lambda'(\mathrm{bd}))^*)$ and $(\Lambda'(\mathrm{bd}))^*\,v = L^+v$. Conversely, suppose that $h \in L_2(G)$ and

$(\Lambda'(\mathrm{bd})\, u,\ h)_0 = (u,\ h^*)_0$ $(u \in \mathfrak{D}(\Lambda'(\mathrm{bd})))$ for some $h^* \in L_2(G)$. Let $v \in W_2^{2m}(\mathrm{bd})^+$ denote the solution to the equation $L^+ v = h^*$. We have

$$(Lu,\ h - v)_0 = (\Lambda'(\mathrm{bd})\, u,\ h)_0 - (Lu,\ v)_0 = (u,\ h^*)_0 - (u,\ L^+ v)_0 = 0$$
$$(u \in W_2^{2m}(\mathrm{bd})).$$

Since Lu exhausts all of $L_2(G)$, $h = v \in W_2^{2m}(\mathrm{bd})^+$. Thus $\mathfrak{D}((\Lambda'(\mathrm{bd}))^*) = W_2^{2m}(\mathrm{bd})^+$; the lemma follows.

In particular, it follows from the lemma that $\Lambda'(\mathrm{bd}) = \Lambda(\mathrm{bd})$.

Proof of theorem. We suppose that $k \geq 0$ is so large that the operator $(\Lambda(\mathrm{bd}) + kE)^{-1}$ exists and acts continuously from $L_2(G)$ into $W_2^{2m}(\mathrm{bd})$; by the imbedding theorem, it is a completely continuous operator from $L_2(G)$ to $L_2(G)$. Consequently, the Fredholm theory applies to the equation $\Lambda(\mathrm{bd})\, u - \lambda u = f$ (i.e. $Lu - \lambda u = f \in L_2(G)$, $u \in W_2^{2m}(\mathrm{bd})$); the equations for eigenfunctions have the form $Lu - \lambda u = 0$ $(u \in W_2^{2m}(\mathrm{bd}))$ and $L^+ v - \lambda v = 0$ $(v \in W_2^{2m}(\mathrm{bd})^+)$. Thus, independently of Theorems 2.3 and 3.5, Chapter II, we have shown that the problem (3.67), considered in terms of smooth solutions and eigenfunctions, is of Fredholm type. On the other hand, every eigenvalue in the sense of the above theorems is taken in the smooth sense and the corresponding subspace of eigenfunctions coincides with the subspace of generalized eigenfunctions. In fact, suppose, for example, that λ_0 is an eigenvalue in the sense of Theorem 2.3 for the problem $L^+ v - \lambda v = 0$, $v \in (\mathrm{bd})^+$, and let M (N) be the corresponding subspace of generalized (smooth) eigenfunctions. Obviously $N \subseteq M$. If $N \subset M$, then by normal solvability the problem $Lu - \bar{\lambda}_0 u = f$, $u \in (\mathrm{bd})$, has smooth solutions for a greater number of $f \in L_2(G)$ than it has generalized solutions, which is absurd. Thus $N = M$ as required. The reverse inclusion for the spectra is obvious. The first assertion of the theorem follows.

If λ is not in the point spectrum for the problem (3.67), then the operator $R_\lambda = (\Lambda(\mathrm{bd}) - \lambda E)^{-1}$ exists and acts continuously from $L_2(G)$ to $L_2(G)$. To prove the second assertion of the theorem we must show that R_λ acts continuously from $L_2(G)$ to $W_2^{2m}(\mathrm{bd})$. However, this follows from the Hilbert identity $R_\lambda = R_{-k} + (\lambda + k)\, R_{-k} R_\lambda$, which is satisfied by R_{-k} with k sufficiently large. The theorem follows.

Corollary 3.2. *Consider the problem* (3.64) *with fixed* L. *If the diameter of the region* G *is sufficiently small, then the assertions in the first part of Theorem* 3.4 *remain valid for this problem, i.e.* 0 *is not an eigenvalue for the problem* $Lu - \lambda u = f \in L_2(G)$, $u \in \mathring{W}_2^m(G) \cap W_2^{2m}(G)$.

This follows from Theorems 2.1 and 3.5.

6. **Significance of the smooth boundary.** We show by an example that *in the case of a piecewise smooth boundary a solution of the boundary value problem* (3.64) *with* $m = 1$ *does not necessarily belong to* $W_2^2(G)$ (*but it always does belong to* $W_2^1(G)$; *see* §2). In fact, in the plane consider the angular sector $G \cup \Gamma$: $0 \leq \rho \leq 1$, $0 \leq \phi \leq \kappa\pi$ ($0 < \kappa < 2$; ρ and ϕ are polar coordinates, radius-vector angle respectively), and in this sector the problem

$$-\Delta u = -u''_{\varrho\varrho} - \frac{1}{\varrho} u'_{\varrho} - \frac{1}{\varrho^2} u''_{\varphi\varphi} = \lambda u, \qquad u|_{\Gamma} = 0. \tag{3.68}$$

Membership in $W_2^2(G)$ of a solution to this problem is equivalent to the inequality

$$\int_0^{\varkappa\pi}\int_0^1 (|u''_{\varrho\varrho}|^2 + \ldots)\, \varrho\, d\varrho\, d\varphi < \infty, \tag{3.69}$$

where the dots denote the remaining derivatives with respect to ρ and ϕ of order ≤ 2. On separating the variables in (3.68), we find that nontrivial solutions exist for eigenvalues $\lambda_\nu > 0$ ($\nu = 1, 2, \cdots$) and are given by

$$u_{\nu l}(\varrho, \varphi) = \sin\frac{l}{\varkappa}\varphi \cdot J_p(\varrho\sqrt{\lambda_\nu}) \quad \left(p = \frac{l}{\varkappa};\ l = 1, 2, \ldots\right), \tag{3.70}$$

where J_p is the Bessel function. The numbers $\lambda_\nu > 0$ are determined from the condition $J_p(\sqrt{\lambda_\nu}) = 0$. As is well known, the functions $J_p(t)$ behave like t^p near $t = 0$, and therefore the solutions (3.70) do not satisfy (3.69) if $p = l/\kappa < 1$. Thus if the opening $\kappa > 1$, then the solutions (3.70) do not belong to $W_2^2(G)$ for $l = 1$. Let u_1 be one of these solutions, and let λ_1 be the corresponding value of the parameter λ; for arbitrary $k \geq 0$, the solution to the problem $-\Delta u + ku = f$ ($u|_\Gamma = 0$) with $f = (\lambda_1 + k)\, u_1 \in L_2(G)$ is equal to u_1 and does not belong to $W_2^2(G)$. This is the required example.

7. **Theorem on homeomorphisms.** We prove an important assertion which, roughly speaking, says that in the passage $u \to Lu$ for an elliptic expression L, the smoothness of u is reduced according to the order of L. We restrict attention to the case where L is strongly elliptic with null boundary conditions, since in this case we have in subsection 4 made a detailed analysis of the boundary value problem. Corresponding results for general elliptic L and (bd) will be presented in §6.10.

Theorem 3.6. *Consider a strongly elliptic expression* L *of order* $2m$ *and the problem* $Lu - \lambda u = f \in L_2(G)$, $u \in$ (bd): $D^\alpha u|_\Gamma = 0$ ($|\alpha| \leq m - 1$); *suppose that*

0 is not an eigenvalue. Let Λ_0 (bd) be the 0-strong operator constructed with respect to L and (bd), i.e. the operator defined by $u \to Lu$ from $\mathring{W}_2^m(G) \cap W_2^{2m}(G) = W_2^{2m}$ (bd) into $L_2(G)$. Assume that this operator (or a suitable restriction) acts in one of the following pairs of spaces:

$$1)\ \mathring{W}_2^m(G) \cap W_2^{2m+s}(G) \to W_2^s(G) \qquad (0 \leqslant s),$$

$$2)\ W_2^m(G) \cap W_2^{2m+s}(G) \to \mathring{W}_2^s(G) \qquad (-m \leqslant s \leqslant 0),$$

$$3)\ \mathring{W}_2^{2m+s}(G) \to W_2'^{s}(G) \qquad (-2m \leqslant s \leqslant -m),$$

$$4)\ W_2^{2m+s}(G) \to W_2'^{s}(G) \qquad (s \leqslant -2m). \tag{3.71}$$

Here $\mathring{W}_2^{-p}(G)$, $W_2'^{-p}(G)$, $p > 0$, are negative spaces constructed with respect to the zero space $L_2(G)$ and positive spaces $\mathring{W}_2^p(G)$, $W'^p_2(G) = \mathring{W}_2^m(G) \cap W_2^p(G)$ (all intersections with $W_2^p(G)$, $p \geq m$, are understood to be subspaces of $W_2^p(G)$).

The closure by continuity of Λ_0 (bd), considered in some pair (3.71), exists and is a homeomorphism between the spaces in this pair (for the first pair, the restriction of Λ_0 (bd), i.e. the s-strong operator Λ_s (bd), serves as this homeomorphism). We require the following smoothness: for the first and second pair, $a_\alpha(x) \in C^{\max(|\alpha|,|s|)}(G \cup \Gamma)$, the boundary Γ is of class $C^{2m+|s|}$; for the third and fourth, $a_\alpha(x) \in C^{|\alpha|+|2m+s|}(G \cup \Gamma)$, Γ is of class $C^{2m+|2m+s|}$ 1)

It is obvious from the statement of the theorem that as s varies from $+\infty$ to $-\infty$, boundary conditions become lost, and moreover the operator $u \to Lu$ can be extended to effect a homeomorphism. On first glance, such a situation is contradictory: for example, for $s = -2m$ the closure of the operator Λ_0 (bd) provides a homeomorphism between $L_2(G)$ and $W_2'^{-2m}(G)$, but it is not clear what happens to functions $u_0 \in W_2^{2m}(G)$ such that $Lu_0 = 0$. This phenomenon is explained by the fact that the space of images can contain a generalized function concentrated on Γ. Namely, u_0 is transformed into such a function.

We proceed to the proof of the theorem. It is based on Theorems 3.1, 3.2, and 3.5. In all that follows, if $s \leq 0$ we set $\sigma = -s \geq 0$. We first establish the following lemma.

---

1) In the case $s = -m$ the assertion concerning existence is already known; it follows easily from Theorem 2.1; the smoothness conditions can be relaxed in this case, as in Theorem 2.1.

Lemma 3.10. *Suppose that the hypotheses of Theorem 3.6 are satisfied. Then*

$$\| Lu \|_s \geqslant C_s \| u \|_{2m+s} \, (C_s > 0; \;\; u \in W_2'^{2m+s}(G); \;\; s = 0, 1, \ldots), \tag{3.72}$$

$$\| Lu \|_{\overset{\circ}{W}_2^{-\sigma}(G)} \geqslant C \| u \|_{2m-\sigma}$$

$$(C > 0; \; u \in W_2'^{2m}(G) = W_2^{2m}(\mathrm{bd}); \; \sigma = 0, \ldots, m). \tag{3.73}$$

Proof. If the inequality (3.72) is not satisfied, then for each $n = 1, 2, \cdots$ we can find $u_n \in W_2'^{2m+s}(G)$ such that $\| Lu_n \|_s < (1/n) \| u_n \|_{2m+s}$. Normalize u_n so that $\| u_n \|_{2m+s} = 1 (n = 1, 2, \cdots)$. Since the inclusion operator $W_2^{2m+s}(G) \to L_2(G)$ is completely continuous, we can choose a subsequence $u_{n'}$ of the sequence u_n such that $u_{n'} \to \phi$ in $L_2(G)$ for some function ϕ belonging to $L_2(G)$. Moreover, because of the inequality (3.1) and the relation $\| Lu_{n'} \|_s < 1/n' \to 0$, as $n', m' \to \infty$,

$$\| u_{n'} - u_{m'} \|_{2m+s}^2 \leqslant \frac{1}{C} (\| Lu_{n'} - Lu_{m'} \|_s^2 + k \| u_{n'} - u_{m'} \|_0^2) \to 0.$$

Thus $u_{n'}$ is fundamental in $W_2^{2m+s}(G)$, and therefore $\phi \in W_2^{2m+s}(G)$ and $u_{n'} \to \phi$ in the metric of this space. Since $u_{n'} \in W_2'^{2m+s}(G)$, and this set is closed in $W_2^{2m+s}(G)$, it follows that $\phi \in W_2'^{2m+s}(G)$ and moreover $\| \phi \|_{2m+s} = 1$. Furthermore, in the sense of convergence in $W_2^s(G)$, $L\phi = \lim Lu_{n'} = 0$, $\phi \in W_2'^{2m+s}(G) \subset W_2^{2m}(\mathrm{bd})$, $\phi \neq 0$. In other words, ϕ is a smooth eigenfunction for the problem $Lu - \lambda u = 0$, $u \in (\mathrm{bd})$, corresponding to the eigenvalue zero, in contradiction to the hypotheses of the lemma. The estimate (3.72) follows.

We prove the inequality (3.73). Repeating the previous argument and using the estimate (3.39) instead of (3.1), we can find a sequence $u_{n'} \in W_2^{2m}(\mathrm{bd})$, $\| u_{n'} \|_{2m-\sigma} = 1$, converging in the metric of $W_2^{2m-\sigma}(G)$ to a function $\phi \in W_2^{2m-\sigma}(G)$, $\phi \neq 0$; for this we have $\| Lu_{n'} \|_{\overset{\circ}{W}_2^{-\sigma}(G)} < 1/n' \to 0$. Since $u_{n'} \in W_2^{2m}(\mathrm{bd}) \subset W_2^m(G)$ and convergence in $W_2^{2m-\sigma}(G)$ implies convergence in $W_2^m(G)$, it follows that $\phi \in \overset{\circ}{W}{}_2^m(G)$. In addition, for any $v \in W_2^{2m}(\mathrm{bd})^+ = W_2^{2m}(\mathrm{bd})$ we have $(\phi, L^+ v)_0 = \lim (u_{n'}, L^+ v)_0 = \lim (Lu_{n'}, v)_0$. However, $W_2^{2m}(\mathrm{bd}) = \overset{\circ}{W}{}_2^m(G) \cap W_2^{2m}(G) \subset \overset{\circ}{W}{}_2^\sigma(G)$, and therefore

$$|(Lu_{n'}, v)_0| \leqslant \| Lu_{n'} \|_{\overset{\circ}{W}_2^{-\sigma}(G)} \| v \|_{\overset{\circ}{W}_2^{\sigma}(G)} < \frac{1}{n'} \| v \|_{\overset{\circ}{W}_2^{\sigma}(G)} \to 0.$$

Thus $(\phi, L^+ v)_0 = 0$ $(v \in W_2^{2m}(\mathrm{bd})^+)$, and moreover $\phi \in \overset{\circ}{W}{}_2^m(G)$, $\phi \neq 0$. This asserts that ϕ is a generalized eigenfunction (in the sense of the definition of Chapter II, §3.7) for the problem under consideration. By Theorem 3.5 $\phi \in W_2^{2m}(\text{bd})$, i.e. ϕ is a smooth eigenfunction, and this is absurd. The inequality (3.73), and along with it the lemma, follow.

Lemma 3.11. *Suppose that the hypotheses of Theorem 3.6 are satisfied. Then there exists a $k \geq 0$ such that for any $t \in [0, 1]$*

$$\|(tL + (1-t)(-\Delta)^m + kE)u\|_s \geqslant C_s \|u\|_{2m+s}$$
$$(C_s > 0;\ \ u \in W_2'^{2m+s}(G);\ \ s = 0, 1, \ldots). \tag{3.74}$$

Proof. The relation (3.74) holds for $s = 0$; this follows from Corollary 3.1 and the proof of Theorem 3.4.

Fix $s > 0$. Since the dependence of k and C in (3.1) on the coefficients of the expression L is like that described in the corollary, there exist $k \geq 0$ and $C > 0$ such that for any $t \in [0, 1]$

$$\|(tL + (1-t)(-\Delta)^m + kE)u\|_s^2 + k\|u\|_0^2 \geqslant C\|u\|_{2m+s}^2$$
$$(u \in W_2'^{2m+s}(G)).$$

Now suppose that (3.74) does not hold. Then for each $n = 1, 2, \cdots$ we can find $u_n \in W_2'^{2m+s}(G)$, $\|u_n\|_{2m+s} = 1$, and $t_n \in [0, 1]$, such that

$$\|(t_nL + (1-t_n)(-\Delta)^m + kE)u_n\|_s < \frac{1}{n}\ (n = 1, 2, \ldots).$$

By the complete continuity of the inclusion operator $W_2^{2m+s}(G) \to L_2(G)$ and the compactness of $[0, 1]$, we can choose subsequences $u_{n'}$ and $t_{n'}$ such that $u_{n'} \to \phi$ in $L_2(G)$ and $t_{n'} \to \tau$. Taking into account that $u_{n'} - u_{m'} \in W_2'^{2m+s}(G)$, we obtain

$$\|(t_{n'}L - (1-t_{n'})(-\Delta)^m + kE)u_{n'} - (t_{m'}L - (1-t_{m'})(-\Delta)^m$$
$$+ kE)u_{m'}\|_s + \|(t_{m'} - t_{n'})(L + (-\Delta)^m)u_{m'}\|_s$$
$$\geqslant \|(t_{n'}L - (1-t_{n'})(-\Delta)^m + kE)(u_{n'} - u_{m'})\|_s$$
$$\geqslant (C\|u_{n'} - u_{m'}\|_{2m+s}^2 - k\|u_{n'} - u_{m'}\|_0^2)^{\frac{1}{2}} \tag{3.75}$$

As $n', m' \to \infty$, the left side of (3.75) tends to zero: for the first term this follows from the construction of $u_{n'}$, and for the second, from the estimate

$$\|(t_{m'} - t_{n'})(L + (-\Delta)^m)u_m\|_s \leqslant C_1|t_{m'} - t_{n'}|\,\|u_{m'}\|_{2m+s} = C_1|t_{m'} - t_{n'}| \to 0.$$

Therefore the right side of (3.75) tends to zero. However, $\| u_{n'} - u_{m'} \|_0 \to 0$, and consequently $\| u_{n'} - u_{m'} \|_{2m+s} \to 0$. Thus $u_{n'}$ is fundamental in $W_2^{2m+s}(G)$, and therefore $\phi \in W_2'^{\,2m+s}(G)$, $\|\phi\|_{2m+s} = 1$, and $u_{n'} \to \phi$ in $W_2^{2m+s}(G)$. Because of this convergence and the convergence $t_{n'} \to \tau$, we have in $W_2^s(G)$:

$$(t_{n'}L + (1 - t_{n'})(-\Delta)^m + kE)\, u_{n'} \to (\tau L + (1 - \tau)(-\Delta)^m + kE)\, \varphi.$$

On the other hand, the left side of this relation tends to zero, and therefore $(\tau L + (1 - \tau)(-\Delta)^m + kE)\,\phi = 0$, in contradiction to (3.74) for $s = 0$. The lemma follows.

We proceed to the proof of the theorem. It is given in steps.

1. We show that the s-strong operator Λ_s (bd) is a homeomorphism between the spaces in the first pair. By the inequality (3.72) and the obvious reverse inequality, it is sufficient to show that $\Re(\Lambda_s(\mathrm{bd})) = W_2^s(G)$.

We first show that the range of the operator $u \to (L + kE)u$ $(u \in W_2'^{\,2m+s}(G))$ fills $W_2^s(G)$; here k is chosen according to Lemma 3.11.

The proof uses arguments similar to those given in the proof of Theorem 3.4: it is sufficient to consider the case where G is the sphere $|x| < 1$. We then apply Lemma 3.8, where B_t is taken to be the transformation $u \to (tL + (1 - t)(-\Delta)^m + kE)\, u$ from the space $E' = W_2'^{\,2m+s}(G)$ to the space $E'' = W_2^s(G)$. As is well known, in the sphere the problem $(-\Delta)^m u + ku = f$, $D^\alpha u|_\Gamma = 0$ $(|\alpha| \le m - 1)$ has sufficiently smooth solutions for sufficiently smooth f, and hence $\Re(B_0)$ is dense in E''; but then by virtue of (3.74), $\Re(B_0) = E''$ and the lemma applies.

Define an operator A in $W_2^s(G)$ by: $u \to (L + kE)\, u$, $\mathfrak{D}(A) = W_2'^{\,2m+s}(G)$ is dense in $W_2^s(G)$, $\Re(A) = W_2^s(G)$. By the imbedding theorem the operator A^{-1} is completely continuous, and therefore $(A^{-1} - \lambda E)^{-1}$ exists if and only if $\lambda \ne 0$ and different from the eigenvalues of the operator A^{-1}. If $(A^{-1} - \lambda E)^{-1}$ exists, then so does $(A - E/\lambda)^{-1}$ (it is easy to see that this is equal to $-\lambda A^{-1}(A^{-1} - \lambda E)^{-1}$), and therefore $\Re(A - E/\lambda) = W_2^s(G)$. Since $(A - E/\lambda)\, u = Lu = \Lambda_s(\mathrm{bd})\, u$ for $\lambda = 1/k$, it follows that $\Re(\Lambda_s(\mathrm{bd})) = W_2^s(G)$ if only this value of λ is not an eigenvalue for A^{-1}. Let $\phi \in W_2^s(G)$ $(\phi \ne 0)$ be such that $A^{-1}\phi = \phi/k$. Then $\phi \in W_2'^{\,2m+s}(G)$ and we obtain $\phi = (1/k) A\phi$, i.e. $0 = (A - kE)\,\phi = L\phi$, which contradicts the hypotheses of the theorem. Thus $\Re(\Lambda_s(\mathrm{bd})) = W_2^s(G)$ and our assertion follows.

2. We prove the theorem in the case of the fourth pair of spaces, assuming

that $a_\alpha(x)$ is sufficiently smooth. We have the estimates

$$C_1 \| u \|_{2m-\sigma} \leqslant \| Lu \|_{W_2'^{-\sigma}(G)} \leqslant C_2 \| u \|_{2m-\sigma}$$

$$(C_1, C_2 > 0;\ u \in W_2'^{2m}(G) = W_2^{2m}(\mathrm{bd})). \tag{3.76}$$

We establish the left inequality. Note that the conclusion of step 1 applies to the expression L^+, since the latter satisfies the hypotheses of the theorem (since the problem is of Fredholm type, 0 is not an eigenvalue; see Theorem 3.5, Chapter II). Thus the mapping $v \longrightarrow L^+v$ is a homeomorphism between $W_2'^{2m+t}(G)$ and $W_2^t(G)$, where $t = -2m + \sigma \geq 0$. Since $(\mathrm{bd})^+ = (\mathrm{bd})$, for $u \in W_2'^{2m}(G)$, $v \in W_2'^{\sigma}(G) = W_2'^{2m+t}(G)$ we have

$$|(u, L^+v)_0| = |(Lu, v)_0| \leqslant \| Lu \|_{W_2'^{-\sigma}(G)} \| v \|_{2m+t}$$

$$\leqslant C_3 \| Lu \|_{W_2'^{-\sigma}(G)} \| L^+v \|_t. \tag{3.77}$$

As v ranges over $W_2'^{\sigma}(G) = W_2'^{2m+t}(G)$, L^+v fills $W_2^t(G)$, and therefore the required estimate $\| u \|_{2m-\sigma} \leq C_3 \| Lu \|_{W_2'^{-\sigma}(G)}$ follows from (3.77).

We prove the right inequality in (3.76). As before, let $u \in W_2'^{2m}(G)$, $v \in W_2'^{\sigma}(G) = W_2'^{2m+t}(G)$; we have

$$|(Lu,v)_0| = |(u, L^+v)_0| \leqslant \| u \|_{-t} \| L^+v \|_t \leqslant C_2 \| u \|_{-t} \| v \|_{2m+t}.$$

Since v varies over all of $W_2'^{\sigma}(G)$ here, $\| Lu \|_{W_2'^{-\sigma}(G)} \leq C_2 \| u \|_{-t}$, as required.

Consider the operator $\Lambda_0(\mathrm{bd})$ as acting from the space $W_2^{2m-\sigma}(G)$ to $W_2'^{-\sigma}(G)$; $\mathfrak{D}(\Lambda_0(\mathrm{bd})) = W_2'^{2m}(G)$ is dense in $L_2(G)$ and moreover in $W_2^{2m-\sigma}(G)$ $(2m - \sigma \leq 0)$; $\mathfrak{R}(\Lambda_0(\mathrm{bd})) = L_2(G)$ is dense in $W_2'^{-\sigma}(G)$. Because of the inequalities (3.76), this operator may be closed, and the closure is obviously a homeomorphism between $W_2^{2m-\sigma}(G)$ and $W_2'^{-\sigma}(G)$.

We clarify the smoothness requirements imposed on a_α in the theorem. It is easy to see that if we impose on the coefficients b_α of the expression L^+ a smoothness restriction of the type $b_\alpha \in C^{\max(|\alpha|, p)}(G)$ $(p \geq 0)$, then for the realization of this restriction it is more natural to require the relations $a_\alpha \in C^{|\alpha|+p}(G)$. Above we used the fact that $v \longrightarrow L^+v$ is a homeomorphism between $W_2'^{2m+t}(G)$ and $W_2^t(G)$. According to step 1, the smoothness requirements are $b_\alpha \in C^{\max(|\alpha|, t)}(G)$, and hence $a_\alpha \in C^{|\alpha|+t}(G)$, $t = -2m + \sigma = |2m + s|$.

3. We prove the theorem for the second pair of spaces. We now also have the estimates (3.76) with $\| \cdot \|_{W_2'^{-\sigma}(G)}$ substituted for $\| \cdot \|_{\overset{\circ}{W}{}_2^{-\sigma}(G)}$. In fact, the left inequality has already been established (see (3.73)), and the right inequality follows from Lemma 3.6.

The proof is now completed as in step 2: consider Λ_0 (bd) as an operator from the space $W_2'^{2m-\sigma}(G)$ to the space $\overset{\circ}{W}_2^{-\sigma}(G)$; obviously $\mathfrak{D}(\Lambda_0(\mathrm{bd})) = W_2'^{2m}(G)$ is dense in $W_2'^{2m-\sigma}(G)$ and $\mathfrak{R}(\Lambda_0(\mathrm{bd})) = L_2(G)$ is dense in $\overset{\circ}{W}_2^{-\sigma}(G)$. Passing to the closure and using the analogue of (3.76), we obtain the required assertion.

4. We prove the theorem in the case of the third pair of spaces; for this we first establish the estimates (3.76) with $\sigma = m, \cdots, 2m$. Apply the result of step 3 to the expression L^+, which is obviously possible. We find that the closure of the operator $v \to L^+v$ ($v \in \overset{\circ}{W}_2'^{2m}(G)$) is a homeomorphism between the spaces $W_2'^{2m+t}(G)$ and $\overset{\circ}{W}_2^t(G)$, where $t = -2m + \sigma = -m, \cdots, 0$. If $u, v \in W_2'^{2m}(G)$, then since $W_2'^{2m}(G) \subseteq W_2'^{\sigma}(G)$,

$$\begin{aligned}|(u, L^+v)_0| = |(Lu, v)_0| &\leqslant \| Lu \|_{W_2'^{-\sigma}(G)} \| v \|_\sigma \\ &\leqslant C_3 \| Lu \|_{W_2'^{-\sigma}(G)} \| L^+v \|_{\overset{\circ}{W}_2^t(G)}. \end{aligned} \tag{3.78}$$

The functions L^+v are dense in $\overset{\circ}{W}_2^t(G)$, and $u \in W_2'^{2m}(G) \subset \overset{\circ}{W}_2^m(G) \subseteq \overset{\circ}{W}_2^{-t}(G)$. Therefore we conclude from (3.78) that $\| u \|_{-t} \leq C_3 \| Lu \|_{W_2'^{-\sigma}(G)}$, i.e. we obtain the left inequality in (3.76). For the right inequality we have

$$\begin{aligned}|(Lu, v)_0| &= |(u, L^+v)_0| \leqslant \| u \|_{-t} \| L^+v \|_{\overset{\circ}{W}_2^t(G)} \\ &\leqslant C_2 \| u \|_{-t} \| v \|_{2m+t} = C_2 \| u \|_{2m-\sigma} \| v \|_\sigma \\ &(u, v \in W_2'^{2m}(G),\ W_2'^{2m}(G) \subset \overset{\circ}{W}_2^{-t}(G)).\end{aligned} \tag{3.79}$$

By the density of $v \in W_2'^{2m}(G)$ in $W_2'^{\sigma}(G)$, it follows from (3.79) that $\| Lu \|_{W_2'^{-\sigma}(G)} \leq C_2 \| u \|_{2m-\sigma}$. The inequalities (3.76) are established.

From the density of $\mathfrak{D}(\Lambda_0(\mathrm{bd})) = W_2'^{2m}(G)$ in $\overset{\circ}{W}_2^{2m-\sigma}(G)$ and $\mathfrak{R}(\Lambda_0(\mathrm{bd})) = L_2(G)$ in $W_2'^{-\sigma}(G)$ and (3.76), it follows that the closure of Λ_0 (bd) is a homeomorphism. The smoothness of the coefficients in this case is taken as in step 2.

The theorem follows.

Corollary 3.3. *Theorem 3.6 holds for any strongly elliptic expression L, with smoothness conditions on the coefficients as in Theorem 3.6, provided that the diameter of the region G is sufficiently small.*

This result follows from Corollary 3.2.

As was already mentioned, a similar theorem can be proved with other boundary conditions; this question is reserved for §6. We only remark that for a strongly elliptic expression L of second order, with the usual smoothness conditions on its coefficients, and the boundary condition (bd): $\partial u/\partial \mu + \sigma(x) u|_\Gamma =$

0 $(\sigma \in C^1(\Gamma))$, and when zero is not an eigenvalue the following homeomorphisms were previously obtained:

1) The operator Λ_0 (bd), i.e. the operator $u \longrightarrow Lu$, $u \in W_2^2(\text{bd})$, $Lu \in L_2(G)$, is a homeomorphism between $W_2^2(\text{bd})$ and $L_2(G)$. Γ is of class C^2 (Theorem 3.5).

2) The operator Λ_0 (bd), considered as an operator from $W_2^1(G)$ to $W_2^{-1}(G)$, after closure, is a homeomorphism between these spaces; Γ is of class C^1. This result follows from Theorem 3.4, Chapter II, for sufficiently positive coefficients for L; this theorem may be applied because we have the inequality $\text{Re}(Lu, u)_0 \geq C \| u \|_1^2$ $(u \in W_2^2(\text{bd}))$ (see §2.3). It should also be kept in mind that $W_2^{\prime m}(G) = W_2^1(G)$ (see the end of §2.2). The passage to the general case where 0 is not an eigenvalue is effected with the help of Theorem 2.3 as on p. 158.

Finally, we remark that from 1) we could obtain homeomorphisms for adjoint spaces, as in the cases 3) and 4) in Theorem 3.6.

§4. SMOOTHNESS OF SOLUTIONS OF ELLIPTIC EQUATIONS

In this section we obtain one of the basic properties of elliptic equations: every generalized solution of such an equation is a smooth function to a sufficient degree. Furthermore, it can be shown that in the case of analytic coefficients, this solution is also analytic; however, we do not dwell on these problems. To analyze smoothness properties up to the boundary, we restrict attention to the case of strongly elliptic equations and null boundary conditions, since it is only for this case that our techniques for dealing with boundary value problems are developed to a sufficient degree. The general case will be considered in §6.12. We remark that throughout this section, we do not use the weakest smoothness conditions on coefficients needed to guarantee the validity of our assertions.

1. **Fundamental solutions.** Let L be an arbitrary differential expression of the form (1.2), Chapter II, with sufficiently smooth coefficients. By a fundamental solution for L with a singularity at the point $\xi \in G$ we mean a solution $e_\xi \in W_2^{-\sigma}(G)$ of the equation

$$Lu = \delta_\xi \tag{4.1}$$

inside G (δ_ξ is the δ-function concentrated at ξ; for the concept of a solution inside G see p. 95). Since $\delta_\xi \in W_2^{-l}(G)$ for $l > n/2$, σ must be such that $r + \sigma > n/2$. A fundamental solution is not uniquely defined. As in Theorem 3.3, Chapter II, it is easy to show that if we have the energy inequality

$$\| L^{+}v \|_{\sigma} \geqslant C \| v \|_{\left[\frac{n}{2}\right]+1} \qquad (C > 0; v \in C_0^{\infty}(G)), \qquad (4.2)$$

then the equation $Lu = f \in W_2^{-([n/2]+1)}(G)$ is always solvable inside G. In particular, e_ξ exists for such L.

By Theorem 1.2, the inequality (4.2) holds for elliptic expressions if the diameter of G is sufficiently small, and moreover we may take $\sigma = \max([n/2] + 1 - r, 0)$. Thus for elliptic expressions of order r with a sufficiently small region and smooth coefficients, fundamental solutions $e_\xi \in W_2^{-\max([n/2]+1-r,0)}(G)$ always exist. Actually, deeper results hold for these expressions. It turns out that e_ξ is an ordinary function except at ξ, where it has a power singularity. The proof of this classical fact is laborious, and we restrict ourselves to its formulation only

Thus, suppose that L is an elliptic expression in an open but not necessarily bounded region G, with coefficients $a_\alpha(x) \in C^{|\alpha|+p}(G)$, where $p \geq 1$[1)] (by ellipticity in an open set G we mean that (1.3) holds for $x \in G$). For $x \neq \xi$ in some neighborhood $W \subseteq G \times G$ of a bounded part of the diagonal $x = \xi$, there exists a function $e(x, \xi)$, the fundamental solution in the classical sense, r times continuously differentiable with respect to each of the variables x, ξ separately, having the following properties:

1) If $v \in C_0^r(V)$ where V is a neighborhood such that $V \times V \subseteq W$, then

$$\int_V e(x, \xi)(L^{\oplus}v)(x)\,dx = v(\xi), \int_V e(x, \xi)(Lv)(\xi)\,d\xi = v(x)$$

$$(\xi, x \in V; L^{\oplus} = \overline{L^{+}}). \qquad (4.3)$$

2) For $x \neq \xi$, the derivatives $D_x^\alpha D_\xi^\beta e(x, \xi)$ exist and are continuous with respect to $(x, \xi) \in W$. Each of these derivatives has the form $A(x, \xi)/|x - \xi|^{n-r+|\alpha|+|\beta|}$ (for $n - r + |\alpha| + |\beta| > 0$) or $A(x, \xi) \log |x - \xi|$ (for $n - r + |\alpha| + |\beta| = 0$), where $A(x, \xi)$ is bounded. For $n - r + |\alpha| + |\beta| < 0$ the derivatives are already bounded.

3) If $f \in C^q(\overline{v})$ $(\overline{v} \times \overline{v} \subset W)$, and moreover $q \geq 1$ and $p \geq r + q$, then

$$u(x) = \int_V e(x, \xi) f(\xi)\,d\xi \in C^{q+r-1}(V),$$

$$v(\xi) = \int_V e(x, \xi) f(x)\,dx \in C^{q+r-1}(\overline{V});$$

---

1) If $r=1$, it is necessary to require an addition that $a_\alpha(x) \in C^{2+p}(G)$ for $|\alpha| = 1$. An expression of the first order can be elliptic only in the case of nonreal coefficients and $n = 2$. In everything that follows, we do not explicitly state the extra smoothness condition in the rarely encountered case of expressions of the first order.

$$Lu = f, \quad L^{\oplus} v = f. \tag{4.4}$$

We relate the classical fundamental solution $e(x, \xi)$ to the generalized solution e_ξ. Corresponding to $e(x, \xi)$ $(x, \xi \in V,\ V \times V \subseteq W)$ we define functionals e_ξ and $e_x^{\oplus}$ on $W_2^{\sigma}(V)$ $(\sigma = \max([n/2] + 1 - r, 0))$ by setting

$$(e_\xi, u)_0 = \int_V e(x, \xi)\, \overline{u(x)}\, dx, \quad (e_x^{\oplus}, u)_0 = \int_V e(x, \xi)\, \overline{u(\xi)}\, d\xi \tag{4.5}$$

(it will be shown below that the functionals defined by (4.5) are continuous on $W_2^{\sigma}(V)$). From (4.3) we then obtain the equations

$$(e_\xi, L^+ v)_0 = (\delta_\xi, v)_0, (e_x^{\oplus}, \bar{L} v)_0 = (\delta_x, v)_0 \ (v \in C_0^{\infty}(V)),$$

i.e. e_ξ and $e_x^{\oplus}$ are solutions inside V corresponding to the equations

$$Lu = \delta_\xi, \quad L^{\oplus} u = \delta_x \tag{4.6}$$

In other words, e_ξ and $e_x^{\oplus}$ are fundamental solutions in $G = V$ for the expressions L and $L^{\oplus}$. We remark that the relations (4.4) follow formally from (4.6); hence by the smoothness of $e(x, \xi)$ with respect to each variable it follows that

$$L_x[e(x, \xi)] = 0, L_\xi^{\oplus}[e(x, \xi)] = 0 \qquad ((x, \xi) \in W, x \neq \xi). \tag{4.7}$$

We show that the expressions (4.5) actually define continuous functionals on $W_2^{\sigma}(V)$. This follows from the following general fact: the formula

$$l(u) = l_\xi(u) = \int_G \frac{B(x)}{|x - \xi|^{n-q}} \overline{u(x)}\, dx$$

(G bounded, $\xi \in G$, $q > 0$, $|B(x)| \leq C$ $(x \in G)$) defines a linear continuous functional on $W_2^k(G)$ if $k \geq \max([n/2] + 1 - q, 0)$. In fact, suppose $q < n$ (the assertion is obvious in the case $q \geq n$). By Hölder's inequality $l(u)$ is a continuous functional on $L_{p'}(G)$, if p is such that $1/|x - \xi|^{p(n-q)} \in L_1(G)$ as a function of x $(1/p + 1/p' = 1)$, i.e. if $p < n/(n - q)$ or $p' > n/q$. By the imbedding theorem,

$$\|u\|_{L_{p'}(G)} \leqslant C_1 \|u\|_{W_2^k(G)} \left(k \geqslant 0,\ p' < \frac{2n}{n-2k}\right);$$

if this norm estimate holds, then $l(u)$ is a continuous functional on $W_2^k(G)$. Suppose $n/q < 2n/(n - 2k)$; between these two numbers we can insert p' and complete the proof; the last inequality is equivalent to $k \geq [n/2] + 1 - q$. The assertion follows.

We remark that the norm of the functional l_ξ (and consequently $\|e_\xi\|_{-\sigma}, \|e_x^{\oplus}\|_{-\sigma}$)

is estimated uniformly with respect to $\xi \in G$ (or $\xi, x \in V$).

2. **Smoothness inside regions. Generalized solutions in the sense of L. Schwartz.** Now, with the help of fundamental solutions, we establish a theorem on the smoothness of generalized solutions for an elliptic equation $Lu = f$. In view of the importance of the problem we will present two methods: for solutions in the sense of L. Schwartz and for solutions taken from spaces with negative norms; in subsection 5 we give another method for proving smoothness. We remark that the results below have a local character: the smoothness of a solution near a point depends on the smoothness of the coefficients of the equation near this point.

Extensions of functions from part of G to all of G will not be explicitly constructed when clear from context; finite functions in part of G are always extended by zero to all of G.

Consider a region $G \subseteq E_n$ (not necessarily bounded), and locally summable functions $f(x)$ and $g(x)$ $(x \in G)$. Let N be a linear differential expression of order $\sigma \geq 0$ with coefficients $b_\alpha(x) \in C^{|\alpha|}(G)$. Let us agree to say that the generalized function Ng is a generalized solution to the equation $Lu = f$ inside $G_1 \subseteq G$, if

$$\int_G g(x)\,\overline{(N^+L^+v)(x)}\,dx = \int_G f(x)\overline{v(x)}\,dx \quad (v \in C_0^\infty(G_1)) \tag{4.8}$$

(we assume that $a_\alpha(x) \in C^{|\alpha|+\sigma}(G)$).

It is clear from this definition that if the coefficients of L and N are infinitely differentiable, then Ng can be regarded as a generalized function in the sense of L. Schwartz, obtained by applying N to g and satisfying the equation $Lu = f$. It is known that every generalized function of L. Schwartz can be obtained from derivatives of continuous g; this shows that actually Ng can be any generalized function in the sense of L. Schwartz.

Theorem 4.1. *Let L be an elliptic expression of order r with coefficients $a_\alpha(x) \in C^{|\alpha|+r+p}(G)$, where $p \geq \sigma + 1$, $\sigma \geq 0$, and let N be an arbitrary expression of order σ with coefficients $b_\alpha(x) \in C^{|\alpha|}(G)$. Then every generalized solution Ng inside G of the equation*

$$Lu = f \in C^q(G) \quad (0 \leqslant q \leqslant p) \tag{4.9}$$

coincides as a functional with an ordinary function $h(x)$ $(x \in G)$ which is also a generalized solution of equation (4.9) *inside G. If the equation is homogeneous,* *i.e.* $f=0$, *then* $h \in C^{r+p}(G)$ *and is therefore a smooth solution of the equation* $Lu=0$. *If* $f \neq 0$, *then* $h \in C^{r+q-1}(G)$; *therefore for* $q=0$, h *is generalized, and for* $q \geq 1$, h *is a smooth solution of equation* (4.9). *The coincidence of* Ng *as a functional with* h *means that*

$$\int_G g(x)\,\overline{(N^+u)(x)}\,dx = \int_G h(x)\,\overline{u(x)}\,dx \qquad (u \in C_0^\infty(G)). \tag{4.10}$$

The proof will be carried out in steps.

1. We fix some point $x_0 \in G$ and first carry out our considerations near this point. We initially reduce the study of the nonhomogeneous equation to the homogeneous one. Choose a neighborhood V ($\overline{V} \subset G$) of the point x_0 so small that $\overline{V} \times \overline{V} \subset W$, where W is a neighborhood in which there exists a fundamental solution $e(x, \xi)$ for L. Let $\theta(x) = \int_V e(x, \xi)\, f(\xi)\, d\xi$ $(x \in V)$ and extend θ arbitrarily into G. From property 3) of the fundamental solution it follows that for $q \geq 1$

$$\theta(x) \in C^{q+r-1}(\overline{V}); \tag{4.11}$$

this relation holds even for $q=0$: by 2) $(D^\alpha\theta)(x) = \int_V D_x^\alpha e(x, \xi)\, f(\xi)\, d\xi$ $(|\alpha| \leq r-1)$, where the last integral is continuous in $\overline{V}$. Moreover, by (4.3) we have

$$\int_V \theta(x)\,\overline{(L^+v)(x)}\,dx = \int_V \left\{\int_V e(x, \xi)\,\overline{(L^+v)(x)}\,dx\right\} f(\xi)\,d\xi$$

$$= \int_V \left\{\int_V e(x, \xi)\,\overline{(L^+v)(x)}\,dx\right\} f(\xi)\,d\xi = \int_V f(x)\,\overline{v(x)}\,dx \qquad (v \in C_0^\infty(V)), \tag{4.12}$$

i.e. $\theta(x)$ is a generalized (and for $q \geq 1$, smooth) solution of the equation $Lu = f$ inside V. From (4.8) and (4.12) it follows that $Ng - \theta$ is a solution of $Lu = 0$ in the generalized sense:

$$\int_V \left\{g(x)\,\overline{(N^+L^+v)(x)} - \theta(x)\,\overline{(L^+v)(x)}\right\} dx = 0 \qquad (v \in C_0^\infty(V)). \tag{4.13}$$

2. We now show that for sufficiently small $U \subset V$ there exists a $w(x) \in C^{r+p}(U)$ such that

$$\int_G \left\{g(x)\,\overline{(N^+v)(x)} - \theta(x)\,\overline{v(x)}\right\} dx = \int_G w(x)\,\overline{v(x)}\,dx \qquad (v \in C_0^\infty(U)). \tag{4.14}$$

In the proof we choose U to be a sphere U_R of radius R with center at x_0. The radius R is chosen so small that the sphere U_{2R} with center at x_0 and radius $2R$ is strictly contained in the neighborhood V of step 1. We assume that

$e(x, \xi)$ is extended in an arbitrary way outside W. Suppose that $k(t) \in C^\infty((-\infty, \infty))$ vanishes for $|t| \geq R$ and is equal to 1 in some neighborhood of zero, and $v_0 \in C_0^\infty(U)$. The function on G

$$v(x) = \int_G \overline{e(\xi, x)}\, k(|\xi - x|)\, v_0(\xi)\, d\xi = \int_{U_{2R}} \overline{e(\xi, x)}\, [k(|\xi - x|) - 1]\, v_0(\xi)\, d\xi$$

$$+ \int_{U_{2R}} \overline{e(\xi, x)}\, v_0(\xi)\, d\xi \qquad (4.15)$$

vanishes outside of U_{2R} and therefore is finite with respect to V. In all cases it is $r+\sigma$ times continuously differentiable: for the first integral in the right side of (4.15), this follows from the fact that the singularity at $x = \xi$ is eliminated, and $e(x, \xi)$, according to 2), is $r + p \geq r + \sigma + 1$ times continuously differentiable with respect to x. For the second integral this follows from 3), since under our assumptions it belongs to $C^{r+\sigma}(\bar{U}_{2R})$.

Thus we may use the function $v(x)$ from (4.15) in (4.13) (it is clear that (4.13) holds for $v \in C_0^{r+\sigma}(V)$). Since by 3),

$$L^+\left[\int_{U_{2R}} \overline{e(\xi, x)}\, v_0(\xi)\, d\xi\right] = \overline{L^{\oplus}\left[\int_{U_{2R}} e(\xi, x)\, \overline{v_0(\xi)}\, d\xi\right]} = v_0(x),$$

it follows from (4.15) that

$$(N^+L^+v)(x) = \int_{U_{2R}} N_x^+ L_x^+ \left[\overline{e(\xi, x)}\, [k(|\xi - x|) - 1]\right] v_0(\xi)\, d\xi + (N^+ v_0)(x)$$

with a similar equation for N^+ replaced by E. Taking this equation into account and making the said substitution, we obtain

$$0 = \int_G \left\{g\overline{N^+L^+v} - \theta\, \overline{L^+v}\right\} dx = \int_{U_{2R}} \{\ldots\}\, dx$$

$$= \int_{U_{2R}} g(x) \overline{\left\{\int_{U_{2R}} N_x^+ L_x^+ \left[\overline{e(\xi, x)}\, [k(|\xi - x|) - 1]\right] v_0(\xi)\, d\xi\right\}}\, dx$$

$$- \int_{U_{2R}} \theta(x) \overline{\left\{\int_{U_{2R}} L_x^+ \left[\overline{e(\xi, x)}\, [k(|\xi - x|) - 1]\right] v_0(\xi)\, d\xi\right\}}\, dx$$

$$+ \int_{U_{2R}} [g(x)\, \overline{(N^+ v_0)(x)} - \theta(x)\, \overline{v_0(x)}]\, dx$$

$$= \int_{U_{2R}} \left\{\int_{U_{2R}} g(x)\, \overline{N_x^+ L_x^+ \left[\overline{e(\xi, x)}\, [k(|\xi - x|) - 1]\right]}\, dx - \right.$$

$$-\int_{U_{2R}} \theta(x)\, \overline{L_x^+\left[\overline{e(\xi, x)}\,[k(|\xi - x|) - 1]\right] dx\}}\, \overline{v_0(\xi)}\, d\xi$$

$$+\int_{U_{2R}} [g\overline{N^+ v_0} - \theta \bar{v}_0]\, dx = -\int_G w(\xi)\overline{v_0(\xi)}\, d\xi + \int_G [g\overline{N^+ v_0} - \theta \bar{v}_0]\, dx, \quad (4.16)$$

where $w(\xi)$ is defined by $w(\xi) = -\{\cdots\}$. It follows from 2) and the expression for w that $w \in C^{r+p}(U)$. We have thus proved (4.14) for any $v = v_0 \in C_0^\infty(U)$.

3. We now construct the function h and prove the representation (4.10). Enclose each point $x \in G$ in a neighborhood O_x, strictly contained in the $U = U_x$ constructed in step 2 for $x_0 = x$. Choose from the covering of G by neighborhoods O_x a countable covering $O_{x_1}, O_{x_2}, \cdots$ such that every subregion of G which is strictly contained in G meets only a finite number of these neighborhoods; let $1 = \sum_{j=1}^\infty \chi_j(x)$ be a decomposition of unity corresponding to the covering O_{x_j}. By steps 1 and 2 we can construct functions $\theta = \theta_j$ and $w = w_j$ for the neighborhoods $U = U_{x_j}$. Since for any $v \in C_0^\infty(G)$, $v\chi_j \in C_0^\infty(U_{x_j})$, it follows that (4.14) holds with v replaced by $v\chi_j$. Taking this equation into account along with the fact that only a finite number of the functions $v\chi_j$ are different from zero, we obtain relation (4.10):

$$\int_G g\overline{N^+ v}\, dx = \int_G g\overline{N^+\left[\sum_{j=1}^\infty v\chi_j\right]}\, dx = \sum_{j=1}^\infty \int_G g\overline{N^+[v\chi_j]}\, dx = \sum_{j=1}^\infty \int_G \theta_j \bar{v}\chi_j\, dx$$

$$+\sum_{j=1}^\infty \int_G w_j \bar{v}\chi_j\, dx = \int_G \left(\sum_{j=1}^\infty (\theta_j + w_j)\chi_j\right)\bar{v}\, dx = \int_G h\bar{v}\, dx,$$

$$h(x) = \sum_{j=1}^\infty \theta_j(x)\chi_j(x) + \sum_{j=1}^\infty w_j(x)\chi_j(x) \qquad (x \in G).$$

Since for each sufficiently small neighborhood of x, only a finite number of terms do not vanish, and $\theta_j \in C^{q+r-1}(U_{x_j})$ (see (4.11)), $w_j \in C^{r+p}(U_{x_j})$, it follows that

$$\sum_{j=1}^\infty \theta_j\chi_j \in C^{q+r-1}(G), \quad \sum_{j=1}^\infty w_j\chi_j \in C^{r+p}(G).$$

Therefore if $f = 0$, then only the second sum figures in the representation for h and $h \in C^{r+p}(G)$. In the general case, $h \in C^{r+q-1}(G)$.

To complete the proof of the theorem, it remains to show that h is a generalized solution of (4.9); i.e. we must verify the identity

$$\int_G h(x)\,\overline{(L^+v)(x)}\,dx = \int_G f(x)\,\overline{v(x)}\,dx \quad (v \in C_0^\infty(G)).$$

In (4.10) replace $u \in C_0^\infty(G)$ by $L^+ v$, where $v \in C_0^\infty(G)$, and use (4.8) (for $G_1 = G$). Then

$$\int_G h\,\overline{L^+ v}\,dx = \int_G g\overline{N^+L^+ v}\,dx = \int_G f\bar{v}\,dx,$$

as required. The theorem follows.

3. Smoothness inside a region. Solutions that are generalized kernels of L. Schwartz. Later we will frequently encounter the situation where a generalized kernel is a solution of an elliptic equation with respect to each variable. We now obtain an analogue of the previous theorem for this case, restricting attention to generalized kernels in the sense of L. Schwartz.

We consider in two regions $G', G'' \subseteq E_n$, possibly unbounded, differential expressions L', N' and L'', N'' respectively; their orders are r', σ' and r'', σ''; L', N' always act with respect to $x' \in G'$, L'', N'' with respect to $x'' \in G''$. The smoothness restrictions on the coefficients are similar to those mentioned in subsection 2. Let $O \subseteq G' \times G''$ be some region, and let $G(x', x'')$ and $F(x', x'')$ be locally summable functions in O. We will say that the generalized derivative $N' N'' G$ is a generalized solution of the equations $L'_{x'} U = F$, $L''_{x''} U = F$, inside $O_1 \subseteq O$, if

$$\iint_O G(x', x'')\overline{(\overset{\prime +}{N}_{x'} \overset{\prime\prime +}{N}_{x''} \overset{\prime +}{L}_{x'} V)(x', x'')}\,dx'dx'' = \iint_O F(x', x'')\overline{V(x', x'')}\,dx'dx'',$$

$$\iint_O G(x', x'')\overline{(\overset{\prime +}{N}_{x'} \overset{\prime\prime +}{N}_{x''} \overset{\prime\prime +}{L}_{x''} V)(x', x'')}\,dx'dx'' = \iint_O F(x', x'')\overline{V(x', x'')}\,dx'dx''$$

$$(V(x', x'') \in C_0^\infty(O_1)). \tag{4.17}$$

By the expansion of a smooth kernel in a bilinear series which is sufficiently well convergent, it is not difficult to see that in this definition, the equations (4.17) can be equivalently replaced by

$$\iint_O G(x', x'')\overline{(N'^+ L'^+ v')(x')}\,\overline{(N''^+ v'')(x'')}\,dx'dx'' =$$

$$= \iint_O F(x', x'') \overline{v'(x') v''(x'')}\, dx' dx'',$$

$$\iint_O G(x', x'') \overline{(N'^{+} v')(x')} \, \overline{(N''^{+} L''^{+} v'')(x'')}\, dx' dx''$$
$$= \iint_O F(x', x'') \overline{v'(x') v''(x'')}\, dx' dx'', \tag{4.18}$$

where $v'(x') \in C_0^\infty(G')$, $v''(x'') \in C_0^\infty(G'')$ are such that the product of their supports lies in O_1.

Theorem 4.2. *Let L' be an elliptic expression of order r' with coefficients $a'_\alpha(x') \in C^{|\alpha| + r' + p'}(G')$, where $p' \geq \sigma' + 1$, $\sigma' \geq 0$, and let N' be an arbitrary expression of order σ' with coefficients $b'_\alpha(x') \in C^{|\alpha|}(G')$. Define L'' and N'' similarly. Then every generalized solution $N' N'' G$ inside a region $O \subseteq G' \times G''$ of the system of equations*

$$L'_{x'} U = F, \qquad L''_{x''} U = F, \tag{4.19}$$

where $F(x', x'')$ $((x', x'') \in O)$ is such that the derivatives $D^{\alpha'}_{x'} D^{\alpha''}_{x''} F$ ($|\alpha| \leq q' \leq p'$, $|\alpha| \leq q'' \leq p''$) exist and depend continuously on $(x', x'') \in O$, coincides as a functional with an ordinary kernel $H(x', x'')$ $((x', x'') \in O)$ which is also a generalized solution of the system (4.19) inside O. If $F = 0$, then the derivatives $D^{\alpha'}_{x'} D^{\alpha''}_{x''} H$, where $|\alpha'| \leq r' + p'$, $|\alpha''| \leq r'' + p''$, exist and depend continuously on $(x', x'') \in O$; therefore this kernel is a smooth solution of the equations $L'_{x'} U = 0$, $L''_{x''} U = 0$. If $F \neq 0$, then the derivatives $D^{\alpha'}_{x'} D^{\alpha''}_{x''} H$, where $|\alpha'| \leq q'$, $|\alpha''| \leq r'' + q'' - 1$ or $|\alpha'| \leq r' + q' - 1$, $|\alpha''| \leq q''$, exist and depend continuously on $(x', x'') \in O$. The coincidence of $N' N'' G$ as a functional with H means that

$$\iint_O G(x', x'') \overline{(N'^{+}_{x'} N''^{+}_{x''} V)(x', x'')}\, dx' dx'' = \iint_O H(x', x'') \overline{V(x', x'')}\, dx' dx''$$
$$(V(x', x'') \in C_0^\infty(O)). \tag{4.20}$$

We will prove a relation equivalent to (4.20): for any $v'(x') \in C_0^\infty(G')$, $v''(x'') \in C_0^\infty(G'')$ such that the product of their supports lies inside O,

$$\iint_O G(x', x'') \overline{(N'^{+} v')(x')} \, \overline{(N''^{+} v'')(x'')}\, dx' dx''$$
$$= \iint_O H(x', x'') \overline{v'(x')} \, \overline{v''(x'')}\, dx' dx''. \tag{4.21}$$

The proof of the theorem is a variation of the proof of the previous theorem, and therefore in part it is only outlined.

1. We fix $(x_0', x_0'') \in G' \times G''$ and choose so small a neighborhood V' (V'') of the point x_0' (x_0'') such that a fundamental solution $e'(x', \xi')$ $(e''(x'', \xi''))$ for the expression L' (L'') exists in $V' \times V'$ $(V'' \times V'')$ and such that $\overline{V' \times V''} \subset O$. If $(x', x'') \in V' \times V''$, we set $\Theta_1(x', x'') = \int_{V'} e'(x', \xi') F(\xi', x'') d\xi'$ and extend this function in an arbitrary way to all of O. It is clear from the discussion in step 1 of the previous proof and the first of the relations (4.19) that this function admits continuous derivatives $D_{x'}^{\alpha'} D_{x''}^{\alpha''} \Theta_1$ $(|\alpha'| \le q' + r' - 1, |\alpha''| \le q'')$ and satisfies the equation

$$\iint_O \{G\overline{N'^{+}L'^{+}v'} \cdot \overline{N''^{+}v''} - \Theta_1 \overline{L'^{+}v'} \cdot \overline{v''}\}\, dx'dx'' = 0 \tag{4.22}$$

$$(v' \in C_0^\infty(V'), \qquad v'' \in C_0^\infty(V'')).$$

2. We now choose a spherical neighborhood $U' = U'_{R'}$ of the point x_0' with radius R' so small that the similar neighborhood $U'_{2R'}$, having radius twice as large, is strictly contained in V'. We construct, similarly to (4.15), a function $V'(x') \in C_0^{r'+\sigma'}(V')$ with respect to $v_0'(x') \in C_0^\infty(U')$, and substitute it into (4.22) ((4.22) holds even for $v' \in C_0^{r'+\sigma'}(V')$). As in the proof of Theorem 4.1, we find that for any $v_0' \in C_0^\infty(U')$, $v'' \in C_0^\infty(V'')$,

$$\iint_O G\overline{N'^{+}v_0'} \cdot \overline{N''^{+}v''} dx'dx'' = \iint_O \{K(x', x'')\overline{v_0'}\; \overline{N''^{+}v''} + L(x', x'')\overline{v_0'}\,\overline{v''}\} dx'dx'',$$

$$K(x', x'') = -\int_{U'_{2R'}} G(\xi', x'') \overline{N_{\xi'}'^{+} L_{\xi'}'^{+} [e'(x', \xi')[\kappa(|x' - \xi'|) - 1]]}\, d\xi',$$

$$L(x', x'') = \int_{U'_{2R'}} \Theta_1(\xi', x'') \overline{L_{\xi'}'^{+} [e'(x', \xi')[k(|x' - \xi'|) - 1]]}\, d\xi' + \Theta_1(x', x''). \tag{4.23}$$

3. We substitute the function $L''^{+}v''$ in (4.23) in place of v'', where $v'' \in C_0^\infty(V'')$. By the second equation in (4.18), the left side of (4.23) then becomes $\iint_O F\overline{v_0'}\,\overline{v''}\, dx'\, dx''$. Therefore, if we introduce the function $\Theta_2(x', x'') = \int_{V''} e''(x'', \xi'') F(x', \xi'') d\xi''$ and use (4.3), we find that for $v_0' \in C_0^\infty(U')$ and $v'' \in C_0^\infty(V'')$

$$\iint_O \{K(x', x'')\bar{v}'_0 \overline{N''^+ L''^+ v''} - (\Theta_2(x', x'') - L(x', x''))\bar{v}'_0 \overline{L''^+ v''}\}\, dx'dx'' = 0.$$

This equation is similar to (4.13). On constructing, as above, a function v'' with respect to $v''_0 \in C_0^\infty(U'')$ (the spherical neighborhood $U'' = U''_R$ of the point x''_0 is so small that $U''_{2R''}$ lies strictly inside V''), we obtain

$$\iint_O K(x', x'')\bar{v}'_0 \overline{N''^+ v''_0}\, dx'dx'' = \iint_O M(x', x'')\bar{v}'_0 \bar{v}''_0\, dx'dx'',$$

$$M(x', x'') = -\int_{U''_{2R''}} K(x', \xi'') \overline{N''^+_{\xi''} L''^+_{\xi''} [\overline{e''(x'', \xi'')}[k(|x'' - \xi''|) - 1]]}\, d\xi''$$

$$+ \int_{U''_{2R''}} (\Theta_1(x', \xi'') - L(x', \xi'')) \overline{L''^+_{\xi''} [\overline{e''(x'', \xi'')}[k(|x'' - \xi''|) - 1]]}\, d\xi''$$

$$+ \Theta_2(x', x'') - L(x', x'')$$

$$(v'_0 \in C_0^\infty(U'), \quad v''_0 \in C_0^\infty(U'')).$$

Substituting this expression for the integral of K in the right part of (4.23) (where v'' is replaced by v''_0), we find that for the v'_0, v''_0 under consideration

$$\iint_O G\overline{N'^+ v'_0} \cdot \overline{N''^+ v''_0}\, dx'dx'' = \iint_O N(x', x'')\bar{v}'_0 \bar{v}''_0\, dx'dx''$$

$$(v'_0 \in C_0^\infty(U'), \quad v''_0 \in C_0^\infty(U'')), \tag{4.24}$$

$$N(x', x'') = \iint_{U'_{2R'} \times U''_{2R''}} G(\xi', \xi'') \overline{N'^+_{\xi'} L'^+_{\xi'} [\overline{e'(x', \xi')}[k(|x' - \xi'|) - 1]]}$$

$$\times \overline{N''^+_{\xi''} L''^+_{\xi''} [\overline{e''(x'', \xi'')}[k(|x'' - \xi''|) - 1]]}\, d\xi' d\xi'' -$$

$$- \iint_{U'_{2R'} \times U''_{2R''}} \Theta_1(\xi', \xi'') \overline{L'^+_{\xi'} [\overline{e'(x', \xi')}[k(|x' - \xi'|) - 1]]} \times$$

$$\times \overline{L''^+_{\xi''} [\overline{e''(x'', \xi'')}[k(|x'' - \xi''|) - 1]]}\, d\xi' d\xi'' +$$

$$+\int_{U''_{2R''}} (\Theta_2(x',\xi'')-\Theta_1(x',\xi''))\,\overset{+}{L''_{\xi''}}\,\overline{[e''(x'',\xi'')[k(|x''-\xi''|)-1]]}\,d\xi''$$

$$+\Theta_2(x',x'') \qquad (4.25)$$

$$(x'\in U',\ x''\in U'').$$

We show that N has the smoothness required for H. The first and second integrals in (4.25) are continuously differentiable by $D^{\alpha'}_{x'}, D^{\alpha''}_{x''}$, where $|\alpha'|\le r'+p'$, $|\alpha''|\le r''+p''$. Since $\Theta_2(x',x'')$ belongs to $C^{q'}(U')$ with respect to x', and $\Theta_1(x',x'')$ belongs to $C^{r'+q'-1}(U')$, the third integral is continuously differentiable by $D^{\alpha'}_{x'}, D^{\alpha''}_{x''}$, $|\alpha'|\le q'$, $|\alpha''|\le r''+p''$. Finally, the term $\Theta_2(x',x'')$ is continuously differentiable by $D^{\alpha'}_{x'} D^{\alpha''}_{x''}$, $|\alpha'|\le q'$, $|\alpha''|\le r''+q''-1$. Thus, if $F=0$, and consequently $\Theta_1=\Theta_2=0$, then $D^{\alpha'}_{x'} D^{\alpha''}_{x''}N$ exists and is continuous in $U'\times U''$ for $|\alpha'|\le r'+p'$, $|\alpha''|\le r''+p''$. If $F\ne 0$, then $D^{\alpha'}_{x'} D^{\alpha''}_{x''}N$ exists and is continuous in $U'\times U''$ for $|\alpha'|\le q'$, $|\alpha''|\le r''+q''-1$.

In the proof we can take in step 2, not v' along with v_0', but v'' along with v_0'', and in step 3, v' along with v_0'. As the result we obtain (4.24) with a new kernel $\tilde N$; by the arbitrariness of v_0' and v_0'', $\tilde N = N$. However, as before, if $F\ne 0$ then $D^{\alpha'}_{x'} D^{\alpha''}_{x''}\tilde N$ exists and is continuous in $U'\times U''$ for $|\alpha'|\le r'+q'-1$ and $|\alpha''|\le q''$. This proves the last smoothness relation for N.

4. We have thus obtained (4.24) with the required smoothness properties for N, i.e. we have proved (4.21) locally. To complete the proof of the theorem, the kernel $H(x',x'')$ must be constructed with respect to the kernels $N(x',x'')$, constructed inside a neighborhood of each point (x_0', x_0'') of the region O. This is done exactly as in the previous theorem, with the help of a decomposition of unity. It follows as before that H is a generalized solution of the equations (4.19) with respect to each variable. The theorem follows.

4. Smoothness inside a region. Generalized solutions as elements of a space with negative norm. We carry over the theorems in subsections 2 and 3 to generalized solutions of this type. For definiteness we will assume that the region G is bounded; in the case of unbounded G, the results remain valid if $W_2^{\sigma}(G)$ is replaced by $W_2^{(\sigma,q)}(G)$.

Theorem 4.3. *Let L be an elliptic expression as in Theorem 4.1, and suppose that $\phi\in W_2^{-\sigma}(G)$ $(\sigma\ge 0)$ satisfies inside G the equation $Lu=f$, where $f\in$*

$C^q(G)$, $0 \le q \le p$. Then ϕ coincides inside G with an ordinary function h, also satisfying this equation inside G, and having the following smoothness: if the equation is homogeneous ($f = 0$), then $h \in W_{2,\mathrm{loc}}^{r+p}(G)$ and is therefore a smooth solution; if $f \neq 0$, then $h \in W_{2,\mathrm{loc}}^{r+q-1}(G)$ and for $q = 0$ this is a generalized, and for $q \ge 1$ a smooth solution.

The proof is similar to the proof of Theorem 4.1.

1. If $x_0 \in G$, choose $V \ni x_0$ and construct $\theta(x)$ as in the earlier proof. We will consider θ as an element of $W_2^{-\sigma}(G)$, and then equation (4.12) asserts that θ satisfies the equation $Lu = f$ inside G. The generalized function $\psi = \phi - \theta \in W_2^{-\sigma}(G)$ is a solution inside G of the homogeneous equation $Lu = 0$:

$$(\psi, L^+v)_0 = 0 \qquad (v \in C_0^\infty(V)). \tag{4.26}$$

2. We now consider the case of a homogeneous equation, as in the previous step 2. Define U, k, v_0, v as there. We have

$$(L^+v)(x) = \int_{U_{2R}} K(x,\xi)\, v_0(\xi)\, d\xi + v_0(x), \tag{4.27}$$

where $K(x, \xi) = \overline{L_x^+[e(\xi, x)\,[k(|\xi - x|) - 1]]}$; it follows from the expression for K that the derivatives $D_x^\alpha D_\xi^\beta K$ exist and are continuous when $|\alpha| \le p$, $|\beta| \le r + p$, $p \ge \sigma + 1$ ($(x, \xi) \in \overline{V} \times \overline{V}$). We extend the kernel $K(x, \xi)$ in an arbitrary way, preserving this smoothness, to $(G \cup \Gamma) \times (G \cup \Gamma)$, and define an operator A by the equation

$$(Au)(x) = \int_G K(x,\xi)\, u(\xi)\, d\xi. \tag{4.28}$$

This operator acts continuously from $W_2^{-r-p}(G)$ to $W_2^\sigma(G)$; i.e. if $u_\nu \in L_2(G)$ converges to 0 in $W_2^{-r-p}(G)$, then $Au_\nu \to 0$ in $W_2^\sigma(G)$: if $|\alpha| \le \sigma$, then

$$|(D^\alpha Au_\nu)(x)| = \left| \int_G (D_x^\alpha K)(x,\xi)\, u_\nu(\xi)\, d\xi \right| = |(u_\nu, \overline{D_x^\alpha K(x,\cdot)})_0|$$

$$\leqslant \| \overline{(D_x^\alpha K)(x,\cdot)} \|_{r+p} \| u_\nu \|_{-r-p} \leqslant C \| u_\nu \|_{-r-p} \qquad (x \in G),$$

from which it follows that $D^\alpha Au_\nu \to 0$ ($|\alpha| \le \sigma$) uniformly for $x \in G$, and hence $\| Au_\nu \|_\sigma \to 0$. Therefore A^+ acts continuously from $W_2^{-\sigma}(G)$ to $W_2^{r+p}(G)$. Substituting (4.15) into (4.26) and using (4.27) and (4.28), we obtain, similarly to (4.14), the equation

$$0 = (\psi, L^+v)_0 = (\psi, Av_0)_0 + (\psi, v_0) = (A^+\psi, v_0)_0 + (\psi, v_0)_0;$$

$$(\psi, v_0) = (w, v_0)_0 \qquad (w = -A^+\psi \in W_2^{r+p}(G); \quad v_0 \in C_0^\infty(U)). \tag{4.29}$$

3. It follows from the equations $\psi = \phi - \theta$ and (4.29) that for each $x_0 \in G$, there exists a neighborhood U_{x_0} sufficiently small that $(\phi, v)_0 = (\theta + w, v)_0$ ($v \in C_0^\infty(U_{x_0})$), and moreover $\theta \in C^{q+r-1}(\bar{U}_{x_0}) \subset W_2^{q+r-1}(U_{x_0})$ (see (4.11)), $w \in W_2^{r+p}(G)$. The proof is now completed exactly as before; see also Lemma 3.2, Chapter II.

By modernizing the proof of Theorem 4.2, it is possible to establish the following assertion, which is similar to that given in the previous theorem (for simplicity, G' and G'' are taken to be bounded).

Theorem 4.4. *Let L', L'', O, F be as in Theorem 4.2. Suppose that $\Phi \in W_2^{-\sigma'}(G') \otimes W_2^{-\sigma''}(G'')$ ($\sigma', \sigma'' \geq 0$) satisfies the system of equations (4.19) inside O, i.e.*

$$(\Phi, (L'^{+}v')(x')v''(x''))_{L_2(G'\times G'')} = (F(x', x''), v'(x')v''(x''))_{L_2(G'\times G'')},$$

$$(\Phi, v'(x')(L''^{+}v'')(x''))_{L_2(G'\times G'')} = (F(x', x''), v'(x')v''(x''))_{L_2(G'\times G'')} \tag{4.30}$$

($v' \in C_0^\infty(G')$, $v'' \in C_0^\infty(G'')$; the product of the supports of v' and v'' lies inside O).

Then Φ coincides inside O with an ordinary kernel $H(x', x'')$ ($(x', x'') \in O$), also a generalized solution to the system (4.19) inside O, and having the following smoothness: if $F = 0$, then in every subregion of O strictly interior to O, $H \in W_2^{r'+p'} \otimes W_2^{r''+p''}$; if $F \neq 0$, then in every such subregion

$$H \in (W_2^{q'} \otimes W_2^{r''+q''-1}) \cup (W_2^{r'+q'-1} \otimes W_2^{q''}).$$

The coincidence inside O of Φ with H means that

$$(\Phi, V)_{L_2(G'\times G'')} = (H, V)_{L_2(G'\times G'')} \quad (V \in C_0^\infty(O)). \tag{4.31}$$

5. **Another method. Smoothness inside a region.** We introduce another method for proving smoothness of generalized solutions of elliptic equations, using results on boundary value problems. This method permits an analysis of smoothness up to the boundary (for clarity of presentation, we restrict attention to an analysis inside G); moreover, we now include the case of generalized right parts, and the results acquire more symmetry. As was already mentioned, in the rest of this section we will consider only strongly elliptic expressions; for the more complicated general case, see §6.12. As in subsection 4, for definiteness, in this subsection and the following we assume that G is bounded.

Theorem 4.5. *Let L be a strongly elliptic expression of order $2m$, with coefficients $a_\alpha(x) \in C^{|\alpha|+p}(G)$, where $p \geq 0$ is some number. Suppose that the function $\phi \in W_2^s(G)$ $(s = \cdots, -1, 0, 1, \cdots)$ is a generalized solution inside G of the equation $Lu = f$, where $f \in W_{2,\text{loc}}^{s-2m}(G)$.*

If actually $f \in W_{2,\text{loc}}^t(G)$, with $t > s - 2m$ *of arbitrary sign, and the coefficients $a_\alpha(x)$ are sufficiently smooth, then ϕ is smoother inside G; for a large degree of smoothness on the coefficients, $\phi \in W_{2,\text{loc}}^{t+2m}(G)$. More precisely:* 1) *if $p < m$, then we can consider $\phi \in W_2^s(G)$, where $s \in [-p, p]$; we assert that automatically $\phi \in W_{2,\text{loc}}^{\min(t+2m,p)}(G)$;* 2) *if $p \geq m$, we may take $s \in [-p, p+2m)$, and then $\phi \in W_{2,\text{loc}}^{\min(t+2m,p+2m)}(G)$.*

Before giving the proof of the theorem, we outline some general ideas (see pp. 138–139). Consider a sequence $W_2^{-l}(G) \supseteq L_2(G) \supseteq W_2^l(G)$. If $a(x) \in C^l(G \cup \Gamma)$, define the product of $\alpha \in W_2^{-l}(G)$ on $a(x)$ as the generalized function $a\alpha$ in $W_2^{-l}(G)$ which acts according to the rule $(a\alpha, u)_0 = (\alpha, \overline{a(x)}\, u(x))_0$ $(u \in W_2^l(G))$. This definition is meaningful: the multiplication operator $u(x) \to a(x)\, u(x)$ is continuous in $W_2^l(G)$, and the transformation $\alpha \to a\alpha$ is its adjoint. If $a(x)$ vanishes outside a region $G_1 \subseteq G$ with piecewise smooth boundary, then $a\alpha$ can be considered as an element of $W_2^{-l}(G_1)$, acting on $u \in W_2^l(G_1)$ according to the rule $(a\alpha, u)_0 = (\alpha, \bar{a}u)_0$; this equation is meaningful, since au belongs to $W_2^l(G)$ and depends continuously on $u \in W_2^l(G_1)$. This interpretation of $a\alpha$ will be used below without further explanation.

Proof. For the proof we will use Theorem 3.6 applied to the adjoint expression L^+. The passage from the required smoothness on the coefficients of L to the corresponding requirements with respect to L^+ in the case of the first and second pairs of spaces in (3.71) is effected as in the proof of Theorem 3.6. This is explained for the smoothness restrictions cited below.

We prove the theorem locally. If $x_0 \in G$, let U be a sphere with center x_0 and sufficiently small radius, and let $V \supset U$ be a sphere with the same center and larger radius. We will assume that the radius of V is small enough that V lies strictly interior to G and that the problem $L^+u = f$ in the region V, with null boundary conditions, is solvable in the sense that Theorem 3.6 holds with s, $|s| \leq N$, where N is some sufficiently large number (its choice will be explained later). Let $\chi(x)$ be a nonnegative function in $C^\infty(E_n)$, vanishing in a neighborhood of the set $E_n \setminus V$. In everything that follows, if $s \leq 0$ we set $\sigma = -s \geq 0$.

1. We show that if $\phi \in W_2^s(G) = W_2^{-\sigma}(G)$ $(s < 0)$ satisfies inside G the equa-

tion $Lu = f$, where $f \in W^t_{2,\mathrm{loc}}(G)$ with $t > s - 2m$ of arbitrary sign, then $\chi\phi \in W_2^{s+1}(V)$.

In fact, if $w \in \mathring{W}_2^m(V) \cap W_2^{2m+\sigma}(V)$, then $v(x) = \chi(x)\, w(x) \in W^{2m+\sigma}_{2,0}(G)$ and it may be substituted into (3.10), Chapter II. We obtain

$$(\varphi, L^+[\chi w])_0 = (f, \chi w)_0 \qquad (w \in \mathring{W}_2^m(V) \cap W_2^{2m+\sigma}(V)). \tag{4.32}$$

However,

$$(L^+[\chi w])(x) = \chi(x)(L^+ w)(x) + (M_\chi w)(x), \tag{4.33}$$

where M_χ is a differential expression of order $2m - 1$; it has sufficiently smooth coefficients that the operator A: $v \longrightarrow M_\chi v$ maps $W_2^{2m+\sigma-1}(V)$ continuously into $W_2^\sigma(V)$. If A^+ is the adjoint operator, then $(\alpha, M_\chi v)_0 = (\alpha, Av)_0 = (A^+\alpha, v)_0$ for any $\alpha \in W_2^{-\sigma}(V)$, $v \in \mathring{W}_2^{2m+\sigma-1}(V)$; here $A^+\alpha \in W_2^{-2m-\sigma+1}(V)$. In particular, $(\phi, M_\chi w)_0 = (\psi, w)_0$ where $\psi = A^+\phi\, (w \in \mathring{W}_2^m(V) \cap W_2^{2m+\sigma}(V) \subset W_2^{2m+\sigma-1}(V))$. Substituting (4.33) into (4.32) and using the relation thus obtained, we find that

$$\begin{aligned}(\chi\varphi, L^+ w)_0 = (\varphi, \chi L^+ w)_0 &= (f, \chi w)_0 - (\varphi, M_\chi w)_0 \\ &= (\chi f - \psi, w)_0 = (\theta, w)_0 \\ &\qquad (w \in \mathring{W}_2^m(V) \cap W_2^{2m+\sigma}(V)),\end{aligned} \tag{4.34}$$

where $\theta = \chi f - \psi \in W_2^{-2m-\sigma+1}(V)$. Because the mapping $w \longrightarrow L^+ w$ is a homeomorphism between $\mathring{W}_2^m(V) \cap W_2^{2m+\sigma-1}(V)$ and $W_2^{\sigma-1}(V)$, we can write

$$|(\theta, w)_0| \leqslant \|\theta\|_{-2m-\sigma+1} \|w\|_{2m+\sigma-1} \leqslant C \|\theta\|_{-2m-\sigma+1} \|L^+ w\|_{\sigma-1}$$
$$(w \in \mathring{W}_2^m(V) \cap W_2^{2m+\sigma-1}(V)).$$

As in the proof of Theorem 3.3, Chapter II, it follows that $(\theta, w)_0 = (\mu, L^+ w)_0$, $\mu \in W^{-\sigma+1}(V)$. From this equation and from (4.34) we have

$$(\chi\varphi, L^+ w)_0 = (\mu, L^+ w)_0\, (w \in \mathring{W}_2^m(V) \cap W_2^{2m+\sigma}(V));$$

but since $L^+ w$ runs through all of $W_2^\sigma(V)$, we obtain $\chi\phi = \mu \in W_2^{-\sigma+1}(V)$, as required.

It is easy to see that for the argument in this proof it is sufficient to require that $a_\alpha \in C^{|\alpha|+|s|}(G)$.

2. Let $u \in W_2^s(V)$ $(s \geq 0)$, $w \in \mathring{W}_2^{2m}(V)$; integrating by parts, we obtain

$$(u, M_\chi w)_0 = \sum_{|\alpha| \leqslant 2m-1} (u, c_\alpha(x) D^\alpha w)_0 = \sum_{|\alpha| \leqslant s,\ |\beta| \leqslant 2m-s-1} (D^\alpha u, c_{\alpha\beta}(x) D^\beta w)_0 \tag{4.35}$$

(surface integrals do not appear here, since c_α and all of its derivatives vanish on the boundary of V because of the presence of the factor χ). Thus, if $s \geq 2m-1$, then for the u and w in question,

$$(u, M_\chi w)_0 = (\psi, w)_0, \tag{4.36}$$

where $\psi \in W_2^{-2m+s+1}(V)$. We show that (4.36) holds even for $0 \leq s \leq 2m-1$. Fix indices α and β ($|\alpha| \leq s$, $|\beta| \leq 2m-s-1$) and consider the operator $A_{\alpha\beta}$: $v \to c_{\alpha\beta}(x) D^\beta v$, which acts continuously from $W_2^{2m-s-1}(V)$ to $L_2(V)$; $A_{\alpha\beta}^+$ acts from $L_2(V)$ to $W_2^{-2m+s+1}(V)$. We have, in particular,

$$(D^\alpha u, c_{\alpha\beta} D^\beta w)_0 = (D^\alpha u, A_{\alpha\beta} w)_0 = (A_{\alpha\beta}^+ D^\alpha u, w)_0 \quad (u \in W_2^s(V), w \in W_2^{2m}(V)),$$

and substituting this expression into (4.35), we obtain (4.36) with

$$\psi = \sum_{|\alpha| \leq s, \ |\beta| \leq 2m-s-1} A_{\alpha\beta}^+ D^\alpha u \in W_2^{-2m+s+1}(V).$$

Below we show that step 1 holds even for $s \geq 0$. For this we meanwhile prove the analogue of (4.34): repeating the arguments for the proof of step 1 and using (4.36), we obtain

$$(\chi\varphi, L^+ w)_0 = (\theta, w)_0 \ (w \in \overset{\circ}{W}{}_2^m(V) \cap W_2^{2m}(U), \ \theta = \chi f - \psi \in W_2^{-2m+s+1}(V)). \tag{4.37}$$

3. We establish step 1 for $0 \leq s < m$; as before, suppose that $f \in W_{2,\mathrm{loc}}^t(G)$ with $t > s-2m$. The mapping $w \to L^+ v$ ($w \in \overset{\circ}{W}{}_2^m(V) \cap \overset{\circ}{W}{}_2^{2m}(V)$) after closure is a homeomorphism between $\overset{\circ}{W}{}_2^m(V) \cap W_2^{2m-s-1}(V)$ and $\overset{\circ}{W}{}_2^{-s-1}(V)$, and therefore

$$|(\theta, w)_0| \leq \|\theta\|_{-2m+s+1} \|w\|_{2m-s-1} \leq C \|\theta\|_{-2m+s+1} \|L^+ w\|_{\overset{\circ}{W}{}_2^{-s-1}(V)}$$
$$(w \in \overset{\circ}{W}{}_2^m(V) \cap W_2^{2m}(V)). \tag{4.38}$$

Again as in Theorem 3.3, Chapter II, it follows that for such w, $(\theta, w)_0 = (\mu, L^+ w)_0$, $\mu \in \overset{\circ}{W}{}_2^{s+1}(V)$. Comparing this equation with (4.37), we conclude that $(\chi\phi, L^+ w)_0 = (\mu, L^+ w)_0$ ($w \in \overset{\circ}{W}{}_2^m(V) \cap W_2^{2m}(V)$); but $L^+ w$ runs through all of $L_2(V)$, and therefore $\chi\phi = \mu \in \overset{\circ}{W}{}_2^{s+1}(V)$, as required. For carrying out the argument in step 3, it is sufficient to require that $a_\alpha \in C^{|\alpha|+s+1}(G)$.

The cases 4, $m \leq s < 2m$ and 5, $s \geq 2m$ are treated similarly; it is only necessary to use the spaces in the last two pairs in (3.71) in the estimate (4.38). The smoothness conditions in these cases take the form $a_\alpha \in C^{|\alpha|+|2m-s-1|}(G)$.

We can now prove a local formulation of the theorem: if $\phi \in W_2^s(G)$ is a solution of the given equation inside G, then $\phi \in W_{2,\mathrm{loc}}^{\min(t+2m,p)}(U)$ ($p < m$, $s \in [-p, p)$)

or $\phi \in W_{2,\mathrm{loc}}^{\min(t+2m,p+2m)}(U)$ $(p \geq m,\ s \in [-p, p+2m))$.

Suppose $s < 0$; we assume first that t is large and positive. Applying step 1, we find that $\chi\phi \in W_2^{s+1}(V)$. Now, in place of χ choose a function which is equal to 1 in a region V', lying strictly inside V, such that $\overline{U} \subset V'$. It follows from the proof that $\phi \in W_{2,\mathrm{loc}}^{s+1}(V')$ and satisfies the equation $Lu = f$. If $s + 1 < 0$, apply step 1 again, but replace V by a subregion $V_1 \supset \overline{U}$ strictly contained in V'; if $s + 1 = 0$, apply step 3. We obtain $\chi\phi \in W_2^{s+2}(V_1)$. Again for χ choose a function which in addition is equal to 1 in a region $V_1' \supset \overline{U}$, lying strictly inside V_1. Extend the argument with V_1 replaced by V_2, etc. If we arrive at $\chi\phi \in W_2^m$,[1] then further use 4; if we go up to $\chi\phi \in W_2^{2m}$, then use 5. The process can terminate only as the result of nonsmoothness of the coefficients. It is also clear that it could be started with $s \geq 0$. We show how the termination occurs in the specified way.

If $p < m$, then 1 can begin with $s = -p$ and extend up to $s = -1$; the last step gives $\chi\phi \in W_2^0 = L_2$. Then use 3; the last step is with $s = p - 1$, and it gives $\chi\phi \in W_2^{s+1} = W_2^p$, i.e. $\phi \in W_{2,\mathrm{loc}}^p$. If now $p \geq m$, then by means of 1 and 3 we may arrive at $\chi\phi \in W_0^m$, and then apply 4 and 5. The last step is with $|2m - s - 1| = p$, i.e. with $-2m + s + 1 = p$. As the result we obtain $\chi\phi \in W_2^{s+1} = W_2^{p+2m}$. Thus $\phi \in W_{2,\mathrm{loc}}^{p+2m}$.

If t is not large and positive, then the termination of this raising process can occur earlier; the last s is that which satisfies the equation $t = s - 2m + 1$; as the result we obtain inclusion in $W_2^{s+1} = W_2^{t+2m}$.

The theorem is proved in its local form. The theorem over all of G follows from this proof and Lemma 3.2, Chapter II.

6. **Smoothness up to the boundary.** We show that the method of the previous subsection can be used to prove smoothness of generalized solutions up to the boundary of the region. We consider the case of null boundary conditions, for which we are able to formulate the most complete results. The general case will be considered in §6.12. Below we use the definitions of §3.5, Chapter II.

Theorem 4.6. *Let L be a strongly elliptic expression of order $2m$, with coefficients $a_\alpha(x) \in C^{|\alpha|+p}(G \cup \Gamma_0)$, where $\Gamma_0 \subseteq \Gamma$ is a piece of class C^{2m+p} $(p \geq 0)$. Assume that the function $\phi \in W_2^s(G)$ $(s = \cdots, -1, 0, 1, \cdots)$ satisfies the equation $Lu = f$ inside G and up to the piece Γ_0 of the boundary,*

1) For simplicity we no longer indicate the region in the notation for the spaces.

where the problem has null boundary conditions (*i.e.* $D^\alpha u|_{\Gamma_0} = 0$, $|\alpha| \le m-1$). *Here* $f \in W^{s-2m}_{2,\mathrm{loc}}(G, \Gamma_0)$, *i.e. it belongs to* W_2^{s-2m} *inside* G *and up to* Γ_0. *The equation is satisfied if*

$$(\varphi, L^+ v)_0 = (f, v)_0 \tag{4.39}$$

for all $v \in \overset{\circ}{W}{}_2^m(G) \cap W_2^{2m+\max(-s,0)}(G)$ *vanishing in a neighborhood of* $\Gamma \backslash \Gamma_0$.

Suppose that, actually, the function $f \in W^t_{2,\mathrm{loc}}(G, \Gamma_0)$, *where* $t > s-2m$ *has arbitrary sign. Then* 1) *for* $p < m$ *and* $s \in [-p, p)$ *we automatically have* $\phi \in W^{\min(t+2m,p)}_{2,\mathrm{loc}}(G, \Gamma_0)$; 2) *for* $p \ge m$ *and* $s \in [-p, p+2m)$ *we have* $\phi \in W^{\min(t+2m,p+2m)}_{2,\mathrm{loc}}(G, \Gamma_0)$. *Moreover, if the* min *is positive, then* ϕ (*more precisely, the function with which* ϕ *coincides*) *vanishes on* Γ_0 *along with some number of its derivatives. Namely, in case* 1), $D^\alpha \phi|_{\Gamma_0} = 0$ *for* $|\alpha| \le \min(t+2m, p) - 1$; *in case* 2), $D^\alpha \phi|_{\Gamma_0} = 0$ *for* $|\alpha| \le \min(t+2m, m) - 1$.

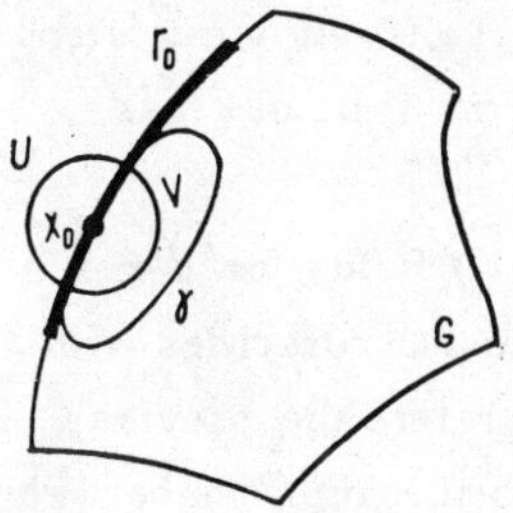

Figure 4.

Proof. The theorem is obtained along the lines of the arguments in the proof of Theorem 4.5, and is based on Theorem 3.6; we outline it. Let x_0 be a point in the interior of the piece Γ_0, U a sphere with center x_0 and sufficiently small radius, and $V \subset G$ a region with sufficiently smooth boundary γ covering $U \cap G$ as indicated in Figure 4. Suppose that the diameter of V is sufficiently small that the problem $L^+ u = f$ in V, with null boundary conditions, is solvable: Theorem 3.6 holds for sufficiently large $|s|$. Let $\chi(x) \in C^\infty(E_n)$ be a nonnegative function vanishing in a neighborhood of the set $G \backslash V$. We now show how the steps 1 – 5 of the previous proof are carried over.

1. Let $s < 0$, $\sigma = -s$; if $\phi \in W_2^s(G) = W_2^{-\sigma}(G)$ satisfies the equation $Lu = f$ in the sense of the definition (4.39) with $f \in W^t_{2,\mathrm{loc}}(G, \gamma \cap \Gamma_0)$ $(t > -\sigma - 2m)$, then

$$\chi\varphi \in W_2^{-\sigma+1}(V). \tag{4.40}$$

The proof of this fact is hardly different from the proof of the previous step 1. As there, the necessary smoothness on the coefficients is $a_\alpha \in C^{|\alpha|+|s|}(G)$; the piece Γ_0 of the boundary must obviously be of class $C^{2m+|s|}$

2. An essential difficulty is encountered in the attempt to prove equation (4.36); it is connected with the fact that $\chi(x)$ does not necessarily reduce to zero near Γ_0 and the free shifting of derivatives in (4.35) is no longer possible. There-

fore step 2 now appears in the following way: let $u \in W_2^s(V)$ $(s > 0)$ be such that for $|\alpha| \leq \min(s-1, m-1)$, $D^\alpha u$ vanishes on part Γ_0' of the boundary of V, lying interior to Γ_0. Then automatically

$$(u, M_\chi w)_0 = (\psi, w)_0 \quad (w \in \mathring{W}_2^m(V) \cap W_2^{2m}(V)), \tag{4.41}$$

where $\psi \in W_2^{-2m+s+1}(V)$; for $s = 0$ equation (4.41) holds for any $u \in L_2(V)$. The proof of this formulation of the assertion is exactly like that of the former. We now prove (4.40) for $s \geq 0$.

3′. Suppose $s = 0$. Equation (4.41) holds for any $u \in L_2(V)$, and therefore the proof of the previous step 3 carries over, and we obtain (4.40). We remark that the function μ, which coincides with $\chi\phi$, belongs to $\mathring{W}_2^1(V)$ by construction.

3″. Suppose $0 < s < m$. The inclusion $\chi\phi \in W_2^{s+1}(V)$ holds for $\phi \in W_2^s(G)$, and in addition $D^\alpha\phi|_{\Gamma_0'} = 0$ for $|\alpha| \leq s-1$; the function $\chi\phi$ coincides with a $\mu \in \mathring{W}_2^{s+1}(V)$. In fact, (4.41) can now be written for $u = \phi$ and the proof of 3 again carries over; by construction μ belongs to $\mathring{W}_2^{s+1}(V)$. To carry out steps 3′ and 3″ it is necessary to have $a_\alpha \in C^{|\alpha|+s+1}(G)$; Γ_0 must be of class C^{2m+s+1}.

4. Suppose $m \leq s < 2m$. The inclusion $\chi\phi \in W_2^{s+1}(V)$ holds for $\phi \in W_2^s(G)$ and in addition $D^\alpha\phi|_{\Gamma_0'} = 0$ for $|\alpha| \leq m-1$; the function $\chi\phi$ coincides with a $\mu \in W_2'^{s+1}(V)$. In fact, we can again write (4.41), and therefore the previous proof carries over. The estimate (4.38), by virtue of the homeomorphism between the third pair of spaces in (3.71), appears as

$$|(\theta, w)_0| \leqslant \|\theta\|_{-2m+s+1} \|w\|_{2m-s-1} \leqslant C \|\theta\|_{-2m+s+1} \|L^+ w\|_{W_2'^{-s-1}(V)}$$

$$(w \in \mathring{W}_2^m(V) \cap W_2^{2m}(V)).$$

Consequently, the expression $(\theta, w)_0$ can be considered as a linear continuous functional of L^+w, which varies by virtue of Theorem 3.6 over a dense set in $W_2'^{-s-1}(V)$. This functional is represented in the form

$$(\theta, w)_0 = (\mu, L^+ w)_0, \quad \mu \in W_2'^{s+1}(V) = \mathring{W}_2^m(V) \cap W_2^{s+1}(V) \subset \mathring{W}_2^m(G).$$

Assertion 4 therefore follows. The required smoothness restrictions are $a_\alpha \in C^{|\alpha|+|2m-s-1|}(G)$, Γ_0 of class $C^{2m+|2m-s-1|}$.

5. The case $s \geq 2m$ is treated similarly to 4; the smoothness restrictions are the same as there.

It is now easy to prove the theorem in a local form: let $\phi \in W_2^s(G)$ be a solution of the equation $Lu = f$ as described in the theorem. Then

$$\varphi \in W_{2,\mathrm{loc}}^{\min(t+2m,p)}(U \cap G, \gamma \cap \Gamma_0) \qquad (p < m, \quad s \in [-p, p))$$

or

$$\varphi \in W_{2,\mathrm{loc}}^{\min(t+2m,p+2m)}(U \cap G, \gamma \cap \Gamma_0) \quad (p \geqslant m, \quad s \in [-p, p+2m)),$$

and moreover ϕ vanishes on $\gamma \cap \Gamma_0$ along with its derivatives in the way described in the theorem. The proof of this fact is carried out exactly as it was for Theorem 4.5; it is only necessary that the regions V_j, V_j' contract in the region and slide along Γ_0. Then (beginning with 3″), the solution ϕ is proper with respect to its vanishing along with a certain number of derivatives on Γ_0'; the previous step guarantees exactly this degree of vanishing for $\chi\phi$.

The passage to the general formulation is effected with the help of the local formulation of Theorem 4.5 and the variation of Lemma 3.2, Chapter II, mentioned on p. 94. The theorem follows.

In conclusion, we formulate an elementary result of this type for a boundary condition

$$\left.\frac{\partial u}{\partial \mu} + \sigma(x) u\right|_{\Gamma_0} = 0 \quad (\sigma \in C^1(\Gamma_0));$$

the proof is based on the homeomorphisms 1) and 2) mentioned at the end of §3.7, and the homeomorphism adjoint to 1) (it is not explicitly stated there).

Theorem 4.7. *Let L be a strongly elliptic expression of the second order with $a_\alpha(x) \in C^{|\alpha|}(G \cup \Gamma)$. Let Γ_0 be a piece of the boundary Γ of class C^2, on which the problem has the boundary condition* (bd):

$$\left.\frac{\partial u}{\partial \mu} + \sigma(x) u\right|_{\Gamma_0} = 0 \qquad (\sigma \in C^1(\Gamma_0));$$

assume that near Γ_0 the coefficients $p_j(x)$ in the representation (2.4) *of the expression L are real. Suppose that $\phi \in W_2^{-1}(G)$ satisfies the equation $Lu = f \in W_{2,\mathrm{loc}}^t(G, \Gamma_0)$ $(t = -1, 0)$ inside G and up to the piece Γ_0. Then $\phi \in W_{2,\mathrm{loc}}^{t+2}(G, \Gamma_0)$, and for $t = 0$ it satisfies the given boundary condition on Γ_0.*

The theorem is proved by arguments similar to those for Theorems 4.5 and 4.6. We mention one difficulty. For the given boundary condition and decreasing diameter of the region V in the problem $Lu = f$, $u \in$ (bd), it is possible that the problem will not be solvable for arbitrary f. Therefore we proceed in this way: if $f \in W_2^{-1}(V)$, then $\phi \in W_2^{-1}(V)$ is a solution of the equation $Lu + \lambda u = f + \lambda\phi \in W_2^{-1}(V)$ for any number λ. Choose λ sufficiently positive that for the expression $Lu + \lambda u$ with the corresponding boundary condition on the boundary of V, the homeomorphism assertion at the end of §3.7 holds. It is then possible to prove that $\phi \in W_{2,\mathrm{loc}}^1(G, \Gamma_0)$. In the case $f \in L_2(V)$, we have $f + \lambda\phi \in W_2^{-1}(V)$, and therefore the previous argument gives $\phi \in W_2^1(V) \subset L_2(V)$. Now $f + \lambda\phi \in L_2(V)$, and repeating the previous argument, we obtain $\phi \in W_{2,\mathrm{loc}}^2(G, \Gamma_0)$.

7. **Application to boundary value problems and eigenvalue problems.** The application of Theorems 4.1, 4.3, 4.5 – 4.7 to boundary value problems is clear: if u is a generalized solution to the equation $Lu = f$ in a region G (bounded or not) in the sense that

$$(u, L^+v)_0 = (f, v)_0 \tag{4.42}$$

for a sufficiently large number of functions, finite with respect to G and ∞, then in the case of ellipticity or strong ellipticity, the order of generality of the solution in a neighborhood of the point $x_0 \in G$ will, generally speaking, decrease if f and the coefficients $a_\alpha(x)$ of the expression L near x_0 are sufficiently smooth. If equation (4.42) holds not only for finite v, but also for v satisfying these or other homogeneous boundary conditions near part of the boundary, then the improved smoothness of the solution can be extended to a neighborhood of a point $x_0 \in \Gamma$, if, in addition to smoothness for f and $a_\alpha(x)$ near x_0, we have smoothness for Γ_0. The smoothness of u always increases with increasing smoothness for f, $a_\alpha(x)$, and Γ_0.

A similar situation holds for eigenfunctions, i.e. generalized solutions of the problem $Lu - \lambda u = 0$, $u \in$ (bd). Since improved smoothness is the same for the expressions $L - \lambda E$ and L, the smoothness properties of eigenfunctions are determined by the coefficients of the expression L and the smoothness of part of the boundary.

8. **The minimal and maximal operators induced by strongly elliptic expressions.** It is now easy to clarify the structure of the domains of these operators. All considerations below are carried out in $L_2(G)$; G bounded.

Theorem 4.8. *Let* L *be a strongly elliptic expression of order* $2m$, *with the usual smoothness conditions on the coefficients* $a_\alpha(x)$; Γ *piecewise smooth. Then*: 1) *the domain of the minimal operator* Λ *coincides with* $\overset{\circ}{W}{}_2^{2m}(G)$; 2) *under the assumption that* $a_\alpha(x) \in C^{|\alpha|+m}(G \cup \Gamma)$, *the maximal operator* Π *coincides* *with the closure of the operator* $u \to Lu(u \in C^\infty(G \cup \Gamma))$.

The proof of 1) follows from the second inequality in (1.29) (for $s = 0$) and the obvious fact that the domains of the operators constructed from L and $L + kE$ coincide.

We use Lemma 2.2, Chapter II, for the proof of the second part. Extend the coefficients of L to all of E_n so as to preserve strong ellipticity and smoothness. Equation (2.15), Chapter II, shows that inside some fixed bounded region G', strictly containing G in its interior, $L^+\hat{u} = h \in L_2(G')$. According to Theorem 4.5 (for $s = 0$, $t = 0$, $p = m$), $\hat{u} \in W_{2,\text{loc}}^{2m}(G')$; at the same time $\hat{u}(x) = 0$, $x \in G' \setminus G$. It follows that u and all derivatives of order $\leq 2m - 1$ vanish on Γ, i.e. $u \in \mathring{W}_2^{2m}(G) = \mathfrak{D}(\Lambda^+)$. Thus the hypotheses of the lemma are satisfied; $\mathcal{L} = \bar{A}$. The theorem follows.

We remark that $\mathfrak{D}(\mathcal{L})$ does not coincide with $W_2^r(G)$. For, suppose $G \subset E_3$, $L = \Delta = L^+$. The functions $u(x) = 1/|x - x_0|$, where $x_0 \in \Gamma$, belong to $\mathfrak{D}(\mathcal{L})$: for any $v \in C_0^\infty(G)$, we have

$$\left(\Delta v, \frac{1}{|x - x_0|}\right)_0 = \left(v, \Delta_x \frac{1}{|x - x_0|}\right)_0 = (v, 0)_0,$$

i.e. $u \in \mathfrak{D}((\Lambda^+)')^* = \mathfrak{D}(\mathcal{L})$ and $\mathcal{L}u = 0$; at the same time it is obvious that $u \bar{\in} W_2^2(G)$.

§5. GREEN'S FUNCTION

We consider the generalized solution of the problem $Lu = f$, $u \in$ (bd), as the action of some operator on f. In the case of elliptic expressions, as a rule, this operator acts continuously in L_2. We now show that it is an integral operator, whose kernel is called Green's function, and we study the properties of this function and also establish some auxiliary results. To study the behavior of Green's function on the boundary we will use Theorem 4.6, and we are therefore forced to restrict attention to strongly elliptic expressions and null boundary conditions. At the same time, the presentation will be made in such a way that the reader will be able to formulate, without difficulty, the corresponding results for general elliptic equations and conditions, using the results in §6.12 concerning improved smoothness. We assume below that G is bounded; the case of unbounded G will be considered in the last subsection.

1. Existence and properties of Green's function inside a region. We prove the following general theorem.

Theorem 5.1. *Let L be an elliptic expression of order r, with coefficients $a_\alpha(x) \in C^{|\alpha|+r+p}(G)$; here $p \geq n+1$. Suppose that there exists an operator R, acting continuously in $L_2(G)$, such that Rf and $R^* f$ are generalized solutions inside G of the respective equations $Lu = f$ and $L^+ u = f$ for any $f \in L_2(G)$. We then have an integral representation*

$$(Ru, v)_0 = \int_G \int_G R(x, y)\, u(y) \overline{v(x)}\, dx dy \qquad (u, v \in C_0(G)). \tag{5.1}$$

The kernel $R(x, y)$ $(x, y \in G,\ x \neq y)$ has the following properties:

1) *all derivatives of the form $D_x^\alpha D_y^\beta R$ $(|\alpha|, |\beta| \leq r + p)$ exist and are continuous with respect to $(x, y) \in G \times G$, $x \neq y$;*

2) *the following equations, with respect to x and y, hold:*

$$(L_x R)(x, y) = \delta_y, \qquad (L_y^{\oplus} R)(x, y) = \delta_x; \tag{5.2}$$

3) *for $|x - y|$ sufficiently small,*

$$R(x, y) = e(x, y) + r(x, y), \tag{5.3}$$

where $e(x, y)$ is a fundamental solution for the expression L, and $r(x, y)$ is continuously differentiable as many times as above with respect to $(x, y) \in G \times G$ (thus for $x = y$, $R(x, y)$ has a singularity of the form $1/|x - y|^{n-r}$ if $n > r$, of the form $\log|x - y|$ if $n = r$, and is bounded if $n < r$).

Proof. According to Theorem 3.4, Chapter I, $(Ru, v)_0 = B(u, v)$ admits a representation

$$(Ru, v)_0 = \int_G \int_G K(x, y)\, (Du)(y)\, (D\overline{v})(x)\, dx dy$$

$$(K(x, y) \in C(E_n \times E_n);\quad D = D_1, \ldots, D_n;\quad u, v \in C_0^n(G)). \tag{5.4}$$

Let $O = (G \times G) \backslash \Omega$, where Ω is the set of points $(x, x) \in E_n \times E_n$. We show that inside O, the generalized kernal $D_x D_y K$ in the sense of L. Schwartz satisfies the equations

$$L_x U = 0, \quad L_y^{\oplus} U = 0 \tag{5.5}$$

in the sense of the definition (4.17). We use the equivalent definition (4.18). Let $v', v'' \in C_0^\infty(G)$ be such that the product of their supports lies inside O; hence their supports do not meet; we obtain the required relation with the help of (5.4) and the equation $D^+ = (-1)^n D$:

$$\int_G\int_G K(x, y)\overline{(D^+L^+v')(x)}\,\overline{(D^+v'')(y)}\,dxdy = (R\bar{v}'', L^+v')_0 = (\bar{v}'', v')_0 = 0,$$

$$\int_G\int_G K(x, y)\,\overline{(D^+v')(x)}\,\overline{(D^+\bar{L}v'')(y)}\,dxdy = (RL\bar{v}'', v')_0 = \overline{(R^*v', L\bar{v}'')_0}$$

$$= \overline{(v', \bar{v}'')_0} = (\bar{v}'', v')_0 = 0. \qquad (5.6)$$

Applying Theorem 4.2, we find a function $R(x, y)$, $(x, y) \in O$, having the smoothness properties stated in 1), satisfying (5.2) (since now $x \neq y$, $\delta_y = \delta_x = 0$), and coinciding inside O with $D_x D_y K$ as a functional:

$$\int_G\int_G R(x, y)\,\overline{V(x, y)}\,dxdy = \int_G\int_G K(x, y)\,\overline{(D_xD_yV)(x, y)}\,dxdy \quad (V \in C_0^\infty(O)). \qquad (5.7)$$

Let $W \subseteq G \times G$ be a neighborhood of the set $\Omega \cap (G \times G)$, in which there exists a fundamental solution $e(x, y)$. The function $e(x, y)$ is summable inside W (see 2) in §4.1) and therefore may be considered as a generalized function T in the sense of L. Schwartz on $C_0^\infty(W)$. We show that inside W, it satisfies the equations

$$L_xU = Д, \quad L_y^{\oplus}U = Д, \qquad (5.8)$$

where $Д$ is a generalized function on $C_0^\infty(W)$ defined by the equation $(Д, U) = \overline{\int_G U(x, x)\,dx}$ $(U \in C_0^\infty(W))$. In fact, let $v', v'' \in C_0^\infty(G)$ be such that the product of their supports lies inside W; using property 1) of a fundamental solution, we obtain the required equations

$$\int_W\int e(x, y)\overline{(L^+v')(x)}\,\overline{v''(y)}\,dxdy = (\bar{v}'', v')_0 = (Д, v'(x)\,v''(y)),$$

$$\int_W\int e(x, y)\,\overline{v'(x)}\,\overline{(\bar{L}v'')(y)}\,dxdy = (\bar{v}'', v')_0 = (Д, v'(x)\,v''(y)).$$

On the other hand, $D_x D_y K$ also satisfies equation (5.8) inside W; this follows from the relations (5.6) in which v', v'' have supports whose product lies inside W. Therefore $D_x D_y K - T$ satisfies equation (5.5) inside W, and Theorem 4.2 can be applied to it. According to this theorem, we can find a sufficiently smooth function $r(x, y)$ $((x, y) \in W)$ such that

$$\int_W\int K(x, y)\overline{(D_xD_yV)(x, y)}\,dxdy - \int_W\int e(x, y)\,\overline{V(x, y)}\,dxdy$$

$$= \int_W\int r(x, y)\,\overline{V(x, y)}\,dxdy \quad (V \in C_0^\infty(W)). \qquad (5.9)$$

Now choose $V(x, y)$ so that in addition it vanishes in a neighborhood of the diagonal Ω. Then both relations (5.7) and (5.9) hold for this function, and hence $\iint_W R\overline{V}dxdy = \iint_W (e+r)\overline{V}dxdy$, which implies (5.3).

We show that equation (5.1) holds. As a preliminary, we obtain V in the form $V = V_1 + V_2$ where $V_1 \in C_0^\infty(G \times G)$ and in addition vanishes in some neighborhood of the diagonal Ω, and $V_2 \in C_0^\infty(G \times G)$ and vanishes outside a strictly interior subregion of the region W. Using (5.7), (5.9), and (5.3), we obtain (5.7) for $V \in C_0^\infty(G \times G)$:

$$\int_G\int_G K\overline{D_x D_y V}\, dxdy = \int_G\int_G K\overline{D_x D_y V_1}dxdy + \int\int_W K\overline{D_x D_y V_2}dxdy$$

$$= \int_G\int_G R\overline{V}_1 dxdy + \int\int_W (e+r)\overline{V}_2 dxdy = \int_G\int_G R\overline{(V_1+V_2)}\, dxdy$$

$$= \int_G\int_G R\overline{V}dxdy.$$

In the proof of this relation, if we set $V(x, y) = v(x)\,\overline{u(y)}$ $(u, v \in C_0^\infty(G))$, then by (5.4) we find that (5.1) holds for such u, v, and hence for $u, v \in C_0(G)$.

It remains to prove (5.2) for any $x, y \in G$. If $v', v'' \in C_0^\infty(G)$, then by (5.1)

$$\int_G\int_G R(x, y)\,\overline{(L^+v')(x)}\,\overline{v''(y)}\, dxdy = (R\overline{v''}, L^+v')_0 = (\overline{v''}, v')_0$$

$$= \int_G \overline{v''(y)}\,\overline{v'(y)}\, dy.$$

Since v'' is arbitrary, it follows that

$$\int_G R(x, y)\overline{(L^+v')(x)}\, dx = \overline{v'(y)}\ (v' \in C_0^\infty(G);\ y \in G), \text{ i. e. } L_x R = \delta_y.$$

The proof of the second equation in (5.2) is similar. The theorem follows.

Consider a problem with parameter λ (L elliptic)

$$Lu - \lambda u = f \in L_2(G), \quad u \in (\text{bd}), \tag{5.10}$$

satisfying the conditions of Theorem 3.5, Chapter II. A solution to this problem, for λ not an eigenvalue λ_k, exists and has the form $u = (A - \lambda E)^{-1} f \in W_2^m(G) \subset L_2(G)$, where A is the operator constructed in Chapter II, §3.7. Since by Lemma 3.3, Chapter II, $(A - \lambda E)^{-1*} f$ solves the adjoint problem; applying the theorem just proved, we conclude that our solution has the form

$$u(x) = \int_G R(x, y; \lambda) f(y)\, dy \quad (f \in C_0(G) \subset L_2(G);\ x \in G). \tag{5.11}$$

For each $\lambda \neq \lambda_k$, the kernel $R(x, y; \lambda)$ exists and has properties 1)–3) in Theorem 5.1. It is called Green's function for the problem (5.10) (or the kernel of the resolvent $R_\lambda = (A - \lambda E)^{-1}$).

It follows from Lemma 3.3 that $\overline{R(x, y; \bar{\lambda})}$ is the Green's function for the adjoint problem. In particular, Green's function exists for problems with null boundary conditions or conditions in the third type of boundary value problem (see Theorems 2.1 – 2.3).

2. Existence and properties of Green's function up to the boundary of the region. Consider again an expression L and operator R as in Theorem 5.1; we suppose in addition that Rf and R^*f are generalized solutions to the problems $Lu = f$, $u \in$ (bd), and $L^+v = f$, $v \in (\text{bd})^+$, respectively for any $f \in L_2(G)$; here (bd) denotes some boundary conditions. Let $l = [n/2] + 1$ and apply Theorem 3.3, Chapter I, to the form $B(u, v) = (Ru, v)_0$. According to this theorem, we can find a generalized kernel $\mathrm{R} \in W_2^{-l}(G) \otimes W_2^{-l}(G)$ such that for any $u, v \in W_2^l(G)$ we have the equation

$$(Ru, v)_0 = (\mathrm{R}, v(x)\overline{u(y)})_0 \, .^{1)} \tag{5.12}$$

It is clear that inside $G \times G$ this kernel coincides with $R(x, y)$, and it is therefore sufficiently smooth there; coincidence follows from the equation (see (5.1)):

$$(\mathrm{R}, v'(x) v''(y))_0 = (R\bar{v}'', v')_0 = \int_G \int_G R(x, y) \overline{v''(y)}\, \overline{v'(x)}\, dx dy = (R(x, y), v'(x) v''(y))_0 \; (v', v'' \in C_0^\infty(G)).$$

At the same time R does not, generally speaking, cease to be singular over all of $(G \cup \Gamma) \times (G \cup \Gamma)$.

Naturally, R satisfies boundary conditions with respect to x and y. However, in view of the singularities of R, this must be suitably interpreted: a generalized function $\alpha \in W_2^{-\sigma}(G)$ $(\sigma \geq 0)$ satisfies the equation $Lu = f \in W_2^{-r-\sigma}(G)$ and boundary conditions (bd), if the equation $(\alpha, L^+v)_0 = (f, v)_0$ holds not only for $v \in C_0^\infty(G)$, but also for $v \in W_2^r(\text{bd})^+ \cap W_2^{r+\sigma}(G)$ (see Chapter 2, §3.3).

We make a useful construction. As before, let Д be the generalized function in $W_2^{-l}(G) \otimes W_2^{-l}(G)$ defined by

$$(Д, U)_0 = \int_G \overline{U(x, x)}\, dx \quad (U \in W_2^l(G) \otimes W_2^l(G)).$$

1) Actually, R is smoother than the elements of the space $W_2^{-l}(G) \otimes W_2^{-l}(G)$ (see (3.7) or (2.20), (2.21), Chapter II). Therefore the smoothness restrictions on functions in the positive spaces in (5.12) and (5.13) can be relaxed with respect to one of the variables x and y.

The definition is meaningful: for $u \in W_2^l(G)$, $|u(x)| \leq C\|u\|_l$ uniformly with respect to $x \in G$, and therefore for $U(x, y) = u'(x)\, u''(y)$ $(u', u'' \in W_2^l(G))$:

$$\Big|\int_G \overline{U(x,x)}\,dx\Big| \leqslant C_1\|u'\|_l\|u''\|_l = C_1\|U\|_{W_2^l(G)\otimes W_2^l(G)};$$

the estimate extends to all $U \in W_2^l(G) \otimes W_2^l(G)$ by the assertion on p. 41.

It follows from (5.2) and (5.12) that R satisfies (5.8) inside $G \times G$. We now show that R satisfies this equation not only inside $G \times G$, but over all $(G \cup \Gamma) \times (G \cup \Gamma)$ with some boundary restriction. Consider the condition $(\mathrm{bd})_x$ for the region $G \times G$, consisting of the subspace $W_2^r(\mathrm{bd}) \otimes W_2^r(G)$ of the space $W_2^r(G) \otimes W_2^r(G)$, and the condition $(\mathrm{bd})_y^{\oplus}$ consisting of the subspace $W_2^r(G) \otimes \overline{W_2^r(\mathrm{bd})^+}$ (the bar denotes passage to complex conjugates). Then

$$(\mathrm{R}, (L_x^+V)(x, y))_0 = (Д, V(x, y))_0 \,(V \in (W_2^r(\mathrm{bd})^+ \cap W_2^{r+l}(G)) \otimes W_2^{\max(r,l)}(G)),$$

$$(\mathrm{R}, (\overline{L}_yV)(x, y))_0 = (Д, V(x, y))_0 (V \in W_2^{\max(r,l)}(G) \otimes \overline{(W_2^r(\mathrm{bd}) \cap W_2^{r+l}(G))}), \tag{5.13}$$

i.e. (5.8) is satisfied with the conditions $(\mathrm{bd})_x$ and $(\mathrm{bd})_y^{\oplus}$ respectively.

We prove, for example, the first equation in (5.13). It is sufficient to consider

$$V(x, y) = v'(x)\, v''(y), \quad v' \in W_2^r(\mathrm{bd})^+ \cap W_2^{r+l}(G), \quad v'' \in W_2^{\max(r,l)}(G);$$

If we use (5.12) and notice that Rf is a generalized solution for the problem $Lu = f$, $u \in (\mathrm{bd})$, we obtain

$$(\mathrm{R}, (L_x^+V)(x, y))_0 = (\mathrm{R}, (L^+v')(x)\, v''(y))_0 = (R\overline{v}'', L^+v')_0$$

$$= (\overline{v}'', v')_0 = (Д, v'(x)\, v''(y))_0.$$

These results are summarized in the following theorem.

Theorem 5.2. *Let L and R be as in Theorem* 5.1, $a_\alpha(x) \in C^{|\alpha|+r+p}(G \cup \Gamma)$, *and in addition suppose it is known that Rf and $R^* f$, for any $f \in L_2(G)$, are generalized solutions for the problems $Lu = f$, $u \in (\mathrm{bd})$, and $L^+ v = f$, $v \in (\mathrm{bd})^+$, respectively* ((bd) *denotes some boundary conditions*). *Then there exists a generalized kernel* $\mathrm{R} \in W_2^{-l}(G) \otimes W_2^{-l}(G)$, *where $l = [n/2] + 1$, such that* $(Ru, v)_0 = (\mathrm{R}, v(x)\, \overline{u(y)})_0$ *for all u, $v \in W_2^l(G)$. Inside the region $G \times G$, this kernel coincides with the kernel $R(x, y)$ given in Theorem* 5.1, *and therefore it is sufficiently smooth there. It satisfies the boundary conditions* (bd) *with respect to the variable x, and the conditions* $(\mathrm{bd})^{\oplus}$ *with respect to the variable y; in other words, it satisfies the relation* (5.13).

It is clear from Lemma 3.3, Chapter II, that Green's function for the problem (5.10) can be defined over all of the region $(G \cup \Gamma) \times (G \cup \Gamma)$ as a generalized kernel $\mathrm{R}_\lambda \in W_2^{-l}(G) \otimes W_2^{-l}(G)$, occurring in the representation (5.12) for the operator $R = (A - \lambda E)^{-1}$. This kernel coincides with $R(x, y, \lambda)$ inside $G \times G$. *Theorem* 5.2 *holds for the kernel* R_λ *for each* $\lambda \neq \lambda_k$.

3. **The concept of Green's function for boundary conditions in the classical sense.** We show that for "nice" boundary conditions with sufficiently smooth coefficients and boundary, Green's function is sufficiently smooth up to the boundary and satisfies these conditions with respect to each of its variables. We give three interdependent approaches to this problem. They are presented respectively in subsections 3, 4, and 5. The first approach gives smoothness of the kernel simultaneously as a function of two variables and is very simple; however, it is suitable only for a very restrictive class of problems. The other two approaches study $R(x, y)$ with respect to each variable separately. In subsections 6 and 7 we present certain supplements.

We make use of an artificial device. Consider a differential expression M with respect to $2n$ variables $x_1, \cdots, x_n; y_1, \cdots, y_n$, acting according to the rule $(MU)(x, y) = (L_x U)(x, y) + (L_y^{\oplus} U)(x, y)$. If L has order $2m$ and is strongly elliptic, then M is also strongly elliptic and has order $2m$; this follows from the fact that for vectors

$$(\xi, \eta) \in E_{2n} (\xi, \eta \in E_n) (\operatorname{Re} M)_c ((x, y), (\xi, \eta)) = (\operatorname{Re} L)_c (x, \xi) + (\operatorname{Re} L)_c (y, \eta).$$

Suppose now that L has order $2m$, and let R be as in Theorem 5.2; R is the kernel in $W_2^{-l}(G) \otimes W_2^{-l}(G)$ corresponding to R. We will consider generalized kernels in $W_2^{-l}(G) \otimes W_2^{-l}(G)$ as generalized functions in $W_2^{-2l}(G \times G)$ (see Theorem 3.2, Chapter I); since the kernel R satisfies (5.8) inside $G \times G$, it follows that $\mathrm{R} \in W_2^{-2l}(G \times G)$ is a generalized solution inside $G \times G$ of the equation

$$MU = 2Д \in W_2^{-2l} (G \times G). \tag{5.14}$$

Moreover, it is not difficult to see that this equation is satisfied up to the boundary; now applying Theorem 4.6 to M and R, we obtain the necessary smoothness for R up to the boundary.

In fact, the boundary of the region $G \times G$ is the set $S = (\Gamma \times (G \cup \Gamma)) \cup ((G \cup \Gamma) \times \Gamma)$. Let Γ_1 (Γ_2) be a piece of Γ, $G_1 \subseteq G$ $(G_2 \subseteq G)$ a subregion adjoining Γ along Γ_1 (Γ_2). Suppose that the distance between G_1 and G_2 is positive; Γ_1 and Γ_2 may be empty. The set $S_0 = (\Gamma_1 \times G_2) \cup (G_1 \times \Gamma_2)$ is a piece of the

$2m-1$-dimensional surface S; if Γ_1 and Γ_2 are $2m+q$ $(q \geq m,\ n+2)$ times continuously differentiable pieces, then S_0 will be a piece with the same smoothness. Let L be a strongly elliptic expression in some neighborhood of the sets $G_1 \cup \Gamma_1$ and $G_2 \cup \Gamma_2$, with coefficients $a_\alpha \in C^{|\alpha|+q}$. Then the expression M is also strongly elliptic in a $2n$-dimensional neighborhood of the set S_0, and its coefficients will have smoothness $C^{|\alpha|+q}$.

Now suppose that (bd) is null on $\Gamma_1 \cup \Gamma_2$: functions in W_2^{2m}(bd) satisfy $D^\alpha u|_{\Gamma_1 \cup \Gamma_2} = 0$ $(|\alpha| \leq m-1)$ on $\Gamma_1 \cup \Gamma_2$. Then both of the relations (5.13) hold for functions $V(x, y) \in W^{2m+n+2}(G \times G)$, all of whose derivatives (with respect to x and y together) vanish on S_0 up to the order $m-1$ inclusive, and which itself vanishes in a $2n$-dimensional neighborhood of the closure of the region $(G \times G)\setminus(G_1 \times G_1)$. This follows from the fact that any such function along with a sufficient number of derivatives may be approximated in the required metric by functions of class

$$(W_2^r(\text{bd})^+ \cap W_2^{r+l}(G)) \otimes W_2^{\max(r,l)}(G) \text{ and } W_2^{\max(r,l)}(G) \otimes \overline{(W_2^r(\text{bd}) \cap W_2^{r+l}(G))},$$

for which (5.13) holds (note that $\mathrm{R} \in W_2^{-l}(G) \otimes W_2^{-l}(G) \subset W_2^{-2l}(G \times G)$, where $l = [n/2]+1$; therefore $(\mathrm{R}, U)_0$ is meaningful for $U \in W_2^{n+2}(G \times G)$, since $2l \leq n+2$).

Since $M^+ = L_x^+ + \overline{L}_y$, from (5.13) for such V, it follows that $(\mathrm{R}, M^+V)_0 = (2Д, V)_0$. The distance between G_1 and G_2, by construction, is positive, and therefore $G_1 \times G_2$ is at a positive distance from the diagonal $x = y$ in the region $G \times G$. Consequently, $V = 0$ in a neighborhood of this diagonal, and since $Д$ is concentrated on the diagonal, $(Д, V)_0 = 0$. Thus we now have $(\mathrm{R}, M^+V)_0 = 0$. On applying Theorem 4.6 (with q instead of p), we conclude that R belongs to the class W_2^{2m+q} inside $G_1 \times G_2$ and up to the piece S_0 of the boundary of this region (i.e. $\mathrm{R} \in W_{2,\text{loc}}^{2m+q}(G_1 \times G_2, S_0)$) and it satisfies null boundary conditions on S_0. Application of this theorem is possible: $q \geq m$ and $s = -2l \in [-q, q+2m)$ $(-2l \geq -(n+2) \geq -q)$. We have arrived at the following theorem.

Theorem 5.3. *Consider an expression L of order $r = 2m$, and let* R *and* (bd) *be as in Theorems 5.1 and 5.2. Let G_1 and G_2 be some subregions of G, at a positive distance from each other and adjoining Γ along pieces Γ_1 and Γ_2 respectively. Take boundary conditions on $\Gamma_1 \cup \Gamma_2$: $D^\alpha u|_{\Gamma_1 \cup \Gamma_2} = 0$ $(|\alpha| \leq m-1)$. If Γ_1 and Γ_2 are of class C^{2m+q} $(q \geq m,\ n+2)$, and if L is strongly elliptic in $G_1 \cup \Gamma_1$ and $G_2 \cup \Gamma_2$ with coefficients $a_\alpha(x) \in C^{|\alpha|+q}(G_j \cup \Gamma_j)$ $(j = 1, 2)$, then*

$$R(\cdot,\cdot)\in W^{2m+c}_{2,\,\mathrm{loc}}(G_1\times G_2,\ (\Gamma_1\times G_2)\cup(G_1\times\Gamma_2)),$$

i.e., with respect to the variable (x, y), *the kernel* $R(x, y)$ *is of class* W_2^{2m+q} *inside* $G_1\times G_2$ *and up to the part* $(\Gamma_1\times G_2)\cup(G_1\times\Gamma_2)$ *of the boundary of this region. The following boundary conditions are satisfied:*

$$(D_x^{\alpha}R)(x, y)\big|_{x\in\Gamma_1, y\in G_2}=0,\ (D_y^{\beta}R)(x, y)\big|_{x\in G_1, y\in\Gamma_2}=0\quad(|\alpha|, |\beta|\leqslant m-1).$$

The presentation of the above method of analysis for the smoothness of $R(x, y)$ can be carried over to certain other boundary conditions (for example, the type $\partial u/\partial\mu+\sigma(x)\,u|_{\Gamma}=0$ for equations of second order). We emphasize that strong ellipticity for L is essential: it guarantees strong ellipticity for M (this requirement on L can be somewhat weakened by the construction of a more general expression M; namely, we may take $(MU)(x, y)=A(x, y)\,(L_xU)(x, y)+B(x, y)\times(L_y^{\oplus}U)(x, y)$, where A and B are appropriate coefficients).

4. **Differential expressions of high order. Second method.** We present a device, suitable for expressions of order $r>n/2$, and not depending on the form of (bd).

Theorem 5.4. *Suppose that only the conditions of Theorem* 5.1 *are satisfied, and the expression* L *has high order:* $r>n/2$. *In this case, the kernel* $R(x, y)$ *belongs to* $L_2(G)$ *with respect to* y (*with respect to* x) *for fixed* $x\in G$ ($y\in G$), *i.e. it is a Carleman kernel. For any* $x\in G$ *and* $f\in L_2(G)$,

$$(Rf)(x)=\int_G R(x, y)\,f(y)\,dy,\quad (R^*f)(x)=\int_G \overline{R(y, x)}\,f(y)\,dy. \tag{5.15}$$

Moreover, the integrals

$$\int_G |R(x, y)|^2\,dy,\quad \int_G |R(x, y)|^2\,dx \tag{5.16}$$

are bounded when x *and* y *remain strictly interior to* G.

The proof is based on the following lemma.

Lemma 5.1. *Inside some sphere* $O\subset G$ *of radius* r, *let the function* $g\in L_2(O)$ *be a generalized solution of the equation* $Lu=f\in L_2(O)$ *for the given* L. *If the radius* r *is sufficiently small, then for* $x\in O_{r/2}$ ($O_{r/2}$ *is the sphere with the same center as* O, *but with radius half as large*) *we have the representation*

$$g(x)=\int_O A(x, \xi)\,g(\xi)\,d\xi+\int_O B(x, \xi)\,f(\xi)\,d\xi, \tag{5.17}$$

where the kernels $A(x, \xi)$ *and* $B(x, \xi)$ $(x, \xi, \in O)$ *belong to* $L_2(O)$ *with respect to* ξ, *and moreover their norms are bounded uniformly for* $x\in O_{r/2}$.

The proof follows from the relation (4.16). In fact, put $N=E$ and $O=U_{2R}$. Since $v_0\in C_0^{\infty}(O_{r/2})$ is arbitrary in (4.16), this relation is equivalent to

$$\int_O (g(x)-\theta(x))\,\overline{L_x^+[\overline{e(\xi,x)}[k(|\xi-x|)-1]]}\,dx+g(\xi)-\theta(\xi)=0$$

$$(\xi\in O_{\frac{r}{2}}), \tag{5.18}$$

where $\theta(x) = \int_O e(x, \eta)\, f(\eta)\, d\eta$ (note that since $e(x, \eta)$ belongs to L_2 with respect to η in our case, the calculations in the first two steps of the proof of Theorem 4.1 can be carried out not only for $f \in C$, but also for $f \in L_2$). Substituting the expression for θ into (5.18) and changing variables, we obtain the representation (5.17), where

$$A(x,\xi)=-\overline{L_\xi^+[\overline{e(x,\xi)}[k(|x-\xi|)-1]]},\quad B(x,\xi)=e(x,\xi)$$
$$+\int_O e(\eta,\xi)\,\overline{L_\eta^+[\overline{e(x,\eta)}[k(|x-\eta|)-1]]}\,d\eta.$$

The properties of the kernels A and B follow from properties of fundamental solutions. The lemma follows.

It is now easy to prove the theorem. By assumption, the function $(Rf)(x)$ ($f \in L_2(G)$) is a generalized solution of the equation $Lu = f$ and therefore it is sufficiently smooth inside G. Consider a neighborhood $O \subset G$ for which the lemma holds; define a linear functional l_x on $f \in L_2(G)$ by setting $l_x(f) = (Rf)(x)$ $(x \in O_{r/2})$. It is continuous and its norm is bounded uniformly with respect to $x \in O_{r/2}$, since, on writing $g = Rf$ in the representation in the lemma, we have

$$|(Rf)(x)|^2\leqslant 2\left|\int_O A(x,\xi)(Rf)(\xi)\,d\xi\right|^2+2\left|\int_O B(x,\xi)f(\xi)\,d\xi\right|^2$$
$$\leqslant 2\int_O |A(x,\xi)|^2 d\xi\cdot\|Rf\|^2_{L_2(O)}+2\int_O |B(x,\xi)|^2 d\xi\cdot\|f\|^2_{L_2(O)}\leqslant C_1\|Rf\|^2_{L_2(G)}$$
$$+C_2\|f\|^2_{L_2(G)}\leqslant C_3\|f\|^2_{L_2(G)}\quad (x\in O_{\frac{r}{2}}).$$

By the Riesz representation $(Rf)(x) = l_x(f) = \int_G h_x(y)\, f(y)\, dy$, where $\|h_x\|_{L_2(G)} \leq C$ for $x \in O_{r/2}$. At the same time, it follows from (5.1) that

$$(Ru)(x)=\int_G R(x,y)\,u(y)\,dy \qquad (u\in C_0(G)); \tag{5.19}$$

from these two representations we conclude that $R(x, y) = h_x(y)$, and therefore $\int_G |R(x, y)|^2\, dy \leq C^2$ $(x \in O_{r/2})$. This proves the first equation in (5.15). Since the neighborhood O can be chosen about any interior point of G, it easily follows from this that the first integral in (5.16) remains bounded when x remains strictly interior to G. The assertion concerning the second equation in (5.15) is proved similarly. The theorem follows.

Remark. A similar theorem can be formulated when the inequality $r > n/2$ fails; in this case L_2 must be replaced by a space L_p (with p chosen such that $A(x, \cdot)$, $B(x, \cdot) \in L_p$). We do not elaborate on these problems.

Suppose, in addition to the conditions in Theorem 5.2, the kernel R satisfies boundary conditions (bd) with respect to x, and (bd)$^\oplus$ with respect to y, now appearing in this way:

For fixed $y \in G$ ($x \in G$), $R(x, y)$ is a generalized solution in $L_2(G)$ of the problem $Lu = \delta_y$ with respect to the other variable, $u \in$ (bd) ($L^\oplus v = \delta_x$, $v \in$ (bd)$^+$), i.e.

$$(R(x, y), (L^+v)(x))_0 = \overline{v(y)} \quad (v \in W_2^r(\mathrm{bd})^+),$$

$$(R(x, y), (\bar{L}v)(y))_0 = \overline{v(x)} \quad (v \in \overline{W_2^r(\mathrm{bd})}). \tag{5.20}$$

Thus if a theorem of the type 4.6 holds for the conditions (bd) *and* (bd)$^+$, *we can conclude that for a fixed value of one variable, $R(x, y)$ will be smooth with respect to the other variable up to the boundary.*

We prove, for example, the first relation. If $u \in C_0(G)$, then by the second equation in (5.16)

$$\int_G (R(x, y), (L^+v)(x))_0\, u(y)\, dy = \int_G \int_G R(x, y)\, \overline{(L^+v)(x)}\, u(y)\, dx\, dy$$

$$= \overline{\int_G \int_G \overline{R(x, y)}\, (L^+v)(x)\, \overline{u(y)}\, dx\, dy} = \overline{\int_G (R^*L^+v)(y)\, \overline{u(y)}\, dy}$$

$$= (Ru, L^+v)_0 = (u, v)_0.$$

The condition follows since u is arbitrary and $(R(x, y), (L^+v)(x))_0 = \overline{(R^*L^+v)(y)}$ depends continuously on $y \in G$.

We emphasize that Theorem 5.4, by itself, does not say anything concerning the behavior of the kernel $R(x, y)$, when x and y lie at a distance $\geq C > 0$ from each other and simultaneously approach the boundary. For example, the convergence of the integral $\int_{G_1}\int_{G_2} |R(x, y)|^2\, dxdy$ is not even clear when G_1 and G_2 are subregions of G bordering on the boundary Γ along pieces at a positive distance from each other.

5. **Third method.** This method is stronger than the previous ones, and is concerned with smoothness with respect to each variable separately.

Theorem 5.5. *Let the conditions of Theorems* 5.1 *and* 5.2 *be satisfied, and let* G_0 *be a subregion of* G *bordering on* Γ *along a piece* Γ_0; *let* $q > n/2 - r$ *be a nonnegative integer. Suppose in addition that* L, Γ_0, *and the boundary conditions* (bd) *are such that the following theorem on improved smoothness holds in* G_0: *let* $G_0' \subseteq G_0$ *be an arbitrary subregion, bordering on* Γ *along a piece* $\Gamma_0' \subseteq \Gamma_0$. *When* $u \in W_2^{-q}(G_0')$ *satisfies the equation* $Lu = f \in W_2^q(G_0')$ *inside* G_0' *and up to* Γ_0', *it automatically follows that* $u \in W_{2,\mathrm{loc}}^{r+q}(G_0', \Gamma_0')$. *Similarly for* L^+ *and* $(\mathrm{bd})^+$.

Then for any fixed $x \in G_0$ $(y \in G_0)$, *we have the inclusions*

$$R(x,\cdot) \in W_{2,\mathrm{loc}}^{r+q}(G_0 \setminus \{x\}, \Gamma_0) \quad (R(\cdot, y) \in W_{2,\mathrm{loc}}^{r+q}(G_0 \setminus \{y\}, \Gamma_0)), \tag{5.21}$$

and moreover, $R(x,\cdot)$ $(R(\cdot, y))$ *satisfies* $L^{\oplus}u = 0$ $(Lu = 0)$ *inside* $G_0 \setminus \{x\}$ $(G_0 \setminus \{y\})$, *and also satisfies the boundary conditions* $(\mathrm{bd})^{\oplus}$ $((\mathrm{bd}))$ *on* Γ_0, *in the sense that*

$$(R(x,\cdot), \overline{Lv})_0 = 0 \qquad ((R(\cdot, y), L^+ v)_0 = 0) \tag{5.22}$$

for all $v \in \overline{W_2^r(\mathrm{bd})}$ $(v \in W_2^r(\mathrm{bd})^+)$ *which vanish in a neighborhood of the set* $G \setminus G_0$.

We explain at once that because of the smoothness of R, (5.22) actually denotes fulfillment of the boundary conditions in the ordinary sense. We first prove a lemma of the type 5.1. The idea of the proof is used later also.

Lemma 5.2. *Let* L *be an expression in a region* G, *let* (bd) *be given boundary conditions, and let* R *be a continuous operator in* $L_2(G)$ *such that for any* $f \in L_2(G)$, Rf *is a generalized solution of the problem* $Lu = f$, $u \in (\mathrm{bd})$. *Consider a subregion* $G_0 \subseteq G$ *bordering on* Γ *along a piece* Γ_0; *let there exist a* $q = 0, 1, \cdots$ *such that whenever* $u \in L_2(G)$ *satisfies the equation and* (bd) *inside* G_0 *and up to* Γ_0, *then* u *belongs to* $W_{2,\mathrm{loc}}^{r+q}(G_0, \Gamma_0)$ *if only* $f \in W_2^q(G)$. *We then have the estimate*

$$\| Rf \|_{W_2^{r+q}(\widetilde{G}_0)} \leqslant C_{\widetilde{G}_0} \| f \|_{W_2^q(G)} \quad (f \in W_2^q(G)), \tag{5.23}$$

where $\widetilde{G}_0$ *is any subregion of* G_0, *having a common boundary* $\widetilde{\Gamma}_0$ *with* G_0 *only in the interior of the piece* Γ_0.

Proof. For any $f \in W_2^q(G)$, the function Rf, considered only on G_0, satisfies the equation $Lu = f$ and (bd) inside G_0 and up to Γ_0. By the hypotheses of the lemma, $Rf \in W_{2,\mathrm{loc}}^{r+q}(G_0, \Gamma_0)$, and hence $Rf \in W_2^{r+q}(\widetilde{G}_0)$. Thus, we have a linear transformation $f \to Rf$ defined on vectors in the complete space $W_2^q(G)$ and mapping into $W_2^{r+q}(\widetilde{G}_0)$. It is closed: suppose $f_n \to f$ in $W_2^q(G)$ and $Rf_n \to g$ in $W_2^{r+q}(\widetilde{G}_0)$. Since a function $f_n \to f$ in $L_2(G)$ and R acts continuously in

$L_2(G)$, $Rf_n \to Rf$ in $L_2(G)$, and hence in $L_2(\widetilde{G}_0)$. On the other hand, $Rf_n \to g$, and therefore $g = Rf$; this proves closure. However, a closed transformation from a complete space into another space is automatically continuous. This gives (5.23). The lemma follows.

Proof of the theorem. The hypotheses of Lemma 5.2 are satisfied by the assumption concerning the theorem on improved smoothness: we need only apply this theorem with $G_0' = G_0$ and $\Gamma_0' = \Gamma_0$, and notice that $f(x) \in W_2^q(G)$ belongs to $W_2^q(G_0)$ as a function of $x \in G_0$. Thus, the estimate (5.23) holds. Since $r + q > n/2$, by the imbedding theorem, $Rf \in C(\widetilde{\widetilde{G}}_0)$ and $|(Rf)(x)| \leq C \| Rf \|_{W_2^{r+q}(\widetilde{G}_0)}$ $(x \in \widetilde{\widetilde{G}})$. Consider the homogeneous and additive functional $l_x(f) = (Rf)(x)$ $(x \in \widetilde{G}_0)$ on $f \in W_2^q(G)$; Since

$$|l_x(f)| = |(Rf)(x)| \leqslant C \|Rf\|_{W_2^{r+q}(\widetilde{G}_0)} \leqslant CC_{\widetilde{G}_0} \|f\|_{W_2^q(G)}$$

this functional is continuous. Therefore there exists an $\eta_x \in W_2^{-q}(G)$ such that

$$(Rf)(x) = l_x(f) = \overline{(\eta_x, f)_0} \quad (f \in W_2^q(G), x \in \widetilde{G}_0). \tag{5.24}$$

Let $v \in W_2^r(\text{bd}) \cap W_2^{r+q}(G)$ also vanish in a neighborhood of the point x and the set $G \setminus G_0$; setting $f = Lv$ in (5.24), we obtain $(\eta_x, Lv)_0 = (RLv)(x) = v(x) = 0$. The equation $(\eta_x, Lv)_0 = 0$ asserts that η_x (considered as an element of $W_2^{-q}(G_0 \setminus \xi x \xi))$ satisfies the equation $L^+ u = 0$ and $(\text{bd})^+$ inside $G_0 \setminus \xi x \xi$ and up to the piece Γ_0 of the boundary; therefore, by the hypotheses of the theorem it belongs to $W_{2,\text{loc}}^{r+q}(G_0 \setminus \xi x \xi, \Gamma_0)$. In other words, we delete from $\widetilde{G}_0$ some closed neighborhood of the point x and denote the remaining set by $\widetilde{\widetilde{G}}_0$. Then we can find a function $h_x(y) \in W_2^{r+q}(\widetilde{\widetilde{G}}_0)$ (depending on $\widetilde{\widetilde{G}}_0$) such that $(h_x, u)_0 = (\eta_x, u)$ for all $u \in W_2^q(G)$ which vanish in a neighborhood of the set $G \setminus \widetilde{\widetilde{G}}_0$. Taking into account (5.1) and (5.24), we obtain for such u which also vanish near Γ:

$$\int_G R(x, y) u(y)\, dy = (Ru)(x) = \overline{(h_x, u)_0} = \int_G \overline{h_x(y)}\, u(y)\, dy. \tag{5.25}$$

It follows that for $y \in \widetilde{\widetilde{G}}_0$, $R(x, y) = \overline{h_x(y)} \in W_2^{r+q}(\widetilde{\widetilde{G}}_0)$ $(x \in \widetilde{G}_0)$. This proves the first of the relations in (5.21), since $\widetilde{\widetilde{G}}_0$ borders on Γ_0 and approximates $G_0 \setminus \{x\}$ arbitrarily well.

The first equation in (5.22) follows from the fact that $\overline{R(x, \cdot)} = h_x(\cdot) = \eta_x$, and, as was shown, $(\eta_x, Lw)_0 = 0$ for $w \in W_2^r(\text{bd}) \cap W_2^{r+q}(G)$ which also vanish in a neighborhood of x and $G \setminus G_0$. Thus, $(R(x, \cdot), Lw)_0 = (R(x, \cdot), \overline{L\overline{w}})_0 = 0$; on approximating functions v in (5.22) by such $\overline{w}$, we arrive at what is to be proved.

It is also clear that from the relation thus obtained we can conclude $(L_y^{\oplus}R)(x, y) = 0$.

The conclusions of the theorem concerning $R(x, y)$ as a function of x are obtained similarly. The theorem follows.

From the proof of this theorem follows

Corollary 1. *Suppose that L has high order $r > n/2$ and satisfies the hypotheses of Theorem 5.5 with $q = 0$. Then the integrals (5.16) are uniformly bounded for $x, y \in G_0'$, where G_0' is any subregion of the region G_0, having a common boundary with G_0 only in a piece lying interior to Γ_0.*

In fact, now $\eta_x \in L_2(G)$; moreover, since $|l_x(f)| \leq CC_{\tilde{G}_0} \|f\|_{L_2(G)}$ for all $x \in \tilde{G}_0$, it follows that $\|\eta_x\|_{L_2(G)}$ is uniformly bounded for $x \in \tilde{G}_0$. It follows from (5.15) and (5.24) that

$$\int_G R(x, y) f(y)\, dy = (Rf)(x) = \overline{(\eta_x, f)_0} = \int_G \overline{\eta_x(y)} f(y)\, dy \quad (f \in L_2(G)).$$

Hence $R(x, \cdot) = \overline{\eta_x(\cdot)}$ and therefore

$$\|R(x, \cdot)\|_{L_2(G)} = \|\overline{\eta}_x\|_{L_2(G)} = \|\eta_x\|_{L_2(C)} \leqslant C_1 \ (x \in \widetilde{C}_0).$$

The assertion follows for the first integral in (5.16) since we may choose $G_0' = \tilde{G}_0$; the second integral is treated similarly.

We now formulate more concrete results concerning the smoothness of $R(x, y)$, which follow from Theorems 5.5, 4.6 and 4.7. As already mentioned, corresponding results for general elliptic expressions L and (bd) can be easily formulated using the theorems concerning improved smoothness given in §6.12. Applying Theorem 4.6, we arrive at the following assertion.

Corollary 2. *Suppose that the conditions of Theorems 5.1 and 5.2 are satisfied; let G_0 be some subregion of G, bordering on Γ along a piece Γ_0; consider an integer $q > n/2 - 2m, m - 1$. We assume that Γ_0 is of class C^{2m+q}, and L is strongly elliptic in $G_0 \cup \Gamma_0$, with coefficients $a_\alpha(x) \in C^{|\alpha|+q}(G_0 \cup \Gamma_0)$. Consider null conditions (bd) on Γ_0: $D^\alpha u|_{\Gamma_0} = 0$ $(|\alpha| \leq m - 1)$.*

Then for any fixed $x \in G_0$ $(y \in G_0)$ we have the inclusion (5.21), and moreover the function $R(x, \cdot)$ $(R(\cdot, y))$ satisfies the equation $L^{\oplus}u = 0$ $(Lu = 0)$ inside $G_0 \backslash \xi x \xi$ $(G_0 \backslash \xi y \xi)$. These functions satisfy null boundary conditions on Γ_0 in the ordinary sense, i.e.

$$(D_y^\beta R)(x, y)|_{y \in \Gamma_0} = 0 \ (|\beta| \leqslant m - 1) \quad ((D_x^\alpha R)(x, y)|_{x \in \Gamma_0} = 0 \ (|\alpha| \leqslant m - 1)) \qquad (5.26)$$

Note that case 2) of Theorem 4.6 applies here with $p = t = q$. The conditions (5.26) are obviously equivalent to (5.22). Corollary 3 follows immediately from Corollary 1.

Corollary 3. *If $2m > n/2$ and the hypotheses of Corollary 2 are satisfied with $q = m$, then the integrals (5.16) are uniformly bounded for x, y as in Corollary 1.*

For $r = 2$ and $n = 3$, Theorem 4.7 is applicable to Theorem 5.5, since we may now write $q = 0$, so that the required improved smoothness is guaranteed by the last theorem. As a result, we are able to investigate the behavior of $R(x, y)$ near the boundary in the case of conditions of the form $\partial u/\partial\mu + \sigma(x)\, u|_{\Gamma_0} = 0$ ($\sigma \in C^1(\Gamma_0)$). We do not formulate the assertion, which is easily done.

6. **Behavior of the kernel $R(x, y)$ for x and y on the boundary.** The method in subsection 3 does not apply in this case: in a neighborhood of $\Gamma_1 \times \Gamma_2$, the boundary of $G \times G$ is not smooth, and so the application of Theorem 4.6 here is not correct (we do not consider refinements of similar theorems). The last method does not succeed directly either, since equation (5.25) is not valid for $x \in \Gamma$. Nevertheless, we now obtain some results by combining the previous approaches. The distance between x and y is assumed to be $\geq C > 0$. We prove some useful equations.

From (5.1) we immediately obtain the representation

$$(Ru)(x) = \int_G R(x, y)\, u(y)\, dy \quad (u \in C_0(G),\ x \in G). \tag{5.27}$$

Let $\Gamma_0 \subseteq \Gamma$; suppose that L near Γ_0 and (bd) on Γ_0 are such that the hypotheses of Theorem 5.5 are satisfied. Then (5.27) holds for any $u \in W_2^q(G)$ which vanishes in an n-dimensional neighborhood of the part $\Gamma\backslash\Gamma_0$ of the boundary. In fact, we first prove (5.27) for such $u = u_2$ which, in addition, vanish in a neighborhood of the point x. Using the notation of the proof of Theorem 5.5, it is even sufficient to assume that $u_2 \in W_2^q(G)$ vanishes in a neighborhood of the set $G\backslash\approx{G}_0$. But then (5.27) follows from (5.24), with f replaced by u_2, and from the equations $(\eta_x, u_2)_0 = (h_x, u_2)_0$, $\overline{h_x(y)} = R(x, y)$ $(y \in \approx{G}_0)$ (see proof of Theorem 5.5). For the proof of (5.27) in the general case, write $u \in W_2^q(G)$, vanishing in an n-dimensional neighborhood of $\Gamma\backslash\Gamma_0$, in the form $u = u_1 + u_2$, where $u_1 \in C_0(G)$ and u_2 is as described above. Since (5.27) holds for each term, it holds for u. The assertion follows.

Until now we have proved that relation (5.27) holds for $x \in G$; we show that in some cases it holds even for $x \in \Gamma$.

Lemma 5.3. *Let $\Gamma_0 \subseteq \Gamma$, and suppose that L and* (bd) *on Γ_0 are such that one of these conditions holds:* a) *for any subregion $G_0 \subset G$ bordering on Γ along Γ_0, and any subregion G_2 at a positive distance from G_0, the conditions of Theorem 5.3 are satisfied (with $G_1 = G_0$);* b) *in some subregion $G_0 \subset G$ bordering on Γ along Γ_0, the conditions of Theorem 5.5 are satisfied, and $r > n/2$. Then for any $y \in G$, $\lim_{x \to x_0} R(x, y) = R(x_0, y)$ $(x_0 \in \Gamma_0)$ exists and*

$$(Ru)(x_0) = \int_G R(x_0, y)\, u(y)\, dy \quad (u \in W^q_{2,0}(G),\ x_0 \in \Gamma_0) \tag{5.28}$$

(here q is a number which is fixed by the conditions in Theorems 5.3 and 5.5).

Proof. Case a). Fix $u \in C_0(G)$ and choose G_0 and G_2 such that $u = 0$ in a neighborhood of $G \setminus G_2$. By Theorem 5.3, $R(\cdot, \cdot) \in W^{2m+q}_{2,\mathrm{loc}}(G_0 \times G_2, \Gamma_0 \times G_2)$. Choose $G_0' \subset G$ such that G_0' and G_0 have a common boundary only along a piece $\Gamma_0' \ni x_0$ strictly interior to Γ_0; choose G_2' strictly inside G_2 such that $u = 0$ outside G_2. Then $R(\cdot, \cdot) \in W^{2m+q}_2(G_0' \times G_2')$. Since $2m + q > n$,

$$|R(x, y)| \leqslant C \| R(\cdot, \cdot) \|_{W^{2m+q}_2(G_0' \times G_2')} = C_1 < \infty \quad (x \in G_0',\ y \in G_2').$$

This estimate permits passage to the limit under the integral sign in (5.27), and we obtain

$$\lim_{x \to x_0} (Ru)(x) = \lim_{x \to x_0} \int_G R(x, y)\, u(y)\, dy = \int_G R(x_0, y)\, u(y)\, dy.$$

On the other hand, by Theorem 4.6, $Ru \in W^{2m+q}_2(G_0')$ for $u \in W^q_{2,0}(G)$, and therefore $\lim_{x \to x_0} (Ru)(x) = (Ru)(x_0)$. Hence (5.28) follows.

Case b). Let G_0 and G_0' be as above. By Corollary 1, $\| R(x, \cdot)\, u(\cdot) \|_{L_2(G)} \leq C < \infty$ $(x \in G_0')$ and therefore we can pass to the limit under the integral sign in (5.27) as $x \to x_0$. Since now $(Ru)(x) \to (Ru)(x_0)$ as $x \to x_0$, we again arrive at (5.28). The lemma follows.

Theorem 5.6. *Suppose that the hypotheses of Theorems 5.1 and 5.2 are satisfied; let $\Gamma_0 \subset \Gamma$, and suppose that L and* (bd) *on Γ_0 are such that one of these conditions holds:* a) *for any subregion $G_0 \subset G$ bordering on Γ along Γ_0, and any subregion $G_2 \subset G$ at a positive distance from G_0, the conditions of Theorem 5.3 are satisfied;* b) *$r > n/2$ and in some subregion $G_0 \subset G$ bordering on Γ along Γ_0, the hypothesis concerning improved smoothness in Theorem 5.5 is satisfied for any $q = 0, 1, \cdots$.*

Then for any fixed $x \in G_0 \cup \Gamma_0$ $(y \in G_0 \cup \Gamma_0)$

$$R(x,\cdot)\in W_{2,\mathrm{loc}}^{r+q}(G_0\setminus\{x\},\quad \Gamma_0'\setminus\{x\})$$
$$(R(\cdot,y)\in W_{2,\mathrm{loc}}^{r+q}(G_0\setminus\{y\},\quad \Gamma_0\setminus\{y\})) \tag{5.29}$$

and the remaining assertions in Theorem 5.5 *hold* (*with the alteration that* $(\mathrm{bd})^+$ ((bd)) *is satisfied on* $\Gamma_0\setminus\{x\}(\Gamma_0\setminus\{y\})$; *this means that in* (5.22), v *should also vanish in a neighborhood of the point* x (y)).

The proof is carried out now exactly as in the proof of Theorem 5.5: we need only assume $x\in\widetilde{G}_0\cup\widetilde{\Gamma}_0$ in the definition of l_x ($\widetilde{\Gamma}_0$ is the piece of the boundary of $\widetilde{G}_0$ bordering on Γ_0). Everything else remains unchanged, except that η_x satisfies the equation $L^+u=0$ and $(\mathrm{bd})^+$ inside $G_0\setminus\{x\}=G_0'$ and up to $\Gamma_0\setminus\{x\}=\Gamma_0'$ (and not Γ_0). Finally, by virtue of (5.28), equation (5.25) may be written for $x\in\widetilde{\Gamma}_0$.

We leave it to the reader to formulate the conditions of Corollary 2 on the basis of Theorem 5.6, so that we obtain the inclusion (5.29) instead of (5.21). It is also easy to formulate the corresponding facts for a boundary condition of the form $\partial u/\partial\mu+\sigma(x)u|_{\Gamma_0}=0$, and for the general L and (bd) occurring in §6.12.

The results in subsections 3–6 apply in a natural way to Green's function $R(x,y;\lambda)$. It would be superfluous to formulate these facts.

7. **Product of resolvents.** For a complete spectral theory, it is necessary to use some of the results in subsections 1–6 in the case where a product $R_{\lambda_1}\cdots R_{\lambda_N}$ plays the role of R. We undertake some general considerations in connection with this.

Let $L_1,\cdots,L_N$ be differential expressions of respective orders $r_1,\cdots,r_N$ in G, with coefficients in $C^\rho(G\cup\Gamma)$, $\rho=r_1+\cdots+r_N$. Then $L=L_1\cdots L_N$ is an expression of order ρ, with coefficients satisfying the usual smoothness conditions. Let $(\mathrm{bd})_j$ be related to L_j, and let $W_2^{r_j}(\mathrm{bd})_j$ be the corresponding subspace of $W_2^{r_j}(G)$ ($j=1,\cdots,N$). We define $W_2^\rho(\mathrm{bd})$ as the collection of functions u in $W_2^\rho(G)$ for which $L_2\cdots L_Nu\in W_2^{r_1}(\mathrm{bd})_1$, $L_3\cdots L_Nu\in W_2^{r_2}(\mathrm{bd})_2,\cdots$, $u\in W_2^{r_N}(\mathrm{bd})_N$. Obviously $W_2^\rho(\mathrm{bd})$ is a subspace of the space $W_2^\rho(G)$ containing $\overset{\circ}{W}{}_{2,0}^{\rho}(G)$, and therefore the conditions (bd) are admissible. It is easy to see that $L^+=L_N^+\cdots L_1^+$ and $W_2^\rho(\mathrm{bd})^+$ are defined with respect to the product $L_N^+\cdots L_1^+$ and $W_2^{r_N}(\mathrm{bd})_N^+,\cdots,W_2^{r_1}(\mathrm{bd})_1^+$ written in this order; $(\mathrm{bd})^{++}=(\mathrm{bd})$.

Suppose that the expressions $L_1,\cdots,L_N$ are elliptic and their coefficients belong to $C^{2\rho+p}(G\cup\Gamma)$ ($p\geq n+1$). Then L is elliptic, and automatically its coefficients $a_\alpha(x) \in C^{|\alpha|+\rho+p}(G \cup \Gamma)$. Let R_j be a continuous operator in $L_2(G)$, connected with L_j and $(\mathrm{bd})_j$ as in Theorem 5.2 ($j = 1, \cdots, N$). We set $R = R_N \cdots R_1$; R is connected with L and (bd) in the same way. In fact, for $f \in L_2(G)$ and $v \in W_2^\rho(\mathrm{bd})^+$ we have

$$(Rf, L^+v)_0 = (R_N \ldots R_1 f,\ L_N^+ \ldots L_1^+ v)_0 = (R_{N-1} \ldots R_1 f,\ L_{N-1}^+ \ldots L_1^+ v)_0 = \ldots = (f, v)_0,$$

i.e. Rf is a generalized solution of the problem $Lu = f$, $u \in$ (bd). Similarly for $R^* f$. Thus, we can apply Theorems 5.1 and 5.2 to L, (bd), and R to obtain: there exists a kernel $\mathrm{R} \in W_2^{-l}(G) \otimes W_2^{-l}(G)$ ($l = [n/2] + 1$) such that $(Ru, v)_0 = (\mathrm{R}, v(x)\overline{u(y)})_0$ ($u, v \in W_2^l(G)$). Inside the region $G \times G$, this kernel coincides with an ordinary kernel $R(x, y)$ ($x, y \in G$), which is smooth for $x \neq y$ (this asserts the existence and continuity with respect to $(x, y) \in G \times G$, $x \neq y$, of all derivatives $D_x^\alpha D_y^\beta R$ ($|\alpha|, |\beta| \leq \rho + p$)), and has for $x = y$ the singularity of the fundamental solution of the elliptic expression L of order ρ. The kernel R satisfies relations of the type (5.13).

On applying Theorem 5.4 to the L, (bd), and R just constructed, we conclude that for the corresponding kernel $R(x, y)$ the integrals (5.16) remain bounded for x interior to G (in the case $\rho > n/2$). Moreover, we have the following theorem.

Theorem 5.7. *Let $L_1, \cdots, L_N$ be elliptic expressions in a region G of orders $r_1, \cdots, r_N$; suppose $\rho > n/2$, where $\rho = r_1 + \cdots + r_N$. Let G_0 be a subregion of G bordering on Γ along the piece Γ_0. Suppose that for G_0 and each L_j, we have the assertion on improved smoothness, formulated in the hypotheses of Theorem 5.5, with $q = r_1 + \cdots + r_{j-1}$ ($j = 2, \cdots, N$) and $q = 0$ for $j = 1$. Let G_0' be any subregion of G_0, having a common boundary with G_0 only in a piece strictly interior to Γ_0.*

Then the vector function $R(x, \cdot)$ ($R(\cdot, y)$) of $x \in \overline{G}_0'$ ($y \in \overline{G}_0'$) with values in $L_2(G)$ is weakly continuously differentiable up to the order $\rho - [n/2] - 1$ inclusive, and moreover all of these derivatives are bounded.

The proof is based on the following fact.

Lemma 5.4. *For ρ and any $f \in L_2(G)$, the function $Rf \in W_2^\rho(G_0')$.*

Proof. Construct a sequence of regions

$$G_0' = \widetilde{G}_0^{(N)} \subset \widetilde{G}_0^{(N-1)} \subset \ldots \subset \widetilde{G}_0^{(1)} \subset \widetilde{G}_0^{(0)} = G_0,$$

for G_0' contained in G_0, with each region contained in the one to the right; let

$$\Gamma_0' = \widetilde{\Gamma}_0^{(N)} \subset \widetilde{\Gamma}_0^{(N-1)} \subset \ldots \subset \widetilde{\Gamma}_0^{(1)} \subset \widetilde{\Gamma}_0^{(0)} = \Gamma_0$$

be the corresponding pieces of the boundaries lying on Γ. Since by hypothesis $R_1 f$ is a generalized solution of the problem $L_1 u = f$, $u \in (\mathrm{bd})_1$, we may consider that $R_1 f \in L_2(\widetilde{G}_0^{(0)})$ satisfies the equation $L_1 u = f \in L_2(\widetilde{G}_0^{(0)})$ inside $\widetilde{G}_0^{(0)}$ and up to $\widetilde{\Gamma}_0^{(0)}$. Therefore $R_1 f \in W_{2,\mathrm{loc}}^{r_1}(\widetilde{G}_0^{(0)}, \widetilde{\Gamma}_0^{(0)})$ and consequently $R_1 f \in W_2^{r_1}(\widetilde{G}_0^{(1)})$. Furthermore, $R_2 R_1 f$ is a generalized solution of the problem $L_2 u = R_1 f$, $u \in (\mathrm{bd})_2$; we can consider that $R_2 R_1 f \in W_2^{r_1}(\widetilde{G}_0^{(1)})$ satisfies the equation $L_2 u = R_1 f \in W_2^{r_1}(\widetilde{G}_0^{(1)})$ inside $\widetilde{G}_0^{(1)}$ and up to $\widetilde{\Gamma}_0^{(1)}$. Therefore $R_2 R_1 f \in W_{2,\mathrm{loc}}^{r_1+r_2}(\widetilde{G}_0^{(1)})$ and consequently $R_2 R_1 f \in W_2^{r_1+r_2}(\widetilde{G}_0^{(2)})$. We consider $R_3 R_2 R_1 f$ and repeat the process. At the end we obtain $Rf = R_N \cdots R_1 f \in W_2^{r_1+\cdots+r_N}(\widetilde{G}_0^{(N)}) = W_2^{\rho}(G_0')$, as required. The lemma follows.

Repeating the proof of Lemma 5.2 and using this assertion, we obtain the inequality

$$\| Rf \|_{W_2^{\varrho}(G_0')} \leqslant C_{G_0'} \| f \|_{L_2(G)} \quad (f \in L_2(G)). \tag{5.30}$$

Since $\rho > n/2$, by the imbedding theorem we find:

$$Rf \in C^{\varrho - \left[\frac{n}{2}\right] - 1}(\overline{G_0'}), \quad |(D^{\alpha} Rf)(x)| \leqslant C_1 \| Rf \|_{W_2^{\varrho}(G_0')} \leqslant C_2 \| f \|_{L_2(G)}$$
$$(f \in L_2(G); \ |\alpha| \leqslant \varrho - \left[\frac{n}{2}\right] - 1, \ x \in \overline{G_0'}). \tag{5.31}$$

The inequality (5.31) with $\alpha = 0$ asserts that for fixed x, the functional $l_x(f) = (Rf)(x)$ is continuous on $L_2(G)$, and therefore admits a representation $(Rf)(x) = l_x(f) = (h_x, f)_0$ $(h_x \in L_2(G))$. Since for any $f \in L_2(G)$,

$$(h_x, f)_0 = \overline{(Rf)(x)} \in C^{\varrho - \left[\frac{n}{2}\right] - 1}(\overline{G_0'}),$$

the vector-function h_x is weakly differentiable, and moreover

$$(D_x^{\alpha} h_x, f)_0 = D_x^{\alpha}(h_x, f)_0 = \overline{(D^{\alpha} Rf)(x)} \left(|\alpha| \leqslant \varrho - \left[\frac{n}{2}\right] - 1 \right).$$

It now follows from (5.31) that $\| D_x^{\alpha} h_x \|_0 \leq C_2$ $(x \in \overline{G}_0')$ for such α. On the other hand, $h_x = R(x, \cdot)$ by (5.27); this proves the assertion of the theorem concerning $R(x, \cdot)$. We can treat $R(\cdot, y)$ in exactly the same way by passing to the adjoint expressions, (bd), and operators. The theorem follows.

From Theorem 4.6 we obtain

Corollary 1. *The assertion in Theorem 5.7 holds if the elliptic expressions* $L_1, \cdots, L_N$, *introduced at the beginning of this subsection, are in addition strongly* *elliptic in* $G_0 \cup \Gamma_0$, *and* (bd) *is null on* Γ_0 *sufficiently smooth.*

Another corollary follows for $L_1 = \cdots = L_N = L$.

Corollary 2. *Let* R_λ *be the resolvent, introduced at the end of subsection* 1, *for the expression* L *of order* $r = 2m$, *and let* $N = 1, 2, \cdots$ *be so large that* $Nr > n/2$. *Assume that the coefficients of* L *belong to* $C^{2Nr+p}(G \cup \Gamma)$ $(p \geq n+1)$ *and that there exists a subregion* G_0 *of the region* $G(0 \subseteq G_0 \subseteq G)$, *bordering on* Γ *along the piece* Γ_0 *of class* $C^{\max(Nr, r+m)}$, *such that* L *is strongly elliptic in* $G_0 \cup \Gamma_0$, *and* (bd) *is null on* Γ_0.

Then every product $R = R_{\lambda_1} \cdots R_{\lambda_N}$ *is an integral operator with kernel* $R(x, y)$ $(x, y \in G)$ *such that the integrals* (5.16) *remain bounded for* x *and* y *strictly interior to* G. *These integrals remain bounded even for* $x, y \in \overline{G}_0'$ *where* G_0' *is an arbitrary subregion of* G_0, *having a common boundary with* G_0 *only in a piece lying strictly interior to* Γ_0. *The kernel* $R(x, y)$ *is sufficiently smooth for* $x \neq y$: *all derivatives* $D_x^\alpha D_y^\beta R$ $(|\alpha|, |\beta| \leq Nr + p)$ *exist and are continuous for* $(x, y) \in G \times G$. *The vector functions* $R(x, \cdot)$ *and* $R(\cdot, y)$ *with values in* $L_2(G)$ *are weakly continuously differentiable up to the order* $Nr - [n/2] - 1$ *inclusive, and moreover all of these derivatives are bounded.*

We will not dwell on the formulation of corollaries to Theorem 5.7 for boundary conditions from the third type of boundary value problem, or for the general elliptic L and (bd) in §6.12.

8. **The case of an unbounded region.. The concept of boundary conditions for such a region.** It is necessary for spectral theory to fomulate the results of these subsections concerning the operator R for the case of unbounded G. The transfer is easily carried out. First of all we observe that both the statement and proof of Theorem 5.1 carry over.

We introduce the concept of boundary conditions (bd) for unbounded G. It is convenient to introduce "finite" conditions, without imposing restrictions on the behavior of functions at ∞; this justifies the following construction. Consider the Sobolev space $W_2^r(G) = W_2^{(r,q)}(G)$, where $q(x) = 1$ $(x \in G)$. Let $\overset{\circ}{W}{}_2^r(G)$ be the closure in $W_2^r(G)$ of the class $C_0^\infty(G)$ of functions finite with respect to G and ∞. Every subspace $W_2^r(\text{bd})$ of the space $W_2^r(G)$, containing $\overset{\circ}{W}{}_2^r(G)$, defines certain boundary conditions (bd). Let L be a differential expression of order r with the usual smoothness: $a_\alpha(x) \in C^{|\alpha|}(G \cup \Gamma)$ (no restrictions are imposed at ∞); let L^+ be the formal adjoint expression. The adjoint boundary conditions $(\text{bd})^+$ are defined by the subspace $W_2^r(\text{bd})^+$ of the space $W_2^r(G)$, consisting of all functions

$v \in W_2^r(G)$ such that $(Lu, v)_0 = (u, L^+v)_0$ for all $u \in W_2^r(\text{bd})$ which, in addition, vanish at ∞. Finiteness of u at ∞ means that we are not interested in the influence of (bd) on functions in $W_2^r(\text{bd})$ at ∞. In all that follows, we are only concerned with boundary conditions (bd) such that $(\text{bd})^{++} = (\text{bd})$. If $g(x)$ $(x \in G)$ coincides with some $u(x) \in W_2^r(\text{bd})$ for x near Γ, then we will say that $g(x)$ satisfied (bd).

A generalized function $u \in W_2^{-(\sigma, q_1)}(G)$ $(\sigma \geq 0,\ q_1(x) \geq 1)$ by definition satisfies the equation $Lu = f \in W_2^{-(r+\sigma, q_2)}(G)$ $(q_2(x) \geq 1)$ and boundary conditions (bd), if $(u, L^+v)_0 = (f, v)_0$ for all $v \in W_2^r(\text{bd})^+ \cap W_2^{r+\sigma}(G)$ which are finite at ∞ (it is assumed that $a_\alpha(x) \in C^{|\alpha|+\sigma}(G \cup \Gamma)$ and $W_2^r(\text{bd}) \cap W_{2,0}^{r+\sigma}(E_n)$ is dense in the functions $W_2^r(\text{bd}) \cap W_{2,0}^r(E_n)$ with this notion of convergence: $v_n \to 0$ if the supports of the v_n lie in a common sphere U and $v_n \to 0$ in $W_2^r(G \cap U)$; cf. p. 89). Fulfillment of this equation inside G and up to a piece $\Gamma_0 \subseteq \Gamma$ means that the previous equation holds, but only for those v also vanishing in a neighborhood of the set $\Gamma \backslash \Gamma_0$.

Note that now, as before in Chapter II, §1.1, the definition of (bd) presents one difficulty: if u satisfies (bd) on all of Γ, what should we mean by fulfillment of these conditions on part of Γ? Our (bd) does not, in general, have a local character, and therefore this problem is not meaningful. We do not formalize the concept of localness, since in concrete cases of conditions, given by equating certain differential expressions to zero on Γ, we can always avoid the situation as in Theorem 5.5; in the case of null boundary conditions, equation (5.22) reduces to (5.26). In connection with this, in general we will not define membership in (bd) for unbounded G by functions which are not small at ∞.

It is now clear that because of Theorem 3.3, Chapter I, in an unbounded region (see p. 60), *Theorem 5.2 holds in the same formulation, if only* $W_2^l(G)$ *is replaced by* $W_2^{(l,q)}(G)$ *where* $l > n/2$ *and* $q(x) \geq 1$ *satisfies* (3.17), Chapter I. *Thus now* $R \in W_2^{-(l,q)}(G) \otimes W_2^{-(l,q)}(G)$. *Realization of the boundary conditions* $(\text{bd})_x$ *and* $(\text{bd})_y^\oplus$ *for* R *means that the relations* (5.13) *hold for* $V(x, y)$ *belonging respectively to* $(W_2^r(\text{bd})^+ \cap W_2^{r+l}(G)) \otimes W_2^{\max(r,l)}(G)$ *and* $W_2^{\max(r,l)}(G) \otimes \overline{(W_2^r(\text{bd}) \cap W_2^{r+l}(G))}$, *and finite at infinity as functions of the point* (x, y).

Since Theorem 5.3 is a local fact, it carries over to the case of unbounded G (G_1, G_2, and also G_0 in the subsequent theorems, must be assumed bounded). Obviously, Theorems 5.4–5.7 and their corollaries hold, with the alteration that the integrals (5.16) remain bounded for x and y in bounded subregions of G

satisfying the conditions of these theorems (the integrals themselves extend over all of G!). *Thus all of Theorems* 5.3–5.7, *with the above alterations in their statements, hold for unbounded* G.

§6. BOUNDARY VALUE PROBLEMS AND SMOOTHNESS OF GENERALIZED SOLUTIONS UP TO THE BOUNDARY FOR ELLIPTIC EQUATIONS IN THE CASE OF GENERAL BOUNDARY CONDITIONS

In this section we study, for general boundary conditions, results of the type in §3 on the solvability of boundary value problems, and of the type in §4 on local smoothness of generalized solutions up to the boundary of the region. The methods used here will often differ from the previous approaches (particularly with respect to §3): however they are frequently only outlined, to prevent an awkward presentation. At the same time, it should be emphasized that the proofs of a majority of the facts stated below are easily reconstructed from the outlined methods. Exceptions are the "difficult to reconstruct" proofs of Theorems 6.1 (necessity), 6.4, and Lemmas 6.1 and 6.4. References to these proofs are given in the "Notes on the Literature."

We do not discuss generalizations of the results in §5, since the presentation there is in such a form that the results are easily extended by using the theorems below.

1. The form of differential expressions and boundary conditions. Energy inequalities. Let G be a bounded region in E_n with sufficiently smooth boundary Γ. Let L be a given elliptic differential expression in G of order $2m$

$$Lu = L(x, \partial)\, u = \sum_{|\alpha| \leqslant 2m} a_\alpha(x)\, \partial^\alpha u, \qquad \partial^\alpha = \partial_1^{\alpha_1} \ldots \partial_n^{\alpha_n}, \qquad \partial_j = \frac{1}{i} D_j \qquad (j = 1, \ldots, n).^{1)} \tag{6.1}$$

As is known, the condition for ellipticity means that for any real vector $\xi = (\xi_1, \cdots, \xi_n) \neq 0$, the form $L_c(x, \xi) = \sum_{|\alpha| = 2m} a_\alpha(x)\, \xi^\alpha$ is different from zero for $x \in G \cup \Gamma$.

We recall the discussions on pp. 122 and 130. Let $x \in \Gamma$ be fixed; fix a vector $\tau \in E_{n-1}$ parallel to the tangent hyperplane to Γ at the point x, and consider the polynomial in the complex variable ζ: $P(\zeta) = L_c(x, \tau + \zeta\nu(x))$ ($\nu(x)$ is the exterior normal at the point x). Since L is elliptic, $P(\zeta)$ has no real roots. In

---

1) It is convenient to use ∂^α instead of D^α in this section.

what follows, we will consider expressions L such that for any $\tau \neq 0$, the polynomial $P(\zeta)$ has m roots in the open upper half-plane, and m in the open lower half-plane. Such an expression L is called regularly elliptic. As we have seen, every elliptic expression for $n \geq 3$ is regularly elliptic, and for $n = 2$, every strongly elliptic expression is regularly elliptic. If L is regularly elliptic, so is L^+. Below we use the factorization

$$P(\zeta) = P_+(\zeta)\, P_-(\zeta),$$

where $P_+(\zeta)$ $(P_-(\zeta))$ is the polynomial of degree m constructed from the roots of $P(\zeta)$ lying in the upper (lower) half-plane.

We take boundary differential expressions on Γ as defining (bd) (see §3.3). Namely, we set

$$B_j u = B_j(x, \partial)\, u = \sum_{|\alpha| \leq m_j} b_{j\alpha}(x)\, \partial^\alpha u \qquad (m_j < 2m;\ j = 1, \ldots, m), \tag{6.2}$$

where $b_{j\alpha}(x)$ are sufficiently smooth coefficients defined for $x \in \Gamma$ (in all cases we assume $b_{j\alpha}(x) \in C(\Gamma)$ $(j = 1, \cdots, m)$). The expression (6.2) can be computed for a smooth function u given in a neighborhood of Γ. As for L, we construct the multilinear form

$$B_{j,c}(x, \xi) = \sum_{|\alpha| = m_j} b_{j\alpha}(x)\, \xi^\alpha \quad (x \in \Gamma;\ \xi \in E_n)$$

and form the polynomial analogous to $P(\zeta)$: $Q_j(\zeta) = B_{j,c}(x, \tau + \zeta\nu(x))$ $(x \in \Gamma$ and $\tau \in E_{n-1}$ fixed).

It turns out that the condition for covering in the sense of §3.3 can be expressed in an algebraic way. Thus we will say that the system of boundary expressions (6.2) covers L if for any point $x \in \Gamma$ and any $\tau \in E_{n-1}$, $\tau \neq 0$, the polynomials $Q_1(\zeta), \cdots, Q_m(\zeta)$ are linearly independent modulo $P_+(\zeta)$, i.e. the equation

$$\sum_{j=1}^{m} C_j Q_j(\zeta) = C(\zeta)\, P_+(\zeta), \tag{6.3}$$

where $C_1, \cdots, C_m$ are complex constants and $C(\zeta)$ is a polynomial, holds only for $C_1 = \cdots = C_m = 0$.[1)]

In this subsection we take as fundamental the nonhomogeneous boundary value problem

1) It is easy to see that $P_+(\zeta)$ can be replaced by $P_-(\zeta)$ in this definition (see the proof of Lemma 3.2).

$$(Lu)(x) = f(x) \qquad (x \in G), \tag{6.4}$$

$$(B_j u)(x) = \varphi_j(x) \qquad (x \in \Gamma;\ j = 1, \ldots, m), \tag{6.5}$$

where L is a regularly elliptic expression and the system $\{B_j\}$ $(j = 1, \cdots, m)$ covers it. Let us agree to call such a problem elliptic.

As was already mentioned in §3.3, the energy inequality can be proved for arbitrary functions on $G \cup \Gamma$, not necessarily satisfying homogeneous boundary conditions (bd); in the inequality there occurs a norm on functions defined on Γ, the so-called boundary norm. We now introduce certain spaces of functions defined on Γ and the corresponding norms.

We assume that the boundary Γ of the region G is of class C^l, where $l > 0$ is an integer. Let $W_2^{l-\frac{1}{2}}(\Gamma)$ be the linear set of functions $\phi(x)$ defined on Γ and having the values on Γ of a function in the space $W_2^l(G)$. This set becomes a complete normed space, if the norm is defined by

$$\langle\!\langle \varphi \rangle\!\rangle_{l-\frac{1}{2}} = \langle\!\langle \varphi \rangle\!\rangle_{W_2^{l-\frac{1}{2}}(\Gamma)} = \inf \| u \|_l, \tag{6.6}$$

where the inf is extended over all functions $u \in W_2^l(G)$ coinciding with $\phi(x)$ on Γ. It is clear that for $k > l$,

$$W_2^{k-\frac{1}{2}}(\Gamma) \subseteq W_2^{l-\frac{1}{2}}(\Gamma), \ \langle\!\langle \varphi \rangle\!\rangle_{l-\frac{1}{2}} \leqslant \langle\!\langle \varphi \rangle\!\rangle_{k-\frac{1}{2}} \ (\varphi \in W_2^{k-\frac{1}{2}}(\Gamma))$$

and $W_2^{k-\frac{1}{2}}(\Gamma)$ forms a complete part of $W_2^{l-\frac{1}{2}}(\Gamma)$. If we fix $C > 1$, then obviously for any $\phi \in W_2^{l-\frac{1}{2}}(\Gamma)$ there is a $u \in W_2^l(G)$ which satisfies the inequality

$$C^{-1} \| u \|_l \leqslant \langle\!\langle \varphi \rangle\!\rangle_{l-\frac{1}{2}} \leqslant C \| u \|_l. \tag{6.7}$$

It is not difficult to see that actually $W_2^{l-\frac{1}{2}}(\Gamma)$ is a Hilbert space. In fact, the given definition can be paraphrased in the following way: consider the subspace M of $W_2^l(G)$ consisting of all functions equal to zero on Γ. Then $W_2^{l-\frac{1}{2}}(\Gamma)$ coincides with the factor space $W_2^l(G)/M$. However, $W_2^l(G)$ is a Hilbert space, and therefore $W_2^{l-\frac{1}{2}}(\Gamma) = W_2^l(G)/M$. coincides with the orthogonal complement of M in $W_2^l(G)$, i.e. it is a Hilbert space. The scalar product in $W_2^{l-\frac{1}{2}}(\Gamma)$ is denoted by $\langle \cdot, \cdot \rangle_{W_2^{l-\frac{1}{2}}(\Gamma)} = \langle \cdot, \cdot \rangle_{l-\frac{1}{2}}$. We remark that the space $W_2^{l-\frac{1}{2}}(\Gamma)$ can be intrinsically described as a Sobolev space W_2^k, in which k, namely the maximal order of derivatives, is fractional (cf. Chapter I §3.5). We do not take up this definition, since it is not needed for the formulation of results (but it is needed for certain proofs).

We now formulate the energy inequality, which is fundamental for the development of the theory.

Theorem 6.1. *Suppose that the coefficients of L and B_j are sufficiently smooth:*

$$a_\alpha(x) \in C^s(G \cup \Gamma),\ b_{j\alpha}(x) \in C^{2m-m_j+s}(\Gamma) \quad (j = 1, \ldots, m),$$

where $s \geq 0$ is an integer; suppose that the surface Γ is of class C^{2m+s}. A necessary and sufficient condition that there exist a constant $C > 0$ such that

$$\| Lu \|_s^2 + \| u \|_0^2 + \sum_{j=1}^{m} \langle\!\langle B_j u \rangle\!\rangle^2_{2m-m_j+s-\frac{1}{2}} \geqslant C \| u \|^2_{2m+s}$$
$$(u \in W_2^{2m+s}(G)) \tag{6.8}$$

is that the problem (6.4) – (6.5) *be elliptic.*

The proof of the sufficiency in Theorem 6.1 is carried out in the same way as in the proof of Theorem 3.1 by passage from local arguments. Actually, the basic difficulty consists in establishing the following lemma concerning expressions with constant coefficients, which is similar to Lemma 3.1.

Lemma 6.1. *Let G_δ $(\delta > 0)$ be the hemisphere $|x| < \delta$, $x_n > 0$. Consider in G_δ homogeneous expressions of the type* (6.1) *and* (6.2) *with constant coefficients:*

$$Lu = \sum_{|\tau|+\nu=2m} a_{\tau\nu} \partial^\tau \partial_n^\nu u, \qquad B_j u = \sum_{|\tau|+\nu=2m-1} b_{j,\,\tau\nu} \partial^\tau \partial_n^\nu u \quad (j = 1, \ldots, m); \tag{6.9}$$

here $\tau = (\tau_1, \cdots, \tau_{n-1})$, and ∂^τ denotes differentiation in a tangetial (with respect to the boundary $x_n = 0$) direction. If the expression L is regularly elliptic and covered by the system $\{B_j\}$ $(j = 1, \cdots, m)$, then for integral $s \geq 0$ the inequality (6.8) *holds on the class of functions $W_2^{2m+s}(G_\delta; 0)$, consisting of functions in $W_2^{2m+s}(G_\delta)$ which also vanish in a neighborhood of the boundary $|x| = \delta$ of the region G_δ. The boundary norm in* (6.8) *is now constructed with respect to some region $G'_\delta \supset G_\delta$ having sufficiently smooth boundary and containing the piece $x_n = 0$, $|x| < \delta$ of the boundary of G_δ.*

Two ways of proving Lemma 3.1 for L of arbitrary order were indicated earlier: using a representation of solutions by means of a singular integral and using Fourier transforms. Both methods are suitable even for the proof of Lemma 6.1, and moreover, as before, it is sufficient to consider only the case $s = 0$: as in the last step of the earlier proof it can be shown that the estimate (6.8) for $s > 0$ follows from the same estimate for $s = 0$. We recall this last argument.

It is clear that it is sufficient to prove Lemma 6.1 for functions

$$u \in C^{2m+s}(\overline{C}_\delta; 0) = W_2^{2m+s}(G_\delta; 0) \cap C^{2m+s}(\overline{G}_\delta),$$

since then we can arrive at $u \in W_2^{2m+s}(G_\delta; 0)$ by a passage to the limit. Suppose it holds for $s = 0$; to prove it for $s = 1$, we proceed as follows. Consider $u \in C^{2m+1}(\overline{G}_\delta; 0)$ and a difference quotient in a tangetial direction

$$u_k^h(x) = \frac{1}{ih}(u(x_1, \ldots, x_{k-1}, x_k + h, x_{k+1}, \ldots, x_n)) - u(x_1, \ldots, x_n) \; (k = 1, \ldots, n-1).$$

If $|h|$ is sufficiently small, then $u_k^h \in C^{2m}(\overline{G}_\delta; 0)$. Therefore we can apply the known inequality to u_k^h, i.e. (6.8) with $s = 0$. Passing to the limit as $h \to 0$, we obtain

$$\| L\partial_k u \|_0^2 + \| \partial_k u \|_0^2 + \sum_{j=1}^m \langle\langle B_j \partial_k u \rangle\rangle^2_{2m - m_j - \frac{1}{2}} \geq C \| \partial_k u \|_{2m}^2. \qquad (6.10)$$

Since $a_{(0, \cdots, 0, 2m)} \neq 0$ by virtue of ellipticity, it follows from the relation $Lu = \sum_{|\tau| + \nu = 2m} a_{\tau\nu} \partial^\tau \partial_n^\nu u$ that

$$\partial_n^{2m+1} u = \frac{1}{a_{(0, \ldots, 0, 2m)}} \left(\partial_n Lu - \sum_{\substack{|\tau| + \nu = 2m \\ \nu < 2m}} a_{\tau\nu} \partial^\tau \partial_n^{\nu+1} u \right),$$

$$\| \partial_n^{2m+1} u \|_0 \leq C_1 \left(\| \partial_n Lu \|_0 + \sum_{\substack{|\tau| + \nu = 2m \\ \nu < 2m}} \| \partial^\tau \partial_n^{\nu+1} u \|_0 \right). \qquad (6.11)$$

From (6.10) and (6.11) and with the help of the Ehrling-Nirenberg inequality, we conclude that (6.8) holds for $s = 1$. Hence, applying this argument, we obtain (6.8) for all natural numbers s. The assertion follows.

By somewhat modifying this proof, it is not difficult to obtain the following fact: if $u \in W_2^{2m}(G_\delta; 0)$, while $f = Lu \in W_2^s(G_\delta)$, $\phi_j = B_j u \in W_2^{2m - m_j + s - 1/2}(G'_\delta)$ $(j = 1, \cdots, m)$, where $s = 0, 1, \cdots$ and G'_δ is a region as in Lemma 6.1, then actually $u \in W_2^{2m+s}(G_\delta; 0)$. This permits the following alternate formulation of the sufficiency in Theorem 6.1: *if*

$$u \in W_2^{2m}(G), \; Lu \in W_2^s(G), \quad B_j u \in W_2^{2m - m_j + s - \frac{1}{2}}(\Gamma) \; (j = 1, \ldots, m),$$

then $u \in W_2^{2m+s}(G)$ *and the inequality* (6.8) *holds*. We have thus obtained an assertion concerning improved smoothness. Of course, it also holds in a local formulation.

2. The operator corresponding to a nonhomogeneous boundary value problem. We will assume that the coefficients in the expressions (6.1) and (6.2) have smoothness

$$a_\alpha(x) \in C(G \cup \Gamma),\ b_{j\alpha}(x) \in C^{2m-m_j}(\Gamma)\ \ (j=1,\dots,m),$$

and that Γ is of class C^{2m}. We construct an operator $\mathfrak{L}$ acting continuously from $W_2^{2m}(G)$ to the orthogonal sum

$$K_{\left(0,\,2m-m_j-\frac{1}{2}\right)} = L_2(G) \oplus \sum_{j=1}^{m} W_2^{2m-m_j-\frac{1}{2}}(\Gamma)$$

by setting

$$\mathfrak{L}u = (Lu, B_1u, \dots, B_mu), \qquad u \in W_2^{2m}(G).$$

Thus the problem (6.4)–(6.5) with f and $\phi_j (j = 1, \cdots, m)$ in their respective spaces can be written in the form

$$\mathfrak{L}u = F \quad \left(u \in W_2^{2m}(G),\quad F = (f, \varphi_1, \dots, \varphi_m) \in K_{\left(0,2m-m_j-\frac{1}{2}\right)}\right).$$

Let N denote the kernel of the operator $\mathfrak{L}$, i.e. the subspace of solutions in $W_2^{2m}(G)$ for the problem (6.4) – (6.5) with $f = 0$, $\phi_1 = 0, \cdots, \phi_m = 0$. We obtain some lemmas which will be used later.

Lemma 6.2. *The kernel N of the operator $\mathfrak{L}$ is finite dimensional.*

In fact, it follows from (6.8) that for $u \in N$, $\| u \|_{2m} \le C_1 \| u \|_0$. Let $w = u/\| u \|_0$ $(u \in N)$. Then $\| w \|_0 = 1$ and $\| w \|_{2m} \le C_1$; therefore by the imbedding theorem the set of all such w is precompact in $L_2(G)$. Thus, in the metric of $L_2(G)$, the subspace N has a precompact sphere, and is hence finite dimensional. The lemma follows.

We remark that by definition N is a subspace of $W_2^{2m}(G)$, but because of finite dimensionality it is closed in $L_2(G)$. We set $H_{2m} = W_2^{2m}(G) \ominus N$, where $\ominus$ denotes orthogonal complementation with respect to $L_2(G)$. It is easy to see that H_{2m} is a subspace of $W_2^{2m}(G)$. Every element $u \in W_2^{2m}(G)$ can be uniquely represented in the form

$$u = u' + u'', \qquad u' \in N, \qquad u'' \in H_{2m} \tag{6.12}$$

Thus we can define (nonorthogonal) projection operators P_N and $P_{\perp N}$ in $W_2^{2m}(G)$ by setting

$$P_N u = u', \; P_{\perp N} u = u'' \; (u \in W_2^{2m}(G)); \; P_N + P_{\perp N} = E.$$

It is useful to observe that these operators are continuous in the metric of $W_2^{2m}(G)$. It is sufficient to prove this for P_N. Since the decomposition (6.12) is orthogonal in $L_2(G)$ and N is finite dimensional, we can write

$$\| P_N u \|_{2m} = \| u' \|_{2m} \leqslant C_1 \| u' \|_0 \leqslant C_1 \| u \|_0 \leqslant C_2 \| u \|_{2m} \qquad (u \in W_2^{2m}(G)),$$

as required.

The following lemma ties together these somewhat connected facts.

Lemma 6.3. *Suppose that the problem* (6.4) – (6.5) *is elliptic, with*

$$a_\alpha(x) \in C(G \cup \Gamma), \; b_{j\alpha}(x) \in C^{2m-m_j}(\Gamma) \; (j = 1, \ldots, m),$$

and Γ *of class* C^{2m}. *Then*

a) *There exists a constant* $C > 0$ *such that*

$$C^{-1} \| u \|_{2m}^2 \leqslant \| Lu \|_0^2 + \sum_{j=1}^{m} \langle\!\langle B_j u \rangle\!\rangle^2_{2m-m_j-\frac{1}{2}} \leqslant C \| u \|_{2m}^2, \qquad (u \in H_{2m}). \tag{6.13}$$

b) *The operator* $\mathfrak{L}$ *considered as acting from* $L_2(G)$ *to* $K_{(0,\, 2m-m_j-1/2)}$ *is closed.*

c) *The range of the operator* L *in* $K_{(0,\, 2m-m_j-1/2)}$ *is closed.*

d) *If* $\mathfrak{L}u = F = (f, \phi_1, \cdots, \phi_m)$, *and in addition*

$$F \in K_{\left(s,\, 2m-m_j+s-\frac{1}{2}\right)} = W_2^s(G) \oplus \sum_{j=1}^{m} W_2^{2m-m_j+s-\frac{1}{2}}(\Gamma) \subseteq K_{\left(0, 2m-m_j-\frac{1}{2}\right)}$$

$$a_\alpha(x) \in C^s(G \cup \Gamma), \; b_{j\alpha}(x) \in C^{2m-m_j+s}(\Gamma) \; (j = 1, \ldots, m),$$

with Γ *of class* C^{2m+s} *for* $s \geq 0$ *an integer, then* $u \in W_2^{2m+s}(G)$.

The proof is carried out for each assertion.

a) The proof of the inequality (6.13) is similar to the arguments used for Lemmas 3.10–3.11. For let us suppose that the left inequality does not hold. Then we can find a sequence $u_n \in H_{2m}$ such that $\| u_n \|_{2m} = 1$ and

$$\| Lu_n \|_0^2 + \sum_{j=1}^{n} \langle\!\langle B_j u_n \rangle\!\rangle^2_{2m-m_j-\frac{1}{2}} \to 0.$$

It follows from the imbedding theorem that there exists a subsequence $u_{n'}$ for which $\| u_{n'} - u_{m'} \|_0 \to 0$ as $n', m' \to \infty$. By virtue of the inequality (6.8) (with $s = 0$), we have

$$C\| u_{n'} - u_{m'} \|_{2m}^2 \leqslant \| L(u_{n'} - u_{m'}) \|_0^2 + \sum_{j=1}^{m} \langle\langle B_j(u_{n'} - u_{m'}) \rangle\rangle^2_{2m-m_j-\frac{1}{2}}$$

$$+ \| u_{n'} - u_{m'} \|_C^2 \xrightarrow[n', m' \to \infty]{} 0.$$

Therefore there exists an element $\phi \in W_2^{2m}(G)$ such that $\| u_{n'} - \phi \|_{2m} \to 0$; since H_{2m} is closed in $W_2^{2m}(G)$, $\phi \in H_{2m}$. On the other hand, from

$$\| Lu_n \|_0^2 + \sum_{j=1}^{m} \langle\langle B_j u_n \rangle\rangle^2_{2m-m_j-\frac{1}{2}} \to 0$$

it follows that $\phi \in N$. Therefore $\phi = 0$. At the same time, $\| \phi \|_{2m} = \lim \| u_n \|_{2m} = 1$. We have arrived at a contradiction. The right inequality in (6.13) is obvious.

b) Suppose that $u_n \to u$ in $L_2(G)$ and $\mathfrak{L}u_n \to (f, \phi_1, \cdots, \phi_m)$ in $K_{(0,2m-m_j-\frac{1}{2})}$. Then the sequences u_n and $\mathfrak{L}u_n$ are fundamental respectively in $L_2(G)$ and $K_{(0,2m-m_j-\frac{1}{2})}$. It follows from the inequality (6.8) (for $s = 0$) that u_n is fundamental in $W_2^{2m}(G)$. Therefore $u_n \to u$ in $W_2^{2m}(G)$ and $\mathfrak{L}u = \lim \mathfrak{L}u_n = (f, \phi_1, \cdots, \phi_m)$.

c) Let $\mathfrak{L}_0$ denote the restriction of $\mathfrak{L}$ to H_{2m}. It follows from the representation (6.12) that the ranges of the operators $\mathfrak{L}$ and $\mathfrak{L}_0$ coincide: $\mathfrak{R}(\mathfrak{L}) = \mathfrak{R}(\mathfrak{L}_0)$. On the other hand, the inequality (6.13) asserts that the inverse operator $\mathfrak{L}_0^{-1}$ exists on $\mathfrak{R}(\mathfrak{L}_0)$ and maps $K_{(0,2m-m_j-\frac{1}{2})}$ continuously into $W_2^{2m}(G)$. Thus, $\mathfrak{L}_0$ effects a homeomorphism between H_{2m} and $\mathfrak{R}(\mathfrak{L}_0) = \mathfrak{R}(\mathfrak{L})$, and this implies that the last set is closed in $K_{(0,2m-m_j-\frac{1}{2})}$.

d) This assertion follows immediately from the discussion at the end of subsection 1.

The lemma is proved. We formulate a corollary to it, which can be interpreted as an analogue of case 1) in Theorem 3.6 on homeomorphisms; it does not require a complete description of the range of the operator.

Corollary. *If the smoothness conditions in* d) *are satisfied, then the restriction* $\mathfrak{L}_s$ *of the operator* $\mathfrak{L}$ *to*

$$H_{2m+s} = H_{2m} \cap W_2^{2m+s}(G) = W_2^{2m+s}(G) \ominus N$$

determines a homeomorphism between H_{2m+s} *and the subspace* $\mathfrak{R}(\mathfrak{L}_s) = R(L) \cap K_{(s,2m-m_j+s-\frac{1}{2})}$ *of the space* $K_{(s,2m-m_j+s-\frac{1}{2})}$ *(*$s \geq 0$ *integral).*

In fact, for $s = 0$ the assertion follows from a); for $s > 0$ it follows from d), the inequality

$$\| Lu \|_s^2 + \sum_{j=1}^{m} \langle\!\langle B_j u \rangle\!\rangle^2_{2m-m_j+s-\frac{1}{2}} \leq C \| u \|^2_{2m+s} \quad (u \in H_{2m+s})$$

and the theorem asserting that the inverse of a continuous operator between two complete spaces, when it exists, is itself continuous.

3. **Noetherian elliptic problems.** Let B be a Banach space, M a subspace. The dimension of the factor space $B \backslash M$ is called the codimension of M. If B is a Hilbert space, then the codimension of M coincides with the dimension of its orthogonal complement.

We now investigate the codimension of $\mathfrak{R}(\mathfrak{L})$ in $K_{(0,2m-m_j-\frac{1}{2})}$ (recall that $\mathfrak{R}(\mathfrak{L})$ is closed in $K_{(0,2m-m_j-\frac{1}{2})}$; see Lemma 6.2c). We mention an "analytical" definition of codimension in this case. It is easy to see that $W_2^{l-\frac{1}{2}}(\Gamma)$ $(l > 0)$ can be considered as a positive space with respect to the zero space $L_2(\Gamma)$; let $W_2^{-(l-\frac{1}{2})}(\Gamma)$ be the corresponding negative space. The scalar products and norms are denoted by $\langle \cdot, \cdot \rangle_{l-\frac{1}{2}}$, $\langle \cdot, \cdot \rangle_0$, $\langle \cdot, \cdot \rangle_{-(l-\frac{1}{2})}$ and $\langle\!\langle \cdot \rangle\!\rangle_{l-\frac{1}{2}}$, $\langle\!\langle \cdot \rangle\!\rangle_0$, $\langle\!\langle \cdot \rangle\!\rangle_{-(l-\frac{1}{2})}$. Considering $K_{(0,2m-m_j-\frac{1}{2})}$ as a positive space with respect to the zero space. $L_2(G) \oplus L_2(\Gamma) \oplus \cdots \oplus L_2(\Gamma)$ ($L_2(\Gamma)$ is repeated m times), we obtain the sequence

$$L_2(G) \oplus \sum_{j=1}^{m} W_2^{-\left(2m-m_j-\frac{1}{2}\right)}(\Gamma) \supseteq L_2(G) \oplus L_2(\Gamma) \oplus \cdots \oplus L_2(\Gamma)$$

$$\supseteq L_2(G) \oplus \sum_{j=1}^{m} W_2^{2m-m_j-\frac{1}{2}}(\Gamma) = K_{\left(0,2m-m_j-\frac{1}{2}\right)}. \tag{6.14}$$

The condition that $\mathfrak{R}(\mathfrak{L})$ has finite codimension in $K_{(0,2m-m_j-\frac{1}{2})}$ can obviously be formulated in the following way: there exist q linearly independent vectors

$$A^{(k)} = (a^{(k)}, \alpha_1^{(k)}, \ldots, \alpha_m^{(k)}) \in L_2(G) \oplus \sum_{j=1}^{m} W_2^{-\left(2m-m_j-\frac{1}{2}\right)}(\Gamma) \quad (k = 1, \ldots, m)$$

such that $F = (f, \phi_1, \cdots, \phi_m) \in K_{(0,2m-m_j-\frac{1}{2})}$ belongs to $\mathfrak{R}(\mathfrak{L})$ if and only if

$$[F, A^{(k)}]_0 = (f, a^{(k)})_0 + \sum_{j=1}^{m} \langle \varphi_j, \alpha_j^{(k)} \rangle_0 = 0 \quad (k = 1, \ldots, q). \tag{6.15}$$

Here $[\cdot, \cdot]_0$ denotes the "scalar product" of generalized and basic vectors in the sequence (6.14).

It turns out that the codimension of $\mathfrak{R}(\mathfrak{L})$ in $K_{(0,2m-m_j-\frac{1}{2})}$ is finite.

Lemma 6.4. *Suppose that the problem* (6.4) – (6.5) *is elliptic and* $a_\alpha(x) \in C(G \cup \Gamma)$, $b_{j\alpha}(x) \in C^{2m-m_j}(\Gamma)$ $(j = 1, \cdots, m)$, *with* Γ *of class* C^{2m}. *Then the codimension of* $\Re(\mathfrak{L})$ *in* $K_{(0,2m-m_j-\frac{1}{2})}$ *is finite.*

We present only the idea of the proof of this important lemma. Let T be a continuous operator acting from $K_{(0,2m-m_j-\frac{1}{2})}$ to $W_2^{2m}(G)$. Then $\mathfrak{L}T$ acts continuously in $K_{(0,2m-m_j-\frac{1}{2})}$. Suppose now that T is such that $\mathfrak{L}T = E + S$, where S is completely continuous in $K_{(0,2m-m_j-\frac{1}{2})}$. Then $\Re(\mathfrak{L}T)$ has finite codimension in $K_{(0,2m-m_j-\frac{1}{2})}$, and since $\Re(\mathfrak{L}) \supseteq \Re(\mathfrak{L}T)$, so does $\Re(\mathfrak{L})$. Thus the proof of the lemma reduces to the construction of T, which is called a regularization operator.

This construction is carried out locally, and it uses in an essential way a formula which, as has been pointed out, could be used to prove Lemmas 3.1 and 6.1 (namely, a formula representing solutions to the problem (6.4) – (6.5) in a half-space G in terms of $f(x)$ $(x \in G)$ and $\phi_1(x), \cdots, \phi_m(x)$ $(x \in \Gamma)$; Γ is a hyperplane). We outline it.

Let V_k be a fixed neighborhood lying inside G. We first construct an auxiliary operator T_k, acting from $K_{(0,2m-m_j-\frac{1}{2})}$ to $W_2^{2m}(V_k)$, such that for any $F = (f, \phi_1, \cdots, \phi_m) \in K_{(0,2m-m_j-\frac{1}{2})}$,

$$\| T_k F \|_{W_2^{2m}(V_k)} \leq C \| F \|_{K_{\left(0,2m-m_j-\frac{1}{2}\right)}} \tag{6.16}$$

$$(L(T_k F))(x) = f(x) + (L'(T_k F))(x) \qquad (x \in V_k),$$

where L' is a differential expression of order $< 2m$. If V_k borders on the piece Γ_k of the boundary Γ, then T_k is constructed as before, acting from $K_{(0,2m-m_j-\frac{1}{2})}$ to $W_2^{2m}(V_k)$, so that besides the relation (6.16), we have the equation

$$(B_j(T_k F))(x) = \varphi_j(x) + (B_j'(T_k F))(x) \tag{6.17}$$
$$(x \in \Gamma_k;\ j = 1, \ldots, m).$$

where B_j' is a differential expression of order $< m_j$.

It can be shown that if $V_k \subset G$ is a sufficiently small neighborhood (bordering on Γ or not), then it is actually possible to construct an operator T_k with the properties (6.16) – (6.17). Its construction, for the case when L and $B_j (j = 1, \cdots, m)$ are homogeneous expressions with constant coefficients and Γ_k is a piece of a hyperplane, follows immediately from the above-mentioned representation formula: in this case T_k is simply locally an inverse operator, i.e. in (6.16) and (6.17) the expressions L' and B_j' reduce to zero. In the general case, the construction of T_k is carried out by the method of successive approximations.

We now form a finite covering of G by neighborhoods $V_1, \cdots, V_N$, in each of which a corresponding operator T_k is constructed: $1 = \Sigma_{k=1}^N \chi_k(x)$ $(x \in G \cup \Gamma)$ is a decomposition of unity corresponding to this covering. It is easy to see that we may use the operator

$$(TF)(x) = \sum_{k=1}^{N} \chi_k(x)(T_k F)(x).$$

We will say that the problem (6.4) – (6.5) is Noetherian if the operator $\mathfrak{L}$, acting from $W_2^{2m}(G)$ to $K_{(0,2m-m_j-\frac{1}{2})}$ constructed with respect to the problem, has the following properties

a) the kernel of the operator $\mathfrak{L}$ is finite dimensional;

b) the range $\mathfrak{R}(\mathfrak{L})$ is closed in $K_{(0,2m-m_j-\frac{1}{2})}$;

c) the codimension of $\mathfrak{R}(\mathfrak{L})$ in $K_{(0,2m-m_j-\frac{1}{2})}$ is finite.[1)]

Thus for a Noetherian problem we have solvability for any $F = (f, \phi_1, \cdots, \phi_m)$ with "finite deficiency." If p denotes the dimension of the kernel of the operator $\mathfrak{L}$, and q its codimension, then the difference $p - q$ is called the index of the problem. Generalizing the concept of Fredholm type, mentioned in Theorem 3.5, Chapter II, the problem (6.4) – (6.5) is said to be of Fredholm type if its index is equal to 0. We do not take up the large number of problems connected with these ideas. From Lemmas 6.2, 6.3c, and 6.4, we obtain

Theorem 6.2. *An elliptic problem* (6.4) – (6.5) *is Noetherian if the following smoothness conditions hold:*

$$a_\alpha(x) \in C(G \cup \Gamma), \quad b_{j\alpha}(x) \in C^{2m-m_j}(\Gamma) \quad (j = 1, \ldots, m),$$

Γ of class C^{2m}.

4. **The adjoint problem in the case of homogeneous (bd).** We study the problem, adjoint to an elliptic problem (6.4) – (6.5) with homogeneous boundary conditions; it is now natural to assume that L satisfies the usual smoothness conditions. Let W_2^{2m}(bd) denote the set of functions $u \in W_2^{2m}(G)$ for which $(B_j u)(x) = 0$ $(x \in \Gamma;\ j = 1, \cdots, m)$. It follows from the imbedding theorem that if L is a surface of class C^{2m}, then W_2^{2m}(bd) is a subspace of the space $W_2^{2m}(G)$, and therefore the introduction of (bd) is meaningful from the point of view of §1.1, Chapter II. Define (bd)$^+$ in the usual way; the equation (bd)$^{++}$ = (bd) is now not auto-

1) An operator acting from one Banach space to another and having the properties a) – c) is also called a Φ-operator.

matically satisfied.

We consider the boundary value problems.

$$Lu = f, \quad u \in (\mathrm{bd}); \tag{6.18}$$

$$L^+ v = g, \quad v \in (\mathrm{bd})^+. \tag{6.19}$$

Suppose $g \in W_2^{-2m}(G)$; by a weak solution (more precisely, 0-solution) of the problem (6.19) we mean any $v \in L_2(G)$ such that $(v, Lu)_0 = (g, u)_0$ for every $u \in W_2^{2m}(\mathrm{bd})$. This definition (when it is assumed that $(\mathrm{bd})^{++} = (\mathrm{bd})$) is consistent with the definition in §3.3, Chapter II; boundary conditions are possibly lost for this. It is easy to prove

Theorem 6.3. *Suppose that the problem (6.4) – (6.5) is elliptic, with*

$$a_\alpha(x) \in C^{|\alpha|}(G \cup \Gamma),\ b_{j\alpha}(x) \in C^{2m-m_j}(\Gamma)\ (j = 1, \ldots, m),$$

and Γ of class C^{2m}. If $g \in W_2^{-2m}(G)$ satisfies $(g, N)_0 = 0$ (N is the kernel of the operator $\mathfrak{L}$), then there exists a weak solution to the problem (6.19). It is clear that the converse holds: if (6.19) admits a weak solution for $g \in W_2^{-2m}(G)$, then $(g, N)_0 = 0$.

The proof easily reduces to an abstract form of Theorem 3.3, Chapter II (see the end of §3.4, Chapter II), but it is simpler to develop it directly. We adopt the second course, and moreover obtain a useful modification of the arguments of §3.4, Chapter II.

Thus it follows from (6.8) that the bilinear form, defined for $u, v \in W_2^{2m}(G)$,

$$B(u, v) = (Lu, Lv)_0 + \sum_{j=1}^{m} \langle B_j u, B_j v \rangle_{2m-m_j-\frac{1}{2}} \tag{6.20}$$

can be taken as a new scalar product in H_{2m}, equivalent to $(\cdot, \cdot)_{2m}$. We consider the conjugate linear continuous functional $l(u'') = (g, u'')_0$ on $u'' \in H_{2m}$. It can be written in terms of the scalar product (6.20): $(g, u'')_0 = B(w, u'')$ $(u'' \in H_{2m})$, where w is some element of H_{2m}. The last equation holds not only for $u'' \in H_{2m}$, but also for $u \in W_2^{2m}(G)$: decomposing u according to (6.12) in the form $u = u' + u''$, where $u' \in N$ and $u'' \in H_{2m}$, we obtain by the conditions $(g, u')_0 = 0$ and $\mathfrak{L}u' = 0$

$$B(w, u) = (Lw, Lu)_0 + \sum_{j=1}^{m} \langle B_j w, B_j u \rangle_{2m-m_j-\frac{1}{2}}$$

$$= B(w, u'') = (g, u'')_0 = (g, u)_0. \tag{6.21}$$

Let $v = Lw \in L_2(G)$ and assume $u \in W_2^{2m}(\mathrm{bd})$. Now $B_j u = 0$ ($j = 1, \cdots, m$), and equation (6.21) gives $(v, Lu)_0 = (g, u)_0$. Thus v is the desired weak solution. The theorem follows.

It turns out that if the coefficients of the differential expressions and Γ are sufficiently smooth, then the weak solution obtained just now will have improved smoothness for smoother g. This result follows from the following general theorem, whose proof is based on techniques similar to those used for the proof of Lemma 6.1 and the end of the proof of Lemma 3.1.

Theorem 6.4. *Suppose that the problem* (6.4) – (6.5) *is elliptic, with*

$$a_\alpha(x) \in C^{2m+\max(|\alpha|, s)}(G \cup \Gamma),\ b_{j\alpha}(x) \in C^{2m+s-1}(\Gamma)\ (j = 1, \ldots, m),$$

Γ *of class* C^{4m+s}, *and* $g \in W_2^s(G)$ ($s \geq 0$ *integral*). *Define the bilinear form* $B(u, v)$ *for* $u, v \in W_2^{2m}(G)$ *by* (6.20). *If* $w \in W_2^{2m}(G)$ *is such that for any* $u \in W_2^{2m}(G)$,

$$B(w, u) = (g, u)_0, \tag{6.22}$$

then automatically $w \in W_2^{4m+s}(G)$.

Corollary 1. *Suppose that the hypotheses of Theorems* 6.3 *and* 6.4 *are satisfied and* $(g, N)_0 = 0$. *Then the weak solution* v *to the problem* (6.19), *given by Theorem* 6.3, *belongs to* $W_2^{2m+s}(G)$.

In fact, $v = Lw$, where w satisfies (6.21). Comparing this equation with (6.22), we conclude that $w \in W_2^{4m+s}(G)$, and hence $v \in W_2^{2m+s}(G)$.

Corollary 2. *If in Theorem* 6.4 *the condition* (6.22) *is replaced by the condition* $B(w, w) = 0$, *then* $w \in W_2^{4m+s}(G)$. *In particular,* $N \subset W_2^{2m+s}(G)$.

For the bilinear form (6.20) on $W_2^{2m}(G)$ is positive definite, and therefore the equation $B(w, w) = 0$ implies $B(w, u) = 0$ ($u \in W_2^{2m}(G)$). Thus (6.22) holds with $g = 0$, and the assertion follows from this.

It follows from Lemma 6.3c that the set $L(W_2^{2m}(\mathrm{bd}))$ is closed in $L_2(G)$, and from Lemma 6.4 that the dimension of the orthogonal complement in $L_2(G)$ is finite. However, this orthogonal complement coincides with M^+, the set of weak solutions of the problem (6.19) with $g = 0$. We denote by N^+ the kernel of an operator which is constructed from L^+; the operator is similar to $\mathfrak{L}$ which is constructed from L. In other words, N^+ is the set of solutions $v \in W_2^{2m}(\mathrm{bd})^+$ of the problem (6.19) with $g = 0$. Clearly $N^+ \subseteq M^+$, and therefore N^+ *is also finite dimensional* (this result does not follow trivially by replacing L by L^+ in subsection 2, since $(\mathrm{bd})^+$ is not, in general, described by differential expressions of the type (6.2)).

We show later (subsection 6) that under a certain additional condition (the normality condition) on the system of boundary expressions (6.2), we have the equation

$$N^+ = M^+. \tag{6.23}$$

We make the following remark in connection with Corollary 1.

Suppose that the conditions of Corollary 1 *are satisfied with* $s = 0$, *and let* (6.23) *hold. Then every weak solution to the problem* (6.19) *with* $g \in L_2(G)$ (*and not only those constructed from Theorem* 6.3) *belongs to* $W_2^{2m}(G)$.

We show first of all that a weak solution to the problem (6.19), which is orthogonal to M^+ in $L_2(G)$, is unique. In fact, if there exist two solutions, then their difference $w \in L_2(G)$ satisfies the equations

$$(w, Lu)_0 = 0 \quad (u \in W_2^{2m}(\mathrm{bd})), \quad (w, M^+)_0 = 0. \tag{6.24}$$

However, the orthogonal complement (in $L_2(G)$) of M^+ coincides with the set $L(W_2^{2m}(\mathrm{bd}))$, since the latter is closed. Therefore it follows from the second equation in (6.24) that $w = Lu_0$, where $u_0 \in W_2^{2m}(\mathrm{bd})$. Setting $u = u_0$ in the first equation in (6.24), we obtain $(w, w)_0 = 0$, i.e. $w = 0$ as required.

Now let $v \in L_2(G)$ be any weak solution for the problem (6.19) with $g \in L_2(G)$, i.e. $(v, Lu)_0 = (g, u)_0$ $(u \in W_2^{2m}(\mathrm{bd}))$. Represent v in the form $v = v' + v''$, where $v' \in M^+$ and v'' is orthogonal to M^+ in $L_2(G)$. Since $(v', Lu)_0 = 0$ $(u \in W_2^{2m}(\mathrm{bd}))$ by the definition of M^+, v'' is also a weak solution of (6.19).

Make a similar decomposition $v_0 = v_0' + v_0''$ for a weak solution v_0 of the problem (6.19) obtained from Theorem 6.3. According to the proof, $v'' = v_0'' = v_0 - v_0'$. Thus $v = v' + v_0 - v_0'$. By Corollary 1, $v_0 \in W_2^{2m}(G)$; by (6.23), $v', v_0' \in M^+ = N^+ \subset W_2^{2m}(G)$. Thus, $v \in W_2^{2m}(G)$ as required.

5. **Normal systems of boundary expressions.** As was already pointed out, the adjoint boundary conditions to (bd), constructed from (6.2), are not, in general, described by expressions of the type (6.2). This accounts for the asymmetry in the presentation and leads to less complete results. We now study a class of (bd) which do not have this shortcoming. A system of boundary expressions (6.2) is called normal if a) $m_j \neq m_l$ whenever $j \neq l$; b) for every $x \in \Gamma$, $B_{j,c}(x, \nu(x)) \neq 0$ $(j = 1, \cdots, m$; $\nu(x)$ is the exterior normal to Γ at the point x).[1]

We will assume that Γ is a surface of class C^l, $l \geq 1$. Then for every

1) The concept of normality on a piece $\Gamma_0 \subseteq \Gamma$ is introduced similarly.

point $x \in \Gamma$, there exists a neighborhood U of x in E_n, such that $\Gamma \cap U$ can be mapped in a one-to-one manner onto the tangent hyperplane at the point x, and moreover such that this mapping, and its inverse, are l times continuously differentiable. We will assume that the point x is the origin for the coordinates, and the equation for the tangent hyperplane at this point is $x_n = 0$. The piece $\Gamma \cap U$ of the surface is represented in the form $x_n = \psi(x_1, \cdots, x_{n-1})$, where $\psi(0, \cdots, 0) = 0$, $\psi \in C^l$. Then, a transformation of the type mentioned on p. 140.

$$x'_k = x_k \quad (k = 1, \ldots, n-1),$$

$$x'_n = x_n - \psi(x_1, \ldots, x_{n-1}) \tag{6.25}$$

maps $\overline{G \cap U}$ into a hemisphere $\overline{G}_\delta$ $(|x'| \leq \delta,\ x'_n \geq 0)$. After such a transformation, any boundary expression $B(x, \partial)$ of the type (6.2) of order $l-1$ passes into an expression

$$B'(x', \partial') = \sum_{s=1}^{l} T_s(x', \partial')\, \partial_n'^{\,s-1} \qquad \left(\partial'_n = \frac{1}{i} \frac{\partial}{\partial x'_n}\right), \tag{6.26}$$

where $T_s(x', \partial')$ is an expression in partial derivatives of order $\leq l - s$ with respect to the variables $x'_1, \cdots, x'_{n-1}$. In other words, the derivative $\partial/\partial x'_n$ is directed along the normal to the boundary $x'_n = 0$ of the region G_δ, and the remaining derivatives which occur in $T_s(x', \partial')$ are tangential. If $B(x, \partial)$ belongs to a normal system, then from condition b) it follows that the function $T_l(x', 0) \neq 0$.

A system of m normal boundary expressions (6.2) is called a Dirichlet system if all of the orders m_j of the expressions are less than m. If $B_1, \cdots, B_m$ is such a system, then after renumbering the expressions, we can assume that the order of B_j is equal to $j-1$. We use this convention in everything that follows.

Lemma 6.5. *Let* (6.2) *be a Dirichlet system, with*

$$b_{j\alpha}(x) \in C^{m-j+1}(\Gamma) \quad (j = 1, \ldots, m);$$

Γ is of class C^m. If $\phi_1(x), \cdots, \phi_m(x)$ is any given system of functions on Γ, where $\phi_j(x) \in W_2^{m-j+1/2}(\Gamma)$, then there exists a function $u \in W_2^m(G)$ such that

$$(B_j u)(x) = \varphi_j(x)(x \in \Gamma;\ j = 1, \ldots, m).$$

The transformation $(\phi_1, \cdots, \phi_m) \to u$ acts continuously from $\oplus \sum_{j=1}^m W_2^{m-j+1/2}(\Gamma)$ to $W_2^m(G)$.

We outline the proof. It is clear that it is sufficient to carry it out locally, and moreover near a plane piece of the boundary (it is necessary to use a decomposition of unity and the transformation (6.25)). This allows us to assume that G is a half-space and to consider functions which are finite for $|x'| \to \infty$.

Suppose now that B_j has the special form: $B_j = \partial_n'^{j-1}$ $(j = 1, \cdots, m)$. In this case the lemma follows from the theory of spaces $W_2^l(G)$, where l is fractional, with the help of the Fourier transformation with respect to $(x_1, \cdots, x_{n-1})$. To treat the general case, we proceed as follows. From the triangular system (see (6.26))

$$B_j(x', \partial') = \sum_{s=1}^{j} T_{js}(x', \partial')\, \partial_n'^{s-1} \qquad (j = 1, \ldots, m) \tag{6.27}$$

it is possible to express $\partial_n'^{j-1}$ in terms of $B_1, \cdots, B_m$:

$$\partial_n'^{j-1} = \sum_{s=1}^{j} \hat{T}_{js}(x', \partial')\, B_s(x', \partial') \qquad (j = 1, \ldots, m), \tag{6.28}$$

where $\hat{T}_{js}(x', \partial')$ are expressions similar to $T_{js}(x', \partial')$. The orders of T_{js} and $\hat{T}_{js}$ are not greater than $j - s$; $T_{jj}(x', 0)$, $T_{jj}(x', 0) \neq 0$ $(j = 1, \ldots, m)$. Now suppose that it is required to find a function $u \in W_2^m(G)$ such that $(B_j u)(x) = \varphi_j(x)$ $(x \in \Gamma;$ $j = 1, \cdots, m)$. Because of (6.27) and (6.28), it is sufficient to find u satisfying on Γ the equation:

$$\partial_n'^{j-1} u = \sum_{s=1}^{j} \hat{T}_{js}(x', \partial')\, \varphi_s \in W_2^{m-j+\frac{1}{2}}(\Gamma) \quad (j = 1, \ldots, m).$$

Thus the problem is reduced to the special case, and this proves the lemma.

Theorem 6.5. *Let the expression (6.1) be elliptic, and suppose that the system (6.2) of boundary expressions is normal. Suppose that*

$$a_\alpha(x) \in C^{|\alpha|}(G \cup \Gamma),\ b_{j\alpha}(x) \in C^{\max(2m-m_j,\, m_j)}(\Gamma) \quad (j = 1, \ldots, m)$$

and Γ is of class C^{2m}. Then we can find a normal system of the type (6.2)

$$B_j' v = B_j'(x, \partial) v = \sum_{|\alpha| \leq m_j'} b_{j\alpha}'(x)\, \partial^\alpha v \qquad (m_j' < 2m;\ j = 1, \ldots, m), \tag{6.29}$$

*such that $W_2^{2m}(\mathrm{bd})^+$ consists of those, and only those, functions $v \in W_2^{2m}(G)$ for which $(B_j' v)(x) = 0$ $(x \in \Gamma;\ j = 1, \cdots, m)$. For this, $W_2^{2m}(\mathrm{bd})^{++} = W_2^{2m}(\mathrm{bd})$.**

We outline the proof. Extend the system $\{B_j\}$ $(j = 1, \cdots, m)$ in an arbitrary way to a Dirichlet system of order $2m$ (this is possible since the orders of the expressions $B_1, \cdots, B_m$ are less than $2m$. We introduce the natural numbering for

* The last inequality holds if the coefficients in (6.1) and (6.2) are sufficiently smooth. In fact, the smoothness must be such that $b_{j\alpha}'(x) \in C^{2m-m_j'}(\Gamma)$, $c_{j\alpha}'(x) \in C^{2m-1_j'}(\Gamma)$ $(j = 1, \cdots, m)$, where these coefficients $b_{j\alpha}'(x)$ and $c_{j\alpha}'(x)$ of the expressions B_j' and C_j' are introduced below.

the obtained system (the jth expression has order $j-1$) Thus our original expressions are written in the notation $B_{m_1+1}, \cdots, B_{m_m+1}$. By means of the transformation (6.25), we may pass to the hemisphere G_δ and expressions of the type (6.26); we assume at once that B_j has the form (6.26). We also take the case where (6.27) and (6.28) hold, with m replaced by $2m$.

Suppose $u \in W_2^{2m}(G_\delta)$, and write the expression L in the form

$$Lu = \sum_{|\tau|+\nu \leqslant 2m} a_{\tau\nu}(x)\, \partial^\tau \partial_n^\nu u, \qquad \partial^\tau = \partial_1^{\tau_1} \ldots \partial_{n-1}^{\tau_{n-1}} \tag{6.30}$$

(we omit the primes from the notation). Consider $v \in W_2^{2m}(G_\delta)$ vanishing in a neighborhood of the boundary $|x| = \delta$ of the region G_δ. In the expression $(Lu, v)_0$, we integrate by parts, shifting the tangential derivatives to v; we obtain

$$(Lu, v)_0 - (u, L^+ v)_0 = \sum_{\nu=0}^{2m} \sum_{s=1}^{\nu} \int_{S_\delta} \partial_n^{s-1} u \cdot \sum_{|\tau| \leqslant 2m-\nu} \overline{\partial_n^{\nu-s} \partial^\tau (\bar{a}_{\tau\nu} v)}\, dx$$

$$= \sum_{s=1}^{2m} \int_{S_\delta} \partial_n^{s-1} u \cdot \sum_{\substack{|\tau|+\nu \leqslant 2m, \\ \nu \geqslant s}} \overline{\partial_n^{\nu-s} \partial^\tau (\bar{a}_{\tau\nu} v)}\, dx,$$

where S_δ is the plane part of the boundary of G_δ.

Taking into account (6.28) (with m replaced by $2m$), we hence obtain

$$(Lu, v)_0 - (u, L^+ v)_0 = \sum_{s=1}^{2m} \sum_{t=1}^{s} \int_{S_\delta} \hat{T}_{st} B_t u \cdot \overline{N_s v}\, dx$$

$$= \sum_{t=1}^{2m} \int_{S_\delta} B_t u \cdot \overline{\sum_{s=t}^{2m} \hat{T}_{st}^{+} N_s v}\, dx = \sum_{t=1}^{2m} \langle B_t u, B'_{2m-t+1} v \rangle_0. \tag{6.31}$$

Here we denote

$$N_s v = \sum_{\nu=s}^{2m} \sum_{|\tau|+\nu \leqslant 2m} \partial_n^{\nu-s} \partial^\tau (\overline{a_{\tau\nu}} v) \qquad (s = 1, \ldots, 2m),$$

$$B'_{2m-t+1} v = \sum_{s=t}^{2m} \hat{T}_{st}^{+} N_s v \qquad (t = 1, \ldots, 2m);$$

$\hat{T}_{st}^{+}$ is the formal adjoint of the expression $\hat{T}_{st}$, which is composed only of tangential derivatives.

It is easy to verify that the order of the expression B'_{2m-t+1} is equal to $2m-t$, and the coefficient of ∂_n^{2m-t} in it is

$$\hat{T}_{tt}^{+}(x, 0)\, \overline{a_{(0,\ldots,0,2m)}(x)} = \overline{\hat{T}_{tt}(x, 0) a_{(0,\ldots,0,2m)}(x)}.$$

This coefficient is different from zero since $T_{tt}(x, 0) \neq 0$ and $a_{(0,\cdots,0,2m)}(x) \neq 0$ by ellipticity. Thus the system $\{B'_{2m-t+1}\}$ $(t = 1, \cdots, 2m)$ of boundary expressions is a Dirichlet system of order $2m$.

Now recall that $\{B_t\}$ for $t = m_1 + 1, \cdots, m_m + 1$ coincides with the original system of boundary expressions. Then by (6.31) and Lemma 6.5 (in which m is replaced by $2m$), it follows that $\{B'_{2m-t+1}\}$, for the remaining values of the indices, forms a system of boundary expressions defining $(\mathrm{bd})^+$. For this, $W_2^{2m}(\mathrm{bd})^{++} = W_2^{2m}(\mathrm{bd})$ (see the proof of Theorem 1.1, Chapter II). This system is taken for (6.29) after a change of index. It is normal since it is part of a Dirichlet system. The theorem follows.

It is clear from the proof of the theorem that the coefficients of the expressions (6.29) satisfy smoothness requirements depending on the assumed smoothness of the coefficients in the original expressions (6.2) (clearly, increased smoothness in (6.2) leads to increased smoothness in (6.29)). We will not formulate this, since later we give more symmetric and conceptually simpler smoothness conditions for both the boundary expressions defining (bd), and the similar expressions defining $(\mathrm{bd})^+$.

In what follows we will need Green's formula, which was incidentally obtained in the proof of the theorem. Namely, the following fact is obtained from (6.31).

Let L be elliptic and satisfy the smoothness requirements of Theorem 6.5. Then for any $u, v \in W_2^{2m}(G)$ we have the equation

$$(Lu, v)_0 + \sum_{j=1}^{m} \langle B_j u, C'_j v \rangle_0 = (u, L^+ v)_0 + \sum_{j=1}^{m} \langle C_j u, B'_j v \rangle_0. \qquad (6.32)$$

Here $\{B_j\}$, $\{B'_j\}$ $(j = 1, \cdots, m)$ are the boundary expressions, of orders $m_j < 2m$ and $m'_j < 2m$ respectively, defining (bd) *and* $(\mathrm{bd})^+$; *the expressions $\{C'_j\}$ and $\{C_j\}$ are of the type* (6.2) *and have orders $l'_j = 2m - m_j - 1$ and $l_j = 2m - m'_j - 1$ respectively; when the latter are taken together with $\{B'_j\}$ and $\{B_j\}$ $(j = 1, \cdots, m)$, we obtain Dirichlet systems of order $2m$ (we emphasize that there is ambiguity in the definitions of $\{B'_j\}$, $\{C_j\}$, and $\{C'_j\}$ $(j = 1, \cdots, m)$).*

To apply the theorem just proved, we need

Theorem 6.6. *Let the expression* (6.1) *be regularly elliptic, let* (6.2) *be the system defining* (bd), *and let* (6.9) *be the system, whose existence is guaranteed by Theorem* 6.5, *defining* $(\mathrm{bd})^+$. *Suppose that the following smoothness conditions* *are satisfied:*

$$a_\alpha(x) \in C^{2m+|\alpha|}(G \cup \Gamma), \quad b_{j\alpha}(x) \in C^{\max(2m-1, 2m-m_j)}(\Gamma), \quad b'_{j\alpha}(x) \in C^{2m-m'_j}(\Gamma) \ (j=1, \ldots, m),$$

with Γ *of class* C^{4m}. *If the original system of boundary expressions* (6.2) *covers* L, *then* (6.29) *covers* L^+.

A direct verification of this theorem is awkward, and we outline another approach to its proof. Namely, we will show that the energy inequality (6.8) holds for L^+ and the expressions (6.29). The covering property then follows from Theorem 6.1.

Let $\mathfrak{L}$ be the operator constructed with respect to the problem (6.4) – (6.5), and let N be its kernel. We consider the problem (6.19), where $g \in L_2(G)$, $(g, N)_0 = 0$. By virtue of Theorem 6.3, it has a weak solution $v \in L_2(G)$, which, because of Corollary 1 above, belongs to $W_2^{2m}(G)$, and hence to $W_2^{2m}(\mathrm{bd})^+$. Let N^+ be a similar kernel, constructed with respect to L^+ and (6.29) (see subsection 2). $H_{2m}(\mathrm{bd})^+ = W_2^{2m}(\mathrm{bd})^+ \ominus N^+$ (the orthogonal complement is taken in $L_2(G)$; $H_{2m}(\mathrm{bd})^+$ has the metric $(\cdot, \cdot)_{2m}$). It is now clear that the operator $w'' \rightarrow L^+ w''$, $w'' \in H_{2m}(\mathrm{bd})^+$ is a continuous one-to-one mapping of this space onto $L_2(G) \ominus N$. But then the inverse operator is continuous, i.e.

$$\| L^+ w'' \|_0 \geqslant C_1 \| w'' \|_{2m} \qquad (C_1 > 0;\ w'' \in H_{2m}(\mathrm{bd})^+). \tag{6.33}$$

By the discussion on p. 216, N^+ is finite dimensional. Using a decomposition as in (6.12), it is easy to see that (6.33) gives the estimate

$$\| L^+ w \|_0^2 + \| w \|_0^2 \geqslant C_2 \| w \|_{2m}^2 \qquad (C_2 > 0;\ w \in W_2^{2m}(\mathrm{bd})^+). \tag{6.34}$$

Now consider an arbitrary $v \in W_2^{2m}(G)$. Complete the system $\{B'_j\}$ $(j = 1, \cdots, m)$ to a Dirichlet system of order $2m$, and apply Lemma 6.5 (with m replaced by $2m$). Here, we take $\phi''_k(x)$ equal to $(B'_j v)(x) \in W_2^{2m-m'_j-1/2}(\Gamma)$ when the index corresponds to a B'_j in the original system, and we take $\phi_k(x)$ equal to 0 for an index in a supplementary expression. As the result, we are able to construct a function $v_0 \in W_2^{2m}(G)$ such that $(B'_j v_0)(x) = (B'_j v)(x)$ $(x \in \Gamma;\ j = 1, \cdots, m)$ and

$$\| v_0 \|_{2m}^2 \leqslant C_3 \sum_{j=1}^{m} \langle\!\langle B'_j v \rangle\!\rangle^2_{2m-m'_j-\frac{1}{2}}, \tag{6.35}$$

where $C_3 > 0$ does not depend on the choice of v. We set $w = v - v_0 \in W_2^{2m}(\mathrm{bd})^+$, so that $v = w + v_0$. Using the estimates (6.34) and (6.35), we find

$$\| v \|_{2m}^2 \leqslant 2 (\| w \|_{2m}^2 + \| v_0 \|_{2m}^2)$$

$$\leqslant C_4 \left(\| L^+ w \|_0^2 + \| w \|_0^2 + \sum_{i=1}^{m} \langle\!\langle B_i' v \rangle\!\rangle^2_{2m-m_i'-\frac{1}{2}} \right)$$

$$= C_4 \left(\| L^+ v - L^+ v_0 \|_0^2 + \| v - v_0 \|_0^2 + \sum_{i=1}^{m} \langle\!\langle B_i' v \rangle\!\rangle^2_{2m-m_i'-\frac{1}{2}} \right)$$

$$\leqslant C_5 \left(\| L^+ v \|_0^2 + \| v \|_0^2 + \| v_0 \|_{2m}^2 + \sum_{j=1}^{m} \langle\!\langle B_j' v \rangle\!\rangle^2_{2m-m_j'-\frac{1}{2}} \right)$$

$$\leqslant C_6 \left(\| L^+ v \|_0^2 + \| v \|_0^2 + \sum_{j=1}^{m} \langle\!\langle B_j' v \rangle\!\rangle^2_{2m-m_j'-\frac{1}{2}} \right).$$

We have thus established the required estimate of the type (6.8), which proves the theorem.

In the case of a normal system of boundary conditions, along with the problem (6.4) – (6.5) we can consider the problem

$$(L^+ v)(x) = g(x) \qquad (x \in G), \tag{6.36}$$

$$(B_j' v)(x) = \psi_j(x) \qquad (x \in \Gamma;\ j = 1, \ldots, m), \tag{6.37}$$

which we agree to call the adjoint problem with respect to (6.4) – (6.5). All of the previous results hold for the problem (6.36) – (6.37) under the corresponding smoothness assumptions.

In what follows we use a series of definitions of spaces and operators. Some of these were introduced in connection with the problem (6.4) – (6.5); others involve the problem (6.36) – (6.37). For the convenience of the reader, we now collect all of these definitions. Below, $s \geq 0$ is an integer.

a) *The original problem* (6.4) – (6.5). We use (bd) to denote corresponding homogeneous boundary conditions. In connection with the problem (6.4) – (6.5), we have introduced the space

$$K_{\left(s, 2m-m_j+s-\frac{1}{2}\right)} = W_2^s(G) \oplus \sum_{j=1}^{m} W_2^{2m-m_j+s-\frac{1}{2}}(\Gamma). \tag{6.38}$$

We assume that

$$a_\alpha(x) \in C(G \cup \Gamma), \quad b_{j\alpha}(x) \in C^{2m-m_j}(\Gamma) \ (j = 1, \ldots, m),$$

with Γ of class C^{2m}. An operator $\mathfrak{L}$, acting continuously from $W_2^{2m}(G)$ to $K_{(0,2m-m_j-\frac{1}{2})}$, is constructed by the rule

$$\mathfrak{L}u = (Lu, B_1u, \ldots, B_mu) \qquad u \in W_2^{2m}(G). \tag{6.39}$$

The kernel of $\mathfrak{L}$ is denoted N; it is a finite-dimensional subspace defined by the equation $\mathfrak{L}(N) = 0$. When the coefficients and Γ are sufficiently smooth, $N \subset W_2^{2m+s}(G)$ (see Corollary 2 above). In addition, we have introduced the subspace of the space $W_2^{2m+s}(G)$

$$H_{2m+s} = W_2^{2m+s}(G) \ominus N = H_{2m} \cap W_2^{2m+s}(G) \tag{6.40}$$

($s = 0, 1, \cdots$; the orthogonal complement is taken in $L_2(G)$). Since N is finite dimensional, we have the direct sum decomposition of $W_2^{2m+s}(G)$:

$$W_2^{2m+s}(G) = N + H_{2m+s}, \tag{6.41}$$

and moreover the nonorthogonal projection operators P_N and $P_{\perp N}$ onto N and H_{2m+s}, defined by the decomposition (6.41), are continuous in $W_2^{2m+s}(G)$.[1] It is clear that by increasing s we produce only restrictions of these operators; therefore the dependence on s is not indicated in the notation.

We have also considered the restriction $\mathfrak{L}_s$ of $\mathfrak{L}$ to H_{2m+s}; this operator acts from H_{2m+s} (equipped, of course, with the metric of $W_2^{2m+s}(G)$) to $K_{(s,2m-m_j+s-\frac{1}{2})}$. For this, we suppose in addition that

$$a_\alpha(x) \in C^s(G \cup \Gamma),\ b_{j\alpha}(x) \in C^{2m-m_j+s}(\Gamma) \quad (j = 1, \ldots, m),$$

and Γ is of class C^s.

b) *The adjoint problem* (6.36) – (6.37). We impose the usual smoothness restrictions on $L\,(a_\alpha(x) \in C^{|\alpha|}(G \cup \Gamma))$ to ensure the existence of L^+. For the existence of boundary expressions (6.29), figuring in (6.37), we require normality for the system of boundary expressions (6.2) and smoothness of their coefficients of the form

$$b_{j\alpha}(x) \in C^{\max(2m-m_j-1,m_j)}(\Gamma)\ (j=1, \ldots, m).$$

As the smoothness of $b_{j\alpha}(x)$, $a_\alpha(x)$, and Γ increases to $+\infty$, the smoothness of the coefficients in (6.29) also increases to $+\infty$. The homogeneous boundary conditions corresponding to (6.36) and (6.37), are naturally denoted $(\mathrm{bd})^+$. In connection with this problem we introduce the space

1) The last fact was proved for $s = 0$ on p. 209–210; the arguments are similar for $s > 0$.

$$K_{\left(s,2m-m_j'+s-\frac{1}{2}\right)} = W_2^s(G) \oplus \sum_{j=1}^m W_2^{2m-m_j'+s-\frac{1}{2}}(\Gamma). \tag{6.42}$$

Assuming in addition

$$b_{j\alpha}'(x) \in C^{2m-m_j'}(\Gamma), \quad (j = 1,\ldots,m),$$

we introduce the operator $\mathfrak{L}^+$, acting continuously from $W_2^{2m}(G)$ to $K_{(0,2m-m_j'-\frac{1}{2})}$ according to the rule

$$\mathfrak{L}^+ v = (L^+ v, B_1' v, \ldots, B_m' v), \qquad v \in W_2^{2m}(G). \tag{6.43}$$

The kernel $N^+ \subset W_2^{2m}(G)$ of $\mathfrak{L}^+$ is finite dimensional. As in a), we define the space H_{2m+s}^+, decompositions of the type (6.41), and operators P_{N^+}, $P_{\perp N^+}$, $\mathfrak{L}_s^+$; it is only necessary to replace N by N^+ in a) and require the smoothness

$$a_\alpha(x) \in C^s(G \cup \Gamma), \; b_{j\alpha}'(x) \in C^{2m-m_j'+s}(\Gamma) \; (j = 1,\ldots,m);$$

Γ of class C^s.

On the basis of Theorem 6.6, we can now make the following assertion.

In addition to the conditions mentioned in b), *suppose that we have the following smoothness*:

$$a_\alpha(x) \in C^{2m+|\alpha|}(G \cup \Gamma), \; b_{j\alpha}(x) \in C^{\max(2m-1,2m-m_j)}(\Gamma), \; b_{j\alpha}'(x) \in C^{2m-m_j'}(\Gamma) \; (j = 1,\ldots,m);$$

Γ of class C^{4m}. If the system (6.2) covers L, then the system (6.9) covers L^+, so that the problem (6.36) – (6.37) is elliptic and all the results in subsections 1 – 4 hold for it, with the definitions a) *replaced by the definitions* b). *Moreover, it must be kept in mind that the system (6.29) is normal.*

In what follows, normal systems (bd) are considered exclusively.

6. **Solvability of boundary value problems in the case of a normal system of homogeneous** (bd). It is easy to prove

Lemma 6.6. *Suppose that the problem (6.4) – (6.5) is elliptic, the system (6.2) is normal, and we have the following smoothness conditions*:

$$a_\alpha(x) \in C^{2m+|\alpha|}(G \cup \Gamma), \; b_{j\alpha}(x) \in C^{\max(2m-1,2m-m_j)}(\Gamma), b_{j\alpha}'(x) \in C^{\max(2m-1,2m-m_j)}(\Gamma) \; (j = 1,\ldots,m),$$

Γ of class C^{4m}. Then the set M^+ of weak solutions of the problem $L^+ v = 0$, $v \in (\mathrm{bd})^+$, coincides with N^+, and therefore every weak solution of the problem $L^+ v = g \in L_2(G)$, $v \in (\mathrm{bd})^+$, belongs to $W_2^{2m}(G)$.

In fact, by the discussion on p. 216, to prove the lemma it is sufficient to show that $M^+ \subseteq N^+$. We assume that this is not true, and choose $h \in M^+ \subseteq L_2(G)$, $h \overline{\in} N^+$.

Decompose $h = h' + h''$, where $h' \in N^+ \subseteq W_2^{2m}(\mathrm{bd})^+$ and $h'' \perp N^+$ (in $L_2(G)$). For every $u \in W_2^{2m}(\mathrm{bd})$ we have

$$(h'', Lu)_0 = (h - h', Lu)_0 = (h, Lu)_0 - (h', Lu)_0 = -(h', Lu)_0 = -(L^+h', u)_0 = 0, \tag{6.44}$$

i.e. $h'' \in M^+$.

On the other hand, since $h'' \perp N^+$, by Theorem 6.3 and Corollary 1 we can find $u_0 \in W_2^{2m}(\mathrm{bd})$ such that $h'' = Lu_0$. Substituting this equation into (6.44) and then taking $u = u_0$, we obtain $(Lu_0, Lu_0)_0 = 0$, i.e. $0 = Lu_0 = h''$. Thus $h = h' \in N^+$, which is a contradiction. The lemma follows.

We collect a series of known facts into a theorem on solvability.

Theorem 6.7. *Suppose that the problem (6.4) – (6.5) is elliptic, the system (6.2) is normal, and we have the following smoothness conditions:*

$a_\alpha(x) \in C^{2m+\max(|\alpha|, s)}(G \cup \Gamma)$, $b_{j\alpha}(x) \in C^{\max(2m+s-1, 2m-m_j+s)}(\Gamma)$, $b'_{j\alpha}(x) \in C^{\max(2m+s-1, 2m-m'_j+s)}(\Gamma)$ $(j = 1, \cdots, m)$, Γ *of class* C^{4m+s} $(s \geq 0$ *integral).*

Then the kernel N is finite dimensional and is contained in $W_2^{2m+s}(G)$ and coincides with the set M of weak solutions of the problem $Lu = 0$, $u \in (\mathrm{bd})$.

The restriction of the 0-strong operator $\Lambda_0(\mathrm{bd})$ for the problem (6.4) – (6.5) (i.e. the operator $u \to Lu$, $u \in W_2^{2m}(\mathrm{bd})$) to

$$H_{2m+s}(\mathrm{bd}) = (W_2^{2m}(\mathrm{bd}) \cap W_2^{2m+s}(G)) \ominus N \tag{6.45}$$

effects a homeomorphism between the space (6.45) in the metric $(\cdot,\cdot)_{2m+s}$ and the space $H_s^+ = W_2^s(G) \ominus N^+$ in the metric $(\cdot,\cdot)_s$ (the orthogonal complement is formed in $L_2(G)$).

Similar assertions hold with M and N replaced by M^+ and N^+, and for the operator $\Lambda_s(\mathrm{bd})^+$ corresponding to the problem (6.36) – (6.37) (this problem is automatically elliptic, and the system (6.29) is normal).

We need only clarify the assertion concerning the homeomorphisms effected by the restrictions of the operator $\Lambda_0(\mathrm{bd})$. Namely, the homeomorphism between $H_{2m+s}(\mathrm{bd})$ and $\Re(\Lambda_0(\mathrm{bd})) \cap W_2^s(G)$ (in the metric $(\cdot,\cdot)_s$) follows from Lemma 6.3d. At the same time, by Theorem 6.3, $\Re(\lambda_0(\mathrm{bd})) = L_2(G) \ominus N^+$. Taking in account that

$$\Re(\Lambda_0(\mathrm{bd})) \cap W_2^s(G) = (L_2(G) \ominus N^+) \cap W_2^s(G) = W_2^s(G) \ominus N^+ = H_s^+,$$

we see that the proof follows.

Note that when we are interested in only one of the problems (6.4) – (6.5) or (6.36) – (6.37), the smoothness restrictions can be somewhat relaxed.

The theorem is a generalization of Theorem 3.6 1) to the case of general homogeneous (bd) and the now present deficiency. We will not determine homeomorphisms of the types remaining in Theorem 3.6 (although this indeed can be done), but instead we study similar problems in the case of nonhomogeneous (bd).

Note also that the development of the theory depends in an essential way on Theorem 6.6, the proof of which uses, in particular, Lemma 6.4 and the construction of the regularization operator. At the same time, as was already mentioned, Theorem 6.6 can be proved directly. In this way, Theorem 6.2 (for normal systems of conditions) becomes a corollary of Theorem 6.7.

7. **Sovability of boundary value problems in the case of a normal system of nonhomogeneous boundary conditions.** In this subsection we carry over the details of Theorem 6.2 for normal systems (6.2) and certain related facts. We will obtain a theorem generalizing Theorem 6.7 to nonhomogeneous boundary conditions. We first give a result of the type Lemma 6.6; the proof uses a well-known device which reduces a problem with nonhomogeneous boundary conditions to one with homogeneous conditions

Lemma 6.7. *Suppose that the hypotheses of Lemma 6.6 are satisfied. In order that the problem*

$$\mathfrak{L}u = F = (f, \varphi_1, \ldots, \varphi_m) \in K_{\left(0, 2m - m_j - \frac{1}{2}\right)} \qquad (u \in W_2^{2m}(G)) \tag{6.46}$$

possess a solution, it is necessary and sufficient that

$$[F, (v, C_1'v, \ldots, C_m'v)]_0 = (f, v)_0 + \sum_{j=1}^{m} \langle \varphi_j, C_j'v \rangle_0 = 0 \quad (v \in N^+). \tag{6.47}$$

Similarly, for the solvability of the problem

$$\mathfrak{L}^+ v = G = (g, \psi_1, \ldots, \psi_m) \in K_{\left(0, 2m - m_j' - \frac{1}{2}\right)} \qquad (v \in W_2^{2m}(G)) \tag{6.48}$$

it is necessary and sufficient that

$$[G, (u, C_1u, \ldots, C_mu)]_0 = (g, u)_0 + \sum_{j=1}^{m} \langle \psi_j, C_ju \rangle_0 = 0 \, (u \in N) \tag{6.49}$$

(in (6.47) and (6.49), the expressions C_j and C_j' are those figuring in Green's formula (6.32)).

In what follows, conditions (6.47) and (6.49) will be written more briefly as $[F, N^+ \cdots]_0 = 0$ and $[G, N \cdots]_0 = 0$.

Proof. We restrict attention to the problem (6.46), i.e. the problem (6.4) – (6.5). By Lemma 6.5, there exists a function $u_0 \in W_2^{2m}(G)$ such that $B_j u_0 = \phi_j (j = 1, \cdots, m)$. Set $w = u - u_0$. Then the solvability of the problem (6.4) – (6.5) is equivalent to the solvability of the problem

$$(Lw)(x) = f(x) - (Lu_0)(x) \qquad (x \in G), \tag{6.50}$$

$$(B_j w)(x) = 0 \qquad (x \in \Gamma;\ j = 1, \ldots, m) \tag{6.51}$$

which has homogeneous boundary conditions. With the help of Theorem 6.7 with $s = 0$ (or Lemma 6.6), we conclude that the problem (6.50) – (6.51) is solvable if and only if

$$(f - Lu_0, v)_0 = (f, v)_0 - (Lu_0, v)_0 = 0 \qquad (v \in N^+). \tag{6.52}$$

Now transform $(Lu_0, v)_0$ by Green's formula (6.32), and consider that $L^+ v = 0$, $B_j' v|_\Gamma = 0$ $(j = 1, \cdots, m)$. The condition for the solvability of (6.52) becomes the condition (6.47). The lemma follows.

We now prove some "projection" lemmas, concerning decompositions of the type (6.12). In all of them we assume sufficient smoothness for the coefficients and the boundary Γ.

Lemma 6.8. *Every element*

$$F = (f, \varphi_1, \ldots, \varphi_m) \in K_{\left(0, 2m - m_j - \frac{1}{2}\right)}$$

can be uniquely written in the form

$$F = (v', 0, \ldots, 0) + F'', v' \in N^+, F'' \in K_{\left(0, 2m - m_j - \frac{1}{2}\right)}, [F'', N^+ \ldots]_0 = 0. \tag{6.53}$$

The nonorthogonal projection operators $Q_{N^+} F = (v', 0, \cdots, 0)$ *and* $Q_{\perp N^+} F = F''$ *are continuous in* $K_{(0, 2m - m_j - \frac{1}{2})}$.

Proof. We consider N^+ as a Hilbert space in the scalar product $(\cdot, \cdot)_0$. If $F \in K_{(0, 2m - m_j - \frac{1}{2})}$ is fixed, then by the finite dimensionality of N^+, for any $v \in N^+$ we obtain

$$|l(v)| = |[F, (v, C_1' v, \ldots, C_m' v)]_0| = |(f, v)_0 + \sum_{j=1}^{m} \langle \varphi_j, C_j' v \rangle_0|$$

$$\leq C_1 \| v \|_{2m} \leq C_2 \| v \|_0.$$

Therefore by Riesz's theorem, there exists an element $v' \in N^+$ such that

$$[F, (v, C_1' v, \ldots, C_m' v)]_0 = (v', v)_0 \qquad (v \in N^+). \tag{6.54}$$

Now set $F'' = F - (v', 0, \cdots, 0)$; it follows immediately from (6.54) that $[F'', N^+ \cdots]_0 = 0$. The decomposition (6.53) follows. It is easy to see that it is direct: for otherwise we could find an element $(v', 0, \cdots, 0)$ $(v' \in N^+)$ of the type F''; in particular, we would then have

$$(v', v')_0 = [(v', 0, \ldots, 0), (v', C_1'v', \ldots, C_m'v')]_0 = 0,$$

which is absurd.

It remains to prove continuity, for example, for the operator $Q_{N^+}F$. By (6.54) and the finite dimensionality of N^+, we have

$$\| Q_{N^+}F \|_{K\left(0,2m-m_j-\frac{1}{2}\right)} = \| (v', 0, \ldots, 0) \|_{K\left(0,2m-m_j-\frac{1}{2}\right)} = \| v' \|_0$$

$$= \sup_{v' \in N^+} \frac{|(v', v)_0|}{\| v \|_0} = \sup_{v \in N^+} \frac{|[F, (v, C_1'v, \ldots, C_m'v)]_0|}{\| v \|_0} \leq C_1 \| F \|_{K\left(0,2m-m_j-\frac{1}{2}\right)}$$

$$\left(F \in K_{\left(0,2m-m_j-\frac{1}{2}\right)}\right),$$

as required. The lemma follows.

With sufficient smoothness, $N^+ \subset W_2^{2m+s}(G)$ $(s > 0$ an integer). Therefore if we decompose

$$F = (f, \varphi_1, \ldots, \varphi_m) \in K_{\left(s,2m-m_j+s-\frac{1}{2}\right)} \subset K_{\left(0,2m-m_j-\frac{1}{2}\right)}$$

according to (6.53), then

$$F'' = (f - v', \varphi_1, \ldots, \varphi_m) \in K_{\left(s,2m-m_j+s-\frac{1}{2}\right)},$$

i.e. (6.53) is a direct sum decomposition in the space $K_{(s,2m-m_j+s-\frac{1}{2})}$. By the finite dimensionality of $(N^+, 0, \cdots, 0)$, the operators $Q_{N^+}F$ and $Q_{\perp N^+}F$ are continuous as operators in $K_{(s,2m-m_j+s-\frac{1}{2})}$.

A lemma similar to 6.8 holds also for negative spaces.

Lemma 6.9. *Let $\sigma > 0$ be an integer. Then every element*

$$A = (a, a_1, \ldots, a_m) \in K_{\left(-\sigma, -\left(\sigma - l_j' - \frac{1}{2}\right)\right)} = W_2^{-\sigma}(G) \oplus \sum_{j=1}^{m} W_2^{-\left(\sigma - l_j' - \frac{1}{2}\right)}(\Gamma)^{1)}$$

can be uniquely written in the form

1) See subsection 3 for the definition of $W_2^{-(k-\frac{1}{2})}(\Gamma)$, $(k > 0)$.

$$A = (v', 0, \ldots, 0) \dotplus A'', \ v' \in N^+, \ A'' \in K_{\left(-\sigma, -\left(\sigma - l_j' - \frac{1}{2}\right)\right)}, \ [A'', N^+ \ldots]_0 = 0. \quad (6.55)$$

Here $l_j' = 2m - m_j - 1$ *are the orders of the expressions* C_j' $(j = 1, \cdots, m)$, *and* $[A'', N^+ \cdots]_0 = 0$ *denotes fulfillment of the relation*

$$[A'', (v, C_1'v, \ldots, C_m'v)]_0 = [(a'', a_1'', \ldots, a_m''), (v, C_1'v, \ldots, C_m'v)]_0$$

$$= (a'', v)_0 + \sum_{j=1}^{m} \langle a_j'', C_j'v \rangle_0 = 0 \qquad (v \in N^+).$$

The nonorthogonal projection operators $Q_{N^+}A = (v', 0, \cdots, 0)$ *and* $Q_{\perp N^+}A = A''$ *are continuous in* $K_{(-\sigma, -(\sigma - l_j' - \frac{1}{2}))}$.

Proof. Consider first the case $\sigma \geq 2m$. Let $v \in W_2^\sigma(G)$. If we assume that the coefficients of the expression C_j' are extended smoothly inside G, then $C_j' v \in W_2^{\sigma - l_j'}(G)$. Therefore $C_j' v \in W_2^{\sigma - l_j' - \frac{1}{2}}(\Gamma)$ and $\langle \alpha_j, C_j' v\rangle_0$ is meaningful for $\alpha_j \in W_2^{-(\sigma - l_j' - \frac{1}{2})}(\Gamma)$. Moreover, by (6.7)

$$|\langle \alpha_j, C_j'v \rangle_0| \leq \langle\langle \alpha_j \rangle\rangle_{-\left(\sigma - l_j' - \frac{1}{2}\right)} \langle\langle C_j'v \rangle\rangle_{\sigma - l_j' - \frac{1}{2}}$$

$$\leq C_1 \langle\langle \alpha_j \rangle\rangle_{-\left(\sigma - l_j' - \frac{1}{2}\right)} \| C_j'v \|_{\sigma - l_j'} \leq C_2 \langle\langle \alpha_j \rangle\rangle_{-\left(\sigma - l_j' - \frac{1}{2}\right)} \| v \|_\sigma. \quad (6.56)$$

With sufficient smoothness, $N^+ \subset W_2^\sigma(G)$. Therefore for any fixed A under consideration and $v \in N^+$, the expression $l(v) = [A, (v, C_1' v, \cdots, C_m' v)]_0$ has meaning; by (6.56) it admits the estimate $|l(v)| \leq C_3 \| v \|_\sigma \leq C_4 \| v \|_0$ $(v \in N^+)$. We now repeat the arguments in the proof of Lemma 6.8: we consider N^+ in the metric $(\cdot, \cdot)_0$, and represent $l(v)$ according to Riesz's theorem, etc.

The analysis for the case $0 < \sigma < 2m$ is now practically obvious: since

$$K_{\left(-\tau, -\left(\tau - l_j' - \frac{1}{2}\right)\right)} \supset K_{\left(-\sigma, -\left(\sigma - l_j' - \frac{1}{2}\right)\right)}$$

for $\tau > \sigma$, and the decomposition in the space $K_{(-\tau, -(\tau - l_j' - \frac{1}{2}))}$ has already been defined for $\tau \geq 2m$, it can be defined in $K_{(-\sigma, -(\sigma - l_j' - \frac{1}{2}))}$ (it should be noticed that $(v', 0, \cdots, 0) \in K_{(-\sigma, -(\sigma - l_j' - \frac{1}{2}))}$ for $v' \in N^+$). Continuity of the operators Q_{N^+} and $Q_{\perp N^+}$ in $K_{(-\sigma, -(\sigma - l_j' - \frac{1}{2}))}$ follows from the finite dimensionality of $(N^+, 0, \cdots, 0)$.

The lemma follows.

In the process of the proof of the lemma, it was actually observed that Q_{N^+} and $Q_{\perp N^+}$, for decreasing values of σ, are obtained simply as restrictions in the space $K_{(-\sigma, -(\sigma - l_j' - \frac{1}{2}))}$ (note that for $\sigma = 0$, $K_{(-\sigma, -(\sigma - l_j' - \frac{1}{2}))}$ coincides with

$K_{(0,2m-m_j-\frac{1}{2})}$, since $l_j' = 2m - m_j - \frac{1}{2}$). In what follows, it is convenient to assume that Q_{N^+} and $Q_{\perp N^+}$ are constructed for $\sigma \geq 0$ sufficiently large and then pass to the appropriate restrictions.

Of course, lemmas similar to the two just proved also hold with N^+ replaced by N and $K_{(-\sigma,-(\sigma-l_j'-\frac{1}{2}))}$ by $K_{(-\sigma,-(\sigma-l_j-\frac{1}{2}))}$ $(\sigma \geq 0)$, where $l_j = 2m - m_j - 1$ is the order of the expression C_j $(j = 1, \cdots, m)$. The corresponding projection operators are denoted Q_N and $Q_{\perp N}$.

Finally, we prove yet another lemma, generalizing the decomposition (6.41) to the space $W_2^{2m+s}(G)$ for any integer $2m + s$.

Lemma 6.10. *Every element $u \in W_2^l(G)$ ($l = \cdots, -1, 0, 1, \cdots$ fixed) can be uniquely written in the form*

$$u = u' + u'', \qquad u' \in N, \ (u'', N)_0 = 0. \tag{6.57}$$

The nonorthogonal projection operators $P_N u = u'$ and $P_{\perp N} u = u''$ ($u \in W_2^l(G)$) are continuous in $W_2^l(G)$.

This lemma has already appeared in the case $l = 2m + s$, $s \geq 0$ (see (6.12) and (6.41)). It is proved similarly for $l \geq 0$. Suppose now that $l = -\sigma < 0$. The argument is close to the proofs of Lemmas 6.8 – 6.9.

We consider N as a Hilbert space in the scalar product $(\cdot, \cdot)_0$. If $u \in W_2^{-\sigma}(G)$, then by the finite dimensionality of N, for any $w \in N$ we obtain

$$|(u, w)_0| \leqslant \|u\|_{-\sigma} \|w\|_\sigma \leqslant C_1 \|u\|_{-\sigma} \|w\|_0.$$

By Riesz's theorem, there exists an element $u' \in N$ such that $(u, w)_0 = (u', w)_0$ $(w \in N)$. We obtain the decomposition (6.57) on setting $u - u' = u''$. Clearly, it is direct.

Further, by the continuity of P_N in $L_2(G)$ and the finite dimensionality of N, we have

$$\|P_N u\|_{-\sigma} \leqslant \|P_N u\|_0 \leqslant \|u\|_0 \leqslant C_2 \|u\|_{-\sigma} \qquad (u \in L_2(G));$$

the continuity of P_N follows from the density of $L_2(G)$ in $W_2^{-\sigma}(G)$. The lemma follows.

Consider projection operators P_N and $P_{\perp N}$ constructed for some $l = \cdots, -1, 0, 1, \cdots$; the analogous operators constructed for $k > l$ are obviously restrictions of these. Therefore, as in the case of operators of the type Q, we can assume that P_N and $P_{\perp N}$ are constructed for some sufficiently negative l, and then form restrictions of these.

Clearly, a lemma of the type 6.10 holds with N replaced by N^+; as before, the corresponding operators are denoted P_{N^+} and $P_{\perp N^+}$.

The following theorem on solvability follows from Lemmas 6.7 and 6.8 and the corollary to Lemma 6.3.

Theorem 6.8. *Suppose that the hypotheses of Theorem 6.7 are satisfied for some integer $s \geq 0$. Then the restriction $\mathfrak{L}_s$ of the operator $\mathfrak{L}$ to*

$$H_{2m+s} = P_{\perp N} W_2^{2m+s}(G) = W_2^{2m+s}(G) \ominus N \tag{6.58}$$

(the orthogonal complement is taken in $L_2(G)$) effects a homeomorphism between the space (6.58) in the metric $(\cdot, \cdot)_{2m+s}$ and the space $\mathfrak{A}_{N^+} K_{(s, 2m-m_j+s-\frac{1}{2})}$ in the metric

$$(\cdot,\cdot)_{K\left(s, 2m-m_j+s-\frac{1}{2}\right)}.$$

A similar assertion holds for the operator $\mathfrak{L}^+$ connected with the adjoint problem (6.36) – (6.37); for this, N and $K_{(s,2m-m_j+s-\frac{1}{2})}$ should be replaced by N^+ and $K_{(s,2m-m_j'+s-\frac{1}{2})}$.

8. **The theorem on homeomorphisms in the case of nonhomogeneous boundary conditions.** We now prove an analogue of Theorem 3.6 on homeomorphisms; the case of homogeneous boundary conditions will be considered in subsection 10. We first introduce a norm in the space which will occur in the theorem on homeomorphisms.

Fix $l = \cdots, -1, 0, 1, \cdots$ and let $\widetilde{W}_2^l(G)$ denote the completion of the space $W_2^{\max(l,2m)}(G)$ in the norm

$$|||u|||_l^2 = \|u\|_l^2 + \sum_{j=1}^{2m} \left\langle\!\left\langle \frac{\partial^{j-1}}{\partial \nu^{j-1}} u \right\rangle\!\right\rangle_{l-j+\frac{1}{2}} \tag{6.59}$$

where $\nu = \nu(x)$ is the exterior normal; Γ is assumed to be of class $C^{\max(l,2m)}$. If $l \geq 2m$, then according to (6.7), for $j = 1, \cdots, 2m$,

$$\left\langle\!\left\langle \frac{\partial^{j-1}}{\partial \nu^{j-1}} u \right\rangle\!\right\rangle_{l-j+\frac{1}{2}} \leq C_1 \sum_{|\alpha|=j-1} \|D^\alpha u\|_{l-j+1} \leq C_2 \|u\|_l$$

and therefore $|||u|||_l \leq C_3 \|u\|_l$; thus in this case the norms $|||\cdot|||_l$, $\|\cdot\|_l$ are equivalent and $\widetilde{W}_2^l(G) = W_2^l(G)$. If $l < 2m$, such an equivalence does not hold,[1] and on account of the inequality $\| u \|_l \leq ||| u |||_l$ $(u \in W_2^{\max(l,2m)}(G))$, in forming the completion we obtain the inclusion $\widetilde{W}_2^l(G) \subset W_2^l(G)$. Clearly, $\widetilde{W}_2^l(G)$ is a Hilbert space in any case. Obviously,

$$\ldots \supseteq \widetilde{W}_2^{-1}(G) \supseteq \widetilde{W}_2^0(G) \supseteq \widetilde{W}_2^1(G) \supseteq \ldots, \tag{6.60}$$

$$\ldots \leqslant ||| u |||_{-1} \leqslant ||| u |||_0 \leqslant ||| u |||_1 \leqslant \ldots,$$

and moreover every $\widetilde{W}_2^l(G)$ is dense in $\widetilde{W}_2^k(G)$ for $k < l$ (note, however, that (6.60) is not a sequence of positive and negative spaces).

The purpose in introducing the norm (6.59) is explained by the following lemma, which is similar to Lemma 3.6.

Lemma 6.11. *Let N be an arbitrary expression of order $r \leq 2m$ with sufficiently smooth coefficients; suppose that Γ is of class $C^{\max(l,2m)}$. Then*

$$\| Nu \|_{l-r} \leqslant C_l ||| u |||_l \quad (u \in W_2^{\max(l,2m)}(G);\ l = \ldots, -1, 0, 1, \ldots). \tag{6.61}$$

Similarly, for an arbitrary boundary expression B of order $r \leq 2m - 1$ with sufficiently smooth coefficients and boundary Γ, we have

$$\langle\!\langle Bu \rangle\!\rangle_{l-r-\frac{1}{2}} \leqslant C_l ||| u |||_l \qquad (u \in W_2^{\max(l,2m)}(G);\ l = \ldots, -1, 0, 1, \ldots). \tag{6.62}$$

Proof. We prove (6.61). The inequality is obvious if $l \geq r$. Suppose $l < r$. By the definition of a negative norm as the norm of a functional, we have

$$\| Nu \|_{l-r} = \sup_{v \in W_2^{r-l}(G)} \frac{|(Nu, v)_0|}{\| v \|_{r-l}}. \tag{6.63}$$

In the case $l \geq 0$, we use integration by parts to shift $r - l$ derivatives in the expression $(Nu, v)_0$ from u to v. The integral obtained over the region G is estimated by $C_1 \| u \|_l \| v \|_{r-l}$. The integral over the surface Γ is estimated by

$$C_2 \left(\| u \|_l + \sum_{j=l+1}^{r} \langle\!\langle \frac{\partial^{j-1}}{\partial \nu^{j-1}} u \rangle\!\rangle_{l-j+\frac{1}{2}} \right) \| v \|_{r-l}.\ ^{2)}$$

---

1) In fact, in the contrary case, we could write for smooth u

$$\langle\!\langle \frac{\partial^{j-1}}{\partial \nu^{j-1}} u \rangle\!\rangle_{l-j+\frac{1}{2}} \leqslant C \| u \|_l \qquad (j = 1, \ldots, 2m).$$

Letting $l = 1$, $j = 2$, we obtain $\langle\!\langle \frac{\partial u}{\partial \nu} \rangle\!\rangle_{-\frac{1}{2}} \leqslant C \| u \|_1$. So for smooth u and v we would have

$$\left| \int_\Gamma \frac{\partial u}{\partial \nu} \bar{v} dx \right| \leqslant \langle\!\langle \frac{\partial u}{\partial \nu} \rangle\!\rangle_{-\frac{1}{2}} \langle\!\langle v \rangle\!\rangle_{\frac{1}{2}} \leqslant C \| u \|_1 \| v \|_1,$$

which is absurd.

2) In connection with the techniques required for these and later estimates, see also the proof of the more complex Lemma 6.14.

Substituting these estimates into (6.63), we arrive at (6.61).

In the case $l < 0$, shift all derivatives in the expression $(Nu, v)_0$ onto v. The integral over G is now estimated: $|(u, N^+v)_0| \leq \|u\|_l \|N^+v\|_{-l} \leq C_1 \|u\|_l \|v\|_{r-l}$; the integral over Γ is estimated as in the case $l \geq 0$, and we again arrive at (6.61).

The estimate (6.62) is proved similarly. Namely, it is again necessary to consider only the case $l < r$. With the help of (6.7), we obtain

$$\langle\!\langle Bu \rangle\!\rangle_{l-r-\frac{1}{2}} = \sup_{v \in W_2^{r-l+\frac{1}{2}}(\Gamma)} \frac{|\langle Bu, v\rangle_0|}{\langle\!\langle v \rangle\!\rangle_{r-l+\frac{1}{2}}} \leqslant C_1 \sup_{v \in W_2^{r-l+1}(G)} \frac{|\langle Bu, v\rangle_0|}{\|v\|_{r-l+1}}. \tag{6.64}$$

In the expression $\langle Bu, v\rangle_0$, we shift part of the tangential derivatives ∂_k from u to v. As the result we obtain an integral of the form

$$\int_\Gamma c_{\tau j\sigma}(x)\, \partial^\tau \frac{\partial^{j-1}}{\partial \nu^{j-1}} u \times \overline{\partial^\sigma v}\, dx,$$

where $j = 1, \cdots, r+1 \leq 2m$, $|\tau| + |\sigma| \leq r - j + 1$. For $j > l$, the transfer is carried out so that $\tau = 0$; the required estimate follows from (6.64) and the inequality

$$\left| \int_\Gamma c_{0j\sigma}(x) \frac{\partial^{j-1}}{\partial \nu^{j-1}} u \cdot \overline{\partial^\sigma v}\, dx \right| \leqslant C_2 \langle\!\langle \frac{\partial^{j-1}}{\partial \nu^{j-1}} u \rangle\!\rangle_{l-j+\frac{1}{2}} \langle\!\langle \partial^\sigma v \rangle\!\rangle_{j-l-\frac{1}{2}}$$

$$\leqslant C_3 |||u|||_l \sum_{|\alpha| \leqslant r-j+1} \|D^\alpha v\|_{j-l} \leqslant C_4 |||u|||_l \|v\|_{r-l+1}.$$

For $j \leq l$, the transfer is carried out so that $|\sigma| \leq r - l$, and then we estimate the integral over Γ by an integral over G. The lemma follows.

For homeomorphisms effected by elliptic operators, spaces of the type $Q_{\perp N^+} K_{(s, 2m-m_j+s-½)}$ serve as spaces of transforms. We now consider the spaces which are to be transformed.

Since for any $l = \cdots, -1, 0, 1, \cdots$, $\widetilde{W}_2^l(G) \subseteq W_2^l(G)$ and $N, N^+ \subset \widetilde{W}_2^l(G)$ (for sufficiently strong smoothness restrictions), the projection operators P_N, $P_{\perp N}$, P_{N^+}, $P_{\perp N^+}$ can be considered as acting in $\widetilde{W}_2^l(G)$. By the finite dimensionality of N and N^+, they are continuous in the space $\widetilde{W}_2^l(G)$. It turns out that spaces of the type $P_{\perp N}\widetilde{W}_2^l(G)$ play the role of the transfomed spaces.

In connection with (6.40) and (6.58), we denote

$$\widetilde{H}_l = P_{\perp N}\widetilde{W}_2^l(G) = \widetilde{W}_2^l(G) \ominus N, \widetilde{H}_l^+ = P_{\perp N^+}\widetilde{W}_2^l(G) = \widetilde{W}_2^l(G) \ominus N^+$$

$$(l = \ldots, -1, 0, 1, \ldots), \tag{6.65}$$

where $\widetilde{H}_l$ and $\widetilde{H}_l^+$ are equipped with the metric $|||\cdot|||_l$; for $l \geq 2m$, $\widetilde{H}_l = H_l$, $\widetilde{H}_l^+ = H_l^+$. By (6.60)

$$\cdots \supset \widetilde{H}_{-1} \supset \widetilde{H}_0 \supset \widetilde{H}_1 \supset \cdots . \qquad \cdots \supset \widetilde{H}_{-1}^+ \supset \widetilde{H}_0^+ \supset \widetilde{H}_1^+ \supset \cdots \tag{6.66}$$

and every space $\widetilde{H}_l$ $(\widetilde{H}_l^+)$ is dense in $\widetilde{H}_k$ $(\widetilde{H}_k^+)$ for $k < l$ (it is necessary to consider the finite dimensionality of N and N^+).

We also introduce a similar notation for the spaces of transforms. Namely, we set

$$K_s = Q_{\perp N} K_{\left(s, 2m - m_j' + s - \frac{1}{2}\right)}, \quad K_s^+ = Q_{\perp N^+} K_{\left(s, 2m - m_j + s - \frac{1}{2}\right)}$$

$$(s = \ldots, -1, 0, 1, \ldots). \tag{6.67}$$

The metric of $K_{\cdot}^{\cdot}$ is that of the corresponding $K_{(\cdot,\,\cdot)}$ (we use the following general notation:

$$K_{\left(s, t_j - \frac{1}{2}\right)} = W_2^s(G) \oplus \sum_{j=1}^{m} W_2^{t_j - \frac{1}{2}}(\Gamma) \Big).$$

Note that

$$K_{\left(s, 2m - m_j' + s - \frac{1}{2}\right)} = K_{\left(s, s + l_j + \frac{1}{2}\right)}, \quad K_{\left(s, 2m - m_j + s - \frac{1}{2}\right)} = K_{\left(s, s + l_j' + \frac{1}{2}\right)}$$

$$(s = \ldots, -1, 0, 1, \ldots),$$

where $l_j = 2m - m_j' - 1$, $l_j' = 2m - m_j - 1$ are the orders of the expressions C_j and C_j' $(j = 1, \cdots, m)$ which occur in Green's formula (6.32).

Clearly, we now have relations of the type (6.66)

$$\cdots \supset K_{-1} \supset K_0 \supset K_1 \supset \cdots, \cdots \supset K_{-1}^+ \supset K_0^+ \supset K_1^+ \supset \cdots, \tag{6.68}$$

$$\cdots \leqslant \|u\|_{K_{-1}} \leqslant \|u\|_{K_0} \leqslant \|u\|_{K_1} \leqslant \cdots, \cdots \leqslant \|u\|_{K_{-1}^+} \leqslant \|u\|_{K_0^+} \leqslant \|u\|_{K_1^+} \leqslant \cdots$$

with similar density properties.

We have the following theorem.

Theorem 6.9. *Suppose that the problem* (6.4) – (6.5) *is elliptic, the system* (6.2) *is normal, and the smoothness conditions listed below are satisfied.*

Consider the pair of spaces $\widetilde{H}_{2m+s}$ *and* K_s^+ $(s = \cdots, -1, 0, 1, \cdots)$ *introduced in* (6.65) *and* (6.67), *and the operator* $\mathfrak{L}$ *associated with the problem* (6.4)–(6.5), *i.e. the operator which acts from* $W_2^{2m}(G)$ *to* $L_2(G) \oplus \sum_{j=1}^m W_2^{2m-m_j-\frac{1}{2}}(\Gamma)$ *according to the rule* $\mathfrak{L}u = (Lu, B_1 u, \cdots, B_m u)$. *If* $s \geq 0$, *then the restriction* $\mathfrak{L}_s$ *of this operator to* $\widetilde{H}_{2m+s}$ *establishes a homeomorphism between* $\widetilde{H}_{2m+s}$ *and* K_s^+; *if* $s < 0$, *such a homeomorphism is established by the closure (which exists) of the operator* $\mathfrak{L}_0$ *considered as an operator from* $\widetilde{H}_{2m+s}$ *to* K_s^+.

A similar assertion holds with respect to the operator $\mathfrak{L}^+$ *associated with the adjoint problem. The spaces* $\widetilde{H}^+_{2m+s}$ *and* K_s $(s = \cdots, -1, 0, 1, \cdots)$ *now appear as the pair of homeomorphic spaces.*

The smoothness assumptions are: 1) *for* $s \geq 0$, $a_\alpha(x) \in C^{2m+\max(|\alpha|,s)}(G \cup \Gamma)$, $b_{j\alpha}(x) \in C^{\max(2m+s-1, 2m-m_j+s)}(\Gamma)$, $b'_{j\alpha}(x) \in C^{\max(2m+s-1, 2m-m'_j+s)}(\Gamma)$ $(j = 1, \ldots, m)$, Γ *of class* C^{4m+s}; 2) *for* $-2m \leq s \leq 0$, *the same as in* 1) *but with* s *replaced by* 0, *and in addition* $c_{j\alpha}(x) \in C^{2m-l_j}(\Gamma)$, $c'_{j\alpha}(x) \in C^{2m-l'_j}(\Gamma)$ $(j = 1, \ldots, m)$; 3) *for* $s \leq -2m$, *the same as in* 1) *but with* s *replaced by* $|2m+s|$, *and in addition*

$$c_{j\alpha}(x) \in C^{|s|-l_j}(\Gamma), c'_{j\alpha}(x) \in C^{|s|-l'_j}(\Gamma) \quad (j = 1, \ldots, m)$$

(*here* $c_{j\alpha}(x)$ *and* $c'_{j\alpha}(x)$ *are the coefficients in the differential expressions* C_j *and* C'_j *respectively*).

Proof. 1. For $s \geq 0$, as we have indicated, $\widetilde{W}_2^{2m+s}(G) = W_2^{2m+s}(G)$ and $\widetilde{H}_{2m+s}$ coincides with (6.58). Therefore the theorem in this case coincides with Theorem 6.8. In what follows, the arguments will be carried out only for $\mathfrak{L}$.

2. We prove the theorem for $-2m \leq s \leq 0$. The operator $\mathfrak{L}_0$ effects a homeomorphism between $\widetilde{H}_{2m}$ and K_0^+, and therefore $\mathfrak{L}_0^{-1}$ exists and acts continuously from K_0^+ to $\widetilde{H}_{2m}$.

We define an operator S on vectors $F \in K_0^+$ by setting

$$SF = (\mathfrak{L}_0^{-1}F, C_1(\mathfrak{L}_0^{-1}F), \ldots, C_m(\mathfrak{L}_0^{-1}F)). \tag{6.69}$$

Obviously $SF \in K_{(2m, 2m-l_j-\frac{1}{2})}$, and S is a continuous operator from $K_0^+ = Q_{\perp N^+} K_{(0, 2m-m_j-\frac{1}{2})}$ to $K_{(2m, 2m-l_j-\frac{1}{2})}$. Consequently, the operator $SQ_{\perp N^+}$ acts continuously from all of $K_{(0, 2m-m_j-\frac{1}{2})}$ to $K_{(2m, 2m-l_j-\frac{1}{2})}$.

The operator S^+ is defined similarly: the operator $\mathfrak{L}_0^+$, namely the restriction of $\mathfrak{L}^+$ to $\widetilde{H}^+_{2m}$, effects a homeomorphism between $\widetilde{H}^+_{2m}$ and K_0, and therefore $(\mathfrak{L}_0^+)^{-1}$ acts continuously from K_0 to $\widetilde{H}^+_{2m}$, and for $G \in K_0$ we can put

$$S^+G = ((\mathfrak{L}_0^+)^{-1}G, G'_1((\mathfrak{L}_0^+)^{-1}G), \ldots, C'_m((\mathfrak{L}_0^+)^{-1}G)). \tag{6.70}$$

Now $S^+G \in K_{(2m, 2m-l'_j-\frac{1}{2})}$ and S^+ acts continuously from K_0 to $K_{(2m, 2m-l'_j-\frac{1}{2})}$, and hence $S^+Q_{\perp N}$ is continuous from all of $K_{(0, 2m-m'_j-\frac{1}{2})}$ to $K_{(2m, 2m-l'_j-\frac{1}{2})}$.

Taking into account (6.69), (6.70), and Green's formula (6.32), we find for

$$F \in K_{\left(0, 2m-m_j-\frac{1}{2}\right)}, \quad G \in K_{\left(0, 2m-m'_j-\frac{1}{2}\right)}$$

$$
\begin{aligned}
&[SQ_{\perp N^+}F, Q_{\perp N}G]_0\\
&= [(\mathfrak{L}_0^{-1}Q_{\perp N^+}F, C_1(\mathfrak{L}_0^{-1}Q_{\perp N^+}F), \dots, C_m(\mathfrak{L}_0^{-1}Q_{\perp N^+}F)), \mathfrak{L}^+(\mathfrak{L}_0^+)^{-1}Q_{\perp N}G]_0\\
&\quad = [(\mathfrak{L}_0^{-1}Q_{\perp N^+}F, C_1(\mathfrak{L}_0^{-1}Q_{\perp N^+}F), \dots, C_m(\mathfrak{L}_0^{-1}Q_{\perp N^+}F)) \qquad (6.71)\\
&\qquad (L^+(\mathfrak{L}_0^+)^{-1}Q_{\perp N}G, B_1(\mathfrak{L}_0^+)^{-1}Q_{\perp N}G, \dots, B_m(\mathfrak{L}_0^+)^{-1}Q_{\perp N}G)]_0\\
&= (\mathfrak{L}_0^{-1}Q_{\perp N^+}F, L^+(\mathfrak{L}_0^+)^{-1}Q_{\perp N}G)_0 + \sum_{j=1}^{m}\langle C_j\mathfrak{L}_0^{-1}Q_{\perp N^+}F, B_j'(\mathfrak{L}_0^+)^{-1}Q_{\perp N}G\rangle_0\\
&= (L\mathfrak{L}_0^{-1}Q_{\perp N^+}F, (\mathfrak{L}_0^+)^{-1}Q_{\perp N}G)_0 + \sum_{j=1}^{m}\langle B_j\mathfrak{L}_0^{-1}Q_{\perp N^+}F, C_j'(\mathfrak{L}_0^+)^{-1}Q_{\perp N}G\rangle_0\\
&= [Q_{\perp N^+}F, S^+Q_{\perp N}G]_0.
\end{aligned}
$$

We set $Q_N G = (v, 0, \dots, 0)$ $(Lv = 0)$. Since $\mathfrak{R}(\mathfrak{L}_0^{-1}) = \widetilde{H}_{2m} \perp N$,

$$[SQ_{\perp N^+}F, Q_N G]_0 = (\mathfrak{L}_0^{-1}Q_{\perp N^+}F, v)_0 = 0. \qquad (6.72)$$

With the help of (6.72) and the similar equation $[Q_{N^+}F, S^+Q_{\perp N}G]_0 = 0$, from (6.71) we obtain the following relation which will be used later:

$$[SQ_{\perp N^+}F, G]_0 = [F, S^+Q_{\perp N}G]_0 \quad (F \in K_{\left(0, 2m - m_j - \frac{1}{2}\right)}, \; G \in K_{\left(0, 2m - m_j' - \frac{1}{2}\right)}. \qquad (6.73)$$

Thus the operator $S^+Q_{\perp N}$ acts continuously from all of $K_{(0, 2m - m_j' - 1/2)}$ to $K_{(2m, 2m - l_j' - 1/2)}$. The corresponding dual spaces with respect to the "scalar product" $[\cdot, \cdot]_0$ are $K_{(0, -(2m - m_j' - 1/2))}$ and $K_{(-2m, -(2m - l_j' - 1/2))}$ respectively (in connection with this, see (6.14) and the proof of Lemma 6.7). We construct the adjoint operator $\widetilde{SQ}_{\perp N^+}$ to $S^+Q_{\perp N}$ with respect to $[\cdot, \cdot]_0$; obviously, it acts continuously from all of $K_{(-2m, -(2m - l_j' - 1/2))}$ to $K_{(0, -(2m - m_j' - 1/2))}$. We compare $\widetilde{SQ}_{\perp N^+}$ with the operator $SQ_{\perp N^+}$. The latter acts continuously from all of

$$K_{\left(0, 2m - m_j - \frac{1}{2}\right)} \subseteq K_{\left(-2m, -\left(2m - l_j' - \frac{1}{2}\right)\right)} \left(0 > -2m, \; 2m - m_j - \frac{1}{2} > -\left(2m - l_j' - \frac{1}{2}\right) = -m_j - \frac{1}{2}\right) \quad \text{to} \quad K_{\left(2m, 2m - l_j - \frac{1}{2}\right)}$$

$$\subseteq K_{\left(0, -\left(2m - m_j' - \frac{1}{2}\right)\right)} \left(2m > 0, \; 2m - l_j - \frac{1}{2} = m_j' + \frac{1}{2} > -\left(2m - m_j' - \frac{1}{2}\right)\right),$$

and therefore it appears that $\widetilde{SQ}_{\perp N^+}$ is an extension of $SQ_{\perp N^+}$.

In fact, the operator $\widetilde{SQ}_{\perp N^+}$ is defined by the equation

$$[A, S^+Q_{\perp N}G]_0 = [\widetilde{SQ}_{\perp N^+}A, G]_0 \; \left(G \in K_{\left(0,2m-m_j-\frac{1}{2}\right)},\, A \in K_{\left(-2m,-\left(2m-l'_j-\frac{1}{2}\right)\right)}\right) \tag{6.74}$$

and setting $A = F \in K_{(0,2m-m_j-\frac{1}{2})}$ and comparing (6.74) with (6.73), we obtain $\widetilde{SQ}_{\perp N^+}F = SQ_{\perp N^+}F$.

Thus the operator $\widetilde{SQ}_{\perp N^+}$ acts continuously in the following pair of spaces:

$$K_{\left(0,2m-m_j-\frac{1}{2}\right)} \to K_{\left(2m,2m-l_j-\frac{1}{2}\right)} \tag{6.75}$$

$$K_{\left(-2m,-m_j-\frac{1}{2}\right)} = K_{\left(-2m,-\left(2m-l'_j-\frac{1}{2}\right)\right)} \to K_{\left(0,-\left(2m-m'_j-\frac{1}{2}\right)\right)} = K_{\left(0,-l_j-\frac{1}{2}\right)}$$

$$\left(\mathfrak{D}(\widetilde{SQ}_{\perp N^+}) = K_{\left(-2m,-m_j-\frac{1}{2}\right)}\right)$$

Later, in subsection 9, we will prove the so-called interpolation theorem, from which it follows that $\widetilde{SQ}_{\perp N^+}$ acts continuously in the spaces "intermediate" to (6.75); namely

$$K_{\left(s,2m-m_j+s-\frac{1}{2}\right)} \to K_{\left(2m+s,2m-l_j+s-\frac{1}{2}\right)}, \quad -2m \leqslant s \leqslant 0. \tag{6.76}$$

We complete the proof, assuming that (6.76) holds.

Thus we have the inequality

$$\|\widetilde{SQ}_{\perp N^+}F\|_{K_{\left(2m+s,2m-l_j+s-\frac{1}{2}\right)}} \leqslant C_1 \|F\|_{K_{\left(s,2m-m_j+s-\frac{1}{2}\right)}} \tag{6.77}$$

$$\left(F \in K_{\left(s,2m-m_j+s-\frac{1}{2}\right)};\; -2m \leqslant s \leqslant 0\right).$$

If $u \in \widetilde{H}_{2m}$, then

$$F = \mathfrak{L}_0 u = (Lu, B_1u, \ldots, B_mu) \in K_0^+ \subseteq K_{\left(s,2m-m_j+s-\frac{1}{2}\right)}.$$

$F = Q_{\perp N^+}F$. Substituting this F into (6.77) and taking into account that now $\widetilde{SQ}_{\perp N^+}F = SQ_{\perp N^+}F$, and (6.69), we obtain

$$\|u\|^2_{2m+s} + \sum_{j=1}^{m} \langle\!\langle C_ju \rangle\!\rangle^2_{2m-l_j+s-\frac{1}{2}} \leqslant C_1^2 \left(\|Lu\|_s^2 + \sum_{j=1}^{m} \langle\!\langle B_ju \rangle\!\rangle^2_{2m-m_j+s-\frac{1}{2}}\right)$$

$$(u \in \widetilde{H}_{2m};\; -2m \leqslant s \leqslant 0). \tag{6.78}$$

In the left-hand side we pass to the norm $|||\cdot|||_{2m+s}$. For this, recall that the $2m$ boundary differential expressions $B_1, \cdots, B_m$; $C_1, \cdots, C_m$ form a Dirichlet system of order $2m$. We introduce new notation $A_1, \cdots, A_{2m}$ for this system, assuming that the expression A_j has order $j-1$. It follows from (6.28) that at every point $x \in \Gamma$, we have a representation

$$\frac{\partial^{j-1}}{\partial \nu^{j-1}} = \sum_{k=1}^{j} \hat{T}_{jk}(x, \partial) A_k \qquad (j = 1, \ldots, 2m),$$

where $\hat{T}_{jk}(x, \partial)$ are differential expressions, containing only tangential derivatives, and of order $\le j-k$. Therefore for $u \in W_2^{2m}(G)$

$$\left\langle\!\left\langle \frac{\partial^{j-1}}{\partial \nu^{j-1}} u \right\rangle\!\right\rangle_{2m-j+s-\frac{1}{2}} = \left\langle\!\left\langle \sum_{k=1}^{j} \hat{T}_{jk}(x, \partial) A_k u \right\rangle\!\right\rangle_{2m-j+s-\frac{1}{2}}$$

$$\leqslant \left\langle\!\left\langle \sum_{k=1}^{j} \hat{T}_{jk}(x, \partial) A_k u \right\rangle\!\right\rangle_{2m-j+s-\frac{1}{2}} \leqslant C_2 \sum_{k=1}^{j} \langle\!\langle A_k u \rangle\!\rangle_{2m-k+s-\frac{1}{2}}$$

$$(j = 1, \ldots, 2m; \ -2m \leqslant s \leqslant 0).$$

Hence

$$\sum_{j=1}^{2m} \left\langle\!\left\langle \frac{\partial^{j-1}}{\partial \nu^{j-1}} u \right\rangle\!\right\rangle^2_{2m+s-j+\frac{1}{2}} \leqslant C_3 \sum_{j=1}^{2m} \langle\!\langle A_j u \rangle\!\rangle^2_{2m+s-j+\frac{1}{2}}$$

$$= C_3 \left(\sum_{j=1}^{m} \langle\!\langle B_j u \rangle\!\rangle^2_{2m+s-m_j-\frac{1}{2}} + \sum_{j=1}^{m} \langle\!\langle C_j u \rangle\!\rangle^2_{2m+s-l_j-\frac{1}{2}} \right) \quad (-2m \leqslant s \leqslant 0). \quad (6.79)$$

The required inequality follows from (6.78) and (6.79):

$$|||u|||^2_{2m+s} \leqslant C_4 \left(\|Lu\|^2_s + \sum_{j=1}^{m} \langle\!\langle B_j u \rangle\!\rangle^2_{2m-m_j+s-\frac{1}{2}} \right)$$

$$(u \in H_{2m}; \ -2m \leqslant s \leqslant 0). \qquad (6.80)$$

With the aid of Lemma 6.11, we conclude that a reverse inequality holds (for $u \in W_2^{2m}(G)$):

$$\|Lu\|^2_s + \sum_{j=1}^{m} \langle\!\langle B_j u \rangle\!\rangle^2_{2m-m_j+s-\frac{1}{2}} \leqslant C_5 |||u|||^2_{2m+s} \quad (-2m \leqslant s \leqslant 0). \quad (6.81)$$

The inequalities (6.80) and (6.81) lead to the estimate

$$\frac{1}{C_4}|||u|||^2_{2m+s} \leqslant \|\mathfrak{L}_0 u\|^2_{K_{\left(s,2m-m_j+s-\frac{1}{2}\right)}} \leqslant C_5 |||u|||^2_{2m+s} \quad (u \in \widetilde{H}_{2m}),$$

which shows that the closure by continuity of $\mathfrak{L}_0$, considered as an operator from $\widetilde{H}_{2m+s}$ to K_s^+ $(-2m \leq s \leq 0)$, exists and effects a homeomorphism between these two spaces.

3. We outline the proof in the case $s \leq -2m$. The arguments are now similar to the previous ones, and they use the passage to adjoints (the interpolation theorem is not needed this time). We set $\sigma = -s \geq 2m$, and define the operator $S^+_{\sigma-2m}$ similarly to (6.70), but with $\mathfrak{L}_0^+$ replaced by $\mathfrak{L}^+_{\sigma-2m}$; it acts continuously from $K_{\sigma-2m}$ to $\widetilde{H}^+_\sigma$. The operator $S^+_{\sigma-2m} Q_{\perp N}$ acts continuously from all of $K_{(\sigma-2m,\sigma-m_j'-\frac{1}{2})}$ to $K_{(\sigma,\sigma-l_j'-\frac{1}{2})}$. The adjoint of $S^+_{\sigma-2m} Q_{\perp N}$ in the sense of $[\cdot,\cdot]_0$ is an operator which acts continuously from all of

$$K_{\left(-\sigma,-\left(\sigma-l_j'-\frac{1}{2}\right)\right)} = K_{\left(s,2m-m_j+s-\frac{1}{2}\right)} \text{ to } K_{\left(-\sigma,-\left(\sigma-m_j-\frac{1}{2}\right)\right)} = K_{\left(2m+s,2m-l_j+s-\frac{1}{2}\right)}$$

It is easy to see that, as before, it is an extension (greater than before) of the operator $SQ_{\perp N^+}$; we preserve the notation $\widetilde{SQ}_{\perp N^+}$ for this adjoint. Thus the inequality (6.77) does indeed hold for the considered s. It only remains to repeat the arguments following (6.77) in step 2.

The theorem follows.

9. **The interpolation theorem.** We present certain general considerations, which, in particular, fill the gap in the proof of Theorem 6.9 (the continuity of the transformation (6.76)).

Let H_0 be a Hilbert space with scalar product $(\cdot,\cdot)_{H_0}$ and norm $\|\cdot\|_{H_0}$. Consider an unbounded positive operator A in H_0, with domain $\mathfrak{D}(A)$, such that $\|u\|_{H_0} \leq \|Au\|_{H_0}$ $(u \in \mathfrak{D}(A))$. The domain $\mathfrak{D}(A^\alpha)$ $(\alpha > 0)$ is a Hilbert space H_α in the scalar product $(u, v)_{H_\alpha} = (A^\alpha u, A^\alpha v)_{H_0}$. Obviously, H_α can be taken as a positive space for the zero space H_0. It follows from the discussion in §3.6 of Chapter I that the corresponding negative space $H_{-\alpha}$ is obtained as the completion of H_0 with respect to the scalar product $(f, g)_{H_{-\alpha}} = (A^{-\alpha}f, A^{-\alpha}g)_{H_0}$; the roles of the operators D and $\mathbf{D}$ for the sequence $H_{-\alpha} \supseteq H_0 \supseteq H_\alpha$ are filled by the operators A^α and the closure by continuity of A^α, considered as an operator from H_0 to $H_{-\alpha}$, respectively. The family $\{H_\alpha\}$ $(\alpha \in (-\infty, \infty))$ of Hilbert spaces so constructed is called a Hilbert scale of spaces.

If E_λ is the resolution of the identity corresponding to A, then

$$(u, v)_{H_\alpha} = \int_1^\infty \lambda^{2\alpha} d(E_\lambda u, v)_{H_0}, \quad \|u\|^2_{H_\alpha} = \int_1^\infty \lambda^{2\alpha} d(E_\lambda u, u)_{H_0}$$

$$(\alpha \in (-\infty, \infty);\ u, v \in H_{\max(\alpha,0)}). \tag{6.82}$$

It is clear from (6.82) that for $\alpha < \beta (\alpha, \beta \in (-\infty, \infty))$, $H_\alpha \supseteq H_\beta$ and $\|u\|_{H_\alpha} \le \|u\|_{H_\beta} (u \in H_\beta)$; then H_β is dense in H_α. Note that $\bigcap_{\alpha \ge 0} H_\alpha$ is nonzero and even dense in H_0, for example, every vector of the form $E(\Delta) f$, where Δ is a finite interval and $f \in H_0$, belongs to this intersection. If $u \in \bigcap_{\alpha \ge 0} H_\alpha$, then for any $N \in (-\infty, \infty)$, $\int_1^\infty \lambda^{2N} d(E_\lambda u, u)_{H_0} < \infty$ and therefore for any $\alpha, \beta \in (-\infty, \infty)$, $A^\alpha u \in H_\beta$.

Theorem 6.10. *Let* $\{H'_\alpha\}$ *and* $\{H''_\alpha\}$ *be two Hilbert scales, and let* B *be a linear operator which acts continuously from* $H'_{\alpha'}$ *to* $H''_{\alpha''}$ *and from* $H'_{\beta'}$ *to* $H''_{\beta''}$ *for some fixed* $\alpha', \alpha'', \beta', \beta'' \ (\alpha' < \beta', \alpha'' < \beta'')$. *Then* B *acts continuously from* $H'_{\gamma'(\mu)}$ *to* $H''_{\gamma''(\mu)}$, *where* $\gamma'(\mu) = (1-\mu)\alpha' + \mu\beta'$, $\gamma''(\mu) = (1-\mu)\alpha'' + \mu\beta''$, $0 \le \mu \le 1$.

Proof. Suppose we have

$$\|Bu\|_{H''_{\alpha''}} \leqslant C_{\alpha',\alpha''} \|u\|_{H'_{\alpha'}}, \quad \|Bv\|_{H''_{\beta''}} \leqslant C_{\beta',\beta''} \|v\|_{H'_{\beta'}} \quad (u \in H'_{\alpha'}, v \in H'_{\beta'}). \tag{6.83}$$

Fix $u_0 \in \bigcap_{\alpha \ge 0} H'_\alpha$ and $v_0 \in \bigcap_{\alpha \ge 0} H''_\alpha$, and consider the function of complex $z = \sigma + i\tau$, varying over the entire plane:

$$F(z) = (BA'^{z(\beta'-\alpha')} u_0, \ A''^{\bar{z}(\alpha''-\beta'')} v_0)_{H_0}; \tag{6.84}$$

here A' and A'' are operators of the type A corresponding to the scales $\{H'_\alpha\}$ and $\{H''_\alpha\}$.

Notice that the "scalar product" (6.84) is meaningful. Since $u_0 \in \bigcap_{\alpha \ge 0} H'_{\alpha_0}$, both $A'^{z(\beta'-\alpha')} u_0$ and $A'^{\sigma(\beta'-\alpha')} u_0$ belong to every H'_α, and in particular to $H'_{\alpha'}$; similarly $A''^{\bar{z}(\alpha''-\beta'')} v_0 \in H''_{-\alpha''}$. Recall that B acts from $H'_{\alpha'}$ to $H''_{\alpha''}$. Further, taking into account (6.83) and (6.82), we obtain

$$|F(z)| \leqslant \|BA'^{z(\beta'-\alpha')} u_0\|_{H''_{\alpha''}} \|A''^{\bar{z}(\alpha''-\beta'')} v_0\|_{H''_{-\alpha''}}$$

$$\leqslant C_{\alpha',\alpha''} \|A'^{z(\beta'-\alpha')} u_0\|_{H'_{\alpha'}} \|A''^{\bar{z}(\alpha''-\beta'')} v_0\|_{H''_{-\alpha''}}$$

$$= C_{\alpha',\alpha''} \|A'^{\sigma(\beta'-\alpha')} u_0\|_{H'_{\alpha'}} \|A''^{\sigma(\alpha''-\beta'')} v_0\|_{H''_{-\alpha''}} = C_{\alpha',\alpha''} \|u_0\|_{H_{\gamma'(\sigma)}} \|v_0\|_{H''_{-\gamma''(\sigma)}}. \tag{6.85}$$

Similarly, we find

$$\begin{aligned}|F(z)| &\leqslant \| BA'^{z(\beta'-\alpha')}u_0\|_{H''_{\beta''}} \| A''^{\bar z(\alpha''-\beta'')}v_0\|_{H''_{-\beta''}} \\ &\leqslant C_{\beta',\beta''} \| A'^{z(\beta'-\alpha')}u_0\|_{H'_{\beta'}} \| A''^{\bar z(\alpha''-\beta'')}v_0\|_{H''_{-\beta''}} \\ &= C_{\beta',\beta''} \| u_0\|_{H'_{-\sigma\alpha'+(1+\sigma)\beta'}} \| v_0\|_{H''_{\sigma\alpha''+(-1-\sigma)\beta''}}\end{aligned} \qquad (6.86)$$

We set in (6.85) $\sigma = \mu$, and in (6.86) $\sigma = \mu - 1$. We obtain

$$|F(\mu + i\tau)| \leqslant C_{\alpha',\alpha''} \| u_0\|_{H'_{\gamma'(\mu)}} \| v_0\|_{H''_{-\gamma''(\mu)}},$$

$$|F(\mu - 1 + i\tau)| \leqslant C_{\beta',\beta''} \| u_0\|_{H'_{\gamma'(\mu)}} \| v_0\|_{H''_{-\gamma''(\mu)}}$$

$$(\tau \in (-\infty, \infty)). \qquad (6.87)$$

Now use the theorem on three lines (see, for example, I. I. Privalov [1], Chapter III, §17, p. 72): if $f(z)$ is an analytic bounded function in the strip $a < \sigma < b$, then the upper bound of $\log|f(z)|$ on any line $\sigma + i\tau$ $(-\infty < \tau < \infty)$ is a convex function of σ. Letting $f(z) = F(z)$, we obtain with the help of (6.87)

$$\begin{aligned}|(Bu_0, v_0)_{H_0}| &= |F(0)| = e^{\log|F(0)|} \leqslant \exp\{\mu \sup_\tau \log|F(\mu-1+i\tau)| \\ &+ (1-\mu)\sup_\tau \log|F(\mu+i\tau)|\} = (\sup_\tau |F(\mu-1+i\tau)|)^{\mu} (\sup_\tau |F(\mu+i\tau)|)^{1-\mu} \\ &\leqslant C^{1-\mu}_{\alpha',\alpha''} C^{\mu}_{\beta',\beta''} \| u_0\|_{H'_{\gamma'(\mu)}} \| v_0\|_{H''_{-\gamma''(\mu)}}\end{aligned}$$

By virtue of the density of the v_0 in $H''_{-\gamma''(\mu)}$, it follows that

$$\| Bu_0\|_{H''_{\gamma''(\mu)}} \leqslant C^{1-\mu}_{\alpha',\alpha''} C^{\mu}_{\beta',\beta''} \|u_0\|_{H'_{\gamma'(\mu)}}.$$

Because of the density of the u_0 in $H'_{\gamma'(\mu)}$, we finally obtain

$$\| Bu\|_{H''_{\gamma''(\mu)}} \leqslant C^{1-\mu}_{\alpha',\alpha''} C^{\mu}_{\beta',\beta''} \| u\|_{H'_{\gamma'(\mu)}} \qquad (u \in H'_{\gamma'(\mu)};\ 0 \leqslant \mu \leqslant 1). \qquad (6.88)$$

The theorem follows.

Note that we have proved somewhat more than was asserted: if the estimates (6.83) hold, then the estimate (6.88) holds, i.e. we have obtained an estimate of the norm of the operator B as it acts from $H'_{\gamma'(\mu)}$ to $H''_{\gamma''(\mu)}$.

For the required application of Theorem 6.10, we must show that each of the sequences of spaces

$K_{(s,\, 2m-m_j+s-\frac{1}{2})}$ $(s = -2m, \ldots, 0)$ and $K_{(2m+s,\, 2m-l_j+s-\frac{1}{2})}$ $(s = -2m, \ldots, 0)$

(see (6.76)) can be considered as part of a certain Hilbert scale, depending on the sequence. Since the space $K_{(\cdot,\cdot)}$ is constructed as an orthogonal sum of Hilbert spaces of the type W_2^l, to prove the inclusion in a scale of spaces, it is obviously sufficient to make the verification only for each W_2^l (the A for the sum is equal to the orthogonal sum of the A's for the terms). Below we restrict attention only to those l's which we need (i.e. integral and integral plus ½). It is possible to treat general indices l in the same way; we do not do this, because the definitions of the corresponding W_2^l have not been mentioned. Note that if all of these considerations were extended, we would obtain estimates of the type (6.80) for all $s \in [-2m, 0]$; however, simpler estimates of the type (6.81) do not hold in this case.

Thus we consider first the spaces $W_2^l(G)$.

Lemma 6.12. *Fix an integer* $\sigma > 0$. *There exists a Hilbert scale* $\{H_\alpha\}$ ($\alpha \in (-\infty, \infty)$) *such that* $H_l = W_2^l(G)$ $(l = -\sigma, \cdots, \sigma)$ (*more precisely, the norms in the spaces* H_l *and* $W_2^l(G)$ *are equivalent*).

Proof. We construct a Hilbert scale $\{H_\alpha\}$ such that $H_{l/\sigma} = W_2^l(G)$ $(l = -\sigma, \cdots, \sigma)$; the required scale is obtained by replacing A by A^σ. Let $H_0 = L_2(G)$, $H_1 = W_2^\sigma(G)$, and consider H_0 as a zero space and H_1 as a positive space. Consider the corresponding operator D ($\mathfrak{D}(D) = H_1$) and construct a scale $\{H_\alpha\}$ by setting $A = D$. We show that it is the desired object. It is sufficient to show only that $H_{l/\sigma} = W_2^l(G)$ for $l = 0, \cdots, \sigma$, since for negative l, both $H_{l/\sigma}$ and $W_2^l(G)$ are constructed in a unique way by passage to negative spaces.

We first consider an analogous problem, where the spaces $W_2^l(G)$ are replaced by $\overset{\circ}{W}{}_2^l(E_n)$ $(l = 0, \cdots, \sigma)$; the corresponding scale is denoted $\{H'_\alpha\}$. As mentioned in Chapter I, §3.5, the scalar product in $\overset{\circ}{W}{}_2^l(E_n)$ can be given by the integral

$$(u, v)_{\overset{\circ}{W}{}_2^l(E_n)} = \int_{E_n} (1 + |\xi|^2)^l \, \tilde{u}(\xi) \overline{\tilde{v}(\xi)} \, d\xi, \tag{6.89}$$

where $\tilde{W}(\xi)$ denotes the Fourier transform of the function $w(x)$. Thus, for $u \in \overset{\circ}{W}{}_2^\sigma(E_n)$,

$$\widetilde{(Au)}(\xi) = \widetilde{(Du)}(\xi) = \sqrt{(1 + |\xi|^2)^\sigma} \, \tilde{u}(\xi), \ \widetilde{(A^{\frac{l}{\sigma}} u)}(\xi) = \left(\sqrt{(1 + |\xi|^2)^\sigma}\right)^{\frac{l}{\sigma}} \tilde{u}(\xi)$$
$$= \sqrt{(1 + |\xi|^2)^l} \, \tilde{u}(\xi) \qquad (l = 0, \ldots, \sigma).$$

We conclude from (6.89) that $(\cdot, \cdot)_{H'_{l/\sigma}} = (\cdot, \cdot)_{\overset{\circ}{W}{}_2^l(E_n)}$. This does in fact give the equation $H'_{l/\sigma} = \overset{\circ}{W}{}_2^l(E_n)$ $(l = 0, \cdots, \sigma)$.

We return to the spaces $W_2^l(G)$. It is not difficult to prove that every function

$u \in W_2^l(G)$ can be extended to a function $Tu \in \overset{\circ}{W}{}_2^l(E_n)$ $(l = 0, \cdots, \sigma)$, where the extension operator T satisfies the inequality

$$C_1 \| u \|_{W_2^l(G)} \leqslant \| Tu \|_{\overset{\circ}{W}{}_2^l(E_n)} \leqslant C_2 \| u \|_{W_2^l(G)}$$
$$(u \in W_2^l(G);\ l = 0, \ldots, \sigma). \tag{6.90}$$

The right inequality in (6.90) for $l = 0$, σ can be written in the form

$$\| Tu \|_{H_0'} \leqslant C_2 \| u \|_{H_0} \ (u \in H_0), \quad \| Tu \|_{H_1'} \leqslant C_2 \| u \|_{H_1} \ (u \in H_1).$$

Applying Theorem 6.10 to T, we conclude that we have the inequality

$$\| Tu \|_{\overset{\circ}{W}{}_2^l(E_n)} = \| Tu \|_{H'_{\frac{l}{\sigma}}} \leqslant C_2 \| u \|_{H_{\frac{l}{\sigma}}} \quad (u \in W_2^\sigma(G);\ l = 0, \ldots, \sigma).$$

Taking into account the left inequality in (6.90), we find

$$\| u \|_{W_2^l(G)} \leqslant C_3 \| u \|_{H_{\frac{l}{\sigma}}} \quad (u \in W_2^\sigma(G);\ l = 0, \ldots, \sigma). \tag{6.91}$$

We prove a reverse estimate. Let S denote the operator which maps a function $v(x) \in \overset{\circ}{W}{}_2^l(E_n)$ into the same function, but considered only for $x \in G$. Obviously, we have

$$\| Sv \|_{W_2^l(G)} \leqslant \| v \|_{\overset{\circ}{W}{}_2^l(E_n)} \quad (v \in \overset{\circ}{W}{}_2^l(E_n);\ l = 0, \ldots, \sigma).$$

Writing this estimate for $l = 0$, σ and then applying Theorem 6.10, we obtain

$$\| Sv \|_{H_{\frac{l}{\sigma}}} \leqslant \| v \|_{H'_{\frac{l}{\sigma}}} = \| v \|_{\overset{\circ}{W}{}_2^l(E_n)} \quad (v \in \overset{\circ}{W}{}_2^\sigma(E_n);\ l = 0, \ldots, \sigma).$$

Replacing v by Tu $(u \in W_2^\sigma(G))$, and using (6.90), we arrive at the estimate

$$\| u \|_{H_{\frac{l}{\sigma}}} \leqslant C_2 \| u \|_{W_2^l(G)} \quad (u \in W_2^\sigma(G);\ l = 0, \ldots, \sigma). \tag{6.92}$$

The inequalities (6.91) and (6.92) show that $\| \cdot \|_{H_{l/\sigma}}$ and $\| \cdot \|_{W_2^l(G)}$ $(l = 0, \cdots, \sigma)$ are equivalent. The lemma follows.

We now consider the spaces

$$W_2^{l-\frac{1}{2}}(\Gamma) \quad (l = \ldots, -1, 0, 1, \ldots).$$

Lemma 6.13. *The assertion of Lemma 6.12 holds with* $W_2^l(G)$ *replaced by*

$$W_2^{l-\frac{1}{2}}(\Gamma) \quad (l = -\sigma + 1, \ldots, \sigma).$$

Proof. As before, it is sufficient to construct a Hilbert scale $\{H_\alpha\}$ such that

$$H_{l-\frac{1}{2}/\sigma-\frac{1}{2}} = H_{\frac{2l-1}{2\sigma-1}} = W_2^{l-\frac{1}{2}}(\Gamma)$$

for the mentioned l. We construct this scale with respect to the space $H_0 = L_2(\Gamma)$ and the operator $A = D$ in it, where D is induced by the zero space $H_0 = L_2(\Gamma)$ and the positive space $H_1 = W_2^{\sigma-1/2}(\Gamma)$. As before, it is sufficient to prove coincidence of the spaces for $l = 1, \cdots, \sigma$.

The proof of the equation

$$H_{\frac{2l-1}{2\sigma-1}} = W_2^{l-\frac{1}{2}}(\Gamma) \quad (l = 1, \dots, \sigma)$$

is carried out by arguments given in the case of Lemma 6.12, with $W_2^l(G)$ playing the role of $\overset{\circ}{W}{}_2^l(E_n)$, and the space $H_{l/\sigma}$ constructed for the proof of Lemma 6.12 playing the role of $H'_{l/\sigma}$. Namely, let Tu denote the extension of $u \in W_2^{l-1/2}(\Gamma)$ to $Tu \in W_2^l(G)$ ocurring in the estimate (6.7); this can now be rewritten in a form similar to (6.90):

$$C_1 \langle\langle u \rangle\rangle_{W_2^{l-\frac{1}{2}}(\Gamma)} \leqslant \| Tu \|_{W_2^l(G)} \leqslant C_2 \langle\langle u \rangle\rangle_{W_2^{l-\frac{1}{2}}(\Gamma)} \quad (u \in W_2^{l-\frac{1}{2}}(\Gamma);\ l = 1, \dots, \sigma). \tag{6.93}$$

With the aid of Theorem 6.10, it follows from the right estimate in (6.93) for $l = 1, \sigma$ that

$$\| Tu \|_{W_2^l(G)} = \| Tu \|_{H'_{\frac{l}{\sigma}}} \leqslant C_2 \| u \|_{H_{\frac{2l-1}{2\sigma-1}}} \quad (u \in W_2^{\sigma-\frac{1}{2}}(\Gamma);\ l=1, \dots, \sigma).$$

Taking into account the left inequality in (6.93), we find

$$\langle\langle u \rangle\rangle_{W_2^{l-\frac{1}{2}}(\Gamma)} \leqslant C_3 \| u \|_{H_{\frac{2l-1}{2\sigma-1}}} \quad (u \in W_2^{\sigma-\frac{1}{2}}(\Gamma);\ l = 1, \dots, \sigma).$$

The reverse inequality is proved as in Lemma 6.12; the role of S is played by the operator which maps a function $u \in W_2^l(G)$ into the same function, considered only on Γ (belonging to $W_2^{l-1/2}(\Gamma)$).

The lemma follows.

As was already explained, it follows from Lemmas 6.12 and 6.13 that there exist Hilbert scales $\{H'_\alpha\}$ and $\{H''_\alpha\}$ such that

$$K_{\left(s, 2m-m_j+s-\frac{1}{2}\right)} = H'_s \text{ and } K_{\left(2m+s, 2m-l_j+s-\frac{1}{2}\right)} = H''_s \ (s = -2m, \dots, 0).$$

Now apply Theorem 6.10 to these scales and the operator $B = \widetilde{SQ}_{\perp N^+}$, we conclude that $\widetilde{SQ}_{\perp N^+}$ *acts continuously from all of*

$$K_{\left(s, 2m-m_j+s-\frac{1}{2}\right)} \text{ to } K_{\left(2m+s, 2m-l_j+s-\frac{1}{2}\right)}.$$

10. **The theorem on homeomorphisms in the case of homogeneous boundary conditions.** Consider the operator induced by the problem (6.4) – (6.5) which effects, by Theorem 6.9, a homeomorphism between $\tilde{H}_{2m+s}$ and K_s^+ $(s = \cdots, -1, 0, 1, \cdots)$. We restrict this operator to functions satisfying homogeneous boundary conditions (bd). More precisely, this denotes the following: for $s \geq 0$, consider the operator Λ_s(bd) which coincides with the restriction of $\mathfrak{L}_s$ to W_2^{2m}(bd), and for $s < 0$, consider the operator which appears as the closure by continuity of Λ_0 (bd), considered as an operator acting from $\tilde{W}_2^{2m+s}(G)$ to $W_2^s(G)$. Clearly, these operators are homeomorphisms with domains $W_2^s(G) \ominus N$ (the orthogonal complement is formed in $L_2(G)$; i.e. $\alpha \in W_2^s(G) \ominus N$ if and only if $(\alpha, N)_0 = 0$). A similar fact holds for the adjoint problem.

We now give another theorem on homeomorphisms for homogeneous (bd), which coincides with Theorem 3.6 in the case of null (bd). We will not derive it from the just now described fact, but instead we give an independent proof. As a preliminary, we elaborate on the general considerations in subsection 9.

Consider a Hilbert scale $\{H_\alpha\}$. Let $H_r (r > 0)$ be a fixed space in this scale, and let N and N^+ be finite-dimensional subspaces of H_r; let $H_0 \ominus N$, $H_0 \ominus N^+$ be their orthogonal complements in H_0. We assume that we are given an operator B, which maps all of $H_0 \ominus N^+$ into a dense subset of $H_0 \ominus N$,[1] and which is continuous with respect to the metric of H_0. The usual adjoint to B is an operator B^* which acts continuously from all of $H_0 \ominus N$ to $H_0 \ominus N^+$. In addition, we assume that $\Re(B), \Re(B^*) \subseteq H_r$. The closures of $\Re(B)$ and $\Re(B^*)$ in the metric of H_s $(0 \leq s \leq r)$ will be denoted by H_s(bd) and $H_s(\text{bd})^+$ respectively. The space H_s(bd) is dense in $H_0 \ominus N$ in the metric $\|\cdot\|_{H_0}$, and $\|u\|_{H_0} \leq \|u\|_{H_s(\text{bd})}$ $(u \in H_s(\text{bd}))$; therefore $H_0 \ominus N$ can be taken as a zero space and H_s(bd) as a positive space. The corresponding negative space is denoted H_{-s}(bd). Similarly, we introduce $H_{-s}(\text{bd})^+$.

Theorem 6.11. *If*

$$\|Bf\|_{H_r} \leqslant C_1 \|f\|_{H_0} \quad (f \in H_0 \ominus N^+), \; \|B^*g\|_{H_r} \leqslant C_2 \|g\|_{H_0} \quad (g \in H_0 \ominus N), \tag{6.94}$$

then for $\lambda \in [-r, 0]$,

$$\|Bf\|_{H_{r+\lambda}} \leqslant C_3 \|f\|_{H_\lambda(\text{bd})^+} \qquad (f \in H_0 \ominus N^+). \tag{6.95}$$

---

1) Later, the role of B will be played by Λ_0(bd); this accounts for the notation introduced below.

Proof. Consider first the case of zero deficiency: $N = N^+ = 0$. Construct the operator $\tilde{B}$ which is adjoint to B^* in the sense of $(\cdot,\cdot)_{H_0}$, i.e. set $\tilde{B} = B^{*+}$; $\tilde{B}$ acts continuously from H_{-r} to H_0. This operator is an extension of the operator B: if $f \in H_0$, then for any $g \in H_0$ we have $(\tilde{B}f, g)_{H_0} = (f, B^*g)_{H_0} = (Bf, g)_{H_0}$, i.e. $\tilde{B}f = Bf$. Since the norm of B^* is not greater than C_2, the same is true for the norm of $B^{*+} = \tilde{B}$:

$$\| \tilde{B}\alpha \|_{H_0} \leqslant C_2 \| \alpha \|_{H_{-r}} \qquad (\alpha \in H_{-r}). \tag{6.96}$$

The first inequality in (6.94) can be rewritten in the form $\| \tilde{B}f \|_{H_r} \leq C_1 \| f \|_{H_0}$ $(f \in H_0)$. Now consider (6.96) and apply the interpolation Theorem 6.10 to $\tilde{B}$ (now $\{H'_\alpha\} = \{H''_\alpha\} = \{H_\alpha\}$, $\mu = -\lambda/r$); we obtain

$$\| \tilde{B}\alpha \|_{H_{r+\lambda}} \leqslant C_1^{1+\frac{\lambda}{r}} C_2^{-\frac{\lambda}{r}} \| \alpha \|_{H_\lambda} \quad (\alpha \in H_\lambda;\ \lambda \in [-r, 0]). \tag{6.97}$$

We pass from the inequality (6.97) to the inequality (6.95). Let V_- denote the subspace of the space H_λ, consisting of all β such that $(\beta, v)_{H_0} = 0$ $(v \in H_{-\lambda}(\mathrm{bd})^+)$. The operator $\tilde{B}$ annihilates V_-: for $\beta \in V_-$ and $u \in H_0$, $(\tilde{B}\beta, u)_{H_0} = (\beta, B^*u)_{H_0} = 0$, since by definition of $H_{-\lambda}(\mathrm{bd})^+$, $B^*u \in H_{-\lambda}(\mathrm{bd})^+$. According to (6.97), we can write

$$\| \tilde{B}\alpha \|_{H_{r+\lambda}} = \| \tilde{B}(\alpha + \beta) \|_{H_{r+\lambda}} \leqslant C_1^{1+\frac{\lambda}{r}} C_2^{-\frac{\lambda}{r}} \| \alpha + \beta \|_{H_\lambda}$$
$$(\alpha \in H_\lambda;\ \beta \in V_-;\ \lambda \in [-r, 0]). \tag{6.98}$$

We now use formula (3.18), Chapter I, for the computation of $\| \cdot \|_{H_\lambda(\mathrm{bd})^+}$:

$$\| \alpha \|_{H_\lambda(\mathrm{bd})^+} = \inf_{\beta \in V_-} \| \alpha + \beta \|_{H_\lambda} \quad (\alpha \in H_\lambda).$$

On taking the inf over $\beta \in V_-$ in the right side of (6.98), we obtain an inequality from which follows (6.95):

$$\| \tilde{B}\alpha \|_{H_{r+\lambda}} \leqslant C_1^{1+\frac{\lambda}{r}} C_2^{-\frac{\lambda}{r}} \| \alpha \|_{H_\lambda(\mathrm{bd})^+} \quad (\alpha \in H_\lambda).$$

We now outline the proof in the general case with the presence of a deficiency. The operator B^* can be considered as acting from all of $H_0 \ominus N$ to H_r. If we form the adjoint of this operator, we obtain an operator $\tilde{B} = B^{*+}$, which acts from all of H_{-r} to $H_0 \ominus N$ and is an extension of B. As before, we can write the inequality (6.96) for $\tilde{B}$.

We introduce the operator $P_{\perp N^+}$ which is the orthogonal projection of H_0

into $H_0 \ominus N^+$, and construct its extension to H_{-r}, as described in Lemma 6.10; the extension is also denoted $P_{\perp N^+}$. The first of the inequalities (6.94) and the inequality (6.96) can be rewritten in the form

$$\| BP_{\perp N^+} f \|_{H_r} \leqslant C_1 \| P_{\perp N^+} f \|_{H_0} \leqslant C_1 \| f \|_{H_0} \quad (f \in H_0),$$

$$\| \widetilde{B} P_{\perp N^+} \alpha \|_{H_0} \leqslant C_2 \| P_{\perp N^+} \alpha \|_{H_{-r}} \leqslant C_4 \| \alpha \|_{H_{-r}} \quad (\alpha \in H_{-r}).$$

These two inequalities permit the application of the Interpolation Theorem 6.10 to the operator $BP_{\perp N^+}$, and we obtain the estimate

$$\| \widetilde{BP}_{\perp N^+} \alpha \|_{H_{r+\lambda}} \leqslant C_1^{1+\frac{\lambda}{r}} C_4^{-\frac{\lambda}{r}} \| \alpha \|_{H_\lambda} \quad (\alpha \in H_\lambda;\ \lambda \in [-r, 0]).$$

For $\alpha \in H_\lambda \ominus N^+$ (orthogonal complementation in H_0), the last estimate can be rewritten in a form analogous to (6.97):

$$\| \widetilde{B} \alpha \|_{H_{r+\lambda}} \leqslant C_1^{1+\frac{\lambda}{r}} C_4^{-\frac{\lambda}{r}} \| \alpha \|_{H_\lambda} \quad (\alpha \in H_\lambda \ominus N^+;\ \lambda \in [-r, 0]).$$

Further passage to the estimate (6.95) is accomplished as in the case of zero deficiency.

The theorem follows.

We describe the general method by which Theorem 6.11 is applied to regularly elliptic expressions L of order $r = 2m$ with sufficiently smooth coefficients. For the scale $\{H_\alpha\}$, we take the scale constructed in Lemma 6.12 for $\sigma = 2m$; thus $H_l = W_2^l(G)$, and we may assume that $(\cdot, \cdot)_{H_l} = (\cdot, \cdot)_l$, $\| \cdot \|_{H_l} = \| \cdot \|_l$ $(l = -2m, \cdots, 2m)$. Consider the operator Λ_0 (bd) induced by L and some (bd); Λ_0 (bd) acts continuously from W_2^{2m}(bd) to $L_2(G)$. We will assume that Λ_0 (bd) acts in $L_2(G)$, and denote this operator by A. Suppose that the following conditions are satisfied:

a) the adjoint A^* of A in $L_2(G)$ coincides with the operator constructed in the same way as A, but with (bd) replaced by (bd)$^+$;

b) the subspaces N and N^+ of solutions of the equations $Au = 0$ and $A^* v = 0$, respectively, are finite dimensional;

c) we have the inequalities

$$\| Au \|_0 \geqslant C_1 \| u \|_{2m} \quad (u \in W_2^{2m}(\text{bd}) \ominus N),$$

$$\| A^* v \|_0 \geqslant C_2 \| v \|_{2m} \quad (v \in W_2^{2m}(\text{bd})^+ \ominus N^+);$$

d) the ranges of A on $W_2^{2m}(\text{bd}) \ominus N$ and A^* on $W_2^{2m}(\text{bd})^+ \ominus N^+$ coincide respectively with $L_2(G) \ominus N^+$ and $L_2(G) \ominus N$ (all orthogonal complements are in the sense of $L_2(G)$).

We now set $B = A^{-1}$, where A^{-1} is the inverse operator from $L_2(G) \ominus N^+$ to $W_2^{2m}(\text{bd})$. Then $B^* = A^{*-1}$ and all of the hypotheses of Theorem 6.11 are satisfied. Thus we obtain the estimate (6.95) for B, which is equivalent to the inequality

$$\| Lu \|_{H_\lambda(\text{bd})^+} \geqslant C^{-1} \| u \|_{2m+\lambda} \qquad (u \in W_2^{2m}(\text{bd}); \quad \lambda \in [-2m, 0]). \tag{6.99}$$

We will show later (Lemma 6.14) that for integral $\lambda \in [-2m, 0]$ we have a reverse inequality to (6.99); thus we obtain the estimate

$$C^{-1} \| u \|_{2m+s} \leqslant \| Lu \|_{H(\text{bd})^+} \leqslant C \| u \|_{2m+s} \ (u \in W_2^{2m}(\text{bd}); \ s = -2m, \ldots, 0). \tag{6.100}$$

This estimate leads to the "middle set" of homeomorphisms, effected by closures of the operator $\Lambda_0(\text{bd})$.

The proof of the existence of the homeomorphisms for $s > 0$ has already been obtained (see Theorem 6.7). The proof for $s < -2m$ is conveniently carried out by passage to adjoints (see Theorem 3.6 in case 4) or Theorem 6.9 for $s > -2m$).

We now show that with sufficient smoothness restriction, conditions a) – d) are satisfied if the system of boundary conditions is normal (cf. proof of Lemma 3.9).

Condition a). Let B be the operator which is constructed in the same way as A, but with (bd) replaced by $(\text{bd})^+$. It is clear that $B \subseteq A^*$. We obtain the reverse inclusion. Suppose $f \in \mathfrak{D}(A^*)$, i.e. $(Lu, f)_0 = (u, A^*f)_0$ for all $u \in W_2^{2m}(\text{bd})$. If we take $u \in N$ here, we obtain $A^*f \perp N$ in $L_2(G)$. By Theorem 6.7 we can find $v \in W_2^{2m}(\text{bd})^+$ such that $L^+v = A^*f$; thus $(Lu, f - v)_0 = (Lu, f)_0 - (Lu, v)_0 = (u, A^*f)_0 - (u, L^+v)_0 = 0$ $(u \in W_2^{2m}(\text{bd}))$. In other words, $w = f - v \in L_2(G)$ is a weak solution of the problem $L^+v = 0$, $v \in (\text{bd})^+$. By Theorem 6.7, w is a smooth solution of this problem, i.e. $w \in W_2^{2m}(\text{bd})^+$ and $L^+w = 0$. Thus $f = v + w \in W_2^{2m}(\text{bd})$ and $L^+f = A^*f$. In other words $A^* \subset B$. The assertion follows.

Conditions b), c), and d) follow from Theorem 6.7.

The indicated proof easily leads to the following theorem.

Theorem 6.12. *Let the problem* (6.4) – (6.5) *be elliptic, and suppose that the system* (6.2) *is normal and the smoothness conditions formulated below are satisfied. We introduce the following spaces (orthogonal complements are formed in* $L_2(G)$; s *is an integer):*

a) $0 \leq s$, $H_{2m+s}(\text{bd}) = W_2^{2m}(\text{bd}) \cap W_2^{2m+s}(G) \ominus N$ *(in the metric* $(\cdot,\cdot)_{2m+s}$);

b) $-2m \leq s < 0$, $H_{2m+s}(\mathrm{bd})$ *is the closure of* $W_2^{2m}(\mathrm{bd}) \ominus N$ *in* $W_2^{2m+s}(G)$;

c) $s < -2m$, $H_{2m+s}(\mathrm{bd})$ *is the negative space constructed for the zero space* $L_2(G) \ominus N$ *and the positive space* $H_{-(2m+s)}(\mathrm{bd})$;

d) $0 \leq s$, $H_s = W_2^s(G) \ominus N$ *(in the metric* $(\cdot, \cdot)_s$*)*;

e) $s < 0$, H_s *is the negative space constructed for the zero space* $L_2(G) \ominus N$ *and the positive space* H_{-s}.

Analogous spaces $H_s(\mathrm{bd})^+$ *and* H_s^+ *are introduced for* $(\mathrm{bd})^+$ *and* N^+.

Consider the 0*-strong operator* $\Lambda_0(\mathrm{bd})$, *constructed with respect to* L *and* (bd) *(i.e. the operator* $u \to Lu$, $u \in W_2^{2m}(\mathrm{bd})$*). Then*

1) *for* $s \geq 0$ *the restriction of* $\Lambda_0(\mathrm{bd})$ *to* $H_{2m+s}(\mathrm{bd})$ *effects a homeomorphism between* $H_{2m+s}(\mathrm{bd})$ *and* H_s^+;

2) *for* $-2m \leq s < 0$, $\Lambda_0(\mathrm{bd})$, *considered as an operator from* $H_{2m+s}(\mathrm{bd})$ *to* $H_s(\mathrm{bd})^+$, *admits a closure by continuity and this closure effects a homeomorphism between* $H_{2m+s}(\mathrm{bd})$ *and* $H_s(\mathrm{bd})^+$;

3) *for* $s < -2m$, $\Lambda_0(\mathrm{bd})$, *considered as an operator from* H_{2m+s} *to* $H_s(\mathrm{bd})^+$, *admits a closure by continuity and this closure effects a homeomorphism between* H_{2m+s} *and* $H_s(\mathrm{bd})^+$.

The smoothness assumptions are: for case 1), $a_\alpha(x) \in C^{2m+\max(|\alpha|,s)}(G \cup \Gamma)$, $b_{j\alpha}(x) \in C^{\max(2m+s-1, 2m-m_j+s)}(\Gamma)$, $b_{j\alpha}(x) \in C^{\max(2m+s-1, 2m-m'_j+s)}(\Gamma)$ $(j = 1, \ldots, m)$, Γ *of class* C^{4m+s}; *for case* 2)(3)) *the same requirements with* s *replaced by* 0 $(|2m+s|)$.

It is easy to see that Theorem 3.6 is a special case of this theorem (this is true if we ignore smoothness restrictions, which are less severe in Theorem 3.6 because of another method of proof for the solvability of the boundary value problem). In fact, suppose that $(\mathrm{bd}) = (\mathrm{bd})^+$ are null and $N = N^+ = 0$. Then $H_s = W_2^s(G)$ $(s = \cdots, -1, 0, 1, \cdots)$, $H_{2m+s}(\mathrm{bd}) = \mathring{W}_2^m(G) \cap W_2^{2m+s}(G)$ $(s = -m, -m+1, \ldots)$, $H_{2m+s}(\mathrm{bd}) = \mathring{W}_2^{2m+s}(G)$ $(s = -2m, \cdots, -m-1)$. For $s = \cdots, -2m-2, -2m-1$, $H_{2m+s}(\mathrm{bd})$ coincides with the negative space for the zero space $L_2(G)$ and positive space $H_{-(2m+s)}(\mathrm{bd})$. Therefore $H_l(\mathrm{bd}) = \mathring{W}_2^l(G)$ $(l = -m, \cdots, -1)$ and $H_l(\mathrm{bd}) = W'^{\,l}_2(G)$ $(l = \cdots, -m-2, -m-1)$, where $W_2'^{-l}(G) = H_{-l}(\mathrm{bd}) = \mathring{W}_2^m(G) \cap W_2^{2m+s}(G)$.

For the proof of Theorem 6.12, it remains to establish the following lemma.

Lemma 6.14. *Suppose that the hypotheses of Theorem* 6.12 *are satisfied in case* 2). *Then*

$$\| Lu \|_{H_s(\mathrm{bd})^+} \leqslant C \| u \|_{2m+s} \quad (u \in W_2^{2m}(\mathrm{bd}); s = -2m, \ldots, 0). \tag{6.101}$$

Proof. In what follows we set $\sigma = -s = 0, \cdots, 2m$. According to the definition of a negative norm, we have

$$\| Lu \|_{H_{-\sigma}(\text{bd})^+} = \sup_{v \in H_\sigma(\text{bd})^+} \frac{|(Lu, v)_0|}{\|v\|_\sigma} = \sup_{v \in W_2^{2m}(\text{bd})^+ \oplus N^+} \frac{|(Lu, v)_0|}{\|v\|_\sigma}$$

$$\leqslant \sup_{v \in W_2^{2m}(\text{bd})^+} \frac{|(Lu, v)_0|}{\|v\|_\sigma}. \tag{6.102}$$

We use integration by parts to transfer σ derivatives in the expression $(Lu, v)_0$ from u to v. The resulting integral over G is estimated above by $C_1 \| u \|_{2m-\sigma} \| v \|_\sigma$; we consider the remaining integrals over Γ. If we can show that these integrals are estimated by $C_2 \| u \|_{2m-\sigma} \| v \|_\sigma$, then (6.101) will follow from (6.102). We now obtain such estimates.

In order to find the form of the integrals over Γ, we use the arguments and notation of subsection 5. Let x be an arbitrary point on Γ. By using a decomposition of unity, we can reduce the argument to the case where v vanishes outside of some neighborhood (in E_n) of the point x; we assume $x = 0$. Then we can construct a "rectification" of the type (6.25), and consider a function $v \in W_2^{2m}(G_\delta)$ vanishing near the hemisphere $|x| = \delta$, $x_n \geq 0$ (G_δ is the region $|x| < \delta$, $x_n > 0$). Using the notation (6.30), we obtain

$$(Lu, v)_0 = \Big(\sum_{|\tau|+\nu \leqslant 2m} a_{\tau\nu}(x) \partial^\tau \partial_n^\nu u, v \Big)_0 = \sum_{\nu=0}^{2m} \Big(\partial_n^\nu u, \sum_{|\tau| \leqslant 2m-\nu} \partial^\tau (\overline{a_{\tau\nu} v}) \Big)_0$$

$$= \sum_{\nu=0}^{2m-\sigma} \Big(\partial_n^\nu u, \sum_{|\tau| \leqslant 2m-\nu} \partial^\tau (\overline{a_{\tau\nu} v}) \Big)_0 + \sum_{\nu=2m-\sigma+1}^{2m} \Big(\partial_n^\nu u, \sum_{|\tau| \leqslant 2m-\nu} \partial^\tau (\overline{a_{\tau\nu} v}) \Big)_0. \tag{6.103}$$

Here we have used the fact that the tangential derivatives ∂^τ can be freely shifted onto v by integration by parts, and integrals over Γ do not appear (v vanishes near $|x| = \delta$, $x_n \geq 0$). Transferring such derivatives in an appropriate way, we obtain for the first sum in the right side of (6.103) the estimate

$$\Big| \sum_{\nu=0}^{2m-\sigma} \cdots \Big| \leqslant C_3 \| u \|_{2m-\sigma} \| v \|_\sigma.$$

We now consider the second sum. In each of its terms, we transfer derivatives ∂_n from u to v until there remain exactly $2m - \sigma$. As was already explained, we need only estimate the integrals over Γ. They have the form

$$\sum_{\nu=2m-\sigma+1}^{2m} \sum_{k=2m-\sigma+1}^{\nu} \int_\Gamma \partial_n^{k-1} u \sum_{|\tau|\leqslant 2m-\nu} \overline{\partial^{\nu-} \partial^\tau(\bar{a}_{\tau\nu} v)}\, dx$$

$$= \sum_{k=2m-\sigma+1}^{2m} \sum_{\nu=k}^{2m} \int_\Gamma \partial_n^{k-1} u \cdot \sum_{|\tau|\leqslant 2m-\nu} \overline{\partial_n^{\nu-k} \partial^\tau(\bar{a}_{\tau\nu} v)}\, dx = \sum_{k=2m-\sigma+1}^{2m} \int_\Gamma \partial_n^{k-1} u \cdot \overline{N_k v}\, dx$$

$$= \sum_{k=2m-\sigma+1}^{2m} \int_\Gamma \sum_{t=1}^{k} \hat{T}_{kt} B_t u \cdot \overline{N_k v} dx = \sum_{k=2m-\sigma+1}^{2m} \sum_{t=1}^{k} \int_\Gamma B_t u \cdot \overline{\hat{T}_{kt}^+ N_k v}\, dx$$

$$= \sum_{k=2m-\sigma+1}^{2m} \left(\sum_{t=1}^{2m-\sigma} \cdots + \sum_{t=2m-\sigma+1}^{k} \cdots \right) = \sum_{k=m-\sigma+1}^{2m} \sum_{t=1}^{2m-\sigma} \cdots$$

$$+ \sum_{t=2m-\sigma+1}^{2m} \sum_{k=t}^{2m} \cdots = \sum_{k=2m-\sigma+1}^{2m} \sum_{t=1}^{2m-\sigma} \int_\Gamma B_t u \cdot \overline{\hat{T}_{kt}^+ N_k v}\, dx$$

$$+ \sum_{t=2m-\sigma+1}^{2m} \int_\Gamma B_t u \cdot \overline{B'_{2m-t+1} v} dx. \tag{6.104}$$

We clarify the calculation. As in the proof of Theorem 6.5, we have set

$$N_k v = \sum_{\nu=k}^{2m} \sum_{|\tau|+\nu\leqslant 2m} \partial^{\nu-k} \partial^\tau (\overline{a_{\tau\nu}} v) \qquad (k = 1, \ldots, 2m),$$

applied the representation (6.28), transferred $\hat{T}_{kt}$ from u to v ($\hat{T}_{kt}$ is constructed from the tangential derivatives), and introduced B_0' by means of $\hat{T}_{\cdot\cdot}^+$, $N_{\cdot}$.

Up to now we have imposed restrictions on u and v on the plane piece of the boundary of the hemisphere G_δ. We now assume that $u \in W_2^{2m}$ (bd), $v \in W_2^{2m}$ (bd)$^+$. Then $B_t u \cdot B'_{2m-t+1} v = 0$ ($t = 2m - \sigma + 1, \cdots, 2m$), and for the estimate (6.104), it will only be necessary to estimate the integral

$$\int_\gamma B_t u \cdot \overline{\hat{T}_{kt}^+ N_k v} dx \qquad (u, v \in W_2^{2m}(G_\delta);\ t = 1, \ldots, 2m - \sigma;$$
$$k = 2m - \sigma + 1, \ldots, 2m), \tag{6.105}$$

which is taken over the plane part γ of the boundary of G_δ. For sufficiently smooth functions $f(x)$, $g(x)$ ($x \in \bar{G}_\delta$), one of which vanishes near the hemisphere $|x| = \delta$, $x_n \geq 0$, we can write

$$\int_\gamma f g dx = -i \int_{G_\delta} (\partial_n f \cdot g + f \partial_n g)\, dx.$$

Therefore, if we first extend the coefficients of B_t and $\hat{T}_{kt}^+$ inside G_δ in a smooth way, then with the help of this formula we obtain

$$\left|\int_{\gamma} B_t u\cdot\overline{\hat{T}_{kt}^{+}N_k v}\,dx\right| \leqslant \left|\int_{G_\delta} \partial_n (B_t u)\cdot\overline{\hat{T}_{kt}^{+}N_k v}\,dx\right|$$

$$+\left|\int_{G_\delta} B_t u\cdot\overline{\partial_n(\hat{T}_{kt}^{+}N_k v)}\,dx\right| \quad (t=1,\ldots,2m-\sigma;\ k=2m-\sigma+1,\ldots,2m). \quad (6.106)$$

If we now consider that the order of the expression B_t is $t-1$, the order of N_k is $2m-k$, and the order of the tangential expression $\hat{T}_{kt}^{+}$ is $k-t$, and also notice that the transferring of tangential derivatives does not give rise to an integrated term, we see that the integrals in the right part of (6.106) are estimated by $C_4\|u\|_{2m-\sigma}\|v\|_{\sigma}$. Thus the required estimates of the integrals over Γ are obtained. The lemma follows.

Thus Theorem 6.12 on homeomorphisms is completely proved.

In conclusion, we remark that negative spaces of the type c) and e) in the statement of this theorem can be interpreted somewhat differently. We mention this interpretation in an abstract form. Suppose that we have a sequence $H_- \supseteq H_0 \supseteq H_+$ and a finite dimensional subspace N of H_+. Consider the subspaces $H_-\ominus N$, $H_0\ominus N$, $H_+\ominus N$ (all of the orthogonal complements are formed in H_0; cf. Lemma 6.10). Then we assert that *the negative space constructed for the zero space $H_0\ominus N$ and the positive space $H_+\ominus N$*[1] *is isometric with the subspace $H_-\ominus N$.*

Actually, this is just a paraphrase of the discussion in Chapter I §3.4: the considered negative space coincides with the factor space H_-/N_-, where N_- is the subspace of those $\alpha\in H_-$ such that $(\alpha, H_+\ominus N)_0=0$. Taking into account the finite dimensionality of N, we conclude that $N_-=N$ and $H_-/N_-=H_-\ominus N$.

11. Smoothness up to the boundary for strong generalized solutions of elliptic equations. In this and the following subsection, as in §§4.5–4.6, we apply the theorem on homeomorphisms to the analysis of the smoothness in the case of general boundary conditions; as before, the considerations will be carried out locally. More complete results are obtained from the application of Theorem 6.9 instead of 6.12. This is connected with the fact that from the inclusions $U(x)\in W_2^{2m}(\mathrm{bd})$, $\chi(x)\in C^\infty(E_n)$, it does not follow that $\chi(x)\,u(x)\in W_2^{2m}(\mathrm{bd})$. We will present only this application. We remark finally, that the assertion below contains

1) Namely, this is a space of the type c) or e).

additional information concerning smoothness inside the region: in particular, we obtain results, not of the type of Theorem 4.1 or 4.3, but of the type of Theorem 4.5, for general elliptic expressions.

We will study an elliptic problem (6.4) – (6.5) with sufficient smoothness for the coefficients of the expressions L and B_j and the boundary Γ. By Lemma 6.11, we have the estimate

$$\| Lu \|_s \leqslant C_s ||| u |||_{2m+s}, \quad \langle\langle B_j u \rangle\rangle_{s-\frac{1}{2}} \leqslant C_s' ||| u |||_{2m+s}$$

$$(C_s > 0;\ u \in W_2^{\max(2m+s, 2m)}(G);\quad s = \ldots, -1, 0, 1, \ldots;\ j = 1, \ldots, m).$$

Thus the operator $u \longrightarrow Lu$, $u \in W_2^{\max(2m+s, 2m)}(G)$, if it is considered as an operator from the space $\widetilde{W}_2^{2m+s}(G)$ to the space $W_2^s(G)$, is continuous. The closure of this operator by continuity is denoted $\mathbf{L}_s$.[1] Similarly, we let $\mathbf{B}_{j,s}$ $(j = 1, \cdots, m)$ denote the closure by continuity of the operator $u \longrightarrow B_j u$, $u \in W_2^{\max(2m+s,\ 2m)}(G)$, acting from $\widetilde{W}_2^{2m+s}(G)$ to $W_2^{s-1/2}(\Gamma)$.

Consider the boundary value problem

$$Lu = f \in W_2^{s-2m}(G),\ B_j u = \varphi_j \in W_2^{s-m_j-\frac{1}{2}}(\Gamma) \qquad (j = 1, \ldots, m) \qquad (6.107)$$

for some $s = \cdots, -1, 0, 1, \cdots$. By a strong generalized solution of this problem we mean a $u \in \widetilde{W}_2^s(G)$ such that

$$\mathbf{L}_{s-2m} u = f, \qquad \mathbf{B}_{j, s-m_j} u = \varphi_j \qquad (j = 1, \ldots, m). \qquad (6.108)$$

The following theorem is easily proved.

Theorem 6.13. *Let $u \in \widetilde{W}_2^s(G)$ $(s = \cdots, -1, 0, 1, \cdots)$ be a strong generalized solution of the problem (6.107), but with more smoothness than in the right part of (6.107):*

$$f \in W_2^{s+1-2m}(G),\ \varphi_j \in W_2^{s+1-m_j-\frac{1}{2}}(\Gamma) \quad (j = 1, \ldots, m).$$

Then $u \in \widetilde{W}_2^{s+1}(G)$.

We assume that the conditions in Theorem 6.9 are satisfied both for s replaced by $s - 2m$ and for s replaced by $s + 1 - 2m$.

Proof. We can make the decomposition $u = u' + u''$, where $u' = P_N u \in N$, $u'' = P_{\perp N} u \in \widetilde{H}_s$ (see p. 244). Obviously, from (6.108) we have

---

1) We introduce the similar notation $\mathbf{N}_s$ for the closure of the operator $u \to Nu$, $u \in W_2^{\max(r+s, r)}(G)$, where N is an arbitrary expression of order r.

$$\mathbf{L}_{s-2m}u'' = f, \qquad \mathbf{B}_{j,s-m_j}u'' = \varphi_j \qquad (j = 1, \ldots, m). \tag{6.109}$$

Let

$$F = (f, \varphi_1, \ldots, \varphi_m) \in K_{\left(s+1-2m, s-m_j+\frac{1}{2}\right)} \subset K_{\left(s-2m, s-m_j-\frac{1}{2}\right)}.$$

Equation (6.109) can be rewritten in the form $\overline{\mathfrak{L}}_0 u'' = F$, where by $\overline{\mathfrak{L}}_0$ we understand the restriction (for $s - 2m \geq 0$) or the closure by continuity (for $s - 2m < 0$) of the operator $\mathfrak{L}_0$, considered as acting from $\widetilde{W}_2^s(G)$ to $K_{(s-2m, s-m_j-1/2)}$. By virtue of Theorem 6.9, $[F, N^+ \cdots]_0 = 0$, and therefore also

$$F \in \dot{Q}_{\perp N^+} K_{\left(s+1-2m,\, s-m_j+\frac{1}{2}\right)} = K^+_{s+1}.$$

Again by virtue of Theorem 6.9, we can find $u''' \in \widetilde{H}_{s+1}$ which corresponds under the homeomorphism to F. However, $\widetilde{H}_{s+1} \subset \widetilde{H}_s$, and therefore the last homeomorphism is the restriction of the homeomorphism $\overline{\mathfrak{L}}_0$ which makes F and u'' correspond. It therefore follows that $u''' = u''$. Thus

$$u = u' + u'' = u' + u''' \in \widetilde{W}_2^{s+1}(G) \quad (u' \in N \subset \widetilde{W}_2^{s+1}(G)).$$

The theorem follows.

We proceed to a local formulation of a result of the type of this theorem. A function $\chi(s)$, as in the following lemma, will be called admissable.

Lemma 6.15. *Let Γ be sufficiently smooth, and let Γ_0 be a piece of Γ on which borders a subregion G_0 of the region G. Suppose that $\chi(x) \in C^\infty(G \cup \Gamma)$ vanishes in some neighborhood of the set $G \setminus G_0$ and $\partial\chi/\partial\nu = 0$ near Γ_0 (ν is in the direction of the exterior normal $\nu(x)$ ($x \in \Gamma$), carried into some neighborhood of Γ_0). Then if $u \in \widetilde{W}_2^l(G)$, we have $\chi(x)\, u(x) \in \widetilde{W}_2^l(G_0)$; the operator $u \to \chi u$ acts continuously from $\widetilde{W}_2^l(G)$ to $\widetilde{W}_2^l(G_0)$ ($l = \cdots, -1, 0, 1, \cdots$).*

We clarify the formulation. This explanation at the same time provides the proof of the lemma.

The inclusion $\chi(x)\, u(x) \in \widetilde{W}_2^l(G_0)$ denotes that

$$\chi(x)\, u(x) \in W_2^l(G_0), \qquad \frac{\partial^{j-1}}{\partial \nu^{j-1}} (\chi(x)\, u(x)) \in W_2^{l-j+\frac{1}{2}}(\widetilde{\Gamma}_0) \tag{6.110}$$
$$(j = 1, \ldots, 2m),$$

where $\widetilde{\Gamma}_0$ is the full boundary of the region G_0. The first inclusion in (6.110) is obvious for $l \geq 0$; for $l < 0$, the inclusion is interpreted as in the footnote on p. 138, and in this sense it again holds. The second inclusion in (6.110) (j fixed) is clear for $l-j\geq 0$. For $l-j<0$, it must be interpreted (according to the definition of the space $\widetilde{W}_2^l(G)$ as the completion of smooth functions with respect to the norm (6.59)) in the following way: if a sequence of smooth functions $u_n(x)$ ($x\in G$; $n=1, 2, \cdots$) converges in the norm $|||\cdot|||_{\widetilde{W}_2^l(G)}$ to an element u, then

$$\frac{\partial^{j-1}}{\partial\nu^{j-1}}(\chi(x)\,u_n(x))$$

is fundamental in the norm of $W_2^{l-j+1/2}(\widetilde{\Gamma}_0)$. However, since $\partial\chi/\partial\nu=0$ near Γ_0 and χ vanishes in a neighborhood of $G\backslash G_0$,

$$\frac{\partial^{j-1}}{\partial\nu^{j-1}}(\chi(x)\,u_n(x))=\chi(x)\,\frac{\partial^{j-1}u_n(x)}{\partial\nu^{j-1}}\qquad(x\in\widetilde{\Gamma}_0).$$

The sequence

$$\frac{\partial^{j-1}u_n(x)}{\partial\nu^{j-1}}$$

is fundamental in $W_2^{l-j+1/2}(\Gamma)$, since $u\in\widetilde{W}_2^l(G)$. Then

$$\chi(x)\frac{\partial^{j-1}u_n(x)}{\partial\nu^{j-1}}$$

is fundamental in $W_2^{l-j+1/2}(\Gamma)$, and hence, by the form of $\chi(x)$, it is even fundamental in $W_2^{l-j+1/2}(\widetilde{\Gamma}_0)$. This follows from the continuity of the multiplication operator on smooth functions in the negative space

$$W_2^{l-j+\frac{1}{2}}(\widetilde{\Gamma}_0)=W_2^{-\left(j-l-\frac{1}{2}\right)}(\widetilde{\Gamma}_0),$$

which is proved exactly as on p. 138. The continuity of the operator $u\longrightarrow\chi u$ is also clear from the discussion. The lemma follows.

Theorem 6.14. *Consider the elliptic problem* (6.107) *in a region G with sufficiently smooth boundary Γ; let $u\in\widetilde{W}_2^s(G)$ be a strong generalized solution ($s=\cdots,-1,0,1,\cdots$ fixed). Suppose that on Γ we have a piece Γ_0, on which borders some subregion $G_0\subseteq G$; further, assume that f and ϕ_j are smoother on G_0 and Γ_0: for any admissable function $\chi(x)$, $\chi f\in W_2^{s+1-2m}(G_0)$ and $\chi\phi_j\in W_2^{s+1-m_j-1/2}(\widetilde{\Gamma}_0)$ ($j=1,\cdots,m$; $\widetilde{\Gamma}_0$ is the full boundary of G_0). Then $\chi u\in\widetilde{W}_2^{s+1}(G_0)$.*

For this we assume that L is regularly elliptic in $G_0\cup\Gamma_0$, the system of boundary conditions is normal on the piece Γ_0 and there covers L; and the smoothness conditions of Theorem 6.9 are satisfied with s replaced both by $s-2m$ and by $s+1-2m$, and with $G\cup\Gamma$ replaced by $G_0\cup\Gamma_0$ and Γ by Γ_0.

Before proving the theorem, we remark that, of course, it could be formulated so as to provide improvement of smoothness by more than one unit, and so that

f, ϕ_j and u appear locally in their respective spaces instead of the products of these functions by χ. Such a formulation bears greater resemblance to Theorems 4.5 and 4.6.

Proof. We fix $\chi(x)$ and slightly compress the region G_0, sliding it along the surface Γ. The obtained region is denoted G_0', and obviously the conditions of the theorem will be satisfied if we replace G_0 by G_0'. It is clear that we can compress G_0 in such a way that G_0' is a region with boundary Γ_0' satisfying the conditions of Theorem 6.9 with s replaced by both $s-2m$ and $s+1-2m$. We consider $L(x, \partial)$ only for $x \in G_0'$; the conditions of Theorem 6.9 (with the mentioned s) on the coefficients of $L(x, \partial)$ in the region G_0' are satisfied. Further, we extend all of the expressions $B_j(x, \partial)$, $B_j'(x, \partial)$, $C_j(x, \partial)$, and $C_j'(x, \partial)$ from Γ_0 to the remaining part of the boundary Γ_0' of the region G_0', in such a way that the rest of the conditions in Theorem 6.9 hold. We denote the operators $\mathbf{L}_{s-2m}$ and $\mathbf{B}_{j,s-m_j}$, constructed for the region G_0', by $\mathbf{L}_{s-2m,G_0'}$ and $\mathbf{B}_{j,s-m_j,G_0'}$.

For sufficiently smooth $u_n(x)$ $(x \in G)$, we have

$$(L[\chi u_n])(x) = \chi(x)(Lu_n)(x) + (M_\chi u_n)(x) \qquad (x \in G),$$
$$(B_j[\chi u_n])(x) = \chi(x)(B_j u_n)(x) + (N_{j,\chi} u_n)(x) \qquad (x \in \Gamma;\ j = 1, \ldots, m). \tag{6.111}$$

Here M_χ and $N_{j,\chi}$ are differential expressions of orders $2m-1$ and $m_j - 1$ respectively, the coefficients of which vanish in the region where $\chi \equiv 0$. Now let $u \in \widetilde{W}_2^s(G)$ be approximated in the metric of $\widetilde{W}_2^s(G)$ by smooth u_n. With the help of Lemmas 6.15 and 6.11, we obtain from (6.111):

$$\mathbf{L}_{s-2m,G_0'}[\chi u] = \chi \mathbf{L}_{s-2m} u + \mathbf{M}_{\chi,s-2m} u = \chi f + \mathbf{M}_{\chi,s-2m} u = f' \in W_2^{s+1-2m}(G_0'),$$

$$\mathbf{B}_{j,s-m_j,G_0'}[\chi u] = \chi \mathbf{B}_{j,s-2m} u + \mathbf{N}_{j,\chi,s-2m} u = \chi \varphi_j + \mathbf{N}_{j,\chi,s-2m} u$$

$$= \varphi_j' \in W_2^{s+1-m_j-\frac{1}{2}}(\Gamma_0') \quad (j = 1, \ldots, m).$$

Applying Theorem 6.13 in the region G_0', we obtain $\chi u \in \widetilde{W}_2^{s+1}(G_0')$. By the vanishing properties of χ, we can write $\chi u \in \widetilde{W}_2^{s+1}(G_0)$. The theorem follows.

12. Smoothness up to the boundary for generalized solutions of elliptic equations. The generalized solutions in the previous subsection were in the strong sense and not consistent with the definition (4.39). We now fill this gap.

Consider the problem (6.107) with fixed $s = \cdots, -1, 0, 1, \cdots$. A function

$u \in \widetilde{W}_2^s(G)$ will be called a weak generalized solution of the problem (6.107) if, for all $v \in W_2^{2m+\max(-s,0)}(G)$,

$$(u, L^+v)_0 + \sum_{j=1}^{m} \langle C_j u, B_j' v\rangle_0 = (f, v)_0 + \sum_{j=1}^{m} \langle \varphi_j, C_j' v\rangle_0 \qquad (6.112)$$

(the coefficients of the expressions L^+, B_j', C_j', and C_j are assumed sufficiently smooth).

It follows easily from Green's formula (6.32) that if $s \geq 2m$, then a weak solution will be a smooth (in $W_2^s(G)$) solution of the problem. Since strong generalized solutions are obtained by a closure procedure from smooth solutions, it is clear that a strong generalized solution is a weak generalized solution. It turns out that a converse fact is true.

Lemma 6.16. *Suppose that the hypotheses of Theorem* 6.9 *are satisfied with* s *replaced by* $s - 2m$. *Then a weak generalized solution of the problem* (6.107) *is a strong generalized solution of this problem; or more precisely, the right side of the problem* (6.109) *can be changed in such a way that its weak generalized solution is not changed and will coincide with the strong for precisely this problem.**

Proof. Let $u \in \widetilde{W}_2^s(G)$ be a weak generalized solution of the problem (6.107). As in the proof of Theorem 6.13, we write u in the form $u = u' + u''$, where

$$u' = P_N u \in N, \quad u'' = P_{\perp N} u \in \widetilde{H}_s^{\bullet}.$$

Since $\mathfrak{L} u' = 0$,

$$(u', L^+v)_0 + \sum_{j=1}^{m} \langle C_j u', B_j' v\rangle_0 = 0 \qquad (v \in W_2^{2m+\max(-s,0)}(G))$$

and equation (6.112) holds with u'' in place of u. It follows from (6.112) that $[(f, \phi_1, \cdots, \phi_m), N^+]_0 = 0$. Therefore, by Theorem 6.9 there exists a strong generalized solution $u''' \in \widetilde{H}_s$ for the problem (6.107). Since a strong generalized solution is also a weak solution,

$$(u'' - u''', L^+v)_0 + \sum_{j=1}^{m} \langle C_j (u'' - u'''), B_j' v\rangle_0 = 0 \qquad (v \in W_2^{2m+\max(-s,0)}(G)). \qquad (6.113)$$

In this we set $v \in W_2^{2m}(\mathrm{bd})^+ \cap W_2^{2m+\max(-s,0)}(G)$, i.e. we assume $B_j' v = 0$

---

*For this lemma and for other results of §§6.8–6.12 and of §5, see also Ju. M. Berezanskiĭ and Ja. A. Roĭtberg, *A theorem on homeomorphisms and the Green function for general elliptic boundary value problems*, Ukrain. Mat. Ž. 19 (1967), no. 5. (Russian) (To appear)

$(j = 1, \cdots, m)$. Then by virtue of Theorem 6.7, L^+v exhausts $H_{\max(-s,0)} = W_2^{\max(-s,0)}(G) \ominus N$ and $(u'' - u''', L^+v)_0 = 0$. Since u'', u''' are orthogonal to N, it follows that $u'' - u'''$ in $W_2^s(G)$. Thus in $W_2^s(G)$ we have $u = u' + u'''$, from which the assertion of the lemma follows easily.

Corollary. *Theorems 6.13 and 6.14 remain valid for strong generalized solutions of the problem (6.107) replaced by weak generalized solutions.*

We pass to the consideration of homogeneous boundary conditions. If in equation (6.112) we set $\phi_j = 0\,(j = 1, \cdots, m)$, then we obtain the definition of a weak generalized solution of the problem (6.107) with homogeneous (bd). This definition is, nevertheless, different from (4.39) and we bring it up to date.

In accordance with the discussion on p. 250, we introduce the following spaces (s is an integer): for $s \geq 0$, $W_2^{2m+s}(\mathrm{bd})^+ = W_2^{2m}(\mathrm{bd})^+ \cap W_2^{2m+s}(G)$ (in the metric $(\cdot,\cdot)_{2m+s}$); for $-2m \leq s < 0$, $W_2^{2m+s}(\mathrm{bd})^+$ is the closure of $W_2^{2m}(\mathrm{bd})^+$ in $W_2^{2m+s}(G)$; for $s < -2m$, $W_2^{2m+s}(\mathrm{bd})^+$ is the negative space with respect to the zero space $L_2(G)$ and the positive space $W_2^{-(2m+s)}(\mathrm{bd})^+$. In other words, $W_2^l(\mathrm{bd})^+$ coincides with $H_l(\mathrm{bd})^+$, constructed under the assumption $N^+ = 0$.

A function $u \in W_2^s(G)$ $(s = \cdots, -1, 0, 1, \cdots)$ will be called a generalized solution of the problem

$$Lu = f \in W_2^{\min(s-2m,0)}(\mathrm{bd})^+, \quad u \in (\mathrm{bd}) \tag{6.114}$$

if for all $v \in W_2^{2m+\max(-s,0)}(\mathrm{bd})^+$ we have the equation

$$(u, L^+v)_0 = (f, v)_0 \tag{6.115}$$

(the coefficients of L^+ are assumed sufficiently smooth). It is clear that a solution by definition (6.112) (with $\phi_j = 0$; $j = 1, \cdots, m$) is also a solution by this definition. We prove the converse.

Lemma 6.17. *Let $u \in W_2^s(G)$ $(s = \cdots, -1, 0, 1, \cdots)$ be a generalized solution of the problem (6.114) in the sense of the last definition. If $f \in W_2^{s-2m}(G)$, then $u \in \widetilde{W}_2^s(G)$ and satisfies the relation (6.112) with $\phi_j = 0\,(j = 1, \cdots, m)$, i.e. it is a weak (and hence strong) generalized solution of the problem (6.107). For this we assume that the conditions of Theorem 6.9 are satisfied with s replaced by $s - 2m$.*

Proof. Represent u in the form

$$u = u' + u'', \quad u' = P_N u \in N, \quad u'' = P_{\perp N} u \in \widetilde{H}_s. \tag{6.116}$$

It is clear that $(u'', L^+v)_0 = (f, v)_0$ for v from (6.115). It follows from (6.115) that $[(f, 0, \cdots, 0), N^+ \cdots]_0 = 0$, and therefore by Theorem 6.9 there exists a $u''' \in \tilde{H}_s$ which satisfies the relation (6.112) with $\phi_j = 0$ $(j = 1, \cdots, m)$ and hence also the relation (6.115). Later, as in Lemma 6.16, it is shown that $u'' = u'''$. The assertion then follows from the representation (6.116). The lemma is proved.

This lemma shows that Theorems 6.13 and 6.14 can be applied to generalized solutions of the problem (6.114). In particular, these theorems imply

Theorem 6.15. *In a region G with sufficiently smooth boundary Γ, consider the problem* (6.114) *with $f \in W_2^{s-2m}(G)$; let $u \in W_2^s(G)$ be a generalized solution $(s = \cdots, -1, 0, 1, \cdots)$. Let Γ_0 be a piece of Γ, on which borders a subregion $G_0 \subseteq G$, and suppose that f has more smoothness in G_0: for any admissible function $\chi(x)$, $\chi f \in W_2^{s+1-2m}(G_0)$. Then $\chi u \in \tilde{W}_2^{s+1}(G_0)$.*

For this we assume that L is regularly elliptic in $G_0 \cup \Gamma_0$, the system of boundary expressions is normal on the piece Γ_0 and there covers L; and the smoothness conditions of Theorem 6.9 *are satisfied with s replaced by both $s - 2m$ and $s + 1 - 2m$, and with $G \cup \Gamma$ replaced by $G_0 \cup \Gamma_0$ and Γ by Γ_0.*

It is clear that for $s + 1 \geq 2m$, the function u properly satisfies (bd). We establish a result in this direction, making a restriction for simplicity to a formulation over all of G. We will assume that the right part in (6.114) is "more generalized" than in Theorem 6.15, and make use of the theorem on homeomorphisms 6.12.

Theorem 6.16. *Let the conditions of Theorem* 6.9 *be satisfied with s replaced by both $s - 2m$ and $s + 1 - 2m$ $(s = \cdots, -1, 0, 1, \cdots$ fixed). Let $u \in W_2^s(G)$ be a generalized solution of the problem* (6.114), *where*

$$f \in \begin{cases} W_2^{s-2m+1}(\mathrm{bd})^+, & s - 2m + 1 < 0, \\ W_2^{s-2m+1}(G), & s - 2m + 1 \geq 0. \end{cases}$$

Then

$$u \in \begin{cases} W_2^{s+1}(\mathrm{bd}), & s + 1 > 0, \\ W_2^{s+1}(G), & s + 1 \leq 0^{1)} \end{cases}$$

1)For $s + 1 \leq 0$, this inclusion denotes the following: there exists an element $u_0 \in W_2^{s+1}(G)$ such that $(u, w)_0 = (u_0, w)_0$ $(w \in W_2^{-s}(G))$, i.e. u coincides as a functional with $u_0 \in W_2^{s+1}(G)$.

Proof. Represent u in the form (6.116). Obviously, $(u'', L^+v)_0 = (f, v)_0$ $(v \in W_2^{2m+\max(-s,0)}(\mathrm{bd})^+)$ and $(f, N^+)_0 = 0$. Since $(f, N^+)_0 = 0$, by Theorem 6.12 there exists an element

$$u''' \in \begin{cases} W_2^{s+1}(\mathrm{bd}), & s+1>0, \\ W_2^{s+1}(G), & s+1 \leq 0, \end{cases} \qquad (u''', N)_0 = 0,$$

which corresponds under the respective homeomorphism to f. It is clear that $(u''', L^+v)_0 = (f, v)_0$ $(v \in W_2^{2m+\max(-s,0)}(\mathrm{bd})^+)$, and hence $(u'' - u''', L^+v)_0 = 0$ for the mentioned v. Since L^+v runs through all $H_{\max(-s,0)} = W_2^{\max(-s,0)}(G) \ominus N$, and u'', u''' are orthogonal to N, u'' coincides as a functional with u'''. The assertion now follows from (6.116). The theorem follows.

These theorems on smoothness completely displace Theorem 4.6, and they can be successfully applied to the study near the boundary of Green's function, eigenfunctions, etc., in the case of general (bd) induced by normal systems of differential expressions on Γ which cover L. For application of these theorems in unbounded regions, a similar notion is introduced for fulfillment of an equation and conditions (bd) locally. A similar change in the definition (6.115), along the lines indicated in §5.8, and the formulation of corresponding results, can easily be carried out by the reader.

CHAPTER IV

BOUNDARY VALUE PROBLEMS. OTHER TYPES OF EQUATIONS

The substance of this chapter is essentially the consideration of a number of examples of "nonclassical" problems, connected with nonelliptic equations, for which one can establish energy inequalities and obtain on the basis of Chapter II some results concerning their generalized solvability. These examples should be considered as illustrations of the methods of Chapter II. But §3 of the present chapter, where equations of mixed type are considered, is "classical". We will pay very little attention to the difficult and insufficiently explored question concerning smoothness of given generalized solutions. The investigations below are carried out, unless otherwise stated, in a bounded region G with piecewise-smooth boundary Γ.

§1. GENERAL DIFFERENTIAL EXPRESSIONS WITH CONSTANT COEFFICIENTS

Such expressions have a number of important properties, the most basic being that there always exist solvable extensions of the minimal operator. In this section we establish this fact, and also some results connected with it.

1. **The fundamental energy inequality.** Differential expressions with constant coefficients can be conveniently written in the form

$$Lu = L(\partial)\,u = \sum_{|\alpha|\leqslant r} a_\alpha \partial^\alpha u, \quad \partial^\alpha = \partial_1^{\alpha_1}\ldots\partial_n^{\alpha_n}, \quad \partial_j = \frac{1}{i}D_j \tag{1.1}$$

$$(j = 1, \ldots, n).$$

For such an expression

$$L^+ u = \sum_{|\alpha|\leqslant r} \bar{a}_\alpha \partial^\alpha u = \bar{L}u. \tag{1.2}$$

We associate with the expression $L(\partial)$ the polynomial $L(\zeta)$ of the n complex variables $\zeta_1, \cdots, \zeta_n$, by setting

$$L(\zeta) = \sum_{|\alpha| \leq r} a_\alpha \zeta^\alpha, \qquad \zeta = (\zeta_1, \ldots, \zeta_n), \qquad \zeta^\alpha = \zeta_1^{\alpha_1} \ldots \zeta_n^{\alpha_n}. \tag{1.3}$$

Conversely, to each polynomial $L(\zeta)$ there corresponds, after substitution of ∂_j for ζ_j, a differential expression of the form (1.1). The Fourier transform of $L(\partial)u$ has the form $(\widetilde{L(\partial)u})(\xi) = L(\xi)\tilde{u}(\xi)$ $(u \in C_0^\infty(E_n))$.

Consider the polynomial

$$L^{(\alpha)}(\zeta) = D^\alpha L(\zeta) = \frac{\partial^{|\alpha|}}{\partial \zeta_1^{\alpha_1} \ldots \partial \zeta_n^{\alpha_n}} L(\zeta), \tag{1.4}$$

and denote the differential expression corresponding to it by $L^{(\alpha)}(\partial)u = L^{(\alpha)}u$. Leibnitz's formula is

$$L[uv] = \sum_\alpha \frac{1}{\alpha!} \partial^\alpha v \cdot L^{(\alpha)}u \qquad (\alpha! = \alpha_1! \ldots \alpha_n!) \tag{1.5}$$

(the sum is taken over all possible α). To prove this formula, note that $L(\partial)[uv] = L(\partial_u + \partial_v)[uv]$, where the latter expression has the following interpretation: in $L(\partial)$ the derivatives ∂_j are replaced by sums $\partial_{j,u} + \partial_{j,v}$ of commuting quantities and then $L(\partial)$ is expressed in powers of $\partial_{j,u}$ and $\partial_{j,v}$. In the action of the expression obtained on uv, derivatives with index u act only on u, and those with index v act only on v. Identity (1.5) follows immediately from this rule of calculation of $L(\partial)[uv]$, if we use Taylor's formula:

$$L(\zeta + \eta) = \sum_\alpha \frac{1}{\alpha!} \eta^\alpha L^{(\alpha)}(\xi).$$

Theorem 1.1. *Let L and M be two differential expressions with constant coefficients of the form (1.1), G some fixed bounded region. A necessary and sufficient condition that the inequality*

$$\| Lu \|_0 \geqslant C \| Mu \|_0 \qquad (C > 0;\ u \in C_0^\infty(G)), \tag{1.6}$$

hold is that the condition

$$\frac{\sum_\alpha | M^{(\alpha)}(\xi) |^2}{\sum_\alpha | L^{(\alpha)}(\xi) |^2} \leqslant C_1 \qquad (C_1 > 0;\ \xi \in E_n) \tag{1.7}$$

is satisfied. As will follow from the proof, a sufficient condition for the validity of inequality (1.6) *is that, instead of* (1.7), *the formally weaker estimate*

$$\frac{|M(\xi)|^2}{\sum |L^{(\alpha)}(\xi)|^2} \leqslant C_2 \qquad (C_2 > 0;\ \xi \in E_n) \tag{1.8}$$

holds.

The proof of the sufficiency is based on the following lemma, the idea of the proof of which is also used later on.

Lemma 1.1. *For any derivatives $L^{(\alpha)}(\zeta)$ of $L(\zeta)$ there exists a constant $C > 0$ such that*

$$\| Lu \|_0 \geqslant C \| L^{(\alpha)} u \|_0 \qquad (u \in C_0^\infty (G)). \tag{1.9}$$

Proof. It is sufficient to carry out the proof in the case when $L^{(\alpha)}(\zeta) = D_k L(\zeta)$ since the general inequality (1.9) follows from the estimate obtained in this case by several iterations. In what follows we denote $L^{[k]}(\zeta) = D_k L(\zeta)$. Taking into account (1.2) and the equation $\overline{L^{[k]}} = \overline{L}^{[k]}$, we obtain by means of integration by parts and formula (1.5) (below $u \in C_0^\infty(G)$)

$$\int_G x_k Lu \cdot \overline{L^{[k]} u}\, dx = \int_G u \overline{L} [x_k \overline{L^{[k]} u}] dx = \int_G u x_k \overline{L} [\overline{L^{[k]} u}]\, dx \tag{1.10}$$

$$+ \frac{1}{i} \int_G u \overline{L^{[k]} [L^{[k]} u]} dx = \int_G u x_k \overline{L^{[k]} [\overline{L} u]}\, dx + \frac{1}{i} \int_G | L^{[k]} u |^2\, dx$$

$$= \int_G \overline{L^{[k]}} [u x_k] \cdot \overline{Lu} dx + \frac{1}{i} \int_G | L^{[k]} u |^2 dx = \int_G x_k \overline{L^{[k]}} u \cdot \overline{Lu} dx$$

$$+ \frac{1}{i} \int_G \overline{L^{[k][k]} u} \cdot \overline{Lu} dx + \frac{1}{i} \int_G | L^{[k]} u |^2\, dx.$$

Hence

$$\int_G | L^{[k]} u |^2\, dx = i \int_G x_k Lu \cdot \overline{L^{[k]} u} dx - i \int_G x_k \overline{L^{[k]} u} \cdot \overline{Lu} dx - \int_G \overline{L^{[k][k]} u} \cdot \overline{Lu} dx$$

$$\leqslant C \{ \| Lu \|_0 \| L^{[k]} u \|_0 + \| \overline{L} u \|_0 \| \overline{L^{[k]} u} \|_0 + \| \overline{L} u \|_0 \| \overline{L^{[k][k]} u} \|_0 \}. \tag{1.11}$$

But for any expression $Nu = \sum_{|\alpha| \leq r} c_\alpha \partial^\alpha u$ of the type (1.1) we obtain, by means of integration by parts, $u \in C_0^\infty(G)$,

$$\| Nu \|_0^2 = \int_G \Big| \sum_{|\alpha| \leqslant r} c_\alpha \partial^\alpha u \Big|^2 dx = \sum_{|\alpha|, |\beta| \leqslant r} c_\alpha \bar{c}_\beta \int_G \partial^\alpha u \cdot \overline{\partial^\beta u} dx$$

$$= \sum_{|\alpha|, |\beta| \leqslant r} c_\alpha \bar{c}_\beta \int_G \partial^\beta \partial^\alpha u \cdot \bar{u} dx = \sum_{|\alpha|, |\beta| \leqslant r} c_\alpha \bar{c}_\beta \int_G \partial^\alpha \partial^\beta u \cdot \bar{u} dx =$$

$$= \sum_{|\alpha|,|\beta|\leqslant r} c_\alpha \bar{c}_\beta \int_G \partial^\beta u \cdot \overline{\partial^\alpha u} dx = \| \bar{N} u \|_0^2,$$

i.e. $\|Nu\|_0 = \|\bar{N}u\|_0$ $(u \in C_0^\infty(G))$. Therefore (1.1) can be rewritten in the form

$$\| L^{[k]}u \|_0^2 \leqslant C \| Lu \|_0 (2 \| L^{[k]}u \|_0 + \| L^{[k][k]}u \|_0). \tag{1.12}$$

If the order of the expression L is $r = 1$, then $L^{[k][k]} = 0$ and inequality (1.12) gives the required inequality $\|L^{[k]}u\|_0 \leq C_1\|Lu\|_0$, after cancellation of $\|L^{[k]}u\|_0$. Assume now that this estimate has been proven for all expressions of order $< r$; we will prove it for L of order r. Since $L^{[k]}$ has order $r - 1$, by the induction hypothesis we have $\|L^{[k][k]}u\|_0 \leq C_2\|L^{[k]}u\|_0$. On substitution of this estimate in (1.12) we obtain $\|L^{[k]}u\|_0^2 \leq C(2 + C_2)\|Lu\|_0\|L^{[k]}u\|_0$, from which the required result follows. The lemma is proved.

We come now to the proof of the sufficiency in the theorem. We will assume that functions of $C_0^\infty(G)$ are extended by zero to all of E_n. Using Parseval's equation for the Fourier transform and estimates (1.8) and (1.9), we obtain

$$\| Mu \|_0^2 = \int_G | Mu |^2 dx = \int_{E_n} | \widetilde{(Mu)} (\xi) |^2 d\xi = \int_{E_n} | M (\xi) |^2 | \tilde{u} (\xi) |^2 d\xi$$

$$\leqslant C_2 \sum_\alpha \int_{E_n} | L^{(\alpha)} (\xi)|^2 | \tilde{u} (\xi) |^2 d\xi = C_2 \sum_\alpha \| L^{(\alpha)} u \|_0^2 \leqslant C_3' \| Lu\|_0^2$$

for $u \in C_0^\infty(G)$, as required.

We prove the necessity. Let $\psi \in C_0^\infty(G)$ be such that its Fourier transform is everywhere different from zero, and set $u(x) = \psi(x)e^{i(x,\xi)}$, where $\xi \in E_n$ is fixed. Applying (1.5), we find that

$$Lu = e^{i(x,\xi)} \sum_\alpha \frac{1}{\alpha!} \partial^\alpha \psi \cdot L^{(\alpha)} (\xi).$$

Similarly, calculate Mu and substitute these expressions in the square of inequality (1.6). We obtain

$$C^2 \sum_{\alpha,\beta} M^{(\alpha)} (\xi)\overline{M^{(\beta)}(\xi)}\, \psi_{\alpha\beta} \leqslant \sum_{\alpha,\beta} L^{(\alpha)} (\xi)\overline{L^{(\beta)}(\xi)}\, \psi_{\alpha\beta}, \tag{1.13}$$

where $\psi_{\alpha\beta} = 1/\alpha!\beta! \int_G \partial^\alpha\psi \cdot \overline{\partial^\beta\psi} dx$.

The indices α and β run through a certain finite set of values (let, for example, $0 \leq |\alpha|, |\beta| \leq m$), hence $\psi_{\alpha\beta}$ can be regarded as coefficients of some quadratic form $\Psi(t)$, where the variable t is used for the collection of numbers t_α $(|\alpha| \leq m)$. This form is strictly positive definite: using Parseval's equation, we obtain

$$\Psi(t) = \sum_{|\alpha|,|\beta|\leqslant m} \psi_{\alpha\beta} t_\alpha t_\beta = \int_G \Big| \sum_{|\alpha|\leqslant m} \frac{1}{\alpha!} t_\alpha \partial^\alpha \psi \Big|^2 dx$$

$$= \int_{-\infty}^{\infty} \Big| \sum_{|\alpha|\leqslant m} \frac{1}{\alpha!} t_\alpha \xi^\alpha \Big|^2 |\tilde{\psi}(\xi)|^2 d\xi \geqslant 0,$$

where equality holds only if $\sum_{|\alpha|\leq m}(1/\alpha!)\,t_\alpha\xi^\alpha = 0$, for all ξ, i.e. if all $t_\alpha = 0$. Consequently, the values of Ψ are bounded below by the length of the vector t; in addition, it is obviously bounded above. Thus we have

$$C_1 \sum_{|\alpha|\leqslant m} |t_\alpha|^2 \leqslant \sum_{\alpha,\beta} \psi_{\alpha\beta} t_\alpha \bar{t}_\beta \leqslant C_2 \sum_{|\alpha|\leqslant m} |t_\alpha|^2.$$

It follows from this inequality and (1.13) that

$$C_1 \sum_{|\alpha|\leqslant m} |M^{(\alpha)}(\xi)|^2 \leqslant \sum_{\alpha,\beta} \psi_{\alpha\beta} M^{(\alpha)}(\xi)\overline{M^{(\beta)}(\xi)} \leqslant \frac{1}{C^2} \sum_{\alpha,\beta} \psi_{\alpha\beta} L^{(\alpha)}(\xi)\overline{L^{(\beta)}(\xi)}$$

$$\leqslant \frac{C_2}{C^2} \sum_{|\alpha|\leqslant m} |L^{(\alpha)}(\xi)|^2,$$

i.e. we arrive at the estimate (1.7). The theorem is proved.

Corollary 1. *If condition* (1.7) *holds, then for any* $s \in (-\infty, \infty)$

$$\| Lu \|_{\mathring{W}_2^s(G)} \geqslant C_s \| Mu \|_{\mathring{W}_2^s(G)} \quad (C_s > 0;\ u \in C_0^\infty(G)). \tag{1.14}$$

Here the constants C_s *can be chosen independent of* $s \in [a, \infty)$.

We prove inequality (1.14) first for $s < -\sigma < 0$. For this we use Theorem 3.6, Chapter I, with $\phi(x)$ in $C_0^\infty(E_n)$ vanishing for $|x| \geq 1$. Now $\phi_\epsilon(x)$ $(0 < \epsilon \leq \epsilon_0)$ is zero for $|x| \geq \epsilon_0$ and therefore $u * \phi_\epsilon$ belongs to $C_0^\infty(G')$ for $u \in C_0^\infty(G)$, where G' is a bounded region which strictly contains G in its interior. It follows from (1.7) that

$$\| Lv \|_{L_2(G')} \geqslant C \| Mv \|_{L_2(G')} \quad (v \in C_0^\infty(G'))$$

by Theorem 1.1. In particular,

$$\| L[u*\varphi_\varepsilon] \|_{L_2(G')} \geqslant C \| M[u*\varphi_\varepsilon] \|_{L_2(G')} (u \in C_0^\infty(G)).$$

For a differential expression P with constant coefficients it is obvious that $P(f*g) = (Pf)*g$, so from the last inequality and (3.21), Chapter I, it follows that $\|Lu\|_{-\sigma} \geq C\|Mu\|_{-\sigma}$. This inequality is equivalent to

$$\| Lu \|_{\mathring{W}_2^{-\sigma}(G)} \geqslant C_1 \| Mu \|_{\mathring{W}_2^{-\sigma}(G)} \quad (u \in C_0^\infty(G)). \tag{1.15}$$

where C_1 can be chosen independently of $-\sigma \in [c, d]$, $-\infty < c < d < 0$. Thus (1.14) is established for $s < 0$ (it is true that dependence of C_s on s is not yet of the form stated).

Assume now that $c < -1 < d < 0$. Replacing u by $D^\alpha u$ $(u \in C_0^\infty(G))$ in (1.15), taking the square and summing, we obtain

$$\sum_{|\alpha|\leqslant t} \| D^\alpha Lu \|^2_{\mathring{W}_2^{-\sigma}(G)} = \sum_{|\alpha|\leqslant t} \| LD^\alpha u \|^2_{\mathring{W}_2^{-\sigma}(G)} \geqslant C_1^2 \sum_{|\alpha|\leqslant t} \| MD^\alpha u \|^2_{\mathring{W}_2^{-\sigma}(G)}$$

$$= C_1^2 \sum_{|\alpha|\leqslant t} \| D^\alpha Mu \|^2_{\mathring{W}_2^{-\sigma}(G)} \quad (t = 1, 2, \ldots). \tag{1.16}$$

By passing to the Fourier transform, it is easy to show that the expression

$$\left(\sum_{|\alpha|\leqslant t} \| D^\alpha v \|^2_{\mathring{W}_2^{-\sigma}(G)} \right)^{\frac{1}{2}} \quad (v \in C_0^\infty(G))$$

is equivalent to the norm $\|v\|_{\mathring{W}_2^{t-\sigma}(G)}$ (cf. Chapter I, Theorem 3.6). From (1.16) we conclude by virtue of this observation that Corollary 1 actually holds.

Corollary 2. *For any expression L with constant coefficients, the energy inequalities*

$$\| Lu \|_0 \geqslant C \| u \|_+ \left(C > 0;\ \| u \|_+^2 = \sum_\alpha \| L^{(\alpha)} u \|_0^2,\ u \in C_0^\infty(G) \right), \tag{1.17}$$

$$\| Lu \|_{\mathring{W}_2^s(G)} \geqslant C_s \| u \|_{\mathring{W}_2^s(G)} \quad (C_s > 0;\ s \in (-\infty, \infty);\ u \in C_0^\infty(G)). \tag{1.18}$$

always hold (dependence of C_s on s is the same as in Corollary 1).

Indeed, inequality (1.17) follows immediately from (1.9). It is only necessary to note that the norm $\|\cdot\|_+$ is in fact positive, i.e. $\|u\|_+ \geq C_1 \|u\|_0$, as follows from the fact that by sucessive differentiation with respect to ζ of the polynomial $L(\zeta)$, we will eventually obtain a constant. Inequality (1.18) is a special case of (1.14); it is sufficient to set $M = E$.

Inequalities (1.17) and (1.18) remain valid if L is replaced by L^+. Hence, in particular, we obtain two facts.

Corollary 3. *Let L be an arbitrary expression of order r with constant coefficients. The equation $Lu = f$ is always solvable inside G. More precisely, this means the following: for any $f \in \mathring{W}_2^s(G)$ there is a $u \in \mathring{W}_2^s(G)$ $(s \in (-\infty, \infty))$ such that the relation*

$$(u, L^+ v)_0 = (f, v)_0 \quad (v \in C_0^\infty(G);\ s < r), \qquad Lu = f \ (s \geqslant r) \tag{1.19}$$

holds.

In fact, by (1.18), the inequality $\|L^+v\|_{\overset{\circ}{W}{}_2^{-s}(G)} \geq C\|v\|_{\overset{\circ}{W}{}_2^{-s}(G)}$ $(v \in C_0^\infty(G))$ holds. As in the proof of Theorem 3.3, Chapter II, consider $(f, v)_0 = l(L^+v)$ $(v \in C_0^\infty(G))$; this expression is a continuous functional of L^+v in the metric $\overset{\circ}{W}{}_2^{-s}(G)$:

$$|l(L^+v)| = |(f, v)_0| \leqslant \|f\|_{\overset{\circ}{W}{}_2^{s}(G)} \times \|v\|_{\overset{\circ}{W}{}_2^{-s}(G)} \leqslant \frac{1}{C}\|f\|_{\overset{\circ}{W}{}_2^{s}(G)} \|L^+v\|_{\overset{\circ}{W}{}_2^{-s}(G)}.$$

By means of the Hahn-Banach Theorem we obtain the first of relations (1.19) for any s, and the second equation in (1.19) then follows for $s \geq r$.

Corollary 4. *An expression with constant coefficients always has solvable extensions.*

This follows from Theorem 2.1, Chapter II, and (1.17).

The last two corollaries show that the equation $Lu = f$ for an expression with constant coefficients is always solvable. This is, in general, not true for variable coefficients.

From (1.17) we obtain $\|Lu\|_0 \geq C\|u\|_0$ $(C > 0;\ u \in C_0^\infty(G))$. Replacing u by $D^\alpha u$ for $|\alpha| \leq \sigma$ we find that $\|Lu\|_\sigma \geq C\|u\|_\sigma$ $(C > 0;\ u \in C_0^\infty(G);\ \sigma = 0, 1, \cdots)$. The same inequality can be written for L^+. Hence from the remarks in §4.1, Chapter III, we have

Corollary 5. *For an expression L with constant coefficients, there always exists a fundamental solution*

$$e_\xi \in W_2^{-\left(\left[\frac{n}{2}\right]+1\right)}(G) \quad (\xi \in G).$$

The assertion is similar to and follows immediately from Corollary 3. We will not be occupied with analytic representations of the given e_ξ. In connection with this, cf. G. E. Šilov [1].

2. **Structure of the domain of a minimal operator.** Consider the minimal operator Λ, constructed with respect to an expression L of order r with constant coefficients. The following theorem shows that the functions of $\mathfrak{D}(\Lambda)$ are characterized by their local behavior.

Theorem 1.2. *If $u \in \mathfrak{D}(\Lambda)$, $\chi \in C^r(G \cup \Gamma)$, then $\chi(x)\,u(x) \in \mathfrak{D}(\Lambda)$. In particular (for χ vanishing outside of a neighborhood), this means that the inclusion $u \in \mathfrak{D}(\Lambda)$ implies that u "belongs locally" to $\mathfrak{D}(\Lambda)$. Conversely, suppose that $u \in L_2(G)$ is such that for each point of $G \cup \Gamma$ there is a neighborhood U of the point and a function $v_U \in \mathfrak{D}(\Lambda)$ such that $u(x) = v_U(x)$ on*

$U \cap G$. Then $u \in \mathfrak{D}(\Lambda)$.

Proof. We establish the first assertion. Let $u \in \mathfrak{D}(\Lambda)$; $u_\nu \in C_0^\infty(G)$ such that $u_\nu \to u$ and $Lu_\nu \to \Lambda u$ in $L_2(G)$. Because of the estimate (1.9), the sequence $L^{(\alpha)}u_\nu$ is fundamental in $L_2(G)$ for any α, but then by (1.5), $L[\chi u_\nu] = \Sigma_\alpha (1/\alpha!)\partial^\alpha \chi \cdot$ $\cdot\, L^{(\alpha)}u_\nu$ is also fundamental; in addition, $\chi u_\nu \to \chi u$. This shows that $\chi u \in \mathfrak{D}(\Lambda)$.

We prove the second assertion. Let $x_0 \in G \cup \Gamma$, and let U_{x_0} be a neighborhood of x_0 satisfying the conditions of the theorem. From the covering of $G \cup \Gamma$ by the neighborhoods U_{x_0}, extract a finite covering $U_{x_1}, \cdots, U_{x_N}$. Let $\chi_1, \cdots$ $\cdots, \chi_N$ be a partition of unity, constructed with respect to this covering, i.e. $\chi_j \in C^\infty(E_n)$ is nonnegative, it vanishes outside U_{x_j}, and is such that $\Sigma_{j=1}^N \chi_j(x) = 1$ $(x \in G)$. We have $u = \Sigma_{j=1}^N \chi_j u = \Sigma_{j=1}^N \chi_j v_{U_{x_j}}$, where each of the terms $\chi_j v_{U_{x_j}} \in \mathfrak{D}(\Lambda)$ by what was proved above. Thus, $u \in \mathfrak{D}(\Lambda)$, as required. The theorem is proved.

Theorem 1.3. *Let Л be the maximal operator, constructed with respect to the expression L. If $u \in \mathfrak{D}(\text{Л})$ vanishes in a strip near the boundary Γ, then $u \in \mathfrak{D}(\Lambda)$.*

Proof. Let $\omega_\epsilon(y) \in C_0^\infty(E_n)$ $(\epsilon > 0)$ be the function defined in §10 of the Introduction. Let

$$u_\varepsilon(x) = (S_\varepsilon u)(x) = (\omega_\varepsilon * u)(x).$$

As is well known, $u_\epsilon \to u$ in $L_2(G)$ as $\epsilon \to 0$. Clearly, for ϵ sufficiently small, $u_\epsilon \in C_0^\infty(G)$; hence the theorem will be proved if it is shown that the sequence Lu_ϵ is fundamental in $L_2(G)$. For $x \in G$ and ϵ small, $\omega_\epsilon(y-x)$ belongs to $C_0^\infty(G)$ with respect to y, and recalling the definition of a maximal operator, we obtain

$$(Lu_\varepsilon)(x) = \int_G L_x[\omega_\varepsilon(y-x)]\, u(y)\, dy = \int_G \overline{L_y^+[\omega_\varepsilon(y-x)]}\, u(y)\, dy$$

$$= \int_G \omega_\varepsilon(y-x)(\text{Л}u)(y)\, dy = ((\text{Л}u) * \omega_\varepsilon)(x).$$

Hence it follows that $Lu_\epsilon \to \text{Л}u$ in $L_2(G)$, as required.

The theorem is proved.

In the study of the structure of the domain of a minimal operator, there arises a natural question: how many derivatives can be taken of functions in $\mathfrak{D}(\Lambda)$? The answer to this is essentially given by Theorem 1.1: if the differential expression M with constant coefficients is such that inequality (1.8) holds, then the estimate

(1.6) holds, and hence

$$\mathfrak{D}(\Lambda) \subset \mathfrak{D}(\mathrm{M}) \tag{1.20}$$

(M is the minimal operator, constructed with respect to M), i.e. the expression M can be applied in the natural sense to functions of $\mathfrak{D}(\Lambda)$.

Conversely, if the inclusion (1.20) holds, then inequality (1.7) is valid. For the proof we use the following argument, analogous to that used for Lemma 5.2, Chapter III. Consider the set $\mathfrak{D}(\Lambda)$ equipped with the norm $\|u\|_1 = \|\Lambda u\|_0$; since the inequality $\|\Lambda u\|_0 \geq C\|u\|_0$ $(u \in \mathfrak{D}(\Lambda))$ holds (it follows from $\|Lu\|_0 \geq C\|u\|_0$, $u \in C_0^\infty(G)$), $\mathfrak{D}(\Lambda)$ is a complete space H in this norm. The correspondence $u \to \mathrm{M}u$, as is not difficult to see, is a closed linear operator from H into $L_2(G)$, defined on all of H; but then, as is well known, it is continuous, i.e. $\|\mathrm{M}u\|_0 \leq C_1\|u\|_1 = C_1\|\Lambda u\|_0$ $(u \in \mathfrak{D}(\Lambda))$. Hence (1.6) follows, and therefore, in view of Theorem 1.1, (1.7) follows also. Summarizing, we have the following result: *a necessary and sufficient condition that an expression M with constant coefficients can be applied to functions in $\mathfrak{D}(\Lambda)$ (i.e, that the inclusion* (1.20) *holds) is that inequality* (1.7) *holds.*

In certain cases $\mathrm{M}u$ will be a continuous function on $G \cup \Gamma$ (after correction on a set of measure 0, of course) for any $u \in \mathfrak{D}(\Lambda)$. We clarify the conditions on L and M for which this will occur.

Theorem 1.4. *If*

$$\int_{E_n} \frac{|M(\xi)|^2}{\sum_\alpha |L^{(\alpha)}(\xi)|^2} d\xi < \infty, \tag{1.21}$$

then $\mathfrak{D}(\Lambda) \subseteq \mathfrak{D}(\mathrm{M})$ and for each $u \in \mathfrak{D}(\Lambda)$ $\mathrm{M}u$ is continuous on $G \cup \Gamma$ and vanishes on Γ. Conversely, if for each $u \in \mathfrak{D}(\Lambda)$, the function $\mathrm{M}u$ is defined (i.e. $\mathfrak{D}(\mathrm{M}) \supseteq \mathfrak{D}(\Lambda)$) and continuous in a fixed neighborhood of some point of G, then (1.21) *holds.*

Proof. We show that (1.21) implies that $\mathrm{M}u$ is continuous and vanishes on Γ. For this, it is sufficient to prove the inequality

$$\max_{x \in G \cup \Gamma} |(Mu)(x)| \leqslant C \| Lu \|_0 \quad (u \in C_0^\infty(G)). \tag{1.22}$$

Using the Fourier transform and then the estimate (1.9), we find

$$|(Mu)(x)|^2 = \left| \frac{1}{\sqrt{(2\pi)^n}} \int_{E_n} M(\xi) \tilde{u}(\xi) e^{i(x,\xi)} d\xi \right|^2 \leqslant \frac{1}{(2\pi)^n} \int_{E_n} \frac{|M(\xi)|^2}{\sum_\alpha |L^{(\alpha)}(\xi)|^2} d\xi \times$$

$$\times \int_{E_n} \sum_\alpha |L^{(\alpha)}(\xi)|^2 |\widetilde{u}(\xi)|^2 d\xi \leqslant C \sum_\alpha \| L^{(\alpha)}u \|_0^2 \leqslant C_1 \| Lu \|_0^2 \quad (u \in C_0^\infty(G))$$

as required.

The proof of the second part of the theorem is more complicated. Without loss of generality, we may assume that $0 \in G$ and that Mu is continuous in a closed neighborhood $U \ni 0$; the conditions of the theorem imply the estimate

$$|(Mu)(0)| \leqslant C \| Lu \|_0 \quad (u \in C_0^\infty(G)). \tag{1.23}$$

In fact, consider the space H – the linear manifold $\mathfrak{D}(\Lambda)$ equipped with the norm $\|u\|_1 = \|\Lambda u\|_0$; as is already noted it is complete. The correspondence $u \longrightarrow (Mu)(x)$ $(u \in H)$ defines a linear operator, mapping all of H into the space $C(\bar{U})$. This operator is closed. Indeed, let $u_\nu \longrightarrow v$ in H and $Mu_\nu \longrightarrow f$ in $C(\bar{U})$. In our case inequality (1.6) and hence also the inequality $\|\Lambda u\|_0 \geq C\|Mu\|_0$ $(u \in \mathfrak{D}(\Lambda))$, are valid (since (1.20) holds). Therefore $Mu_\nu \longrightarrow Mv$ in $L_2(G)$. Since $Mu_\nu \longrightarrow f$ in $C(\bar{U})$, then $Mv = f$. This proves that our operator is closed; since it is defined on all of H, it is continuous. Hence (1.23) follows.

Let $\phi(\xi) \in C_0^\infty(E_n)$ be arbitrary, consider the function

$$v(x) = \frac{1}{\sqrt{(2\pi)^n}} \int_{E_n} \frac{\varphi(\xi)}{\sqrt{\sum_\alpha |L^{(\alpha)}(\xi)|^2}} e^{i\langle x,\xi\rangle} d\xi$$

and set $u = \chi v$, where $\chi(x) \in C_0^\infty(G)$ is equal to 1 in a neighborhood of 0. It is obvious that $u \in C_0^\infty(G)$ and therefore it may be substituted in (1.23). Noting that $(Mu)(0) = (Mv)(0)$ and

$$Lu = \sum_\alpha \frac{1}{\alpha!} \partial^\alpha \chi \cdot L^{(\alpha)} v,$$

we find

$$\left| \frac{1}{\sqrt{(2\pi)^n}} \int_{E_n} \frac{M(\xi)}{\sqrt{\sum_\alpha |L^{(\alpha)}(\xi)^2|}} \varphi(\xi)\, d\xi \right|^2 = |(Mv)(0)|^2 = |(Mu)(0)|^2 \leqslant C^2 \| Lu \|_0^2$$

$$= C^2 \left\| \sum_\alpha \frac{1}{\alpha!} \partial^\alpha \chi \cdot L^{(\alpha)} v \right\|_0^2 \leqslant C_1 \sum_\alpha \| L^{(\alpha)} v \|_0^2 =$$

$$=C_1\sum_\alpha\left\|\frac{1}{\sqrt{(2\pi)^n}}\int\limits_{E_n}\frac{L^{(\alpha)}(\xi)\varphi(\xi)}{\sqrt{\sum_\alpha|L^{(\alpha)}(\xi)|^2}}e^{i\langle x,\xi\rangle}d\xi\right\|_0^2=C_1\int\limits_{E_n}|\varphi(\xi)|^2d\xi.$$

Since, in this inequality, ϕ runs through a dense set in $L_2(L_n)$, it follows that

$$M(\xi)/\sqrt{\sum_\alpha|L^{(\alpha)}(\xi)|^2}$$

is square summable, i.e. (1.21) holds. The theorem is proved.

Thus, if $(\Sigma_\alpha|L_{(\alpha)}(\xi)|^2)^{-1}\in L_2(E_n)$, then the functions of $\mathfrak{D}(\Lambda)$ are continuous and therefore they may be examined on manifolds of lower dimensions, contained in $G\cup\Gamma$. It is natural to pose the last problem independently: for a given expression, determine conditions on manifolds so that on these manifolds there are values of functions of $\mathfrak{D}(\Lambda)$ (and even their derivatives). We will not get involved with the results here.

3. **The domain of a maximal operator.** We have the following important fact.

Theorem 1.5. *If L is an expression with constant coefficients, then the maximal operator Л coincides with the closure in $L_2(G)$ of the operator defined by the correspondence $u\to Lu$ $(u\in C_0^\infty(G\cup\Gamma))$.*[1]

The proof, as in the case of strongly elliptic expressions, is based on Lemma 2.2, Chapter III. In order to apply it, it is sufficient to establish the following: let $u\in L_2(E_n)$ be such that $Lu\in L_2(E_n)$ in the sense of generalized functions (i.e. there is an $h\in L_2(E_n)$ for which

$$(u,L^+v)_{L_2(E_n)}=(h,v)_{L_2(E_n)}\quad(v\in C_0^\infty(E_n))):$$

If u vanishes outside G, then the restriction of u to G belongs to $\mathfrak{D}(\Lambda)$. For the proof, cover $G\cup\Gamma$ by a finite number of neighborhoods $U_1,\cdots,U_N$ so small that for each U_j there is a sequence of translations by vectors $\rho_\nu^{(j)}$ ($\nu=1,2,\cdots$; $|\rho_\nu^{(j)}|\to 0$ as $\nu\to\infty$) which transform the set $U_j\cap G$ into the strict interior of G $((U_j\cap G)+\rho_\nu^{(j)}\subset G)$. Construct a partition of unity $\chi_1,\cdots,\chi_N$ with respect to the system $U_1,\cdots,U_N$; $\chi_j\in C_0^\infty(U_j)$, $\Sigma_{j=1}^N\chi_j(x)=1$ in a neighborhood of $G\cup\Gamma$. We show that

$$u^{(j)}(x)=\chi_j(x)u(x)\in\mathfrak{D}(\text{Л})\quad(j=1,\ldots,N).\tag{1.24}$$

In fact, let G' be a bounded region which strictly contains G in its interior.

---

[1] The boundary of the region G must be sufficiently regular so that the condition expressed below concerning translation by $\rho_\nu^{(j)}$ is fulfilled.

It follows from the fact that $Lu \in L_2(E_n)$ that $u \in \mathfrak{D}(\mathbb{L}')$, where $\mathbb{L}'$ is the maximal operator constructed with respect to L and G'. Applying Theorem 1.3, we conclude that $u \in \mathfrak{D}(\Lambda')$, where Λ' is the minimal operator corresponding to $\mathbb{L}'$. Using Theorem 1.2, we find that $\chi_j u \in \mathfrak{D}(\Lambda') \subseteq \mathfrak{D}(\mathbb{L}')$. But if $h \in \mathfrak{D}(\mathbb{L}')$, then its restriction to G obviously belongs to $\mathfrak{D}(\mathbb{L})$. Therefore the inclusion $\chi_j u \in \mathfrak{D}(\mathbb{L}')$ implies (1.24). Consider the function $v_\nu^{(j)}(x) = u^{(j)}(x - \rho_\nu^{(j)})$ $(x \in E_n)$ on G. It is easy to see that $v_\nu^{(j)} \in \mathfrak{D}(\mathbb{L})$ and $(\mathbb{L} v_\nu^{(j)})(x) = (\mathbb{L} u^{(j)})(x - \rho_\nu^{(j)})$ in $L_2(G)$ as $\nu \to \infty$. Moreover, each $u_\nu^{(j)}$ vanishes in a strip near Γ and therefore belongs to $\mathfrak{D}(\Lambda)$ by Theorem 1.3. Thus, the last two limits mean that $u^{(j)} \in \mathfrak{D}(\Lambda)$ and hence $u = \sum_{j=1}^N u^{(j)} \in \mathfrak{D}(\Lambda)$. The assertion, and at the same time the theorem, are proved.

4. **Complete continuity of the inverse of a minimal operator.** Let L and M be expressions with constant coefficients; let Λ and M be the corresponding minimal operators. We will assume that $\mathfrak{D}(\mathrm{M}) \supseteq \mathfrak{D}(\Lambda)$ and will explain under what conditions the operator $\mathrm{M}\Lambda^{-1}$ is completely continuous; in other words, when the mapping

$$Lu \to Mu \quad (u \in C_0^\infty(G)) \tag{1.25}$$

in $L_2(G)$ is completely continuous.

By (1.17), for expressions N with constant coefficients the norms $\|Nu\|_0$ and

$$\| u \|_{+,N} = \left(\sum_\alpha \| N^{(\alpha)} u \|_0^2 \right)^{\frac{1}{2}}$$

are equivalent on $C_0^\infty(G)$; hence complete continuity of (1.25) is equivalent to complete continuity of the inclusion operator from the space with norm $\|u\|_{+,L}$ to the space with norm $\|u\|_{+,M}$ $(u \in C_0^\infty(G))$.

Theorem 1.6. *A necessary and sufficient condition that the mapping* (1.25) *be completely continuous is that*

$$\frac{\sum_\alpha | M^{(\alpha)}(\xi) |^2}{\sum_\alpha | L^{(\alpha)}(\xi) |^2} \underset{|\xi| \to \infty}{\longrightarrow} 0 \tag{1.26}$$

for real ξ.

Proof. First we establish the sufficiency: if (1.26) holds, then from a sequence of functions $u_\nu \in C_0^\infty(G)$ such that $\|Lu_\nu\|_0 \leq 1$, we can select a subsequence $u_{\nu'}$, for which $Mu_{\nu'}$, converges in $L_2(G)$. By virtue of Parseval's equation it is sufficient to establish precompactness of the sequence $\widetilde{(Mu_\nu)}(\xi) = M(\xi)\tilde{u}_\nu(\xi)$.

in $L_2(E_n)$. Since these functions are Fourier transforms of functions Mu_ν which vanish outside a compactum and are uniformly bounded in the norm of $L_2(G)$ ($\|Mu\|_0 \le C\,\|Lu\|_0$ ($u \in C_0^\infty(G)$) by (1.26) and Theorem 1.1), they are uniformly bounded, equicontinuous, and vanish at ∞. If we apply the theorem of Arzelà, we can select a subsequence $(\widetilde{Mu_{\nu'}})(\xi)$ which converges uniformly to $\xi \in E_n$.

To complete the proof it remains to show that $\widetilde{Mu_{\nu'}}$ is fundamental in the norm of $L_2(E_n)$. Let $\epsilon > 0$ be given; by (1.26) we can find $R > 0$ such that

$$|\xi| > R \quad |M(\xi)|^2 \leqslant \sum_\alpha |M^{(\alpha)}(\xi)|^2 < \varepsilon \sum_\alpha |L^{(\alpha)}(\xi)|^2$$

for $|\xi| > R$. By means of this inequality and (1.9) we obtain

$$\int_{E_n} |\widetilde{Mu_{\nu'}} - \widetilde{Mu_{\mu'}}|^2 d\xi = \int_{|\xi|\leqslant R} |\widetilde{Mu_{\nu'}} - \widetilde{Mu_{\mu'}}|^2 d\xi + \int_{|\xi|>R} |M(\xi)|^2 |\tilde{u}_{\nu'} - \tilde{u}_{\mu'}|^2 d\xi$$

$$< \int_{|\xi|\leqslant R} \cdots + \varepsilon \int_{E_n} \sum_\alpha |L^{(\alpha)}(\xi)|^2 |\tilde{u}_{\nu'} - \tilde{u}_{\mu'}|^2 d\xi = \int_{|\xi|\leqslant R} \cdots$$

$$+ \varepsilon \sum_\alpha \| L^{(\alpha)}(u_{\nu'} - u_{\mu'}) \|_0^2 \leqslant \int_{|\xi|\leqslant R} \cdots + \varepsilon C_1 \| L(u_{\nu'} - u_{\mu'}) \|_0^2$$

$$\leqslant \int_{|\xi|\leqslant R} |\widetilde{Mu_{\nu'}} - \widetilde{Mu_{\mu'}}|^2 d\xi + 4\varepsilon C_1$$

and the required result follows.

We prove the necessity of condition (1.26). It is sufficient to show that if $\xi_\nu \to \infty$ is a sequence through which the limit in (1.26) exists (and is finite or infinite) then this limit is zero. Selecting, if necessary, a subsequence of ξ_ν, we may assume that $\xi_\nu - \xi_\mu \to \infty$ as $\nu, \mu \to \infty$ ($\nu \neq \mu$).

Let $\psi \in C_0^\infty(G)$ be such that its Fourier transform is everywhere different from zero. If we consider the sequence of functions

$$u_\nu(x) = \psi(x) \frac{e^{i\langle x, \xi_\nu\rangle}}{\sqrt{\sum_\alpha |L^{(\alpha)}(\xi_\nu)|^2}} \in C_0^\infty(G),$$

by Leibnitz's formula (1.5)

$$(Lu_\nu)(x) = \frac{e^{i\langle x, \xi_\nu\rangle}}{\sqrt{\sum_\alpha |L^{(\alpha)}(\xi_\nu)|^2}} \sum_\alpha \frac{1}{\alpha!} \partial^\alpha \psi \cdot L^{(\alpha)}(\xi_\nu), \tag{1.27}$$

and hence $\|Lu_\nu\|_0 \leq C$ $(\nu = 1, 2, \cdots)$. Thus, because of complete continuity of the mapping (1.25), some subsequence $Mu_{\nu'}$, converges in $L_2(G)$. Using the equation analogous to (1.27), we obtain as $\nu', \mu' \longrightarrow \infty$

$$\| Mu_{\nu'} \|_0^2 + \| Mu_{\mu'} \|_0^2 - 2\mathrm{Re}\,(Mu_{\nu'}, Mu_{\mu'})_0 = \| Mu_{\nu'} - Mu_{\mu'} \|_0^2 \to 0,$$

$$2\mathrm{Re}\,(Mu_{\nu'}, Mu_{\mu'})_0 = 2\mathrm{Re}\left\{\sum_{\alpha,\beta} \frac{M^{(\alpha)}(\xi_{\nu'})}{\sqrt{\sum_\alpha |L^{(\alpha)}(\xi_{\nu'})|^2}}\right.$$

$$\left.\times \frac{M^{(\beta)}(\xi_{\mu'})}{\sqrt{\sum_\alpha |L^{(\alpha)}(\xi_{\mu'})|^2}} \frac{1}{\alpha!\beta!} \int_G \partial^\alpha \psi \cdot \overline{\partial^\beta \psi} \cdot e^{i\langle x, \xi_{\nu'} - \xi_{\mu'}\rangle}\, dx\right\}.$$

The latter integral approaches zero as $\nu', \mu' \longrightarrow \infty$, since it is the Fourier transform of a summable function; the factor in front of it is bounded by virtue of the estimate (1.7), which according to Theorem 1.1 automatically occurs; but the mapping (1.25) is not only continuous, but also completely continuous. Therefore $2\mathrm{Re}\,(Mu_{\nu'}, Mu_{\mu'})_0 \longrightarrow 0$ and consequently $\|Mu_{\nu'}\|_0 \longrightarrow 0$. If we introduce $\psi_{\alpha\beta}$ in the same way as on p. 266 we obtain

$$\| Mu_{\nu'} \|_0^2 = \frac{1}{\sum_\alpha |L^{(\alpha)}(\xi_{\nu'})|^2} \sum_{\alpha,\beta} M^{\alpha}(\xi_{\nu'})\, \overline{M^{(\beta)}(\xi_{\nu'})}\, \psi_{\alpha\beta}. \qquad (1.28)$$

As was established on p. 266, the form with coefficients $\psi_{\alpha\beta}$ is strictly positive definite; consequently, the numerator in (1.28) is not less than $\epsilon \Sigma_{\alpha,\beta} |M^{(\alpha)}(\xi_{\nu'})|^2$ $(\epsilon > 0)$. Thus,

$$\frac{\sum_\alpha |M^{(\alpha)}(\xi_{\nu'})|^2}{\sum_\alpha |L^{(\alpha)}(\xi_{\nu'})|^2} \leqslant \frac{1}{\varepsilon} \| Mu_{\nu'} \|_0^2 \underset{\nu' \to \infty}{\longrightarrow} 0,$$

as required. The theorem is proved.

In particular, we obtain from this theorem a corollary important for considerations of the type of Chapter II, §2.4.

Corollary. *A necessary and sufficient condition that the operator Λ^{-1} be completely continuous (or that the inclusion operator of the space $C_0^\infty(G)$ with the norm $\|u\|_{+,L}$ to $L_2(G)$ be completely continuous) is that the relation*

$$\sum_\alpha |L^{(\alpha)}(\xi)|^2 \underset{|\xi| \to \infty}{\longrightarrow} \infty. \qquad (1.29)$$

hold.

We seek a simpler expression of condition (1.29); to this end we introduce a general concept. Consider a polynomial $P(\xi)$ of the real vector $\xi \in E_n$ of the form (1.3); the subspace $C(P)$ of vectors $\eta \in E_n$, each of which have the property that for any real t

$$P(\xi + t\eta) = P(\xi) \quad (\xi \in E_n), \tag{1.30}$$

will be called the subspace of linearity of the polynomial P (we will clarify that the set of all vectors, which satisfy (1.30) for any $\xi \in E_n$ and $t \in (-\infty, \infty)$, actually form a subspace). We note at once that if $P = \sum_{k=0}^{r} P_k$ is a decomposition of the polynomial into homogeneous parts (P_k has degree k), then the determination of $C(P)$ reduces immediately to the determination of $C(P_k)$ $(k = 0, \cdots, \cdots, r)$, because of the equation

$$C(P) = \bigcap_{k=0}^{r} C(P_k). \tag{1.31}$$

We prove (1.31). The inclusion $\bigcap_{k=0}^{r} C(P_k) \subseteq C(P)$ is obvious; now let $\eta \in C(P)$, i.e. it satisfies (1.30). Replace ξ and t by $\epsilon\xi$ and ϵt in (1.30), where ϵ is a scalar parameter, and equate the coefficients of powers of ϵ. As a result we obtain the equation $P_k(\xi + t\eta) = P_k(\xi)$, i.e. $\eta \in C(P_k)$ $(k = 0, \cdots, r)$. Thus $C(P) \subseteq \bigcap_{k=0}^{r} C(P_k)$. The relation (1.31) is established.

The polynomial $P(\xi)$ is called complete, if its subspace of linearity consists only of zero, i.e. if it actually depends on all n variables.

Theorem 1.7. *Relation* (1.29) *holds if and only if the polynomial* $L(\xi)$ *is complete.*

Proof. If we assume that $L(\xi)$ is not complete, then there is a vector $\eta \neq 0$ such that $L(\xi + t\eta) = L(\xi)$ for all $\xi \in E_n$ and $t \in (-\infty, \infty)$. Differentiating this equation with respect to ξ, we obtain $L^{(\alpha)}(\xi + t\eta) = L^{(\alpha)}(\xi)$, whence

$$\sum_{\alpha} |L^{(\alpha)}(\xi + t\eta)|^2 = \sum_{\alpha} |L^{(\alpha)}(\xi)|^2.$$

In particular,

$$\sum_{\alpha} |L^{(\alpha)}(t\eta)|^2 = \sum_{\alpha} |L^{(\alpha)}(0)|^2 \not\to \infty$$

as $|t| \to \infty$. Thus, by (1.29), it must be that $L(\xi)$ is complete.

We come to the proof of the second part of the theorem. First we establish the following: let $P(\xi)$ be a homogeneous polynomial of degree r such that for some $\eta \in E_n$, $P^{(\alpha)}(\eta) = 0$ for all $|\alpha| = r - 1$. We assert that $\eta \in C(P)$. To prove this we use induction on the degree of the polynomial. For $r = 1$ the assertion is obvious; we assume that it is valid for degree $\leq r-1$. If $P(\xi)$ is of degree r, then $\partial P/\partial \xi_k$ is of degree $r-1$ and $(D^\alpha\, \partial P/\partial \xi_k)(\eta) = 0$ for $|\alpha| = r-2$. By the inductive hypothesis, $(\partial P/\partial \xi_k)(\xi + t\eta) = (\partial P/\partial \xi_k)(\xi)$ $(\xi \in E_n;\ t \in (-\infty, \infty);$ $k = 1, 2, \cdots)$. Consequently $P(\xi + t\eta) - P(\xi)$ does not depend on ξ and therefore has the form

$$P(\xi + t\eta) - P(\xi) = P(t\eta) = t^r P(\eta). \tag{1.32}$$

Setting $t = 1$ and $\xi = \eta$ here, we find that $2^r P(\eta) = P(2\eta) = 2P(\eta)$. Thus $P(\eta) = 0$ and it follows from (1.32) that $P(\xi + t\eta) = P(\xi)$, i.e. $\eta \in C(P)$. The assertion is proved.

We continue the proof of the theorem. We introduce a useful definition: a set in E_n is bounded mod H where H is a subspace of E_n if the projection of the set on the orthogonal complement of H is bounded. It is easy to see that if $H = \bigcap_{k=1}^m H_k$ where H_k is a subspace of E_n, then boundedness of a set mod H is equivalent to boundedness mod H_k $(k = 1, \cdots, m)$.

Instead of the assertion of the theorem, we prove the following general fact.

Lemma 1.2. *Let $P(\xi)$ be an arbitrary polynomial. The set π_t of $\xi \in E_n$ which satisfy the inequality*

$$\sum_\alpha |P^{(\alpha)}(\xi)|^2 \leqslant t, \tag{1.33}$$

where t is a fixed constant is always bounded mod $C(P)$.

The relation (1.29) for complete polynomials follows immediately since now $C(P) = 0$ and π_t is simply bounded, i.e. there are no such points $\xi = \xi_\nu \to \infty$ for which the sum in (1.29) can be bounded with respect to ν.

The proof is carried out by induction on the degree of the polynomial. The lemma is obvious for $r = 1$; assume that it is valid for degree $\leq r$. Consider a polynomial P of degree r; by (1.31) it is sufficient to prove that π_t is bounded mod $C(P_k)$ $(k = 0, \cdots, r)$. First of all we show that it is bounded mod $C(P_r)$. This will follow from the boundedness mod $C(P_r)$ of the larger set, namely the set of all points $\xi \in E_n$ which satisfy the inequality $\sum_{|\alpha| = r-1} |P^{(\alpha)}(\xi)|^2 \leq t$. But $P^{(\alpha)}(\xi)$ and $P_r^{(\alpha)}(\xi)$ $(|\alpha| = r-1)$ differ from each other only by an additive constant, hence boundedness mod $C(P_r)$ of the latter set is equivalent to boundedness mod $C(P_r)$ of the set of $\xi \in E_n$ for which

$$\sum_{|\alpha| = r-1} |P_r^{(\alpha)}(\xi)|^2 < t. \tag{1.34}$$

The expressions $P_r^{(\alpha)}(\xi)$ $(|\alpha| = r - 1)$ are linear forms on E_n. By the assertion proved before the lemma, the corresponding hyperplanes have a common intersection only in $C(P_r)$, hence the ξ which satisfy (1.34) can approach infinity only along $C(P_r)$. In other words, the set of ξ which satisfy (1.34) is bounded $\operatorname{mod} C(P_r)$ and this implies the same such boundedness of π_t.

Consider the polynomial $R(\xi) = P(\xi) - P_r(\xi) = \Sigma_{k=0}^{r-1} P_k(\xi)$. It has degree $r - 1$; P_k is its group of homogeneous summands. Therefore, by the induction hypothesis, the set $\rho_{t'}$ of vectors ξ for which $\Sigma_\alpha |R^{(\alpha)}(\xi)|^2 \le t'$ is bounded $\operatorname{mod} C(P_k)$ $(k = 0, \cdots, r-1)$. If we can show that $\rho_{t'}$ contains $\pi_{t'}$ for sufficiently large t', then it will follow that π_t is bounded mod $C(P_k)$ and the assertion will be proved. Thus it remains to show that $\Sigma_\alpha |R^{(\alpha)}(\xi)|^2$ is bounded on π_t. We have

$$\left(\sum_\alpha |R^{(\alpha)}(\xi)|^2\right)^{\frac{1}{2}} = \left(\sum_\alpha |P^{(\alpha)}(\xi) - P_r^{(\alpha)}(\xi)|^2\right)^{\frac{1}{2}}$$

$$\leqslant \left(\sum_\alpha |P^{(\alpha)}(\xi)|^2\right)^{\frac{1}{2}} + \left(\sum_\alpha |P_r^{(\alpha)}(\xi)|^2\right)^{\frac{1}{2}}. \qquad (1.35)$$

The next to last sum is bounded on $\pi_{t'}$, and the last is also bounded: since π_t is bounded $\operatorname{mod} C(P_r)$, the points of this set can approach infinity only along $C(P_r)$ and along this path both P_r and $P_r^{(\alpha)}$ do not vary by the definition of $C(P_r)$. Thus, expression (1.35) is bounded on π_t. The lemma, and simultaneously Theorem 1.7 are completely proved.

Remark. It is easily observed from the proof of the theorem that for a complete polynomial a relation actually stronger than (1.29) is valid: there exists a $\gamma > 0$ such that

$$\sum_\alpha |L^{(\alpha)}(\xi)|^2 \geqslant C(\xi_1^2 + \ldots + \xi_n^2)^\gamma \quad (C > 0;\ \xi \in E_n). \qquad (1.36)$$

§2. THE PROBLEM OF DIRICHLET TYPE FOR SECOND ORDER DIFFERENTIAL EXPRESSIONS WITH CONSTANT COEFFICIENTS

By the general results of §1, the energy inequality is valid for such expressions for finite functions and therefore solvable extensions exist. We show now that it is possible to obtain both inequalities (2.12) of Chapter II for the condition $u|_\Gamma = 0$ and special regions G. Their derivations are suggested by the proof of the estimate (1.9): carry out the transformations, analogous to those described in the proof of Lemma 1.1, assuming that u is not finite and write down the integrals with respect to Γ wherever they appear. In order to obtain the inequality for a larger class of functions than the finite functions, we will choose Γ and impose boundary conditions on u so that all these integrals vanish or have a definite sign, which does not impede the derivation of the estimate. As a result we obtain the desired conditions, which depend both on L and on Γ. It is usually necessary to modify this procedure for each individual class of equations.

1. **Methods of obtaining energy inequalities.** We establish certain identities. Below, $A(x)$ real and $u(x)$ complex are sufficiently smooth functions; we integrate by parts, interchange positions of u and $\bar{u}$, and moreover carry out the integration so as to avoid the appearance of third derivatives:

$$\int_G AD_j^2u\cdot D_k\bar{u}dx = -\int_G D_ju\cdot D_k\bar{u}\cdot D_jAdx - \int_G D_ju\cdot D_jD_k\bar{u}\cdot Adx$$

$$+\int_\Gamma D_ju\cdot D_k\bar{u}\cdot Av_jdx = -\int_G D_ju\cdot D_k\bar{u}\cdot D_jAdx + \int_G |D_ju|^2D_kAdx$$

$$+\int_G D_kD_ju\cdot D_j\bar{u}\cdot Adx - \int_\Gamma |D_ju|^2Av_kdx + \int_\Gamma D_ju\cdot D_k\bar{u}\cdot Av_jdx$$

$$= -2\operatorname{Re}\int_G D_ju\cdot D_k\bar{u}\cdot D_jAdx + \int_G |D_ju|^2D_kAdx - \int_G D_ku\cdot D_j^2\bar{u}\cdot Adx$$

$$-\int_\Gamma |D_ju|^2Av_kdx + 2\operatorname{Re}\int_\Gamma D_ju\cdot D_k\bar{u}\cdot Av_jdx.$$

Hence from analogous but simpler relations, we obtain

$$2\operatorname{Re}\int_G AD_j^2u\cdot D_k\bar{u}dx = \int_G |D_ju|^2D_kAdx - 2\operatorname{Re}\int_G D_ju\cdot D_k\bar{u}\cdot D_jAdx$$

$$-\int_\Gamma |D_ju|^2Av_kdx + 2\operatorname{Re}\int_\Gamma D_ju\cdot D_k\bar{u}\cdot Av_jdx \quad (j,\ k=1,\dots,n); \tag{2.1}$$

$$2\operatorname{Re}\int_G AD_j^2u\cdot\bar{u}dx = -2\int_G A|D_ju|^2dx + \int_G |u|^2D_j^2Adx$$

$$+2\operatorname{Re}\int_\Gamma AD_ju\cdot\bar{u}v_jdx - \int_\Gamma |u|^2D_jA\cdot v_jdx \quad (j=1,\dots,n); \tag{2.2}$$

$$2\operatorname{Re}\int_G AD_ju\cdot\bar{u}dx = -\int_G |u|^2D_jAdx + \int_\Gamma |u|^2Av_jdx \quad (j=1,\dots,n). \tag{2.3}$$

We will use equations (2.1)–(2.3) below in the case when $u|_\Gamma = 0$. For such u the integrals over Γ in (2.2)–(2.3) generally vanish, and the sum of the integrals over Γ in (2.1) has the form

$$\int_\Gamma |N_u|^2 A\nu_j^2\nu_k dx, \tag{2.4}$$

where N_u is a normalizing factor such that $(D_j u)(x) = N_u(x)\nu_j(x)$ $(x \in \Gamma)$.

Consider a general second order differential expression L with constant coefficients, with boundary condition $u|_\Gamma = 0$. By rotation of the coordinate system, L can be reduced to the form

$$Lu = \sum_{j=1}^n c_j D_j^2 u + \sum_{j=1}^n b_j D_j u + bu. \tag{2.5}$$

Let $A_1(x), \cdots, A_n(x)$, and $A(x)$ be sufficiently smooth, real functions, and let $u|_\Gamma = 0$. Using equations (2.1)–(2.4), we easily find

$$2\mathrm{Re}\int_G Lu\left(\sum_{k=1}^n A_k D_k\bar u + A\bar u\right)dx = \int_G\left\{\sum_{j=1}^n\left[c_j\left(\sum_{k=1}^n D_k A_k - 2D_j A_j - 2A\right)\right.\right.$$

$$\left. + 2b_j A_j\right]|D_j u|^2 + \sum_{\substack{j,k=1\\ j\neq k}}^n (-c_j D_j A_k - c_k D_k A_j + b_j A_k + b_k A_j) D_j u\cdot D_k\bar u\Big\} dx$$

$$+\int_G\left\{\sum_{j=1}^n (c_j D_j^2 A - b_j D_j A - bD_j A_j) + 2bA\right\}|u|^2 dx$$

$$+\int_\Gamma |N_u|^2\left(\sum_{k=1}^n A_k\nu_k\right)\left(\sum_{j=1}^n c_j\nu_j^2\right)dx. \tag{2.6}$$

Assume that $A_1, \cdots, A_n$ and A can be chosen so that for each $x \in G \cup \Gamma$ the quadratic form

$$\sum_{j=1}^n\left[c_j\left(\sum_{k=1}^n D_k A_k - 2D_j A_j - 2A\right) + 2b_j A_j\right]|\zeta_j|^2 + \sum_{\substack{j,k=1\\ j\neq k}}^n (-c_j D_j A_k$$

$$- c_k D_k A_j + b_j A_k + b_k A_j)\zeta_j\zeta_k \tag{2.7}$$

(with respect to ζ) is strictly positive definite and satisfies the inequalities

$$\sum_{j=1}^n (c_j D_j^2 A - b_j D_j A - bD_j A_j) + 2bA \geqslant 0 \ (x\in G);$$

$$\left(\sum_{k=1}^n A_k\nu_k\right)\left(\sum_{j=1}^n c_j\nu_j^2\right) \geqslant 0 \ (x\in\Gamma). \tag{2.8}$$

Then from (2.6) it follows that

$$2\operatorname{Re}\int_G Lu\cdot\left(\sum_{k=1}^n A_kD_k\bar u+A\bar u\right)dx\geqslant C_1\int_G\sum_{j=1}^n|D_ju|^2dx\geqslant C_2\|u\|_1^2\ (C_1,C_2>0)\qquad(2.9)$$

(recall that since $u|_\Gamma=0$, $\int_G\sum_{j=1}^n|D_ju|^2dx$ is equivalent to $\|u\|_1^2$). Estimating the left side of (2.9) by $C_3\|Lu\|_0\|u\|_1$, we obtain

$$\|Lu\|_0\geqslant C\|u\|_1\ (C>0;\ u\in\mathring{W}_2^1(G)\cap W_2^2(G)).\qquad(2.10)$$

Thus if there exist real functions $A_j(x)\in W_2^1(G)$ $(j=1,\cdots,n)$ and $A(x)\in W_2^2(G)$ such that for each $x\in G\cup\Gamma$ the quadratic form (2.7) is strictly positive definite and inequalities (2.8) are satisfied, then (2.10) holds.

The following problem arises: how to choose the region G for the expression (2.5) so that inequality (2.10) holds. On the basis of the above, it can be solved in the following way. Choose functions $A_k(x)$ and $A(x)$ so that the form (2.7) is strictly positive definite and the first of the inequalities (2.8) holds. Now we seek solutions $f(x)$ of the equation $\sum_{k=1}^n A_k(x)D_kf=0$. On the surfaces $f(x)=H\in(-\infty,\infty)$, the second of the relations (2.8) becomes an equality: by deforming these surfaces in the proper way, we obtain a sufficiently rich family of surfaces on which the second of the inequalities (2.8) holds. If the boundary of some region G can be formed from a finite number of these surfaces, then G will be as desired. Clearly, such a construction, if continued indefinitely, gives a whole family of regions G, in which inequality (2.10) is valid.

2. **Existence of regions in which the problem of Dirichlet type is solvable.** We will show that for any expression of the form (2.5) there exists a family of regions in which the problem $Lu=f\in L_2(G)$, $u|_\Gamma=0$ has a weak solution $u\in L_2(G)$ for any f, and any strong solution is unique. More precisely, we will prove that the boundary condition $u|_\Gamma=0$ is almost correct for L in these regions.

Theorem 2.1. *Let L be an arbitrary differential expression with constant coefficients of the form* (2.5); *assume that all the $c_j\neq0$ $(j=1,\cdots,n)$. There exist bounded regions $G\subset E_n$ with piecewise-smooth boundary Γ not containing any characteristic pieces of the expression* (2.5), *for which the energy inequalities*

$$\|Lu\|_0\geqslant C\|u\|_1,\quad\|L^+v\|_0\geqslant C\|v\|_1^*\ (C>0;\ u,v\in\mathring{W}_2^1(G)\cap W_2^2(G))^{1)}\qquad(2.11)$$

[1] From this inequality it follows that there exists a generalized solution even for $f\in W_2^{-1}(G)$ (cf. Theorem 3.3, Chapter II).

are valid. Small deformations of Γ give rise to regions with boundaries without characteristic pieces, for which inequalities (2.11) *remain valid (the idea of a small deformation is described below). Since Γ does not contain any characteristic pieces, the zero condition is adjoint to itself (see Theorem* 1.1, *Chapter* II), *and therefore the inequalities* (2.11) *mean, in fact, that the problem under consideration is almost correct.*

The proof is reduced to an explicit construction of the required regions G; such regions are of course not unique. Let the p coefficients $c_1, \cdots, c_p$ be positive and the q coefficients $c_{p+1}, \cdots, c_n$ $(p + q = n)$ be negative. We present only the case when $p, q > 0$, since in the contrary case L is elliptic and the assertion of the theorem follows from the results of §3, Chapter III. We may assume without loss of generality that $c_1 = \cdots = c_p = 1$, $c_{p+1} = \cdots = c_n = -1$. Set

$$A_k(x) = -x_k (k = 1, \ldots, p), \; A_k(x) = x_k (k = p+1, \ldots, n),$$
$$A(x) = \frac{1}{2}(\operatorname{sign} b - p + q);$$

the first of the relations (2.8) obviously holds. We have

$$c_j\left(\sum_{k=1}^{n} D_k A_k - 2D_j A_j - 2A\right) = \begin{cases} -p+q+2-2A = 2 - \operatorname{sign} b > 0 & (j = 1, \ldots, p), \\ p-q+2+2A = 2 + \operatorname{sign} b > 0 & (j = p+1, \ldots, n) \end{cases} \tag{2.12}$$

If we place G in a sphere U of sufficiently small radius with center at the origin, each of the quantities $|b_j A_k(x)|$ $(j, k = 1, \cdots, n)$ becomes sufficiently small. Since $D_j A_k = 0$ $(j \neq k)$ then, taking into account (2.12), we can take the radius of the sphere U so small that the form (2.7) is strictly positive for $x \in G \cup \Gamma$.

We must now choose the boundary of the region G to ensure validity of the second of the inequalities (2.8): we will arrange it sufficiently close to the origin. The equation $\sum_{j=1}^{n} A_k D_k f = 0$ acquires the form

$$-x_1 D_1 f - \ldots - x_p D_p f + x_{p+1} D_{p+1} f + \ldots + x_n D_n f = 0.$$

To determine its solutions, we form the system of ordinary differential equations

$$\frac{dx_1}{-x_1} = \ldots = \frac{dx_p}{-x_p} = \frac{dx_{p+1}}{x_{p+1}} = \ldots = \frac{dx_n}{x_n}.$$

We arrange these equations in such a way that in each of them one minus and one plus appear in the denominator; moreover, we form a minimal number of such equations, requiring only that each of the variables $x_1, \cdots, x_n$ appear in one of these (this process is, in general, not unique). We obtain, for example, N equations of the form

$$\frac{dx_1}{-x_1} = \frac{dx_{p+1}}{x_{p+1}}, \quad \frac{dx_2}{-x_2} = \frac{dx_{p+2}}{x_{p+2}}, \ldots \tag{2.13}$$

(if $p \neq q$, then among the equations, recurrence of variables will occur in designated places). Integrating (2.13), we find that we can take as f the functions $x_1 x_{p+1}$, $x_2 x_{p+2}, \cdots$. Thus the surfaces $f(x) = h$ have the form $x_1 x_{p+1} = h$, $x_2 x_{p+2} = h, \cdots$. These surfaces cannot enclose a bounded region in E_n; we must deform them. Consider, for example, in the $x_1 O x_{p+1}$ plane four branches of hyperbolas of the form $x_1 x_{p+1} = h_1$ (see Figure 5) and close the segments by curves AA_1, AA_2, $BB_1, \cdots$. These curves are arbitrary with the exception that the angles between the tangents to them and the corresponding axes are in modulus not larger than $\pi/4$ and not smaller than the analogous angles for the hyperbolas $x_1 x_{p+1} = h_1$ at the points under consideration (see Figure 5). As a result we obtain a bounded region $\tilde{G}_1$ in the plane $x_1 O x_{p+1}$; consider the cylinder $G_1 = \tilde{G}_1 \times E_{n-2}$ where E_{n-2} denotes the $n-2$ dimensional space, spanned by all the coordinate axes except Ox_1 and Ox_{p+1}. Similarly, we construct cylinders $G_2, \cdots, G_N$ and set $G = \bigcap_{\alpha=1}^N G_\alpha$; G is a bounded region with a boundary which consists of a finite number of pieces of smooth surfaces. We need only clarify the boundedness of G, which follows from the fact that for points of G_1 the coordinates x_1, x_{p+1} are bounded, for points of G_2 the coordinates x_2, x_{p+2} are bounded etc., where by construction all the coordinates are considered. On choosing the constants h in the equations of the hyperbolas sufficiently small and points of the type A, B, C, D sufficiently near the origin, we can make the diameter of G sufficiently small so that the form (2.7) turns out to be strictly positive for $x \in G \cup \Gamma$. We show that the second of the relations (2.8) also holds. Let $x = x^0$ be an interior point of some smooth piece, lying on Γ; assume, for instance, that x^0 lies on the lateral surface of the cylinder G_1. If x^0 lies on $(A_2 B_1) \times E_{n-2}$, $(B_2 C_1) \times E_{n-2}, \cdots$, then by construction $\sum_{k=1}^n A_k(x^0) \nu_k(x^0) = 0$. It remains to consider the cases when x^0 lies on $(AA_2) \times E_{n-2}$, $(BB_1) \times E_{n-2}, \cdots$; they are examined similarly. For definiteness, assume that $x^0 \in (CC_1) \times E_{n-2}$; let $\tilde{x}^0$ denote the point (x_1^0, x_{p+1}^0) of the plane

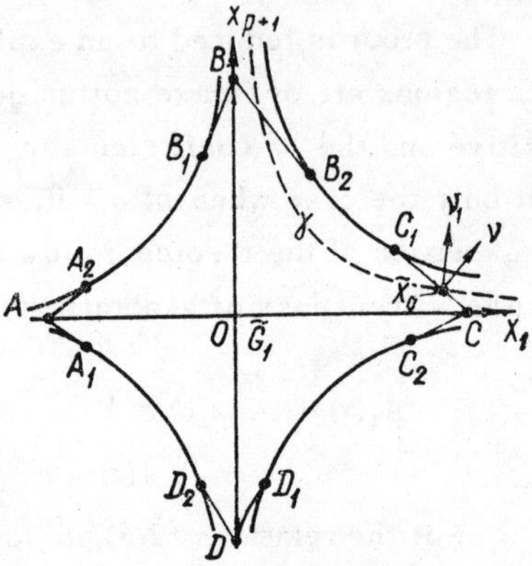

Figure 5.

x_1Ox_{p+1}. The unit normal vector $\nu(x^0) = \nu$ lies in this plane; hence the second inequality in (2.8) acquires the form

$$(-x_1^0\nu_1 + x_{p+1}^0\nu_{p+1})(\nu_1^2 - \nu_{p+1}^2) \geqslant 0 . \tag{2.14}$$

We show that it actually holds. We draw through $\tilde{x}^0$ a hyperbola γ of the form $x_1x_{p+1} = h$, and let ν' be a unit vector normal to it (see Figure 5). Clearly, $\nu_1 \geq \nu_1' > 0$, $\nu_{p+1}' \geq \nu_{p+1} > 0$, therefore $-x_1^0\nu_1 + x_{p+1}^0\nu_{p+1} \leq -x_1^0\nu_1' + x_{p+1}^0\nu_{p+1}' = 0$ Moreover $\nu_1^2 - \nu_{p+1}^2 \leq 0$; consequently, inequality (2.14) is valid. Thus, (2.8) holds and therefore the first of the inequalities (2.11) is valid. The second inequality in (2.11) also holds for the region G constructed; this follows from the fact that the leading terms in L and L^+ are identical.

It is easy to see from the proof of the inequalities (2.11) that they are valid in the case of a region G' close to G. In this connection *we say that G' is close to G, if its boundary Γ' is close to Γ in the sense of uniform closeness of the functions which assign the surface together with their derivatives. In addition, near the $(n-2)$-faces of the generated points of the type A, $B, \cdots$, the boundary Γ' has the same form as Γ.*

In order to examine the regions G' it is necessary to use functions $A_k(x) + \epsilon_k(x)$ instead of the previous functions $A_k(x)$, where $\epsilon_k(x)$ is sufficiently smooth and vanishes in neighborhoods of the $(n-2)$-faces mentioned. For sufficiently small $|\epsilon_k(x)|$ and $|D_j\epsilon_k(x)|$ the form (2.7) remains positive definite and inequalities (2.8) remain valid, and we arrive at the previous estimates.

It remains to remark that the regions G constructed do not contain pieces of characteristic of the expression L. The theorem is proved.

3. Examination of the problem of Dirichlet type by means of separation of variables.[1] We establish some simple general facts. Let L be a formally selfadjoint strongly elliptic expression of the second order with the usual smoothness conditions on the coefficients, considered in a bounded region G, whose boundary Γ is of class C^2. By Lemma 3.9, Chapter III, the operator $Au = Lu$, $u \in \mathfrak{D}(A) = \overset{\circ}{W}{}_2^1(G) \cap W_2^2(G)$ is selfadjoint in $L_2(G)$. This operator has a countable number of eigenfunctions $\phi_k(x)$, corresponding to eigenvalues λ_k $(k = 1, 2, \cdots)$, and in addition $\phi_k \in \overset{\circ}{W}{}_2^1(G) \cap W_2^2(G)$, λ_k is real and $\rightarrow +\infty$ (see Theorem 3.5, Chapter III). Later on we will show that the system $\phi_k(x)$ $(k = 1, 2, \cdots)$ is

1) For a general point of view of separation of variables see §4, Chapter VI.

complete in $L_2(G)$ (see Chapter VI, §2.5).

Now consider $G = G' \times G'' \subseteq E_n$, where $G'(G'')$ is a bounded region in the space E_p of points $(x_1, \cdots, x_p)$ (E_q of points $(x_{p+1}, \cdots, x_n)$, $p + q = n$; $p, q \geq 1$) with boundary of class C^2. In G' and G'' we define corresponding elliptic expressions L' and L'' of the form stated above and set

$$Lu = L'u - L''u + c(x)\, u; \tag{2.15}$$

$c(x)$ is a bounded real function. It is obvious that L is formally selfadjoint and ultrahyperbolic. Associate with L the zero boundary condition (bd): $u|_\Gamma = 0$ and construct the strong operator of the problem Λ(bd) – the closure in $L_2(G)$ of the operator $u \to Lu$ ($u \in \overset{\circ}{W}{}_2^1(G) \cap W_2^2(G)$).

Theorem 2.2. *The operator* Λ(bd) *is selfadjoint: thus the weak operator* Л(bd) *coincides with the strong.*

Proof. It is well known that selfadjointness of an operator B is equivalent to selfadjointness of $B + C$, $\|C\| < \infty$, $C^* = C$.[1] Since the operator $(Cu)(x) = c(x)\, u(x)$ is bounded in $L_2(G)$, it is sufficient to give a proof for the case $c(x) = 0$. Construct with respect to L' and L'' in G' and G'' the operators analogous to A; let $\phi'_\mu(x_1, \cdots, x_p)$ and $\phi''_\nu(x_{p+1}, \cdots, x_n)$ ($\mu, \nu = 1, 2, \cdots$) be complete orthonormal sets of eigenfunctions, corresponding to the eigenvalues λ'_μ and λ''_ν. These functions belong to $W_2^2(G')$ and $W_2^2(G'')$ and vanish on the boundaries of G' and G''. The system of functions $\phi_{\mu\nu}(x) = \phi'_\mu(x_1, \cdots, x_p)\, \phi''_\nu(x_{p+1}, \cdots, x_n)$ is orthonormal and complete in $L_2(G)$; hence for any $f \in L_2(G)$ and any nonreal z the series

$$u(x) = \sum_{\mu,\nu=1}^{\infty} \frac{f_{\mu\nu}}{\lambda'_\mu - \lambda''_\nu - z} \varphi_{\mu\nu}(x), \quad f_{\mu\nu} = \int_G f(x)\, \overline{\varphi_{\mu\nu}(x)}\, dx, \tag{2.16}$$

converges in $L_2(G)$. It is easy to see that

$$u \in \mathfrak{D}(\Lambda(\text{bd})), \quad \Lambda(\text{bd})\, u - zu = f. \tag{2.17}$$

In fact, the function $u_{MN}(x)$, which differs from $u(x)$ in that the summation in (2.16) is taken up to $\mu = M$, $\nu = N$, belongs to $\mathfrak{D}(\Lambda(\text{bd}))$ and is such that

$$Lu_{MN} - zu_{MN} = \sum_{\mu,\nu=1}^{M,N} f_{\mu\nu}\varphi_{\mu\nu}(x).$$

---

[1] See the corollary to Lemma 1.2, Chapter VI.

On passing to the limit here as $M, N \to \infty$, we arrive at (2.17). Thus the equation $\Lambda(\mathrm{bd})u - zu = f$ is solvable for any $f \in L_2(G)$, and this shows that $\Lambda(\mathrm{bd})$ is selfadjoint. The theorem is proved.

It follows from (2.16) that the equation $\Lambda(\mathrm{bd}) - zu = f$ is solvable for any $f \in L_2(G)$ for those and only those z for which $|\lambda'_\mu - \lambda''_\nu - z| \geq \epsilon$ $(\mu, \nu = 1, 2, \cdots)$, for some $\epsilon > 0$; in this case $\|u\|_0 \leq (1/\epsilon)\|f\|_0$. In other words, *the spectrum of the operator* $\Lambda(\mathrm{bd})$ (*for* $c(x) \equiv 0$) *is the closure of the set of numbers*

$$\lambda'_\mu - \lambda''_\nu \quad (\mu, \nu = 1, 2, \ldots). \tag{2.18}$$

Outside the spectrum the solution of this equation is given by formula (2.16). The smoothness character of such a solution also follows from (2.16): if $f_{\mu\nu}$ is decreasing sufficiently fast, then $u(x)$ is smooth. It is also clear that the equation $\Lambda(\mathrm{bd})u - zu = f$ may have a solution (for specific f) in the case when z belongs to the spectrum of the operator $\Lambda(\mathrm{bd})$: for z of the form $\lambda'_{\mu_0} - \lambda''_{\nu_0}$, in some neighborhood of which there is no number $\lambda'_\mu - \lambda''_\nu \neq z$, f must be orthogonal to all $\phi_{\mu\nu}$, $\lambda'_\mu - \lambda''_\nu = z$. For z a bound for $\lambda'_\mu - \lambda''_\nu$ and not coinciding with one of these, the corresponding Fourier coefficients $f_{\mu\nu}$ must decrease so fast that convergence of the series (2.16) is insured; if $z = \lambda'_{\mu_0} - \lambda''_{\nu_0}$ is a bound of $\lambda'_\mu - \lambda''_\nu$, then it is necessary to require in addition that f be orthogonal to all $\phi_{\mu\nu}$ for which $\lambda'_\mu - \lambda''_\nu = z$.

Thus if z does not belong to the spectrum of the operator $\Lambda(\mathrm{bd})$, induced by the expression (2.15), then the boundary value problem

$$Lu - zu = f \in L_2(G), \quad u|_\Gamma = 0, \tag{2.19}$$

always has a weak solution in $L_2(G)$; it is, at the same time, strong; therefore it depends continuously on f: $\|u\|_0 \leq C\|f\|_0$ $(f \in L_2(G))$. (The strong and weak operators, constructed with respect to $L - zE$, coincide with $\Lambda(\mathrm{bd}) - zE$ and $\Pi(\mathrm{bd}) - zE$ respectively.)

Consider the differential equation of the vibrating string, a special case of (2.15): $Lu = -D_1^2u + D_2^2u$. The region is $G = (0, l_1) \times (0, l_2)$ $(0 < l_1, l_2 < \infty)$, $u|_\Gamma = 0$. By the above, $\Lambda(\mathrm{bd})$ is selfadjoint and its spectrum, in view of (2.18), is the closure of the set of points of the form

$$\pi^2\left(\frac{\mu^2}{l_1^2} - \frac{\nu^2}{l_2^2}\right) \quad (\mu, \nu = 1, 2, \ldots). \tag{2.20}$$

We explain in what cases the operator $\Lambda(\mathrm{bd})$ is invertible in $L_2(G)$, i.e. in what cases 0 is not a point of the spectrum and the problem $Lu = f \in L_2(G)$,

$u|_\Gamma = 0$ is solvable in the stated sense only. It is not difficult to prove the following assertion: *if $\alpha = l_2/l_1$ is irrational and is expanded as a continued fraction of the form*

$$\alpha = a_0 + \cfrac{1}{a_1 + \cfrac{1}{a_2 + \dots}}$$

($a_0 = [\alpha]$, $a_1 = |1/\alpha - a_0|$ u etc.) in which the numbers $a_0 a_1, \cdots$ are bounded, then 0 is not a point of the spectrum of the operator Λ(bd). *In all the remaining cases 0 belongs to the spectrum.*

By (2.20), for the proof we must study all possible representations of 0 by numbers of the form $\alpha^2\mu^2 - \nu^2$ $(\mu, \nu = 1, 2, \cdots)$. If α is rational, then $\alpha^2 q^2 - p^2 = 0$ where p and q are natural numbers such that $\alpha = p/q$. Now suppose that α is irrational. It is known (see, for example, A. Ja. Hinčin [1], Theorem 23) that if for given α the numbers a_j are bounded, then for any $\epsilon > 0$ there is an infinite set of natural numbers p, q such that $|\alpha - p/q| < \epsilon/q^2$; if the numbers a_j are bounded, then there exists $\epsilon_0 > 0$ such that for all natural numbers p, q $|\alpha - p/q| \geq \epsilon_0/q^2$. Therefore in the second case we obtain

$$|\alpha^2\mu^2 - \nu^2| = \mu^2 \left|\alpha + \frac{\nu}{\mu}\right| \left|\alpha - \frac{\nu}{\mu}\right| \geqslant \mu^2\alpha \cdot \frac{\varepsilon_0}{\mu^2} = \alpha\varepsilon_0 > 0,$$

i.e. 0 does not belong to the spectrum. In the first case, for given $\epsilon > 0$ there exist μ, ν such that $|\alpha - \nu/\mu| < \epsilon/\mu^2$. Then $\nu/\mu < \alpha + \epsilon/\mu^2$ and we obtain

$$|\alpha^2\mu^2 - \nu^2| = \mu^2 \left|\alpha + \frac{\nu}{\mu}\right| \left|\alpha - \frac{\nu}{\mu}\right| < \mu^2 \left(2\alpha + \frac{\varepsilon}{\mu^2}\right) \frac{\varepsilon}{\mu^2} \leqslant (2\alpha + \varepsilon)\,\varepsilon,$$

and the assertion is proved.

Thus, for our problem, the following situation occurs: there exists, on the semi-axis, a dense set of fractions l_2/l_1 (for instance squares of irrationals; for these the a_j are bounded), for which the problem is solvable in $L_2(G)$ for any $f \in L_2(G)$ and its solution depends continuously on f. Moreover, by slightly varying the ratio l_2/l_1 we can always pass to an unsolvable case, in other words, solvability of the problem is unstable with respect to small variations of the region.

Let l_2/l_1 be such that 0 is not a point of the spectrum. Then the solution $u(x)$ of the problem (2.19) is regenerated by formula (2.16), where $z = 0$ and

$$\varphi_{\mu\nu}(x) = \frac{2}{\sqrt{l_1 l_2}} \sin\frac{\pi\mu x_1}{l_1} \cdot \sin\frac{\pi\nu x_2}{l_2} \quad (\mu, \nu = 1, 2, \dots).$$

If for some k $f(x) \in W_2^k(G)$ and vanishes together with its derivatives up to order $k-1$ inclusive on Γ, then integrating the expression for $f_{\mu\nu}$ (see (2.16)) by parts, we find that

$$f_{\mu\nu} = \frac{1}{\mu^{k_1}\nu^{k_2}} g_{\mu\nu}^{(k_1, k_2)}, \qquad \sum_{\mu, \nu=1}^{\infty} | g_{\mu\nu}^{(k_1, k_2)} |^2 < \infty,$$

where k_1, k_2 are any fixed natural numbers such that $k_1 + k_2 = k$. Using this property, it is easy to see that the series (2.16), expressed for our $u(x)$, can be differentiated termwise; therefore also $u \in W_2^k(G)$. Thus, for $k \geq 2$, the solution found is a smooth solution of the problem.

Suppose that $l_2/l_1 = \alpha$ is irrational and such that 0 is a point of the spectrum, but that this fraction can be approximated sufficiently poorly by rational numbers, i.e. there exist $d > 2$ and $\epsilon_0 > 0$ such that $|\alpha - p/q| \geq \epsilon_0/q^d$ $(p, q = 1, 2, \cdots)$, (for example, α could be an algebraic number of degree > 2). Then for sufficiently smooth f and the vanishing of its derivatives on Γ the solution of our problem nevertheless exists and is sufficiently smooth. This follows from the estimate

$$\lambda_\mu' - \lambda_\nu''| = \frac{\pi^2}{l_2^2} | \alpha^2\mu^2 - \nu^2 | = \frac{\pi^2\mu^2}{l_2^2} \left| \alpha + \frac{\nu}{\mu} \right| \left| \alpha - \frac{\nu}{\mu} \right| \geqslant \frac{\pi^2}{l_1 l_2} \frac{\varepsilon_0}{\mu^{d-2}},$$

since now the decrease of the denominator in (2.16) can be neglected by the sufficiently rapid decrease of the numerator $f_{\mu\nu}$ if only the previous requirement concerning f is realized for sufficiently large k.

Finally, if $l_2/l_1 = \alpha$ is rational, then 0 is a point of the spectrum. However, it is easy to see now that the spectrum is discrete and therefore by the above, a solution of the problem exists, if f is orthogonal to the eigenfunctions

$$\sin \frac{\pi\mu x_1}{l_1} \cdot \sin \frac{\pi\nu x_2}{l_2} \left(\mu = mq, \ \nu = mp \ \text{ where } \ m = 1, 2, \ldots; \ \alpha = \frac{p}{q} \right).$$

4. The problem of Dirichlet type for the equation of the vibrating string. Other regions; analysis of the smoothness of a solution. We consider as before the problem

$$Lu = D_1^2 u - D_2^2 u = f \in L_2(G), \quad u|_\Gamma = 0. \tag{2.21}$$

On comparison of the results of subsections 2 and 3 it is obvious that althongh in the rectangles $G = (0, l_1) \times (0, l_2)$, solvability is unstable with respect to small perturbations of the region, there exist regions where such stability occurs. For example, one can take the region of Figure 5 (for $x_{p+1} = x_2$), where its size may be arbitrary, since the decrease in the diameter is due only to the presence of first derivatives in the general expression (2.5) (see subsection 2). We mention still another example of similar regions.

Set $A_1(x) = -x_1$, $A_2(x) = 0$ (see the end of subsection 1); the equation for f acquires the form $-x_1 D_1 f = 0$ and the curves $f(x) = h$ are lines $x_2 = h$. The region G can be formed as indicated in Figure 6: it is required that the unit vector $\nu(x)$ satisfy the inequalities $|\nu_1(x)| \leq |\nu_2(x)|$ and $x_1\nu_1(x) \geq 0$ on the whole boundary. In this case (2.7) acquires the form $|\zeta_1|^2 + |\zeta_2|^2$, the first of inequalities (2.8) is obviously satisfied, and for the second we have $-x_1\nu_1(x) \times (\nu_1^2(x) - \nu_2^2(x)) \geq 0$. *Thus in this region, the energy inequality* (2.10) *holds.*

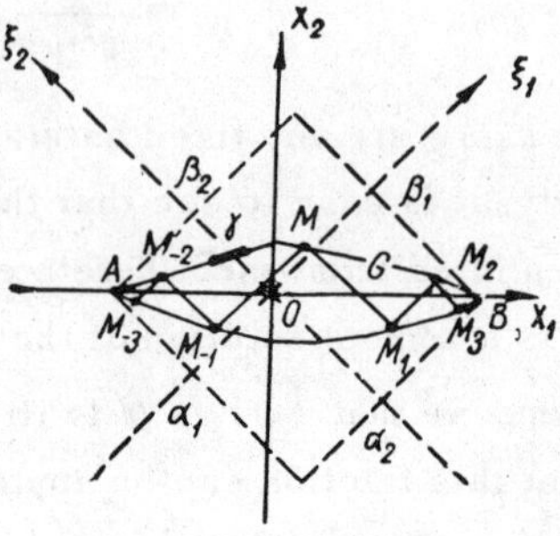

Figure 6.

We investigate smoothness of a weak solution of the problem (2.21) (if it exists) in an arbitrary region G, with a bounded closed piecewise-smooth curve Γ not containing pieces of the characteristics $x_1 \pm x_2 = C$. It is convenient to pass, in the x_1Ox_2 plane, to the coordinates $\xi_1 O \xi_2$ directed along the characteristics (see Figure 6). Making the change of variables, we pass from the problem (2.21) to the problem

$$Lu = \frac{\partial^2 u}{\partial \xi_1 \partial \xi_2} = f(\xi) \in L_2(G), \quad u|_\Gamma = 0 \quad (\xi = (\xi_1, \xi_2)). \tag{2.22}$$

Theorem 2.3. *A weak solution* $u(\xi) \in L_2(G)$ *of the problem* (2.22) *has the form*

$$u(\xi) = \int_0^{\xi_1}\int_0^{\xi_2} f(\eta)\, d\eta + \omega(\xi). \tag{2.23}$$

Here $f \in L_2(G)$ *is extended from* G *to the whole plane by zero, and* $\omega(\xi)$ *is a function which is represented in the form* $\phi(\xi_1) + \psi(\xi_2)$ *in each part of* G *where the boundary is intersected by the lines* $\xi_1 = C_1$, $\xi_2 = C_2$ *in at most two points;* ϕ *and* ψ *belong to* $L_2(\Delta)$ *for the corresponding intervals* Δ.

Functions of the form (2.23) *are defined on the boundary* Γ *of our region. For a weak solution* u *of problem* (2.22) *the values on the boundary are zero.*

If the boundary of G intersects the characteristics $\xi_1 = C_1$, $\xi_2 = C_2$ in at most two points, then the representation $\omega(\xi) = \phi(\xi_1) + \psi(\xi_2)$ is unique to within an additive constant. In the general case G must be partitioned into a finite number of subregions $O_1, \cdots, O_N$ of the required form and a similar representation will hold for each subregion; the functions ϕ and ψ now depend on the partition. Thus in the case of the region of Figure 6 the representation is unique and $\phi \in L_2((\alpha_1, \beta_1))$, $\psi \in L_2((\alpha_2, \beta_2))$.

We establish first of all two lemmas.

Lemma 2.1. *Let* $Q = (\alpha_1, \beta_1) \times (\alpha_2, \beta_2)$ *be a rectangle, circumscribed around some region* G *(see Figure 6), and let the sequence* $u_n(\xi_1, \xi_2) = \phi_n(\xi_1) + \psi_n(\xi_2)$, $\phi_n \in L_2((\alpha_1, \beta_1)), \psi_n \in L_2((\alpha_2, \beta_2))$ *converge in the sense of* $L_2(G)$ *to a function in* (ξ_1, ξ_2). *Then* $u(\xi_1, \xi_2) = \phi(\xi_1) + \psi(\xi_2)$, *where* $\phi \in L_2((\alpha_1, \beta_1))$, $\psi \in L_2((\alpha_2, \beta_2))$, *and moreover the inequalities*

$$\| \varphi \|_{L_2((\alpha_1, \beta_1))} \leqslant C \| u \|_{L_2(G)}, \quad \| \psi \|_{L_2((\alpha_2, \beta_2))} \leqslant C \| u \|_{L_2(G)} \tag{2.24}$$

hold with the constant C *depending only on the region* G.

The proof reduces to the case $\phi_n \in C^2([\alpha_1, \beta_1])$ and $\psi_n \in C^2([\alpha_2, \beta_2])$. In fact, let $\phi_n' \in C^2([\alpha_1, \beta_1])$ and $\psi_n' \in C^2([\alpha_2, \beta_2])$ be such that

$$\| \varphi_n - \varphi_n' \|_{L_2((\alpha_1, \beta_1))} < \frac{1}{n}, \quad \| \psi_n - \psi_n' \|_{L_2((\alpha_2, \beta_2))} < \frac{1}{n}; \quad u_n'(\xi_1, \xi_2)$$
$$= \varphi_n'(\xi_1) + \psi_n'(\xi_2).$$

Then $\|u_n - u_n'\|_{L_2(Q)} \to 0$ and therefore a fortiori $u_n' \to u$ in $L_2(G)$. Thus we can assume that ϕ_n and ψ_n are smooth.

We show that u_n is fundamental in the metric of $L_2(Q)$. For this it is sufficient to show that u_n is fundamental in $L_2(O)$, where O is a small region adjoining G. Suppose that $u(x)$ is a function which satisfies the equation $Lu = D_1^2 u - D_2^2 u = 0$ in Q; then, as is well known, it has the form (see Figure 7)

$$u(x) = \frac{u(A') + u(D')}{2} + \frac{1}{2} \int_{A'}^{D'} (D_2 u)(y)\, dy.$$

We integrate this equation over the coordinate x_2 of the point A'. Letting $C_1, C_2, \cdots$ denote certain constants, we obtain

$$u(x) = C_1 \left(\int_A^B + \int_D^C \right) u(s)\, ds + C_2 \iint_{ABCD} (D_2 u)(y)\, dy$$

$$= C_3 \left(\int_A^B + \int_D^C \right) u(s)\, ds + C_2 \left(\int_B^C - \int_A^D \right) u(s)\, ds;$$

$$| u(x) |^2 \leqslant C_4 \left(\int_A^B + \int_D^C \right) | u(s) |^2 ds + C_5 \left(\int_B^C + \int_A^D \right) | u(s) |^2 ds.$$

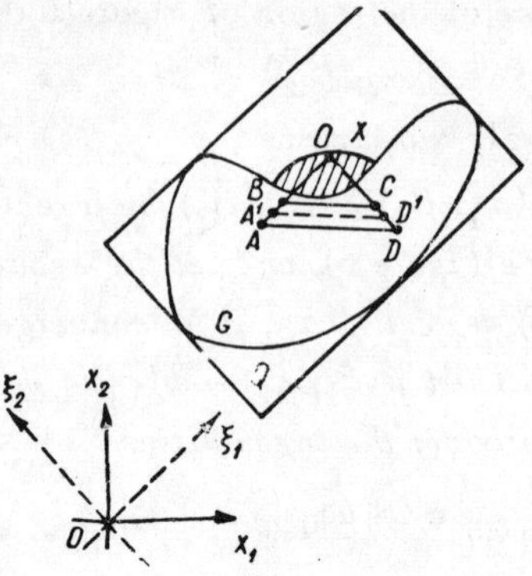

Figure 7.

We integrate the last equation over $x \in O$, where O is taken so small that for variable $x \in O$ the trapezoid $ABCD$ does not fall outside the limits of G. Continuing the estimate, we obtain

$$\| u \|_{L_2(O)} \leqslant C \| u \|_{L_2(G)}. \tag{2.25}$$

Since $u_n - u_m$ satisfies the equation $Lu = 0$ in Q, on the basis of (2.25) we conclude that $\|u_n - u_m\|_{L_2(O)} \to 0$. Thus, u_n is fundamental in $L_2(Q)$.

Denote by $v \in L_2(Q)$ the limit of u_n in $L_2(Q)$; obviously, $v(\xi) = u(\xi)$ for $\xi \in G$. Set

$$\widehat{\varphi}_n(\xi_1) = \varphi_n(\xi_1) - \frac{1}{\beta_1 - \alpha_1} \int_{\alpha_1}^{\beta_1} \varphi_n(\xi_1)\, d\xi_1, \quad \check{\psi}_n(\xi_2) = \psi_n(\xi_2) + \frac{1}{\beta_1 - \alpha_1} \int_{\alpha_1}^{\beta_1} \varphi_n(\xi_1) d\xi_1.$$

We have as before $u_n(\xi) = \widehat{\phi}_n(\xi_1) + \check{\psi}_n(\xi_2)$. We show that $\lim \widehat{\phi}_n$ exists in the sense of weak convergence in $L_2((\alpha_1, \beta_1))$. In fact, let $f \in L_2((\alpha_1, \beta_1))$ be arbitrary,

$$\widehat{f}(\xi_1) = f(\xi_1) - \frac{1}{\beta_1 - \alpha_1} \int_{\alpha_1}^{\beta_1} f(\xi_1)\, d\xi_1.$$

We have

$$(\beta_2 - \alpha_2) \int_{\alpha_1}^{\beta_1} \widehat{\varphi}_n f d\xi_1 = (\beta_2 - \alpha_2) \int_{\alpha_1}^{\beta_1} \widehat{\varphi}_n \widehat{f} d\xi_1$$

$$= \int_{\alpha_1}^{\beta_1} \int_{\alpha_2}^{\beta_2} (\widehat{\varphi}_n(\xi_1) + \check{\psi}_n(\xi_2))\, \widehat{f}(\xi_1)\, d\xi_1 d\xi_2$$

$$= \int_Q u_n(\xi) \widehat{f}(\xi_1)\, d\xi_1 d\xi_2 \to \int_Q v(\xi) \widehat{f}(\xi_1)\, d\xi_1 d\xi_2, \tag{2.26}$$

as required: set $\phi = \lim \hat{\phi}_n \in L_2((\alpha_1, \beta_1))$. A weak limit $\lim \check{\psi}_n$ also exists in $L_2((\alpha_2, \beta_2))$: for any $f \in L_2((\alpha_2, \beta_2))$ we have

$$(\beta_1 - \alpha_1) \int_{\alpha_2}^{\beta_2} \hat{\hat{\psi}}_n f d\xi_2 = \int_{\alpha_1}^{\beta_1}\int_{\alpha_2}^{\beta_2} (\hat{\varphi}_n(\xi_1) + \check{\psi}_n(\xi_2)) f(\xi_2)\, d\xi_1 d\xi_2$$

$$= \int_Q u_n(\xi) f(\xi_2)\, d\xi_1 d\xi_2 \to \int_Q v(\xi) f(\xi_2)\, d\xi_1 d\xi_2. \tag{2.27}$$

Set $\psi = \lim \check{\psi}_n \in L_2((\alpha_2, \beta_2))$.

We show that $v(\xi) = \phi(\xi_1) + \psi(\xi_2)$. Let $g \in L_2(Q)$: taking into account that single integrals of g belong to L_2 with respect to the other variable, we find

$$\int_Q u_n g d\xi = \int_{\alpha_1}^{\beta_1} \hat{\varphi}_n(\xi_1) \left(\int_{\alpha_2}^{\beta_2} g(\xi_1, \xi_2)\, d\xi_2 \right) d\xi_1 + \int_{\alpha_2}^{\beta_2} \check{\psi}_n(\xi_2) \left(\int_{\alpha_1}^{\beta_1} g(\xi_1, \xi_2)\, d\xi_1 \right) d\xi_2$$

$$\to \int_{\alpha_1}^{\beta_1} \varphi(\xi_1) \left(\int_{\alpha_2}^{\beta_2} g(\xi_1, \xi_2)\, d\xi_2 \right) d\xi_1$$

$$+ \int_{\alpha_2}^{\beta_2} \psi(\xi_2) \left(\int_{\alpha_1}^{\beta_1} g(\xi_1, \xi_2)\, d\xi_1 \right) d\xi_2 = \int_Q (\varphi + \psi)\, g d\xi.$$

At the same time $\int_Q u_n g d\xi \to \int_Q v g d\xi$, and in view of the arbitrariness of g we have $v = \phi + \psi$.

To finish the proof of the lemma we must establish the inequalities (2.24). From (2.26) and (2.27), we easily obtain the estimates

$$\| \varphi \|_{L_2((\alpha_1, \beta_1))} \leqslant C_1 \| v \|_{L_2(Q)}, \quad \| \psi \|_{L_2((\alpha_2, \beta_2))} \leqslant C_1 \| v \|_{L_2(Q)}, \tag{2.28}$$

where C_1 depends only on the size of Q. For large n $\|v\|_{L_2(Q)} \leq 2\, \|u_n\|_{L_2(Q)}$. The inequality (2.25) shows that we can write the estimate $\|u_n\|_{L_2(Q)} < C_2 \|u_n\|_{L_2(G)}$ where the constant C_2 depends on the form of the boundary of the region G. The inequalities (2.24) follow from (2.28), the last two inequalities, and the convergence $u_n \to u$ in $L_2(G)$. The lemma is proved.

Remark. It is clear from the proof of the inequalities (2.24) that if G_ν is an expanding sequence of regions of the form considered, which converges to a limiting region G, where the boundaries converge in the uniform metric, then the constant C in (2.24) can be chosen to hold for all G_ν.

Lemma 2.2. *Let G be a region with the property that each line $\xi_1 = C_1$, $\xi_2 = C_2$ intersects its boundary in at most two points. A function $u \in C^2(G \cup \Gamma)$ which satisfies the equation $\partial^2 u/\partial\xi_1\partial\xi_2 = 0$ inside G has the form (see Figure 6)*

$$u(\xi_1, \xi_2) = \varphi(\xi_1) + \psi(\xi_2), \quad \varphi \in C([\alpha_1, \beta_1]) \quad \psi \in C([\alpha_2, \beta_2]). \tag{2.29}$$

Proof. Let $\xi_2 = \chi(\xi_1) \in C([\alpha_1, \beta_1])$ be the equation of the lower part (with respect to the system $\xi_1 O \xi_2$) of the boundary of the region G. Integrating the equation $(\partial^2 u/\partial\xi_1\partial\xi_2)(\xi_1^0, \xi_2) = 0$ with respect to ξ_2 from $\chi(\xi_1^0)$ to ξ_2^0 (here $(\xi_1^0, \xi_2^0) \in G$), we obtain

$$\left(\frac{\partial u}{\partial \xi_1}\right)(\xi_1^0, \xi_2^0) - f(\xi_1^0) = 0, \text{ where } f(\xi_1^0) = \left(\frac{\partial u}{\partial \xi_1}\right)(\xi_1^0, \chi(\xi_1^0)) \in C([\alpha_1, \beta_1]).$$

Set

$$v(\xi_1, \xi_2^0) = u(\xi_1, \xi_2^0) - \int_{\alpha_1}^{\xi_1} f(t)\, dt \quad ((\xi_1, \xi_2^0) \in G),$$

for fixed ξ_2^0 in the corresponding interval of the variable ξ_1, $(\partial v/\partial\xi_1)(\xi_1, \xi_2^0) = 0$. Let $\xi_1 = \kappa(\xi_2) \in C([\alpha_2, \beta_2])$ be the equation of the left side (with respect to $\xi_1 O \xi_2$) of the boundary of the region G; integrating the last equation with respect to ξ_1 from $\kappa(\xi_2^0)$ to ξ_1^0, we find that $v(\xi_1^0, \xi_2^0) - v(\kappa(\xi_2^0), \xi_2^0) = 0$. Thus

$$u(\xi_1^0, \xi_2^0) = v(\xi_1^0, \xi_2^0) + \int_{\alpha_1}^{\xi_1^0} f(t)\, dt = \int_{\alpha_1}^{\xi_1^0} f(t)\, dt + v(\varkappa(\xi_2^0), \xi_2^0).$$

The representation (2. 29) is obtained. The lemma is proved.

We turn to the proof of the first part of the theorem—the representation (2.23). This representation already follows from the fact that $u \in L_2(G)$ is a solution of the equation (2.22) inside G. In fact, let O be a part of G, as in the statement of the theorem, on which $\omega(\xi)$ is to have the specified form. It follows from (2.21) that $(u, Lv)_0 = (f, v)_0$, $v \in C_0^2(O)$. An analogous equation, as is easily computed, holds with u replaced by the integral of (2.23); hence

$$(\omega, Lv)_0 = 0 \quad (v \in C_0^2(O)). \tag{2.30}$$

Denote by S_ϵ $(\epsilon > 0)$ the averaging operator, constructed from the function $\omega_\epsilon(y)$, which in addition is even. Let $\delta > 0$ be fixed, O_δ the subregion of O consisting of those points $\xi \in O$ such that $\rho(\xi, \gamma) > \delta$, where γ is the boundary of O. If $w \in C(O)$ is different from zero only for $\xi \in O_\delta$, then $v = S_\epsilon w \in C_0^\infty(O)$ for ϵ sufficiently small. Substituting this function in (2.30) and using properties of the averaging operator, we obtain

$$0 = (\omega, L[S_\varepsilon w])_0 = (\omega, S_\varepsilon Lw)_0 = (S_\varepsilon \omega, Lw)_0 = (L[S_\varepsilon \omega], w)_0$$

($S_\epsilon^* = S_\epsilon$ because of the evenness of $\omega_\epsilon(y)$). In view of the arbitrariness of w it follows that $(L[S_\epsilon \omega])(\xi) = 0$ for $\xi \in O_\delta$ and all sufficiently small ϵ; the function $S_\epsilon\omega \in C^\infty(\bar{O}_\delta)$. For $\delta > 0$ sufficiently small the boundary of the region O_δ intersects each line parallel to the ξ_1 and ξ_2 axes in at most two points, but then by Lemma 2.2 the smooth solution of the equation $\partial^2 u/\partial\xi_1\partial\xi_2 = 0$ $(\xi \in O_\delta)$ is restored by formula (2.29). Thus $(S_\epsilon\omega)(\xi) = \phi_\epsilon(\xi_1) + \psi_\epsilon(\xi_2)$ with continuous ϕ_ϵ and ψ_ϵ. Now take the limit as $\epsilon \to 0$. Since $\omega \in L_2(0)$, $S_\epsilon\omega \to \omega$ in the sense of $L_2(O_\delta)$, i.e. $\phi_\epsilon(\xi_1) + \psi_\epsilon(\xi_2)$ has a limit in $L_2(O_\delta)$. By Lemma 2.1 this limit has the form $\phi(\xi_1) + \psi(\xi_2)$ where $\phi \in L_2((\alpha_1^{(\delta)}, \beta_1^{(\delta)}))$, $\psi \in L_2((\alpha_2^{(\delta)}, \beta_2^{(\delta)}))$; $(\alpha_1^{(\delta)}, \beta_1^{(\delta)})$ and $(\alpha_2^{(\delta)}, \beta_2^{(\delta)})$ are determined by the region O_δ. Thus

$$\omega(\xi) = \varphi(\xi_1) + \psi(\xi_2) \quad (\xi \in O_\delta),$$

$$\|\varphi\|_{L_2((\alpha_1^{(\delta)}, \beta_1^{(\delta)}))} \leqslant C\|\omega\|_{L_2(O_\delta)}, \quad \|\psi\|_{L_2((\alpha_2^{(\delta)}, \beta_2^{(\delta)}))} \leqslant C\|\omega\|_{L_2(O_\delta)}. \tag{2.31}$$

Now let $\delta \to 0$. It is not difficult to see that the functions ϕ and ψ are defined on larger intervals than the original $(\alpha_1^{(\delta)}, \beta_1^{(\delta)})$ and $(\alpha_2^{(\delta)}, \beta_2^{(\delta)})$. As a result we obtain the first of the relations (2.31) for all $\xi \in O$. The functions ϕ and ψ belong to L_2 on the intervals corresponding to O: this follows from the remark to Lemma 2.1 and inequalities (2.31); in addition, it is necessary to consider that $\omega \in L_2(O)$. Thus, the representation (2.23) is proved.

We turn to the proof of the second part. The integral in (2.23) is continuous with respect to ξ and therefore has values on Γ. The function $\omega(\xi)$ is locally equal to $\phi(\xi_1) + \psi(\xi_2)$, where $\phi, \psi \in L_2$: on each piecewise-smooth curve, not containing pieces of the lines $\xi_1 = C_1$, $\xi_2 = C_2$, it is defined almost everywhere. Thus, each function of the type (2.23) has values almost everywhere on Γ. We show that if such a function is a weak solution of the problem (2.22), then $u|_\Gamma = 0$. We need the following lemma.

Lemma 2.3. *Let $u(\xi)$ be a function of the form (2.23). For any $v \in \mathring{W}_2^1(G) \cap W_2^2(G)$ which vanishes in addition in a neighborhood of each point of the boundary, at which the tangent is a characteristic, the equation*

$$(\omega, Lv)_0 = \int_\Gamma \omega \frac{\partial \bar{v}}{\partial \mu} dx, \tag{2.32}$$

holds, where $\mu = (\nu_1, -\nu_2)$ is the unit conormal of the expression L.

We clarify that the function $\omega(\xi)$ is locally of the form $\phi(\xi_1) + \psi(\xi_2)$, where ϕ and ψ belong to L_2, and hence that ω is also square summable on each section of Γ which is at a positive distance from the points P_k with tangents parallel to the ξ_1 or ξ_2 axis. This shows that the integral in (2.32) makes sense.

Proof of the Lemma. Let O_j be the subregions mentioned above, γ_j their boundaries; construct N infinitely differentiable functions $\chi_j(x) \geq 0$ $(x \in E_2)$, each of which vanishes in $G \setminus O_j$ and in a neighborhood of the piece $\gamma_j \setminus \Gamma$ of the boundary, such that $\Sigma_{j=1}^N \chi_j(x) = 1$ $(x \in G)$. Since $v(x) = \Sigma_{j=1}^N v(x)\chi_j(x)$, then in order to prove equation (2.32) it is sufficient to show that

$$(\omega, Lv)_{L_2(O_j)} = \int_{\gamma_j} \omega \frac{\partial \bar{v}}{\partial \mu} dx, \tag{2.33}$$

where $v \in W_2^2(O_j)$, $v|_\Gamma = 0$ is any function which vanishes in a neighborhood of the points P_k and in a neighborhood of $\gamma_j \setminus \Gamma$. We limit consideration to the more complicated case, when $\gamma_j \cap \Gamma$ is not empty. In the region O_j, $\omega(\xi) = \phi(\xi_1) + \psi(\xi_2)$; hence (2.33) can be rewritten in the form

$$(\varphi(\xi_1) + \psi(\xi_2), Lv)_{L_2(O_j)} = \int_{(\gamma_j \cap \Gamma) \setminus \Delta} (\varphi(\xi_1) + \psi(\xi_2)) \frac{\partial \bar{v}}{\partial \mu} dx; \tag{2.34}$$

here Δ is the set of intervals on $\gamma_j \cap \Gamma$, obtained from the intersection of the neighborhoods of the points P_k with $\gamma_j \cap \Gamma$. We establish (2.34). For this we construct sequences of smooth $\phi_n(\xi_1)$ and $\psi_n(\xi_2)$ such that $\phi_n \to \phi$ in $L_2((\alpha_1, \beta_1))$ and $\psi_n \to \psi$ in $L_2((\alpha_2, \beta_2))$ ($(\alpha_1, \beta_1) \times (\alpha_2, \beta_2)$ is the minimal rectangle containing O_j). Equation (2.34) with ϕ replaced by ϕ_n and ψ replaced by ψ_n is an obvious consequence of Green's formula. Write down (2.34) for ϕ_n and ψ_n and pass to the limit as $n \to \infty$. This is possible since $\phi_n + \psi_n \to \phi + \psi$ both in $L_2(O_j)$ and in $L_2((\gamma_j \cap \Gamma) \setminus \Delta)$. As a result we obtain (2.34) for ϕ and ψ. The lemma is proved.

We conclude the proof of the theorem. Let u be a weak solution of the problem (2.22); if $w(\xi)$ denotes the integral in (2.23), we have $u = w + \omega$. By means of (2.32) and Green's formula we find

$$(u, Lv)_0 - (f, v)_0 = (w, Lv)_0 - (f, v)_0 + (\omega, Lv)_0$$
$$= (Lw, v)_0 - (f, v)_0 + \int_\Gamma w \frac{\partial \bar{v}}{\partial \mu} dx + \int_\Gamma \omega \frac{\partial \bar{v}}{\partial \mu} dx = \int_\Gamma u \frac{\partial \bar{v}}{\partial \mu} dx, \tag{2.35}$$

where $v \in W_2^2(G)$ is arbitrary except that $v|_\Gamma = 0$ and that it vanishes in arbitrarily small neighborhoods of the points P_k. Since $(\partial v/\partial \mu)|_\Gamma$ assumes sufficiently arbitrary values outside of these neighborhoods, and $(u, Lv)_0 - (f, v)_0 = 0$, it follows from (2.35) that $u|_\Gamma = 0$. The theorem is proved.

In any case, for regions whose boundary does not contain any points with tangent parallel to the ξ_1 or ξ_2 axis (for example, G in Figure 6), any function u of the form (2.23), which vanishes on Γ, is a weak solution of problem (2.22);

this follows immediately from the identity (2.35).

Thus we have clarified the smoothness character of weak solutions of the problem (2.22). It is shown above that there is stability with respect to variations of the boundaries, for regions for which a weak solution exists for any $f \in L_2(G)$. The question arises as to whether these solutions will also be strong. In the case of problem (2.22), $L^+ = L$, $(\mathrm{bd})^+ = (\mathrm{bd})$, and $\|Lu\|_0 \geq C\|u\|_0$ $(u \in W_2^2(\mathrm{bd}))$; hence $\Pi(\mathrm{bd}) < \Lambda(\mathrm{bd})$ in those and only those cases when the weak solution of the problem $Lu = 0$, $u|_\Gamma = 0$ is unique (this follows from the assertions in §2.3, Chapter II). It is not difficult to show, with the help of Theorem 2.3, that in the examples of regions described at the beginning of this subsection such uniqueness is not the case and therefore $\Lambda(\mathrm{bd}) \subset \Pi(\mathrm{bd})$. It is also easy to see that functions of $\mathfrak{D}(\Lambda(\mathrm{bd}))$ do not all belong to $W_2^2(\mathrm{bd})$; consequently $\Lambda'(\mathrm{bd}) \subset \Lambda(\mathrm{bd})$.

We establish the nonuniqueness of weak solutions, limiting ourselves to the case of the region of Figure 6. Let M be some point on its boundary, different from A and B, and construct the sequence of points $M_1, M_2, \cdots; M_{-1}, M_{-2}, \cdots$ with respect to M as indicated in the figure. Consider the interval (α_1, β_1) and associate with M the even set of ξ_1-coordinates of the points M_j: $M \to \Xi_{1,M}$. As a result we obtain a partition of the interval (α_1, β_1) into a union of even classes $\Xi_{1,M}$. By an analogous consideration of the ξ_2-coordinates of the points M_j, we obtain a partition of the interval (α_2, β_2) into a union of classes $\Xi_{2,M}$. Let $\phi(\xi_1)$ be a measurable step function on (α_1, β_1), the set of constancy of which consists entirely of classes of the type $\Xi_{1,M}$, and let $\psi(\xi_2)$ be a similar function on the interval (α_2, β_2). Let ϕ admit at least two distinct values and let $\psi(\xi_2) = -\phi(\xi_1)$ in the case when $\xi_1 \in \Xi_{1,M}$ and ξ_2 belongs to the class $\Xi_{2,M}$ generated by the same point M; from Figure 6, it is obvious that such functions are easily constructed. Then $\omega(\xi_1, \xi_2) = \phi(\xi_1) + \psi(\xi_2) \not\equiv 0$ for $(\xi_1, \xi_2) \in G$ and $\omega(\xi_1, \xi_2)|_\Gamma = 0$. By Theorem 2.3 and the remark on it made above, $\omega(\xi_1, \xi_2)$ is different from zero and is a weak solution of the problem $Lu = 0$, $u|_\Gamma = 0$, as required.

It is not difficult to see that the subspace Z of all weak solutions of the problem under consideration (i.e. the set of zeros of the operator $\Pi(\mathrm{bd})$) changes substantially for small variations of the boundary; a variation of Z implies a variation of the operator L of Theorem 2.2, Chapter II. Therefore, although we are able to establish weak solvability of the problem (2.22), and stability with respect to small variations of the boundary, we can not guarantee the choice of a unique solution, depending continuously on f, by means of superposition of simple additional conditions, common for all close regions. Apparently, a similar situation arises in the case of the general Theorem 2.1..

5. **Stronger uniqueness theorems. Conditional solvability.** For the region of Figure 6, the uniqueness theorem for smooth solutions follows naturally from the energy inequality: if $u \in W_2^2(G)$, $u|_\Gamma = 0$, and $Lu = 0$, then $u(x) = 0$ $(x \in G)$. In fact, for the validity of the uniqueness theorem, it is optional that u vanish on all of Γ. We show this: *if $u \in W_2^2(G)$, $u|_{\Gamma \setminus \gamma} = 0$ (see Figure 6; γ must be of sufficiently small length), and $Lu = 0$, then $u(x) = 0$ $(x \in G)$*. In fact, it is obvious from the proof of Lemma 2.2 that the lemma itself is valid in case $u \in W_2^2(G)$; hence the representation (2.29) holds. Since $u|_{\Gamma\setminus\gamma} = 0$, it is easy to see that $\phi(\xi_1)$ is constant on the whole class $\Xi_{1,M}$, if only $M \in \Gamma \setminus (\bigcup_{j=-\infty}^{\infty} \gamma_j)$, $\gamma_0 = \gamma$, and $\psi(\xi_2)$ is constant on all $\Xi_{2,M}$, where $\psi(\xi_2) = -\phi(\xi_1)$ if $\xi_2 \in \Xi_{2,M}$, $\xi_1 \in \Xi_{1,M}$. Since the points α_1 and β_1 are bounds for any class $\Xi_{1,M}$, by the continuity of ϕ on $[\alpha_1, \beta_1]$ $\phi(\xi_1) = \phi(\alpha_1) = \phi(\beta_1) = C$ for the coordinates ξ_1 of the mentioned points M. Similarly, for the coordinates ξ_2 of these points $\psi(\xi_2) = \psi(\alpha_2) = \psi(\beta_2) = -C$. In a similar way if we move away from the point $M \in \Gamma\setminus\gamma$ either toward the side of the point A or toward the side of the point B, we conclude that in general $\phi(\xi_1) = C$ $(\xi_1 \in [\alpha_1, \beta_1])$ and $\psi(\xi_2) = -C$ $(\xi_2 \in [\alpha_2, \beta_2])$. Thus $u(\xi) = \phi(\xi_1) + \psi(\xi_2) = C - C = 0$ $(\xi \in G)$. Uniqueness is proved.

By Theorem 1.1, Chapter II, the adjoint conditions to the conditions $u|_{\Gamma\setminus\gamma} = 0$, $u|_\gamma$ ~ are $v|_{\Gamma\setminus\gamma} = 0$, $v|_\gamma = \partial v/\partial\mu|_\gamma = 0$. Applying Theorem 3.1 of this chapter, we conclude that *the problem $Lu = f$, $u|_\Gamma = 0$, $\partial u/\partial\mu|_\gamma = 0$, is conditionally solvable for any $f \in W_2^{-2}(G)$*. It is clear that the arguments of this subsection can be generalized to regions of more complicated structure than that depicted in Figure 6.

§3. EQUATIONS OF MIXED TYPE

In this section we show how the methods of determining reasonable formulations of boundary value problems, designated in the beginning of §2, can be applied to equations with variable coefficients. Equations of mixed type will be studied, i.e. equations which are elliptic in one part of the space and hyperbolic in the other. Only the simplest equations and formulations of problems are considered, but these considerations can be carried over, in the large, to more complicated cases. The technique used below can be considered as a development of the so-called *abc*-method of proof of uniqueness theorems for such equations.

1. **Form of the differential expression.** Let G be a region in the plane (x_1, x_2), bounded by a closed, piecewise-smooth curve Γ which intersects the axis Ox_1; $-h < x_2 < H$ $(-h = \inf_{x \in G} x_2,\ H = \sup_{x \in G} x_2)$ is the strip in which this region is situated. Consider in G a differential expression, for simplicity with real coefficients, of the form

$$Lu = \sum_{j,k=1}^{2} D_j (b_{jk}(x) D_k u) + \sum_{j=1}^{2} p_j(x) D_j u + p(x) u. \tag{3.1}$$

Assume that L is elliptic in the region $G_e = G \cap \{x_2 > 0\}$ in the sense that for some $\epsilon > 0$

$$\sum_{j,k=1}^{2} b_{jk}(x) \xi_j \xi_k \geq \varepsilon |\xi_2|^2;$$

in addition, let

$$p(x) - \frac{1}{2} \sum_{j=1}^{2} (D_j p_j)(x) \leqslant 0 \ (x \in G_e)$$ [1];

the coefficients $b_{jk}(x), p_j(x) \in C^1(\overline{G}_e)$, $p(x) \in C(\overline{G}_e)$. Under transition of x to the hyperbolic region $G_h = G \cap \{x_2 < 0\}$ the coefficients of L turn continuously into the coefficients of the hyperbolic expression

$$k(x_2) D_1^2 + D_2^2. \tag{3.2}$$

Here $k(x_2)$ is continuous in $[-h, 0]$ and continuously differentiable in $[-h, 0)$, where

$$k(x_2) < 0, \quad k'(x_2) > 0 \text{ in } [-h, 0), \quad \lim_{x_2 \to 0} \frac{k(x_2)}{k'(x_2)} = 0$$

and $(k/k')'$ is summable in $[-h, 0]$.

The expression L under consideration is called Čaplygin's expression if it also has the form (3.2) in the elliptic part G_e with $k(x_2) > 0$; the corresponding equation $Lu = 0$ plays an important part in transonic gas dynamics. Čaplygin's expression is transformed into the so-called Tricomi expression, if $k(x_2) = x_2$.

We will find the characteristics of the expression L in the hyperbolic region G_h. For the unit vector $\nu(x)$ normal to the characteristic we have

$$k(x_2) \nu_1^2(x) + \nu_2^2(x) = 0. \tag{3.3}$$

---

[1] In this section it is convenient to neglect consideration of the respective choices of sign of the form for the elliptic expression, adopted at the beginning of Chapter III.

If $x_2 = x_2(x_1)$ is the equation of the characteristic, then (dx_1, dx_2) is a vector along its tangent, and $(-dx_2, dx_1)$ along its normal. Substituting the coordinates of the latter vector in (3.3), we obtain the differential equation of the characteristic $k(x_2)(dx_2)^2 + (dx_1)^2 = 0$, i.e., $dx_1 = \pm\sqrt{-k(x_2)}\, dx_2$. Integrating this equation, we obtain two families of characteristics:

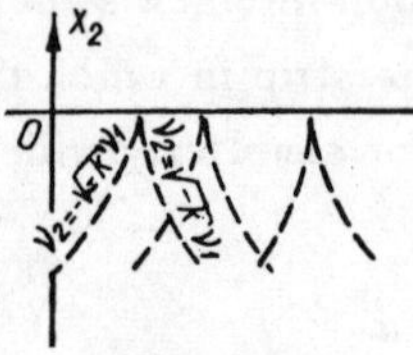

Figure 8.

$$x_1 = \pm \int_0^{x_2} \sqrt{-k(t)}\, dt + C. \tag{3.4}$$

The derivative $dx_1/dx_2 = \pm\sqrt{-k(x_2)}$ never becomes ∞; hence the tangent to a characteristic is never parallel to the axis Ox_1, i.e. $\nu_1(x) \neq 0$. Thus $B(x)\nu(x) = (k(x_2)\nu_1(x), \nu_2(x)) \neq 0$ $(x_2 < 0)$, i.e. the characteristics are weak; for $x_2 = 0$ we have degeneration: $B(x_1, 0)\nu(x_1, 0) = 0$. The form of the characteristics is shown in Figure 8.

Our next aim is to establish energy inequalities for certain boundary value problems connected with the expression (3.1)–(3.2). In accord with what was shown in §2.1, to obtain these inequalities we consider the integral

$$2\,\mathrm{Re} \int_G (Lu)(x)\, \overline{(a(x)\, D_1 u + b(x)\, D_2 u + c(x) u)}\, dx \qquad (u \in W_2^2(G)). \tag{3.5}$$

with sufficiently smooth real functions a, b, and c of the variable $x \in G$, and by means of integration by parts and special choices of these functions, we try to extract definite sums from it. The examination is based on an identity for the expression (3.2), which is obtained by means of a direct application of equations (2.1) and (2.2). If $G' \subseteq G$ is some subregion of G, Γ' its boundary, then the identity has the form

$$\begin{aligned}
2\,\mathrm{Re} \int_{G'} (kD_1^2 u + D_2^2 u)\, \overline{(aD_1 u + bD_2 u + cu)}\, dx &= \int_{G'} \{(-kD_1 a + D_2(kb) - 2kc)|D_1 u|^2 \\
&\quad - 2\,\mathrm{Re}\,(kD_1 b + D_2 a)\, D_1 u \cdot \overline{D_2 u} + (D_1 a - D_2 b - 2c)\, |D_2 u|^2\}\, dx + \int_{G'} (kD_1^2 c \\
&\quad + D_2^2 c)\, |u|^2 dx + \int_{\Gamma'} \{-k(-a\nu_1 + b\nu_2)\, |D_1 u|^2 - 2\,\mathrm{Re}\,(-kb\nu_1 - a\nu_2) D_1 u \cdot \overline{D_2 u} \\
&\quad + (-a\nu_1 + b\nu_2)\, |D_2 u|^2\}\, dx + 2\,\mathrm{Re} \int_{\Gamma'} c\, (k\nu_1 D_1 u + \nu_2 D_2 u)\, \bar{u}\, dx \\
&\quad - \int_{\Gamma'} (k\nu_1 D_1 c + \nu_2 D_2 c)\, |u|^2 dx
\end{aligned}$$

$$(u \in W_2^2(G')). \tag{3.6}$$

2. Derivation of energy inequalities. We will now derive energy inequalities for the expression (3.1)–(3.2), using the identity (3.6) in G_h, and the usual estimate of an elliptic expression in G_e. Set

$$q(x_2) = -\frac{4k(x_2)}{k'(x_2)} > 0 \; (-h \leqslant x_2 < 0,\; q(0) = 0),\; a = \sqrt{-kq}c,\; b = -qc. \tag{3.7}$$

Take $G' = G_h$ in (3.6) and substitue the given expressions for a and b. Observing that $k(0) = q(0) = 0$, we find after a simple calculation ($\Gamma_h = \Gamma \cap \{x_2 < 0\}$, $\Gamma_m = G \cap \{x_2 = 0\}$):

$$2\operatorname{Re}\int_{G_h} Lu\cdot\overline{(aD_1u + bD_2u + cu)}\,dx = 2\operatorname{Re}\int_{G_h} Lu\cdot \overline{c\,[q(\sqrt{-k}D_1u - D_2u) + u]}\,dx$$

$$= \int_{G_h} (\sqrt{-kq}D_1c + D_2(qc) - 2c)\,|\sqrt{-k}D_1u - D_2u|^2dx +$$

$$+ \int_{G_h} (kD_1^2c + D_2^2c)\,|u|^2\,dx - \int_{\Gamma_h} qc(\sqrt{-k}\nu_1 + \nu_2)\,|\sqrt{-k}D_1u - D_2u|^2dx$$

$$+ 2\operatorname{Re}\int_{\Gamma_h} c\,(k\nu_1D_1u + \nu_2D_2u)\,\bar{u}dx - \int_{\Gamma_h} (k\nu_1D_1c + \nu_2D_2c)\,|u|^2\,dx$$

$$+ 2\operatorname{Re}\int_{\Gamma_m} c\,(x_1, 0)\,D_2u\cdot\bar{u}dx - \int_{\Gamma_m} (D_2c)(x_1, 0)\,|u|^2dx \tag{3.8}$$

$$(u \in W_2^2(G_r)).$$

For functions $u \in W_2^2(G_e)$, $u|_{\Gamma_e} = 0$ ($\Gamma_e = \Gamma \cap \{x_2 > 0\}$) we obtain in the usual way (see p. 115)

$$2\operatorname{Re}\int_{G_e} Lu\cdot\bar{u}dx = -2\int_{G_e}\sum_{j,k=1}^{2} b_{jk}D_ku\cdot D_j\bar{u}dx + \int_{G_e}\Big(2p - \sum_{j=1}^{2} D_jp_j\Big)\,|u|^2dx$$

$$-2\operatorname{Re}\int_{\Gamma_m} D_2u\cdot\bar{u}dx. \tag{3.9}$$

If $c(x_1, 0) = c(0)$ is a constant, multiplying (3.9) by $c(0)$ and combining it with (3.8), we obtain ($\kappa_E(x)$ is the characteristic function of the set E):

$$2\operatorname{Re}\int_{G} Lu\cdot \overline{\{\varkappa_{G_h}c\,[q(\sqrt{-k}D_1u - D_2u) + u] + \varkappa_{G_e}c(0)\,u\}}\,dx$$

$$= -2c(0)\int_{G_e}\sum_{j,k=1}^{2} b_{jk}D_ku\cdot D_j\bar{u}dx + \int_{G_h} (\sqrt{-kq}D_1c + D_2(qc) - 2c)\,|\sqrt{-k}D_1u,$$

$$-D_2u|^2dx + c(0)\int_{G_e}\Big(2p - \sum_{j=1}^{2} D_jp_j\Big)\,|u|^2dx + \int_{G_h} (kD_1^2c + D_2^2c)\,|u|^2dx -$$

$$-\int_{\Gamma_m} (D_2c)(x_1, 0) \, |u|^2 dx + I_{\Gamma_h}, \tag{3.10}$$

where

$$I_{\Gamma_h} = -\int_{\Gamma_h} qc(\sqrt{-k}\nu_1 + \nu_2) \, |\sqrt{-k}D_1u - D_2u|^2 dx + 2\,\mathrm{Re} \int_{\Gamma_h} c\,(k\nu_1 D_1 u \tag{3.11}$$

$$+ \nu_2 D_2 u)\bar{u}dx - \int_{\Gamma_h} (k\nu_1 D_1 c + \nu_2 D_2 c) \, |u|^2 dx.$$

Assume that we have chosen Γ_h, the boundary conditions for u on Γ_h, and a real function $c(x)$ $(x \in \bar{G}_h)$ such that

$$I_{\Gamma_h} \geqslant 0; \tag{3.12}$$

$$c(0) < 0, \; (D_2c)(x_1, 0) \leqslant 0 \; ((x_1, 0) \in \Gamma_m), \; \sqrt{-k}qD_1c + D_2(qc) - 2c \geqslant \delta > 0 (x \in G_h),$$

$$kD_1^2 c + D_2^2 c \geqslant 0 \quad (x \in G_h). \tag{3.13}$$

In relation to the smoothness of $c(x)$, as is obvious from the indicated calculations, it is sufficient to require that it be twice piecewise-continuously differentiable. We show that under these assumptions and certain additional restrictions the energy inequality of Lemma 3.1 holds. In fact, in this lemma, we show that under broad boundary conditions on u the estimate

$$\int_{G_e} \sum_{j,k=1}^{2} b_{jk} D_k u \cdot D_j \bar{u} dx + \int_{G_h} |\sqrt{-k}D_1 u - D_2 u|^2 dx \geqslant C \int_G |u|^2 dx \tag{3.14}$$

holds. If a positive norm is introduced by the equation

$$\|u\|^2_{+,\ell} = \int_G |u|^2 dx + \int_{G_e} \sum_{j,k=1}^{2} b_{jk} D_k u \cdot D_j \bar{u} dx + \int_{G_h} |\sqrt{-k}D_1 u - D_2 u|^2 dx \tag{3.15}$$

$$(u \in W_2^1(G)),$$

then for functions $u \in W_2^2(G)$, which satisfy the required boundary conditions, we have the estimate (following from (3.10))

$$C_1 \|Lu\|_0 \|u\|_{+,\ell}$$

$$\geqslant \left| 2\,\mathrm{Re} \int_G Lu \cdot \{\varkappa_{G_h} [qc(\sqrt{-k}D_1 u - D_2 u) + cu] + \varkappa_{G_e} c(0) u\} \, dx \right| \geqslant C_2 \|u\|^2_{+,\ell},$$

i.e. $\|Lu\|_0 \geq C_3 \|u\|_{+,\ell}$.

Thus, if the boundary Γ_h, *and the boundary conditions on it can be chosen so that inequalities* (3.12) *and* (3.13) *hold and inequality* (3.14) *holds on* $W_2^2(\mathrm{bd})$, *then the energy inequality*

$$\|Lu\|_0 \geq C \|u\|_{+,\ell} \quad (u \in W_2^2(\mathrm{m})) \tag{3.16}$$

holds.

We will explain somewhat the possible choice of Γ_h and the boundary conditions on it, below. We show now that the same inequality (3.14) holds under sufficiently general assumptions.

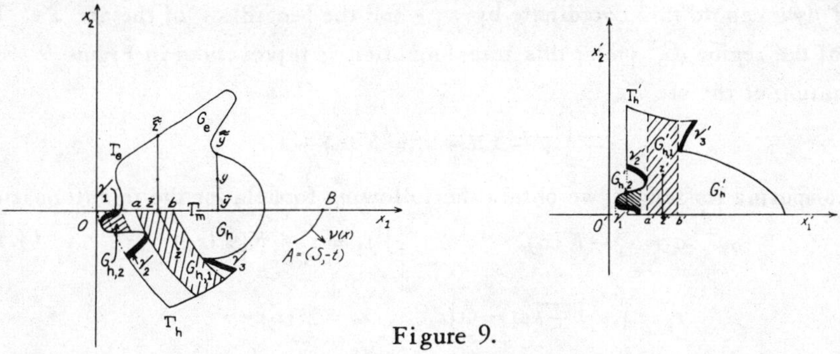

Figure 9.

Lemma 3.1. *Let* Γ *be an arbitrary piecewise-smooth curve, let* $u_{\Gamma_e} = 0$ *and* u *vanish on all those sections of the curve* Γ_h *which are "upper" with respect to the family of characteristics of the form* $\nu_2 = \sqrt{-k\nu_1}$ *(sections* $\gamma_1, \gamma_2, \gamma_3$ *in Figure 9). Estimate (3.14) is valid for functions* $u \in W_2^1(G)$ *which satisfy such boundary conditions.*

Proof. First of all note that

$$\int_{G_e} |D_2u|^2 dx \geqslant C_1 \int_{G_e} |u|^2 dx \quad (u \in W_2^1(G_e),\ u|_{\Gamma_e} = 0). \tag{3.17}$$

In fact, let $y \in G_e$ be arbitrary, and let $(\tilde{y}, \tilde{\tilde{y}})$ be the largest vertical segment lying entirely in G_e, which passes through the point y (see Figure 9). Integrating $\partial u/\partial x_2$ over $(y, \tilde{\tilde{y}})$ and observing that $u(\tilde{\tilde{y}}) = 0$, we obtain

$$-u(y) = \int_y^{\tilde{\tilde{y}}} \frac{\partial u}{\partial x_2}\, dx.$$

Hence

$$\int_{\tilde{y}}^{\tilde{\tilde{y}}} |u(y)|^2 dy = \int_{\tilde{y}}^{\tilde{\tilde{y}}} \left| \int_y^{\tilde{\tilde{y}}} D_2u\,dx \right|^2 dy \leqslant H \int_{\tilde{y}}^{\tilde{\tilde{y}}} \int_y^{\tilde{\tilde{y}}} |D_2u|^2 dx\,dy \leqslant C_2 \int_{\tilde{y}}^{\tilde{\tilde{y}}} |D_2u|^2 dx.$$

Since this inequality holds for each interval $(\tilde{y}, \tilde{\tilde{y}})$, then by integrating over all such intervals, we obtain (3.17).

We now establish the inequality

$$\int_{G_e} |D_2u|^2\, dx + \int_{G_h} |\sqrt{-k}D_1u - D_2u|^2 dx \geqslant C_1 \int_{G_h} |u|^2 dx, \tag{3.18}$$

valid for all functions $u \in W_2^1(G)$, which satisfy the boundary conditions stated in the lemma. To this end we go over to new coordinates in the half-plane $x_2 \leq 0$, regarding as the coordinates of the point z (see Figure 9) the x_1-coordinate of the point $\tilde{z}$ (we denote this coordinate by x_1') and the length x_2' of the arc $\tilde{z}z$. The image of the region G_h under this transformation is represented in Figure 9. Since the equation of the arc $\tilde{z}z$ is

$$x_1 = -\int_0^{x_2} \sqrt{-k}dt + x_1' = K(x_2) + x_1',$$

then, computing its length, we obtain the following formula for the transformation:

$$x_1 = x_1 - K(x_2), \qquad x_1 = x_1' + K(\Psi(x_2')), \tag{3.19}$$

$$x_2 = \int_{x_2}^{0} \sqrt{1-k}dt = \Phi(x_2), \qquad x_2 = \Psi(x_2');$$

$$\left|\frac{dx'}{dx}\right| = |\Phi'(x_2)| = \sqrt{1-k(x_2)}.$$

Here Ψ denotes the inverse of the monotone function Φ; dx'/dx is the Jacobian of the transformation from the variables $x' = (x_1', x_2')$ to the variables $x = (x_1, x_2)$; obviously, in the bounded region, $1 \leq |dx'/dx| \leq C < \infty$. Since $K' = -\sqrt{-k}$,

$$\frac{\partial u}{\partial x_2'} = \frac{\partial u}{\partial x_1}\frac{\partial x_1}{\partial x_2'} + \frac{\partial u}{\partial x_2}\frac{\partial x_2}{\partial x_2'} = -\Psi'(x_2')\left(\sqrt{-k(x_2)}\frac{\partial u}{\partial x_1} - \frac{\partial u}{\partial x_2}\right) = -\Psi'(x_2')\mathfrak{M}u. \tag{3.20}$$

We now deduce the estimate (3.18) in which the region G_h is replaced by the region $G_{h,1}$ (see Figure 9). Integrating the derivative $\partial u/\partial x_2'$ over the interval $(\tilde{z}', z')$, we obtain

$$u(z') - u(\tilde{z}') = \int_{\tilde{z}'}^{z'} \frac{\partial u}{\partial x_2'} dx_2',$$

and hence

$$|u(z')|^2 \leqslant 2|u(\tilde{z}')|^2 + 2\left|\int_{\tilde{z}'}^{z'} \frac{\partial u}{\partial x_2'} dx_2'\right|^2 \leqslant 2|u(\tilde{z}')|^2 + C_2 \int_{\tilde{z}'}^{z'} \left|\frac{\partial u}{\partial x_2'}\right|^2 dx_2'.$$

Using relations (3.19) and (3.20), we find

$$\int_{G_{h,1}} |u|^2 dx = \int_{G_{h,1}'} |u|^2 \left|\frac{dx}{dx'}\right| dx' \leqslant C_3 \int_{G_{h,1}'} |u|^2 dx' \leqslant C_4 \int_{a'}^{b'} |u(z_1', 0)|^2 dz_1'$$

$$+ C_2C_3 \int_{G_{h,1}'} \int_{\tilde{z}'}^{z'} \left|\frac{\partial u}{\partial x_2'}\right|^2 dx_2' dz' \leqslant C_4 \int_{a'}^{b'} \ldots + C_5 \int_{G_{h,1}'} \left|\frac{\partial u}{\partial x_2'}\right|^2 dz' = C_4 \int_{a'}^{b'} \ldots +$$

$$+C_5 \int\limits_{G'_{h,1}} |\Psi'(z_2')|^2 |\mathfrak{M}u|^2 dz' \leqslant C_4 \int\limits_{a'}^{b'} \dots + C_6 \int\limits_{G'_{h,1}} |\mathfrak{M}u|^2 dz'$$

$$= C_4 \int\limits_{a'}^{b'} \dots + C_6 \int\limits_{G_{h,1}} |\mathfrak{M}u|^2 \left|\frac{dx'}{dx}\right| dx \leqslant C_4 \int\limits_{a'}^{b'} |u(z_1', 0)|^2 dz_1 + C_7 \int\limits_{G_{h,1}} |\mathfrak{M}u|^2 dx. \quad (3.21)$$

We estimate the first integral in the first part of (3.21). First of all, note that for $x_2' = 0$, $x_1' = x_1$; hence this equals $\int_a^b |u(x_1, 0)|^2 dx_1$. Integrating $\partial u/\partial x_2$ over $(\tilde{z}, \tilde{\tilde{z}})$ and observing that $u(\tilde{\tilde{z}}) = 0$, we obtain

$$-u(\tilde{z}) = \int\limits_{\tilde{z}}^{\tilde{\tilde{z}}} \left(\frac{\partial u}{\partial x_2}\right)(z_1, x_2)\, dx_2, \quad |u(z_1, 0)|^2 = |u(\tilde{z})|^2 \leqslant C_8 \int\limits_{\tilde{z}}^{\tilde{\tilde{z}}} |D_2 u|^2 dx.$$

Integrating the last inequality with respect to z_1 from a to b, we find

$$\int\limits_a^b |u(z_1, 0)|^2 dz_1 \leqslant C_8 \int\limits_a^b \left(\int\limits_{\tilde{z}}^{\tilde{\tilde{z}}} |D_2 u|^2 dx \right) dz_1 \leqslant C_8 \int\limits_{G_e} |D_2 u|^2 dx.$$

Substituting this estimate in (3.21), we arrive at (3.18), where G_h is replaced by $G_{h,1}$. Similarly, (3.18) can be established with G_h replaced by $G_{h,2}$ (see Figure 9), where here the situation is even simpler since in (3.21) the integral $\int_{a'}^{b'} |u(z_1', 0)|^2 dz_1'$ is absent — the function $u(x)$ vanishes for $x \in \gamma_1$. Partitioning the region G_h by subregions of the type $G_{h,1}$ and $G_{h,2}$ and combining the inequalities (3.18) for them, we obtain (3.18) in the required form.

Combining (3.17) and (3.18), we find

$$\int\limits_{G_e} |D_2 u|^2 dx + \int\limits_{G_h} |\sqrt{-k}\, D_1 u - D_2 u|^2 dx \geqslant C \int\limits_G |u|^2 dx. \quad (3.22)$$

From the assumptions made at the beginning of this section corresponding to the form of L it follows that

$$\sum_{j,k=1}^{2} b_{jk} \zeta_j \bar{\zeta}_k \geqslant \varepsilon |\zeta_2|^2,$$

and hence the inequality

$$\int\limits_{G_e} \sum_{j,k=1}^{2} b_{jk} D_k u \cdot D_j \bar{u}\, dx \geqslant \varepsilon \int\limits_{G_e} |D_2 u|^2 dx \quad (u \in W_2^1(G_e))$$

follows. This and equality (3.22) reduce to inequality (3.14). The lemma is proved.

We make still another recommendation concerning the obtaining of inequality (3.12).

Let X be a piece of characteristic of the type AB (see Figure 9). If

$$-kD_1c+\sqrt{-k}D_2c+D_2(\sqrt{-k}c)\geqslant 0 \tag{3.23}$$

on X then the expression

$$J_X=2\,\mathrm{Re}\int_X c\,(k\nu_1D_1u+\nu_2D_2u)\,\bar{u}\,dx-\int_X (k\nu_1D_1c+\nu_2D_2c)\,|\,u\,|^2dx \tag{3.24}$$

(the unit normal vector $\nu(x)$ is as in Figure 9) is nonnegative for $u(x)$ such that $u(A)=0$.

In fact, it is easy to compute that

$$\nu(x)=\left(\frac{1}{\sqrt{1-k}},\ -\frac{\sqrt{-k}}{\sqrt{1-k}}\right);$$

hence if we introduce the function

$$U(x_2)=u\left(\int_0^{x_2}\sqrt{-k}\,dt+C,\ x_2\right)\ (-h\leqslant x_2\leqslant 0),$$

where

$$\left(\int_0^{x_2}\sqrt{-k}\,dt+C,\ x_2\right)$$

is a point on AB, then

$$\frac{dU(x_2)}{dx_2}=\sqrt{-k}D_1u+D_2u=-\frac{\sqrt{1-k}}{\sqrt{-k}}(k\nu_1D_1u+\nu_2D_2u). \tag{3.25}$$

Taking into account this relation and the equalities $dx=\sqrt{1-k}\,dx_2$ $(x\in X)$, $k(0)=0$, $U(-t)=u(A)=0$, we obtain by integration by parts

$$J_X=-2\,\mathrm{Re}\int_{-t}^{0}\frac{dU}{dx_2}\bar{U}\sqrt{-k}\,c\,dx_2+\int_{-t}^{0}(-kD_1c+\sqrt{-k}D_2c)\,|\,U\,|^2dx_2$$

$$=-\int_{-t}^{0}\frac{d}{dx_2}|\,U\,|^2\cdot\sqrt{-k}\,c\,dx_2+\int_{-t}^{0}(-kD_1c+\sqrt{-k}D_2c)\,|\,U\,|^2dx_2$$

$$=\int_{-t}^{0}(D_2(\sqrt{-k}\,c)-kD_1c+\sqrt{-k}D_2c)\,|\,U\,|^2dx_2.$$

Condition (3.23) implies nonnegativity of the last integral. The assertion is proved.

3 Some formulations of boundary value problems. We will now find elementary boundary conditions for which the energy inequality (3.16) holds and make some reasonable formulations of boundary value problems. It will be necessary to impose some additional requirements on the function $k(x_2)$; we will assume now that the simplest of these holds, namely the so-called Frankl′ condition

$$2\left(\frac{k(x_2)}{k'(x_2)}\right)' + 1 \geqslant \delta > 0 \text{ (i.e. } q'(x_2) \leqslant 2 - \delta), \; -h \leqslant x_2 < 0. \tag{3.26}$$

The conditions on the arc Γ_e are the same as usual –piecewise-smoothness.

I. *The Tricomi problem.* The region G has the form shown in Figure 10.

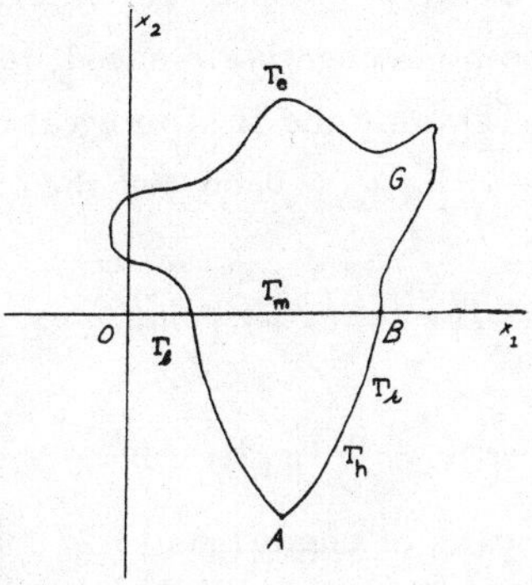

Figure 10.

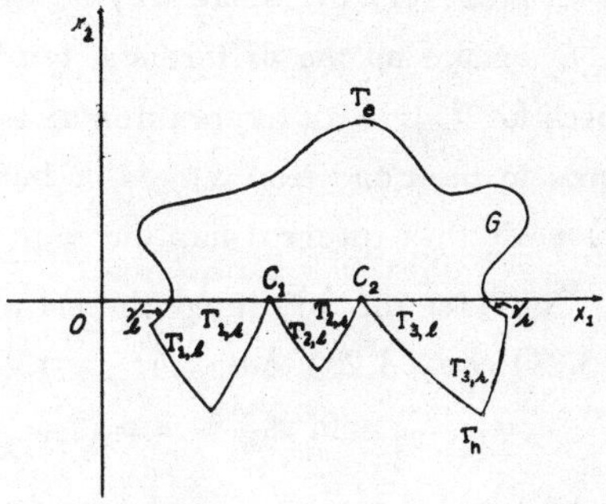

Figure 11.

The boundary Γ_h consists of two parts: Γ_ℓ and Γ_r, each of which are characteristics of our expression. The boundary conditions are

$$u|_{\Gamma_e \cup \Gamma_\ell} = 0, \; u|_{\Gamma_r} \sim. \tag{3.27}$$

Inequality (3.16) holds for these boundary conditions. Indeed, Lemma 3.1 can be applied to them. Further, using the natural notation $I_{\Gamma_h} = I_{\Gamma_\ell} + I_{\Gamma_r}$, we show that $I_{\Gamma_h} \geq 0$ if only (3.23) holds. Since $u|_{\Gamma_\ell} = 0$, the last two integrals in the expression for I_{Γ_ℓ} vanish; the first integral also vanishes since $D_1 u = \lambda\nu_1$, $D_2 u = \lambda\nu_2$ on Γ_ℓ and therefore $|\sqrt{-k}D_1 u - D_2 u| = |\lambda|\,|\sqrt{-k}\nu_1 - \nu_2| = 0$. In the expression for I_{Γ_r} the first integral equals zero, since $(\sqrt{-k}\nu_1 + \nu_2)|_{\Gamma_r} = 0$; the sum of the last two is nonnegative by (3.23).

Thus for (3.16) to be valid we must find a function $c(x)$ $(x \in G)$ such that inequalities (3.13) and (3.23) hold. Because of the assumption (3.26) we can take for this the function $c(x) \equiv -1$.

II. *The generalized Tricomi problem.* The region G is shown in Figure 11. Here $\Gamma_{1,\ell}, \Gamma_{1,r}, \cdots, \Gamma_{N,\ell}, \Gamma_{N,r}$ are arcs of characteristics ($N \geq 1$; in the figure $N = 3$); γ_ℓ and γ_r are two arcs having the equations $x_2 = \phi_\ell(x_1)$ and $x_2 = \phi_r(x_1)$ respectively, where

$$\varphi_\ell \geqslant 0, \; \varphi'_\ell < (-k)^{-\frac{1}{2}}; \; \varphi'_r \leqslant 0, \; |\varphi'_r| < (-k)^{-\frac{1}{2}}$$

One or both of the arcs γ_ℓ, γ_π may be absent. The boundary conditions are

$$u|_{\Gamma_e \cup \Gamma_{1,\ell} \cup \ldots \cup \Gamma_{N,\ell} \cup \gamma_\ell \cup \gamma_\pi} = 0, \qquad (3.28)$$

$$u|_{\Gamma_{1,\pi} \cup \ldots \cup \Gamma_{N,\pi}} \sim .$$

(3.16) also holds for the boundary conditions under consideration. We show this in precisely the same way as in the case of the problem I. The integrals I_{γ_ℓ}, I_{γ_π} make up the difference, but they are both nonnegative. Indeed, for example, for I_{γ_ℓ} in an expression of the type (3.11), only the first integral remains thanks to the condition $u|_{\gamma_\ell} = 0$, but since $\sqrt{-k}\nu_1 + \nu_2 > 0$ on γ_ℓ, then for $c(x) \equiv -1$ this integral has the sign +.

Consider the adjoint problems to I and II. *The boundary conditions, adjoint to* (3.27) *and* (3.28), *have the form*

$$v|_{\Gamma_e \cup \Gamma_\pi} = 0, \; v|_{\Gamma_\ell} \sim \quad u \quad v|_{\Gamma_e \cup \Gamma_{1,\pi} \cup \ldots \cup \Gamma_{N,\pi} \cup \gamma_\ell \cup \gamma_\pi} = 0, \; v|_{\Gamma_{1,\ell} \cup \ldots \cup \Gamma_{N,\ell}} \sim . \qquad (3.29)$$

We show this, for example, in the simpler case of conditions (3.27). By the general Theorem 1.1, Chapter II, the adjoint conditions are $v|_{\Gamma_e} = 0$, $v|_{\Gamma_\ell} \sim$, $(\mathfrak{M}^+ v - \overline{\mathfrak{M}}v)|_{\Gamma_\pi} = 0$, where $\mathfrak{M}$ is constructed with respect to (3.2) and the characteristic Γ_π. We compute $\mathfrak{M}$. We construct, with respect to the function $v(x_1, x_2)$, defined on Γ_π, the function $V(x_2)$ $(-h \le x_2 < 0)$ in the manner done above. Taking into account the expression for $\mathfrak{M}$ ((1.15), Chapter II) and equation (3.25), we obtain

$$\mathfrak{M}v = kD_1 v \cdot \nu_1 + D_2 v \cdot \nu_2 = -\frac{\sqrt{-k}}{\sqrt{1-k}} (\sqrt{-k} D_1 v + D_2 v) = -\frac{\sqrt{-k}}{\sqrt{1-k}} \frac{d}{dx_2} V. \qquad (3.30)$$

Since $dx = \sqrt{1-k}\, dx_2$,

$$\int_{\Gamma_\pi} \mathfrak{M}v \cdot \bar{v}\, dx = -\int_{-h}^{0} \sqrt{-k} V'(x_2) \overline{V(x_2)}\, dx_2,$$

from which it is clear that

$$\mathfrak{M}^+ v = \frac{1}{\sqrt{1-k}} \frac{d}{dx_2} (\sqrt{-k} V). \qquad (3.31)$$

It follows from (3.30) and (3.31) that the condition $(\mathfrak{M}^+ v - \overline{\mathfrak{M}}v)|_{\Gamma_\pi} = 0$ is equivalent to the equation $(\sqrt{-k}V)' + \sqrt{-k}V' = 0$; hence $V' + k'V/4k = 0$ $(-h \le x_2 < 0)$. The general solution of the latter equation is $V(x_2) = C(-k(x_2))^{-1/4}$. Since $|v(B)| < \infty$, $|V(0)| < \infty$ and hence $C = 0$. Thus, $V(x_2) = 0$ $(-h \le x_2 \le 0)$, i.e. $v|_{\Gamma_\pi} = 0$ and the first of conditions (3.29) is in fact adjoint to (3.27). The assertion is proved.

Thus in going over from the problems I – II to their adjoints it is only necessary to remember the roles of arcs of the types Γ_ℓ and Γ_π. The expression L^+

as before has the form shown at the beginning of this section. This shows that an energy inequality of the type (3.16) is valid for L^+ and $(\mathrm{bd})^+$, in which $\|v\|_+$ is easily computed by means of the symmetry to (3.15) of the relation

$$\|v\|^2_{+,\varkappa} = \int_G |v|^2 dx + \int_{G_e} \sum_{j,k=1}^{2} b_{jk} D_k v \cdot D_j \bar{v} dx + \int_{G_h} |\sqrt{-k} D_1 v + D_2 v|^2 dx. \qquad (3.32)$$

We obtain the following theorem.

Theorem 3.1. *In the case of the Tricomi problem (ordinary or generalized) under the Frankl' condition* (3.26), *both energy inequalities*

$$\|Lu\|_0 \geqslant C\|u\|_{+,\ell} \ (C>0;\ u \in W_2^2(\mathrm{bd})),\quad \|L^+ v\|_0 \geqslant C\|v\|_{+,\varkappa} (C>0; v \in W_2^2(\mathrm{bd})^+)$$

hold, where the positive norms are defined by relations (3.15) *and* (3.32). *Thus the problem* $Lu = f,\ u \in (\mathrm{bd})$ *under consideration is almost correct and is weakly solvable for any* $f \in L_2(G)$.

Furthermore, there exists a generalized solution of this problem for f in the space with negative norm, constructed with respect to the positive norm $\|\cdot\|_{+,\ell}$ *and the zero norm of the space* $L_2(G)$.

4. Generalizations. We show now how one can replace the Frankl' condition (3.26) by a less stringent condition; it is not possible to avoid such conditions completely (if special requirements are not imposed on the form of Γ_e; cf. subsection 5). First of all we show that *the energy inequality* (3.16) *remains valid if the second of the conditions* (3.13) *is replaced by the weaker condition*

$$(D_2 c)(x_1, 0) < -\frac{2\varepsilon}{H} c(0) \quad ((x_1, 0) \in \bar{\Gamma}_m) \qquad (3.33)$$

(*here* $\epsilon > 0$ *is the same as that appearing on p. 299 for the estimate of the form for* L).

In fact,

$$\int_{G_e} \sum_{j,k=1}^{2} b_{jk} D_k u \cdot D_j \bar{u} dx \geqslant \varepsilon \int_{G_e} |D_2 u|^2 dx.$$

Moreover, in the notation of Figure 9, for u such that $u|_{\Gamma_e} = 0$ we have

$$\int_{\Gamma_m} |u(\tilde{y})|^2 d\tilde{y} = \int_{\Gamma_m} \left| \int_{\tilde{y}}^{\tilde{\tilde{y}}} (D_2 u)(y)\, dy \right|^2 d\tilde{y} \leqslant \int_{\Gamma_m} \left(|\tilde{\tilde{y}} - \tilde{y}| \int_{\tilde{y}}^{\tilde{\tilde{y}}} |D_2 u|^2 dy \right) d\tilde{y}$$

$$\leqslant H \int_{G_e} |D_2 u|^2 dx.$$

Thus

$$\int_{G_e}\sum_{j,k=1}^{2} b_{jk}D_k u\cdot D_j\bar{u}\,dx \geqslant \frac{\varepsilon}{H}\int_{\Gamma_m} |\,u\,\widetilde{(y)}|^2 d\widetilde{y} \quad (u|_{\Gamma_e}=0). \tag{3.34}$$

Taking this into account, we rewrite (3.10) in the following way ($c(0)<0$, $2>\epsilon_1>0$):

$$2\,\mathrm{Re}\int_G Lu\cdot\overline{\{\varkappa_{G_h} c\,[q\sqrt{-k}D_1u - D_2u) + u] + \varkappa_{G_e} c\,(0)\,u\}}\,dx$$

$$\geqslant -\varepsilon_1 c\,(0)\int_{G_e}\sum_{j,k=1}^{2} b_{jk}D_k u\cdot D_j\bar{u}\,dx + \int_{G_h}(\sqrt{-k}qD_1c + D_2(qc) - 2c)\,|\sqrt{-k}D_1u$$

$$-D_2u|^2 dx + c\,(0)\int_{G_e}\Big(2p - \sum_{j=1}^{2} D_jp_j\Big)|\,u\,|^2 dx + \int_{G_h}(kD_1^2c + D_2^2c)\,|\,u\,|^2 dx$$

$$+\int_{\Gamma_m}\Big[-(2-\varepsilon_1)\frac{\varepsilon}{H}c\,(0) - (D_2c)\,(x_1,0)\Big]|\,u\,|^2 dx + I_{\Gamma_h}. \tag{3.35}$$

It follows from condition (3.33) that for $\epsilon_1 > 0$ sufficiently small $-(2-\epsilon_1)\,\epsilon c(0)/H - (D_2c)\,(x_1, 0) \geq 0$ on Γ_m. If we fix such an ϵ_1, the integral over Γ_m in (3.35) can then be neglected without affecting the sign of the inequality. If we then choose c such that the remaining relations (3.12)–(3.13) are fulfilled, and if we carry out such estimates precisely as on p. 302, we arrive at inequality (3.16). The assertion is proved.

Theorem 3.2. *The results of Theorem 3.1 remain valid, if the Frankl' condition (3.26) is replaced by the conditions:* a) *the function $k(x_2)$ is thrice continuously differentiable on $[-h, 0)$ and $k''(x_2)$ is bounded near 0;* b) *the set of those x_2, where $2(k/k')' + 1 < 0$ consists of a finite number of intervals in $[-h, 0)$ and on each such interval $k'''(x_2) \leq 0$.*

Proof. By what was said at the beginning of subsection 3 it reduces to the construction of the required function c; we will construct it as a function of the variable x_2 only. First we reduce it to a subsidiary construction. Let $[\alpha, \beta] \subset [-h, 0)$ be such that $q'(x_2) > 2$ in its interior (i.e. $2(k/k')' + 1 < 0$) and $q'(\beta) = 2$. We construct the function $c(x_2)$ only on $[\alpha, \beta]$ by setting

$$c\,(x_2) = -e^{\int_{x_2}^{\beta}\frac{q'(t)-\lambda}{q(t)}dt} \tag{3.36}$$

where the constant $\lambda < 2$. This function satisfies the third and fourth conditions of (3.13) and the inequality (3.23), if $2 - \lambda = \eta$ is sufficiently small.

Indeed, for the function $c(x) = c(x_2)$, conditions (3.13), the second of which is replaced by (3.33), and (3.23) have the form

$$c(0) < 0,\ c'(0) < -\frac{2\varepsilon}{H} c(0),\ (qc)' - 2c \geqslant \delta > 0,\ c'' \geqslant 0, \tag{3.37}$$

$$2\sqrt{-kc'} - \frac{k'}{2\sqrt{-k}} c \geqslant 0 \text{ (or } qc' - c \geqslant 0), \quad -h \leqslant x_2 < 0.$$

The last three of these are of interest to us on the segment $[\alpha, \beta]$. Differentiating (3.36), we obtain

$$c'(x_2) = e^{\int_{x_2}^{\beta} \frac{q'-\lambda}{q} dt} \frac{q'(x_2) - \lambda}{q(x_2)} > 0. \tag{3.38}$$

Since $c(x_2) < 0$ ($x_2 \in [\alpha, \beta]$), $qc' - c \geq 0$. Moreover,

$$(qc') - 2c = \exp\left(\int_{x_2}^{\beta} \frac{q' - \lambda}{q} dt\right)(2 - \lambda) > 2 - \lambda = \eta > 0.$$

Finally, we prove the fourth of the conditions (3.37). Computing c'', we find

$$c'' = \frac{1}{q^2} e^{\int_{x_2}^{\beta} \frac{q'-\lambda}{q} dt} (-2q'^2 + qq'' + 3q'\lambda - \lambda^2).$$

We must show that the quantity in the last parentheses is nonnegative on $[\alpha, \beta]$. Since $q' \geq 2$,

$$-2q'^2 + qq'' + 3q'\lambda - \lambda^2 \geqslant -2q'^2 + qq'' + 8 - 2\eta - \eta^2.$$

Therefore if

$$-2q'^2 + qq'' + 8 > 0 \quad (x_2 \in [\alpha, \beta]), \tag{3.39}$$

then choosing η sufficiently small, we obtain $c'' \geq 0$. Substituting the expression (3.7) for q in (3.39) and noting that $k' > 0$, we rewrite this inequality in the form $-k'^3 + 2kk'k'' - 2k^2k'''/3 > 0$. On $[\alpha, \beta]$

$$2(k/k')' + 1 \leqslant 0, \text{ i.e. } -3k'^2 + 2kk'' \geqslant 0.$$

By means of this inequality and the relations $k' > 0$, $k''' \leq 0$ we find

$$-k'^3 + 2kk'k'' - \frac{2}{3}k^2k''' > -3k'^3 + 2kk'k'' - \frac{2}{3}k^2k''' \geqslant 0.$$

Thus, (3.39), and together with it the inequality $c'' \geq 0$ are established.

We show now that if the hypotheses of the theorem hold, then there exists a twice piecewise-differentiable function $c(x_2)$ ($-h \leq x_2 \leq 0$) which satisfies the requirements (3.37). Let $[\alpha_1, \beta_1], \ldots, [\alpha_m, \beta_m]$ be maximal intervals of the Ox_2 axis inside of which $q' > 2$. Since

$$2(k/k')' + 1 = \frac{1}{k'^2}(3k'^2 - 2kk''),\ k(0) = 0$$

and k'' is bounded near 0, $2(k/k')' + 1 > 0$ near 0, i.e. $q' < 2$. Thus, our segments lie to the left of the origin; suppose that $-h \leq \alpha_m < \beta_m < \alpha_{m-1} < \cdots < \alpha_1 < \beta_1 < 0$. Obviously, $q'(\alpha_j) = q'(\beta_j) = 2$ $(j = 1, \cdots, m)$.

Define the function $c(x_2)$ on $[\alpha_1, \beta_1]$ by equation (3.36) with $[\alpha, \beta] = [\alpha_1, \beta_1]$. We have

$$c(\beta_1) = -1; \; c'(\beta_1) = \frac{2-\lambda}{q(\beta_1)} > 0$$

(see (3.38)) and therefore for λ sufficiently near 2, $c'(\beta_1)$ can be made arbitrarily small. Make $c'(\beta_1)$ so small that c can be extended to $(\beta_1, 0]$ in such a way as to preserve the properties $c' > 0$ and $c'' \geq 0$, so that $c(0) < 0$, $c'(0) < -2\epsilon c(0)/H$. Further, define c on $[\alpha_2, \beta_2]$ by (3.36), multiplying the integral by a certain factor $\mu > 0$ and setting $[\alpha, \beta] = [\alpha_2, \beta_2]$. It is clear that by again choosing λ here sufficiently near 2 and changing $\mu > 0$, we can extend c to the interval (β_2, α_1) such that $c' > 0$, $c'' \geq 0$, and keep the required smoothness properties on $[\alpha_2, 0]$. Then define c on $[\alpha_3, \beta_3]$ etc.; on the left of α_m c is extended arbitrarily but preserving the inequalities $c' > 0$ and $c'' \geq 0$. We show that this $c(x_2)$ satisfies the requirements (3.37). In fact, we need only consider the case when $x_2 \notin [\alpha_j, \beta_j]$ $(j = 1, \cdots, m)$, $x_2 \neq 0$. Since $c < 0$, $c' > 0$, and $c'' \geq 0$, the fourth and fifth conditions of (3.37) hold. Further, by construction $q' \leq 2$ outside the intervals $[\alpha_j, \beta_j]$; hence $(qc)' - 2c = qc' + (q' - 2)c \geq qc'$; the last expression is always $\geq \delta > 0$, outside of a small neighborhood of 0. Near the origin $qc' \geq 0$, but $q' < 2$ there; hence $qc' + (q' - 2)c \geq (q' - 2)c > 0$. Thus the constructed c satisfies (3.37). The theorem is proved.

We also make the following remark. Assume that the conditions of Theorem 3.1 are fulfilled, and let $(-\sigma, 0]$ be the largest half-open interval in which the inequality $q' < 2$ holds. According to this theorem, the energy inequalities hold in case $h < \sigma$. They are also valid for h somewhat larger than σ. It is easy to see this if we assume that $c(x_2) = x_2 - a$, where $a > H/(2\epsilon)$ is fixed; conditions (3.37) hold for such a function.

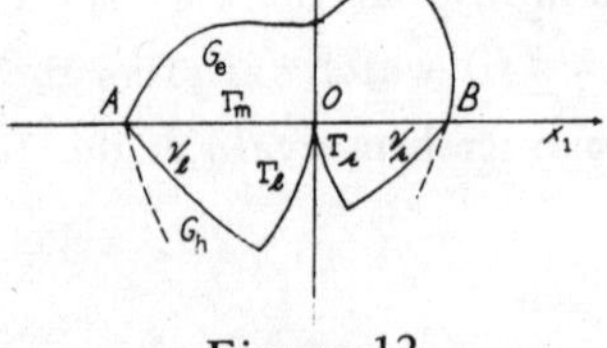

Figure 12.

5. A modification of the method of obtaining energy inequalities. The Frankl' problem. The relation (3.7) between the functions a, b and c does not lead to our aim in all problems and then these functions must be chosen differently; in this connection additional restrictions on Γ_e ofter appear.

As an illustration, we consider the so-called Frankl' problem for Čaplygin's expression (3.2);

assume that $k(x_2) \in C^1([-h, H])$, $k'(x_2) > 0$ $(x_2 \in [-h, H], x_2 \neq 0)$ and, naturally, as x_2 passes through 0, $k(x_2)$ changes sign from $-$ to $+$. The expression is considered in the region sketched in Figure 12. Here Γ_r and Γ_ℓ are the characteristic arcs; γ_ℓ and γ_r are two arcs having the equations $x_2 = \phi_\ell(x_1)$ and $x_2 = \phi_r(x_1)$ respectively, where

$$\varphi_\ell \leqslant 0, \ |\varphi_\ell'| \leqslant (-k)^{-\frac{1}{2}} \text{ and } \varphi_r \geqslant 0, \varphi_r' < (-k)^{-\frac{1}{2}}.$$

One of the arcs γ_ℓ, γ_r may be absent, and then the point A or B corresponding to it coincides with 0. The arc Γ_e is assumed to be piecewise-smooth and such that $x_1\nu_1(x) + x_2\nu_2(x) \geq 0$ $(x \in \Gamma_e)$ (star-like condition). The boundary conditions are

$$u|_{\Gamma_e \cup \gamma_\ell \cup \gamma_r} = 0, \ u|_{\Gamma_r \cup \Gamma_\ell} \sim. \tag{3.40}$$

Applying Theorem 1.1, Chapter II, and the reasoning of subsection 3, it is easy to see that the adjoint conditions to (3.40) have the form

$$v|_\Gamma = 0. \tag{3.41}$$

First of all we show that in the case of conditions (3.41) a certain energy inequality is valid. We introduce with respect to $H_0 = L_2(G)$ the positive norms

$$\|u\|_{+1}^2 = \int_G \frac{1}{|k|} |u|^2 dx, \ \|u\|_{+2}^2 = \int_G |u|^2 dx + \int_G (|k| |D_1 u|^2 + |D_2 u|^2) dx, \tag{3.42}$$

where the first of these is introduced first for functions of $L_2(G)$ which vanish near Γ_m, and then the completion is taken; we denote the space obtained by H_{+1}. The positive space corresponding to the norm $\|\cdot\|_{+2}$ is denoted by H_{+2}. We assert that *the inequality*

$$\|Lu\|_{+1} \geqslant C \|u\|_{+2} \tag{3.43}$$

holds for functions $u \in W_2^2(G)$ *which satisfy condition* (3.41) *and are such that* $Lu \in H_{+1}$.

First we make a general remark. Consider the fourth integral in (3.6), extended to a certain piece Γ_0 of the boundary, on which $u = 0$. It is easy to compute that it acquires the form (cf. (2.6)):

$$\int_{\Gamma_0} |N_u|^2 (a\nu_1 + b\nu_2)(k\nu_1^2 + \nu_2^2)\, dx, \tag{3.44}$$

where N_u is as in (2.6).

Now set $G' = G$, $a = x_1$, $b = \max\{0, x_2\}$, and $c = -1/4$ in the identity (3.6); $u|_\Gamma = 0$. Using (3.44), we obtain

$$2\,\mathrm{Re}\int_G Lu\cdot\overline{\left(x_1D_1u+bD_2u-\frac{1}{4}u\right)}\,dx=\int_{G_e}\left\{\left(\frac{1}{2}k+k'x_2\right)|D_1u|^2+\frac{1}{2}|D_2u|^2\right\}dx$$

$$+\int_{G_h}\left\{\left(-\frac{1}{2}k\right)|D_1u|^2+\frac{3}{2}|D_2u|^2\right\}dx+\int_{\Gamma_e}|N_u|^2(x_1\nu_1+x_2\nu_2)(k\nu_1^2+\nu_2^2)\,dx$$

$$+\int_{\Gamma_h}|N_u|^2x_1\nu_1(k\nu_1^2+\nu_2^2)\,dx. \tag{3.45}$$

It is necessary here to explain that, in spite of the break of $b(x_2)$ at $x_2=0$, the integrals over Γ_m in (3.45) do not appear; this is easily seen if (3.45) is written separately for G_e and G_h and the results combined.

By assumption $(x_1\nu_1+x_2\nu_2)\big|_{\Gamma_e}\geq 0$, hence $\int_{\Gamma_e}\cdots dx\geq 0$. Also,

$$(k\nu_1^2+\nu_2^2)\,|_{\Gamma_n\cup\Gamma_\ell}=0,\quad (k\nu_1^2+\nu_2^2)\,|_{\gamma_\ell\cup\gamma_n}\geqslant 0 \text{ and } x_1\nu_1|_{\gamma_\ell\cup\gamma_n}\geqslant 0;$$

consequently $\int_{\Gamma_h}\cdots dx\geq 0$. For $x_2>0$, $k'x_2>0$, and we can write

$$\int_{G_e}\left\{\left(\frac{1}{2}k+k'x_2\right)|D_1u|^2+\frac{1}{2}|D_2u|^2\right\}dx+\int_{G_h}\left\{\left(-\frac{1}{2}k\right)|D_1u|^2+\frac{3}{2}|D_2u|^2\right\}dx$$

$$\geqslant C\int_G(|k|\,|D_1u|^2+|D_2u|^2)\,dx.$$

Taking into account the obtained estimates of the integrals and estimating (3.45) we find

$$C\int_G(|k|\,|D_1u|^2+|D_2u|^2)\,dx\leqslant 2\left|\int_G Lu\cdot\overline{\left(x_1D_1u+bD_2u-\frac{1}{4}u\right)}\,dx\right|$$

$$\leqslant 2\left(\int_G\frac{1}{|k|}|Lu|^2dx\right)^{\frac{1}{2}}\left(\int_G|k|\,|x_1D_1u+bD_2u-\frac{1}{4}u|^2dx\right)^{\frac{1}{2}}\leqslant C_1\|Lu\|_{+1}\|u\|_{+2}. \tag{3.46}$$

On the other hand, obviously,

$$\int_{G_e}(k|D_1u|^2+|D_2u|^2)\,dx$$

$$+\int_{G_h}|\sqrt{-k}D_1u-D_2u|^2dx\leqslant C_2\int_G(|k|\,|D_1u|^2+|D_2u|^2)dx.$$

The left side of this is estimated from below by Lemma 3.1 applied for the k under consideration; we obtain

$$\int_G|u|^2dx\leqslant C_3\int_G(|k|\,|D_1u|^2+|D_2u|^2)\,dx,$$

This shows that the first integral in (3.46) can be estimated from below by $\|u\|^2_{+2}$. Cancelling $\|u\|_{+2}$ from the resulting inequality, we get (3.43). The assertion is proved.

Inequality (3.43) implies a certain weak solvability of the Frankl′ problem, as follows from general considerations of the type mentioned in Chapter II, §3.4. We formulate the corresponding result below in Theorem 3.3.

One cannot prove an energy inequality for the original boundary conditions (3.40), but a uniqueness theorem for smooth solutions holds in this case. In fact, let $u \in W^2_2(G)$ be such that $Lu = 0$ and conditions (3.40) are satisfied. We apply identity (3.6), setting $G' = G$, $a = x_1$, $b = \max\{0, x_2\}$ and $c = 0$. Taking into account (3.44), we obtain

$$0 = \int_{G_e} k' x_2 |D_1 u|^2 dx + \int_{G_h} \{(-k)|D_1 u|^2 + |D_2 u|^2\}\, dx$$

$$+ \int_{\Gamma_e} |N_u|^2 (x_1\nu_1 + x_2\nu_2)(k\nu_1^2 + \nu_2^2)\, dx + \int_{\gamma_\ell \cup \gamma_r} |N_u|^2 x_1\nu_1 (k\nu_1^2 + \nu_2^2)\, dx$$

$$+ \int_{\Gamma_r} (-x_1\nu_1) |\sqrt{-k} D_1 u + D_2 u|^2 dx + \int_{\Gamma_\ell} (-x_1\nu_1) |\sqrt{-k} D_1 u - D_2 u|^2 dx. \qquad (3.47)$$

Also, as before, $\int_{\Gamma_e} \cdots dx \geq 0$, $\int_{\gamma_\ell \cup \gamma_r} \cdots dx \geq 0$. Further, it is obvious that $-x_1\nu_1|_{\Gamma_r \cup \Gamma_\ell} \geq 0$; hence the last two integrals in (3.47) are also nonnegative. Thus

$$0 \geqslant \int_{G_e} k' x_2 |D_1 u|^2 dx + \int_{G_h} \{(-k)|D_1 u|^2 + |D_2 u|^2\}\, dx,$$

i.e. $D_1 u = 0$ in G_e and $D_1 u = D_2 u = 0$ in G_h. It follows from the boundary conditions (3.40) that $u = 0$ in G. The assertion is proved.

We formulate the results obtained in the form of a theorem. In it, H_{-k} denotes the negative space constructed with respect to $H_0 = L_2(G)$ and H_k ($k = 1, 2$). Clearly, H_{-1} coincides with the space L_2 with weight $|k|$ ($\|f\|^2_{-1} = \int_G |k|\,|f|^2 dx$).

Theorem 3.3. *Let* (bd) *be the boundary conditions* (3.40) *of the Frankl′ problem. Each function* $u \in W^2_2(\text{bd})$, *for which* $Lu = 0$, *is equal to zero. For the adjoint boundary conditions* $(\text{bd})^+$ *(which have the form* (3.41)) *we have the energy inequality*

$$\|Lv\|_{+1} \geqslant C\|v\|_{+2} \qquad (C > 0;\ v \in W^2_2(\text{bd})^+,\ Lv \in H_{+1}). \qquad (3.48)$$

The Frankl′ problem $Lu = f$, $u \in (\text{bd})$ *has a weak solution* $u \in H_{-1}$ *for any*

$f \in H_{-1}$, *i.e. there exists a* $u \in H_{-1}$ *such that*

$$(u, Lv)_0 = (f, v)_0 \quad (v \in W_2^{2}(\text{bd})^{+},\ Lv \in H_{+1}). \tag{3.49}$$

More precise estimates, in comparison with (3.48), can be obtained for the Frankl' problem; it is possible to study other problems in a similar way, but we shall not go into them here. We note only that the proved uniqueness of smooth solutions with condition (3.40) allows us to affirm, on the basis of Theorem 3.1, Chapter II, the conditional solvability of the problem $Lu = f$, $u|_\Gamma = 0$ for any $f \in W_2^{-2}(G)$.

CHAPTER V

GENERAL THEORY OF EXPANSIONS OF SELFADJOINT OPERATORS IN GENERALIZED EIGENVECTORS

Every selfadjoint operator in a finite-dimensional Hilbert space has a complete system of eigenvectors. For this reason it is natural to seek a similar result in an arbitrary Hilbert space H. However, simple examples show that not every selfadjoint operator A acting on H has such a system, and therefore it is impossible to obtain a strict generalization of the finite-dimensional theorem.

As an example, A may be taken to be multiplication by x in $L_2(0, 1)$. An eigenfunction $\phi(x)$ corresponding to an eigenvalue λ satisfies the equation $(A\phi)(x) = x\phi(x) = \lambda\phi(x)$. The solution to this equation is the δ-function δ_λ concentrated at the point $x = \lambda$. Since $\delta_\lambda \overline{\in} L_2(0, 1)$, the operator A does not have an eigenfunction. Instead, this example shows that although A, in general, does not have an eigenfunction, it has generalized eigenfunctions.

It turns out that a similar occurrence takes place in the general case of a separable Hilbert space H. (The assumption of separability is necessary.) More precisely, suppose there are spaces $\Phi' \supseteq H \supseteq \Phi$. Then with some extra conditions related to the spaces Φ, Φ', each selfadjoint operator A in H has a complete system of eigenvectors in the space Φ'. It is desirable that the space Φ' be as "near" as possible to H (in the finite-dimensional case $\Phi' = H = \Phi$) and therefore that Φ be picked so that it most fully exhausts H.

§1. PROCEDURE FOR DEFINING RESOLUTION OF THE IDENTITY

1. **Some facts about Hilbert-Schmidt operators.** As already mentioned in Chapter I, §2.4, an operator A from a separable Hilbert space H_1 to a Hilbert space H_2 is called a Hilbert-Schmidt operator if for some (and hence every) orthonormal basis $e_1, e_2, \cdots$ in the space H_1, the series $\sum_{j=1}^{\infty} \|Ae_j\|_{H_2}^2$ converges. One may

show that a Hilbert-Schmidt operator is always completely continuous. We set

$$|A|^2 = \sum_{j=1}^{\infty} \|Ae_j\|_{H_2}^2. \tag{1.1}$$

The number $|A|$ is called the Hilbert norm of the operator A. It is easy to verify that $|\lambda A| = |\lambda|\,|A|$; $|A+B| \leq |A| + |B|$; $\|A\| \leq |A|$.

If H_2 is separable and B is a continuous transformation from H_2 into H_3, then BA is defined from H_1 into H_3 and is a Hilbert-Schmidt operator, since the first of the inequalities

$$|BA| \leq \|B\|\,|A|, \quad |AB| \leq |A|\,\|B\| \tag{1.2}$$

is obvious.

For the second inequality it is assumed that B is continuous from H_1 to H_2, A is defined from H_2 into H_3 and that all the spaces are separable. This inequality follows from the first inequality and the following remark: If C is a Hilbert-Schmidt operator defined from a separable space H_1 to a separable space H_2, then C^* is also a Hilbert-Schmidt operator and $|C^*| = |C|$. To verify this, note that if $e_1, e_2, \cdots$ is a basis in H_2, then

$$|C|^2 = \sum_{j,k=1}^{\infty} |(Ce_j, l_k)_{H_2}|^2 = \sum_{j,k=1}^{\infty} |(e_j, C^* l_k)_{H_1}|^2 = |C^*|^2.$$

We will now consider operators defined on a single separable Hilbert space H; let $e_1, e_2, \cdots$ be an orthonormal basis in H. The nonnegative operator A has a finite trace if

$$\operatorname{tr}(A) = \sum_{j=1}^{\infty} (Ae_j, e_j) < \infty. \tag{1.3}$$

It is easy to verify that the definition of the trace of A is independent of the choice of orthonormal basis. *If A is nonnegative and B is bounded, the inequalities*

$$|A| \leq \operatorname{tr}(A), \quad \operatorname{tr}(B^* AB) \leq \|A\|\,|B|^2,$$
$$\operatorname{tr}(B^* AB) \leq \|B\|^2 \operatorname{tr}(A) \tag{1.4}$$

are valid.

Proof. The first inequality follows from the expression

$$|A|^2 = \sum_{j,k=1}^{\infty} |(Ae_k, e_j)|^2 \tag{1.5}$$

and from the estimate $|(Ae_k, e_j)|^2 \le (Ae_k, e_k)\,(Ae_j, e_j)$, which follows from the nonnegativity of A. For the proof of the second,

$$\operatorname{tr}(B^*AB) = \sum_{j=1}^{\infty} (B^*ABe_j, e_j) = \sum_{j=1}^{\infty} (ABe_j, Be_j)$$

$$\le \|A\| \sum_{j=1}^{\infty} \|Be_j\|^2 = \|A\|\, |B|^2.$$

For the proof of the third inequality choose an orthonormal basis of eigenvectors $e_1, e_2, \cdots$ for the completely continuous selfadjoint operator A. Then $a_{jk} = a_{jj}\,\delta_{jk}$, where $a_{jk} = (Ae_k, e_j)$ and we put $(b_{jk} = (Be_k, e_j))$:

$$\operatorname{tr}(B^*AB) = \sum_{j=1}^{\infty} (B^*ABe_j, e_j)$$

$$= \sum_{j=1}^{\infty}\left(\sum_{k=1}^{\infty} \bar{b}_{kj} a_{kk} b_{kj}\right) = \sum_{k=1}^{\infty} a_{kk}\left(\sum_{j=1}^{\infty} |b_{kj}|^2\right)$$

$$= \sum_{k=1}^{\infty} a_{kk} \|B^*e_k\|^2 \leqslant \|B^*\|^2 \sum_{k=1}^{\infty} a_{kk} = \|B\|^2 \operatorname{tr}(A).$$

2. **Differentiation of an operator-valued measure.** Let H be a separable Hilbert space and let $\Theta(\Delta)$ be a function defined on the bounded Borel sets of the real line, whose values are bounded operators on H. The function $\Theta(\Delta)$ is called a nonnegative operator-valued measure, if it takes the value zero on the empty set, if the operators $\Theta(\Delta)$ are nonnegative and if they satisfy the requirement of weak countable additivity: for disjoint Δ_j, the equation

$$\Theta\left(\bigcup_{j=1}^{\infty} \Delta_j\right) = \sum_{j=1}^{\infty} \Theta(\Delta_j) \tag{1.6}$$

holds in the sense of weak convergence.

Suppose that the measure Θ has a locally bounded trace: for bounded Δ $\operatorname{tr}(\Theta(\Delta)) < \infty$. It is not difficult to verify that $\rho(\Delta) = \operatorname{tr}(\Theta(\Delta))$ is an ordinary nonnegative measure defined on all of the Borel sets (for unbounded Δ, the definition is that the natural one—$\rho(\Delta) = \lim_{n\to\infty} \rho(\Delta \cap (-n, n)) \le \infty$).

Theorem 1.1. *For almost all* $\lambda(\rho)$, *there exists an operator-valued function* $\Psi(\lambda) \geq 0$ *satisfying* $|\Psi(\lambda)| \leq \operatorname{tr}(\Psi(\lambda)) = 1$ *and such that for an arbitrary Borel set* Δ

$$\Theta(\Delta) = \int_{\Delta} \Psi(\lambda)\, d\rho(\lambda). \tag{1.7}$$

The function $\Psi(\lambda)$ *is defined up to a set of* ρ*-measure zero. At almost all* λ, *the function* $\Psi(\lambda)$ *may be taken as the weak limit of the sequence of operators* $(1/\rho(\Delta_\nu))\Theta(\Delta_\nu)$ *where* Δ_ν *is some sequence of intervals contracting to* λ. *The integral converges in norm (and even in the Hilbert norm) to an operator for each* Δ *such that* $\rho(\Delta) < \infty$.

Proof. The numerical measure $(\Theta(\Delta)f, g)$, $(f, g \in H)$ is absolutely continuous with respect to ρ, since if $\rho(\Delta) = 0$, then $|(\Theta(\Delta)e_k, e_j)|^2 \leq (\Theta(\Delta)e_k, e_k) \times (\Theta(\Delta)e_j, e_j) \leq \rho^2(\Delta) = 0$, i.e. $\theta(\Delta) = 0$. So, by the Radon-Nikodym theorem (see Introduction, §2), the representation

$$(\Theta(\Delta)f, g) = \int_{\Delta} \Psi_{f,g}(\lambda)\, d\rho(\lambda), \tag{1.8}$$

follows, where the function $\Psi_{f,g}(\lambda)$ is defined almost everywhere on the set $\Lambda_{f,g}$, and the definition may be taken to be $\Psi_{f,g}(\lambda) = \lim (1/\rho(\Delta_\nu))(\Theta(\Delta_\nu)f, g)$, where Δ_ν is a sequence of intervals on some line segment containing λ and contracting to λ. Let R be a dense set in H. If we put $\Lambda = \bigcap_{f,g\in R} \Lambda_{f,g}$, the complement of this set also has ρ-measure zero; for λ in Λ the limit of $((\theta(\Delta_\nu)/\rho(\Delta_\nu))f, g)$, for arbitrary f, g in R, exists. We show that for λ in Λ the sequence of operators $(\Theta(\Delta_\nu)/\rho(\Delta_\nu))$ converges weakly to some limiting operator $\Psi(\lambda)$. For this it is necessary to verify that $\|\Theta(\Delta_\nu)/\rho(\Delta_\nu)\|$ is bounded. We establish the stronger inequality $|\Theta(\Delta_\nu)/\rho(\Delta_\nu)| \leq 1$ from which it will follow that $|\Psi(\lambda)| \leq 1$. The required inequality follows from the estimates

$$|\Theta(\Delta_\nu)|^2 = \sum_{j,k=1}^{\infty} |(\Theta(\Delta_\nu)e_k, e_j)|^2$$

$$\leqslant \sum_{j,k=1}^{\infty} (\Theta(\Delta_\nu)e_k, e_k)(\Theta(\Delta_\nu)e_j, e_j) = \rho^2(\Delta_\nu).$$

The operator $\Psi(\lambda)$, the weak limit of a sequence of nonnegative operators, is nonnegative. Further for $\lambda \in \Lambda$ and $f, g \in R$ $\Psi_{f,g}(\lambda) = (\Psi(\lambda)f, g)$ and therefore it follows from (1.8) that

$$(\Theta(\Delta) f, g) = \int_\Delta (\Psi(\lambda) f, g)\, d\varrho(\lambda) \quad (f, g \in R).$$

Since $\|\Psi(\lambda)\| \le |\Psi(\lambda)| \le 1$, the equality is obtained by passing to a limit over all f, g in H. But this implies the equality (1.7).

We now show, that $\operatorname{tr}(\Psi(\lambda)) = 1$ for almost all $\lambda(\rho)$. Let $e_1, e_2, \cdots$ be some orthonormal basis in H; using (1.7) and Fubini's theorem, we obtain, for arbitrary Δ,

$$\int_\Delta d\varrho(\lambda) = \varrho(\Delta) = \operatorname{tr}(\Theta(\Delta)) = \sum_{j=1}^{\infty} (\Theta(\Delta) e_j, e_j)$$

$$= \sum_{j=1}^{\infty} \int_\Delta (\Psi(\lambda) e_j, e_j)\, d\varrho(\lambda) = \int_\Delta \left(\sum_{j=1}^{\infty} (\Psi(\lambda) e_j, e_j) \right) d\varrho(\lambda),$$

and hence the verification is completed.

Suppose (1.7) holds with another function $\Psi_1(\lambda)$. Since for an arbitrary Borel set Δ, $\int_\Delta (\Psi(\lambda) f, g)\, d\rho(\lambda) = \int_\Delta (\Psi_1(\lambda) f, g)\, d\rho(\lambda)$, it follows that for fixed f, g we have $(\Psi(\lambda) \Delta f, g) = (\Psi_1(\lambda) f, g)$ for almost all $\lambda(\rho)$. Then from the separability of H it follows that $\Psi(\lambda) = \Psi_1(\lambda)$ almost everywhere. Throughout the above, we have understood the integral (1.7) in the weak sense. However, for $\rho(\Delta) < \infty$ it converges in the Hilbert norm of the operators and from the inequality $|\Psi(\lambda)| \le 1$ we obtain the estimate $\int_\Delta |\Psi(\lambda)|\, d\rho(\lambda) \le \rho(\Delta) < \infty$. The theorem follows.

Below, on the basis of Theorem 1.1, we construct a theory of expansions in generalized eigenvectors. For some problems in this theory, an additional theorem on the differentiation of a "signed" operator-valued measure is needed. Let B_1, B_2 be separable Banach spaces, B_2' the dual space of anti-linear functionals l on B_2: (l, f) $(f \in B_2)$. We consider the function $\Theta(\Delta)$ on the Borel sets Δ of the real line, the values of which are bounded operators from B_1 into B_2'. Such a function is called an operator-valued measure if it is equal to zero on the null set and is countably additive: the equality (1.6) is correct with weak convergence of the series. The variation of Θ on the Borel set Δ is given by

$$\varrho(\Delta) = \operatorname*{Var}_\Delta \Theta = \sup \sum \|\Theta(\Delta_j)\|, \tag{1.9}$$

where the sup is taken over all finite sums of disjoint intervals Δ_j contained in Δ. We assume that Θ is locally of bounded variation: $\rho(\Delta) < \infty$ for bounded Δ. It is easy to check that for an arbitrary Borel set Δ, $\rho(\Delta)$ is a nonnegative measure, where we put, as earlier, $\rho(\Delta) = \lim_{n\to\infty} \rho(\Delta \cap (-n, n)) \le \infty$.

Theorem 1.2. *For almost all* $\lambda(\rho)$, *there exists an operator-valued function* $\Psi(\lambda)$ ($\Psi(\lambda)$ *defined from* B_1 *into* B_2^1), $\|\Psi(\lambda)\| = 1$, *such that the representation* (1.7) *is correct and the remaining conclusions of Theorem* 1.1 *are valid* (*with the exclusion of the fact that the integral in* (1.7) *converges in the usual operator norm and not in the Hilbert norm*).

Proof. We may proceed by the scheme of Theorem 1.1: the measure $(\Theta(\Delta)f, g)$ ($f \in B_1$, $g \in B_2$) is absolutely continuous with respect to $\rho(\Delta)$, and hence according to the Radon-Nikodym theorem the representation (1.8) is valid. Further, to repeat the previous argument, it is necessary to use the estimate $\|\Theta(\Delta_2)/\rho(\Delta_2)\| \leq 1$, which is true by definition (1.9). It follows from this estimate that $\|\Psi(\lambda)\| \leq 1$. We show that $\|\Psi(\lambda)\| = 1$ almost everywhere. By assuming the contrary we find a $q < 1$ and a Δ, $\rho(\Delta) > 0$, such that $\|\Psi(\lambda)\| \leq q$ ($\lambda \in \Delta$). Then for a finite number of disjoint Δ_j defined on Δ we have by (1.7)

$$\sum_j \|\Theta(\Delta_j)\| = \sum_j \left\| \int_{\Delta_j} \Psi(\lambda)\, d\varrho(\lambda) \right\| \leqslant \sum_j \int_{\Delta_j} \|\Psi(\lambda)\|\, d\varrho(\lambda) \leqslant q\varrho(\Delta).$$

Passing to the sup on the left of this inequality, we obtain $\rho(\Delta) \leq q\rho(\Delta)$, which is absurd. So we have $\|\Psi(\lambda)\| = 1$. The theorem follows.

We note that the proofs of these two theorems are formally the same and are valid in the multi-dimensional case: $\lambda = (\lambda_1, \cdots, \lambda_q)$ is a point in a q-dimensional space (the Δ_2 are now parallelepipeds; see p. 8). They are true for measures defined on subsets of an abstract space, with the change that now it is impossible to write a relation of the form $(1/\rho(\Delta_\nu))\, \Theta(\Delta_\nu) \to \Psi(\lambda)$; the proof has several complications.

Theorems 1.1 and 1.2 are easily given in the form of the usual Radon-Nikodym theorem. Namely, the operator-valued measure $\Theta(\Delta)$ will be called absolutely continuous with respect to the nonnegative scalar measure $\mu(\Delta)$ if $\mu(\Delta) = 0$ implies $\Theta(\Delta) = 0$. Then for such a measure $\Theta(\Delta)$, satisfying the supplementary condition of local boundedness of the trace $\mathrm{tr}(\Theta(\Delta))$ or of the variation $\mathrm{Var}_\Delta \Theta$, one may differentiate with respect to $\mu(\Delta)$ and express $\Theta(\Delta)$ by means of an integral of the derivative. This immediately follows from (1.7) if we observe that $\rho(\Delta) = \mathrm{tr}(\Theta(\Delta))$ (or $\mathrm{Var}_\Delta \Theta$) is absolutely continuous with respect to $\mu(\Delta)$.

3. Theorems on expansions. Let A be a selfadjoint operator in H and $E(\Delta)$ its resolution of the identity. If λ_0 is a point of the discrete spectrum, then the jump $E_{\lambda_0+0} - E_{\lambda_0}$ is a projection operator onto the eigenmanifold corresponding to Λ_0. In the general case the role of the projection operator naturally must be played by a derivative $dE_\lambda/d\rho_\lambda$ with respect to some measure ρ. But it is impossible to apply Theorem 1.1 (or 1.2) to the operator-valued measure $E(\Delta)$ since $\operatorname{tr}(E(\Delta))$ (as $\operatorname{Var}_\Delta E$) will not be locally finite. However it is possible to proceed in the following way. We choose in H some unbounded operator T with dense domain $\mathfrak{D}(T)$, for which there is an everywhere defined left inverse (i.e., $T^{-1}T = E$) which is a Hilbert-Schmidt operator. We consider the operator-valued measure

$$\Theta(\Delta) = T^{-1^*} E(\Delta)\, T^{-1}. \tag{1.10}$$

With the help of the second of the inequalities (1.4) we have for an arbitrary Borel set $\Delta \subseteq (-\infty, \infty)$: $\rho(\Delta) = \operatorname{tr}(\Theta(\Delta)) \leq \|E(\Delta)\|\, |T|^2 < \infty$. Thus Theorem 1.1 may already be applied to the measure (1.10) and we obtain for $f, g \in \mathfrak{D}(T)$ and an arbitrary Borel set Δ

$$(E(\Delta) f, g) = (E(\Delta)\, T^{-1}\, Tf,\ T^{-1}\, Tg) = (T^{-1^*}\, E(\Delta) T^{-1}\, Tf,\ Tg)$$
$$= (\Theta(\Delta)\, Tf,\ Tg) = \int_\Delta (\Psi(\lambda)\, Tf,\ Tg)\, d\rho(\lambda).$$

If $\Psi(\lambda)$ were constructed from $\Theta(\Delta) = E(\Delta)$, it would be the projection operator onto the eigenmanifold corresponding to the eigenvalue λ. In our case the role of the projection operator must be understood, generally speaking, in some modified sense of the expression $T^*\Psi(\lambda)\, T$; the vectors $T^*\, \Psi(\lambda)\, Tf$ for arbitrary f would have to be eigenvectors and therefore for arbitrary $u \in \mathfrak{D}(A)$

$$(T^*\Psi(\lambda)\, Tf,\ (A - \lambda E)\, u) = ((A - \lambda E)\, T^*\, \Psi(\lambda)\, Tf,\ u) = 0. \tag{1.11}$$

It turns out that in spite of the roughness of the above formulation it is possible to put it in an exact sense and to write an analog of equation (1.11) (see the equality (1.14) below). The following theorem is true.

Theorem 1.3. *Let $E(\Delta)$ be a resolution of the identity, corresponding to the selfadjoint operator A, on a separable Hilbert space H, and let T be an arbitrary unbounded operator with dense domain $\mathfrak{D}(T)$, for which there is a left inverse T^{-1} (i.e. $T^{-1}T = E$), defined on all of H and which is of Hilbert-Schmidt class. Then for an arbitrary Borel set Δ the Parseval equality*

$$(E(\Delta) f, g) = \int_\Delta (\Psi(\lambda)\, Tf,\ Tg)\, d\rho(\lambda) \quad (f, g \in \mathfrak{D}(T)) \tag{1.12}$$

is true where $d\rho(\lambda)$ is a nonnegative finite measure ($\rho((-\infty, \infty)) < \infty$) defined on the Borel sets of the line and $\Psi(\lambda)$, defined ρ-almost everywhere, is an operator-

valued function with values which are operators in H*, where*

$$\Psi(\lambda) \geq 0, \ |\Psi(\lambda)| \leq \operatorname{tr}(\Psi(\lambda)) = 1. \tag{1.13}$$

Roughly speaking, the operator $T^*\Psi(\lambda)T$ *is a projector onto the eigenmanifold corresponding to* λ*. Precisely this means that for each countable collection of vectors* $u \in \mathfrak{D}(A) \cap \mathfrak{D}(T)$ *such that* $Au \in \mathfrak{D}(T)$*, the equality*

$$\Psi(\lambda)T(A - \lambda E)u = 0 \tag{1.14}$$

is true for almost all $\lambda(\rho)$*.*

This theorem is basic in the theory of expansions of selfadjoint operators in generalized eigenvectors. While in its statement we do not encounter the notion of a generalized eigenvector, namely an element of some space with a negative norm, such an interpretation of the theorem is easily possible to obtain. This will be done in the next section.

Proof. The Parseval equality (1.12) has already been obtained, and the relations (1.13) follow directly from Theorem 1.1. It remains to show that (1.14) holds. Let U be some countable set of vectors $u \in \mathfrak{D}(A) \cap \mathfrak{D}(T)$ such that $Au \in \mathfrak{D}(T)$; let R be a countable dense set in H. From Theorem 1.1 for $u \in U$ and $f \in R$ we have

$$\begin{aligned}(\Psi(\lambda)T(A - \lambda E)u, f) &= \lim_{\nu\to\infty}\left(\frac{\Theta(\Delta_\nu)}{\varrho(\Delta_\nu)}T(A - \lambda E)u, f\right)\\ &= \lim_{\nu\to\infty}\frac{1}{\varrho(\Delta_\nu)}(T^{-1*}E(\Delta_\nu)(A - \lambda E)u, f)\\ &= \lim_{\nu\to\infty}\frac{1}{\varrho(\Delta_\nu)}(E(\Delta_\nu)(A - \lambda E)u, T^{-1}f)\\ &= \lim_{\nu\to\infty}\frac{1}{\varrho(\Delta_\nu)}\int_{\Delta_\nu}(\mu - \lambda)\,d(E_\mu u, T^{-1}f).\end{aligned} \tag{1.15}$$

The measure $\omega(\Delta) = (E(\Delta)u, T^{-1}f)$ is absolutely continuous with respect to $\rho(\Delta)$. In fact if $\rho(\Delta) = 0$, then $\Theta(\Delta) = 0$ (see proof of Theorem 1.1), and for g, $h \in \mathfrak{D}(T)$ we have $(E(\Delta)g, h) = (\Theta(\Delta)Tg, Th) = 0$. Since $\mathfrak{D}(T)$ is dense in H, we have $E(A) = 0$, and the absolute continuity of ω follows.

This absolute continuity implies that the limit in the right side of the equality (1.15) is equal to zero on the set $M_{u,f}$ whose complement N is of measure zero:

$$\frac{1}{\varrho(\Delta_\nu)}\left|\int\limits_{\Delta_\nu}(\mu-\lambda)\,d\,(E_\mu u,\ T^{-1}f)\right| = \frac{1}{\varrho(\Delta_\nu)}\left|\int\limits_{\Delta_\nu}(\mu-\lambda)\frac{d\omega}{d\varrho}\,d\varrho(\lambda)\right|$$

$$\leqslant \sup_{\mu\in\Delta_\nu}|\mu-\lambda|\frac{1}{\varrho(\Delta_\nu)}\int\limits_{\Delta_\nu}\left|\frac{d\omega}{d\varrho}\right|d\varrho(\lambda)\to 0$$

for those λ for which $\lim_{\nu\to\infty}(1/\rho(\Delta_\nu))\int_{\Delta_\nu}|d\omega/d\rho|\,d\rho(\lambda)$ is finite. But then on the set $M=\bigcap_{u\in U,f\in R}M_{u,f}$ whose complement is of measure zero, it is equal to zero for arbitrary $u\in U$, $f\in R$. For fixed $u\in U$, $(\Psi(\lambda)\,T(A-\lambda E)\,u,\ f)=0$ for each f in R and since R is dense in H (1.14) follows. The theorem is proved.

The Parseval equality is easily written (not uniquely) in an equivalent form involving individual eigenvectors rather than operators $\Psi(\lambda)$. For this we denote by $\omega_\alpha(\lambda)$ $(\alpha=1,\cdots,N_\lambda\leq\infty)$ a complete orthonormal set of vectors for the continuous nonnegative operator $\Psi(\lambda)$ (λ fixed), corresponding to the eigenvalues $\nu_\alpha(\lambda)>0$, and we put $\psi_\alpha(\lambda)=\sqrt{\nu_\alpha(\lambda)}\,\omega_\alpha(\lambda)$. Expanding $(\Psi(\lambda)\,Tf,\ Tg)$ in a bilinear series in $\psi_\alpha(\lambda)$, we obtain

$$(\Psi(\lambda)\,Tf,\ Tg) = \sum_{\alpha=1}^{N_\lambda}\overline{(\psi_\alpha(\lambda),\ Tf)}\,(\psi_\alpha(\lambda),\ Tg) \tag{1.16}$$

Substituting the expansion (1.16) in (1.12) we obtain a basic part of the proof of the following theorem.

Theorem 1.4. *For arbitrary $f,\,g\in\mathfrak{D}(T)$ and Borel set Δ, the Parseval equality is true in the form*

$$(E(\Delta)\,f,\ g) = \int\limits_{\Delta}\sum_{\alpha=1}^{N_\lambda}\overline{(\psi_\alpha(\lambda),\ Tf)}\,(\psi_\alpha(\lambda),\ Tg)\,d\varrho(\lambda)\quad(N_\lambda\leqslant\infty). \tag{1.17}$$

Here $\psi_\alpha(\lambda)$ are orthogonal vectors in H for which $T^*\psi_\alpha(\lambda)$ is an eigenvector of the operator A, corresponding to the eigenvalue λ in the sense that for such u appearing in Theorem 1.3

$$(\psi_\alpha(\lambda),\quad T(A-\lambda E)u) = 0 \quad (\alpha = 1, \ldots, N_\lambda), \tag{1.18}$$

where

$$\sum_{\alpha=1}^{N_\lambda} \| \psi_\alpha(\lambda) \|^2 = 1 . \tag{1.19}$$

Conversely, if the Parseval equality holds in the form (1.17) *with orthogonal vectors* $\psi_\alpha(\lambda)$ *satisfying* (1.18) *and* (1.19), *then it holds in the form* (1.12).

We finish the proof of the theorem. The equality (1.14) is equivalent to the relation

$$(\Psi(\lambda)f,\ T(A-\lambda E)u) = (f,\ \Psi(\lambda)\,T(A-\lambda E)u) = 0\ (f \in H,\ u \in U). \tag{1.20}$$

Supposing in (1.20), $f = \psi_\alpha(\lambda)$, we come to (1.18). Further

$$\sum_{\alpha=1}^{N_\lambda} \| \psi_\alpha(\lambda) \|^2 = \sum_{\alpha=1}^{N_\lambda} \nu_\alpha(\lambda) = \operatorname{tr}\,(\Psi(\lambda)) = 1 .$$

We prove the second part. Let $\omega_\alpha(\lambda)$ be the normalizations of the $\psi_\alpha(\lambda)$ (i.e. $\psi_\alpha(\lambda) = \|\psi_\alpha(\lambda)\|\,\omega_\alpha(\lambda)$). We define the nonnegative operator $\Psi(\lambda)$, by setting

$$(\Psi(\lambda)f, g) = \sum_{\alpha=1}^{N_\lambda} \overline{(\psi_\alpha(\lambda), f)}\,(\psi_\alpha(\lambda), g)$$

$$= \sum_{\alpha=1}^{N_\lambda} \| \psi_\alpha(\lambda) \|^2\, \overline{(\omega_\alpha(\lambda), f)}\,(\omega_\alpha(\lambda), g)$$

$$(f, g \in H)$$

(by (1.9) the last series converges). Thus a continuous operator is defined. Moreover $\operatorname{tr}(\Psi(\lambda)) = 1$. For let us extend the orthonormal sequence $\omega_\alpha(\lambda)$ to an orthonormal basis e_α in H. Then $(\Psi(\lambda)\,e_\alpha, e_\alpha) = 0$ for all α with the exclusion of those for which e_α coincides with some $\omega_\gamma(\lambda)$; in this case $(\Psi(\lambda)\,e_\alpha, e_\alpha) = \|\psi_\gamma(\lambda)\|^2$. From (1.19),

$$\operatorname{tr}\,(\Psi(\lambda)) = \sum_{\alpha=1}^{\infty} (\Psi(\lambda)\,e_\alpha,\ e_\alpha) = \sum_{\gamma=1}^{N_\lambda} \| \psi_\alpha(\lambda) \|^2 = 1 .$$

From the definition of the operator $\Psi(\lambda)$ it follows that equation (1.17) implies (1.12). It remains to prove (1.14). This relation is equivalent to (1.20) since f may be expanded in the basis e_α and the definition of $\Psi(\lambda)$ and (1.18) may be applied. The theorem follows.

In conclusion of this subsection we write a given function of A in terms of $\Psi(\lambda)$. For this, let $F(\lambda)$ be some complex valued Borel measurable function on the spectrum of A. The operator $F(A)$ is defined by means of the equation

$$F(A)f = \int_{-\infty}^{\infty} F(\lambda)\, dE_\lambda f \tag{1.21}$$

on all vectors f, for which

$$\int_{-\infty}^{\infty} |F(\lambda)|^2 d(E_\lambda f, f) < \infty;$$

they form the domain $\mathfrak{D}(F(A))$ of the operator $F(A)$. Taking the inner product with the vector g in (1.21) and using (1.12) we may write

$$(F(A)f, g) = \int_{-\infty}^{\infty} F(\lambda)(\Psi(\lambda)Tf, Tg)\, d\rho(\lambda) \quad (f \in \mathfrak{D}(F(A)) \cap \mathfrak{D}(T),\ g \in \mathfrak{D}(T)) \tag{1.22}$$

Analogously, this may be used in the form of (1.17).

4. **Converse theorem.** In the previous article we proved the Parseval equality, assuming that T^{-1} has a finite Hilbert norm. We now show that this assumption on T is necessary if we want to use it to construct expansions for arbitrary selfadjoint operators in H. The following theorem is valid.

Theorem 1.5. *Let T be an unbounded operator in a separable Hilbert space with everywhere dense domain $\mathfrak{D}(T)$, for which there exists a bounded inverse T^{-1}. If for an arbitrary selfadjoint operator in H the Parseval equality* (1.12) *is true for some nonnegative finite measure $d\rho(\lambda)$, and $\Psi(\lambda)$ defines for almost all λ a collection of uniformly bounded operators ($\|\Psi(\lambda)\| \leq C < \infty$), then T^{-1} is a Hilbert-Schmidt operator.*

Proof. Substituting in (1.12) for f and g respectively $T^{-1}f_1$, $T^{-1}g_1$(f_1, $g_1 \in H$) and assuming the existence of T^{-1}, a two sided inverse, we obtain $T^{-1*}E(\Delta)T^{-1} = \int_\Delta \Psi(\lambda)\, d\rho(\lambda)$. For an arbitrary finite collection of disjoint Borel sets Δ_j on the line we have

$$\sum_j \|T^{-1^*} E(\Delta_j) T^{-1}\| \le \sum_j \int_{\Delta_j} \|\Psi(\lambda)\| \, d\rho(\lambda)$$

$$\le C\rho(\bigcup_j \Delta_j) \le C\rho((-\infty, \infty)),$$

i.e. $\mathrm{Var}_{(-\infty,\infty)}(T^{-1^*} E(\Delta) T^{-1}) < \infty$. Therefore the theorem will be proved if we can show the following basic fact.

Let a bounded operator C in H be such that $\mathrm{Var}_{(-\infty,\infty)}(C^* E(\Delta) C) < \infty$ *for an arbitrary resolution of the identity $E(\Delta)$. Then C is necessarily a Hilbert-Schmidt operator.*

For the proof of this assertion we will use the following easily verified remark: if a bounded operator A in H yields, with respect to the orthonormal basis $e_1, e_2, \cdots$, a matrix of the form $\|a_{jk}\|_1^\infty = \|\bar{\alpha}_j \alpha_k\|_1^\infty$ then $\|A\| = \sum_{j=1}^\infty |\alpha_j|^2 = |A|$.

Consider now an orthonormal basis $e_1, e_2, \cdots$, in H and a sequence of distinct real numbers $\lambda_1, \lambda_2, \cdots$; we define a resolution of the identity E_λ by the equality $E_\lambda = \sum_{\lambda_j < \lambda} P_j$, where P_j is the projection operator onto the span of the vector e_j. Denoting by $\|C_{jk}\|_1^\infty$ the matrix of the operator C with respect to the basis $e_1, e_2, \cdots$, we find that the matrix $\|d_{jk}\|_1^\infty$ of the operator $C^* P_{j_0} C$ with respect to this basis has the form: $\|d_{jk}\|_1^\infty = \|\bar{c}_{j_0 j} c_{j_0 k}\|_1^\infty$. By the above remark $\|C^* P_{j_0} C\| = \sum_{k=1}^\infty |c_{j_0 k}|^2$. Thus

$$\infty > \mathop{\mathrm{Var}}_{(-\infty,\infty)} (C^* E(\Delta) C) = \sum_{j=1}^\infty \|C^* P_j C\| = \sum_{j,k=1}^\infty |c_{jk}|^2,$$

i.e. C is a Hilbert-Schmidt operator. The theorem is proved.

If T has only a left inverse T^{-1}, then from (1.12) alone it does not follow that $|T^{-1}| < \infty$, in view of the arbitrariness of the values of this operator on the orthogonal complement of $\Re(T)$. In place of the above proof it is easily seen that if we assume that T is closed and consider T^{-1} as an operator from the Hilbert space $H_1 = \Re(T)$ to H, then it will be of Hilbert-Schmidt type if it satisfies (1.2).

5. **Generalizations.** Theorems 1.3 and 1.4 may be carried over to a wider class of operators than the selfadjoint ones. Such extensions are not difficult and their existence will be used in what follows. We consider four classes of operators A.

a) Let A be a Hermitian operator on H and let E_λ be its generalized resolution of the identity, i.e., $E_\lambda = P\widetilde{E}_\lambda$, where $\widetilde{E}_\lambda$ is the usual resolution of the identity in some larger Hilbert space $\widetilde{H}$, and P is an orthogonal projection operator from $\widetilde{H}$ onto H. All of the arguments of subsection 3 may be applied to the nonnegative measure $E(\Delta)$; Theorems 1.3 and 1.4 remain without change for the Hermitian operator A and the generalized resolution of the identity E_λ.

b) Let A be a normal operator in H, i.e. a closed operator with dense domain such that $A^*A = AA^*$. One may construct a resolution of the identity $E(\Delta)$ for A, a nonnegative operator-valued measure defined on the Borel sets of the complex plane. All of our constructions carry over to such an $E(\Delta)$; it is only necessary to use the remarks at the end of subsection 2 and to replace the ordinary integral by a double one, and λ by a complex number. As in a) one may also consider operators admitting normal extensions either in H or in a larger space $\widetilde{H}$.

c) Let $A_1, \cdots, A_q$ be q selfadjoint operators on H with resolutions of identity $E^{(1)}_{\lambda_1}, \cdots, E^{(q)}_{\lambda_q}$. The operators A_j are said to be commuting if for arbitrary $\lambda_1, \cdots, \lambda_q$ their resolutions of identity commute. In this case one can construct a q-dimensional resolution of the identity, namely an operator-valued measure $E(\Delta)$ on the Borel sets in the q-dimensional space E_q of points $\lambda = (\lambda_1, \cdots, \lambda_q)$, with properties analogous to those of the usual resolution of the identity (nonnegativity: $E(\Delta) \geq 0$; orthogonality: $E(\Delta')E(\Delta'') = E(\Delta' \cap \Delta'')$); here also, for every $f, g \in H$ and bounded Δ, the equality

$$(E(\Delta)f, g) = \int_\Delta d(E_\lambda f, g), \quad (A_jE(\Delta)f, g) = \int_\Delta \lambda_j d(E_\lambda f, g) (j = 1, \ldots . q). \tag{1.23}$$

is valid.

Using the remarks at the end of subsection 2, it is possible to differentiate the measure (1.10) (constructed from $E(\Delta)$) with respect to $\rho(\Delta) = \operatorname{tr}(\Theta(\Delta))$ and to obtain an operator-valued function $\Psi(\lambda)$ $(\lambda \in E_q)$. The relations (1.12) and (1.13) are obvious, differing only in that the integral will be q-dimensional in the first of them. The relation (1.14) is replaced by q relations,

$$\Psi(\lambda) T (A_j - \lambda_j E) u = 0 \qquad (j = 1, \ldots, q), \tag{1.24}$$

which are obtained in exactly the same way as (1.14), using the second of the equalities in (1.23). In (1.24) u takes values in some countable set of vectors U_j such that $U_j \subseteq \mathfrak{D}(A_j) \cap \mathfrak{D}(T)$ and $A_jU_j \subseteq \mathfrak{D}(T)$.

Theorem 1.4 also holds when the vectors $\psi_\alpha(\lambda)$ depend on $\lambda \in E_q$ and the equality (1.19) acquires the form

$$(\psi_\alpha(\lambda), T(A_j - \lambda_j E) u) = 0 \qquad (\alpha = 1, \ldots, N_\lambda;\ u \in U_j;\ j = 1, \ldots, q). \tag{1.25}$$

d) Let $A_1, \cdots, A_q$ be q densely defined Hermitian operators which admit commuting selfadjoint extensions in the sense of c): $\widetilde{A}_1 \supseteq A_1, \cdots, \widetilde{A}_q \supseteq A_q$, in a larger space $\widetilde{H} \supseteq H$. We denote by $\widetilde{E}(\Delta)$ the q-dimensional resolution of the identity, corresponding to $\widetilde{A}_1, \cdots, \widetilde{A}_q$, and we introduce a q-dimensional generalized resolution of the identity $E(\Delta)$, putting $E(\Delta) = P\widetilde{E}(\Delta)P$, where P is an orthogonal projection operator of $\widetilde{H}$ on H. The operator valued measure $E(\Delta)$ obviously possesses all of the characteristics of a q-dimensional resolution of the identity with the exception of orthogonality. Since the relation (1.23) is true for A_j and $E(\Delta)$, then all that was said in c) may be repeated without change in the formulas for the Hermitian operators $A_1, \cdots, A_q$ and their q-dimensional generalized resolution of the identity $E(\Delta)$.

§2. EXPANSION IN GENERALIZED EIGENVECTORS

1. Notation for the theorem on decomposition in terms of generalized eigenvectors. It is a remarkable fact that formal expressions of the type $T^*\Psi(\lambda)T$, $T^*\psi_\alpha(\lambda)$ in §1.3 are readily given in an exact sense if we use the notation of a generalized vector given in Chapter I.

Let $H_0 = H$ be a separable Hilbert space, and let A be a selfadjoint operator on H; we will construct an expansion in generalized eigenvectors for this operator. Often it is possible to assume that H_0 is associated with separable Hilbert spaces H_+ and H_- with positive and negative norms:

$$H_- \supseteq H_0 \supseteq H_+. \tag{2.1}$$

We will assume that the imbedding $H_+ \to H_0$ is a quasi-nuclear (see Chapter I, §2.4), and that the remaining choice of H_+ is arbitrary.

We carry out the construction of §1.3 taking for T the operator D, defined in Theorem 1.1, Chapter I and considered as an operator on H_0. This is possible since $T^{-1} = \hat{J}$, and the latter operator thanks to the quasi-nuclearity of the imbedding $H_+ \to H_0$ is a Hilbert-Schmidt operator (see Chapter I, §2.4). Using equation (1.16) of Chapter I, we may write

$$(\Psi(\lambda)Du,\ Dv)_0 = (\mathbf{D}\Psi(\lambda)Du, v)_0\ (u, v \in H_+ = \mathfrak{D}(D)). \tag{2.2}$$

For fixed λ, the operator $P(\lambda) = \mathbf{D}\Psi(\lambda)D$ is defined from H_+ to H_- and is a Hilbert-Schmidt operator since the product of two continuous operators is a Hilbert-Schmidt operator if one of them is. Moreover, from (1.2), from the estimate $|\Psi(\lambda)| \le 1$ and from the isometric nature of D and $\mathbf{D}$, it follows that

$$|P(\lambda)| = |\mathbf{D}\Psi(\lambda)D| \leq \|\mathbf{D}\|\,|\Psi(\lambda)|\,\|D\| = |\Psi(\lambda)| \leq 1. \tag{2.3}$$

The range $\Re(P(\lambda))$ of $P(\lambda)$ is, generally speaking, a nonclosed linear subspace of H_-; it is naturally called the generalized eigenmanifold corresponding to the point λ of the spectrum. The operator $P(\lambda)$ "projects" H_+ onto this subspace, where the "projection" is orthogonal in the usual sense: if $u \in H_+$ is such that $(\Re(P(\lambda)), u)_0 = 0$, then $P(\lambda)u = 0$. In fact, for arbitrary $v \in H_+$ and selfadjoint $\Psi(\lambda)$, by (1.16) in Chapter I we have

$$(P(\lambda)u, v)_0 = (\mathbf{D}\Psi(\lambda)Du, v)_0 = (\Psi(\lambda)Du, Dv)_0 = (Du, \Psi(\lambda)Dv)_0$$
$$= (u, \mathbf{D}\Psi(\lambda)Dv)_0 = (u, P(\lambda)v)_0 = 0.$$

In view of (2.2), the Parseval equality (1.12) may be written in the form

$$(E(\Delta)u, v)_0 = \int_\Delta (P(\lambda)u, v)_0\, d\varrho(\lambda) \qquad (u, v \in H_+),$$

i.e. in each case the integral

$$E(\Delta) = \int_\Delta P(\lambda)\, d\varrho(\lambda) \tag{2.4}$$

converges weakly.

In fact, according to the estimate (2.3) and the finiteness of ρ, this integral converges in the Hilbert norm of the operators (from H_+ to H_-). The Parseval equality (2.4) is now written in the form of the finite case; i.e. the projection operator $E(\Delta)$ is decomposed as a continuous sum of "projection" operators $P(\lambda)$.

We now rewrite the Parseval equality in the form of (1.17) in terms of generalized vectors. By (1.16), Chapter I, we have

$$\begin{gathered}(\psi_\alpha(\lambda), Du)_0 = (\varphi_\alpha(\lambda), u)_0, \quad \varphi_\alpha(\lambda) = \mathbf{D}\psi_\alpha(\lambda) \in H_- \\ (u \in H_+;\ \alpha = 1, \ldots, N_\lambda).\end{gathered} \tag{2.5}$$

The generalized vector $\phi_\alpha(\lambda)$ is "an individual generalized eigenvector" corresponding to the value λ. The vectors $\phi_\alpha(\lambda)$, as D-images of the $\psi_\alpha(\lambda)$, form in the metric of H_- an orthogonal basis for the (generally speaking) nonclosed linear space $\Re(P(\lambda))$. We relate to each $u \in H_+$ its "Fourier transform", a vector of the form

$$\widetilde{u}(\lambda) = (u_1(\lambda), u_2(\lambda), \ldots), \ u_\alpha(\lambda) = (\varphi_\alpha(\lambda), u)_0 \ (\alpha = 1, \ldots, N_\lambda).$$

The vector $\widetilde{u}(\lambda)$, which is defined for almost all $\lambda(\rho)$, consists for each λ of N_λ

coordinates. The equality (1.17) then takes the form

$$(E(\Delta)u, v)_0 = \int_\Delta \sum_{\alpha=1}^{N_\lambda} \overline{u_\alpha(\lambda)}\, v_\alpha(\lambda)\, d\rho(\lambda) \qquad (u, v \in H_+). \tag{2.6}$$

It is clear also that one may write equality (1.22) in terms of $P(\lambda)$ and $\phi_\alpha(\lambda)$. One may get the impression that the results of this subsection are a special case (with $T = D$) of the results in §1.3. However, in Chapter I, §3.6 it was shown that H_0 may be equipped by an arbitrary operator T as in §1.3 (with an additional inessential condition of boundedness $\|T^{-1}\| \leq 1$). In this case D is metrically equal to T and the construction described above essentially coincides with the general construction of §1.

In the following subsection we will discuss the notion of a generalized eigenvector in more detail, after which the facts presented will be summed up in the form of a theorem.

2. **The notion of a generalized eigenvector.** Let us make clear in what sense the vectors of $\mathfrak{R}(P(\lambda))$ are generalized eigenvectors for the operator A. If some further boundedness condition is not imposed on A, then nothing more than a relation of the type (1.14) or (1.20) can be obtained. However, the following situation is often encountered, which we describe in the general case of nonselfadjoint A.

Let A be a densely defined operator with domain $\mathfrak{D}(A)$ in the equipped Hilbert space H_0 $(H_- \supseteq H_0 \supseteq H_+)$. We will say that A admits an extension of the equipment if there exists a linear topological space $Д \subseteq H_+$ which is dense in H_+ (the inclusion is topological), contained in $\mathfrak{D}(A^*)$ and such that A^* is continuously defined from $Д$ to H_+. A vector $\phi \in H_-$ is called a generalized eigenvector of the operator A corresponding to the eigenvalue λ if

$$(\varphi, (A^* - \bar{\lambda}E)u)_0 = 0 \qquad (u \in Д). \tag{2.7}$$

For the Hermitian operator A such that $Д \subseteq \mathfrak{D}(A)$ and such that A maps $Д$ contintinuously into H_+ we may replace A^* by A in (2.7), since $A^* \supseteq A$.

If ϕ is an ordinary vector from $\mathfrak{D}(A)$, then it will satisfy the equality $A\phi = \lambda\phi$, i.e. it will be an ordinary eigenvector. In fact, by (2.7)

$$(A\varphi - \lambda\varphi, u)_0 = (\varphi, (A^* - \bar{\lambda}E)u)_0 = 0 \qquad (u \in Д);$$

Since $Д$ is obviously dense in H_0, it follows that $A\phi - \lambda\phi = 0$.

The definition of a generalized eigenvector depends on the choice of H_+ and Д. If Д is restricted, the collection of eigenvectors will be enlarged: we fix λ and a Д so small that $(A^* - \bar{\lambda}E)$Д is not dense in H_+. Then there is a w in H_+ which is orthogonal to $(A^* - \bar{\lambda}E)$Д. Then $(\mathrm{I}^{-1}w, (A^* - \bar{\lambda}E)u)_0 = (w, (A^* - \bar{\lambda}E)u)_+ = 0$ ($u \in$ Д), i.e. $\phi - \mathrm{I}^{-1}w$ is a generalized vector corresponding to the eigenvalue λ. It is clear that one may construct examples where a selfadjoint operator has generalized eigenvectors corresponding to normal λ.

It is not difficult to see that the above construction is essentially connected with some extension of the operator A. In fact, since Д $\subseteq H_+$, then Д$' \supseteq H'_+ = H_-$, and we have the chain

$$Д' \supseteq H_- \supseteq H_0 \supseteq H_+ \supseteq Д, \tag{2.8}$$

generalizing (1.10) of Chapter I in the sense that Д is a linear topological space and not a Hilbert space. But by repeating the arguments of Chapter I, §1.3 it is easy to see that for each continuous operator C from Д to H_+ there exists a continuous operator C^+ from H_- to Д$'$ connected with C by the relation

$$(C^+\alpha, u)_0 = (\alpha, Cu)_0 \qquad (\alpha \in H_-, u \in Д). \tag{2.9}$$

Corresponding to the above operator A we now construct an operator $\tilde{A} = A^{*+}A$ defined continuously from H_- into Д$'$. On $\mathfrak{D}(A)$ it coincides with A: $(\tilde{A}f, u)_0 = (A^{*+}f, u)_0 = (f, A^*u)_0 = (Af, u)_0$ $(f \in \mathfrak{D}(A), u \in Д \subseteq \mathfrak{D}(A^*))$ i.e. $\tilde{A} \supseteq A$. Now the definition of a generalized eigenvector (2.7) is equivalent to the equation

$$\tilde{A}\varphi = \lambda\varphi. \tag{2.10}$$

In the preceding definition an essential role is played by the fact that A^*, defined in a Hilbert space H_0, may be restricted so that $\mathfrak{D}(A^*)$ is contained in H_+ and dense in that space, and so that $\mathfrak{R}(A^*) \subseteq H_+$. Then $\mathfrak{D}(A^*)$ takes on the topology of the space Д $=$ Д$_+$ (and even the topology of a Hilbert space (generally not complete)) if the scalar product

$$(u, v)_{Д_+} = (u, v)_+ + (A^*u, A^*v)_+ \; (u, v \in \mathfrak{D}(A^*) = Д_+).$$

is introduced. Clearly all of the earlier requirements on Д are now satisfied; one may assume Д$' \supseteq$ Д$'_+$. In particular, it follows that we may assume that Д is always a Hilbert space.

We proceed to the application of these notions to the theorem on expansions, assuming in every case that Д is separable.

Lemma 2.1. *Let the selfadjoint operator A considered in subsection* 1 *admit an extension of the equipment* (2.1). *Then each vector in $\Re(P(\lambda))$ is a generalized eigenvector corresponding to the eigenvalue λ.*

Proof. Let $\phi \in \Re(P(\lambda))$, i.e., $\phi = P(\lambda)v = \mathrm{D}\Psi(\lambda)Dv$. We choose as the countable collection appearing in Theorem 1.3 a countable set U dense in $Д$. Then by (1.14) for each $u \in U$

$$(\phi, (A - \lambda E)u)_0 = (\mathrm{D}\Psi(\lambda)Dv, (A - \lambda E)u)_0$$

$$= (\Psi(\lambda)Dv, D(A - \lambda E)u)_0 + (Dv, \Psi(\lambda)D(A - \lambda E)u)_0 = 0. \tag{2.11}$$

The mapping $u \to (A - \lambda E)u$ is continuous from $Д$ to H_+ and therefore, by approximating the vector u with arbitrary vectors from $Д$, we see that (2.11) is valid for arbitrary $u \in Д$. The lemma follows.

We will clarify the construction of preceding subsection and an analog to this lemma for the extensions given in §1.5. In the case a) (Hermitian operator A, generalized resolution of the identity E_λ) all of the previous formulas are obvious. We consider in more detail the case b), where the operator A is normal. Now $E(\Delta)$ is a nonnegative complex-valued measure on the Borel sets of the complex plane and therefore the function $\Psi(\lambda)$ obtained by differentiating $T^{-1^*}E(\Delta)T^{-1}$ with respect to $\rho(\Delta) = \mathrm{tr}(T^{-1^*}E(\Delta)T^{-1})$ is a function of a complex variable λ, the values of which are nonnegative Hilbert-Schmidt operators on H. Repeating the construction of subsection 1 we obtain the operator-valued function $P(\lambda) = \mathrm{D}\Psi(\lambda)D$, the values of which are Hilbert-Schmidt operators from H_+ to H_-. We describe $\Re(P(\lambda))$ as in Lemma 2.1. Repeating the argument in this proof of Theorem 1.3, in which the Δ_ν are rectangles in the plane tending to λ, we obtain the relation (1.14). As in (2.11), this relation yields the equality $(\phi, (A - \lambda E)u)_0 = 0$ $(u \in Д_2)$ for each $\phi \in \Re(P(\lambda))$. Here $Д_2 \subseteq \mathfrak{D}(A) = \mathfrak{D}(A^{**})$ where we assume that A^* admits an equipped extension. This equality shows that ϕ is a generalized eigenvector of the operator A^*, corresponding to the eigenvalue $\bar\lambda$.

Moreover, ϕ is a generalized eigenvector of the operator A, corresponding to λ. In fact along with the equality (1.14) one may obtain for A the equation $\Psi(\lambda)T(A^* - \bar\lambda E)u = 0$ $(u \in U)$. For this it is necessary to proceed as in the proof of Theorem 1.3 and to use the fact that $A^* = \int_{E_2} \bar\mu \, dE_\mu$. The equation obtained under the natural assumption implies the required relation $(\phi, (A^* - \bar\lambda E)u)_0 = 0$ $(u \in Д_1)$, where $Д_1 \subseteq \mathfrak{D}(A^*)$. Thus $\phi \in \Re/(p(\lambda))$ is in general a generalized eigenvector for A and A^*:

$$\tilde{A}\phi = \lambda\phi, \quad \tilde{A}^*\phi = \bar{\lambda}\phi \quad (\tilde{A} = A^{*+}, \ \tilde{A}^* = A^+).$$

The topologies of the spaces $Д_1$ and $Д_2$ are different, in general, but may be chosen so as to coincide.

Consider the case c) where there are q commuting selfadjoint operators $A_1, \cdots, A_q$ (such a situation may be considered as a general case of b), if one sets $A_1 = (1/2)(A + iA^*)$, $A_2 = (1/2i)(A - iA^*)$). Here again the argument of subsection 1 is repeated. As a result we obtain the operator-valued function $P(\lambda) = \mathrm{D}\Psi(\lambda)D$ defined for ρ-almost all $\lambda = (\lambda_1, \cdots, \lambda_q)$. We assume that each of the operators A_j admits an equipped extension with spaces $Д_j$ (the $Д_j$ are not necessarily distinct). An obvious analog of Lemma 2.1 now takes the following form: each vector $\phi \in \Re(P(\lambda))$ appears as a generalized eigenvector of the system of operators $A_1, \cdots, A_q$, i.e., we have the equalities

$$(\phi, (A_j - \lambda_j E)u)_0 = 0 \quad (u \in Д_j; \ j = 1, \cdots, q),$$

or equivalently, the equations

$$\tilde{A}_j\phi = \lambda_j\phi \quad (\tilde{A}_j = A_j^+; \ j = 1, \cdots, q).$$

3. Formulation of the theorem on expansions in generalized eigenvectors. We now sum up the results of the two preceding subsections. *From here until the end of this section we assume the separability of all spaces encountered.*

Theorem 2.1. *Let*

$$H_- \supseteq H_0 \supseteq H_+ \tag{2.12}$$

be an equipment of the Hilbert space H_0 where the inclusion $H_+ \to H_0$ is quasinuclear. For an arbitrary selfadjoint operator A on H_0 there is a nonnegative finite measure $d\rho(\lambda)$ defined on the Borel sets of the real line, and an almost everywhere (ρ) defined operator-valued function $P(\lambda)$ $(-\infty < \lambda < \infty)$, the values of which are Hilbert-Schmidt operators from H_+ to H_-, where

$$|P(\lambda)| \le 1, \quad (P(\lambda)u, u)_0 \ge 0 \quad (u \in H_+),^* \tag{2.13}$$

such that the Parseval equality is valid: for an arbitrary Borel set Δ and resolution of the identity $E(\Delta)$ corresponding to A, the integral representation

* Moreover, $P(\lambda)$ has a finite trace, equal to 1, i.e. for an arbitrary orthonormal basis $e_1, e_2, \cdots$ in H_+, $\mathrm{tr}(P(\lambda)) = \sum_{j=1}^{\infty}(P(\lambda)e_j, e_j)_0 = 1$. This property of $P(\lambda)$ easily follows from the equation $\mathrm{tr}(\Psi(\lambda)) = 1$; in what follows the definition of the trace for operators from H_+ to H_- will not be used.

$$E(\Delta) = \int_{\Delta} P(\lambda)\, d\rho(\lambda) \tag{2.14}$$

converges in the Hilbert norm. Let the operator A admit an extension of the equipment (2.12), *i.e. there exists a linear topological space* $Д \subseteq H_+$, *dense in* H_+, *such that* $Д \subseteq \mathfrak{D}(A)$ *and that* $A\colon Д \to H_+$ *is continuous. Then* $\Re(P(\lambda))$ *consists of generalized eigenvectors, corresponding to the generalized eigenvalue* λ.

If there is some equipment (2.12) *for which there is a* $\rho(\Delta)$ *and a* $P(\lambda)$ *for each selfadjoint operator in* H_0, *which has the above properties, then the inclusion* $H_+ \to H_0$ *is necessarily quasi-nuclear.*

Clarification is necessary only for the last assertion of the theorem. We consider the chain (2.12); since these operators respectively map H_0 into H_+, and H_- into H_0, then the operator $\Phi(\lambda) = \mathrm{J}P(\lambda)J$ is a Hilbert-Schmidt operator in the space H_0 satisfying $\|\Phi(\lambda)\| \leq 1$. If we consider J as a selfadjoint operator $\hat{J}$ acting on H_0, then taking into account that $E(\Delta)$ is defined in H_0, one may write $\mathrm{J}E(\Delta)J = \hat{J}E(\Delta)\hat{J}$. Now from (2.14) after multiplying by J and J it follows that

$$\hat{J}E(\Delta)\hat{J} = \int_{\Delta} \Phi(\lambda)\, d\varrho(\lambda), \qquad \|\Phi(\lambda)\| \leqslant 1$$

From this, as in the proof of Theorem 1.5, we obtain that $\mathrm{Var}_{(-\infty,\infty)}(\hat{J}E(\Delta)\hat{J}) < \infty$. If we apply the assertion in that proof, we now note that $\hat{J}$ is a Hilbert-Schmidt operator, i.e. the inclusion $H_+ \to H_0$ is quasi-nuclear. But this is what was required.

From (2.14), in particular, the following equalities are obtained:

$$E(\Delta)u = \int_{\Delta} P(\lambda)\, u\, d\varrho(\lambda), \qquad u = \int_{-\infty}^{\infty} P(\lambda)\, u\, d\varrho(\lambda),$$

$$(u, v)_0 = \int_{-\infty}^{\infty} (P(\lambda)u, v)_0\, d\varrho(\lambda) \qquad (u, v \in H_+). \tag{2.15}$$

The representation (1.22) for functions $F(A)$ appear now as

$$(F(A)u, v)_0 = \int_{-\infty}^{\infty} F(\lambda)(P(\lambda)u, v)_0\, d\varrho(\lambda) \qquad (u \in \mathfrak{D}(F(A)) \cap H_+,\ v \in H_+). \tag{2.16}$$

The measure $d\rho(\lambda)$ is called a spectral measure of the operator A, and is concentrated on its spectrum. The operator $P(\lambda)$ will be called a generalized projection operator onto the generalized eigenmanifold $\Re(P(\lambda))$, corresponding to λ. Since

$$P(\lambda)\,d\varrho(\lambda) = \frac{1}{M(\lambda)} P(\lambda)\,M(\lambda)\,d\varrho(\lambda),$$

where $M(\lambda)$ is an arbitrary, nonnegative ρ-locally summable function unequal to zero almost everywhere (ρ), it is also convenient to call $\rho_1(\Delta) = \int_\Delta M(\lambda)\,d\rho(\lambda)$ and $P_1(\lambda) = (1/M(\lambda))\,P(\lambda)$, a generalized spectral measure and generalized projection operator. In other words, our definitions are exact up to multiplications. The measure $d\rho_1(\lambda)$ is completely characterized by the fact that $d\rho_1(\lambda)$ is absolutely continuous with respect to $d\rho(\lambda)$ and $d\rho(\lambda)$ is absolutely continuous with respect to $d\rho_1(\lambda)$, i.e. they are equivalent measures.

If along with (2.14) we have the representation $E(\Delta) = \int_\Delta P_1(\lambda)\,d\rho_1(\lambda)$ where $P_1(\lambda)$ is defined continuously from H_+ to H_- and $d\rho_1(\lambda)$ is concentrated on the spectrum of A, then $d\rho(\lambda)$ will be absolutely continuous with respect to $d\rho_1(\lambda)$. If moreover $d\rho_1(\lambda)$ is absolutely continuous with respect to $d\rho(\lambda)$, then we may assume that $d\rho_1(\lambda) = M(\lambda)\,d\rho(\lambda)$ and $P_1(\lambda) = P(\lambda)/m(\lambda)$ are spectral measures and generalized projection operators. We will sometimes use these terms in the case where $d\rho_1(\lambda)$ is not absolutely continuous with respect to $d\rho(\lambda)$.

Since $|P(\lambda)| \leq 1$, to the operator $P(\lambda)$, generally speaking, there corresponds a generalized kernel $\Phi(\lambda)$, a so-called generalized spectral kernel. The kernel $\Xi_\lambda = \int_{-\infty}^{\lambda} \Phi_\mu\,d\rho(\mu)$ corresponds to the operator $E_\lambda = \int_{-\infty}^{\lambda} P(\mu)\,d\rho(\mu)$ and is called a (generalized) spectral function. For the details of these notions see pp. 347–348, 351–359.

We now formulate an analog of Theorem 1.4.

Theorem 2.2. *Let the conditions of the previous theorems be fulfilled (together with the condition that A admits an extension of the equipment). Then it is possible to choose (not uniquely) a system of orthogonal (in H_-) generalized eigenvectors $\phi_\alpha(\lambda)$ $(\alpha = 1, \cdots, N_\lambda \leq \infty)$ from the generalized eigenmanifold $\Re(P(\lambda))$ of the operator A corresponding to λ such that*

$$\sum_{\alpha=1}^{N_\lambda} \|\varphi_\alpha(\lambda)\|_-^2 = 1, \tag{2.17}$$

and the Parseval equality may be written in the form

$$(E(\Delta)\,u, v)_0 = \int_\Delta \sum_{\alpha=1}^{N_\lambda} u_\alpha(\lambda)\,\overline{v_\alpha(\lambda)}\,d\varrho(\lambda) \qquad (u, v \in H_+); \tag{2.18}$$

$$\widetilde{u}(\lambda) = (u_1(\lambda), u_2(\lambda), \ldots), \; u_\alpha(\lambda) = (\varphi_\alpha(\lambda), u)_0 \; (\alpha = 1, \ldots, N_\lambda) \qquad (2.19)$$

is the "Fourier series" of a vector u in H_+.

Conversely, if the Parseval equality holds in the form (2.18) *with the vectors $\phi_\alpha(\lambda)$ as above, then it holds in the form* (2.14).

Here it is only necessary to point out that the last assertion follows from the last part of Theorem 1.4, since the vectors $\psi_\alpha(\lambda) = J\phi_\alpha(\lambda)$ satisfy the requirements of that theorem.

From (1.16) it follows that

$$(P(\lambda)u, v)_0 = \sum_{\alpha=1}^{N_\lambda} \overline{u_\alpha(\lambda)}\, v_\alpha(\lambda) \qquad (u, v \in H_+). \qquad (2.20)$$

almost everywhere with respect to ρ. Substituting this expression in (2.15) and (2.16), we may write the respective equations in terms of Fourier expansions. We note that N_λ is equal to the dimension of the generalized eigenmanifold corresponding to the point λ of the spectrum and is called the multiplicity of λ. If $N_\lambda = 1$, then the point λ is called simple. If almost all λ are simple (ρ), then equations (2.17)–(2.20) are simplified in that their sums are replaced by one term.

Since the construction is not unique, Theorem 2.2 is, generally speaking, less useful than Theorem 2.1. However, it is useful in that it facilitates the writing of the Parseval equality for general vectors u, v. For consider the Hilbert space $L_2(\infty; d\rho(\lambda)) = L_2(l_2([1, \infty)); (-\infty, \infty), d\rho(\lambda))$ of vector-functions $\widetilde{f}(\lambda) = (f_1(\lambda), f_2(\lambda), \cdots)$ $(-\infty < \lambda < \infty)$ with the inner product

$$(\widetilde{f}, \widetilde{g})_{L_2(\infty;\, d\rho(\lambda))} = \int_{-\infty}^{\infty} \sum_{\alpha=1}^{\infty} f_\alpha(\lambda)\, \overline{g_\alpha(\lambda)}\, d\rho(\lambda)$$

(for greater detail see §4.4). Below we will call a finite vector of the form $\widetilde{u}(\lambda) = (u_1(\lambda), \cdots, u_{N_\lambda}(\lambda), 0, 0, \cdots)$ a Fourier transform, noting that such an agreement causes no change in the previous formulas. Now for each $u \in H_+$ $\int_{-\infty}^{\infty} \sum_{\alpha=1}^{\infty} |u_\alpha(\lambda)|^2 d\rho(\lambda) < \infty$, $\widetilde{u}(\lambda) \in L_2(\infty; d\rho(\lambda))$. Equation (2.18) with $\Delta = (-\infty, \infty)$ is written for $L_2(\infty; d\rho(\lambda))$ in the form

$$(u, v)_0 = (\widetilde{v}, \widetilde{u})_{L_2(\infty;\, d\rho(\lambda))}.$$

It is possible to extend it by continuity to $u, v \in H_0$, where in this connection the Fourier transform $\widetilde{f}(\lambda)$ of the vector f in H_0 is understood as a vector of $L_2(\infty; d\rho(\lambda))$, and appears as a limit in $L_2(\infty; d\rho(\lambda))$ of $\widetilde{u}_n(\lambda)$, where H_+ is such that $u_n \to f$ in H_0. As a result we have the Parseval equality

$$(f, g)_0 = (\widetilde{g}, \widetilde{f})_{L_2(\infty, d\varrho(\lambda))} (f, g \in H_0). \tag{2.21}$$

It is clear that the Fourier transforms $f(\lambda)$ of vectors $f \in H_0$ do not fill all of $L^2(\infty; d\rho(\lambda))$. For example this will be the case when $N_\lambda \leq C < \infty$ for almost all $\lambda(\rho)$.

For convenience we form as a theorem the generalization mentioned in §1.5 and at the end of the previous subsection.

Theorem 2.3. *Let A be a Hermitian operator on an equipped Hilbert space H_0 and $E(\Delta)$ some generalized resolution of the identity for A. Then Theorems 2.1 and 2.2 remain valid in this case without any change in the formulations.*

Theorem 2.4. *Let the chain (2.12) occur, when the inclusion $H_+ \to H_0$ is quasi-nuclear. For an arbitrary normal operator A defined on H_0 there exists a nonnegative finite measure $\rho(\Delta)$ defined on the Borel sets of the complex plane C_1, and a ρ-almost-everywhere-defined operator-valued function $P(\lambda)$ $(\lambda \in C_1)$ such that relations (2.13) and (2.14) hold.*

Let the operators A and A^* admit extensions of the equipment (2.12), i.e., there exist linear topological spaces $Д_1$ and $Д_2$, each densely contained in H_+ and respectively in $\mathfrak{D}(A^*)$ and $\mathfrak{D}(A)$, such that $A^*\colon Д_1 \to H_+$ and $A\colon Д_2 \to H_+$ are continuous. Then $\mathfrak{R}(P(\lambda))$ consists of generalized eigenvectors ϕ for both A and A^*, i.e. the relations

$$(\varphi, (A^* - \lambda E) u)_0 = 0 \ (u \in Д_1), \quad (\varphi, (A - \lambda E) u)_0 = 0 \ (u \in Д_2) \tag{2.22}$$

are satisfied. In other words, for the extensions $\widetilde{A} = A^{*+}$ and $\widetilde{A}^* = A^+$ corresponding to the operators A and A^* the equations

$$\widetilde{A}\varphi = \lambda\varphi, \quad \widetilde{A}^*\varphi = \bar{\lambda}\varphi \tag{2.23}$$

are valid.

Theorem 2.2 carries over without change in its formulation, noting only that λ is complex valued (strictly speaking, the spectrum of A is changed since $\rho(\Delta)$ is obviously concentrated on the spectrum).

Theorem 2.5. *Let the chain (2.21) occur, where the inclusion $H_+ \to H_0$ is quasi-nuclear. If $A_1, \cdots, A_q$ is an arbitrary commuting family of selfadjoint oper-*

ators, there exists a nonnegative finite measure $\rho(\Delta)$, *defined on the Borel sets of the q-dimensional space* E_q, *and an almost everywhere* (ρ) *defined operator-valued function* $P(\lambda)$ ($\lambda \in E_q$), *such that relations* (2.13) *and* (2.14) *hold.*

Let each of the selfadjoint operators A_j *admit an extension of the equipment* (2.12) *in which* $\Phi = \Phi_j$ ($j = 1, \cdots, q$). *Then* $\mathfrak{R}(P(\lambda))$ *consists of generalized eigenvectors* ϕ, *for the system of operators* $A_1, \cdots, A_q$, *i.e., they satisfy the relations*

$$(\phi, (A_j - \lambda_j E)u)_0 = 0 \quad (u \in \Phi_j;\ j = 1, \cdots, q). \tag{2.24}$$

In other words the equations

$$\tilde{A}_j\varphi = \lambda_j\varphi \qquad (j = 1, \ldots, q). \tag{2.25}$$

are valid for the extensions $\tilde{A}_j = A_j^+$.

Theorem 2.2 *carries over without exception if* λ *is understood to be a point of the space* E_q.

Theorem 2.6. *Let* H_0 *be an equipped Hilbert space,* $A_1, \cdots, A_q$ *a system of Hermitian operators on* H_0 *with commuting selfadjoint extensions, and* $E(\Delta)$ *a generalized q-dimensional resolution of the identity. Then Theorem* 2.5 *carries over to this case without change in the formulation.*

Equations of the type (2.15)–(2.16) are easily written for Theorems 2.3–2.6; we will also use the definitions of the spectral measure and generalized projection operators which correspond in a natural way to the generalizations considered. It is also clear that we can introduce a Fourier transformation for vectors of H_0, using a space of the type $L_2(\infty; d\rho(\lambda))$, where λ is a point of a multi-dimensional space.

Thus we have constructed generalized eigenvector expansions for an important class of operators. As shown in the last part of Theorem 2.1, the space of generalized eigenvectors H_- is chosen as close as possible to H_0. In conclusion, we make the following remark related to Theorem 2.1. The operator $E(\Delta)$ may be thought of as being defined from H_+ to H_-. Since $E(\Delta)$ takes H_0 into itself continuously, and the inclusion of H_+ into H_0 and H_0 into H_- are quasi-nuclear, it follows that $E(\Delta)$ will automatically be a Hilbert-Schmidt operator from H_+ into H_-. Formula (2.14) shows that its derivative, $dE_\lambda/d\rho(\lambda) = P(\lambda)$, exists in the Hilbert norm. Analogous remarks may be made concerning Theorems 2.3–2.6.

4. Another proof of the theorems of the preceding subsection. We outline another approach to Theorems 2.3–2.6 which uses the spectral theorem in the form of Neĭman. We restrict ourselves to the introduction of formula (2.18) from which it is possible to obtain the remaining basic assertions. According to the Neĭman theorem, if A is a selfadjoint operator on a separable Hilbert space H_0, it is possible to construct a subspace L_0 of the space $L_2(\infty;\, d\rho(\lambda))$, which is unitarily equal to $H_0 (f \to \tilde{f}(\lambda))$ where $f \in H_0$; $\tilde{f}(\lambda) = (\tilde{f}_1(\lambda), \tilde{f}_2(\lambda), \ldots) \in L_0 \subseteq L_2(\infty;\, d\rho(\lambda))$ is such that the image $\tilde{A}$ of the operator A will admit a diagonal form. In other words,

$$(E(\Delta) f, g)_0 = (\tilde{E}(\Delta) \tilde{f}(\lambda), \tilde{g}(\lambda))_{L_2(\infty;\, d\rho(\lambda))}$$

$$= \int_{\Delta} \sum_{\alpha=1}^{\infty} \tilde{f}_\alpha(\lambda) \overline{\tilde{g}_\alpha(\lambda)}\, d\rho(\lambda) \qquad (f, g \in H_0,\ E(\Delta) \leftrightarrow \tilde{E}(\Delta)). \tag{2.26}$$

Let H_0 be equipped as in (2.12) with a quasi-nuclear inclusion $H_+ \to H_0$. We show that for all λ, excluding possibly a set of ρ-measure zero, for arbitrary $u \in H_+$ the representation

$$\tilde{u}_\alpha(\lambda) = \overline{(\varphi_\alpha(\lambda), u)_0} = \overline{(\omega_\alpha(\lambda), u)_+} = (u, \omega_\alpha(\lambda))_+ \quad (\alpha = 1, 2, \ldots), \tag{2.27}$$

is valid, where the vectors $\phi_\alpha(\lambda) \in H_-$; $w_\alpha(\lambda) = \mathrm{I}\phi_\alpha(\lambda) \in H_+$. For the proof, we denote by O the inclusion operator of H_+ into H_0 and by V the unitary operator taking H_0 onto L_0. Then $\tilde{u}(\lambda) = VOu$. Let $e_1, e_2, \cdots$ be an orthonormal basis in H_+; for arbitrary u in H_+ we have

$$u = \sum_{j=1}^{\infty} (u, e_j)_+ e_j; \qquad \tilde{u}_\alpha(\lambda) = (VOu)_\alpha(\lambda) = \sum_{j=1}^{\infty} (u, e_j)_+ (VOe_j)_\alpha(\lambda)$$

$$(\alpha = 1, 2, \ldots). \tag{2.28}$$

The operator VO, constructed from a bounded operator V and a Hilbert-Schmidt operator O, will be a Hilbert-Schmidt operator. It follows that

$$\infty > \sum_{j=1}^{\infty} \| VOe_j \|^2_{L_2(\infty;\, d\rho(\lambda))} = \sum_{j=1}^{\infty} \int_{-\infty}^{\infty} \sum_{\alpha=1}^{\infty} |(VOe_j)_\alpha(\lambda)|^2\, d\rho(\lambda)$$

$$= \sum_{\alpha=1}^{\infty} \int_{-\infty}^{\infty} \sum_{j=1}^{\infty} |(VOe_j)_\alpha(\lambda)|^2\, d\rho(\lambda).$$

Therefore for each α the last integral converges and therefore $\sum_{j=1}^{\infty} |(VOe_j)_\alpha(\lambda)|^2 < \infty$ for all $\lambda \overline{\in} \Lambda_\alpha$, $\rho(\Lambda_\alpha) = 0$. For $\lambda \overline{\in} \bigcup_{\alpha=1}^{\infty} \Lambda_\alpha (\rho(\bigcup_{\alpha=1}^{\infty} \Lambda_\alpha) = 0)$ the last series converges for arbitrary α. For such λ, the vector

$$w_\alpha(\lambda) = \sum_{j=1}^{\infty} (VOe_j)_\alpha(\lambda)\, e_j$$

is defined and contained in H_+; therefore by (2.28)

$$\widetilde{u}_\alpha(\lambda) = \sum_{j=1}^{\infty} (u, e_j)_+ (VOe_j)_\alpha(\lambda) = \left(u, \sum_{j=1}^{\infty} (VOe_j)_\alpha(\lambda)\, e_j\right)_+ = (u, w_\alpha(\lambda))_+.$$

Equation (2.27) is established.

Assume $u_\alpha(\lambda) = \overline{\widetilde{u}_\alpha(\lambda)} = (\phi_\alpha(\lambda), u)_0$ ($\alpha = 1, 2, \cdots$; $u \in H_+$). Then (2.26) implies

$$(E(\Delta)u, v)_0 = \int_\Delta \sum_{\alpha=1}^{\infty} \overline{u_\alpha(\lambda)}\, v_\alpha(\lambda)\, d\varrho(\lambda) \quad (u, v \in H_+).$$

Thus we find that (2.18) is true without interpreting the vectors $\phi_\alpha(\lambda)$ as generalized eigenvectors. Such an interpretation is easy to give by using the fact that $\widetilde{A}$ is the operator of multiplication by λ; we omit the details.

Although this approach to the previous results is very simple, the previous approach is more natural. In it a uniform procedure for differentiating E_λ is sufficient for all of the complex questions arising in the theory of expansions and among them the theorem of Neĭman itself.

5. **The form of the preceding results in the case where the equipped Hilbert space is nuclear.** Sometimes a somewhat different approach to the theory of generalized expansions appears suitable. We illustrate this now. Assume that the Hilbert space H_0 is equipped with a linear topological space Φ and its dual space Φ', i.e. H_0 contains a dense linear space Φ, itself a linear topological space with respect to some new topology stronger than the topology of H_0 (i.e. $H_0 \supseteq \Phi$ is a topological inclusion). Then $\Phi' \supseteq H_0$ and we obtain the chain

$$\Phi' \supseteq H_0 \supseteq \Phi. \tag{2.29}$$

Let A be an operator on H_0 such that its adjoint operator A^* is continuous on Φ, and $\Phi \subseteq \mathfrak{D}(A^*)$, $A^*\Phi \subseteq \Phi$. We will consider A^* as an operator on Φ and construct its adjoint $A^{*\prime}$. It is easy to see that $\widetilde{A} = A^{*\prime}$ takes the space Φ' continuously onto itself. By a generalized eigenvector of the operator A corresponding to the eigenvalue λ we will now mean a vector $\phi \in \Phi'$ such that

$$\tilde{A}\phi = \lambda\phi. \tag{2.30}$$

If A is Hermitian and such that $\Phi \subseteq \mathfrak{D}(A)$, $A\Phi \subseteq \Phi$ and if A is continuous on Φ, then A may be replaced by A^*.

We recall (see Chapter 1, §4) that a sequential-Hilbert space Φ, the intersection of Hilbert spaces Φ_n $(n = 1, 2, \cdots)$, is called nuclear if for each n we can find an $m > n$, such that $\Phi_m \to \Phi_n$ is quasi-nuclear. We will now consider the equipment (2.29) with nuclear Φ.

One may consider the following scheme. *We assume that we have the chain* (2.29) *with nuclear* Φ. *There is a selfadjoint operator* A *on* H_0 *continuous on* H_0 *and such that* Φ *remains invariant under* A. *The question is, can one assert that* A *has a complete system of generalized eigenvectors in* Φ', *i.e. a system with which it is possible to construct the expansions* (2.18)–(2.19) *with* u, $v \in \Phi$? *It is easy to see that the preceding results at once give a positive answer to this question.*

Since the topology of Φ is stronger than the topology of H_0, then each neighborhood of H_0 contains a neighborhood of Φ. Therefore there is some neighborhood of the space Φ in the ball $\|f\|_0 < 1$, i.e., a ball of the form $\|u - a\|_n < \epsilon$ for some $a \in \Phi$, $\epsilon > 0$ and $n > 0$. By the linearity of the spaces this means that Φ_n is imbedded in H_0 continuously. Again find a number $m > n$ such that Φ_m is imbedded in Φ_n quasi-nuclearly, so that the inclusion $\Phi_m \to H_0$ will also be quasi-nuclear as a composition of a quasi-nuclear with a continuous imbedding. We use Φ_m for H_+ in some renormalizations: multiplying all norms by constants, it turns out that $\|u\|_0 \le \|u\|_m$ $(u \in \Phi_m)$. We then have the chain (2.12) with the quasi-nuclear inclusion $H_+ \to H_0$.

The operator A takes Φ into Φ continuously and thus also takes Φ into $\Phi_m = H_+$ continuously, since the topology of Φ_m is weaker than the topology of Φ. Thus A admits an equipped extension, where $\mathcal{D} = \Phi$, and therefore all the hypotheses of Theorems 2.1 and 2.2 are satisfied. The eigenvectors $\phi_\alpha(\lambda)$ from Theorem 2.2 are contained in $H_- = \Phi'_m \subseteq \bigcup_{n=1}^\infty \Phi'_n = \Phi'$ are desired.

It is clear that the results obtained on pp. 335–338 are more precise than those established just now. Moreover the theorem on expansions mentioned above often appears more convenient, since but one nuclear space Φ figures in it, for an arbitrary Hilbert space H_0 containing Φ topologically. An almost arbitrarily chosen selfadjoint operator A on H_0 has a complete system of eigenvectors among the vectors of Φ.

It may be possible to extend the above scheme to the case of inductive limits of nuclear sequential-Hilbert spaces. It is natural in addition to formulate the remaining theorems in subsection 3 for the case of an equipment (2.29) with nuclear Φ.

§3. EXPANSIONS IN GENERALIZED EIGENFUNCTIONS OF OPERATORS ON THE SPACE $L_2(G)$

1. **The form of the positive space.** Let A be a selfadjoint operator (or one of the operators considered in §1.5) on $H_0 = L_2(G)$, where G is a (not necessarily bounded) region of the n-dimensional space E_n with boundary Γ. According to Theorem 2.1, the space $H_+ \subseteq H_0$ must be such that the imbedding $H_+ \to H_0$ is quasi-nuclear. We indicate some convenient choices of H_+.

a) Let G be a bounded region. Then we may take $H_+ = w_2^l(G)$, where $l > n/2$. By Corollary 2 of Chapter I, §3.1 the inclusion $H_+ \to H_0$ will be quasi-nuclear. If G is not bounded, then one may take $W_2^{(l,q)}(G)$ $(l > n/2)$ for H_+ with the scalar product $(u, v)_{(l,q)} = (uq, vq)_{W_2^l(G)}$, where $q(x) \geq 1$ is a function in the region G such that

$$\int_G \frac{A^2(x)}{q^2(x)}\, dx < \infty. \tag{3.1}$$

Here $A(x)$ $(x \in G)$ is the function appearing in the estimate

$$|u(x)| \leqslant A(x) \| u \|_{W_2^l(G)} \quad (u \in W_2^l(G))$$

(see Chapter I, §3.3). In the case of a finite region G $(A(x)) = C(1 + |x|^{l-n/2})$, the integral (3.1) will converge with $q(x) = 1 + |x|^{l+\epsilon}$ $(\epsilon > 0)$. Thus for such a region $H_+ = W_2^{(l, 1+|x|^{l+\epsilon})}(G)$ $(l > n/2,\ \epsilon > 0)$.

Below we will see that it is possible to estimate at infinity integrals of eigenfunctions. For this purpose it is convenient to make another choice of the positive space H_+ or, equivalently, of the operator T. We recall first the proof of Theorem 3.4, Chapter I.

Let $x \in E_n$. We consider $\omega(x, \xi)$ and put

$$\mathrm{D}u = D_1 \ldots D_n u, \qquad \mathrm{D}^+ = (-1)^n \mathrm{D}. \tag{3.2}$$

It is easy to verify that for a locally summable function $f(x)$ in E_n and $u(x) \in C_0^n(E_n)$, the equations

$$D_x \int_{E_n} \omega(x, \xi) f(\xi)\, d\xi = f(x), \qquad \int_{E_n} \omega(x, \xi)(D^+ u)(x)\, dx = u(\xi),$$

$$\int_{E_n} \omega(x, \xi)(Du)(\xi)\, d\xi = u(x) \tag{3.3}$$

are valid (for the last of these it is necessary to assume that the support of u lies in the region $x_1 \geq 0, \cdots, x_n \geq 0$).

b) Let G be such that it may be shifted into the first octant, $x_1 \geq 0, \cdots, x_n \geq 0$. Let $(Tu)(x) = D[q(x)u(x)]$, $u \in \mathfrak{D}(T) = C_0^n(G)$, where $q(x) = (1 + |x_1|)^{1+\epsilon} \cdots (1 + |x_n|)^{1+\epsilon}$ $(\epsilon > 0)$ (in the case of bounded G, the multiplier q is superfluous). Then by the last of the formulas (3.3) the left inverse T^{-1} has the form

$$(T^{-1}f)(x) = \int_G K(x, \xi) f(\xi)\, d\xi, \qquad K(x, \xi) = \frac{1}{q(x)} \omega(x, \xi)\ (x, \xi \in G);$$

$$\int_G \int_G |K(x, \xi)|^2\, dx d\xi \leqslant \int_0^\infty \cdots \int_0^\infty \frac{1}{q^2(x)} \omega(x, \xi)\, dx d\xi$$

$$= \left(\int_0^\infty \frac{t}{(1+t)^{2+2\varepsilon}}\, dt \right)^n < \infty. \tag{3.4}$$

Thus T^{-1} is a Hilbert-Schmidt operator and hence T may be used for the construction of expansions (the construction was outlined in Chapter I, §3.6).

c) We consider the general case $G \subseteq E_n$. Since the last of the formulas (3.3) is now generally inapplicable, the preceding construction of T is not immediately suitable. We will modify this construction. Let $(Tu)(x) = q(x)(D^+u)(x)$, $u \in \mathfrak{D}(T) = C_0^n(G)$, where $q(x)$ is as in b). Using the second of the formulas (3.3), we find that the left inverse T^{-1} is an integral operator:

$$(T^{-1}f)(x) = \int_G K(x, \xi) f(\xi)\, d\xi, \qquad K(x, \xi) = \frac{1}{q(\xi)} \omega(\xi, x) \quad (x, \xi \in G). \tag{3.5}$$

In a manner analogous to (3.4), we see that T^{-1} is a Hilbert-Schmidt operator and therefore the stated form of T is possible.

It is clear that the choice of D in (3.2) is not unique. For example, for D one might have chosen an elliptic expression of order $r > n/2$ and for $\omega(x, \xi)$, its fundamental solution. Then $\omega(x, \xi)$ is locally square summable in (x, ξ), and equation (3.3) follows from formulas (4.3) and (4.4) of Chapter III.

2. **Formulation of the theorem on expansions.** Finally the theorem on expansions mentioned in §2.3 is valid with any choice of the above spaces H_+. However, it is sometimes useful to phrase these results in the form of theorems such as 1.3 and 1.4 in which T takes the form c) or b) of the preceding subsection. We consider the case c) with an arbitrary region G.

The operator $\Psi(\lambda)$ encountered in (1.12) is a Hilbert-Schmidt operator, where $|\Psi(\lambda)| \leq 1$ for almost all λ (ρ). Therefore it is the integral operator

$$(\Psi(\lambda) f)(x) = \int_G \hat{\Psi}(x, y; \lambda) f(y)\, dy, \quad \iint_{GG} |\hat{\Psi}(x, y; \lambda)|^2\, dx dy = |\Psi(\lambda)|^2 \leqslant 1. \tag{3.6}$$

We now utilize the fact that $\mathrm{tr}\,(\Psi(\lambda)) = 1$. Any operator B with a finite trace is of the form $B = CC^*$ where C is a Hilbert-Schmidt operator. For operators on $L_2(G)$ then $B(x, y) = \int_G C(x, \xi)\overline{C(y, \xi)}\, d\xi$, where $B(x, y)$ and $C(x, y)$ are the kernels of B and C.

Since $C(x, y) \in L_2(G \times G, dx\, dy)$, therefore $B(x, x)$, defined for almost all x in G, is nonnegative and $\int_G B(x, x)\, dx = \mathrm{tr}\,(B)$. Using this fact, we conclude that for almost all $x \in G$ $\hat{\Psi}(x, x; \lambda) \geq 0$ and

$$\int_G \hat{\Psi}(x, x; \lambda)\, dx = 1. \tag{3.7}$$

From the positive defiteness of the kernel $\hat{\Psi}(x, y; \lambda)$ it follows that

$$|\hat{\Psi}(x, y; \lambda)|^2 \leqslant \hat{\Psi}(x, x; \lambda)\, \hat{\Psi}(y, y; \lambda).$$

for all $(x, y) \in G \times G$. (see page 46).

Taking into account that $T = qD^+ = (-1)^n qD$, with the help of (3.6) and (3.7) we obtain

$$(\Psi(\lambda)Tu, Tv)_0 = \int_G\int_G \Psi(x, y; \lambda)(\mathrm{D}u)(y)\overline{(\mathrm{D}v)(x)}\,dxdy \quad (u, v \in C_0^n(G)).$$

$$\Psi(x, y; \lambda) = q(x)q(y)\hat{\Psi}(x, y; \lambda) \ (x, y \in G), \quad \int_G\int_G \frac{|\Psi(x, y; \lambda)|^2}{q^2(x)q^2(y)}\,dxdy \leqslant 1, \tag{3.8}$$

$$\int_G \frac{\Psi(x, x; \lambda)}{q^2(x)}\,dx = 1.$$

The positive definite kernel $\Psi(x, y; \lambda)$ will be called the spectral integral kernel. The Parseval equality (1.12) is rewritten as

$$(E(\Delta)u, v)_0 = \int_\Delta \left\{\int_G\int_G \Psi(x, y; \lambda)(\mathrm{D}u)(y)\overline{(\mathrm{D}v)(x)}\,dxdy\right\} d\varrho(\lambda)$$
$$(u, v \in C_0^n(G)). \tag{3.9}$$

The vectors $\psi_\alpha(\lambda) = \hat{\psi}_\alpha(x; \lambda)$ now appear as functions of $L_2(G)$. From the form of T and (1.19) we see that

$$(\psi_\alpha, Tu)_0 = \int_G \psi_\alpha(x; \lambda)\overline{(\mathrm{D}u)(x)}\,dx \qquad (u \in C_0^n(G)); \tag{3.10}$$

$$\psi_\alpha(x; \lambda) = (-1)^n q(x)\hat{\psi}_\alpha(x; \lambda) \ (x \in G); \quad \sum_{\alpha=1}^{N_\lambda}\int_G \frac{|\psi_\alpha(x; \lambda)|^2}{q^2(x)}\,dx = 1, \tag{3.11}$$

where the last equation is satisfied almost everywhere. The functions $\psi_\alpha(x; \lambda)$ are integral eigenfunctions. *Thus Theorems* 1.3 *and* 1.4 *are valid for selfadjoint operators in* $L_2(G)$, *in which* (1.12) *holds in the form* (3.9), $(\psi_\alpha, Tu)_0$ *is computed with the help of*-(3.10), *and the estimates* (1.13) *and* (1.19) *hold in the form* (3.8) *and* (3.11).

The above formulas are conveniently interpreted with the help of generalized functions of the type used by L. Schwartz, namely continuous functionals $\alpha \in D'(G)$ on a linear topological space $D(G) = C_0^\infty(G)$, where the convergence $u_n(x) \to 0$ means that the supports of the functions $u_n(x)$ are contained in a single compact set in G and these functions with all of their derivatives converge uniformly to zero. In (3.9) and (3.10) if we throw a D into the first factor of the inner product we obtain the generalized kernel $\Phi_\lambda = \mathrm{D}_x\mathrm{D}_y\Psi(x, y; \lambda) \in D'(G) \otimes D'(G)$ as the spectral kernel and the generalized function

$$\phi_\alpha(\lambda) = (-1)^n \mathrm{D}\psi_\alpha(x;\lambda) \in D'(G)$$

as an eigenfunction. Obviously these notions coincide exactly with the notions of generalized functions introduced in §2.

Suppose the operator A admits an equipped extension with $\mathbb{A} = D(G)$. Then equation (1.18) holds for all $u \in C_0^\infty(G)$ and means that $\phi_\alpha(\lambda)$ is a generalized eigenfunction for A in the sense of the theory of L. Schwartz: $A\phi_\alpha(\lambda) = \lambda\phi_\alpha(\lambda)$. Analogously, from (1.14) and the symmetry of $\Psi(\lambda)$, equations $A_x\Phi_\lambda = \lambda\Phi_\lambda$, $A_y\overline{\Phi}_\lambda = \lambda\overline{\Phi}_\lambda$ are established.

The case b) is considered similarly, the only changes occurring in the constructions of the operations D and the multiplication by $q(x)$. As we will see later, constructions of spaces of the type b) and c) yield growth estimates but they are not based on eigenfunctions near the boundary of the region, since functions of these spaces vanish close to the boundary. The construction a) is made with essentially this point of view.

It is clear that all that was said above carries over to the generalizations considered in §1.5 and in Theorems 2.3–2.6.

In conclusion, we note that the Parseval equality (3.8) may be proved differently. Namely, as in Theorem 3.4 in Chapter I, we represent the operator $E(\Delta)$ in the form

$$(E(\Delta)u, v)_0 = \int_G\int_G \Theta(x, y; \Delta)(Du)(y)\overline{(Dv)(x)}\,dxdy \qquad (u, v \in C_0^n(G)),$$

where $\Theta(x, y; \Delta) = (E(\Delta)\omega(y, \cdot), \omega(x, \cdot))_0$ is a continuous kernel in $(G \cup \Gamma) \times (G \cup \Gamma)$. Further for fixed x, y we will differentiate the measure $\Theta(x, y; \Delta)$ with respect to some suitable measure $\rho(\Delta)$ [1]. This derivative will exist almost everywhere (ρ). If we succeed in showing that it exists independently of the choice of x, y (from the line), then this derivative will be equal to $\Psi(x, y; \lambda)$. This independence may be established with the help of an argument similar to the proof of Theorem 1.1. We omit the details (See also Lemma 3.1, Chapter VI).

We may use Theorem 3.3 of Chapter I to reduce the proof to the case where H_+ is of the form a), and applying the abstract Theorem 2.2 of Chapter I, we obtain the case of a general space H_0.

3. **The structure of the generalized eigenfunctions.** Let us re-emphasize the

1) For example, one may put $\rho(\Delta) = \int_G (\theta(x, x; \Delta)/p(x)\,dx$, where $p(x) \geq 1\ (x \in G)$ so that the convergence of this integral is guaranteed.

general nature of the eigenfunctions of an operator in $L_2(G)$, $G \subseteq E_n$. When the space H_+ is of type a), and the region is bounded, the generalized functions belonging to $W_2^{-l}(G)$ with $l > n/2$. In case of an unbounded conical region they are contained in $W_2^{-(l, 1+|x|^{l+\epsilon})}(G)$ $(\epsilon > 0)$ which may be interpreted as a growth restriction with respect to the polynomial $C(1 + |x|^{l+\epsilon})$ of the eigenfunction and certain integrals of it.

The last case is illustrated more clearly if we choose H_+ to be of type c). The spectral kernel now has the form $\Phi_\lambda = D_x D_y \Psi(x, y; \lambda)$, and the eigenfunctions the form $\phi_\alpha(\lambda) = (-1)^n D\psi_\alpha(x; \lambda)$ (the derivative is understood in the sense of L. Schwartz), where

$$\int_G \int_G \frac{|\psi(x, y; \lambda)|^2}{q^2(x) q^2(y)} dxdy \leqslant 1, \qquad \sum_{\alpha=1}^{N_\lambda} \int_G \frac{|\psi_\alpha(x; \lambda)|^2}{q^2(x)} dx = 1$$

$$(q(x) = (1 + |x_1|)^{1+\varepsilon} \dots (1 + |x_n|)^{1+\varepsilon}, \ \varepsilon > 0). \tag{3.12}$$

If G is contained in the octant $x_1 \geq 0, \cdots, x_n \geq 0$, then one may choose H_+ to be of type b). The spectral kernel and eigenfunctions take the form $\Phi_\lambda = q(x)q(y) D_x D_y \hat{\Psi}(x, y; \lambda)$, $\phi_\alpha(\lambda) = (-1)^n q(x) D\hat{\psi}_\alpha(x; \lambda)$, where for almost all λ (with respect to ρ),

$$\int_G \int_G |\hat{\Psi}(x, y; \lambda)|^2 dxdy \leqslant 1, \qquad \sum_{\alpha=1}^{N_\lambda} \int_G |\hat{\psi}_\alpha(x; \lambda)|^2 dx = 1; \tag{3.13}$$

4. **Operators on a space $L_2(G)$ with a weight function.** We will consider generalized eigenfunction expansions in the space $H_0 = L_2(G, pdx)$ with scalar product

$$(f, g)_{L_2(G, pdx)} = \int_G f(x) \overline{g(x)} p(x) dx = (f\sqrt{p}, g\sqrt{p})_{L_2(G)}. \tag{3.14}$$

Here $p(x) \geq 1$ is a sufficiently smooth function on G, generally not bounded as it approaches the boundary of G.

The problem of establishing the general representations of §§1–2 reduces to the choice of a space $H_+ \subseteq H_0$ such that the inclusion $H_+ \to H_0$ is quasi-nuclear. This choice may be made as follows.

Let $\mathfrak{H} \subset L_2(G)$ be a positive space relative to the zero space $L_2(G)$ such that the inclusion $\mathfrak{H} \to L_2(G)$ is quasi-nuclear. We define a scalar product in

H_+ *by putting*

$$(u, v)_+ = (u\sqrt{p}, v\sqrt{p})_{\mathfrak{H}} \tag{3.15}$$

It turns out that the inclusion $H_+ \to L_2(G, pdx)$ *is quasi-nuclear.*

In fact, if $e_1, e_2, \cdots$ is an orthonormal basis in H_+ then $e_1\sqrt{p}, e_2\sqrt{p}, \cdots$ is an orthonormal basis in $\mathfrak{H}$. We have $\sum_{j=1}^{\infty}\|e_j\|^2_{L_2(G,pdx)} = \sum_{j=1}^{\infty}\|e_j\sqrt{p}\|^2_{L_2(G)}$ and by the convergence of the last series, the quasi-nuclearity of the inclusion $\mathfrak{H} \to L_2(G)$ is established. But this implies that $H_+ \to L_2(G, pdx)$ is quasi-nuclear. (In this connection, see the argument on p. 49).

Choosing for $\mathfrak{H}$ one of the spaces a)–c), by (3.15) the construction of H_+ is obtained.

§4. EIGENFUNCTION EXPANSIONS OF CARLEMAN OPERATORS

1. **A basic remark.** Let T be a densely defined operator with domain $\mathfrak{D}(T)$ and a left inverse T^{-1}. As it was shown in §1, the finiteness of the Hilbert norm of T^{-1} is a sufficient and (if T^{-1} is an ordinary inverse) necessary condition for such an operator to be used for a generalized eigenfunction expansion of a given selfadjoint operator A. However, for a fixed selfadjoint A, the choice of T is less restricted: As consequences of Theorems 1.3 and 1.4 we may show that *it is only required that* $\operatorname{tr}(T^{-1*}E(\Delta)T^{-1})$ *remain finite for bounded* Δ. *A sufficient condition for this finiteness is the existence of a nonzero bounded continuous function* $\gamma(\lambda)$ *defined on the spectrum of* A, *such that* $|\gamma(A)T| < \infty$. Indeed, for arbitrary bounded Δ on the spectrum of A there exists $\epsilon_\Delta > 0$ such that the characteristic function $\kappa_\Delta(\lambda) \le \epsilon_\Delta|\gamma(\lambda)|^2$ on the spectrum of A. Hence

$$E(\Delta) \leqslant \varepsilon_\Delta \int_{-\infty}^{\infty} |\gamma(\lambda)|^2\, dE_\lambda = \varepsilon_\Delta (\gamma(A))^* \gamma(A).$$

and therefore

$$\begin{aligned}\operatorname{tr}(T^{-1*}E(\Delta)T^{-1}) &\leqslant \varepsilon_\Delta \operatorname{tr} T^{-1*}(\gamma(A))^*\gamma(A)T^{-1}) \\ &= \varepsilon_\Delta |\gamma(A)T^{-1}| < \infty.\end{aligned}$$

and the assertion is verified.

This remark is particularly applicable to the constructions in §2: If the operator J connected with the equipment $H_- \supseteq H_0 = H \supseteq H_+$ is such that $|\gamma(A)\hat{J}| < \infty$, then a generalized eigenvector expansion of A may be constructed using this equipment.

We note that the functions $\gamma(\lambda) = 1/(\lambda^N - z)$ or $\gamma(\lambda) = 1/(\lambda - z)$ are usually suitable, where N is some sufficiently large natural number and $\operatorname{Im} z \neq 0$.

Remarks similar to the one just verified can also be shown to hold for the generalizations made in §1.5 and in Theorems 2.3–2.6. The rest of the constructions which we shall make in this section can likewise be transferred to these generalizations.

2. Definition of a Carleman operator and theorems on expansions. We will consider operators defined on $H_0 = L_2(Q, dx)$. Here Q is a locally compact separable space, and dx is a nonnegative measure on the Borel sets of Q, finite on compact sets and positive on the open sets. A selfadjoint operator A is called a Carleman operator if there exists a bounded, continuous, nonzero function $\gamma(\lambda)$ defined on the spectrum of A, such that the operator $\gamma(\lambda)$ is an integral operator with kernel $C(x, y)$ $(x, y \in Q)$ which satisfies

$$\int_Q |C(x, y)|^2 \, dx < \infty \left((\gamma(A) f)(x) = \int_Q C(x, y) f(y) \, dy, \; f \in L_2(Q, dx) \right). \tag{4.1}$$

for almost all y.

We now show that the generalized eigenfunctions of the operator under consideration will be ordinary functions, but not functions of $L_2(Q, dx)$. For this purpose, we construct an equipped Hilbert space $H_0 = L_2(Q, dx)$, setting $H_+ = L_2(Q, p dx)$, where $p(x) \geq 1$ $(x \in Q)$ is some Borel measurable function. Since $(f, u)_0 = ((1/p)f, u)_+$ for $f \in H_0$ and $u \in H_+$, then $(If)(x) = (1/p(x)) f(x)$, therefore $(f, g)_- = (If, g)_0 = ((1/p) f, g)_0$ $(f, g \in H_0)$, i.e. $H_- = L_2(Q, (1/p)dx)$. The operator J is equal to the square root of I and is taken as an operator on H_0, i.e.

$$(Jf)(x) = \frac{1}{\sqrt{p(x)}} f(x) \quad (f \in H_0).$$

Let the Carleman operator A be such that

$$\int_Q \int_Q |C(x, y)|^2 \frac{1}{p(y)} \, dx dy < \infty. \tag{4.2}$$

for some function $p(x) \geq 1$. The kernel $C(x, y)\sqrt{p(y)}$ is the kernel of the operator $\gamma(A)\hat{J}$ and condition (4.2) means that the operator is a Hilbert-Schmidt operator. Considering what was done in subsection 1, we conclude that the chain

$$L_2\left(Q, \frac{1}{p}\,dx\right) \supseteq L_2(Q, dx) \supseteq L_2(Q, p dx). \tag{4.3}$$

may be used to construct an eigenfunction expansion for A. Thus the eigenfunctions of a Carleman operator are usually functions of $L_2(Q, (1/p)\,dx)$.

A more detailed eigenfunction expansion is described in the following theorem.

Theorem 4.1. *Let A be a selfadjoint Carleman operator and $p(x) \geq 1$ $(x \in Q)$ a Borel measurable function such that the integral (4.2) converges. Then one may use the chain (4.3) to obtain an eigenfunction expansion for A, and consequently each generalized eigenfunction will be an ordinary function from the space $L_2(Q, (1/p)dx)$.*

The generalized projection operator $P(\lambda)$ onto the generalized eigenmanifold is an integral operator:

$$(P(\lambda)u)(x) = \int_Q \Phi(x, y; \lambda)\, u(y)\, dy \quad (u \in L_2(Q, p dx)). \tag{4.4}$$

The spectral kernel of A, the positive definite function $\Phi(x, y; \lambda)$, satisfies the estimate

$$\int_Q \int_Q \frac{|\Phi(x, y; \lambda)|^2}{p(x)\,p(y)}\, dx dy \leq 1 \left\{\textit{more precisely}: \int_Q \frac{\Phi(x, x; \lambda)}{p(x)}\, dx = 1\right\}. \tag{4.5}$$

Also, an arbitrary function $F(\lambda)$ is an integral operator if $F(\lambda)$ is bounded on the spectrum of A and is finite at ∞; moreover the kernel $K(x, y)$ of this operator can be represented as an integral which is absolutely convergent for almost all (x, y) with respect to the measure $dxdy$:

$$K(x, y) = \int_{-\infty}^{\infty} F(\lambda)\, \Phi(x, y; \lambda)\, d\rho(\lambda); \quad \int_Q \int_Q \frac{|K(x, y)|^2}{p(x)\,p(y)}\, dx dy < \infty. \tag{4.6}$$

Proof. The first assertions of the theorem have already been verified. We will show that $P(\lambda)$ is an integral operator. Since $P(\lambda) = D\Psi(\lambda)D$, by equation (2.2) we have $(P(\lambda)u, v)_0 = (\Psi(\lambda)Du, Dv)_0$ $(u, v \in H_+)$. The operator $D = J^{-1}$ is the operator of multiplication by $\sqrt{p(x)}$, so that if we denote the kernel of the operator $\Psi(\lambda)$ by $\hat{\Psi}(x, y; \lambda)$, we obtain

$$(P(\lambda)u, v)_0 = \int_Q\int_Q \hat{\Psi}(x, y; \lambda)\sqrt{p(x)p(y)}u(y)\overline{v(x)}\,dxdy$$

$$= \int_Q\int_Q \Phi(x, y; \lambda)u(y)\overline{v(x)}dxdy; \quad \Phi(x, y; \lambda) = \sqrt{p(x)p(y)}\hat{\Psi}(x, y, \lambda)$$

$$(x, y \in Q;\ u, v \in L_2(Q, pdx)). \tag{4.7}$$

Since $\int_Q\int_Q |\hat{\Psi}(x, y; \lambda)|^2 dxdy = |\Psi(\lambda)| \leq 1$, the estimate (4.5) follows from (4.7). The relation $\int_Q (\Phi(x, x; \lambda)/p(x))\,dx = 1$ follows from the equation $\operatorname{tr}(\Psi(\lambda)) = 1$.

Further by (4.5) and the Cauchy-Bunjakovskiĭ inequality we have

$$\int_Q\int_Q \frac{1}{p(x)p(y)}\left(\int_{-N}^{N} |F(\lambda)\Phi(x, y; \lambda)|\,d\rho(\lambda)\right)^2 dxdy$$

$$\leqslant \int_{-N}^{N} |F(\lambda)|^2 d\rho(\lambda)\cdot \int_Q\int_Q \frac{1}{p(x)p(y)} \int_{-N}^{N} |\Phi(x, y; \lambda)|^2 d\rho(\lambda)\,dxdy$$

$$\leqslant \rho([-N, N)) \int_{-N}^{N} |F(\lambda)|^2 d\rho(\lambda) < \infty \quad (0 < N < \infty).$$

From this estimate and the finiteness of $F(\lambda)$ we obtain the convergence of the first of the integrals in (4.6) and the existence of the second. Then, from the basic equation (2.16), it follows that $K(x, y)$ is the kernel of the operator $F(A)$. The theorem is proved.

In particular it follows from (4.5) that *the spectral kernel* $\Phi(x, y; \lambda)$ *as a function of the point* $(x, y; \lambda) \in Q \times Q \times E_1$ *is locally square summable, with respect to the measure* $dxdyd\rho(\lambda)$. [1)]

We will discuss the individual eigenfunctions. By the general scheme on p. 325 there is a bilinear series expansion of the kernel $\Psi(x, y; \lambda)$ of the operator $\Psi(\lambda)$ in terms of its eigenfunctions $\hat{\Psi}(x, y; \lambda) = \sum_{\alpha=1}^{N_\lambda} \psi_\alpha(x; \lambda)\overline{\psi_\alpha(y; \lambda)}$. This series converges in the metric of $L_2(Q \times Q, dxdy)$. We multiply it by $\sqrt{p(x)p(y)}$. Noting that $\sqrt{p(x)}\psi_\alpha(x; \lambda) = D\psi_\alpha(x; \lambda) = \phi_\alpha(x; \lambda)$ are generalized eigenfunctions of the operator A, and are in $L_2(Q, (1/p)dx)$, we obtain the generalized eigenfunction expansion of the spectral kernel:

1) The proof of the fact that the function $\Phi(x, y; \lambda)$ of the point $(x, y; \lambda) \in Q \times Q \times E_1$ is a Borel measurable is left to the reader.

$$\Phi(x, y; \lambda) = \sum_{\alpha=1}^{N_\lambda} \phi_\alpha(x; \lambda)\overline{\phi_\alpha(y; \lambda)} \quad (x, y \in Q). \tag{4.8}$$

The series (4.8) converges in the metric of $L_2(Q \times Q, (1/p(x)p(y))\,dxdy)$. Equations (4.8) may of course be obtained directly by expanding the kernel $\Phi(x, y; \lambda)$ by its eigenfunctions. For a Carleman operator, the Fourier transform (2.19) of a function $u \in L_2(Q, pdx)$ is obviously given by the formula

$$\widetilde{u}(\lambda) = (u_1(\lambda), u_2(\lambda), \ldots), \quad u_\alpha(\lambda) = \int_Q \varphi_\alpha(x; \lambda)\overline{u(x)}dx \; (\alpha = 1, \ldots, N_\lambda). \tag{4.9}$$

In conclusion, we note that the spectral measure and kernel are essentially unchanged if we vary $\gamma(\lambda)$ and $p(x)$. For suppose $\gamma_1(\lambda)$ is a function of the type $\gamma(\lambda)$, and $p_1(x)$ a weight constructed from $\gamma_1(\lambda)$; $d\rho_1(\lambda)$ and $\Phi(x, y; \lambda)$ are respectively the corresponding spectral measure and kernel. Since ρ and ρ_1 are obviously absolutely continuous with respect to each other we let (for example) $d\rho_1(\lambda) = M(\lambda)\,d\rho(\lambda)$. Then for arbitrary Borel sets P' and P'' and Δ with compact closure,

$$\int_{P'}\int_{P''}\int_{\Delta} \Phi(x, y; \lambda)\,dxdyd\rho(\lambda) = (E(\Delta)\varkappa_{P''}, \varkappa_{P'})_0$$

$$= \int_{P'}\int_{P''}\int_{\Delta} \Phi_1(x, y; \lambda)\,dxdyd\rho_1(\lambda) = \int_{P'}\int_{P''}\int_{\Delta} \Phi_1(x, y; \lambda)\,M(\lambda)\,dxdyd\rho(\lambda),$$

from which $M(\lambda)\Phi_1(x, y; \lambda) = \Phi(x, y; \lambda)$ for almost all $(x, y; \lambda)$ with respect to the measure $dxdyd\rho(\lambda)$.

3. **The case of a continuous spectral kernel.** The preceding results may now be given in a more detailed form.

Theorem 4.2. *For fixed λ, let the spectral kernel $\Phi(x, y; \lambda)$ be continuous with respect to $(x, y) \in Q \times Q$. Then each of the eigenfunctions $\phi_\alpha(x; \lambda)$ coincides almost everywhere with a continuous function and therefore may be considered to be continuous (redefine the function on a set of measure zero). The series (4.8) converges absolutely and uniformly on each compact subset of $Q \times Q$.*

Proof. The theorem follows directly from the following basic lemma.

Lemma 4.1. *Let $K(x, y)$ $(x, y \in Q)$ be a positive definite and continuous kernel with respect to $(x, y) \in Q \times Q$. Assume that the representation*

$$K(x, y) = \sum_{\alpha=1}^{\infty} \varphi_\alpha(x)\overline{\varphi_\alpha(y)}, \tag{4.10}$$

holds in the metric of $L_2(P \times P, dxdy)$ $(P \subseteq Q$ *is compact), where* $\phi_\alpha(x)$ *are locally square summable. Then the* $\phi_\alpha(x)$ *coincide almost everywhere with continuous functions and therefore, by redefining the functions on sets of measure zero, they may be assumed continuous. The series* (4.10) *converges absolutely and uniformly on each compact subset of* $Q \times Q$.

Proof. Consider the integral equation $\int_P K(x, y)\chi(y)\,dy = \nu\chi(x)$ with a continuous positive definite kernel. Let $\chi_\beta(x)$ $(\beta = 1, 2, \cdots; x \in P)$ be a complete orthonormal system of eigenfunctions corresponding to the eigenvalues $\nu_\beta > 0$. These functions are continuous, and by Mercer's theorem the series representation

$$K(x, y) = \sum_{\beta=1}^{\infty} \nu_\beta \chi_\beta(x)\overline{\chi_\beta(y)} \qquad (x, y \in P). \tag{4.11}$$

holds absolutely and uniformly.

Set

$$\psi_\alpha(x) = \sum_{\beta=1}^{\infty} a_{\alpha\beta}\sqrt{\nu_\beta}\,\chi_\beta(x) \qquad (x \in P), \tag{4.12}$$

where $a_{\alpha\beta}\sqrt{\nu_\beta} = \int_P \phi_\alpha(x)\overline{\chi_\beta(x)}\,dx$. We will show that this series converges absolutely and uniformly. Multiplying (4.10) by $\overline{\chi_\beta(x)}\chi_\gamma(y)$ and integrating over $P \times P$, we obtain

$$\begin{aligned}\sqrt{\nu_\beta \nu_\gamma}\sum_{\alpha=1}^{\infty} a_{\alpha\beta}\bar{a}_{\alpha\gamma} &= \int_P\int_P K(x, y)\,\overline{\chi_\beta(x)}\chi_\gamma(y)\,dxdy \\ &= \nu_\gamma \int_P \chi_\gamma(x)\,\overline{\chi_\beta(x)}\,dx = \nu_\gamma \delta_{\gamma\beta},\end{aligned}$$

i.e. $\sum_{\alpha=1}^{\infty} \bar{a}_{\alpha\beta}a_{\alpha\gamma} = \delta_{\beta\gamma}$. For each finite sequence $f \in l_2([1, \infty))$ we set $(Af)_\alpha = \sum_{\beta=1}^{\infty} a_{\alpha\beta}f_\beta$ $(\alpha = 1, 2, \cdots)$; thus an isometric linear operator A is defined: $(Af, Ag) = (f, g)$. A may be extended by continuity to all of $l_2([1, \infty))$, and will be represented by the matrix $\|a_{\alpha\beta}\|_1^\infty$. The extension remains isometric. Thus we arrive at the relation (which we will use in what follows):

$$\sum_{\alpha=1}^{\infty}\left(\sum_{\beta=1}^{\infty} a_{\alpha\beta}f_\beta\,\overline{\sum_{\gamma=1}^{\infty} a_{\alpha\gamma}g_\gamma}\right) = \sum_{\beta=1}^{\infty} f_\beta \bar{g}_\beta \quad (f, g \in l_2([1, \infty))). \tag{4.13}$$

Since the norm of an isometric operator is equal to one, then $\|A^*\| = \|A\| = 1$ and

$$\sum_{\beta=1}^{\infty} |a_{\alpha\beta}|^2 \leqslant 1 \qquad (\alpha = 1, 2, \ldots). \tag{4.14}$$

On the other hand, taking $x = y$ in the expansion (4.1) it follows that the series $\Sigma_{\beta=1}^{\infty} |\sqrt{\nu_\beta}\chi_\beta(x)|^2$ converges uniformly. Using this, (4.14) and the Cauchy-Bunjakovskiĭ inequality, we conclude that the series (4.12) converges absolutely and uniformly. In particular, the function $\psi_\alpha(x)$ is continuous. We set $r_\alpha(x) = \phi_\alpha(x) - \psi_\alpha(x)$ $(x \in P)$ and show that $r_\alpha(x) = 0$ almost everywhere. Since $r_\alpha(x)$ is orthogonal to all the $\chi_\beta(x)$, by (4.10) and (4.11) we have

$$\sum_{\nu=1}^{\infty} \Big| \int_P \varphi_\nu(x)\overline{r_\alpha(x)}dx \Big|^2 = \int_P \int_P K(x, y)\overline{r_\alpha(x)}r_\alpha(y)\,dxdy$$

$$= \sum_{\beta=1}^{\infty} \nu_\beta \Big| \int_P \chi_\beta(x) r_\alpha(x)\,dx \Big|^2 = 0,$$

from which $\int_P \phi_\alpha(x) r_\alpha(x)\,dx = 0$. Moreover, since $r_\alpha(x)$ is orthogonal to $\psi_\alpha(x)$ (see (4.12)), we have

$$0 = \int_P \varphi_\alpha(x)\overline{r_\alpha(x)}\,dx = \int_P [\varphi_\alpha(x) - \psi_\alpha(x)]\overline{r_\alpha(x)}dx = \int_P |r_\alpha(x)|^2\,dx,$$

i.e. $r_\alpha(x) = 0$ almost everywhere in P. By the arbitrariness of P, we conclude that the functions $\phi_\alpha(x)$ are continuous. We redefine the $\phi_\alpha(x)$ and consider these functions to be functions to be continuous. We will show that the series (4.10) converges absolutely and uniformly. Above we saw that

$$\varphi_\alpha(x) = \psi_\alpha(x) = \sum_{\beta=1}^{\infty} a_{\alpha\beta}\sqrt{\nu_\beta}\,\chi_\beta(x) \qquad (x \in P).$$

From the relation (4.13) with $f_\beta = \sqrt{\nu_\beta}\chi_\beta(x)$, $g_\beta = \sqrt{\nu_\beta}\chi_\beta(y) \in l_2([1, \infty))$ and from (4.11) it follows that

$$\sum_{\alpha=1}^{\infty} \varphi_\alpha(x)\overline{\varphi_\alpha(y)} = \sum_{\beta=1}^{\infty} \nu_\beta\chi_\beta(x)\overline{\chi_\beta(y)} = K(x, y) \qquad (x, y \in P).$$

Since P is arbitrary, the series (4.10) converges pointwise to $K(x, y)$ $(x, y \in Q)$. The convergence is uniform on each compact set $P \times P$. Moreover $\Sigma_{\alpha=1}^{\infty}|\phi_\alpha(x)|^2 =$

$K(x, x) \in C(P)$, and by applying Dini's theorem we conclude that this series, and hence the series (4.10), converges absolutely and uniformly for $(x, y) \in P \times P$. The lemma and the theorem are proved.

It is clear that the theorem is true for arbitrary expansions of type (4.10) independent of the method in which they were obtained.

Theorem 4.3. *Suppose that the integral* (4.1) *is a locally bounded function of* $y \in Q$, *and that* $\Phi(x, y; \lambda)$ *is continuous almost everywhere with respect to* ρ *on the set* $(x, y) \in Q \times Q$. *Then if* $F(\lambda)$ *is such that* $|F(\lambda)| \leq C|\gamma(\lambda)|^2$ *on the spectrum of* A, *the first of the integrals in* (4.6) *represents the kernel of the operator* $F(A)$, *converges absolutely, and is a locally bounded function of* $(x, y) \in Q \times Q$.

If in addition the kernel of the operator $(\gamma(A))^* \gamma(A)$ *is continuous on* $Q \times Q$, *then this integral will continuously depend on* $(x, y) \in Q \times Q$.

Proof. To establish the first part of the theorem it is sufficient to verify the convergence and locally boundedness of the integral

$$\int_{-\infty}^{\infty} |\gamma(\lambda)|^2 |\Phi(x, y; \lambda)| \, d\rho(\lambda). \tag{4.15}$$

We have

$$\int_{-\infty}^{\infty} |\gamma(\lambda)|^2 \left\{ \int_Q \int_Q \Phi(x, y; \lambda) u(y) \overline{v(x)} \, dx dy \right\} d\rho(\lambda) = \int_{-\infty}^{\infty} |\gamma(\lambda)|^2 (\Psi(\lambda) Du,$$

$$Dv)_0 \, d\rho(\lambda) = ((\gamma(A))^* \gamma(A) u, v)_0 = \int_Q \int_Q \left\{ \int_Q \overline{C(\xi, x)} C(\xi, y) \, d\xi \right\} u(y) \overline{v(x)} dx dy. \tag{4.16}$$

If $P \subseteq Q$ is some compact set, by the assumption that $\int_Q |C(x, y)|^2 dx \leq C_P < \infty (y \in P)$, and the Cauchy-Bunjakovskiĭ inequality, we have $|\int_Q \overline{C(\xi, x)} C(\xi, y)| \leq C_P$, $x, y \in P$. Put $u = v = \chi_\nu$ in (4.16), where $\chi_\nu(x)$ is the characteristic function of the sphere of radius $1/\nu$ centered at s, divided by its volume, since the integral (4.1) is locally bounded, $p(x)$ may be chosen to be locally bounded and therefore $\chi_\nu \in L_2(Q, p dx)$. The point s lies in some component P' strictly inside the compact set P. After substituting the last integral in (4.16), the bound C_ρ is uniform in ν and we obtain

$$\int_{-\infty}^{\infty} |\gamma(\lambda)|^2 \left\{ \int_Q \int_Q \Phi(x, y; \lambda) \chi_\nu(y) \chi_\nu(x) \, dx dy \right\} d\rho(\lambda) \leqslant C_P \; (\nu = 1, 2, \ldots). \tag{4.17}$$

We pass to a limit in this expression as $\nu \to \infty$. By the continuity of $\Phi(x, y; \lambda)$

in (x, y) under the integral sign, the integral (4.17) tends to $\Phi(s, s; \lambda)$ and is nonnegative by the positive definiteness of the kernel $\Phi(x, y; \lambda)$. Applying Fatou's lemma, we obtain $\int_{-\infty}^{\infty} |\gamma(\lambda)|^2 \Phi(s, s; \lambda)\, d\rho(\lambda) \leq C_P (s \in P')$. The convergence and local boundedness of the integral (4.15) now follow from the established estimate, the inequality $|\Phi(x, y; \lambda)|^2 \leq \Phi(x, x; \lambda)\Phi(y, y; \lambda)$ and the Cauchy-Bunjakovskiĭ inequality. The first part of the theorem is proved.

The second part will be established with the help of the following lemma.

Lemma 4.2. *Let $K(x, y)$, $L(x, y)$ be ordinary positive-definite kernels, defined for each $x, y \in Q$ with $K \leqslant L$ (i.e. the kernel $L(x, y) - K(x, y)$ is also positive definite. Then if $L(x, y)$ is a continuous function of $(x, y) \in Q \times Q$, it follows that $K(x, y)$ is a continuous kernel.*

Proof. We reduce the lemma to an important construction in the theory of positive-definite kernels. Let $F(x, y)$ be such a kernel defined for arbitrary $(x, y) \in Q$. We associate with each point $x \in Q$ the abstract vector e_x and consider the finite sum $\xi = \sum_j \xi_j e_{x_j}$, where x_j is a point of Q, and ξ_j is a complex number; these sums define a vector space if we define $\xi + \eta = \sum_j (\xi_j + \eta_j) e_{x_j}$ (the points x in the expressions for ξ and η may be combined in one sequence of points x_j), and $\lambda\xi = \sum_j \lambda\xi_j e_{x_j}$. We define a scalar product for vectors ξ, putting

$$(\xi, \eta)_F = \sum_{j,k} F(x_j, x_k)\, \xi_k \eta_j. \tag{4.18}$$

Identifying with zero all vectors ξ for which $(\xi, \xi)_F = 0$, we obtain, in general, the incomplete Hilbert space $\mathfrak{H}_F$. In what follows, when speaking of vectors e_x, ξ, etc. we will mean the equivalence classes of elements corresponding to these vectors. We note that the equation

$$F(x, y) = (e_y, e_x)_F \, (x, y \in Q). \tag{4.19}$$

follows from (4.18).

It is easy to see from this equation that the continuity of the kernel $F(x, y)$ as a function of $(x, y) \in Q \times Q$, and the continuity of the vector-function $e_x \in \mathfrak{H}_F$ are equivalent notions.

We apply this to the proof of the lemma. We construct the spaces $\mathfrak{H}_K$ and $\mathfrak{H}_L$ and note that since $K \leqslant L$, then for each combination, $\sum_j \xi_j e_{x_j} = \xi$ $(\xi, \xi)_K \leq (\xi, \xi)_L$. It follows that, after the identification, the inclusion $\mathfrak{H}_L \subseteq \mathfrak{H}_K$ may be considered correct as well as the inequality $\|\xi\|_K \leq \|\xi\|_L$ $(\xi \in \mathfrak{H}_L)$. Since the continuity of $L(x, y)$ implies that e_x is a continuous function of $x \in Q$ in the norm of L, by the preceding inequality, e_x will also be continuous in the norm $\|\cdot\|_K$ of the space $\mathfrak{H}_K$. But this implies that the kernel $K(x, y)$ is continuous with respect to $(x, y) \in Q \times Q$. The lemma is proved.

We complete the proof of the theorem. We represent $F(\lambda)$ in the form

$$F(\lambda) = F_1(\lambda) - F_2(\lambda) + i(F_3(\lambda) - F_4(\lambda)), \tag{4.20}$$

where $F_1(\lambda) = \max(\operatorname{Re} F(\lambda), 0)$, $F_2(\lambda) = -\min(\operatorname{Re} F(\lambda), 0)$; $F_3(\lambda)$ and $F_4(\lambda)$ are introduced analogously for $\operatorname{Im} F(\lambda)$. The expansion $F(A) = F_1(A) - F_2(A) + i(F_3(A) - F_4(A))$ corresponds to the expansion (4.20) and therefore to establish the continuity of the kernel of the operator $F(A)$, it is sufficient to establish the continuity of the kernels of each of the operators $F_j(A)$. We do this for $F_1(A)$. Since $0 \leq F_1(\lambda) \leq |F(\lambda)| \leq C|\gamma(\lambda)|^2$, we have

$$0 \leqslant \int_{-\infty}^{\infty} F_1(\lambda)\, \Phi(x, y; \lambda)\, d\rho(\lambda) \leqslant C \int_{-\infty}^{\infty} |\gamma(\lambda)|^2\, \Phi(x, y; \lambda)\, d\rho(\lambda). \tag{4.21}$$

The integral on the left in (4.21) represents the kernel of the operator $F_1(A)$; the one on the right, the operator $(\gamma(A))^* \gamma(A)$. By hypothesis the latter kernel is continuous on $Q \times Q$, and therefore by Lemma 4.2 and the inequality (4.21), the operator $F_1(A)$ is continuous. The theorem is completely proved.

Corollary. *If the integral* (4.1) *is a locally bounded function of* $y \in Q$, *and* $\Phi(x, y; \lambda)$ *is a continuous function of* $(x, y) \in Q \times Q$ *for almost all* λ (ρ) *then every bounded Borel set* Δ *has the integral representation*

$$\Xi(x, y; \Delta) = \int_{\Delta} \Phi(x, y; \lambda)\, d\rho(\lambda) \tag{4.22}$$

with a locally bounded kernel (*the spectral function of the operator* A).

If in addition $(\gamma(A))^* \gamma(A)$ *is an integral operator whose kernel is continuous on* $Q \times Q$, *then the spectral function is continuous with respect to* $(x, y) \in Q \times Q$.

4. **The case of a discrete space** Q. By the separability assumption on Q, this space consists of a countable collection of points, so without loss of generality the dx measure of each may be taken to be equal to one. Numbering the points of Q, 1, 2, $\cdots$ we obtain that $H_0 = L_2(Q, dx)$ coincides with the space of sequences $l_2([1, \infty))$. In the space $l_2([1, \infty))$ every selfadjoint operator is a Carleman operator: one may use $\gamma(A) = E$, and for its kernel (it is now natural to

say, its matrix), $C(j, k) = C_{jk} = \delta_{jk}$. In this connection the results of subsections 1–3 are valid for arbitrary selfadjoint operators on the space $l_2([1, \infty))$.

The condition (4.2) carries over to the condition that $\sum_{j=1}^{\infty} 1/p_j < \infty$, and therefore one might for example choose $p_j = j^{1+\epsilon}$ $(\epsilon > 0)$. The chain becomes

$$l_2\left([1, \infty), \frac{1}{p_j}\right) \supset l_2([1, \infty)) \supset l_2([1, \infty), p_j), \tag{4.23}$$

where $l_2([1, \infty), m_j)$ $(m_j > 0;\ j = 1, 2, \cdots)$ denotes the space $l_2([1, \infty))$ with weights m_j: the scalar product in this space is defined by $(f, g)_{l_2([1,\infty), m_j)} = \sum_{j=1}^{\infty} f_j \bar{g}_j m_j$. Thus every generalized eigenvector is an ordinary vector in the space $l_2([1, \infty), 1/p_j)$. The generalized projection operator $P(\lambda)$ is a matrix operator; its matrix $\Phi_{jk}(\lambda)$, the spectral kernel of the operator A, is positive definite and has the property that for almost all (λ)

$$\sum_{j,k=1}^{\infty} \frac{|\Phi_{jk}(\lambda)|^2}{p_j p_k} \leqslant 1 \left(\text{more precisely: } \sum_{j=1}^{\infty} \frac{\Phi_{jj}(\lambda)}{p_j} = 1\right) \tag{4.24}$$

If $F(\lambda)$ is an arbitrary bounded function on the spectrum of A, the function $F(A)$ is a matrix operator where the matrix K_{ik} appears in the form of an absolutely convergent integral:

$$K_{jk} = \int_{-\infty}^{\infty} F(\lambda)\,\Phi_{jk}(\lambda)\,d\varrho(\lambda); \qquad \sum_{j,k=1}^{\infty} \frac{|K_{jk}|^2}{p^j p_{j_k}} < \infty. \tag{4.25}$$

§5. GROWTH ESTIMATES OF EIGENFUNCTIONS AT INFINITY

The results of the preceding two sections lead to the subject of growth estimates at infinity for eigenfunctions of operators on L_2. We will now present the case of a bounded selfadjoint operator; the extension to a more general class of operators for which the expansion theorems 2.3–2.6 are valid, is not difficult. For a simple calculation of the behavior at ∞, one can estimate by step functions. However, from the proofs, it is apparent that more precise estimates may be desired (this refers to §§3, 4–the functions $q(x)$ and $p(x)$ may have a more subtle behavior than a step function).

These growth estimates at ∞ are consequences of the fact that the generalized eigenfunctions are contained in the space H_-, which in the case $H_0 = l_2$

consists of functions with a restricted structure at ∞. Extremely simple estimates appear in the case $H_0 = l_2$. Considering (4.24), (2.17) and the fact that $H_- = l_2([1, \infty), 1/p_j)$, we obtain: for fixed $\epsilon > 0$

$$\sum_{j,k=1}^{\infty} \frac{|\Phi_{jk}(\lambda)|^2}{j^{1+\varepsilon} k^{1+\varepsilon}} \leqslant 1, \qquad \sum_{j=1}^{\infty} \frac{|\varphi_j(\lambda)|^2}{j^{1+\varepsilon}} = 1; \tag{5.1}$$

for almost all λ; here $\phi_j(\lambda)$ is a generalized eigenvector (above we used $p_j = j^{1+\epsilon}$). From (5.1) it follows in any case, that for almost all $\lambda(\rho)$,

$$\Phi_{jk}(\lambda) \underset{j,k\to\infty}{=} O(j^{\frac{1}{2}+\delta} k^{\frac{1}{2}+\delta}), \qquad \varphi_j(\lambda) \underset{j\to\infty}{=} O(j^{\frac{1}{2}+\delta}) \qquad (\delta > 0). \tag{5.2}$$

In the case of nondiscrete Q the situation is more subtle. Below for simplicity we limit ourselves to the case of L_2 on all of E_n.

1. **Estimates of indefinite integrals of eigenfunctions in $L_2(E_n)$.** These estimates will be obtained for operators having ordinary eigenfunctions.

Theorem 5.1. *Suppose A is a selfadjoint operator on $L_2(E_1)$ and that the construction* c) *of* §3.1 *yields an ordinary eigenvector: for arbitrary $u \in C_0^\infty(E_1)$ $(\phi_\alpha(\lambda), u)_0 = (\phi_\alpha(x; \lambda), u)_0$, where $\phi_\alpha(x; \lambda)$ is a locally summable function of x. Then if $\epsilon > 0$ is fixed, the estimate*

$$\int_{-\infty}^{\infty} \frac{1}{(1+|x|)^{2+\varepsilon}} \left| \int_0^x \varphi_\alpha(\xi; \lambda)\, d\xi \right|^2 dx < \infty, \tag{5.3}$$

is satisfied ρ-almost everywhere for these functions, and hence the indefinite integral $\int_0^x \phi_\alpha(\xi; \lambda)\, d\xi$ grows, roughly speaking, no faster than $|x|^{1/2+\delta}$ $(\delta > 0)$.

Proof. For now $D = d/dx$, and therefore, integrating by parts, we obtain

$$\int_{-\infty}^{\infty} \psi_\alpha(x; \lambda)\overline{u'(x)}dx = (\psi_\alpha(x; \lambda), u')_0 = (\varphi_\alpha(\lambda), u)_0 = (\varphi_\alpha(x; \lambda), u)_0$$

$$= \int_{-\infty}^{\infty} \overline{u(x)}\, d_x \left(\int_0^x \varphi_\alpha(\xi; \lambda)\, d\xi \right) = \int_{-\infty}^{\infty} \left(- \int_0^x \varphi_\alpha(\xi; \lambda)\, d\xi \right) \overline{u'(x)}\, dx \tag{5.4}$$

where $u \in C_0^\infty(E_1)$ is arbitrary. Consequently,

$$\psi_\alpha(x; \lambda) = -\int_0^x \varphi_\alpha(\xi; \lambda)d\xi + C \quad (x \in E_1). \tag{5.5}$$

From (3.12) it follows that for ρ-almost all λ $\int_{-\infty}^{\infty} |\psi_\alpha(x; \lambda)|^2/(1 + |x|)^{2+\epsilon}\, dx < \infty$. Since the integral under consideration differs from that for $\psi_\alpha(x; \lambda)$ by a constant, (5.3) follows from the convergence of the integral for $\psi_\alpha(x; \lambda)$. The theorem is proved.

It is clear that this kind of theorem may be formulated for the space $L_2((0, \infty))$. In this one may use, in addition, the construction b) of the operator T (§3.1). Then, using (3.13) in place of (5.3) we obtain the estimate

$$\int_0^\infty \left| \int_0^x \frac{\varphi_\alpha(\xi; \lambda)}{(1+|\xi|)^{1+\varepsilon}} d\xi - C(\alpha, \lambda) \right|^2 dx < \infty, \tag{5.6}$$

where $C(\alpha, \lambda)$ is some constant.

Analogous attempts for spaces $L_2(G)$, $G \subseteq E_n$, $(n \geq 2)$ are not successful, since then from an equality similar to (5.4) we obtain an equality of type (5.5) in which the constant C depends on a solution $C(x)$ of the equation $Du = 0$. The integral $\int_{E_n} C(x)\, dx/(1 + |x_1|)^{2+\epsilon} \cdots (1 + |x_n|)^{2+\epsilon}$ may turn out to be convergent (for example with $n = 2$ $C(x) = f(x_1) + g(x_2)$, where f and g are arbitrary) and therefore from the estimate $\int_{E_n} |\psi_\alpha(x; \lambda)|^2\, dx/(1 + |x_1|)^{2+\epsilon} \cdots (1 + |x_n|)^{2+\epsilon} < \infty$ the analogous estimate in which $\psi_\alpha(x; \lambda)$ depends on the integral $\int_0^{x_1} \cdots$ $\cdots \int_0^{x_n} \phi_\alpha(\xi; \lambda)\, d\xi$, does not follow. However, estimates of the type (5.3) and (5.6) may be obtained in the multi-dimensional case if we further require that A be of Carleman type.

Theorem 5.2. *Suppose A is a Carleman operator on the Hilbert space $L_2(E_n)$ and such that the integral (4.1) is locally bounded for $y \in E_n$. Then if $\epsilon > 0$ is arbitrary, the spectral kernel $\Phi(x, y; \lambda)$ and the eigenfunctions $\phi_\alpha(x, \lambda)$ satisfy the estimates*

$$\int_{E_n}\int_{E_n}\left|\int_0^{x_1}\cdots\int_0^{x_n}\int_0^{y_1}\cdots\int_0^{y_n}\Phi(\xi,\eta;\lambda)\,d\xi d\eta\right|^2\frac{dxdy}{(1+|x|)^{2n+\varepsilon}(1+|y|)^{2n+\varepsilon}}<\infty,$$

$$\int_{E_n}\left|\int_0^{x_1}\cdots\int_0^{x_n}\varphi_\alpha(\xi;\lambda)\,d\xi\right|^2\frac{dx}{(1+|x|)^{2n+\varepsilon}}<\infty \tag{5.7}$$

for ρ-almost all λ.

Proof. The first estimate is based on the following lemma.

Lemma 5.1. *Given the assumptions of the theorem on the spectral integral kernel $\Psi(x, y; \lambda)$, the equality*

$$\Psi(x, y; \lambda)\,M(\lambda)=\int_0^{x_1}\cdots\int_0^{x_n}\int_0^{y_1}\cdots\int_0^{y_n}\Phi(\xi,\eta;\lambda)\,d\xi d\eta \tag{5.8}$$

is valid for almost all $(x, y; \lambda)\in E_n\times E_n\times E_1$ with respect to the measure $dxdyd\rho(\lambda)$, where $M(\lambda)$ is some ρ-almost everywhere positive and finite function.

Proof. Let $f, g\in C_0(E_n)$ and let Δ be a bounded Borel set. We transform the expression $(\Theta(\Delta)f, g)_0=(T^{-1*}E(\Delta)T^{-1}f, g)_0=(E(\Delta)T^{-1}f, T^{-1}g)_0$ by taking into consideration the form (3.5) of the operator T^{-1} in Theorem 4.1. Since the integral (4.1) is locally bounded, the function $p(x)$ introduced in equation (4.2) must also be locally bounded, and therefore, by (4.5), $\Phi(x, y; \lambda)$ is locally square summable for $(x, y; \lambda)\in E_n\times E_n\times E_1$ with respect to the measure $dxdyd\rho(\lambda)$. This renders the following calculation possible:

$$(\Theta(\Delta)f, g)_0=\int_{E_n}\left(E(\Delta)\int_{E_n}\frac{\omega(\xi,\cdot)}{q(\xi)}f(\xi)\,d\xi\right)(x)\int_{E_n}\frac{\omega(\eta,x)}{q(\eta)}\overline{g(\eta)}\,d\eta dx$$

$$=\int_{E_n}\int_{E_n}(E(\Delta)\omega(\xi,\cdot),\omega(\eta,\cdot))_0\frac{f(\xi)\overline{g(\eta)}}{q(\xi)q(\eta)}\,d\xi d\eta=$$

$$= \int_{E_n}\int_{E_n}\left\{\int_{E_n}\int_{E_n}\int_{\Delta}\Phi(\eta',\xi';\lambda)\,\omega(\xi,\xi')\,\omega(\eta,\eta')\,d\xi'd\eta'd\varrho(\lambda)\right\}$$

$$\times\frac{f(\xi)\overline{g(\eta)}}{q(\xi)\,q(\eta)}d\xi d\eta = \int_{E_n}\int_{E_n}\int_{\Delta}\left\{\frac{1}{q(x)\,q(y)}\int_0^{x_1}\cdots\int_0^{x_n}\int_0^{y_1}\cdots\int_0^{y_n}\Phi(\xi,\eta;\lambda)d\xi d\eta\right\} \tag{5.9}$$
$$\times f(y)\,\overline{g(x)}\,dxdy\,d\varrho(\lambda).$$

On the other hand, using the construction of the expansion described in §3.2 we obtain $\Theta(\Delta) = \int_\Delta \Psi(\lambda)\,d\rho_1(\lambda)$; $\rho_1(\Delta)$ is the spectral measure encountered there. Obviously, $\rho(\Delta)$ and $\rho_1(\Delta)$ are absolutely continuous with respect to each other, and therefore, writing $d\rho_1(\lambda)/d\rho(\lambda) = M(\lambda)$, we find that $\Theta(\Delta) = \int_\Delta \Psi(\lambda)\,M(\lambda)\,d\rho(\lambda)$. By (3.6) we obtain

$$(\Theta(\Delta)f,g)_0 = \int_\Delta\left\{\int_{E_n}\int_{E_n}\hat{\Psi}(x,y;\lambda)\,f(y)\,\overline{g(x)}dxdy\right\}M(\lambda)\,d\varrho(\lambda). \tag{5.10}$$

Equating (5.9) and (5.10) we obtain, by the arbitrariness of f, g and Δ,

$$\hat{\Psi}(x,y;\lambda)\,M(\lambda) = \frac{1}{q(x)\,q(y)}\int_0^{x_1}\cdots\int_0^{x_n}\int_0^{y_1}\cdots\int_0^{y_n}\Phi(\xi,\eta;\lambda)\,d\xi d\eta.$$

for all $(x, y; \lambda)$. Since $\Psi = q(x)\,q(y)\,\hat{\Psi}$, (5.8) follows. The lemma is proved.

Now the first of the inequalities (5.7) follows from (3.8), where $q^2(x) = (1+|x_1|)^{2+\epsilon/n}\cdots(1+|x_n|)^{2+\epsilon/n})$, (5.8) and the estimate $q(x) \le (1+|x|)^{2n+\epsilon}$.

The following basic lemma is necessary for the second part of the proof.

Lemma 5.2. *Let $K(x, y)$ be a positive definite kernel defined for each x, y in some space Q. Assume that the expansion*

$$K(x,y) = \sum_{\alpha=1}^{\infty}\psi_\alpha(x)\,\overline{\psi_\alpha(y)} \tag{5.11}$$

converges for arbitrary $x, y \in Q$, where the functions $\psi_\alpha(x)$ have the property that $a_\alpha = 0$ $(\alpha = 1, 2, \cdots)$ whenever $\Sigma_{\alpha=1}^\infty a_\alpha \psi_\alpha(x) = 0$ $(x \in Q)$, $\Sigma_{\alpha=1}^\infty |a_\alpha|^2 < \infty$. If another expansion $K(x, y) = \Sigma_{\alpha=1}^\infty \phi_\alpha(x)\overline{\phi_\alpha(y)}$ converges for each $x, y \in Q$, then

$$\varphi_\alpha(x) = \sum_{\beta=1}^{\infty}u_{\alpha\beta}\psi_\beta(x),\quad \sum_{\beta=1}^{\infty}|u_{\alpha\beta}|^2 \leqslant 1\ (x\in Q;\ \alpha = 1, 2, \ldots). \tag{5.12}$$

Proof. Setting $y = x$ in (5.11), we conclude that the vector $(\psi_1(x), \psi_2(x), \cdots) \in l_2([1, \infty))$; we denote it by s_x. Analogously, we introduce the vector $t_x = (\phi_1(x), \phi_2(x), \cdots) \in l_2([1, \infty))$. The linear span of the vectors s_x $(x \in Q)$ is dense in $l_2([1, \infty))$, since if $(a, s_x) = \Sigma_{\alpha=1}^{\infty} a_\alpha \overline{\psi_\alpha(x)} = 0$ $(a = (a_1, a_2, \cdots) \in l_2([1, \infty)))$, then $a = 0$ by the hypotheses. We place the vectors s_x and t_x in a one to one correspondence and we consider this correspondence as a linear transformation on the linear combinations of the s_x. The resulting linear operator U is densely defined in $l_2([1, \infty))$ and is an isometry since $(s_x, s_y) = K(x, y) = (t_x, t_y) = (Us_x, Us_y)$. Consequently U may be extended to an isometric operator on all of $l_2([1, \infty))$. We denote the matrix of this operator with respect to the basis $\delta_\alpha = (\delta_{\alpha 1}, \delta_{\alpha 2}, \cdots)$ by $\|u_{\alpha\beta}\|_1^\infty$; we then have

$$\varphi_\alpha(x) = (t_x, \delta_\alpha) = (Us_x, \delta_\alpha) = \sum_{\beta=1}^{\infty} u_{\alpha\beta}(s_x, \delta_\beta) = \sum_{\beta=1}^{\infty} u_{\alpha\beta}\psi_\beta(x).$$

Since $\|U\| = 1$, then $\|U^*\| = \|U\| = 1$, it follows that $\Sigma_{\beta=1}^{\infty} |u_{\alpha\beta}|^2 \leq 1$ $(\alpha = 1, 2, \cdots)$. The lemma is proved.

We finish the proof of the theorem. For definiteness we will consider the case $N_\lambda = \infty$. By the general scheme of §1, the functions $\hat{\psi}_\alpha(x; \lambda)$, encountered in §3.2, are orthogonal in $L_2(E_n)$ and yield the convergence of the expansion $\hat{\Psi}(x, y; \lambda) = \Sigma_{\alpha=1}^{\infty} \hat{\psi}_\alpha(x; \lambda) \overline{\hat{\psi}_\alpha(y; \lambda)}$ in the metric of $L_2(E_n \times E_n)$. Therefore the expansion

$$\Psi(x, y; \lambda) = \sum_{\alpha=1}^{\infty} \psi_\alpha(x; \lambda) \overline{\psi_\alpha(y; \lambda)} \tag{5.13}$$

converges in the sense of $L_2(E_n \times E_n, 1/q(x)q(y))\, dx\, dy)$ $(q^2(x) = (1 + |x_1|)^{2+\epsilon/n} \cdots (1 + |x_n|)^{2+\epsilon/n})$, and, in particular, it converges in the sense of L_2 relative to $dxdy$ on arbitrary compact sets. On the other hand, by (5.8) $\Psi(x, y; \lambda)$ is a continuous function of $(x, y) \in E_n \times E_n$. By Lemma 4.1, the functions $\psi_\alpha(x; \lambda)$ may be taken to be continuous in $x \in E_n$, and the series (5.13) converges absolutely and uniformly on compacta. Further if $a \in l_2([1, \infty))$ and $\Sigma_{\alpha=1}^{\infty} a_\alpha \psi_\alpha(x; \lambda) = 0$ $(x \in Q)$, then it follows from the orthogonality of the functions $\psi_\alpha(x; \lambda)$ in the space $L_2(E_n, 1/q^2\, dx)$ that $a = 0$. Thus the kernel $K(x, y) = \Psi(x, y; \lambda)$ and the functions $\psi_\alpha(x; \lambda)$ satisfy the hypothesis of Lemma 5.2.

We now consider the equation of $\Phi(x, y; \lambda)$ in a bilinear series in $\phi_\alpha(x; \lambda)$: $\Phi(x, y; \lambda) = \Sigma_{\alpha=1}^{\infty} \overline{\phi_\alpha(y; \lambda)}$. Integrating this expansion and using (5.8) we obtain the convergence of the series

$$\Psi(x, y; \lambda) = \sum_{\alpha=1}^{\infty} \varphi_\alpha(x)\overline{\varphi_\alpha(y)}, \ \varphi_\alpha(x) = \frac{1}{\sqrt{M(\lambda)}} \int_0^{x_1} \cdots \int_0^{x_n} \varphi_\alpha(\xi; \lambda)\, d\xi$$

$$(x, y \in E_n;\ \alpha = 1, 2, \ldots) \tag{5.14}$$

for each $x, y \in E_n$. Applying Lemma 5.2 we conclude that (5.12) holds for $\psi_\beta = \psi_\beta(x; \lambda)$. Therefore, by the orthogonality of the functions $\psi_\beta(x; \lambda)$ in $L_2(E_n, 1/q^2\, dx)$ and the estimate $\int_{E_n} |\psi_\beta(x; \lambda)|^2\, dx/q^2(x) \le 1$ (see (3.11)),we have

$$\int_{E_n} |\varphi_\alpha(x)|^2 \frac{dx}{q^2(x)} = \int_{E_n} \left| \sum_{\beta=1}^{\infty} u_{\alpha\beta} \psi_\beta(x; \lambda) \right|^2 \frac{dx}{q^2(x)}$$

$$= \sum_{\beta=1}^{\infty} |u_{\alpha\beta}|^2 \int_{E_n} |\psi_\beta(x; \lambda)|^2 \frac{dx}{q^2(x)} \leqslant \sum_{\beta=1}^{\infty} |u_{\alpha\beta}|^2 \leqslant 1 \ (\alpha = 1, 2, \ldots).$$

This inequality together with (5.14) yields the second of the estimates (5.7). We note that in all of the above arguments it was only necessary that λ lie in some set with a complement of ρ-measure zero.

The theorem is completely proved.

2. **Estimates of averaged eigenfunctions of a Carleman operator in $L_2(E_n)$.** We prove the following theorem.

Theorem 5.3. *Let A be an operator defined as in Theorem 5.2. Let ϵ, δ', δ'' be fixed. Then for ρ-almost all λ, the estimates*

$$\int\limits_{|x-\xi''|<\delta''} \int\limits_{|\xi''-\xi'|<\delta'} \int\limits_{|y-\eta''|<\delta''} \int\limits_{|\eta''-\eta'|<\delta'} \Phi(\xi', \eta'; \lambda)\, d\xi' d\eta' d\xi'' d\eta \underset{|x|,|y|\to\infty}{=} O\left(|x|^{\frac{n}{2}+\varepsilon} |y|^{\frac{n}{2}+\varepsilon}\right), \tag{5.15}$$

$$\int\limits_{|x-\xi''|<\delta''} \int\limits_{|\xi''-\xi'|<\delta'} \varphi_\alpha(\xi'; \lambda)\, d\xi' d\xi'' \underset{|x|\to\infty}{=} O\left(|x|^{\frac{n}{2}+\varepsilon}\right) \ (\alpha = 1, \ldots, N_\lambda).$$

are valid.

The following lemma is necessary for the proof.

Lemma 5.3. *Let J_δ be an integral operator on $L_2(E_n)$ with kernel $\chi_\delta(x, y) = \kappa_{(0,\delta)}(|x-y|)$ $(\delta > 0)$, where $\kappa_{(0,\delta)}$ is the characteristic function of the interval $(0, \delta)$. If C is an arbitrary bounded operator on $L_2(E_n)$ the operator $J_\delta CJ_\delta$ is an integral operator with the bounded and continuous (as a function of two variables) kernel $K(x, y) = (C\chi_\delta(\cdot, y), \chi_\delta(\cdot, x))_0$.*

Proof. The kernel $K(x, y)$ is continuous since $\chi_\delta(\cdot, x)$ is a continuous vector-valued function of x with values in $L_2(E_n)$. It is bounded: $|(C\chi_\delta(\cdot, y), \chi_\delta(\cdot, x))_0| \le \|C\| \, \|\chi_\delta(\cdot, y)\|_0 \|\chi_\delta(\cdot, x)\|_0 \le Cm^2$, where m is the measure of the sphere $|x| < \delta$. If f and g are bounded we have

$$\int_{E_n}\int_{E_n} K(x, y) f(y) \overline{g(x)}\, dxdy = \int_{E_n}\int_{E_n} (C\chi_\delta(\cdot, y), \chi_\delta(\cdot, x))_0 f(y) \overline{g(x)}\, dxdy$$
$$= \left(C\int_{E_n} \chi_\delta(\cdot, y) f(y)\, dy, \int_{E_n} \chi(\cdot, x) g(x)\, dx\right)_0 = (CJ_\delta f, J_\delta g)_0 = (J_\delta CJ_\delta f, g)_0 \tag{5.16}$$

(these calculations are correct since an integral of the type $\int_{E_n} \chi_\delta(\cdot, y) f(y)\, dy$ may be understood as an integral of a vector-function with values in $L_2(E_n)$). This proves this lemma.

We turn to the proof of the theorem. We let F denote an integral operator with kernel

$$F(x, y) = \frac{\chi_{\delta''}(x, y)}{(1 + |y|)^{\frac{n}{2}+\varepsilon}}.$$

Since

$$\int_{E_n} |(Ff)(x)|^2\, dx = \int_{E_n} \left| \int_{|x-\xi| < \delta''} \frac{f(\xi)}{(1 + |\xi|)^{\frac{n}{2}+\varepsilon}}\, d\xi \right|^2 dx$$
$$\leqslant \int_{E_n} \frac{1}{(1 + |x| - \delta'')^{n+2\varepsilon}} \left(\int_{|x-\xi| - \delta''} |f(\xi)|\, d\xi \right)^2 dx$$
$$\leqslant \|f\|^2_{L_1(E_n)} \int_{E_n} \frac{dx}{(1 + |x| - \delta'')^{n+2\varepsilon}}, \tag{5.17}$$

then F may be regarded as a continuous transformation from $L_1(E_n)$ into $L_2(E_n)$.

The adjoint operator F^* yielding the kernel $F^*(x, y) = \overline{F(y, x)} = F(y, x)$, will be a continuous operator from $L_2(E_n)$ to $L_1(E_n)' = M(E_n)$ ($M(E_n)$ is the space of essentially bounded functions on E_n, $\|f\|_{M(E_n)} = \operatorname{vrai\,max}_{x\in E_n} |f(x)|$). Let $E(\Delta)$ be a resolution of the identity of the operator A so that the product $\Phi(\Delta) = F^* J_{\delta'} E(\Delta) J_{\delta'} F$, a continuous operator from $L_1(E_n)$ into $M(E_n)$, defines an operator valued measure on Δ. We show that $\operatorname{Var}\Theta$ is strongly bounded on the whole real line.

We denote by $P_\Delta(x, y) = (E(\Delta)\chi_{\delta'}(\cdot, y), \chi_{\delta'}(\cdot, x))_0$ the kernel of the operator $J_{\delta'} E(\Delta) J_{\delta'}$ (see Lemma 5.3). It is positive definite, $P_\Delta(x, x) \leq C_1 (x \in E_n)$, and moreover, for fixed x, $P_\Delta(x, x)$ represents a measure on Δ. Let $\Delta_1, \cdots, \Delta n$ be disjoint. Since $\Theta(\Delta)$ is an operator from $L_1(E_n)$ into $M(E_n)$, then the norm of this operator is equal to the sup of the modulus of its kernel. Denoting $p(x) = (1 + |x|)^{n+2\epsilon}$, we have

$$\sum_{j=1}^{N} \|\Theta(\Delta_j)\| = \sum_{j=1}^{N} \sup_{x,y} \left| \int_{E_n}\int_{E_n} F(\xi, x) P_{\Delta_j}(\xi, \eta) F(\eta, y)\, d\xi d\eta \right|$$

$$\leqslant \sum_{j=1}^{N} \sup_{x,y} \left\{ \int_{E_n} F(\xi, x) \sqrt{P_{\Delta_j}(\xi, \xi)}\, d\xi \cdot \int_{E_n} F(\eta, y) \sqrt{P_{\Delta_j}(\eta, \eta)}\, d\eta \right\}$$

$$= \sum_{j=1}^{N} \sup_{x} \left\{ \int_{E_n} F(\xi, x) \sqrt{P_{\Delta_j}(\xi, \xi)}\, d\xi \right\}^2 \leqslant \sum_{j=1}^{N} \sup_{x} \int_{E_n} F^2(\xi, x)\, p(\xi)\, d\xi$$

$$\times \int_{E_n} \frac{P_{\Delta_j}(\xi, \xi)}{p(\xi)}\, d\xi = \sup_{x} \int_{E_n} F^2(\xi, x)\, p(\xi)\, d\xi \cdot \int_{E_n} \frac{P_{\bigcup_{j=1}^{N} \Delta_j}(\xi, \xi)}{p(\xi)}\, d\xi$$

$$\leqslant C_1 \int_{E_n} \frac{d\xi}{p(\xi)} \cdot \sup_{x} \left\{ \frac{1}{(1 + |x|)^{n+2\varepsilon}} \int_{|x-\xi| < \delta''} (1 + |\xi|)^{n+2\varepsilon}\, d\xi \right\} = C_2. \tag{5.18}$$

In this estimate C_2 does not depend on the choice of Δ_j from the interval $(-\infty, \infty)$, and therefore $\operatorname{Var}_{(-\infty,\infty)}\Phi < \infty$.

Using Theorem 1.2, we differentiate $\Phi(\Delta)$ with respect to $\sigma(\Delta) = \operatorname{Var}_\Delta \Theta$. The resulting derivative is an operator-valued measure $\Psi(\lambda)$ whose values are continuous operators from $L_1(E_n)$ into $M(E_n)$, where $\Theta(\Delta) = \int_\Delta \Psi(\lambda) d\sigma(\lambda)$. If $\rho(\Delta) = 0$ then

$E(\Delta) = 0$ and consequently, $\Theta(\Delta') = 0$ for all $\Delta' \subseteq A$, i.e. $0 = \mathrm{Var}_\Delta \Theta = \sigma(\Delta)$. Thus $\sigma(\Delta)$ is absolutely continuous with respect to $\rho(\Delta)$; denoting $d\sigma(\lambda)/d\rho(\lambda) = R(\lambda)$, we have

$$\Theta(\Delta) = \int_\Delta \Psi(\lambda) R(\lambda)\, d\varrho(\lambda). \tag{5·19}$$

To this point, we have not used the convergence of the integral (4.1). Since it is locally bounded by assumption, then $\Phi(x, y; \lambda)$ is locally square summable with respect to the measure $dxdyd\rho(\lambda)$, and the operator $E(\Delta)$ is an integral operator with kernel $\Xi(x, y; \Delta) = \int_\Delta \Phi(x, y; \lambda) \times d\rho(\lambda)$ (see Theorem 4.1). Therefore $\Theta(\Delta)$ is also an integral operator, with kernel

$$\int_{E_n}\int_{E_n} F(\xi'', x) F(\eta'', y) \int_{|\xi''-\xi'|<\delta'} \int_{|\eta''-\eta'|<\delta'} \left\{\int_\Delta \Phi(\xi', \eta'; \lambda)\, d\varrho(\lambda)\right\} d\xi' d\eta' d\xi'' d\eta''.$$

Considering the local summability of the kernel $\Phi(x, y; \lambda)$ in $(x, y; \lambda)$, (5.19), and the arbitrariness of Δ, we obtain

$$\int_\Delta R(\lambda) (\Psi(\lambda) f, g)_0\, d\varrho(\lambda) = (\Theta(\Delta) f, g)_0$$

$$= \int_\Delta R(\lambda) \int_{E_n}\int_{E_n} S(x, y; \lambda) f(y) \overline{g(x)}\, dxdyd\varrho(\lambda), \tag{5.20}$$

$$S(x, y; \lambda)$$

$$= \frac{1}{R(\lambda)} \int_{E_n}\int_{E_n} F(\xi'', x) F(\eta'', y) \int_{|\xi''-\xi'|<\delta'} \int_{|\eta''-\eta'|<\delta'} \Phi(\xi', \eta'; \lambda) d\xi' d\eta' d\xi'' d\eta'',$$

for bounded f, g, i.e. $S(x, y; \lambda)$ is the kernel of the continuous operator $\Psi(\lambda)$: $L_1(E_n) \to M(E_n)$. But then this kernel is essentially bounded; in view of this and the form of $F(x, y)$, the first of the relations (5·15) follows from (5·20)·

To obtain the second, we substitute (4.8) for $\Phi(\xi', \eta'; \lambda)$ in the estimate just now obtained, interchange the order of summation and integration and then set $y = x$. As a result we obtain

$$\sum_{\alpha=1}^{N_\lambda} \left| \int_{|x-\xi''|<\delta''} \int_{|\xi''-\xi'|<\delta'} \varphi_\alpha(\xi'; \lambda)\, d\xi' d\xi'' \right|^2 \underset{|x|\to\infty}{=} O(|x|^{n+2\varepsilon}), \tag{5.21}$$

from which the second of the estimates (5.15) follows. The theorem is proved.

A particular characteristic of the estimates in Theorems 5.2 and 5.3 is that they are valid for an arbitrary Carleman operator, independent of the behavior of the integral (4.1) in y_0. We proceed, by a simple argument, to obtain other estimates which take this behavior into account.

It follows from the inequality (4.5) (see also (4.7)), that

$$\Phi(x, y; \lambda) = \sqrt{p(x)\,p(y)}\,\widehat{\Psi}(x, y; \lambda)\ (x, y \in E_n);\ \int_{E_n}\int_{E_n} |\widehat{\Psi}(x, y; \lambda)|^2 dx dy \leqslant 1 \quad (5.22)$$

for ρ-almost all λ. Let $\delta > 0$ be fixed; by (5.22) and the Cauchy-Bunjakovskiĭ inequality, we conclude that

$$\begin{aligned} \left| \int_{|x-\xi|<\delta} \int_{|y-\eta|<\delta} \Phi(\xi, \eta; \lambda)\, d\xi d\eta \right| &\leqslant \sqrt{\int_{|x-\xi|<\delta} p(\xi)\, d\xi} \\ &\times \sqrt{\int_{|y-\eta|<\delta} p(\eta)\, d\eta} \sqrt{\int_{|x-\xi|<\delta} \int_{|y-\eta|<\delta} |\widehat{\Psi}(\xi, \eta; \lambda)|^2\, d\xi d\eta} \\ &= \sqrt{\int_{|x-\xi|<\delta} p(\xi)\, d\xi} \sqrt{\int_{|y-\eta|<\delta} p(\eta)\, d\eta} \cdot \underset{|x|,|y|\to\infty}{o(1)}. \end{aligned} \quad (5.23)$$

Analogously, for the individual eigenfunction $\phi_\alpha(x; \lambda)$ considered as an inclusion operator $\phi_\alpha(\cdot\,; \lambda) \in L_2(E_n, (1/p)\,dx)$ we are led to the estimate

$$\int_{|x-\xi|<\delta} \varphi_\alpha(\xi; \lambda)\, d\xi = \sqrt{\int_{|x-\xi|<\delta} p(\xi)\, d\xi} \cdot \underset{|x|\to\infty}{o(1)}\ (\alpha = 1, \ldots, N_\lambda). \quad (5.24)$$

We extract the following theorem from (5.23) and (5.24).

Theorem 5.4. *Let A be an operator defined as in Theorem* 5.2, *and denote*

$$C(y) = \int_{E_n} |C(x, y)|^2\, dx \quad (y \in E_n),$$

where $C(x, y)$ is the kernel of the operator $\gamma(A)$. Fix ϵ, $\delta > 0$; then the estimates

$$\begin{aligned} \int_{|x-\xi|<\delta} \int_{|y-\eta|<\delta} \Phi(\xi, \eta; \lambda)\, d\xi d\eta &\underset{|x|,|y|\to\infty}{=} O\left(\sqrt{\widetilde{C}(x)}\, |x|^{\frac{n}{2}+\varepsilon} \sqrt{\widetilde{C}(y)}\, |y|^{\frac{n}{2}+\varepsilon}\right), \\ \int_{|x-\xi|<\delta} \varphi_\alpha(\xi; \lambda)\, d\xi &\underset{|x|\to\infty}{=} O\left(\sqrt{\widetilde{C}(x)}\, |x|^{\frac{n}{2}+\varepsilon}\right) (\alpha = 1, \ldots, N_\lambda), \end{aligned} \quad (5.25)$$

are valid almost everywhere with respect to ρ, *where* $\widetilde{C}(x) = \sup_{|x-\xi|<\delta}(1 + C(\xi))$.

In fact we may set $p(y) = (1 + C(y))(1 + |y|)^{n+2\epsilon}$ $(y \in E_n)$. This is possible since the integral in (4.2) will then converge. Using such a function $p(x)$ in (5.23) and (5.24) we arrive at (5.25). The theorem follows.

It is clear that from (5.22) and the inclusion $\phi_\alpha(\cdot\,; \lambda) \in L_2(E_n, (1/p)\,dx)$ it would also be possible, in a similar way, to obtain estimates at ∞ of the integrals

$$\int_0^{x_1} \cdots \int_0^{x_n} \int_0^{y_1} \cdots \int_0^{y_n} \Phi(\xi, \eta; \lambda)\, d\xi d\eta, \quad \int_0^{x_1} \cdots \int_0^{x_n} \varphi_\alpha(\xi; \lambda)\, d\xi.$$

But we will not dwell on these.

3. **Eigenfunction estimates for Carleman operators on** $L_2(Q, dx)$. It is clear that some of the relationships of §4 may be understood as some sort of growth estimates: as previously we denote

$$C(y) = \int_Q |C(x, y)|^2\, dx \quad (y \in Q), \tag{5.26}$$

where $C(x, y)$ is the kernel of the operator $\gamma(A)$, and we fix an arbitrary function $p(x) \geq 1$ such that

$$\int_Q \frac{C(y)}{p(y)}\, dy < \infty. \tag{5.27}$$

Then for ρ-almost all λ the relations

$$\int_Q \int_Q \frac{|\Phi(x, y; \lambda)|^2}{p(x)\,p(y)}\, dx dy \leqslant 1, \quad \sum_{\alpha=1}^{N_\lambda} \int_Q \frac{|\varphi_\alpha(x; y)|^2}{p(x)}\, dx = 1 \tag{5.28}$$

are valid, by the known relations characterizing the behavior of $\Phi(x, y; \lambda)$ and $\phi_\alpha(x; \lambda)$ at ∞. On the other hand, we will now show that with one additional restriction, we may obtain estimates on the modulus from (5.28).

Theorem 5.5. *Let A be a selfadjoint Carleman operator in the space* $L_2(Q, dx)$, *for which the function* (5.26) *is locally bounded. Suppose* $p(y)$ *is a locally bounded function which satisfies* (5.27), *and is such that the integral*

$$\int_Q |C(x, y)|^2\, p(y)\, dy = B(x) \quad (x \in Q) \tag{5.29}$$

is locally summable. Then for ρ-almost all λ, the estimates

$$|\Phi(x, y; \lambda)| \leqslant \frac{1}{|\gamma(\lambda)|^2}\sqrt{B(x)B(y)}, \quad \sum_{\alpha=1}^{N_\lambda} |\varphi_\alpha(x; \lambda)|^2 \leqslant \frac{1}{|\gamma(\lambda)|^2} B(x). \tag{5.30}$$

are valid. The first of these is valid for almost all (x, y); *the second is valid under the additional assumption that the function* $\Phi(x, y; \lambda)$ *is continuous in* (x, y) *for ρ-almost all λ.*

Proof. We show that the validity of the equation

$$\int_Q \int_Q C(x, \xi)\overline{C(y, \eta)}\,\Phi(\xi, \eta; \lambda)\, d\xi d\eta = |\gamma(\lambda)|^2 \Phi(x, y; \lambda), \tag{5.31}$$

for almost all (x, y) is, in actuality, equivalent to the fact that the eigenfunctions of the operator A are eigenfunctions for $(\gamma(A))^* \gamma(A)$. By the Cauchy-Bunjakovskiĭ inequality, we obtain

$$\int_Q \int_Q |C(x, \xi)\overline{C(y, \eta)}\,\Phi(\xi, \eta; \lambda)|\, d\xi d\eta$$

$$\leqslant \left(\int_Q \int_Q |C(x, \xi)\overline{C(y, \eta)}|^2 p(\xi)\, p(\eta)\, d\xi d\eta\right)^{\frac{1}{2}}$$

$$\times \left(\int_Q \int_Q \frac{|\Phi(\xi, \eta; \lambda)|^2}{p(\xi)\, p(\eta)}\, d\xi d\eta\right)^{\frac{1}{2}} \leqslant \sqrt{B(x)B(y)}, \tag{5.32}$$

from which follows, in particular, the absolute convergence of the integral on the left side of (5.31) for almost all $(x, y) \in Q \times Q$. Further, we show that for finite $f \in L_2(Q, dx) = H_0$

$$(\gamma(A))^* f \in L_2(Q, p dx) = H_+.$$

For, suppose f vanishes outside the compact set Q_0. Then

$$\int_Q |((\gamma(A))^* f)(\xi)|^2 p(\xi)\, d\xi = \int_Q \left|\int_{Q_0} \overline{C(x, \xi)}\, f(x)\, dx\right|^2 p(\xi)\, d\xi$$

$$\leqslant \|f\|^2 \int_Q \int_{Q_0} |C(x, \xi)|^2 dx\, p(\xi)\, d\xi = \|f\|^2 \int_{Q_0} B(x)\, dx < \infty.$$

If $u, v \in L_2(Q, pdx)$ we have $(P(\lambda)u, v)_0 = \int_Q \int_Q \Phi(\xi, \eta; \lambda) u(\eta) \overline{v(\xi)} d\xi d\eta$. Therefore for finite $f, g \in L_2(Q, dx)$ and bounded Δ we obtain

$$(\gamma(A) E(\Delta)(\gamma(A))^* f, g)_0 = (E(\Delta)(\gamma(A))^* f, (\gamma(A))^* g)_0$$
$$= \int_\Delta (P(\lambda)(\gamma(A))^* f, (\gamma(A))^* g)_0 \, d\rho(\lambda) \cdot$$

$$= \int_\Delta \int_Q \int_Q \Phi(\xi, \eta; \lambda) \int_Q \overline{C(y, \eta)} f(y)\, dy \cdot \overline{\int_Q \overline{C(x, \xi)} g(x)\, dx}\, d\xi d\eta d\rho(\lambda)$$

$$= \int_\Delta \int_Q \int_Q \left\{ \int_Q \int_Q C(x, \xi) \overline{C(y, \eta)} \Phi(\xi, \eta; \lambda)\, d\xi d\eta \right\} f(y) \overline{g(x)}\, dx dy d\rho(\lambda). \qquad (5.33)$$

On the other hand, by Theorem 4.1, $\gamma(A) E(\Delta)(\gamma(A))^*$ is an integral operator with kernel $\int_\Lambda |\gamma(\lambda)|^2 \Phi(x, y; \lambda)\, d\rho(\lambda)$. Consequently

$$(\gamma(A) E(\Delta)(\gamma(A))^* f, g)_0 = \int_\Delta \int_Q \int_Q |\gamma(\lambda)|^2 \Phi(x, y; \lambda) f(y) \overline{g(x)}\, dx dy d\rho(\lambda).$$

Comparing this equation with (5.33) we obtain (5.31) since f, g and Δ are arbitrary. The first of the estimates (5.30) follows from (5.31) and (5.32). To obtain the second estimate from the first, we assume that $\Phi(x, y; \lambda)$ is continuous in (x, y), then expand $\Phi(x, y; \lambda)$ in a bilinear expansion and set $y = x$. The theorem follows.

In conclusion we remark that it would seem at a glance that the inequality (5.28) yields a stronger estimate than (5.30). For example let $C(y) \leq C < \infty$; so that any nonnegative function in $L_1(Q, dx)$ may be used for $1/p(y)$. The boundedness of $\phi_\alpha(x; \lambda)$ in x appears to follow (see (5.28)) from the convergence of the integral $\int_Q (|\phi_\alpha(x; \lambda)|^2 / p(x))\, dx$. But this is not so, since $\Phi(x, y; \lambda)$ and hence $\phi_\alpha(x; \lambda)$ exist for ρ-almost all λ, and the set on which they exist is generally independent of p since p defines the operator T and hence the measure $\rho(\Delta) = \mathrm{tr}(T^{-1*} E(\Delta) T^{-1})$.

CHAPTER VI

SPECTRAL THEORY FOR SELFADJOINT PARTIAL DIFFERENTIAL OPERATORS

In this chapter we present the theory of expansions in eigenfunctions (generalized and ordinary) for differential operators in the space $L_2(G)$. After disposing of the problem of selfadjointness for such operators, we proceed to the detailed construction of spectral theory for elliptic operators and study the behavior of expansions up to the boundary of the region. We also present general results on the spectral analysis of nonelliptic operators, and these are illustrated by special examples. In the last section, we indicate the spectral theory of ordinary differential operators. Below, unless stated to the contrary, the region G is understood to be a possibly unbounded region with piecewise smooth boundary Γ.

§1. DIFFERENTIAL OPERATORS IN AN UNBOUNDED REGION

In this section we carry over certain concepts from Chapter II to the case of unbounded G. We will not dwell on the question of solvability of boundary value problems in an unbounded region (although a similar theory can be constructed using the method of the energy inequalities), but we study the more specialized problem concerning selfadjointness of operators in $L_2(G)$ induced by formally selfadjoint expressions and boundary conditions. The problem of existence amounts to obtaining equations of the type $\Lambda(\mathrm{bd}) = \mathbb{J}(\mathrm{bd})$. The greatest number of results in this direction are obtained for elliptic operators, with selfadjointness determined by the behavior of the coefficients of the expression at ∞. These results will be very incomplete, but at the same time we will present some general methods and facts for nonelliptic operators. Below, unless stated to the contrary, all operators are assumed to act in $H_0 = L_2(G)$, $G \subseteq E_n$.

1. Minimal, maximal, strong, and weak operators for an unbounded region. Let L be an expression of order r in an unbounded region G, and make the usual smoothness assumptions on the coefficients. Recall (see Chapter III, §5.8) that the class of functions satisfying certain (bd) is defined as a subspace W_2^r (bd) $\subseteq$ $W_2^r(G) = W_2^{(r,q)}(G)$, $(q(x) = 1, x \in G)$, containing $\overset{o}{W}{}_2^r(G)$ – the closure in $W_2^r(G)$ of the class $C_0^\infty(G)$ of functions finite with respect to G and ∞. Since we understand that (bd) does not account for behavior at ∞, W_2^r(bd)$^+$ is constructed as the subspace of $W_2^r(G)$ consisting of all v for which $(Lu, v)_0 = (u, L^+v)_0$ for every $u \in W_2^r$(bd) which is finite at ∞. We consider only (bd) for which (bd)$^{++}$ = (bd).

The minimal operator Λ is defined similarly as in the case of bounded G (see Chapter II, §2.1): set $\Lambda'u = Lu$, $\mathfrak{D}(\Lambda') = C_0^\infty(G)$. It is easy to show that Λ' admits a closure, and then by definition, $\Lambda = \overline{\Lambda}'$. It is not difficult to show that every function $u \in \overset{o}{W}{}_2^r(G) \cap W_{2,0}^r(E_n)$ (i.e., $u \in \overset{o}{W}{}_2^r(G)$ and is finite at ∞) belongs to $\mathfrak{D}(\Lambda)$ and $\Lambda u = Lu$.

If Λ^+ is the minimal operator constructed with respect to L^+, then the maximal operator $\mathit{Л}$ is defined as $(\Lambda^+)^*$. We consider functions $u \in L_2(G)$ which belong to $W_2^r(G_R)$ for every $R > 0$, where G_R is the intersection of G with the sphere $|x| < R$. The operator $Au = Lu$, which is defined on these functions when, in addition, $Lu \in L_2(G)$, is in general a restriction of $\mathit{Л}$: for $v \in C_0^\infty(G) = \mathfrak{D}((\Lambda^+)')$ $(Au, v)_0 = (Lu, v)_0 = (u, L^+v)_0 = (u, (\Lambda^+)'v)_0$, and hence $A \subseteq ((\Lambda^+)')^* = (\Lambda^+)^* = \mathit{Л}$.

Suppose that certain (bd) are given on Γ. We define Λ'(bd) by the equation Λ'(bd)$u = Lu$, $\mathfrak{D}(\Lambda'$(bd)$) = W_2^r$(bd)$\cap W_{2,0}^r(E_n)$ (i.e., $u \in W_2^r$(bd) and is finite at ∞). Obviously, Λ'(bd)$\subseteq \mathit{Л}$ and therefore the strong operator $\overline{\Lambda'$(bd)$} = \Lambda$(bd) exists. By definition, $\mathit{Л}$(bd) = $(\Lambda^+$(bd)$^+)^*$ is the weak operator. Obviously,

$$\Lambda \subseteq \Lambda \text{ (bd) } \subseteq \mathit{Л}\text{(bd)} \subseteq \mathit{Л}. \tag{1.1}$$

As in the case of bounded G, Λ and some restriction of $\mathit{Л}$ are partial cases of the operators Λ(bd) and $\mathit{Л}$(bd).

2. **Local structure of the domains of definition of the maximal and minimal operations in the case of elliptic expressions.** In this and in the following subsections we will formulate, in a manner similar to §§4–5, Chapter III, our results are only for the simplest cases (strong elliptic expressions with boundary conditions of a boundary value problem of type zero or three), leaving the general formulation to the reader. Let L be an expression of order $r = 2m$ with the usual requirements of smoothness on the coefficients. We assume that the expression L is elliptic in some subregion $G_0 \subseteq G$. The smoothness of $u \in \mathfrak{D}(\mathit{Л})$ inside the region G_0 is easily verified with the help of the theorems in §§4 and 6, Chapter III.

We thus have the following theorem.

Theorem 1.1. *Let the coefficients of* L *be given by* $a_\alpha(x) \in C^{|\alpha|+p}(G_0)$, $p \geq m$. *Then every function of* $\mathfrak{D}(\mathcal{J})$ *is contained in* $W^{2m}_{2,\mathrm{loc}}(G_0)$ *on* G_0.

In fact, if $g \in \mathfrak{D}(\mathcal{J})$, then $(g, L^+v)_0 = (f, v)_0$ for some $f \in L_2(G)$ $(v \in C_0^\infty(G_0))$. In other words: $g \in L_2(G_0)$ satisfies the equation $Lu = f \in L_2(G_0)$ on G_0. By Theorem 4.5, Chapter III, $g \in W^{2m}_{2,\mathrm{loc}}(G_0)$, as required.

Generally speaking the smoothness properties of the functions in $\mathfrak{D}(\mathcal{J}(\mathrm{bd}))$ and $\mathfrak{D}(\mathcal{J})$ do not carry up to the boundary Γ_0 of G_0 in G. So, we let $G_0 = G$ be bounded, and $W_2^r(\mathrm{bd}) = W_2^r(G)$. Then $\mathfrak{D}(\mathcal{J}(\mathrm{bd})) = \mathfrak{D}(\mathcal{J})$, and $\mathfrak{D}(\mathcal{J})$ does not densely fill the space $W_2^r(G)$ (an example was given at the end of Chapter III, §4). Similar smoothness restrictions are made for Γ_0, L and (bd) for several theorems on local increments in the smoothness up to the boundary. In particular the following theorem is true.

Theorem 1.2. *Let* Γ_0 *be a bounded piece of* Γ *on which borders a bounded subregion* $G_0 \subseteq G$. *Then:* 1) *if* L *is strongly elliptic of order* $2m$ *in* $G_0 \cup \Gamma$, *and its coefficients* $a_\alpha(x) \in C^{|\alpha|+p}(G_0 \cup \Gamma_0)$ $(p \geq m)$, *if the piece* Γ_0 *is of class* C^{2m+p} *and the conditions* (bd) *are null* $(D^\alpha u|_{\Gamma_0} = 0,\ |\alpha| \leq m-1)$, *then each function of* $\mathfrak{D}(\mathcal{J}(\mathrm{bd}))$ *is in* $W^{2m}_{2,\mathrm{loc}}(G_0, \Gamma_0)$ *on* $G_0 \cup \Gamma_0$ *and satisfies the null conditions*; 2) *if* L *is strongly elliptic of second order in* $G_0 \cup \Gamma_0$, $a_\alpha(x) \in C^{|\alpha|}(G_0 \cup \Gamma_0)$ *and the coefficients* $p_j(x)$ *of the representation* (2.4) *of Chapter* III *are real, if the piece* Γ_0 *is of class* C^2 *and the conditions* (bd) *here take the form* $\partial u/\partial\mu + \sigma(x)u|_{\Gamma_0} = 0$ $(\sigma \in C^1(\Gamma_0))$; *then each function of* $\mathfrak{D}(\mathcal{J}(\mathrm{bd}))$ *is in* $W^2_{2,\mathrm{loc}}(G_0, \Gamma_0)$ *on* $G_0 \cup \Gamma_0$ *and satisfies the* (bd) *under consideration on* Γ_0.

We verify the assertion in case 1). If $g \in \mathfrak{D}(\mathcal{J}(\mathrm{bd}))$, then $(g, L^+v)_0 = (f, v)_0$ with $f \in L_2(G)$ for all $v \in W_2^{2m}(\mathrm{bd})^+ \cap W^{2m}_{2,0}(E_n)$. In particular $(g, L^+v)_{L_2(G_0)} = (f, v)_{L_2(G_0)}$ for all $v \in W_2^{2m}(\mathrm{bd})^+$, which are equal to zero on some neighborhood of the set $G \setminus G_0$, i.e., $g \in L_2(G_0)$ and inside G_0 satisfies the equation $Lu = f \in L_2(G_0)$ up to Γ_0. By Theorem 4.6, Chapter III, $g \in W^{2m}_{2,\mathrm{loc}}(G_0, \Gamma_0)$ and satisfies (bd) on Γ_0, the required result. The proof in case 2) now requires only the use of Theorem 4.7, Chapter III. The theorem follows.

We indicate the importance of Theorem 1.2 first in the case of bounded G. Let $G_0 = G$ satisfy the conditions of the theorem. Then $\mathfrak{D}(\mathcal{J}(\mathrm{bd})) = W_2^r(\mathrm{bd}) = \mathfrak{D}(\Lambda'(\mathrm{bd}))$. But $\Lambda'(\mathrm{bd}) \subseteq \mathcal{J}(\mathrm{bd})$ and therefore we now have $\Lambda'(\mathrm{bd}) = \mathcal{J}(\mathrm{bd}) = (\Lambda^{+\prime}(\mathrm{bd})^+)^*$.

This, on one hand, shows that $\Lambda'(\mathrm{bd})$ is closed, and on the other it gives a rule for computation of $((\Lambda^+(\text{bd})^+)')^*$. It is clear that the conditions of the theorem are satisfied for L^+, $(\text{bd})^+ = (\text{bd})$. Therefore $\Lambda^{+\prime}(\text{bd})^+$ is also closed. We thus obtain

Corollary 1.[1] *Let the requirements of Theorem* 1.2 *be satisfied with G bounded and $G_0 = G$. Then $\Lambda'(\text{bd})$ and $\Lambda^{+\prime}(\text{bd})^+$ are closed (and therefore are equal respectively to $\Lambda(\text{bd})$ and $\Lambda^+(\text{bd})^+$) and*

$$(\Lambda'(\text{bd}))^* = \Lambda^{+\prime}(\text{bd})^+, \quad (\Lambda^{+\prime}(\text{bd})^+)^* = \Lambda'(\text{bd}). \tag{1.2}$$

In the case of unbounded G, a similar relation does not generally hold (since the result that $\mathfrak{D}(\bar{\mathbb{J}}(\text{bd})) = W_2^r(\text{bd})$ is already impossible). However, the preceding arguments show that with L, Γ, and (bd) as indicated in Theorem 1.2, the bulk of the proof of the equalities (1.2) is connected with the behavior of L, Γ and (bd) at ∞. We note that without requiring some boundedness condition at ∞, these equations are not valid. In this connection another corollary is useful.

Corollary 2. *Let the requirements of Theorem* 1.2 *be satisfied for an arbitrary bounded subregion G_0 of G, where G is unbounded. Then $\mathbb{J}(\text{bd})u = Lu$ ($u \in \mathfrak{D}(\mathbb{J}(\text{bd}))$), and $\mathfrak{D}(\mathbb{J}(\text{bd}))$ consists of functions of $W_{2,\text{loc}}^r(G, \Gamma) \cap L_2(G)$ which satisfy* (bd) *and are such that $Lu \in L_2(G)$.*

Indeed, let u have the indicated form. For arbitrary $v \in \mathfrak{D}(\Lambda^{+\prime}(\text{bd})^+) = W_2^r(\text{bd})^+ \cap W_{2,0}^r(E_n)$ we have $(\Lambda^{+\prime}(\text{bd})^+ v, u)_0 = (L^+ v, u)_0 = (v, Lu)_0$, i.e., $u \in (\Lambda^{+\prime}(\text{bd})^+)^* = \mathbb{J}(\text{bd})$ and $\mathbb{J}(\text{bd})\,u = Lu$. Conversely, let $u \in \mathfrak{D}(\mathbb{J}(\text{bd}))$. By Theorem 1.2, $u \in W_{2,\text{loc}}^r(G, \Gamma)$ and satisfies (bd). Therefore for the introduced v, $(Lu, v)_0 = (u, L^+v)_0 = (u, \Lambda^{+\prime}(\text{bd})^+ v)_0 = (\mathbb{J}(\text{bd})u, v)_0$, i.e., $Lu = \mathbb{J}(\text{bd})\,u \in L_2(G)$. The corollary is established.

As already mentioned, Theorem 1.2 and its corollaries are valid for general elliptic L and more general (bd). It is sufficient to satisfy the following assumption on the increment in smoothness. *If $u \in L_2(G_0)$ satisfies the equation $Lu = f \in L_2(G_0)$ inside G_0 up to Γ_0 then $u \in W_{2,\text{loc}}^r(G_0, \Gamma_0)$ and satisfies* (bd) *on* Γ_0 (G_0 and Γ_0 are as in Theorem 1.2 and (bd) are given by means of the differential expressions B_1 on Γ and therefore are local in nature). From what was said in §6.12 of Chapter III, it is clear that this assumption holds for L and (bd) as described.

---

1) This corollary is another form of Lemma 3.9, Chapter III.

3. Selfadjoint operators induced by formally selfadjoint elliptic expressions in bounded regions. Let $L = L^+$ be such an expression of order r defined in the bounded region and satisfying the usual requirements of smoothness of the coefficients. Let $(\mathrm{bd}) = (\mathrm{bd})^+$ be some formally selfadjoint boundary conditions. We construct the operator $\Lambda'(\mathrm{bd}) = Lu$, $u \in \mathfrak{D}(\Lambda'(\mathrm{bd})) = W_2^r(\mathrm{bd})$ on $L_2(G)$. Obviously $\Lambda'(\mathrm{bd})$ is Hermitian. Then the following theorem is a consequence of Corollary 1 of the preceding subsection.

Theorem 1.3. *Let the strongly elliptic expression $L = L^+$ of order $r = 2m$ be given in the bounded region G with coefficients $a_\alpha(x) \in C^{|\alpha|+p}(G \cup \Gamma)$ $(p \geq m)$. The boundary Γ is assumed to be of class C^{2m+p} and* (bd) *on Γ are null* $(D^\alpha u|_\Gamma = 0,\ |\alpha| \leq m-1)$. *Then the operator $\Lambda'(\mathrm{bd}) = \Lambda(\mathrm{bd})$ is selfadjoint.*

If $L = L^+$ is a strongly elliptic expression of second order with $a_\alpha(x) \in C^{|\alpha|}$ $(G \cup \Gamma)$, if Γ is of class C^2 and if (bd) *have the form $\partial u/\partial\mu + \sigma(x)u|_\Gamma = 0$ ($\sigma \in C^1(\Gamma)$ is real), then $\Lambda'(\mathrm{bd}) = \Lambda(\mathrm{bd})$ is selfadjoint.*

We point out that in the formulation of the second part of the theorem the requirement that $p_j(x)$ is real is missing, being replaced by the condition on L and (bd) that $\sigma(x)$ is real. It is clear that the theorem mentioned at the end of subsection 2 also remains valid for these (bd).

4. Questions of selfadjointness in the case of an unbounded region. Let L be a formally selfadjoint expression of order r on the unbounded region G with the usual smoothness requirements on the coefficients $a_\alpha(x)$; let $(\mathrm{bd}) = (\mathrm{bd})^+$ on Γ. We construct the corresponding strong operator $\Lambda(\mathrm{bd})$, the closure of the operator $\Lambda'(\mathrm{bd})u = Lu$, $\mathfrak{D}(\Lambda'(\mathrm{bd})) = W_2^r(\mathrm{bd}) \cap W_{2,0}^r(E_n)$. The operators $\Lambda'(\mathrm{bd})$ and $\Lambda(\mathrm{bd})$ are Hermitian. But even with smooth a_α and Γ, $\Lambda(\mathrm{bd})$ will not, in general, be selfadjoint. As mentioned above, the behavior of L, Γ, and (bd) at ∞ is crucial here. Therefore for the construction of eigenfunction expansions in what follows we will use a selfadjoint extension of $\Lambda(\mathrm{bd})$.

We will not consider the finding of criteria for the selfadjointness of $\Lambda(\mathrm{bd})$ as a goal in itself, but for now we only show that by changing L, Γ, and (bd) anywhere but at ∞ we do not affect the selfadjointness (some criteria will however be introduced in subsections 5–7). The arguments used carry over to general (bd).

Lemma 1.1. *Let $L = L^+$ and $(\mathrm{bd}) = (\mathrm{bd})^+$ be such that the assumptions on increase in smoothness indicated at the end of subsection 2 are satisfied for an arbitrary bounded subregion $G_0 \subset G$; G unbounded. A necessary and sufficient* *condition for the operator* $\Lambda(\text{bd})$ *to be selfadjoint is that* (bd) *are satisfied for arbitrary* $u, v \in W^r_{2,\text{loc}}(G, \Gamma) \cap L_2(G)$ *which are such that* $Lu, Lv \in L_2(G)$ *with*

$$(Lu, v)_0 = (u, Lv)_0. \tag{1.3}$$

By Corollary 2 of Theorem 1.2, the relation (1.3) means that $(\Pi(\text{bd})\, u, v)_0 = (u, \Pi(\text{bd})\, v)_0\ (u, v\mathfrak{D}(\Pi(\text{bd})))$, i.e., it is equivalent to the symmetry $\Lambda^*(\text{bd}) = \Pi(\text{bd})$. But the symmetry of $\Lambda^*(\text{bd})$ is a necessary and sufficient condition for the selfadjointness of $\Lambda(\text{bd})$. The lemma follows.

Theorem 1.4. *Let the elliptic expressions* $L_j = L_j^+$ *be given on the unbounded regions* $G_j \subseteq E_n$ *with the usual smoothness conditions on the coefficients, with* $(\text{bd})_j = (\text{bd})_j^+$ $(j = 1, 2)$ *on the boundaries* Γ_j. *Assume that for* $j = 1, 2$ *the requirements of increase in smoothness formulated at the end of subsection* 2 *are met. Suppose there is a sphere* $U \subseteq E_n$ *such that* $G_1 \cap (E_n \setminus U) = G_2 \cap (E_n \setminus U)$ *and that on this region* L_1 *and* L_2 *coincide;* $(\text{bd})_1$ *and* $(\text{bd})_2$ *coincide on the piece of the boundary* $\Gamma_1 \cap (E_n \setminus U) = \Gamma_2 \cap (E_n \setminus U)$. *Then* $\Lambda_1(\text{bd})_1$ *and* $\Lambda_2(\text{bd})_2$ *are either both selfadjoint or both fail to be selfadjoint.*

Proof. As in the case of a second order expression, if G is bounded and L is of order r and such that $a_\alpha \in C^{|\alpha|}(G \cup \Gamma)$ then one may write Green's formula (see (1.18) of Chapter II)

$$\int_G Lu \cdot \bar{v}\, dx - \int_G u\overline{L^+ v}\, dx = \int_\Gamma \mathfrak{R}[u, v]\, dx \quad (u, v \in W_2^r(G)), \tag{1.4}$$

where $\mathfrak{R}[u, v]$ is some bilinear form in $D^\alpha u|_\Gamma$ and $D^\alpha v|_\Gamma$ $(|\alpha| \leq r - 1)$, obtained by integrating by parts. The coefficients of this form depend only on the coefficients of L near Γ. We denote by G_R, the intersection of G from Lemma 1.1 with the sphere $|x| \leq R$, and by Γ_R the piece of the boundary of G_R which is not part of Γ. Using (1.4) we find that (1.3) is equivalent to the relation

$$\lim_{R\to\infty} \int_{G_R} (Lu \cdot \bar{v} - u\overline{Lv})\, dx = \lim_{R\to\infty} \int_{\Gamma_R} \mathfrak{R}[u, v]\, dx = 0, \tag{1.5}$$

and the theorem easily follows.

5. Selfadjointness of an operator, arising from a formally selfadjoint differential expression with constant coefficients in the space $L_2(E_n)$. In this and in the following subsection we will consider questions of selfadjointness for expressions which are not necessarily elliptic. Let

$$Lu = \sum_{|\alpha| \leq r} a_\alpha \partial^\alpha u, \ \partial^\alpha = \partial_1^{\alpha_1} \ldots \partial_n^{\alpha_n}, \ \partial_j = \frac{1}{i} D_j \ (j = 1, \ldots, n) \tag{1.6}$$

have constant coefficients. (Now it is convenient to use the notation ∂_j.) Since $L^+ = \overline{L}$, the condition of formal selfadjointness of L implies that the a_α are real.

Theorem 1.5. *The minimal operator, induced on* $L_2(E_n)$ *by expression* (1.6) *with real constant coefficients is always selfadjoint. Its spectrum consists of the set of values of the polynomial* $L(\xi) = \Sigma_{|\alpha| \leq r} a_\alpha \xi^\alpha$ $(\xi \in E_n)$.

As a preliminary we recall some facts about the space S (see for example I. M. Gel'fand, G. E. Šilov [1], Chapter I, §2, Russian pp. 31–32). This space is the set of functions $u(x) \in C^\infty(E_n)$ which along with their derivatives decrease faster than any power of x: $|x^\alpha (D^\beta u)(x)| \leq C_{\alpha\beta} < \infty$ $(x \in E_n)$ for arbitrary vectors, α, β with nonnegative integer coordinates. Convergence in S is introduced as follows: the sequence $u_\nu \longrightarrow 0$ if the estimates $|x^{\alpha_0} (D^{\beta_0} u_\nu)(x)| \leq C_{\alpha_0\beta_0} < \infty$ $(x \in E_n;\ \nu = 1, 2, \cdots)$ hold for some α_0, β_0, with $C_{\alpha_0\beta_0}$ independent of ν and if $u_\nu(x) \longrightarrow 0$ uniformly along with all of their derivatives on bounded sets. It is not difficult to show that $C_0^\infty(E_n)$ is dense in S. The ordinary Fourier transformation carries S $(S \subset L_2(E_n))$ into itself, i.e., $\widetilde{S} = S$.

Proof of the theorem. The minimal operator Λ is the closure of the operator $\Lambda' u = Lu$, where $u \in \mathfrak{D}(\Lambda') = C_0^\infty(E_n)$, in $L_2(E_n)$. Applying the Fourier transform to the functions $u(x)$, $u(x) \longrightarrow \widetilde{u}(\xi)$, we obtain that the Fourier-equivalent of the operator Λ', is the operator $\widetilde{\Lambda}'$ in $L_2(E_n)$, defined on $\mathfrak{D}(\widetilde{\Lambda}') = \widetilde{C_0^\infty(E_n)}$ and satisfying $(\widetilde{\Lambda}' \widetilde{u})(\xi) = L(\xi) \widetilde{u}(\xi)$. The Fourier-equivalent $\widetilde{\Lambda}$ of the operator Λ is defined as the closure of the operator $\widetilde{\Lambda}'$. In this sense, $\widetilde{\Lambda}$ is the operator, multiplication by the polynomial $L(\xi)$.

In the space $L_2(E_n)$ of functions of x, we define the operator $\Lambda'' \supset \Lambda'$: $\Lambda'' u = Lu$, $u \in \mathfrak{D}(\Lambda'') = S \supset C_0^\infty(E_n)$. Obviously $\Re(\Lambda'') \subseteq S$. It follows from the density of $C_0^\infty(E_n)$ in S, that $\Lambda'' \subset \overline{\Lambda'} = \Lambda$. Therefore $\overline{\Lambda''} = \Lambda$. The Fourier-equivalent $\widetilde{\Lambda}''$ of the operator Λ'' coincides with the operator of multiplication by the polynomial $L(\xi)$ on S, i.e., $(\widetilde{\Lambda}'' \widetilde{u})(\xi) = L(\xi) \widetilde{u}(\xi)$, $\widetilde{u} \in S$; $\Re(\widetilde{\Lambda}'') \subseteq S$. $\widetilde{\Lambda}$ may be considered as the closure of the operator $\widetilde{\Lambda}''$.

For the completion of the proof it is sufficient to show that for $z \overline{\in} \{L(\xi), \xi \in E_n\}$ $\Re(\widetilde{\Lambda}'' - zE) = S$ and $\|(\widetilde{\Lambda}'' - zE) u\|_0 \geq \epsilon \|u\|_0$ $(\epsilon > 0;\ u \in S)$. The first relation follows from the fact that the functions of S may be divided by a nonzero polynomial, yielding another function of S. The second is a consequence of an elementary estimate. The theorem follows.

We note that the interpretation of the operator Λ in the proof (in particular, its Fourier-equivalent) as the closure of the operator of multiplication by $L(\xi)$ on S, is useful in itself.

6. Selfadjointness of operators which are "almost selfadjoint". We first present one simple method of establishing the selfadjointness of operators in a general Hilbert space H with scalar product $(\cdot,\cdot)$ and norm $\|\cdot\|$. Let A and B be two arbitrary operators in H. By $A+B$ we will mean the operator defined by the equation $(A+B)f = Af + Bf$ for $f \in \mathfrak{D}(A+B) = \mathfrak{D}(A) \cap \mathfrak{D}(B)$, and by AB, the operator defined by $(AB)f = A(Bf)$ for all f such that $f \in \mathfrak{D}(B)$ and $Bf \in \mathfrak{D}(A)$ (these f constitute $\mathfrak{D}(AB)$). The following simple relations are well known.

a) If $\mathfrak{D}(A+B)$ is dense in H, then $(A+B)^* \supseteq A^* + B^*$;

b) If $\mathfrak{D}(AB)$ is dense in H, then $(AB)^* \supseteq B^*A^*$;

c) If $\mathfrak{D}(A)$ is dense in H, then $(A+zE)^* = A^* + \bar{z}E$.

For completeness we present the proof again of a well-known lemma.

Lemma 1.2. *Let $\mathfrak{D}(A)$ be dense in H, and let C be a bounded operator on all of H. Then*

$$(A+C)^* = A^* + C^*, \quad (CA)^* = A^*C^*. \tag{1.7}$$

Proof. According to a), $(A+C)^* \supseteq A^* + C^*$; we establish the reverse inclusion. Let $f \in \mathfrak{D}((A+C)^*)$. Then for arbitrary $g \in \mathfrak{D}(A+C) = \mathfrak{D}(A)$, $((A+C)g, f) = (g, (A+C)^*f)$. On the other hand, $((A+C)g, f) = (Ag, f) + (Cg, f) = (Ag, f) + (g, C^*f)$. Therefore, $(Ag, f) = (g, (A+C)^*f) - (g, C^*f) = (g, (A+C)^*f - C^*f)$ for all $g \in \mathfrak{D}(A)$, and consequently $f \in \mathfrak{D}(A^*)$ and $A^*f = (A+C)^*f - C^*f$. In other words, $\mathfrak{D}((A+C)^*) \subseteq \mathfrak{D}(A^*) = \mathfrak{D}(A^* + C^*)$ and $(A+C)^*f = A^*f + C^*f$ $(f \in \mathfrak{D}((A+C)^*))$, i.e., $(A+C)^* \subseteq A^* + C^*$. This establishes the first equation in (1.7).

We establish the second one. By b) $(CA)^* \supseteq A^*C^*$; we establish the reverse inclusion. Let $f \in \mathfrak{D}((CA)^*)$, then for arbitrary $g \in \mathfrak{D}(CA) = \mathfrak{D}(A)$, $((CA)g, f) = (g, (CA)^*f)$; on the other hand, $((CA)g, f) = (Ag, C^*f)$. Therefore, $(Ag, C^*f) = (g, (CA)^*f)$ for all $g \in \mathfrak{D}(A)$ and consequently $C^*f \in D(A^*)$ and $A^*(C^*f) = (CA)^*f$. In other words $\mathfrak{D}((CA)^*) \subseteq \mathfrak{D}(A^*C^*)$ and $(CA)^*f = A^*C^*f$ $(f \in \mathfrak{D}((CA)^*))$, i.e., $(CA)^* \subseteq A^*C^*$. The second equation and consequently the lemma follows.

Corollary. *If A and C are selfadjoint operators and C is bounded, then $A + C$ is selfadjoint.*

A verification of selfadjointness based on the following lemma is possible.

Lemma 1.3. *Let A and B be two operators on H, where $\mathfrak{D}(A)$ is dense in H, $\mathfrak{D}(A) \subseteq \mathfrak{D}(B)$ and $A+B$ is Hermitian. If for some $z \neq \bar{z}$ there is a bounded operator $(A - zE)^{-1}$, defined on all of H and such that*

$$\| Bf \| \leqslant \alpha \| (A - zE) f \| \qquad (0 \leqslant \alpha < 1; f \in \mathfrak{D}(A)), \tag{1.8}$$

then the closure of the operator $A+B$ is selfadjoint.

Proof. It follows from (1.8) that the operator $C = B(A - zE)^{-1}$ is defined on all of H, is continuous, and is such that $\|C\| \leq \alpha < 1$. Also from the existence of $(A - zE)^{-1}$ it follows that the null space of the operator $(A - zE)^*$ consists only of the zero vector. From b) and the second inequality in (1.7) we have

$$(A+B)^* = ((A - zE) + B + zE)^* = ((A - zE) + B)^* + \bar{z}E = ((E + C)$$
$$\times (A - zE))^* + \bar{z}E = (A - zE)^* (E + C)^* + \bar{z}E = (A - zE)^* (E + C^*) + \bar{z}E. \tag{1.9}$$

Let $\phi \in H$ be such that $(A+B)^*\phi = \bar{z}\phi$. According to (1.9) $(A - zE)^*(E + C^*)\phi = 0$, and consequently $(E + E^*)\phi = 0$. But $\|C^*\| = \|C\| < 1$ so therefore $\phi = 0$. Thus $(A+B)^*$ has no nonreal eigenvalues, i.e., the closure of $A+B$ is selfadjoint. The lemma follows.

We will say that a polynomial $Q(\xi)$ is respectively strong or weak with respect to the polynomial $P(\xi)$ if the equations

$$\lim_{|\xi| \to \infty} \frac{|Q(\xi)|}{1 + |P(\xi)|} = 0 \quad \text{or} \quad \lim_{|\xi| \to \infty} \int\limits_{|\xi - \eta| < 1} \frac{|Q(\eta)|^2}{1 + |P(\eta)|^2} d\eta = 0 \tag{1.10}$$

hold for all $\xi \in E_n$. It is clear that the strong condition implies the weak. Even if Q is weak with respect to P the degree of Q is less than the degree of P.

Theorem 1.6. *Let a formally selfadjoint differential expression L, satisfying the usual smoothness restrictions on the coefficients, take the form*

$$Lu = L_0 u + c_1(x) L_1 u + \ldots + c_q(x) L_q u, \tag{1.11}$$

where $L_0, \cdots, L_q$ are expressions with constant coefficients of type (1.6); the coefficients of L_0 are assumed to be real. Each of the polynomials $L_j(\xi)$ $(j = 1, \cdots, q)$ is either strong with respect to $L_0(\xi)$, in which case the corresponding coefficient $C_j(x)$ is bounded in E_n, or weak, in which case $c_j(x)$ is such that the derivatives $D^\alpha c_j$ $(|\alpha| \leq n+1)$ are in $L_1(E_n)$.

With these assumptions, the minimal operator induced on $L_2(E_n)$ by the expression L is selfadjoint.

Proof. Let Λ, Λ_0 and B denote minimal operators induced by the expressions L, L_0 and $\sum_{j=1}^{q} c_j(x) L_j$. By Theorem (1.5) Λ_0 is selfadjoint and therefore $(\Lambda_0 - zE)^{-1}$ exists for arbitrary nonreal z. Assume that we have verified the equation

$$\left\| \sum_{j=1}^{q} c_j L_j u \right\|_0 \leqslant \alpha \| (L_0 - zE) u \|_0 \qquad (0 \leqslant \alpha < 1; u \in C_0^\infty(E_n)) \tag{1.12}$$

for some nonreal z. It follows that $\mathfrak{D}(\Lambda_0) \subseteq \mathfrak{D}(B)$ and that the remaining hypotheses of Lemma 1.3 are satisfied with $A = \Lambda_0$ and the indicated B. Then the closure of $\Lambda_0 + B$ will coincide with Λ and will be selfadjoint, and the theorem will be proved.

To establish (1.12) it is sufficient to verify that for each $j = 1, 2, \cdots, q$, if an arbitrary $\epsilon > 0$ is chosen, there is a $\tau_\epsilon > 0$ such that

$$\| c_j L_j u \|_0 \leqslant \varepsilon \| (L_0 - i\tau E) u \|_0 \qquad (u \in C_0^\infty(E_n); \tau > \tau_\varepsilon). \tag{1.13}$$

If $L_j(\xi)$ is strong subject to $L_0(\xi)$ then the assertion (1.13) is trivial: using the Fourier transformation $u \longrightarrow \tilde{u}$ we obtain

$$\| c_j L_j u \|_0 \leqslant C \| L_j u \|_0 = C \left(\int_{E_n} | L_j(\xi) |^2 | \tilde{u}(\xi) |^2 d\xi \right)^{\frac{1}{2}} \tag{1.14}$$

$$(C = \sup_{x \in E_n} | c_j(x) |).$$

The right side of (1.13), equal to the integral in (1.14), is such that only $L_j(\xi)$ depends on $L_0(\xi) - i\tau$. But by (1.10) with $|\xi| \geq R$, for $R > 0$, sufficiently large and $\tau \geq 1$, $|L_j(\xi)| \leq (\epsilon/C) |L_0(\xi) - i\tau|$. Thus $|L_j(\xi)| \leq (\epsilon/C) |L_0(\xi) - i\tau|$ $(\xi \in E_n)$ with $\tau > \tau_\epsilon > 0$. From here (1.13) follows easily.

Now let $L_j(\xi)$ be weak with respect to $L_0(\xi)$. Again writing (1.13) for $u \in S$, and then taking the Fourier transform, we see that (1.13) is equivalent to the relation $\| A L_j(\xi) / (L_0(\xi) - i\tau) \| \longrightarrow 0$ as $\tau \longrightarrow +\infty$, where A is the operator of convolution with $\tilde{c}_j(\xi)$, and $L_j(\xi) / L_0(\xi) - i\tau$ is the operator of multiplication by this function (the operators are taken to be defined on the space $L_2(E_n)$).

Passing to the adjoint operator, we find that it is necessary to show that the norm of the following integral operator tends to zero in $L_2(E_n)$ as $\tau \longrightarrow +\infty$:

$$(K_\tau f)(\xi) = \frac{1}{\sqrt{(2\pi)^n}} \int_{E_n} \frac{\overline{L_j(\xi)}}{L_0(\xi) + i\tau} \overline{\tilde{c}_j(\eta - \xi)} f(\eta)\, d\eta \qquad (f \in L_2(E_n)). \tag{1.15}$$

Denoting $l(\xi) = (2\pi)^{-n/2}\overline{L_j(\xi)}/(L_0(\xi) + i\tau)$, since $|\tilde{c}_j(\xi)| \le C_1(1+|\xi|^{n+1})^{-1}$ $(\xi \in E_n)$ by the form of c_j, we obtain

$$\|K_\tau f\|^2_{L_2(E_n)} = \int_{E_n} \left| l(\xi) \int_{E_n} \overline{\tilde{c}_j(\eta - \xi)} f(\eta)\, d\eta \right|^2 d\xi \leqslant \int_{E_n} \Bigl(|l(\xi)|^2 \cdot \int_{E_n} |\tilde{c}_j(\eta - \xi)|\, d\eta$$

$$\times \int_{E_n} |\tilde{c}_j(\eta - \xi)|\, |f(\eta)|^2 d\eta \Bigr) d\xi \leqslant C_2 \int_{E_n} \left(\int_{E_n} |l(\xi)|^2 |\tilde{c}_j(\eta - \xi)|\, d\xi \right) |f(\eta)|^2 d\eta$$

$$\leqslant C_2 \sup_{\eta \in E_n} \left(\int_{E_n} |l(\xi)|^2 |\tilde{c}_j(\eta - \xi)|\, d\xi \right) \cdot \|f\|^2_{L_2(E_n)}$$

$$\leqslant C_3 \sup_{\eta \in E_n} \left(\int_{E_n} \frac{|l(\xi)|^2}{1 + |\eta - \xi|^{n+1}}\, d\xi \right) \cdot \|f\|^2_{L_2(E_n)},$$

and consequently

$$\|K_\tau\|^2 \leqslant C_3 \sup_{\eta \in E_n} \left(\int_{E_n} \frac{|l(\xi)|^2}{1 + |\xi - \eta|^{n+1}}\, d\xi \right).$$

But $(1+|\xi|^{n+1})^{-1} \le C_4 \int_{|t|<1} (1+|\xi - t|^{n+1})^{-1} dt$ $(\xi \in E_n)$ and therefore for arbitrary $\eta \in E_n$,

$$\int_{E_n} \frac{|l(\xi)|^2}{1 + |\xi - \eta|^{n+1}}\, d\xi \leqslant C_4 \int_{E_n} \int_{|t|<1} \frac{|l(\xi)|^2}{1 + |\xi - \eta - t|^{n+1}}\, dt\, d\xi$$

$$= C_4 \int_{E_n} \left(\frac{1}{1 + |s|^{n+1}} \int_{|t|<1} |l(\eta + t + s)|^2 dt \right) ds \leqslant C_5 \sup_{s \in E_n} \int_{|t|<1} |l(s+t)|^2 dt$$

$$= C_6 \sup_{s \in E_n} \int_{|t|<1} \frac{|L_j(s+t)|^2}{|L_0(s+t)|^2 + \tau^2}\, dt.$$

Thus $\|K_\tau\|^2 \le C_3 C_6 \sup_{s \in E_n} \int_{|\xi - s|<1} (|L_j(\xi)|^2/(|L_0(\xi)|^2 + \tau^2))\, d\xi$. By the definition of relative weakness, (1.10), the last expression may be made as small as we please, by increasing τ. So $\|K_\tau\| \to 0$ as $\tau \to \infty$ and the theorem follows.

It follows from the Corollary to Lemma 1.2 that if L satisfies the conditions of Theorem 1.6, then the expression $Lu + c(x)u$ is real and bounded, where $c(x) \in C(E_n)$, and that the induced minimal operator on $L_2(E_n)$ is selfadjoint.

Of the important applications of Theorem 1.6 we will limit ourselves to the following. *Let*

$$Lu = \sum_{|\alpha| \leqslant r} a_\alpha(x) D^\alpha u \tag{1.16}$$

be a formally selfadjoint elliptic expression on E_n, *the coefficients of which satisfy the usual smoothness restrictions. If the highest order coefficients* $a_\alpha(|\alpha| = r)$ *are constants, and the remaining* $a_\alpha(x)$ *are bounded, then the corresponding minimal operator* Λ *is selfadjoint in* $L_2(E_n)$. In fact, from the equation $L^+ = L$, it follows that $a_\alpha(|\alpha| = r)$ is real. But then by (1.3), Chapter III, $r = 2m$ is even and $|\Sigma_{|\alpha|=2m} a_\alpha \xi^\alpha| \geq \epsilon |\xi|^{2m}$ $(\epsilon > 0;\ \xi \in E_n)$. Set $L_0 = \Sigma_{|\alpha|=2m} a_\alpha D^\alpha$, $L_\alpha = D^\alpha(|\alpha| < 2m)$. The expression L is written in the form (1.11) where $L_j(\xi)$ will be strong relative to $L_0(\xi)$, and $C_j(x)$, bounded. Thus, our assertion follows from Theorem 1.6.

One may show (we do not) that selfadjointness of Λ occurs even when the high order coefficients in (1.16) are not constant, but bounded.

We further note, that it is possible to show that the integral operator (1.15) is completely continuous, if we assume only that the derivatives $D^\alpha c_j$ are in $L_1(E_n)$ for all $|\alpha| \leq \max(n+1, r_j)$, where r_j is the order of the expression L_j. Consequently, it is easy to conclude that *the limit spectrum*[1] *of the minimal operator* Λ *on* $L_2(E_n)$ *corresponding to* (1.11), *coincides with the set of values of the polynomial* $L_0(\xi)$ $(\xi \in E_n)$, *if all of the* $L_j(\xi)$ $(j = 1, 2, \cdots, q)$ *are weak relative to* $L_0(\xi)$, *and* $C_j(x)$ *has the behavior here indicated at* ∞.

In particular, *the limit spectrum of the operator* Λ *corresponding to* $Lu = L_0 u + c(x)u$ *will coincide with the set of values of* $L_0(\xi)$ $(\xi \in E_n)$ *if* 1 *is weak relative to the polynomial* $L_0(\xi)$ *and* $D^\alpha c \in L_1(E_n)$ *for* $|\alpha| \leq n+1$.

If $L_0 = -\Delta$ (i.e., L is a Schrödinger expression), then 1 is obviously strong, and hence weak, relative to $(-\Delta)(\xi) = \xi_1^2 + \cdots + \xi_n^2$, and therefore, by the

---

1) We recall that a point λ belongs to the limit spectrum of the operator A, by definition, if there exists a bounded nonprecompact sequence $f_n \in \mathfrak{D}(A)$ such that $(A - \lambda E) f_n \to 0$.

indicated behavior of $c(x)$, the limit spectrum of the operator Λ of the Schrödinger expression coincides with the half-line $[0, \infty)$ (in actuality, the restrictions on $c(x)$ may be somewhat weakened). Moreover, if L_0 is not elliptic, then 1 will not in general be strong with respect to $L_0(\xi)$ (for example, 1 is not strong relative to the polynomial $L_0(\xi) = \xi_1^2 - \xi_2^2$ corresponding to $L_0 = -D_1^2 + D_2^2$). In this connection, the general question of the case where 1 is weak relative to $L_0(\xi)$ arises. It turns out that if $L_0(\xi)$ is a complete polynomial (i.e., a polynomial which actually depends on all of the variables; see p. 277), then 1 will be weak relative to $L_0(\xi)$, and conversely.

In conclusion, we introduce an example of a selfadjoint operator where the test of selfadjointness is not based on Lemma 1.2. Other such examples were introduced earlier in §2.3, Chapter IV.

We consider the formal selfadjoint expression on E_n $(n \geq 1)$,

$$Lu = ia(x)D_1u + \left(b(x) + \frac{i}{2}(D_1a)(x)\right)u,$$

where $a(x) \in C^1(E_n)$, $b(x) \in C(E_n)$ are real; let Λ be a corresponding minimal operator on $L_2(E_n)$. If $a(x)$, $(D_1a)(x)$ and $b(x)$ are bounded in E_n and $|a(x)| \geq \epsilon > 0$, $x \in E_n$, then Λ is selfadjoint.

For this, we denote the minimal operator induced by the expression iD_1 by Λ_0, and the operators of multiplication by $a(x)$ and $b(x) + (i/2)(D_1a)(x)$ by A and B respectively. By Theorem 1.5, Λ_0 is selfadjoint; A and B are bounded where A is selfadjoint and B^* is the operator of multiplication by $b(x) - (i/2)(D_1a)(x)$. Since $\Lambda \supseteq A\Lambda_0 + B$, then, in view of (1.7), we have $\Lambda^* \subseteq (A\Lambda_0 + B)^* = (A\Lambda_0)^* + B^* = \Lambda_0 A + B^* \subseteq \Lambda$, and consequently $\Lambda^* = \Lambda$.

7. Selfadjointness of operators and uniqueness of solutions to the Cauchy problem. We will now introduce an approach to the investigation of selfadjointness which is different from that of subsection 6. The investigation is more conveniently carried out in an abstract Hilbert space H with scalar product $(\cdot, \cdot)$ and norm $\|\cdot\|$.

Let S be a densely defined operator on H with domain $\mathfrak{D}(S)$. We consider the differential equation $(r = 1, 2, \cdots)$:

$$\frac{d^r u}{dt^r} - S^*u = 0 \qquad (0 \leqslant t < \infty). \tag{1.17}$$

By a weak solution to the equation (1.17) we mean a vector-function $u(t)$ $(0 \leq t < \infty)$ with values in H, r times weakly differentiable in t and satisfying the equation

$$\frac{d^r}{dt^r}(u(t), f) - (u(t), Sf) = \left(\frac{d^r u(t)}{dt^r}, f\right) - (u(t), Sf) = 0 \qquad (1.18)$$

$$(f \in \mathfrak{D}(S),\ 0 \leqslant t < \infty).$$

We will say that there is a unique weak solution of the Cauchy problem for (1.17) if each weak solution $u(t)$ such that $(d^\alpha u/dt^\alpha)(0) = 0$ $(\alpha = 0, \cdots, r-1)$ is equal to zero for all $t > 0$.

Theorem 1.7. *Let A be an Hermitian operator on H with equal deficiency indices. The closure of this operator is selfadjoint if one of the following is satisfied:*

1) *for both equations*

$$\frac{du}{dt} \pm (iA)^* u = 0 \qquad (0 \leqslant t < \infty) \qquad (1.19)$$

there is a unique solution to the Cauchy problem.

2) *the operator A is semi-bounded from above (i.e. $(Af, f) \leq a\|f\|^2$, $f \in \mathfrak{D}(A)$, $a < +\infty$) and the Cauchy problem for the equation*

$$\frac{du}{dt} - A^* u = 0 \ (0 \leqslant t < \infty) \quad or \quad \frac{d^2u}{dt^2} - A^* u = 0 \ (0 \leqslant t < \infty) \qquad (1.20)$$

has a unique weak solution.

Conversely, if the closure of the operator A is selfadjoint, then the weak solutions to the Cauchy problems for equations (1.19)–(1.20) *are unique (here it is even unnecessary to assume the semi-boundedness of A in case* 2).

Proof in Case 1. Suppose the closure of A is not selfadjoint. Then A has two distinct ordinary resolutions of the identity E'_λ and E''_λ. For an arbitrary $g \in \mathfrak{D}(A)$, the integral $\int_{-\infty}^{\infty} \lambda^2 d(E'_\lambda g, g)$ converges and therefore the vector-function

$$u'(t) = \int_{-\infty}^{\infty} e^{i\lambda t} dE'_\lambda g \qquad (0 \leqslant t < \infty) \qquad (1.21)$$

will be strongly differentiable and $(du'(t)/dt) = i \int_{-\infty}^{\infty} \lambda e^{i\lambda t} dE'_\lambda g$. It is easy to see that it will be a weak solution to equation (1.19) with a minus sign. In fact, for $f \in \mathfrak{D}(A) = \mathfrak{D}(iA)$ we have

$$\frac{d}{dt}(u'(t), f) - (u'(t), iAf) = \left(\frac{du'(t)}{dt}, f\right) - (u'(t), iAf) =$$

$$= \int_{-\infty}^{\infty} i\lambda e^{i\lambda t} d(E'_\lambda g, f) - \int_{-\infty}^{\infty} i e^{i\lambda t} d(E'_\lambda g, Af) = 0,$$

since $d(E'_\lambda g, Af) = d\int_{-\infty}^{\lambda} \mu d(E'_\mu g, f) = \lambda d(E'_\lambda g, f)$.

Analogously, the function $\mu''(t)$ constructed by using E''_λ in (1.21) will be a weak solution of this same equation; $u'(0) = u''(0) = g$. Therefore $u(t) = u'(t) - u''(t)$ is a weak solution of this equation, where $u(0) = 0$. By assumption $u(t) = 0$ for $t \geq 0$, and consequently

$$\int_{-\infty}^{\infty} e^{i\lambda t} d((E'_\lambda - E''_\lambda) g, h) = 0 \; (g \in \mathfrak{D}(A); h \in H; 0 \leqslant t < \infty). \qquad (1.22)$$

We now consider equation (1.19) with the plus sign. We differentiate with respect to the variable $t = -\tau$, and obtain the equation $du/d\tau - (iA)^* u = 0$ where $t \leq 0$, for which there is a unique weak solution to the Cauchy problem. Repeating the previous argument, we arrive at relation (1.22) with $t \in (-\infty, 0]$. Therefore, if we introduce the function of bounded variation $\omega(\lambda) = ((E'_\lambda - E''_\lambda)g, h)$, then $\int_{-\infty}^{\infty} e^{i\lambda t} d\omega(\lambda) = 0$ for all $t \in (-\infty, \infty)$. By the uniqueness theorem on Fourier-Stieltjes transforms, it follows that $d\omega(\lambda) = 0$ $(-\infty < \lambda < \infty)$, i.e. $((E'_\lambda - E''_\lambda) g, h) = 0$ $(g \in \mathfrak{D}(A),\; h \in H)$. Since $\mathfrak{D}(A)$ is dense in H, we conclude that $E'_\lambda = E''_\lambda$ $(-\infty < \lambda < \infty)$, a contradiction. This completes the verification of the assertion.

We examine 2) in the case of the first of the equations (1.20). Again we assume that the closure of A is not selfadjoint. Since A is semi-bounded above by the number a, then,as is well known, there are two distinct selfadjoint extensions of A, A' and A'', on H, which are semi-bounded above by the number $b \geq a$. Let E'_λ and E''_λ be resolutions of the identity corresponding to these. Instead of a function of the type (1.21) we construct the function

$$u'(t) = \int_{-\infty}^{b} e^{\lambda t} dE'_\lambda g \qquad (0 \leqslant t < \infty), \qquad (1.23)$$

where $g \in H$, and the analogous function $u''(t)$ with respect to E''_λ. Since $b < \infty$, then the integral (1.23) exists and is sufficiently regular in t; as earlier, it is easy to convince oneself that $u'(t)$ is a weak solution of the first of the equations (1.20). The same may be said of $u''(t)$. From the assumption of uniqueness of the solution of the Cauchy problem for this equation, it follows that $\int_{-\infty}^{b} e^{\lambda t} d\omega(\lambda) = 0$ $(0 \leq t < \infty)$ where the function of bounded variation $\omega(\lambda)$ is given by

$\omega(\lambda) = ((E'_\lambda - E''_\lambda)g, h)$ $(h \in H)$. By the uniqueness theorem for Laplace-Stieltjes transform, we conclude that $d\omega(\lambda) = 0$, i.e. $E'_\lambda = E''_\lambda$ $(-\infty < \lambda < \infty)$, a contradiction.

Finally we consider 2) in the case of the second of the equations (1.20). It is easy to see that if the hypotheses of the theorem are satisfied for the operator A, then they are also satisfied for arbitrary operators $A - kE$, $k \in (-\infty, \infty)$. Since selfadjointness of the closure of any of these is equivalent to selfadjointness of the closure of A, we may assume that $a < 0$.

Let E'_λ and E''_λ be constructed as in the case of the first of the equations in (1.20), with $b = 0$. We introduce the function

$$u'(t) = \int_{-\infty}^{0} \cos\sqrt{-\lambda}\, t\, dE'_\lambda g_0 + \int_{-\infty}^{0} \frac{\sin\sqrt{-\lambda}\, t}{\sqrt{-\lambda}}\, dE'_\lambda g_1 \quad (0 \leqslant t < \infty), \tag{1.24}$$

where $g \in \mathfrak{D}(A)$, and $g_1 \in \mathfrak{D}(\sqrt{-A})$. We construct the analogous function $u''(t)$ from E''_λ. Then we obviously have, in the strong sense,

$$\frac{d^2u'(t)}{dt^2} = \int_{-\infty}^{0} \lambda \cos\sqrt{-\lambda}\, t\, dE'_\lambda g_0 + \int_{-\infty}^{0} \lambda \frac{\sin\sqrt{-\lambda}\, t}{\sqrt{-\lambda}}\, dE'_\lambda g_1 \quad (0 \leqslant t < \infty); \tag{1.25}$$

the existence of these integrals follows from the fact that the inclusions $g_0 \in \mathfrak{D}(A)$, and $g_1 \in \mathfrak{D}(\sqrt{-A})$ imply that $\int_{-\infty}^{0} \lambda^2 d(E'_\lambda g_0, g_0)$ $\int_{-\infty}^{0} |\lambda|\, d(E'_\lambda g_1, g_1) < \infty$. We easily conclude from (1.25) that (1.24) is a weak solution to the second equation in (1.20) satisfying the initial conditions: $u'(0) = g_0$, $(du'/dt)(0) = g_1$. Therefore $u(t) = u'(t) - u''(t)$ will also be such a solution with $u(0) = (du/dt)(0) = 0$; by the uniqueness requirement for weak solutions to the Cauchy problem, it follows that $u(t) = 0$ for $t \geq 0$.

We denote $\omega(\lambda) = ((E'_\lambda - E''_\lambda)g, h)$, where $g \in \mathfrak{D}(A)$, $h \in H$. Then

$$\int_{-\infty}^{0} \cos\sqrt{-\lambda}\, t\, d\omega(\lambda) = 0, \quad \int_{-\infty}^{0} \sin\sqrt{-\lambda}\, t\, d\omega(\lambda) = 0 \quad (0 \leqslant t < \infty). \tag{1.26}$$

The first of these relations follows from the relation $u(t) = 0$ $(0 \leq t < \infty)$, if $u'(t)$ and $u''(t)$ are constructed with $g_0 = g \in \mathfrak{D}(A)$, and $g_1 = 0$. To obtain the second, let $g_0 = 0$ and $g_1 = \sqrt{-A}\, g \in \mathfrak{D}(\sqrt{-A})$. Then

$$0 = (u(t), h) = \int_{-\infty}^{0} \frac{\sin\sqrt{-\lambda}\, t}{\sqrt{-\lambda}}\, d\,((E'_\lambda - E''_\lambda)\, g_1, h)$$

$$= \int_{-\infty}^{0} \sin\sqrt{-\lambda}\, t\, d\,((E'_\lambda - E''_\lambda)\, g, h) = \int_{-\infty}^{0} \sin\sqrt{-\lambda}\, t\, d\omega(\lambda).$$

Thus (1.26) holds. Therefore $\int_{-\infty}^{0} e^{i\sqrt{-\lambda}t}\, d\omega(\lambda) = 0$ $(0 \leq t < \infty)$ and it follows that $d\omega(\lambda) = 0$, i.e. $E'_\lambda = E''_\lambda$ $(-\infty < \lambda < \infty)$. Again we have reached a contradiction.

Thus the first part of the theorem is proved. We turn to the proof of the second part – the establishment of the uniqueness of the solutions of equations (1.19) and (1.20) under the supposition that the closure of A is selfadjoint. We will prove two lemmas, the first of which will be used again later on.

Let Q be an operator in H with domain $\mathfrak{D}(Q)$ (possibly not dense in H). By a strong solution of the equation

$$\frac{d^r u}{dt^r} - Qu = 0 \quad (0 \leqslant t < \infty; r = 1, 2, \ldots) \tag{1.27}$$

we mean an r-times strongly differentiable vector-function $u(t)$ $(0 \leq t < \infty)$ such that $u(t) \in \mathfrak{D}(Q)$ for all t and $d^r u(t)/dt^r - Q(u(t)) = 0$. It is clear that a strong solution of the equation (1.7) will at the same time be a weak solution. Conversely, if a weak solution $u(t)$ of equation (1.7) is an r-times strongly differentiable vector-function such that $u(t) \in \mathfrak{D}(S^*)$, for each t then $u(t)$ will be a strong solution of this equation.

Lemma 1.4. *Consider equation* (1.17). *Suppose there exists a linearly dense subset* Φ *of* H *such that for arbitrary* $t_0 > 0$ *and* $\phi_0, \cdots, \phi_{r-1} \in \Phi$, *there is a strong solution* $\phi(t)$ *of the equation*

$$\frac{d^r \varphi}{dt^r} - (-1)^r S\varphi = 0 \quad (0 \leqslant t \leqslant t_0). \tag{1.28}$$

satisfying the conditions $(d^\alpha \phi/dt^\alpha)(t_0) = \phi_\alpha$ $(\alpha = 0, \cdots, r-1)$. *Then the weak solution of the Cauchy problem* (1.17) *is unique.*

Proof. The proof of the lemma depends on the formula for integration by parts for vector-functions with values in H. We derive this. Let $v(t)$ and $\psi(t)$ be respectively weak and strong derivatives of the vector-function on the segment $[0, T]$. We show first that $(v(t), \psi(t))$ is differentiable on $[0, T]$ and

$$\frac{d}{dt}(v(t), \psi(t)) = \left(\frac{dv(t)}{dt}, \psi(t)\right) + \left(v(t), \frac{d\psi(t)}{dt}\right) \quad (0 \leqslant t \leqslant T). \tag{1.29}$$

We have

$$\frac{1}{h}[(v(t+h), \psi(t+h)) - (v(t), \psi(t))] = \left(v(t+h), \frac{1}{h}[\psi(t+h) - \psi(t)]\right) + \left(\frac{1}{h}[v(t+h) - v(t)], \psi(t)\right) \quad (h \neq 0).$$

As $h \longrightarrow 0$, $v(t+h) \longrightarrow v(t)$ weakly (a weakly differentiable function is weakly continuous) so the first term tends to $(v(t), d\psi(t)/dt)$. The second term obviously converges to $(dv(t)/dt, \psi(t))$, and consequently, (1.29) follows. If we take the integral of both sides of this equation $\int_0^T \cdots dt$, we obtain the required formula:

$$\int_0^T \left(\frac{dv(t)}{dt}, \psi(t)\right) dt = (v(T), \psi(T)) - (v(0), \psi(0)) - \int_0^T \left(v(t), \frac{d\psi(t)}{dt}\right) dt. \tag{1.30}$$

We pass to the proof of the lemma itself. Let $u(t)$ be a weak solution of equation (1.17) satisfying the conditions $(d^\alpha u/dt^\alpha)(0) = 0$ $(\alpha = 0, \cdots, r-1)$; $t_0 > 0$. Let $\phi(t)$ be as in the statement of the lemma. Using formula (1.30) several times with $T = t_0$, we obtain

$$\int_0^{t_0} \left(\frac{d^r u(t)}{dt^r}, \varphi(t)\right) dt = \left(\left(\frac{d^{r-1}u}{dt^{r-1}}\right)(t_0), \varphi(t_0)\right) - \left(\left(\frac{d^{r-1}u}{dt^{r-1}}\right)(0), \varphi(0)\right)$$

$$- \int_0^{t_0} \left(\frac{d^{r-1}u(t)}{dt^{r-1}}, \frac{d\varphi(t)}{dt}\right) dt = \left(\left(\frac{d^{r-1}u}{dt^{r-1}}\right)(t_0), \varphi_0\right)$$

$$- \left(\left(\frac{d^{r-2}u}{dt^{r-2}}\right)(t_0), \left(\frac{d\varphi}{dt}\right)(t_0)\right) + \left(\left(\frac{d^{r-2}u}{dt^{r-2}}\right)(0), \left(\frac{d\varphi}{dt}\right)(0)\right)$$

$$+ \int_0^{t_0} \left(\frac{d^{r-2}u(t)}{dt^{r-2}}, \frac{d^2\varphi(t)}{dt^2}\right) dt = \dots = \left(\left(\frac{d^{r-1}u}{dt^{r-1}}\right)(t_0), \varphi_0\right) -$$

$$-\left(\left(\frac{d^{r-2}u}{dt^{r-2}}\right)(t_0), \varphi_1\right) + \ldots + (-1)^{r+1}(u(t_0), \varphi_{r-1})$$

$$-(-1)^{r+1}\int_0^{t_0}\left(u(t), \frac{d^r\varphi(t)}{dt^r}\right)dt.$$

Consequently, using (1.18) (where $f = \phi(t)$) and (1.30) we obtain

$$\left(\left(\frac{d^{r-1}u}{dt^{r-1}}\right)(t_0), \varphi_0\right) - \left(\left(\frac{d^{r-2}u}{dt^{r-2}}\right)(t_0), \varphi_1\right) + \ldots + (-1)^{r+1}(u(t_0), \varphi_{r-1})$$

$$= \int_0^{t_0}\left[\left(\frac{d^r u(t)}{dt^r}, \varphi(t)\right) + (-1)^{r+1}\left(u(t), \frac{d^r\varphi(t)}{dt^r}\right)\right]dt$$

$$= \int_0^{t_0}[(u(t), S(\varphi(t))) - (u(t), S(\varphi(t)))]\,dt = 0.$$

By the arbitrariness of $\phi_0, \cdots, \phi_{r-1} \in \Phi$ and the fact that Φ is dense in H, we conclude that $u(t_0) = 0$. The lemma follows.

Lemma 1.5. *Let $S = \zeta B$, where B is a selfadjoint operator and ζ is a complex number. For such S, equation (1.28) has a strong solution $\phi(t)$, satisfying the conditions of Lemma 1.4. Here Φ may be chosen to be $\bigcup_\Delta E(\Delta)H$, where E_λ is the resolution of the identity corresponding to B, and the union is taken over all finite intervals.*

Proof. We let $\chi_\alpha(t; \lambda)$ $(\alpha = 0, \cdots, r-1)$ denote a fundamental system of solutions of the equation $d^r u/dt^r - (-1)^r\zeta\lambda u = 0$ $(0 \le t \le t_0)$, satisfying the conditions $(d^\alpha\chi_\beta/dt^\alpha)(t_0) = \delta_{\alpha\beta}$ $(\alpha, \beta = 0, \cdots, r-1)$. Then we may set

$$\varphi(t) = \sum_{\alpha=0}^{r-1}\int_{-\infty}^{\infty}\chi_\alpha(t; \lambda)\,dE_\lambda\varphi_\alpha \quad (0 \leqslant t \leqslant t_0;\ \ \varphi_0, \ldots, \varphi_{r-1} \in \Phi = \bigcup E(\Delta)H). \tag{1.31}$$

The integral terms are taken over finite intervals in (1.31) and therefore $\phi(t)$ will be r-times strongly differentiable and for each t, $\phi(t) \in \mathfrak{D}(B) = \mathfrak{D}(S)$. It is easy to check that equation (1.28) is satisfied (similarly to the way it was done in the proof of Theorem 1.7 in case 1)). It is also clear that $\phi(t)$ satisfies the required conditions at the point $t = t_0$. The lemma follows.

From Lemmas 1.4 and 1.5 we may conclude the following result, which is more general than that formulated in both parts of Theorem 1.7: *let A be an Hermitian operator on H, the closure of which is selfadjoint, and let ζ be an arbitrary complex number. Then the weak solutions to the Cauchy problem (if they exist) for the equation*

$$\frac{d^r u}{dt^r} - \bar{\zeta} A^* u = 0 \qquad (0 \leqslant t < \infty; r = 1, 2, \ldots) \tag{1.32}$$

will be unique.

Indeed, if $u(t)$ is a weak solution to (1.32), then it will be a weak solution to the similar equation obtained by replacing A by $\bar{A}$. It now remains to apply Lemmas 1.4 and 1.5 setting $S = \zeta \bar{A}$, $B = \bar{A}$. The assertion and the theorem follow.

We note that in the first part of the theorem it is possible to omit the requirement that A have equal deficiency indices; several complications arise since the requirements of part 1) reduce to the maximality of the closure of A (in this connection see the assertion of §2.2, Chapter VIII). It is possible to establish additional results by considering equation (1.32) as a generalization of equations (1.19)–(1.20). We will not formulate these.

Applications of results of the type of Theorem 1.7, 1) will be given in §2.2, Chapter VIII. By using Theorem 1.7, 2) for the first of equations (1.20), one may establish the selfadjointness of elliptic differential operators which are similar to those considered in subsection 6; for this it is further necessary to require the known theorems on uniqueness of solutions to the Cauchy problem for parabolic equations. We will not state these results, but rather limit ourselves to the analogous facts obtained with the help of the second of the equations (1.20).

Theorem 1.8. *Let L be a formally selfadjoint elliptic differential expression of order 2, on E_n, with real coefficients $a_\alpha(x) \in C^{2+[n/2]}(E_n)$. If this expression is bounded from below on the finite functions, i.e. $(Lu, u)_0 \geq C \|u\|_0^2$ $(u \in C_0^\infty(E_n))$ for some $C > -\infty$, then the corresponding minimal operator Λ is selfadjoint in $L_2(E_n)$.*

Proof. It is convenient for us to place a minus sign in fromt of the expression L in the statement of the theorem; it is sufficient to show that the corresponding operator Λ is selfadjoint. We consider the equation

$$\frac{\partial^2 u(x, t)}{\partial t^2} - L_x[u(x, t)] = 0 \tag{1.33}$$

on the space $(x, t) \in E_n \times (-\infty, \infty)$. It will be hyperbolic: [1] every straight line in the real space passing through the origin, intersects the surface $1-\Sigma_{|\alpha|=2}\, a_\alpha(x)\xi^\alpha = 0$ in two distinct points (for each fixed $x \in E_n$). It follows from the inequality (1.3), Chapter III, that $\Sigma_{|\alpha|=2}\, a_\alpha(x)\,\xi^\alpha \geq \epsilon(x)\,|\xi|^2$ where $\epsilon(x) > 0$ $(x \in E_n)$.

We fix $t_0 > 0$. It is known that if we are given $t = t_0$ and arbitrary functions $\phi_0(x), \phi_1(x) \in C^{3+[n/2]}(E_n)$, then we may obtain the solution $u(x, t) \in C^2(E_3 \times (-\infty, t_0])$ of equation (1.33) such that $u(x, t_0) = \phi_0(x)$, $(\partial u/\partial t)(x, t_0) = \phi_1(x)$ $(x \in E_n)$. At each point (x, t) this solution depends only on the values of $\phi_0(x)$ and $\phi_1(x)$, where x is in the bounded region cut out of the space $E_n \times (-\infty, \infty)$ at the point $t = t_0$ by the characteristic cone with vertex at the point (x, t), corresponding to equation (1.33). If ϕ_0 and ϕ_1 are finite, then for each $t \leq t_0$, $u(x, t)$ will be finite.

Now it is easy to complete the proof of the theorem. We consider the second of equations (1.20), where $H = L_2(E_n)$ and $A = \Lambda'$ (i.e. $\Lambda' f = Lf$, $f \in \mathfrak{D}(\Lambda') = C_0^\infty(E_n)$); the operator Λ' is semi-bounded above by $a = -C$. The weak solutions of the Cauchy problem for this equation are unique. For this we apply Lemma 1.4, taking the equation

$$\frac{d^2\varphi}{dt^2} - \Lambda'\varphi = 0 \quad (0 \leqslant t \leqslant t_0) \tag{1.34}$$

for (1.28) where $\Phi = C_0^\infty(E_n)$. The solutions $u(x, t)$ to the equation (1.33) described above with $\phi_0, \phi_1 \in \Phi$, may be interpreted as strong solutions $\phi(t)$ to equation (1.34), since $u(x, t)$ is a finite function of x for each t. Thus the required strong solutions to equation (1.34) exist; therefore the relevant uniqueness exists, and finally by Theorem 1.7, 2), Λ' is closed, i.e. the operator Λ is selfadjoint. The theorem follows.

By combining this theorem with Theorem 1.4, it is possible to show the selfadjointness of the operator $\Lambda(\mathrm{bd})$ of the type in Theorem 1.8, but considered on a closed surface, where formal selfadjoint (bd) are given and the requirement of increase in smoothness is as indicated at the end of subsection 2. The result may be formulated easily by the reader.

In conclusion, we note that the idea of the proof of Theorem 1.8 may sometimes be carried through in the case of non-semi-bounded L. For a Schrödinger expression, for example, it is possible to use the ideas of Theorem 2.9 and then

---

1) For the facts on hyperbolic equations used above, see, for example, I. G. Petrovskiĭ [1], Chapter 2, §16 (also §2.9).

to apply the uniqueness theorems similar to Theorem 3, 18, Chapter VIII. Some bound on the coefficient $c(x)$ implies the applicability of the uniqueness theorem and therefore results in a sufficient condition for the selfadjointness of Λ.

§2. SPECTRAL THEORY OF SELFADJOINT ELLIPTIC OPERATORS

This theory will be constructed in the so-called singular case, when the region $G \subseteq E_n$ is unbounded. The simplification in the case of bounded G (regular case) is indicated in subsection 6. As earlier, all operators are considered in the space $H_0 = L_2(G)$ (unless the contrary is indicated). We will not formulate the results for the most general boundary conditions. This, however, may easily be done by the reader with the help of the considerations of §6, Chapter III.

1. **Spectral theory inside the region.** We consider the formally selfadjoint elliptic expression $L = L^+$ of order r on the unbounded region G with the usual smoothness requirements on the coefficients: $a_\alpha(x) \in C^{|\alpha|}(G \cup \Gamma)$; on Γ we define the formally selfadjoint conditions (bd) = (bd)$^+$ by requiring that $W_2^r(\text{bd}) \subset W_2^r(G)$. As mentioned in §1, the strong operator $\Lambda(\text{bd})$ is an Hermitian closed operator in $L_2(G)$. Let A be one of its selfadjoint extensions on $L_2(G)$ or on the larger space $\widetilde{L_2(G)}$ and $E(\Delta)$ its usual or generalized resolution of the identity. Here we construct the spectral resolution induced by $E(\Delta)$. In this subsection we discuss its properties inside G, so the nature of the (bd) is irrelevant.

Let $\gamma(\lambda)$ be a bounded continuous function on the spectrum of A, and let the generalized function $\gamma(A)$ of the operator A be defined by means of the integral $\gamma(A) = \int_{-\infty}^{\infty} \gamma(\lambda)dE_\lambda$. In other words, if P is an orthogonal projection operator from $\widetilde{L_2(G)}$ onto $L_2(G)$, then $\gamma(A) = P\,\widetilde{\gamma(A)}\,P$, where $\widetilde{\gamma(A)}$ is a function of A considered as an operator on $\widetilde{L_2(G)}$. As indicated on p. 351, all of the assertions of §4, Chapter V, are valid if the selfadjoint operator A on $L_2(G)$ is replaced by one on $\widetilde{L_2(G)}$; $\gamma(A)$ must be considered as a generalized function of the operator A. The application of the results of this section to our case establishes the following lemma.

Lemma 2.1. *Let* $a_\alpha(x) \in C^{2r+n+p}(G)$, $p \geq n+1$, *be the coefficients of the expression* L. *Then the generalized function* $\gamma(A)$ *of the operator* A *is an integral operator if* $\gamma(\lambda) = 1/(\lambda^N - z)$, $N = |n/2r| + 1$, $\text{Im}\, z \neq 0$. *The kernel* $C(x, y)$ *is sufficiently smooth in that* $D_x^\alpha D_y^\beta C$ ($|\alpha|, |\beta| \leq Nr + p$) *exist and are continuous in* $(x, y) \in G \times G$, $x \neq y$, *and the integrals*

$$\int_G |C(x, y)|^2 dy, \quad \int_G |C(x, y)|^2 dx \tag{2.1}$$

are bounded for x, y strictly inside G and bounded.

Proof. Since $2r + n + p \geq 2Nr + p = 2r([n/2r] + 1) + p$, then automatically $a_\alpha \in C^{2n+p}(G)$. Therefore the expression L^N makes sense and its coefficients are $b_\alpha \in C^{|\alpha|+Nr+p}(G)$. We show that for arbitrary $f \in L_2(G)$, $\gamma(A)f$ and $(\gamma(A))^* f$ are generalized solutions inside G of the equations $(L^N - zE)u = f$ and $(L^N - zE)^+ u = f$ respectively, i.e. for arbitrary $v \in C_0^\infty(G)$,

$$(\gamma(A) f, (L^N - zE)^+ v)_0 = (f, v)_0, \quad ((\gamma(A))^* f, (L^N - zE) v)_0 = (f, v)_0. \tag{2.2}$$

For, $\gamma(A) = P\widetilde{R}_z P$ where $\widetilde{R}_z$ is the resolvent of the operator A^N (in $\widetilde{L_2(G)}$). Therefore, since $(L^N)^+ = (L^+)^N = L^N$,

$$(\gamma(A) f, (L^N - zE)^+ v)_0 = (\widetilde{R}_z f, (L^N - \bar{z}E) v)_{\widetilde{L_2(G)}}$$

$$= (f, \widetilde{R}_{\bar{z}} (A^N - \bar{z}E) v)_{\widetilde{L_2(G)}} = (f, v)_{\widetilde{L_2(G)}} = (f, v)_0.$$

The second equation in (2.2) is established analogously:

$$((\gamma(A))^* f, (L^N - zE)v)_0 = (f, \gamma(A)(L^N - zE) v)_0$$

$$= (f, \widetilde{R}_z (L^N - zE) v)_{\widetilde{L_2(G)}} = (f, \widetilde{R}_z (A^N - zE) v)_{\widetilde{L_2(G)}} = (f, v)_{\widetilde{L_2(G)}} = (f, v)_0.$$

Applying Theorem 5.1, Chapter III, where L is replaced by $L^N - zE$ and R by $\gamma(A)$, we obtain that $\gamma(A)$ is an integral operator, the kernel of which has the desired smoothness. Since $L^N - zE$ is of order $Nr > n/2$, then we may apply Theorem 5.4, Chapter III, in view of which the integrals in (2.1) have the required boundedness. The lemma follows.

Since this lemma shows that A is a Carleman operator in the space $L_2(G) = L_2(G, dx)$ ($G \subseteq E_n$ is locally compact), the results of §4, Chapter V may be applied. We choose a function $p(y) \geq 1$ of class $C^\infty(G)$ such that

$$\int_G \int_G |C(x, y)|^2 \frac{1}{p(y)} dx dy < \infty; \tag{2.3}$$

$p(x)$ may increase to ∞ for x near Γ and ∞. Then, by using the chain $H_- \supseteq H_0 \supseteq H_+$ of the form

$$L_2\left(G, \frac{1}{p} dx\right) \supseteq L_2(G) \supseteq L_2(G, p dx). \tag{2.4}$$

a generalized eigenfunction expansion may be constructed.

The operator A admits an extension of the equipment: for $Д$ we take $W^r_{2,0}(G) \subset W^r_2(\mathrm{bd}) \cap W^r_{2,0}(E_n) \subset \mathfrak{D}(A)$ with the topology defined, for example, by the scalar product $(u, v)_{Д} = (u, v)_+ + (Au, Av)_+$. Since $W^r_{2,0}(G)$ is dense in $L_2(G, pdx)$ and the operator A takes $Д$ continuously into $L_2(G, pdx)$, this choice is an admissible one. It follows that each generalized eigenfunction ϕ of the operator A corresponding to the real eigenvalue λ is in this case an ordinary function $\phi(x)$ in the space $L_2(G, (1/p)\,dx)$ such that for each $v \in W^r_{2,0}(G)$

$$(\phi, (L - \lambda E)\,v)_0 = 0. \tag{2.5}$$

It is not difficult to show that the spectral kernel $\Phi = \Phi(x, y; \lambda) \in L_2(G \times G, (1/p(x)p(y))\,dxdy)$ is in each of its variables a generalized solution in G of the equation

$$L_x\Phi = \lambda\Phi, \ \overline{L_y}\Phi = \lambda\Phi, \ \text{i.e.} \ (\Phi, \ ((L^+ - \lambda E)\,v')\,(x)\,v''\,(y))_0 = 0,$$
$$(\Phi, \ v'(x)\,((L^{\oplus} - \lambda E)\,v'')\,(y))_0 = 0 \ (v', v'' \in C_0^\infty(G)). \tag{2.6}$$

In fact, since $P(\lambda)\overline{v}''$ is a generalized eigenfunction, we have $(P(\lambda)\overline{v}'', (L^+ - \lambda E)v')_0 = 0$. Using (4.4) of Chapter V, we obtain

$$(\Phi(x, \ y; \ \lambda), \ ((L^+ - \lambda E)\,v')\,(x)\,v''\,(y))_0 = \int_G\int_G \Phi(x, \ y; \ \lambda)$$
$$\times \overline{((L^+ - \lambda E)\,v')\,(x)\,v''\,(y)}\,dxdy = (P(\lambda)\,\overline{v}'', \ (L^+ - \lambda E)\,v')_0 = 0,$$

which establishes the first of the equations in (2.6). The second equation is obtained from the first by using the relation $\overline{\Phi(y, x; \lambda)} = \Phi(x, y; \lambda)$.

Lemma 2.2. *Suppose that the coefficients of L satisfy $a_\alpha(x) \in C^{|\alpha| + r + p'}(G)$, $p' \geq 1$. Then each generalized eigenfunction $\phi \in L_2(G, (1/p)dx)$ of the operator A is an element of $C^{r+p'}(G)$. The spectral kernel is sufficiently smooth: all of the derivatives $D_x^\alpha D_y^\beta \Phi_\lambda$ exist and are continuous for $|\alpha|, |\beta| \leq r + p'$.*

This lemma follows directly from Theorems 4.1 and 4.2, Chapter III.

Lemmas 2.1 and 2.2 show that all of the results of §4, Chapter V are valid in our case (the only open question is the last assertion of Theorem 4.3 and the corollaries of that theorem). Thus, we have the following basic theorem in the spectral theory of elliptic operators.

Theorem 2.1. *Let L be a formally selfadjoint elliptic expression of order r on the region G (not necessarily bounded) with coefficients*

$$a_\alpha(x) \in C^{2r+n+p}(G \cup \Gamma),\ p \geqslant n+1;$$

the formally selfadjoint boundary conditions (bd) = (bd)$^+$ *are given on* Γ *by means of the inclusion* $W_2^r(\mathrm{bd}) \subset W_2^r(G)$. *The closure of the corresponding operator* $u \longrightarrow Lu$ $(u \in W_2^r(\mathrm{bd}) \cap W_{2,0}^r(E_n))$ *is Hermitian; let* A *be a selfadjoint extension (in* $L_2(G)$ *or into a larger space),* E_λ *a corresponding (in general) generalized resolution of the identity.*

There exists a function $p(x) \in C^\infty(G)$, $p(x) \geq 1$ *(possibly becoming large for* x *near* Γ *and* ∞*) such that the chain (2.4) is suitable for a generalized eigenfunction expansion of the operator* A.

The generalized projection operator $P(\lambda)$ *(defined for* ρ*-almost all* λ*) onto a generalized eigenmanifold is an integral operator*

$$(P(\lambda)u)(x) = \int_G \Phi(x,\ y;\ \lambda)\, u(y)\, dy \quad (u \in L_2(G,\ pdx)). \tag{2.7}$$

The positive definite kernel $\Phi(x, y;\ \lambda)$ $(x, y \in G)$, *the spectral kernel of the operator* A, *is an element of* $L_2(G \times G, (1/p(x)\,p(y))\,dxdy)$ *where*

$$\|\Phi(.\ ,.\ ;\ \lambda)\|_{L_2\left(G\times G,\ \frac{1}{p(x)p(y)}dxdy\right)} \leqslant 1 \left(\text{exactly: } \int_G \frac{\Phi(x,\ x;\ \lambda)}{p(x)}\, dx = 1\right).$$

Besides this, it is sufficiently smooth (all derivatives of the form $D_x^\alpha D_y^\beta \Phi$; $|\alpha|$, $|\beta| \leq r+n+p$ *exist and are continuous) and is an eigenfunction in each of its variables:*

$$L_x\Phi(x,\ y;\ \lambda) = \lambda\Phi(x,\ y;\ \lambda),\ \overline{L}_y\Phi(x,\ y;\ \lambda) = \lambda\Phi(x,\ y;\ \lambda) \quad (x,\ y \in G). \tag{2.8}$$

Any generalized function $F(A) = \int_{-\infty}^{\infty} F(\lambda)\,dE_\lambda$ *of the operator* A, *satisfying* $|F(\lambda)| \leq C/(\lambda^{2N}-1)$, $N = [n/2r]+1$, *on the spectrum of* A *is an integral operator. The kernel* $K(x, y)$ *of this opertator may be expressed in the form of the absolutely convergent integral*

$$K(x,\ y) = \int_{-\infty}^{\infty} F(\lambda)\,\Phi(x,\ y;\ \lambda)\, d\varrho(\lambda), \tag{2.9}$$

and is itself a locally bounded function of $(x, y) \in G \times G$.

Each generalized eigenfunction $\phi \in L_2(G, (1/p)\,dx)$ *of the operator* A *is sufficiently smooth:* $\phi \in C^{r+n+p}(G)$. *The expansion of the spectral kernel in eigenfunctions*

$$\Phi(x,\ y;\ \lambda) = \sum_{\alpha=1}^{N_\lambda} \varphi_\alpha(x;\ \lambda)\,\overline{\varphi_\alpha(y;\ \lambda)}\quad (x,\ y \in G) \tag{2.10}$$

converges in the metric of $L_2(G \times G,\ (1/p(x)\,p(y))\,dxdy)$. *The series* (2.10) *converges absolutely and uniformly on every strictly bounded region* $G \times G$. *Moreover it may be differentiated term by term—derivatives of the form* $D_x^\alpha D_y^\beta$ *may be taken for* $|\alpha|,\ |\beta| \le r + n + p$, *where, as previously, the series obtained after differentiation converges absolutely and uniformly on the indicated subregion.*

It is useful to stress that $p(x)$ is chosen to satisfy a single condition: the theorem then shows that the operator $\gamma(A) = \int_{-\infty}^{\infty} (\lambda^N - z)^{-1}\, dE_\lambda$ $(N = [n/2r] + 1$, $\operatorname{Im} z \neq 0)$ is an integral operator with a Carleman kernel. The function $p(x)$ is chosen such that the integral (2.3) converges for some z and $1 \le p(x) \in C^\infty(G)$.

For the proof, it remains to establish only the fact that the series (2.10) may be differentiated. This fact follows by applying the following basic lemma several times.

Lemma 2.3. *Let* $K(x, y)$ *be a positive definite kernel which is continuous with respect to* $(x, y) \in G \times G$ *and represented in the form of the pointwise convergent series*

$$K(x,\ y) = \sum_{\alpha=1}^{\infty} \varphi_\alpha(x)\,\overline{\varphi_\alpha(y)}\quad (x,\ y \in G). \tag{2.11}$$

If each of the derivatives $(\partial^2/\partial x_j \partial y_j)\,K(x, y)$ *exist and are continuous in* (x, y), *then each of the derivatives* $(\partial/\partial x_j)\,\phi_\alpha(x)$ *exist and are continuous, and to calculate* $(\partial^2/\partial x_j \partial y_j)\,K(x, y)$, *one may differentiate the series* (2.11) *term by term. The differentiated series converges absolutely and uniformly on each bound subregion of* $G \times G$, *strictly contained in* $G \times G$.

Proof. Setting $x = y$ in (2.11) we conclude that the vector $(\phi_1(x), \phi_2(x), \cdots) \in l_2([1, \infty))$; denote this vector by e_x. From the existence and continuity of $(\partial^2/\partial x_j \partial y_j) K(x, y)$ and the equation $(e_x,\ e_y) = K(x, y)$, the existence and strong continuity of the strong derivative $\partial e_x/\partial x_j$ follows. Let δ_k $(k = 1, 2, \cdots)$ denote the orthonormal system of vectors of $l_2([1, \infty))$ of the form $\delta_k = (\delta_{k1}, \delta_{k2}, \cdots)$; evidently $\phi_\alpha(x) = (e_x,\ \delta_\alpha)$. The existence and continuity of the derivatives $(\partial/\partial x_j)\,\phi_\alpha(x) = (\partial/\partial x_j)\,(e_x,\ \delta_\alpha) = ((\partial/\partial x_j)\,e_x,\ \delta_\alpha)$ $(\alpha = 1, 2, \cdots)$ follow from the above. Moreover, we have

$$\frac{\partial^2}{\partial x_j \partial y_j} K(x, y) = \frac{\partial^2}{\partial x_j \partial y_j}(e_x, e_y) = \left(\frac{\partial}{\partial x_j} e_x, \frac{\partial}{\partial y_j} e_y\right)$$

$$= \sum_{\alpha=1}^{\infty} \left(\frac{\partial}{\partial x_j} e_x, \delta_\alpha\right) \overline{\left(\frac{\partial}{\partial y_j} e_y, \delta_\alpha\right)} = \sum_{\alpha=1}^{\infty} \frac{\partial}{\partial x_j} \varphi_\alpha(x) \cdot \frac{\partial}{\partial y_j} \overline{\varphi_\alpha(y)} \quad (x, y \in G). \tag{2.12}$$

It remains to verify that the series (2.12) converges absolutely and uniformly on each bounded subregion strictly inside $G \times G$. Since $(\partial^2/\partial x_j \partial y_j) K(x, y)$ is a positive definite continuous kernel and the expansion (2.12) holds for arbitrary (x, y), this may be verified by using Dini's theorem exactly as in the proof of Lemma 4.1, Chapter V. The lemma follows.

We make one addition to the theorem just proved concerning the smoothness of the kernel $K(x, y)$ of the operator $F(A)$. Although similar results may be proved in the general case, we limit ourselves to the case of strongly elliptic L (see the remark at the end of subsection 4 below).

Theorem 2.2. *Let the hypotheses of Theorem 2.2 hold for* p *sufficiently large, and strongly elliptic* L. *If*

$$F(\lambda) | \leqslant \frac{C}{|\lambda|^{2N+t} + 1} \quad \left(N = \left|\frac{n}{2r}\right| + 1;\ t = 0, 1, \ldots\right)$$

on the spectrum of A, *then* $K(x, y)$, *the kernel of the operator* $F(A)$, *is an element of* $W_{2,\mathrm{loc}}^{rt}(G \times G)$.

Proof. Since the coefficients of the expression L are sufficiently smooth, L^t makes sense and its coefficients are also sufficiently smooth. Let $v', v'' \in C_0^\infty(G)$. By (2.8) we have

$$(K(x, y), ((L^t)^+ v')(x) v''(y))_0 = \int_{-\infty}^{\infty} F(\lambda) \left(\int_G \int_G \Phi(x, y; \lambda) \overline{((L^+)^t v')(x)} \right.$$

$$\left. \times \overline{v''(y)}\, dx dy \right) d\varrho(\lambda) = \int_{-\infty}^{\infty} F(\lambda) \left(\int_G \int_G \lambda \Phi(x, y; \lambda) \right.$$

$$\left. \times \overline{((L^+)^{t-1} v')(x)}\, \overline{v''(y)}\, dx dy \right) d\varrho(\lambda) = \ldots$$

$$\ldots = \left(\left(\int_{-\infty}^{\infty} \lambda^t F(\lambda) \Phi(x, y; \lambda)\, d\varrho(\lambda) \right), v'(x) v''(y) \right)_0. \tag{2.13}$$

By Theorem 2.1

$$\int_{-\infty}^{\infty} \lambda^t F(\lambda)\,\Phi(x,\ y;\ \lambda)\,d\varrho(\lambda) = M(x,\ y) \in L_{2,\mathrm{loc}}G \times G).$$

Equation (2.13) shows that K is a generalized solution of the equation $L_x^t K = M$ inside $G \times G$. Analogously, we verify that $\bar{L}_y^t K = M$ inside $G \times G$. Therefore $(L_x^t + \bar{L}_y^t) K = 2M \in L_{2,\mathrm{loc}}(G \times G)$. The expression L^t and consequently $L_x^t + \bar{L}_y^t$ is strongly elliptic and of order rt (see Chapter III, §5.3) so that by Theorem 4.5, Chapter III, $K \in W_{2,\mathrm{loc}}^{rt}(G \times G)$. The theorem follows.

2. Spectral theory up to the boundary. We will discuss the behavior of the spectral kernel, of the eigenfunctions, and of expansions of type (2.10), etc. near the boundary, for the case of sufficiently nice boundary conditions. As before we limit ourselves to the simplest case, leaving the formulation for general elliptic L and general (bd) to the reader. Below, we only consider selfadjoint extensions of the operator Λ(bd) in the space $L_2(G)$; this limitation is essential.

Suppose that the conditions of Theorem 2.1 are satisfied with $r = 2m$. In addition we will suppose that there is a bounded subregion $G_0 \subseteq G$ bordering Γ on a sufficiently smooth piece Γ_0, in which L is strongly elliptic, and such that the (bd) are null on Γ_0 (we consider G_0 and not all of G in order to stress the local character of the results). Let A be a selfadjoint extension of the operator Λ(bd) in $L_2(G)$. Corollary 2 of Theorem 5.7, Chapter III obviously applies to the resolvents R_z of this operator: R_z^N is an integral operator with kernel $R(x, y)$ $(x, y \in G)$, for which the integral (2.1) is bounded when x, y ranges over a bounded region strictly inside G. These integrals are bounded in the case when $x, y \in \overline{G_0'}$ where G_0' is an arbitrary subregion of G_0 having a common boundary with G_0 only on the piece Γ_0'. In addition the smoothness conditions mentioned in Corollary 2 hold for $R(x, y)$.

We will apply the construction of §4, Chapter V, taking $Q = G \cup \Gamma_0$ and $\gamma(A) = R_z^N$.[1)] The boundedness of the second of the integrals (2.1) allows us to choose the function $p(x) \geq 1$ and satisfying (2.3) from the space $C^\infty(G \cup \Gamma_0)$. Thus, the functions of $L_2(G, (1/p)\,dx)$ are square summable near each piece Γ_0'. In what follows we choose for $Д$, the set of all functions $u \in W_2^r(G)$ which

1) As indicated on page 354, $\Phi(x, y;\ \lambda)$ and $d\rho(\lambda)$ are essentially unchanged by changing the form of the function $\gamma(\lambda)$. It is of no consequence, therefore, that now $\gamma(\lambda) = (\lambda - z)^{-N}$, which is not the same as in subsection 1.

vanish in neighborhoods of $\Gamma \backslash \Gamma_0$ and of ∞, and for Γ_0, the null boundary conditions $D^\alpha u|_{\Gamma_0} = 0$ $(|\alpha| \leq m-1)$. Now $\phi(x)$ and $\Phi(x, y; \lambda)$ will satisfy their respective equations up to Γ, and will be square summable near each piece Γ'_0. Applying Theorem 4.6, Chapter III, we conclude that they are smooth up to Γ'_0 and satisfy the null conditions. We use all of the above to formulate the following theorem.

Theorem 2.3. *Let the conditions of Theorem 2.1 be satisfied with* $r = 2m$. *Suppose there is a bounded subregion* $G_0 \subseteq G$ *bordering* Γ *on the piece* Γ_0, *of class* C^{2m+q} $(q \geq m,\ n/2)$ *and such that* L *is strongly elliptic on* $G_0 \cup \Gamma_0$, *where the coefficients* $a_\alpha(x) \in C^{|\alpha|+q}(G_0 \cup \Gamma_0)$, *and the conditions* (bd) *on* Γ_0 *are null:* $D^\alpha u|_{\Gamma_0} = 0$ $(|\alpha| \leq m-1)$. *Let* A *be a selfadjoint extension on* $L_2(G)$.

Then the function $p(x)$ *may be chosen from* $C^\infty(G \cup \Gamma_0)$ *and therefore each* $u \in L_2(G, (1/p)dx)$ *lies in* $L_{2,\mathrm{loc}}(G_0, \Gamma_0)$, *and* $U \in L_2(G \times G, (1/p(x)p(y))\,dxdy)$ *is in* $L_{2,\mathrm{loc}}(G \times G, ((G_0 \cup \Gamma_0) \times \Gamma_0) \cup (\Gamma_0 \times (G_0 \cup \Gamma_0)))$.

For fixed $x \in G$, *the spectral kernel* $\Phi(x, y; \lambda)$ *is an element of* $W^{2m+q}_{2,\mathrm{loc}}(G_0, \Gamma_0)$ $(y \in G)$ *and satisfies the null conditions*

$$(D^\beta_y \Phi)(x, y; \lambda)|_{y\in\Gamma_0} = 0, \quad |\beta| \leqslant m-1,$$

$$((D^\alpha_x \Phi)(x, y; \lambda)|_{x\in\Gamma_0} = 0, \quad |\alpha| \leqslant m-1).$$

Each generalized eigenfunction $\phi \in L_2(G, (1/p)\,dx)$ *also has these properties. The expansion* (2.10) *of the spectral kernel in generalized eigenfunctions converges absolutely and uniformly in each bounded subregion of the region* $G \times G$ *which borders the boundary on a piece strictly contained in the piece* $((G_0 \cup \Gamma_0) \times \Gamma_0) \cup (\Gamma_0 \times (G_0 \cup \Gamma_0))$.

Proof. The theorem obviously follows from what was said earlier. We sketch the argument. The application of Corollary 2 is valid: $N = [n/2r] + 1$, $Nr > n/2$; further $2r + n + p \geq 2Nr + p$ and $a_\alpha \in C^{2r+n+p}(G \cup \Gamma)$ satisfies the necessary smoothness requirement; Γ_0 is $2m + q$ times continuously differentiable, and so since $q \geq n/2 \geq r\,|n/2r| = (N-1)r$, it follows that $2m + q \geq Nr$ and therefore that Γ_0 is sufficiently smooth. The character of the convergence of the expansion (2.10) is insured by Theorem 4.2, Chapter V.

In order to obtain theorems of type 2.3 in which the null conditions on Γ_0 are replaced by general ones, it is necessary to require that the general ones satisfy Theorem 5.7 of Chapter III with $L_1 = \cdots = L_N = L - zE$. Such a theorem, as we have pointed out earlier, may be proved with the help of the results of §6.12, Chapter III on increase in smoothness. These results guarantee the smoothness of $\phi(x)$ and $\Phi(x, y; \lambda)$ up to Γ_0. For Д we now choose the class of functions W_2^r (bd) which vanish in neighborhoods of $\Gamma \setminus \Gamma_0$ and of ∞.

We formulate still another analog of Theorem 2.3 for boundary conditions of a type three boundary value problem, which may be obtained without applying the general results of §6, Chapter III.

Theorem 2.4. *Let the hypotheses of Theorem 2.1 be satisfied (with $n = 2, 3$ and $r = 2$) in the weakened form $a_\alpha(x) \in C^{|\alpha|+2+p}(G \cup \Gamma)$, $p \geq n+1$. Then all of the conclusions of that theorem are correct if we require only the indicated smoothness of $\Phi(x, y; \lambda)$ and $\phi(x)$, and in the differentiation of (2.10), replace $r + n + p$ by $2 + p$. Now $N = 1$ and $\gamma(A)$ coincides with the generalized resolvent.*

Assume in addition that there exists a bounded subregion of $G_0 \subseteq G$ bordering on Γ on the piece Γ_0 of class C^2, such that L is strongly elliptic on $G_0 \cup \Gamma_0$. On Γ_0, the (bd) correspond to a type three boundary value problem: $\partial u/\partial\mu + \sigma(x)u|_{\Gamma_0} = 0$, where $\sigma \in C^1(\Gamma_0)$ and is real valued. The operator A is a selfadjoint extension on $L_2(G)$. Then all of the conclusions of Theorem 2.3 are valid if the class $W_{2,\mathrm{loc}}^{2m+q}(G_0, \Gamma_0)$ is replaced by the class $W_{2,\mathrm{loc}}^2(G_0, \Gamma_0)$ and the null (bd) are as indicated in the above hypotheses.

The proof of this theorem exactly follows those of Theorems 2.1 and 2.3. We clarify only a few peculiarities. For the proof of the first part, Theorems 5.1 and 5.4 of Chapter III are used directly since here $r > n/2$. For the proof of the second part, we use what was said at the end of §5.5, Chapter III, concerning the form of Theorem 5.5 of that chapter for type three boundary value problems. The limitations are essentially connected with the requirement that (bd) = (bd)$^+$; a consequence of the equation $L = L^+$ is that the coefficients $p_j(x)$ in the representation (2.4) of Chapter III are equal to zero. For the smoothness of the functions $\Phi(x, y; \lambda)$ and $\phi(x)$ up to Γ_0, it is then natural to apply Theorem 4.7, Chapter III.

3. **Behavior of the spectral kernel as a function of the point (x, y) near the boundary of $G \times G$ in the case of a strongly elliptic operator.** In subsection 2, we examined the function $\Phi(x, y; \lambda)$ near the piece $\Gamma_0 \subseteq \Gamma$ by fixing one of the points $x, y \in G$ and considering the behavior of this function as a function of the second point. Using these observations, and applying the method of §5.3 of Chapter III, it is easy to draw several conclusions about $\Phi(x, y; \lambda)$ as a function of both x and y.

In this connection, let the bounded regions $G_1, G_2 \subseteq G$ border on Γ on the respective pieces Γ_1 and Γ_2, not necessarily disjoint. Suppose that L is strongly elliptic on $G_1 \cup \Gamma_1$ and on $G_2 \cup \Gamma_2$, and has sufficiently smooth coefficients. Then $M = L_x + \overline{L}_y$ is strongly elliptic on $(G_1 \cup \Gamma_1) \times (G_2 \cup \Gamma_2)$ and also has sufficiently smooth coefficients. We suppose that null (bd) are given on Γ_1 and Γ_2. Then Theorem 2.2 shows that $p(x)$ is bounded near Γ_1 and Γ_2, and therefore that $\Phi \in L_{2,\mathrm{loc}}(G_1 \times G_2, ((G_1 \cup \Gamma_1) \times \Gamma_2) \cup (\Gamma_1 \times (G_2 \cup \Gamma_2)))$. It is also clear that $M\Phi = 2\lambda\Phi$ on $G_1 \times G_2$ up to the piece of the boundary of $G_1 \times G_2$ just now indicated. This yields the possibility of an exterior corner point of this piece, i.e. outside of $\Gamma_1 \times \Gamma_2$. Theorem 4.6 of Chapter III may be applied to obtain the smoothness of Φ. This consideration leads us to the following theorem.

Theorem 2.5. *Let the conditions of Theorem* 2.1 *be satisfied with* $r = 2m$. *Assume that there are everywhere-bounded regions (possibly intersecting)* $G_1, G_2 \subseteq G$ *bordering* Γ *on the pieces* Γ_1 *and* Γ_2 *of class* C^{2m+q} $(q \geq m,\ n/2)$ *such that* L *is strongly elliptic on* $G_j \cup \Gamma_j$ *and* $a_\alpha(x) \in C^{|\alpha|+q}(G_j \cup \Gamma_j)$ $(j = 1, 2)$. *On* $\Gamma_1 \cup \Gamma_2$ *the* (bd) *are null. The operator* A *is a selfadjoint extension in* $L_2(G)$.

Then the spectral kernel

$$\Phi(\cdot, \cdot;\ \lambda) \in W_{2,\mathrm{loc}}^{2m+q}(G_1 \times G_2, (\Gamma_1 \times G_2) \cup (G_1 \times \Gamma_2))$$

and satisfies the null boundary conditions in each of its variables, i.e. the relations (2.14) *are satisfied where* Γ_0 *is replaced by* $\Gamma_1 \cup \Gamma_2$.

A similar theorem may be obtained for L and (bd) as considered at the end of subsection 2. We do not formulate these results.

4. **Behavior of the spectral kernel as x and y together tend towards the boundary.** This question naturally cannot be investigated using the approach of subsection 2. The method of subsection 3 does not immediately apply even in the case of strongly elliptic L, since it reduces to the investigation of the function $\Phi(x, y; \lambda)$ as a function of the point (x, y) near $\Gamma_1 \times \Gamma_2$, an unsmooth part of the boundary of the region $G_1 \times G_2$. At the same time this question is of considerable importance; for a number of problems it is necessary to guarantee at least the continuity of $\Phi(x, y; \lambda)$ as $x, y \longrightarrow \Gamma$. The method which we will use for this is commonly used in similar situations. We limit ourselves to the case where G is the exterior of some closed sufficiently smooth surface Γ. The arguments will be carried out for strongly elliptic L and null (bd) but will be such that they easily extend to other L and (bd) for which the theorems in §6.12, Chapter III, on increase in smoothness hold.

We consider the formally selfadjoint elliptic expression L of order $r = 2m$ with coefficients $a_\alpha(x) \in C^{2Nr+p'}(G \cup \Gamma)$ $(p' \geq n+1)$ where $Nr > n/2$. Suppose that L and Γ satisfy the following assertions on increase in smoothness: let an arbitrary bounded region $G'_0 \subseteq G$ border Γ on the piece Γ'_0. Suppose that $u \in W^{r+q}_{2,\mathrm{loc}}(G'_0, \Gamma'_0)$, $D^\alpha u|_{\Gamma'_0} = 0$ $(|\alpha| \leq m-1)$ whenever $u \in W_2^{-q}(G'_0)$ and satisfies the equation $(L - zE)u = f \in W_2^q(G'_0)$ inside G'_0 up to Γ'_0. Here $q = 0, \cdots, (N-1)r$ and z is an arbitrary complex number. We consider some selfadjoint extension A of Λ (bd) with resolvents R_z. A conclusion of Theorems 1.1 and 1.2 is that each $u \in \mathfrak{D}(A)$ lies in some bounded part of G in W_2^r and satisfies (bd). In addition $Au = Lu$. Conversely each u of a similar form, which is finite at infinity, is an element of $\mathfrak{D}(A)$.

We fix $z \neq \bar{z}$ and introduce the operator $R = R_z^N$. Obviously Theorem 5.7 of Chapter III applies to R and $L_1 = \cdots = L_N = L - zE$. Let $R(x, y)$ $(x, y \in G)$ be the kernel of the operator R. Since now G'_0 is an arbitrary bounded subregion of G in Theorem 5.7, the vector-function of y with values in $L_2(G)$, $R(\cdot, y)$, is weakly continuously differentiable of orders up to $Nr - [n/2] - 1$, for arbitrary y in $G \cup \Gamma$. Also, by Lemma 5.4 of Chapter III, $Rf \in W_2^{Nr}(G'_0)$ for $f \in L_2(G)$; again by the arbitrariness of G'_0, Rf belongs to W_2^{Nr} on arbitrary bounded parts of G. By (5.15), Chapter III,

$$(Rf)(x) = \int_G R(x, y) f(y)\, dy \quad (f \in L_2(G))$$

for $j = 0, 1, \cdots, N$, we have

$$(L - zE)_x^j \int_G R(x, y) f(y)\, dy = (L - zE)_x^j (Rf)(x) =$$
$$= (L - zE)_x^{j-1} ((A - zE) R_z R_z^{N-1} f)(x) = (L - zE)_x^{j-1} (R_z^{N-1} f)(x)$$
$$= \ldots = (R_z^{N-j} f)(x). \tag{2.15}$$

Obviously the function (2.15) restricted to any bounded part of G is in $W_2^{(N-j)r}$ for $j < N$ and satisfies (bd), and for $j = N$ is equal to $f(x)$.

We denote by U some bounded subregion of the region G bordering on the entire boundary Γ ("a strip near Γ"). Let $h(x) \in C^\infty(G \cup \Gamma)$ be nonnegative, equal to one on U and zero for $|x| \geq d$ where $d > 0$ is some sufficiently large fixed number. We show that the representation

$$u(x) = \int_G (L - zE)_x^N [R(x, y)(1 - h(x))] u(y)\, dy$$

$$+ (L - zE)_x^N \int_G R(x, y) h(x) u(y)\, dy \quad (x \in G) \tag{2.16}$$

holds for each function $u \in C_0(U)$ (extended to zero on all of G).

First, we show that the expression in (2.16) makes sense. In the first integral, the variable y varies in a subregion contained strictly inside U, and $1 - h(x)$ is different from zero only off U. Therefore the singularity of the kernel $R(x, y)$ is removable when $x = y$, and the application of $(L - zE)_x^N$ is valid. It follows from the smoothness of the integral $\int_G R(x, y) u(y) dy$ that the second integral is also sufficiently smooth. Then, by (2.15) with $j = N$, we may write

$$\int_G (L - zE)_x^N [R(x, y)(1 - h(x))] u(y)\, dy + (L - zE)_x^N$$

$$\times \int_G R(x, y) h(x) u(y)\, dy = (L - zE)_x^N \int_G R(x, y) u(y)\, dy = u(x) \quad (x \in G).$$

We denote

$$A_1(x, y) = (L - zE)_x^N [R(x, y)(1 - h(x))], \qquad A_2(x, y) = R(x, y) h(x)$$

$$(x \in G,\ y \in U). \tag{2.17}$$

We note, at once, that these functions vanish for $|x| \geq d$. For A_2 this is obvious and for A_1 this follows from relation (5.2) of Chapter III: since $h(x) = 0$, we have $A_1(x, y) = (L - zE)_x^N R(x, y) = 0$.

Let $\phi(x) \in W^r_{2,\mathrm{loc}}(G, \Gamma)$ and satisfying (bd), be an eigenfunction: $(L\phi)(x) = \lambda\phi(x)$ $(x \in G)$. We denote by G_d the intersection of G with the sphere $|x| < d$. The representation

$$\varphi(y) = \int_{G_d} \overline{(A_1(x, y) + (\lambda - z)^N A_2(x, y))}\, \varphi(x)\, dx \quad (y \in U) \tag{2.18}$$

is valid. In fact, let $u \in C_0(U)$. Then, by (2.16),

$$\int_G \int_G A_1(x, y) \overline{\varphi(x)} u(y)\, dx dy + (\lambda - z)^N \int_G \int_G A_2(x, y) \overline{\varphi(x)} u(y)\, dx dy$$

$$= \int_G \int_G A_1 \ldots + (\lambda - z)^{N-1} \int_G \left(\int_G A_2(x, y) u(y)\, dy \right) \overline{((L - \bar{z}E)\varphi)(x)}\, dx =$$

$$= \int_G \int_G A_1 \ldots + (\lambda - z)^{N-2} \int_G (L - zE)_x \left(\int_G A_2(x, y) u(y)\, dy \right)$$

$$\times \overline{((L - \bar{z}E)\varphi)(x)}\, dx = \ldots = \int_G \int_G A_1 \ldots$$

$$+ \int_G (L - zE)_x^N \left(\int_G A_2(x, y) u(y)\, dy \right) \cdot \overline{\varphi(x)}\, dx = \int_G \left(\int_G A_1(x, y) u(y)\, dy \right.$$

$$\left. + (L - zE)_x^N \int_G A_2(x, y) u(y)\, dy \right) \overline{\varphi(x)}\, dx = \int_G u(x) \overline{\varphi(x)}\, dx. \qquad (2.19)$$

We point out that above, on each sphere, we have integrated by parts, throwing $L - \bar{z}E$ over to ϕ in the expression

$$(L - zE)_x^j \left(\int_G A_2(x, y) u(y)\, dy \right) = (L - zE)_x^j \left[h(x) \int_G R(x, y) u(y)\, dy \right]$$

$$(j = 0, \ldots, N-1). \qquad (2.20)$$

This operation is permissible since ϕ and each of the integrals in (2.20) is sufficiently smooth and satisfies (bd), the latter based on (2.15) and the fact that $h(x) = 1$ near Γ. (2.18) now follows from (2.19) and the arbitrariness of u.

We will assume that the spectral kernel $\Phi(x, y; \lambda)$ of our problem lies in $W_{2,\mathrm{loc}}^r(G, \Gamma)$ as a function of each variable and satisfies (bd). Since $L_x\Phi = \lambda\Phi$ and $L_y\overline{\Phi} = \lambda\overline{\Phi}$ (see (2.8)), then using equation (2.18) for each of the variables (and the analogous equation for $\overline{\Phi}$), we have

$$\Phi(x, y; \lambda) = \int_{G_d} \int_{G_d} (\overline{A_1(\xi, x)} + (\lambda - \bar{z})^N \overline{A_2(\xi, x)}) (A_1(\eta, y)$$

$$+ (\lambda - z)^N A_2(\eta, y)) \Phi(\xi, \eta; \lambda)\, d\xi d\eta \qquad (x, y \in U). \qquad (2.21)$$

The representation (2.21) provides a method of investigating the smoothness of $\Phi(x, y; \lambda)$ up to $x, y \in \Gamma$: this kernel is expressed by means of the kernels in (2.17) and the regularity of Φ is established by showing that A_1 and A_2 are sufficiently regular.

From the weak differentiability of $R(\cdot, y)$ considered as a vector-function with values in $L_2(G)$ and from the equation $A_2(x, y) = h(x) R(x, y)$ ($h(x) = 0$ for $|x| \geq d$) it follows that the vector-function $A_2(\cdot, y)$, with values in $L_2(G_d)$, is weakly continuously differentiable up to the order $Nr - [n/2] - 1$ for $y \in U \cup \Gamma$.

We establish the same such smoothness for $A_1(\cdot, y)$. Fix $y \in U$. Then since

$1 - h(x) = 0$ $(x \in U)$, the singularity of $A_1(x, y)$ is removable in expression (2.17) and therefore $A_1(x, y)$, as a function of $x \in G$ is sufficiently smooth, and vanishes for $x \in U$ and $|x| \geq d$. Consequently, the integral $\int_{G_d} A_1(x, y)\overline{g(x)}\,dx = (A_1(\cdot, y), g)_{L_2(G_d)}$ exists. We show that it takes values in $L_2(U)$. For this, let $u \in C_0(U)$. Then by the estimate $\|Rf\|_{W_2^{Nr}(G_d)} \leq C_1 \|f\|_{L_2(G)}$ $(f \in L_2(G))$ which follows from (5.30), Chapter III, we have[2]

$$\left|\int_U (A_1(\cdot, y), g)_{L_2(G_d)} u(y)\,dy\right| = \left|\int_{G_d} g(x)\,\overline{(L - zE)_x^N [(Ru)(x)(1 - h(x))]}\,dx\right|$$

$$\leqslant \|g\|_{L_2(G_d)} \|(L - zE)_x^N [(Ru)(x)(1 - h(x))]\|_{L_2(G_d)}$$

$$\leqslant C_2 \|g\|_{L_2(G_d)} \|Ru\|_{W_2^{Nr}(G_d)} \leqslant C_1 C_2 \|g\|_{L_2(G_d)} \|u\|_{L_2(G)}$$

$$= C_1 C_2 \|g\|_{L_2(G_d)} \|u\|_{L_2(U)}, \tag{2.22}$$

and the assertion follows.

Thus, the vector-function $A_1(\cdot, y)$ $(y \in U)$ with values in $L_2(G_d)$ is such that $g \in L_2(G_d)$ $(A_1(\cdot, y), g)_{L_2(G_d)} \in L_2(U)$. Our aim will be to show that $(A_1(\cdot, y), g)_{L_2(G_d)} \in W_2^{Nr}(U')$, where $U' \subset U$ is some smaller strip near Γ. It follows from the basic inclusion theorem, that $(A_1(\cdot, y), g)_{L_2(G_d)} \in C^{Nr-[n/2]-1}(U')$, i.e. the required smoothness of the vector-function $A_1(\cdot, y)$.

We show that $\psi(y) = \overline{(A_1(\cdot, y), g)}_{L_2(G_d)}$ is a generalized solution in $L_2(U)$ of the equation $(L - \bar{z}E)^N u = 0$, inside U up to Γ. In this connection we define $(\mathrm{bd})_1$ on the boundary $\Gamma \cup \gamma$ of the strip U from (bd) as in Chapter III, §5.7: $W_2^{Nr}(\mathrm{bd})_1$ consists of all functions $u \in W_2^{Nr}(U)$ for which $(L - zE)^j u \in W_2^r(\mathrm{bd}) \cap W_2^r(U)$ $(j = 0, \cdots, N-1)$. Obviously, $(\mathrm{bd})_1^+$ on Γ takes the previous form. So for $v \in W_2^{Nr}(\mathrm{bd})_1$, zero in a neighborhood of γ, and extended by zero on G, we have

$$(\psi, (L - zE)^N v)_{L_2(U)} = \int_U \left(\int_{G_d} \overline{(L - zE)_x^N [R(x, y)(1 - h(x))]\, g(x)\,dx}\right)$$

$$\times \overline{((L - zE)^N v)(y)}\,dy$$

$$= \int_{G_d} g(x)\,\overline{(L - zE)_x^N \left[(1 - h(x)) \int_G R(x, y)((L - zE)^N v)(y)\,dy\right]}\,dx$$

$$= \int_{G_d} g(x)\,\overline{(L - zE)_x^N [(1 - h(x))(R(L - zE)^N v)(x)]}\,dx =$$

$$= \int_{G_d} g(x) \overline{(L - zE)_x^N [(1-h(x))(R_z^N (A-zE)^N v)(x)]}\, dx$$

$$= \int_{G_d} g(x) \overline{(L - zE)_x^N [(1 - h(x)) v(x)]}\, dx = 0.$$

We point out that above we changed the order of integration in the expression $\int_U (\int_{G_d} A_1(x, y) g(x)\, dx) f(y) dy$ ($f \in L_2(U)$, $g \in L_2(G_d)$); the validity of this interchange is easy to establish from the estimate (2.22). Further, since all of the $(L - zE)^j v \in \mathfrak{D}(A)$ $(j = 0, \cdots, N-1)$, then $(L - zE)^N v = (A - zE)^N v$.

The required smoothness of $A_1(\cdot, y)$ now follows from the following basic lemma.

Lemma 2.4. *Let $\psi \in L_2(U)$ be a generalized solution of the equation $(L - \bar{z}E)^N u = 0$ inside U up to Γ, where* (bd)$_1$ *are given as above. Then $\psi \in W_2^{Nr}(U')$ ($U' \subset U$ is a strip near Γ), and ψ satisfies* (bd)$_1$ *on Γ.*

Proof. If $v \in W_2^{Nr}$(bd) vanishes in some neighborhood of $G \setminus U$ we have $(\psi, (L - zE)^N v)_{L_2(U)} = 0$. For $f \in L_2(G)$ the function $Rf = R_z^N f$ obviously satisfies (bd)$_1$ on Γ and therefore in the above we may put $v(x) = \chi(x)(Rf)(x)$ where $\chi \in C^\infty(G \cup \Gamma)$, is equal to one near Γ, 0 in a neighborhood of $G \setminus U$, and is nonnegative. We obtain

$$0 = (\psi, (L - zE)^N (\chi Rf))_{L_2(U)} = (\psi, \chi (L - zE)^N Rf)_{L_2(U)}$$

$$+ (\psi, M_\chi Rf)_{L_2(U)} = (\chi\psi, f)_{L_2(U)} + (\psi, M_\chi Rf)_{L_2(U)}. \tag{2.23}$$

Here M_χ is a differential expression of order $Nr - 1$ obtained by commuting χ with $(L - zE)^N$. In (2.23) we let $f = (L - zE)w$ where $w \in W_2^r(U)$ vanishes in a neighborhood of $G \setminus U$, satisfies (bd) on Γ and is extended to zero elsewhere on G. We then obtain

$$0 = (\chi\psi, (L - zE)\, w)_{L_2(U)} + (\psi, M_\chi R_z^{N-1} w)_{L_2(U)}. \tag{2.24}$$

We consider the subspace H of the space $W_2^{r-1}(U)$ consisting of functions u such that $D^\alpha u|_\gamma = 0$ ($|\alpha| \leq r - 2$). We extend these functions by setting them equal to zero on the rest of G so that each of the extended u's lies in $W_2^{r-1}(G) \cap L_2(G)$. Similarly, as shown in Lemma 5.4, Chapter III, it is easy to establish that $R_z^{N-1} u \in W_2^{(N-1)r+r-1}(U) = W_2^{Nr-1}(U)$. The transformation $H \ni u \longrightarrow R_z^{N-1} u \in W_2^{Nr-1}(U)$ is defined on the whole space H and is closed, so it is continuous (cf. the proof of Lemma 5.2, Chapter III):

$$\| R_z^{N-1} u \|_{W_2^{Nr-1}(U)} \leqslant C \| u \|_{W_2^{r-1}(U)} \; (u \in H).$$

But then the transformation $B: H \longrightarrow L_2(U)$, defined by $Bu = M_\chi R_z^{N-1} u$, is continuous. Let $\widetilde{B}$ be some extension of B to a continuous operator from all of $W_2^{r-1}(U)$ into $L_2(U)$ so that $\widetilde{B}^+$ takes $L_2(U)$ into $W_2^{-(r-1)}(U)$, where

$$(\widetilde{B}^+ f, u)_{L_2(U)} = (f, \widetilde{B}u)_{L_2(U)} = (f, Bu)_{L_2(U)} = (f, M_\chi R_z^{N-1} u)_{L_2(U)}$$
$$(f \in L_2(U),\ u \in H).$$

In particular, setting $\alpha = -\widetilde{B}^+ \psi \in W_2^{-r+1}(U)$ and $u = w$, we may rewrite (2.24) in the form

$$(\chi\psi, (L - zE)\, w)_{L_2(U)} = (\alpha, w)_{L_2(U)}. \tag{2.25}$$

This means that $\chi\psi \in L_2(U)$ satisfies the equation $(L - zE)\, u = \alpha \in W_2^{-r+1}(U)$ inside U up to Γ, when the null (bd) are given. By Theorem 4.6 of Chapter III, $\chi\psi \in W_2^1(U)$ and $\chi\psi|_{\Gamma \cup \gamma} = 0.$[1)] In particular $\psi \in W_2^1(U_1)$ where $U_1 \subset U$ is a slightly more narrow strip near Γ, and $\psi|_\Gamma = 0$.

We write equation (2.23) with a new $\chi = \chi_1$ which vanishes on a neighborhood not of $G \setminus U$ but of $G \setminus U_1$:

$$0 = (\chi_1\psi, f)_{L_2(U_1)} + (\psi, M_{\chi_1} Rf)_{L_2(U_1)} = (\chi_1\psi, f)_{L_2(U_1)} + (\psi_1, M_{\chi_1}^{(1)} Rf)_{L_2(U_1)}. \tag{2.26}$$

Above we took the first derivative of M_{χ_1} and carried it over to ψ (integration by parts). This is valid since $\psi \in W_2^1(U_1)$, $\psi|_\Gamma = 0$ and χ_1, along with the coefficients of M_{χ_1}, is zero in a neighborhood of $G \setminus U_1$. Sufficiently many interchanges may be obtained by differentiating so that the resulting expression $M_{\chi_1}^{(1)}$ in (2.26) obtained from M_χ is of order $r - 2$; the derivative of ψ, denoted by ψ_1, is in $L_2(U_1)$.

Now we may again repeat the earlier argument used on the expression (2.23). We arrive at a relation of the type (2.25) but with $\alpha \in W_2^{-r+2}(U_1)$ since $M_{\chi_1}^{(1)}$ is of order $r - 2$. With the help of Theorem 4.6, Chapter III we obtain $\psi \in W_2^2(U_2)$, $U_2 \subset U_1$. Again stepping through (2.23)–(2.26), we remove another order from M_{χ_2}; that is, $M_{\chi_2}^{(2)}$ will be of order $r - 3$. Repeating the argument, we obtain that

---

1) So far we have applied the results on increase in smoothness formulated at the beginning of this subsection. Here and in what follows the situation is more delicate. This is necessary in view of the transference of the results to general (bd).

$\psi \in W_2^3(U_3)$, $U_3 \subset U_2$. Continuing this process we obtain $\psi \in W_2^r(U_r)$ $(U_r \subset U_{r-1} \subset \cdots \subset U_1 \subset U)$ and satisfies (bd) on Γ.

In the beginning of the proof, we had $(\psi, (L - zE)^N v)_{L_2(U)} = 0$ for arbitrary $v \in W_2^{Nr}$ $(\mathrm{bd})_1$, which vanishes on some neighborhood of $G \setminus U$. It is clear that in the above U may be replaced by U_r. We then transfer $L - zE$ to ψ (this is possible by the nature of ψ). We obtain $((L - zE)\psi, (L - zE)^{N-1}v)_{L_2(U_r)} = 0$ for arbitrary $v \in W_2^{(N-1)r}$ $(\mathrm{bd})_1$ which vanishes in a neighborhood of $G \setminus U_r$. Repeating the pattern of the proof with ψ replaced by $(L - zE)\psi \in L_2(U_r)$ we obtain $(L - zE)\psi \in W_2^r(U_{2r})$ $(U_{2r} \subset U_{2r-1} \subset \cdots \subset U_{r+1} \subset U_r)$ and satisfies (bd) on Γ. Continuing the process of transferring $L - zE$ we obtain the proof of the lemma.

Thus, the required smoothness of $A_1(\cdot, y)$ is established. From the smoothness of $A_1(\cdot, y)$ and $A_2(\cdot, y)$ it follows that the vector-function of $y \in U \cup \Gamma$, $g_y = A_1(\cdot, y) + (\lambda - z)^N A_2(\cdot, y)$ with values in $L_2(G_d)$ will be weakly continuously differentiable up to order $Nr - [n/2] - 1$ inclusive. The vector-function $f_x = \overline{A_1(\cdot, x) + (\lambda - \bar{z})^N A_2(\cdot, x)} = \bar{g}_x$ $(x \in U \cup \Gamma)$ will contain the same degree of smoothness.

Lemma 2.5. *Let H be a Hilbert space, G a region (or a region with part of its boundary) in E_n, and f_x, g_x, weakly continuous vector-functions of $x \in G$ with values in H (the derivatives $D^\alpha f_x$, $D^\alpha g_x$, $|\alpha| \le k$, exist and are continuous). Then $f_x \otimes g_y$ will be a weakly continuous vector-function on $G \times G$ with values in $H \otimes H$, i.e., the derivatives $D_x^\alpha D_y^\beta (f_x \otimes g_y)$, where $|\alpha|$, $|\beta| \le k$, exist and are continuous.*

Proof. Since $D_x^\alpha D_y^\beta (f_x \otimes g_y) = (D_x^\alpha f_x) \otimes (D_y^\beta g_y)$, everything is reduced to the proof of the continuity of the vector-function $f_x \otimes g_x$ given that f_x and g_x are each continuous. For elements of the form $\sum_{j=1}^N u_j \otimes v_j \in H \otimes_0 H$ we have

$$\left(f_x \otimes g_y, \sum_{j=1}^N u_j \otimes v_j \right)_{H \otimes H} = \sum_{j=1}^N (f_x, u_j)_H (g_y, v_j)_H;$$

the last expression is obviously continuous as a function of $(x, y) \in G \times G$. Since the sums $\sum_{j=1}^N u_j \otimes v_j$ are dense in $H \otimes H$, to prove the continuity of $f_x \otimes g_y$ it remains to point out this vector-function is bounded on each compact set of $G \times G$ in view of the relation $\|f_x \otimes g_y\|_{H \otimes H} = \|f_x\|_H \|g_y\|_H$. The lemma follows.

This lemma immediately applies to our case: by Theorem 2.3, the function $\Phi(x, y; \lambda)$ is a square integrable function of (x, y) on every bounded subset of

$G \times G$, so in particular $\overline{\Phi(\cdot, \cdot; \lambda)} \in L_2(G_d \times G_d) = L_2(G_d) \otimes L_2(G_d)$. Therefore, by considering the indicated smoothness of $g_y = A_1(\cdot, y) + (\lambda - z)^N A_2(\cdot, y)$ and hence of $f_x = \overline{g}_x$, and the representation (2.21), we conclude that the derivatives $(D_x^\alpha D_y^\beta \Phi)(x, y; \lambda)$ $(|\alpha|, |\beta| \le Nr - [n/2] - 1)$ exist and are continuous in $(x, y) \in (U \cup \Gamma) \times (U \cup \Gamma)$ and hence for $(x, y) \in (G \cup \Gamma) \times (G \cup \Gamma)$. We have essentially arrived at the following theorem.

Theorem 2.6. *Let Γ be a closed surface of class C^{2m+q} $(q \ge m, n/2)$, G the exterior of this surface. Assume that the hypotheses of Theorems* 2.1 *and* 2.3 *are satisfied in the entire region G.*

In this case all derivatives of the form $(D_x^\alpha D_y^\beta \Phi)(x, y; \lambda)$ exist and are continuous, where

$$|\alpha|, |\beta| \leqslant r\left\{\min\left(\left[\frac{q}{r}\right], \left[\frac{p-1}{2r}\right]\right) + 1\right\} - \left[\frac{n}{2}\right] - 1 = M(r, n, p, q) \geqslant 0.$$

The expansion (2.10) *converges absolutely and uniformly on each bounded part of $G \times G$ where the series may be differentiated term by term without weakening this convergence; namely, the above derivatives may be taken term by term.*

Proof. The proof reduces to some details of the argument just introduced. In it, we set $N = \min([q/r], [(p-1)/2r]) + 1$ and show that such a choice is suitable. By the hypotheses of Theorem 2.1, $a_\alpha \in C^{2r+n+p}(G \cup \Gamma)$ $(p \ge n+1)$. But $2r + n + p \ge 2([(p-1)/2r] + 1)r + n + 1$ and thus $2r + n + p = 2Nr + p'$ $(p' \ge n+1)$, i.e., a_α has the smoothness required on p. 194. Furthermore, for the validity of the assertion on increase in smoothness with null (bd), which is necessary for Theorem 5.7, Chapter III, it is sufficient to require that $2m + q = r + q \ge Nr$ (see Corollary 2 of that theorem). But $r + q \ge ([q/r] + 1)r$ and so this condition is fulfilled. Finally since $p \ge n + 1$ and $q \ge n/2$, it is easy to verify that $Nr \ge n/2$. This shows that the above choice of N is satisfactory. The last assertion of the theorem, on the differentiability of the series (2.10), follows from the proof of the differentiability of $\Phi(x, y; \lambda)$ and Lemma 2.3, if we note only that this lemma is valid in the case when G is replaced by $G \cup \Gamma$. The theorem is then completely proved.

Corollary. *Suppose the assumptions of the theorem are such that $M(r, n, p, q) \ge m - 1$. Then a boundary condition of the form*

$$(D_x^\alpha D_y^\beta \Phi)(x, y; \lambda)\big|_{x,y \in \Gamma} = 0 \quad (|\alpha|, |\beta| \leqslant m - 1) \tag{2.27}$$

is satisfied.

Indeed, by (2.14) we have $(D_y^\beta \Phi)\,(x, y;\, \lambda)|_{y \in \Gamma} = 0$ with $x \in G$ and $|\beta| \leq m-1$. This equation may be differentiated with respect to x inside G: $(D_x^\alpha D_y^\beta \Phi)\,(x, y;\, \lambda)|_{y \in \Gamma} = 0$ $(x \in G)$. Passing to the limit here as $x \longrightarrow \Gamma$ and applying the theorem, we obtain (2.27).

It is obvious from the proof that Theorem 2.6 is valid for a wide class of (bd). We leave the general results to the reader, limiting ourselves now to the case of a type three boundary condition with $n = 2, 3$ $(r = 2)$. In this case the role of Theorems 2.1 and 2.3 is played by Theorem 2.4 and Theorem 4.7 of Chapter III is used in place of Theorem 4.6 of that same chapter. The increase in smoothness mentioned in the footnote on p. 411 will be guaranteed. Now $N = 1$, $Nr - [n/2] - 1 = 0$ and the corresponding result appears as follows. *Let the hypotheses of Theorem 2.4 be satisfied with* $G_0 = G$. *Then* $\Phi(x, y;\, \lambda)$ *is continuous with respect to* $(x, y) \in (G \cup \Gamma) \times (G \cup \Gamma)$ *and the series* (2.10) *converges absolutely and uniformly in each bounded subset of* $G \times G$. To obtain a greater degree of smoothness for Φ and the validity of a relation of type (2.27) it is necessary to require more smoothness of Γ, the coefficients L and of $\sigma(x)$.

In conclusion, we make the following remark. Let $F(\lambda)$ be as in Theorem 2.1. Then $F(A)$ exists and is an integral operator with kernel (2.9). Multiplying (2.21) by $F(\lambda)$ and integrating with respect to $d\rho(\lambda)$ we obtain

$$K(x, y) = \int_{G_d}\int_{G_d} \overline{(A_1(\xi, x) + (\lambda - \bar{z})^N A_2(\xi, x))}\,(A_1(\eta, y) + (\lambda - z)^N A_2(\eta, y))\,K(\xi, \eta)\,d\xi d\eta \qquad (x, y \in U).$$

Hence, exactly as above, it is possible to make various smoothness conclusions on $K(x, y)$ as a function of the point (x, y) (inside $G \times G$ up to the boundary). We leave this to the reader.

5. Another construction of the spectral theory of selfadjoint elliptic operators. Suppose the same situation as in subsection 1 takes place: given a formal selfadjoint elliptic expression L and $(\mathrm{bd}) = (\mathrm{bd})^+$ we construct the operator A as a selfadjoint extension of $\Lambda(\mathrm{bd})$. One may construct a generalized eigenfunction expansion for A by using the general construction of §3, Chapter V. For such, it is possible to take $l > n/2$ and for the chain $H_- \supseteq H_0 \supseteq H_+$, $W_2^{-(l,q)}(G) \supseteq L_2(G) \supseteq W_2^{(l,q)}(G)$ where $q(x) \geq 1$ grows so fast, as $|x| \longrightarrow \infty$, that the inclusion $W_2^{(l,q)}(G) \longrightarrow L_2(G)$ is quasi-nuclear. We obtain the existence of the operator

$P(\lambda)$, for A, a complete set of generalized eigenfunctions in $W_2^{-(l,q)}(G)$, etc.

We assume that the coefficients of L, $a_\alpha \in C^{|\alpha|+l}(G \cup \Gamma)$. In this case a vector $\phi \in \Re(P(\lambda)) \subseteq W_2^{-(l,q)}(G)$ may be interpreted as a generalized solution of the equation $Lu - \lambda u = 0$ with (bd) on Γ. In fact, A now admits an extension of the equipment. For $\mathcal{D}$ we may use W_2^r (bd) $\cap W_{2,0}^{r+l}(E_n)$; the topology may be defined, for example, as follows: $v_n \longrightarrow 0$ if the supports of v_n lie in a single sphere U and $v_n \longrightarrow 0$ in $W_2^{r+l}(G \cap U)$. By Lemma 2.1, Chapter V, ϕ satisfies the relation

$$(\varphi, (A - \lambda E)v)_0 = 0, \quad \text{i.e.} \quad (\varphi, (L - \lambda E)v)_0 = 0 \; (v \in W_2^r(\text{bd}) \cap W_{2,0}^{r+l}(E_n)). \quad (2.28)$$

In other words, (2.28) shows that ϕ is a generalized solution of the equation $Lu - \lambda u = 0$ up to Γ, lying in $W_{2,\text{loc}}^{-l}(G, \Gamma)$ (in addition, one must presuppose the density of W_2^r (bd) $\cap W_{2,0}^{r+l}(E_n)$ in W_2^r (bd) $\cap W_{2,0}^r(E_n)$ in the sense of the convergence: $v_n \longrightarrow 0$ if the supports of v_n lie in some sphere U and $v_n \longrightarrow 0$ in $W_2^r(G \cap U)$; see §5.8, Chapter III.

Using theorems on the smoothness of generalized solutions of elliptic equations we find that ϕ satisfies (2.28) and is a sufficiently smooth function. This shows that, in the relations formulated in §§2 and 3, Chapter V, instead of generalized $\phi_\alpha(x)$, smooth functions occur, i.e., we obtain an expansion in ordinary eigenfunctions. But for estimating the convergence, the behavior of the kernel $\Phi(x, y; \lambda)$ etc., the representation discussed here is not sufficient, and it will be necessary to repeat the arguments of subsections 1–4 and §4 of Chapter V in some form or another, to show that A is Carleman, and consequently to draw the related conclusions.

It is clear that we might have used other chains $H_- \supseteq H_0 \supseteq H_+$ mentioned in §3 Chapter V, for the above.

6. The case of a bounded region. Several simplifications, which do not make sense in Theorems 2.1–2.5, arise in the formulations and proofs in this case. We recall only that the spectrum is now discrete and converges to infinity. (See Theorems 3.5 of Chapter II, and 2.3 and 3.5 of Chapter III). Essentially, the simplifications are that here, in Theorem 2.6, we do not have to "cut off" $R(x, y)$ with the help of a function $h(x)$; in fact, now $\Phi(x, y; \lambda)$ is contained in $L_2(G \times G)$. The change in (2.16) is obvious: $u(x) = (L - zE)^N \int_G R(x, y)\, u(y)\, dy$ $(u \in L_2(G))$; the basic relation (2.21) becomes the representations

$$\Phi(x, y; \lambda) = |\lambda - z|^{2N} \int_G \int_G \overline{R(\xi, x)}\, R(\eta, y)\, \Phi(\xi, \eta; \lambda)\, d\xi d\eta \quad (x, y \in G).$$

7. Behavior of the eigenfunctions at ∞. The growth estimate for general Carleman operators obtained in §5, Chapter V, is valid for the eigenfunction expansion of a selfadjoint elliptic operator on the unbounded region G. Thus Theorems 5.2 and 5.3 of that chapter are valid without any refinements in the formulas, (we note that the local boundedness of the integral (4.1) of Chapter V always holds in our case; see Lemma 2.1). It is clear that Theorem 5.4 is also valid, and moreover, it is often possible to study the behavior of the function $C(y)$ at ∞. Below we carry out such a study for the Schrödinger operator, which will in addition allow us to verify the conditions of Theorem 5.5 of Chapter V.

8. Examples. We will not dwell on the well-known examples of eigenfunction expansions in bounded regions, constructed by means of separation of variables. Instead we introduce two examples in an unbounded region. Some additional examples are given in §4.4.

a) *The Laplace expression on* E_n. We construct the spectral theory of the operator extension of the expression

$$L = -\Delta = -D_1^2 - \cdots - D_n^2 \tag{2.29}$$

on all of E_n $(n \geq 2)$. Let Λ be a minimal operator corresponding to (2.29), i.e., the operator $u \longrightarrow -\Delta u$ $(u \in C_0^\infty(E_n))$. As is well known, Λ is selfadjoint, and its spectrum fills the interval $[0, \infty)$, namely the region of values of the function $L(\xi) = |\xi|^2$ $(\xi \in E_n)$. First of all, we have the form of the kernel $R(x, y; z)$ of the resolvents of the operator Λ; its existence follows from what was said in §§5.1 and 5.8 of Chapter III.

Since Δ has constant coefficients, then to find $R(x, y; z)$ it is natural to use the usual Fourier transform, $u(x) \longrightarrow \widetilde{u}(\xi)$. For $f \in C_0(E_n)$ $R_z f \in L_2(E_n) \cap W^2_{2,\mathrm{loc}}(E_n)$ (see Theorem 1.1), and $((-\Delta - zE)R_z f)(x) = f(x)$ $(x \in E_n)$. Consequently

$$(|\xi|^2 - z)\widetilde{(R_z f)}(\xi) = \widetilde{((-\Delta - zE)R_z f)}(\xi) = \widetilde{f}(\xi),$$

$$\widetilde{(R_z f)}(\xi) = \frac{1}{|\xi|^2 - z}\widetilde{f}(\xi) \qquad (\xi \in E_n;\ z \overline{\in} [0, \infty)). \tag{2.30}$$

Therefore

$$(R_z f)(x) = \frac{1}{\sqrt{(2\pi)^n}} \int_{E_n} \widetilde{(R_z f)}(\xi)\, e^{i\langle x, \xi\rangle}\, d\xi = \int_{E_n} R(x - y; z) f(y)\, dy;$$

$$R(x; z) = \frac{1}{\sqrt{(2\pi)^n}} \left(\widetilde{\frac{1}{|\xi|^2 - z}}\right)(x) \qquad (x \in E_n;\ z \overline{\in} [0, \infty)).$$

Thus

$$R(x, y; z) = R(x - y; z),\ R(x; z) = \frac{1}{(2\pi)^n} \int\limits_{E_n} \frac{e^{i<x,\xi>}}{|\xi|^2 - z}\, d\xi$$

$$(x, y \in E_n;\ z \overline{\in} [0, \infty)). \tag{2.31}$$

Let $n \geq 3$. We calculate the last integral in spherical coordinates $\rho = |\xi|$, $\phi_1, \cdots, \phi_{n-1}$ where the angle ϕ_1 is equal to the angle between the vectors ξ and x. Taking into consideration that the surface of a sphere of radius one in E_q is equal to $\Omega_q = 2\pi^{q/2}/\Gamma(q/2)$, we obtain

$$R(x;\ z) = \frac{1}{(2\pi)^n} \int\limits_0^\infty \int\limits_0^\pi \cdots \int\limits_0^\pi \int\limits_0^{2\pi} \frac{e^{i|x|\varrho\cos\varphi_1}}{\varrho^2 - z}$$

$$\times\ \varrho^{n-1} \sin^{n-2}\varphi_1 \ldots \sin\varphi_{n-2}\, d\varrho\, d\varphi_1 \ldots d\varphi_{n-2}\, d\varphi_{n-1} =$$

$$= \frac{1}{2^{n-1}\pi^{\frac{n+1}{2}}\Gamma\left(\frac{n-1}{2}\right)} \int\limits_0^\infty \int\limits_0^\pi \frac{e^{i|x|\varrho\cos\varphi_1}}{\varrho^2 - z}\, \varrho^{n-1} \sin^{n-2}\varphi_1\, d\varrho\, d\varphi_1. \tag{2.32}$$

But it is known that

$$\int\limits_0^\pi e^{i|x|\varrho\cos\varphi_1} \sin^{n-2}\varphi_1\, d\varphi_1 = 2^{\frac{n}{2}-1} \sqrt{\pi}\, \Gamma\left(\frac{n-1}{2}\right) \frac{J_{\frac{n}{2}-1}(|x|\varrho)}{(|x|\varrho)^{\frac{n}{2}-1}};$$

$$\int\limits_0^\infty \frac{\varrho^{\frac{n}{2}}}{\varrho^2 + \zeta} J_{\frac{n}{2}-1}(|x|\varrho)\, d\varrho = (\sqrt{\zeta})^{\frac{n}{2}-1} K_{\frac{n}{2}-1}(\sqrt{\zeta}\,|x|), \tag{2.33}$$

where K_q is a cylindrical function with an imaginary argument $\zeta > 0.$ [1] By analytic continuation of the last equation in ζ, we conclude that it is valid for arbitrary ζ in the complex plane, with a slit along the ray $(-\infty, 0]$. We make the change of variables $\zeta = -z$ so that $\sqrt{\zeta} = -i\sqrt{z}$; here z varies in the complex plane slit at $[0, \infty)$, and by $\sqrt{z}$ we mean the branch of the square root equal to $i\sqrt{\sigma}$ where $z = -\sigma < 0$, i.e., positive on the positive axis.

---

1) See, for example, I. M. Ryšik, I. C. Gradšteĭn [1], formulas 6.412, 6 and 4.412, 2.

Thus we obtain

$$\int_0^\infty \frac{\varrho^{\frac{n}{2}}}{\varrho^2 - z} J_{\frac{n}{2}-1}(|x|\varrho)\,d\varrho = (-i\sqrt{z})^{\frac{n}{2}-1} K_{\frac{n}{2}-1}(-i\sqrt{z}|x|)$$

$$(z \bar{\in} [0, \infty)). \tag{2.34}$$

Substituting (2.33) and (2.34) in (2.32) and using (2.31) we finally have

$$R(x, y; z) = R(x - y; z)$$

$$= \frac{1}{(2\pi)^{\frac{n}{2}}} \left(-\frac{i\sqrt{z}}{|x-y|} \right)^{\frac{n}{2}-1} K_{\frac{n}{2}-1}(-i\sqrt{z}|x-y|)$$

$$(x, y \in E_n;\ z \bar{\in} [0, \infty)). \tag{2.35}$$

In the case $n = 2$ the calculation proceeds analogously; we arrive at the same formula in (2.35):

$$R(x, y; z) = \frac{1}{2\pi} K_0(-i\sqrt{z}|x-y|) = \frac{1}{2\pi} \log \frac{i}{\sqrt{z}\,|x-y|} + \dots$$

$$(x, y \in E_2;\ z \bar{\in} [0, \infty)) \tag{2.36}$$

(here the expansion is written with $|x - y|$ small).

We note the case $n = 3$. Since $K_{1/2}(s) = \sqrt{\pi/2s}\, e^{-s}$, we have from (2.35)

$$R(x, y; z) = \frac{1}{4\pi} \cdot \frac{e^{i\sqrt{z}|x-y|}}{|x-y|} \quad (x, y \in E_3;\ z \bar{\in} [0, \infty)). \tag{2.37}$$

Knowing expression (2.35) for the kernel of the resolvent operator, it is easy to find the spectral kernel. For this we use the general formula expressing the resolution of the identity E_λ of a selfadjoint operator by its resolvent R_z:

$$E(\Delta) = \lim_{\varepsilon \to +0} \frac{1}{2\pi i} \int_{\Delta + i\varepsilon} (R_z - R_{\bar{z}})\,dz, \tag{2.38}$$

the limit being understood in the weak sense. Let $f, g \in C_0(E_n)$. Then it follows from (2.35) and (2.38), that

$$(E(\Delta)f, g)_0 = \lim_{\varepsilon\to+0}\frac{1}{2\pi i}\int\limits_{\Delta+i\varepsilon}((R_z - R_{\bar z})f, g)_0\,dz$$

$$= \lim_{\varepsilon\to+0}\frac{1}{2\pi i}\int\limits_{\Delta+i\varepsilon}((R_z - R_z^*)f, g)_0\,dz \tag{2.39}$$

$$= \lim_{\varepsilon\to+0}\frac{1}{\pi}\int\limits_{\Delta+i\varepsilon}\left\{\int\limits_{E_n}\int\limits_{E_n}\operatorname{Im} R(x, y; z)\, f(y)\,\overline{g(x)}\,dxdy\right\}dz.$$

Here we use the fact that the kernel of the operator R_z^* is equal to $\overline{R(y, x; z)}$, which is equal to $\overline{R(x, y; z)}$ in view of the symmetry of the function (2.35) in x and y.

Since the kernels in (2.35) and (2.39) are sufficiently regular, we may take the limit under the integral sign. We calculate this limit. Using the expression $K_p(s) = (\pi i/2)\,e^{\pi p i/2}H_p^{(1)}(is)$ of the function K_p by means of the Hankel cylindrical functions $H_p^{(1)}$, we find that

$$\operatorname{Im} R(x, y; z) = \frac{1}{2^{\frac{n}{2}+1}\pi^{\frac{n}{2}-1}}\operatorname{Re}\left[\left(\frac{\sqrt{z}}{|x-y|}\right)^{\frac{n}{2}-1} H^{(1)}_{\frac{n}{2}-1}(\sqrt{z}\,|x-y|)\right]$$

$$(x, y \in E_n;\ z \overline{\in} [0, \infty)).$$

As z tends towards the half-line $(-\infty, 0)$ in the upper half plane, $\operatorname{Im} R(x, y; z)$ obviously tends to zero; as z tends towards the point $\lambda \in (0, \infty)$ we have

$$\lim_{z\to\lambda+i0}\operatorname{Im} R(x, y; z) = \frac{1}{2^{\frac{n}{2}+1}\pi^{\frac{n}{2}-1}}\left(\frac{\sqrt{\lambda}}{|x-y|}\right)^{\frac{n}{2}-1} J_{\frac{n}{2}-1}(\sqrt{\lambda}\,|x-y|) \tag{2.40}$$

(recall that $H_p^{(1)}(s) = J_p(s) + iN_p(s)$ where the functions $J_p(s)$ and $N_p(s)$ are real for $s > 0$). Hence from (2.39) we obtain

$$(E(\Delta)f, g)_0 = \int\limits_{\Delta\cap(0,\infty)}\left\{\int\limits_{E_n}\int\limits_{E_n}\Phi(x, y; \lambda)\, f(y)\,\overline{g(x)}\,dxdy\right\}d\lambda \tag{2.41}$$

$$(f, g \in C_0(E_n)),$$

$$\Phi(x, y; \lambda) = \Phi(x - y; \lambda) = \frac{1}{2^{\frac{n}{2}+1} \pi^{\frac{n}{2}}} \left(\frac{\sqrt{\lambda}}{|x-y|} \right)^{\frac{n}{2}-1} J_{\frac{n}{2}-1}$$

$$\times (\sqrt{\lambda}\,|x - y|) \quad (x, y \in E_n;\ \lambda > 0),$$

$$d\varrho(\lambda) = \begin{cases} d\lambda & \text{for } \lambda > 0, \\ 0 & \text{for } \lambda \leqslant 0. \end{cases}$$

In particular, for $n = 3$

$$\Phi(x, y; \lambda) = \frac{1}{4\pi^2} \cdot \frac{\sin(\sqrt{\lambda}\,|x-y|)}{|x-y|} \quad (x, y \in E_3;\ \lambda > 0). \tag{2.42}$$

We note that the Parseval equation (2.41) with $\Delta = (-\infty, \infty)$ is essentially the Parseval equation for the ordinary n-dimensional Fourier transform if the latter is put in spherical coordinates.

We now consider some integrals of the type (2.1), where $C(x, y)$ is the kernel of the operator $\gamma(\Lambda)$; $\gamma(\lambda) = 1/\lambda^N - z$, $N = [n/4] + 1$, $\operatorname{Im} z \neq 0$ (for $n = 2, 3$ $\gamma(\Lambda) = R_z$). As in the above, we find that these kernels depend on the difference $C(x, y) = C(x - y)$, $C(\cdot) \in L_2(E_n)$. Therefore, the integrals in question are constant. Consequently, for $p(x)$ used in the assertions of subsection 1, we may here choose an arbitrary function $p(x) \geq 1$ $(x \in E_n)$ such that $\int_{E_n} (1/p(x))dx < \infty$. For example, we may set $p(x) = (1 + |x|)^{n+\epsilon}$ $(\epsilon > 0)$.

b) *Schrödinger expressions.* They are of the form

$$Lu = -\Delta u + c(x)u, \tag{2.43}$$

where $c(x)$ is real; it is clear that L is formally selfadjoint. Now, certainly, all of the results of §§1 and 2 may be applied. We give the details of some of these. Let Λ be a minimal operator induced by the expression (2.43), considered on all of E_n $(n \geq 2)$. Applying Theorem 1.8, we conclude that if L is semi-bounded below on $C_0^\infty(E_n)$ then Λ is selfadjoint; here we assume that $c(x) \in C^{2+[n/2]}(E_n)$. In each case, with $n = 2, 3$, the amount of smoothness may be somewhat lowered. For example, we may take $c(x) \in C^2(E_n)$. The latter follows from the fact that for such a $c(x)$ it is possible to establish the hypotheses for the proofs of Theorem 1.8, and the solvability of the Cauchy problem for equation (1.33), now in the form $\partial^2 u/\partial t^2 - \Delta u + c(x)u = 0$ (see the following subsection).

Further, the semi-boundedness of L will automatically hold if $c(x) \geq C > -\infty$ $(x \in E_n)$: $(-\Delta u + c(x)u, u)_0 = -(\Delta u, u)_0 + (c(x)u, u)_0 \geq C\|u\|_0^2$ $(u \in C_0^\infty(E_n))$.

Therefore for $c(x) \geq C > -\infty$ $(x \in E_n)$, Λ is selfadjoint and its spectrum lies on $[C, \infty)$.

More detailed results connected with the estimation of the integrals in (2.1) will be given in subsection 10. In subsection 9 we state some results on hyperbolic equations.

9. **Some facts about hyperbolic equations.** We cite some formulas for the solution of hyperbolic equations which are of independent interest and of use in the study of the Schrödinger equation.

Let $x = (x_1, \cdots, x_n) \in E_n$, $t \in (-\infty, \infty)$, $p = (x, t) \in E_n \times (-\infty, \infty)$, $u = u(p)$. We set

$$\Box u = \frac{\partial^2 u}{\partial t^2} - D_1^2 u - \ldots - D_n^2 u,$$

$$\Gamma(p, q) = \sqrt{(t-\tau)^2 - (x_1 - y_1)^2 - \ldots - (x_n - y_n)^2} \tag{2.44}$$

$$(p = (x, t),\ q = (y, \tau) \in E_n \times (-\infty, \infty))$$

(i.e. $\Gamma(p, q)$ is the Lorentz distance between the points p and q). We denote by K_p the interior (below the pole) of the cone $\Gamma^2(p, q) = 0$ $(p = (x, t),\ t > 0)$, bounded above by the surfact $t = 0$. For the point $p, q \in E_n \times [0, \infty)$, we will write $q \prec p$ if $q \in K_p$ and $q \preccurlyeq p$ if $q \in \overline{K}_p$. We denote by $\hat{C}^2(\overline{K}_{p_0})$, the class of functions $u(p) \in C(\overline{K}_{p_0})$, for which the derivatives $(D_1^\alpha u)(x, t), \cdots, (D_n^\alpha u)(x, t)$ $(\alpha = 1, 2)$ exist for each t and are in $C(\overline{K}_{p_0})$.

We first consider the case $n = 2$.

Theorem 2.7. *Let $u(x, t) \in C^2(\overline{K}_{p_0})$ be a solution of the equation*

$$\Box u - a(x, t) u = f(x, t) \quad (a, f \in \hat{C}^2(\overline{K}_{p_0})); \tag{2.45}$$

here $p_0 = (x_0, t_0) \in E_2 \times (0, \infty)$ is fixed. Then a solution of class $C^2(\overline{K}_{p_0})$ of the perturbed equation

$$\Box v - [a(x, t) + \alpha(x, t)] v = f(x, t) + \varphi(x, t) \quad (\alpha, \varphi \in \hat{C}^2(\overline{K}_{p_0})), \tag{2.46}$$

satisfying the conditions $v(x, 0) = u(x, 0)$, $(\partial v/\partial t)(x, 0) = (\partial u/\partial t)(x, 0)$ $(|x - x_0| < t_0)$ exists and has the form

$$v(p) = u(p) + \int_{q \prec p} T(p, q)[\alpha(q) u(q) + \varphi(q)]\, dq. \tag{2.47}$$

Here the kernel $T(p, q)$ *is such that* $T(p, q)\Gamma(p, q)$ *is continuous in* (p, q) $(q \lesssim p \lesssim p_0)$. *If for* $a' \geq 0$

$$a' \leqslant a(p) + \alpha(p) \leqslant a'' \quad (p \lesssim p_0), \tag{2.48}$$

then

$$\sqrt{a'}\,\Omega(\sqrt{a'}\,\Gamma(p, q)) \leqslant T(p, q) \leqslant \sqrt{a''}\,\Omega(\sqrt{a''}\,\Gamma(p, q)) \quad (q < p \lesssim p_0); \tag{2.49}$$

$$\Omega(s) = \frac{1}{2\pi s}\operatorname{ch} s$$

(*the satisfaction of one of the inequalities in* (2.48) *implies the corresponding inequality in* (2.49)).

As a preliminary, we establish the following lemma.

Lemma 2.6. *If* $\mu(p) \in \hat{C}^2(\overline{K}_{p_0})$, *then*

$$g(p) = \frac{1}{2\pi}\int_{q \prec p} \frac{\mu(q)}{\Gamma(p, q)}\, dq \quad (p \lesssim p_0) \tag{2.50}$$

is in $C^2(\overline{K}_{p_0})$ *and satisfies the equation* $(\square g)(p) = \mu(p)$ $(p \precsim p_0)$ *with initial conditions* $g(x, 0) = 0$, $(\partial g/\partial t)(x, 0) = 0$ $(|x - x_0| < t_0)$.

Proof. We introduce cylindrical coordinates with the origin at the point $(x, 0)$ $(p = (x, t))$. Then $q = (y, \tau) = (y_1, y_2, \tau) = (x_1 + \rho\cos\phi,\ x_2 + \rho\sin\phi,\ \tau)$ and formula (2.50) takes the form

$$g(x, t) = \frac{1}{2\pi}\int_0^t \left[\int_0^{t-\tau} \frac{\varrho M(x; \varrho, \tau)}{\sqrt{(t-\tau)^2 - \varrho^2}}\, d\varrho\right] d\tau, \tag{2.51}$$

$$M(x; \varrho, \tau) = \int_0^{2\pi} \mu(x_1 + \varrho\cos\varphi,\ x_2 + \varrho\sin\varphi,\ \tau)\, d\varphi;$$

$M(x; \rho, \tau)$ is twice continuously differentiable in x_1, x_2 and ρ.

We establish the differentiability of $g(x, t)$ in t and calculate $\partial^2 g/\partial t^2$. For this we integrate by parts in the inner integral in (2.51):

$$g(x, t) = \frac{1}{2\pi}\int_0^t \left[M(x; 0, \tau)(t - \tau) + \int_0^{t-\tau} \sqrt{(t-\tau)^2 - \varrho^2}\left(\frac{\partial M}{\partial \varrho}\right)(x; \varrho, \tau)\, d\varrho\right] d\tau.$$

Differentiating this expression with respect to t, and then integrating by parts, we find that

$$\left(\frac{\partial g}{\partial t}\right)(x,t)=\frac{1}{2\pi}\int_0^t\left[M(x;0,\tau)+\int_0^{t-\tau}\frac{(t-\tau)\left(\frac{\partial M}{\partial \varrho}\right)(x;\varrho,\tau)}{\sqrt{(t-\tau)^2-\varrho^2}}\,d\varrho\right]d\tau$$

$$=\frac{1}{2\pi}\int_0^t\left[M(x;0,\tau)+(t-\tau)\left(\frac{\pi}{2}\left(\frac{\partial M}{\partial \varrho}\right)(x;t-\tau,\tau)\right.\right.$$

$$\left.\left.-\int_0^{t-\tau}\arcsin\frac{\varrho}{t-\tau}\cdot\left(\frac{\partial^2 M}{\partial \varrho^2}\right)(x;\varrho,\tau)\,d\varrho\right)\right]d\tau. \tag{2.52}$$

Hence

$$\left(\frac{\partial^2 g}{\partial t^2}\right)(x,t)=\frac{1}{2\pi}M(x;0,t)+\frac{1}{2\pi}\int_0^t\left[\frac{\pi}{2}\left(\frac{\partial M}{\partial \varrho}\right)(x;t-\tau,\tau)\right.$$

$$\left.-\int_0^{t-\tau}\arcsin\frac{\varrho}{t-\tau}\cdot\left(\frac{\partial^2 M}{\partial \varrho^2}\right)(x;\varrho,\tau)\,d\varrho+\int_0^{t-\tau}\frac{\varrho\left(\frac{\partial^2 M}{\partial \varrho^2}\right)(x;\varrho,\tau)}{\sqrt{(t-\tau)^2-\varrho^2}}\,d\varrho\right]d\tau$$

$$=\mu(p)+\frac{1}{2\pi}\int_0^t\left[\int_0^{t-\tau}\frac{1}{\sqrt{(t-\tau)^2-\varrho^2}}\left(\left(\frac{\partial M}{\partial \varrho}\right)(x;\varrho,\tau)\right.\right.$$

$$\left.\left.+\varrho\left(\frac{\partial^2 M}{\partial \varrho^2}\right)\right)(x;\varrho,\tau)\right)d\varrho\Bigg]d\tau.$$

Differentiating M in (2.51) with respect to ρ and integrating by parts, it is clear that $(\partial M/\partial\rho)\ (x;\rho,\tau)+\rho\,(\partial^2M/\partial\rho^2)\ (x;\rho,\tau)=\rho((D_1^2+D_2^2)M)\ (x;\rho,\tau)$. Thus

$$\left(\frac{\partial^2 g}{\partial t^2}\right)(x,t)=\mu(\varrho)+\frac{1}{2\pi}\int_0^t\left[\int_0^{t-\tau}\frac{\varrho\left(\left(\frac{\partial^2 M}{\partial x_1^2}\right)(x;\varrho,\tau)+\left(\frac{\partial^2 M}{\partial x_2^2}\right)(x;\varrho,\tau)\right)}{\sqrt{(t-\tau)^2-\varrho^2}}\,d\varrho\right]d\tau. \tag{2.53}$$

Differentiating g in (2.51) with respect to x_1 and x_2 and equating the result with (2.53), we obtain that $(\square g)\ (p)=\mu(p)$.

The continuity of $\partial^2 g/\partial t^2$, $D_1^2 g$ and $D_2^2 g$ as functions of $(x,\ t)\in\overline{K}_{p0}$

follows from the above expression for these derivatives and the following easily verified basic remark (cf. the proof of the continuity of the integral (2.64)): if $f(x;\ \rho, \tau)$ is continuous in x and bounded as a function of all of the variables, then

$$\int_0^t \left[\int_0^{t-\tau} \frac{\varrho f(x; \varrho, \tau)}{\sqrt{(t-\tau)^2 - \varrho^2}} d\varrho \right] d\tau = F(x, t) \in C(\overline{K}_{p_0}). \tag{2.54}$$

It remains to note that it follows from (2.51) and (2.52) that $g(x, 0) = 0$, $(\partial g/\partial t)\ (x, 0) = 0\ (|x - x_0| < t_0)$. The lemma is proved.

Proof of the theorem. We will seek a solution of the form

$$v(p) = u(p) + \frac{1}{2\pi} \int_{q \prec p} \frac{\mu(q)}{\Gamma(p, q)} dq \qquad (p \prec p_0) \tag{2.55}$$

where the function $\mu \in \hat{C}^2(\overline{K}_{p_0})$ is subject to definition. Applying the expression $\square - (a + \alpha)E$ to (2.55) and using Lemma 2.6 we obtain

$$\square v - (a + \alpha)\, v = (\square - aE)\, v - \alpha v = (\square - aE) \left(u + \frac{1}{2\pi} \int \ldots \right)$$

$$- \alpha u - \frac{\alpha}{2\pi} \int \ldots = f + (\square - aE) \left(\frac{1}{2\pi} \int \ldots \right) - \alpha u - \frac{\alpha}{2\pi} \int \ldots$$

$$= f(p) + \mu(p) - \alpha(p)\, u(p) - \frac{1}{2\pi} [a(p) + \alpha(p)] \int_{q \prec p} \frac{\mu(q)}{\Gamma(p, q)} dq.$$

Thus for the function (2.55) to be a solution of (2.46), it is sufficient to choose for $\mu(p)$ a solution of

$$\mu(p) = \alpha(p)\, u(p) + \varphi(p) + \frac{1}{2\pi} [a(p) + \alpha(p)] \int_{q \prec p} \frac{\mu(q)}{\Gamma(p, q)} dq \qquad (p \leqslant p_0), \tag{2.56}$$

which is a function of class $\hat{C}^2(\overline{K}_{p_0})$. This equation is conveniently written in the form

$$\mu(p) = h(p) + (AB\mu)(p);$$

$$h(p) = \alpha(p)\, u(p) + \varphi(p), \qquad (Ag)(p) = [a(p) + \alpha(p)]\, g(p) = A(p)\, g(p),$$

$$(Bg)(p) = \frac{1}{2\pi} \int_{q \prec p} \frac{g(q)}{\Gamma(p, q)} dq \qquad (p \prec p_0). \tag{2.57}$$

Equation (2.57) will be considered on the space $M(K_{p_0})$ of bounded functions on K_{p_0} with the uniform norm $\|\cdot\|$. The formal solution to this equation has the form

$$\mu(p)=\sum_{j=0}^{\infty}((AB)^j h)(p), \tag{2.58}$$

$$((AB)^j h)(p)=\frac{1}{2\pi}\int\limits_{s_1\prec p}\frac{A(p)}{\Gamma(p,s_1)}((AB)^{j-1}h)(s_1)\,ds_1$$

$$=\frac{1}{(2\pi)^2}\iint\limits_{s_2\prec s_1\prec p}\frac{A(p)\,A(s_1)}{\Gamma(p,s_1)\,\Gamma(s_1,s_2)}((AB)^{j-2}h)(s_2)\,ds_2ds_1=\dots$$

$$=\frac{1}{(2\pi)^j}\iint\cdots\iint\limits_{s_j\prec s_{j-1}\prec\dots\prec s_2\prec s_1\prec p}\frac{A(p)\,A(s_1)\dots A(s_{j-2})\,A(s_{j-1})}{\Gamma(p,s_1)\,\Gamma(s_1,s_2)\dots\Gamma(s_{j-2},s_{j-1})\,\Gamma(s_{j-1},s_j)}$$
$$\times\, h(s_j)\,ds_jds_{j-1}\dots ds_2ds_1$$

$$=\int\limits_{s_j\prec p_0}\left[\frac{1}{(2\pi)^j}\int\limits_{s_j\prec s_{j-1}\prec\dots\prec s_2\prec s_1\prec p}\dots\int\frac{A(p)\dots A(s_{j-1})}{\Gamma(p,s_1)\dots\Gamma(s_{j-1},s_j)}ds_{j-1}\dots ds_1\right]h(s_j)\,ds_j$$
$$(p\prec p_0;\ j=1,2,\dots).$$

For the proof of the convergence of the series (2.58) we use the following formula (M. Riesz [1], pp. 31–33):

$$\int\limits_{q\prec s\prec p}\Gamma^{\beta-n-1}(p,s)\,\Gamma^{\gamma-n-1}(s,q)\,ds=\frac{C(\beta)\,C(\gamma)}{C(\beta+\gamma)}\Gamma^{\beta+\gamma-n-1}(p,q), \tag{2.59}$$

$$C(\beta)=\pi^{\frac{n-1}{2}}2^{\beta-1}\Gamma\left(\frac{\beta}{2}\right)\Gamma\left(\frac{\beta-n+1}{2}\right)\qquad(\beta,\gamma>n-1),$$

written for the general case of the space E_n.

Applying this formula several times with $n=2$, we obtain

$$\int\limits_{q\prec s_N\prec\dots\prec s_1\prec p}\cdots\int\frac{ds_1\dots ds_N}{\Gamma(q,s_N)\dots\Gamma(s_1,p)}=\frac{(2\pi)^N}{(2N)!}\Gamma^{2N-1}(p,q) \tag{2.60}$$
$$(N=1,2,\dots).$$

We estimate $\|(AB)^j\|$. If we note that the norm of the integral operator $(Kf)(p)=\int_{q\prec p_0}K(p,q)\,f(q)\,dq$ is equal to $\sup_{p\prec p_0}\int_{q\prec p_0}|K(p,q)|\,dq$, we may use (2.60) to obtain

$$\|(AB)^j\|=\sup_{p\prec p_0}\int\limits_{s_j\prec p_0}\left|\frac{1}{(2\pi)^j}\int\limits_{s_j\prec s_{j-1}\prec\dots\prec s_1\prec p}\dots\int\frac{A(p)\dots A(s_{j-1})}{\Gamma(p,s_1)\dots\Gamma(s_{j-1},s_j)}ds_{j-1}\dots ds_1\right|ds_j\leqslant$$

$$\leqslant \left(\frac{C}{2\pi}\right)^j \sup_{p \prec p_0} \int\limits_{s_j \prec p_0} \left(\int\limits_{s_j \prec s_{j-1} \prec \ldots \prec s_1 \prec p} \cdots \int \frac{ds_{j-1} \ldots ds_1}{\Gamma(p, s_1) \ldots \Gamma(s_{j-1}, s_j)} \right) ds_j$$

$$= \left(\frac{C}{2\pi}\right)^j \sup_{p \prec p_0} \int\limits_{s_j \prec p_0} \left(\frac{(2\pi)^{j-1}}{(2j-2)!} \Gamma^{2j-3}(s_j, p) \right) ds_j \leqslant \frac{C^j C_1^{2j-2}}{2\pi(2j-2)!} \sup_{p \prec p_0} \int\limits_{s_j \prec p_0} \frac{ds_j}{\Gamma(s_j, p)}$$

$$\leqslant \frac{C_2^j}{(2j-2)!} \qquad (j = 1, 2, \ldots; C = \sup_{p \prec p_0} |A(p)|). \tag{2.61}$$

Therefore the series (2.58) converges in the norm of the space $M(K_{p_0})$.

From the observation that the integral (2.54) is continuous, we conclude that ABh, $(AB)^2 h$, etc., lie in $C(\overline{K}_{p_0})$. Since the series (2.58) converges uniformly, $\mu \in C(\overline{K}_{p_0})$. To show that $\mu \in \hat{C}^2(\overline{K}_{p_0})$, it is necessary to establish the existence of the first and second continuous derivatives of $\mu(x, t)$ with respect to x_1 and x_2. We show, for example, that $D_1^2 \mu \in C(\overline{K}_{p_0})$.

First of all, we note that D_1 and B commute for sufficiently smooth w: $D_1 Bw = BD_1 w$. In fact, writing the action of B in the form of the integral (2.51), we obtain

$$(D_1 Bw)(x, t) = D_1 \int_0^t \left[\int_0^{t-\tau} \left(\int_0^{2\pi} w(x_1 + \varrho \cos \varphi, x_2 + \varrho \sin \varphi, \tau)\, d\varphi \right) \frac{\varrho\, d\varrho}{\sqrt{(t-\tau)^2 - \varrho^2}} \right] d\tau$$

$$= \int_0^t \left[\int_0^{t-\tau} \left(\int_0^{2\pi} (D_1 w)(x_1 + \varrho \cos \varphi, x_2 + \varrho \sin \varphi, \tau)\, d\varphi \right) \frac{\varrho\, d\varrho}{\sqrt{(t-\tau)^2 - \varrho^2}} \right] d\tau$$

$$= (BD_1 w)(x, t) \qquad ((x, t) \leqslant p_0).$$

We will now compute $D_1(AB)^j w$, by moving D_1 under the integral sign. In result, we obtain a sum consisting of the following terms: $(AB)^j (D_1 w)$ and j expressions of the form $(AB) \cdots (AB)w$ (j times) in each of which the operator A is replaced by the operator of multiplication by $(D_1 A)(x, t)$. We compute $D_1^2 (AB)^j w = D_1(D_1(AB)^j w)$, analogously inserting D_1 into each of $j + 1$ indicated terms. We obtain a sum of $(j + 1)^2$ terms of the form $(AB) \cdots (AB)w$ (j times) in which A and w are replaced by $D_1 A$, $D_1^2 A$, $D_1 w$, $D_1^2 w$, where the sum of the orders of the derivatives in each term is equal to 2. Estimating $\|D_1^2 (AB)^j w\|$ similarly to (2.61), we obtain

$$\| D_1^2 (AB)^j w \| \leqslant (j+1)^2 \frac{C_3^j}{(2j-2)!} (\| w \| + \| D_1 w \| + \| D_1^2 w \|)$$

$$(j = 1, 2, \ldots).$$

If $w \in \hat{C}^2(\overline{K}_{p_0})$, it follows from Lemma 2.6 that w is sufficiently smooth for the calculation just completed. Therefore the resulting estimate is valid with $w = h = \alpha u + \phi \in \hat{C}^2(\overline{K}_{p_0})$. Hence the series $\mu(x, t) = \Sigma_{j=0}^{\infty} ((AB)^j h)(x, t)$ may be twice termwise differentiated with respect to x_1 and the series obtained are uniformly convergent for $(x, t) \preccurlyeq p_0$. Since each term $D_1^2 (AB)^j h$ is in $C(\overline{K}_{p_0})$ by Lemma 2.6, $D_1^2 \mu \in C(\overline{K}_{p_0})$ as was required.

So the solution μ of equation (2.41) is in the class $\hat{C}^2(\overline{K}_{p_0})$, and consequently, v of form (2.55) satisfies equation (2.46) and is in $C^2(\overline{K}_{p_0})$. As established in Lemma 2.6, the integral (2.50) satisfies the null Cauchy conditions at $t = 0$ and therefore the Cauchy conditions for u and v are identical.

We construct the kernel $T(p, q)$. For this we evaluate the sum in (2.58):

$$\mu(q) = \sum_{j=0}^{\infty} ((AB)^j h)(q) = h(q)$$

$$+ \sum_{j=1}^{\infty} \int_{s_j \prec p_0} \left[\frac{1}{(2\pi)^j} \int_{s_j \prec s_{j-1} \prec \dots \prec s_1 \prec q} \cdots \int \frac{A(q) \dots A(s_{j-1})}{\Gamma(q, s_1) \dots \Gamma(s_{j-1}, s_j)} ds_{j-1} \dots ds_1 \right] h(s_j)\, ds_j \tag{2.62}$$

$$= h(q) + \int_{s_j \prec p_0} \left[\sum_{j=1}^{\infty} \frac{1}{(2\pi)^j} \int_{s_j \prec s_{j-1} \prec \dots \prec s_1 \prec q} \cdots \int \frac{A(q) \dots A(s_{j-1})}{\Gamma(q, s_1) \dots \Gamma(s_{j-1}, s_j)} ds_{j-1} \dots ds_1 \right] h(s_j)\, ds_j.$$

Inserting (2.62) in (2.55) we find that v has the form (2.47), where

$$T(p, s) = \frac{1}{2\pi\Gamma(p, s)} + \sum_{j=1}^{\infty} \frac{1}{(2\pi)^{j+1}} \int_{s \prec s_j \prec \dots \prec s_1 \prec p} \cdots \int \frac{A(s_1) \dots A(s_j)}{\Gamma(p, s_1) \dots \Gamma(s_j, s)} ds_j \dots ds_1. \tag{2.63}$$

The term f_j of this series is bounded above in modulus by the expression $(1/(2j)!)\, C^j \Gamma^{2j-1}(p, s)$ ($C = \sup_{p \prec p_0} |A(p)|$) (see formula (2.60)). Therefore the series converges uniformly for $s \preccurlyeq p \preccurlyeq p_0$ so that differentiating, integrating, and rearranging are permissible. Further, the estimate (2.48) yields the inequalities $(1/(2j)!)\, a'^j \Gamma^{2j-1}(p, s) \le f_j \le (1/(2j)!)\, a''^j \Gamma^{2j-1}(p, s)$, the sum of which gives (2.49).

It remains for us to verify the continuity of the kernel $T(p, q)\Gamma(p, q)$ with respect to (p, q) $(q \preccurlyeq p \preccurlyeq p_0)$. It is clear from the uniform convergence of the series in (2.64) that it is sufficient to prove that *if* $f(p, q, s)$ $(q \preccurlyeq s \preccurlyeq p \preccurlyeq p_0)$ *are continuous in* (p, q) *and bounded in all of the variables, then the integral*

$$\int_{q \prec s \prec p} \frac{f(p, q, s)}{\Gamma(p, s)\,\Gamma(s, q)}\, ds = F(p, q) \tag{2.64}$$

is continuous in (p, q). We show this by passing to the limit under the integral sign. This passage is possible since by (2.59), we have, for some $\delta > 1$ (e.g. $\delta = 3/2$)

$$\int_{q \prec s \prec p} \left| \frac{f(p, q, s)}{\Gamma(p, s)\,\Gamma(s, q)} \right|^{\delta} ds \leqslant C \int_{q \prec s \prec p} \frac{ds}{\Gamma^{\frac{3}{2}}(p, s)\,\Gamma^{\frac{3}{2}}(s, q)} = C_1$$

uniformly in (p, q) $(q \leqslant p \leqslant p_0)$. The theorem is proved.

We now derive some relations for the kernel $T(p, q)$ of (2.47). We set

$$T_{a+\alpha}(p, q) = \begin{cases} T(p, q) & \text{for } q < p, \\ 0 & \text{for } q \,\overline{\in}\, K_p \end{cases} \quad (p, q \in E_2 \times [0, \infty)) \tag{2.65}$$

(it follows from (2.63) that the kernel $T(p, q)$ depends only on the sum $a(p) + \alpha(p) = A(p)$). Formula (2.47) may be rewritten in the form

$$v(p) = u(p) + \int_{E_2 \times [0, \infty)} T_{a+\alpha}(p, q)[\alpha(q)\, u(q) + \varphi(q)]\, dq \quad (p \leqslant p_0). \tag{2.66}$$

We consider the initial conditions $u(x, 0) = (\partial u/\partial t)(x, 0) = 0$ $(|x - x_0| < t_0)$ and set $a = f = 0$. Then after replacing α by a and ϕ by f we find that *the solution of the equation* $\Box u - a(x, t)\, u = f(x, t)$, *where* $a, f \in \hat{C}^2(\overline{K}_{p_0})$, *satisfies the null Cauchy condition with* $t = 0$, *is in* $C^2(\overline{K}_{p_0})$ *and takes the form*

$$u(p) = \int_{E_2 \times [0, \infty)} T_a(p, q)\, f(q)\, dq = \int_{q \prec p} T_a(p, q)\, f(q)\, dq \quad (p \leqslant p_0) \tag{2.67}$$

$$\left(T_0(p, q) = \frac{1}{2\pi} \frac{1}{\Gamma(p, q)},\quad q < p \right).$$

Inserting (2.67) into (2.66) and setting $\phi = 0$, we find the following expression for the solution $v \in C^2(\overline{K}_{p_0})$ satisfying the null boundary conditions of equation (2.46):

$$v(p) = u(p) + \int_{E_2 \times [0, \infty)} T_{a+\alpha}(p, s)\, \alpha(s)\, u(s)\, ds$$

$$= \int_{E_2 \times [0, \infty)} \left| T_a(p, q) + \int_{E_2 \times [0, \infty)} T_{a+\alpha}(p, s)\, \alpha(s)\, T_a(s, q)\, ds \right| f(q)\, dq. \tag{2.68}$$

On the other hand, by (2.67) we obtain

$$v(p) = \int_{E_2 \times [0,\infty)} T_{a+\alpha}(p, q) f(q)\, dq. \tag{2.69}$$

Since solutions of a Cauchy problem are unique, the right-hand sides of (2.68) and (2.69) are equal for arbitrary $f \in \hat{C}^2(\overline{K}_{p0})$. Therefore

$$T_{a+\alpha}(p,q) = T_a(p,q) + \int_{E_2 \times [0,\infty)} T_{a+\alpha}(p,s)\,\alpha(s)\,T_a(s,q)\,ds$$

$$= T_a(p,q) + \int_{q \prec s \prec p} T_{a+\alpha}(p,s)\,\alpha(s)\,T_a(s,q)\,ds \quad (p, q \leqslant p_0;\ a, \alpha \in \hat{C}^2(\overline{K}_{p_0})). \tag{2.70}$$

Integrating (2.70), we obtain a series representation for $T_{a+\alpha}$ in the form

$$T_{a+\alpha}(p,q) = T_a(p,q) + \int_{q \prec s_1 \prec p} T_a(p,s_1)\,\alpha(s_1)\,T_a(s_1,q)\,ds_1$$

$$+ \iint_{q \prec s_1 \prec s_2 \prec p} T_a(p,s_1)\,\alpha(s_1)\,T_a(s_1,s_2)\,\alpha(s_2)\,T_a(s_2,q)\,ds_1 ds_2 + \ldots \quad (p, q \leqslant p_0). \tag{2.71}$$

From the estimate (2.49) for T_α and formula (2.60) it follows that this series converges uniformly.

We now sketch the situation for the case of any dimension $n \geq 2$. We introduce the integral operator I^β (β is complex):

$$(I^\beta \mu)(p) = \frac{1}{C(\beta)} \int_{q \prec p} \Gamma^{\beta-n-1}(p,q)\,\mu(q)\,dq \qquad (p \in E_n \times [0,\infty)). \tag{2.72}$$

For the existence of the integral in (2.71) we must assume that $\operatorname{Re}\beta > n-1$. By formula (2.59) the operators I^β have the semigroup property:

$$I^\beta I^\gamma = I^{\beta+\gamma} \quad (\operatorname{Re}\beta, \operatorname{Re}\gamma > n-1).$$

As in Lemma 2.6 it can be shown, for sufficiently smooth μ, that $\mu \,\Box I^{\beta+2}\mu = I^\beta \mu$ $(\operatorname{Re}\beta > n-1)$. It turns out that this equation has an analytic continuation into the half-plane $\operatorname{Re}\beta > 0$, where on letting $\beta \longrightarrow 0$ we obtain that $\Box I^2 \mu = I^0\mu = \mu$. In the case of $n = 2$, $2 > n-1$, and therefore $I^2\mu$ can be computed immediately by using formula (2.72). It corresponds to $B\mu$ in the notation of the proof of Theorem 2.7. If $n = 3$, then $I^2\mu$ is computed as $\lim_{\epsilon \to +0} I^{2+\epsilon}\mu$. Here the expression for I^2 is more complicated; it is a generalized kernel $T_0(p,q)$, concentrated on the cone K_p. For $n > 3$ an analytic continuation is necessary as a preliminary.

These assertions may be used in place of Lemma 2.6 in an attempt to prove an analog of Theorem 2.7 with $n > 2$. Namely, one may act as follows. Following the formal scheme of the proof of Theorem 2.7, by (2.63) $T(p, q)$ appears as the kernel of the operator $\Sigma_{j=0}^{\infty} I^2(AI^2)^j$. The series $\Sigma_{j=0}^{\infty} I^{\beta_0}(AI^{\beta_1} \dots AI^{\beta_j})$ is then constructed with $\operatorname{Re} \beta_k > n - 1$ $(k = 0, 1, \cdots)$. This series converges nicely to an operator with a kernel, the structure of which is easily obtained by using arguments similar to those used for the case $n = 2$. Then in this resulting kernel $T(p, q; \beta_0, \beta_1, \cdots)$ the limit $\beta_j \longrightarrow 2$ is taken to obtain the desired kernel $T(p, q)$. For $n = 3$, it is simply necessary to take the limit; such a passage is possible and, in fact, reduces to an analog of Theorem 2.7. For $n > 3$ an analytic continuation is necessary; we will not dwell on this case.

We formulate such an analog for the case $n = 3$.

Theorem 2.8. *If $n = 3$ Theorem 2.7 remains valid in its entirety with the following changes in the formulas:* 1) $a(x, t) + \alpha(x, t)$ *is continuously differentiable in t for each x;* 2) *representation* (2.47) *acquires the form*

$$u(p) = u(p) + \frac{1}{4\pi} \int\limits_{|x-y|<t} \frac{a(y, t-|x-y|)\, u(y, t-|x-y|) + \varphi(y, t-|x-y|)}{|x-y|} dy \tag{2.73}$$

$$+ \int\limits_{q \prec p} T_{\mathrm{reg}}(p, q)\, [\alpha(q)\, u(q) + \varphi(q)]\, dq \qquad (p = (x, t), q = (y, \tau)),$$

i.e. the kernel $T(p, q)$ consists of two terms: the singular term T_{sing}, concentrated on K_p, and the regular one, $T_{\mathrm{reg}}(p, q)$; 3) *the estimate* (2.49) *acquires the form*

$$a'\Omega(\sqrt{a'}\Gamma(p, q)) \leqslant T_{\mathrm{reg}}(p, q) \leqslant a''\Omega(\sqrt{a''}\Gamma(p, q)) \quad (q \prec p \leqslant p_0); \tag{2.74}$$

$$\Omega(s) = \frac{t}{4\pi s} J_{-1}(is).$$

If, in analogy with (2.65), a kernel $T_{a+\alpha}$ is introduced for T_{reg}, then it is possible to obtain relations of the type (2.66)–(2.71).

In conclusion we note that the constructions of this subsection remain valid if the functions are of class $\hat{C}^2(\overline{K}_{p_0})$ and not of type C^2 and have sufficiently weak discontinuities in the derivatives. For example, one may define $\hat{C}^2(\overline{K}_{p0})$ to consist of functions $u(p) \in C(\overline{K}_{p0})$, the derivatives of which exist below the plane $x_1 = 0$ and are continuous up to the boundary of this plane (for each fixed t).

10. The Schrödinger expression. Further investigation. As previously, we will consider the expression (2.43) on all of E_n. First we will let $n = 2$. By (2.67), the solution $u(x, t)$ of the problem

$$\frac{\partial^2 u}{\partial t^2} - \Delta u + c(x) u = g(x), \quad u(x, 0) = \left(\frac{\partial u}{\partial t}\right)(x, 0) = 0$$

$$(x \in E_2;\ t \in [0, \infty)) \tag{2.75}$$

is in $C^2(E_2 \times [0, \infty))$ and takes the form

$$u(x, t) = \int_{E_2} W_{-c}(x, t;\ y)\, g(y)\, dy, \tag{2.76}$$

$$W_{-c}(x, t;\ y) = \int_0^\infty T_{-c}((x, t), (y, \tau))\, d\tau = \int_0^{t-|x-y|} T_{-c}((x, t), (y, \tau))\, d\tau$$

$$(x, y \in E_2;\ t \in [0, \infty)).$$

The kernel $W_{-c}(x, t;\ y)$ is obviously analytic for $|x - y| > t$. We establish some facts related to the kernels T_{-c} and W_{-c}.

Lemma 2.7. *The estimate*

$$\left| T_{-c}(p_0, q) - \frac{1}{2\pi\Gamma(p_0, q)} \operatorname{ch}\left(\sqrt{-c(x_0)}\, \Gamma(p_0, q)\right) \right|$$

$$\leqslant \frac{1}{2\pi\Gamma(p_0, q)} \left(\operatorname{ch}\left(\sqrt{c_-(x_0) + \omega(x_0, t_0)}\, \Gamma(p_0, q)\right)\right.$$

$$\left. - \operatorname{ch}\left(\sqrt{c_-(x_0)}\, \Gamma(p_0, q)\right)\right) \quad (q < p_0 = (x_0, t_0) \in E_2 \times (0, \infty)) \tag{2.77}$$

holds, where $c_-(x_0) = \max(-c(x_0), 0)$ *and* $\omega(x_0, \delta)$ *denotes the modulus of continuity of the function* $c(x)$ *at the point* x_0.

Proof. We fix $x_0 \in E_2$ and set $-c(x) = a + \alpha(x)$, where $a = -c(x_0)$, $\alpha(x) = c(x_0) - c(x)$; $|\alpha(x)| \leq \omega(x_0, t_0)$ for x contained in the sphere $|x_0 - x| \leq t_0$. It follows from (2.60) that, independent of the sign of a,

$$T_a(p, q) = \frac{1}{2\pi\Gamma(p, q)} \operatorname{ch}(\sqrt{a}\,\Gamma(p, q)) \quad (q \prec p; \quad a = \text{const}). \tag{2.78}$$

By (2.71) and (2.78) with $c(x_0) \leq 0$, we have

$$|T_{-c}(p_0, q) - \frac{1}{2\pi\Gamma(p_0, q)} \operatorname{ch}(\sqrt{-c(x_0)}\,\Gamma(p_0, q))| = |T_{a+\alpha}(p_0, q)$$

$$- T_a(p_0, q)| \leqslant \int_{q \prec s_1 \prec p_0} |T_a(p_0, s_1)|\,|\alpha(s_1)|\,|T_a(s_1, q)|\,ds_1$$

$$+ \ldots \leqslant \int_{q \prec s_1 \prec p_0} T_a(p_0, s_1)\,\omega(x_0, t_0)\,T_a(s_1, q)\,ds_1 + \ldots$$

$$= T_a(p_0, q) + \int_{q \prec s_1 \prec p_0} T_a(p_0, s_1)\,\omega(x_0, t_0)\,T_a(s_1, q)\,ds_1 + \ldots - T_a(p_0, q)$$

$$= T_{a+\omega(x_0, t_0)}(p_0, q) - T_a(p_0, q) =$$

$$= \frac{1}{2\pi\Gamma(p_0, q)} (\operatorname{ch}(\sqrt{a + \omega(x_0, t_0)}\,\Gamma(p_0, q)) - \operatorname{ch}(\sqrt{a}\,\Gamma(p_0, q))), \tag{2.79}$$

i.e., (2.77). If $c(x_0) > 0$ we have $a < 0$ and

$$|T_a(p_0, q)| = \frac{1}{2\pi\Gamma(p_0, q)} |\operatorname{ch}(\sqrt{a}\,\Gamma(p_0, q))|$$

$$\leqslant \frac{1}{2\pi\Gamma(p_0, q)} = T_0(p_0, q).$$

Therefore the last part of the estimate (2.79) (starting with the second $\leq$ sign) is changed: a must be replaced by 0. As a result we again arrive at (2.77). The lemma is proved.

Lemma 2.8. *Let* $c(x)$, $c_-(x)$ *and* $\omega(x_0, t_0)$ *be as in Lemma 2.7. The kernel* $W_{-c}(x, t; y)$ *is continuous as a function of* $(x, t, y) \in E_2 \times [0, \infty) \times E_2$ *in the region* $|x - y| > 0$, *vanishes for* $|x - y| \geq t$ *and as a function of* x *and* y, *is in* $L_2(E_n)$. *The inequality*

$$|W_{-c}(x_0, t_0; y) - W_{-c(x_0)}(x_0, t_0; y)| \leqslant W_{c_-(x_0)+\omega(x_0, t_0)}(x_0, t_0; y)$$

$$- W_{c_-(x_0)}(x_0, t_0; y) \quad ((x_0, t_0, y) \in E_2 \times [0, \infty) \times E_2) \tag{2.80}$$

is valid.

Proof. From Theorem 2.7, it follows that for each fixed τ, $T_{-c}((x, t), (y, \tau)) \longrightarrow$

$T_{-c}((x_0, t_0), (y_0, \tau))$ as $(x, t, y) \longrightarrow (x_0, t_0, y_0)$, with $|x_0 - y_0| < t_0 - \tau$. Therefore, by definition (2.76) of the kernel W_{-c}, to establish the continuity of this kernel at the point (x_0, t_0, y_0) where $0 < |x_0 - y_0| < t_0$, it is sufficient to show that one may take the limit under the integral sign in (2.76). For this, it is sufficient to show, for example, that $\int_0^\infty |T_{-c}((x, t), (y, \tau))|^{3/2}\, d\tau \le C < \infty$ uniformly for (x, t, y) sufficiently near (x_0, t_0, y_0) (we note that all of the $T_{-c}((x, t), (y, \tau))$ vanish off some finite interval of variation of τ). Since the kernel $T_{-c}(p, q)\Gamma(p, q)$ is bounded in bounded regions of the point (p, q) (Theorem 2.7), we have, for some $\eta > 0$

$$\int_0^\infty |T_{-c}((x, t), (y, \tau))|^{\frac{3}{2}}\, d\tau \leqslant C_1 \int_0^{t-|x-y|} \frac{d\tau}{[(t-\tau)^2 - |x-y|^2]^{\frac{3}{4}}}$$

$$< \frac{C_1}{\eta^{\frac{3}{4}}} \int_0^{t-|x-y|} \frac{d\tau}{[t-\tau-|x-y|]^{\frac{3}{4}}} \leqslant C_2 < \infty,$$

which was required. Therefore, the continuity of $W_{-c}(x, t; y)$ in the region $0 < |x - y| < t$ is established.

For the proof of the stated continuity of the kernel W_{-c}, it remains to show that $W_{-c}(x, t; y) \longrightarrow 0$, if $(x, t, y) \longrightarrow (x_0, t_0, y_0)$, where $|x - y| \longrightarrow t \geq \eta > 0$. This relation follows from the following inequality, which follows, in turn, from the boundedness of $T_{-c}(p, q)\Gamma(p, q)$ in bounded regions of (p, q):

$$|W_{-c}(x, t; y)| \leqslant C \int_0^{t-|x-y|} \frac{d\tau}{\sqrt{(t-\tau)^2 - |x-y|^2}}$$

$$= C[\log(t + \sqrt{t^2 - |x-y|^2}) - \log|x-y|] \underset{|x-y|\to t}{\to} 0. \qquad (2.81)$$

From (2.81) we also obtain the inclusion $W_{-c}(\cdot, t; y)$, $W_{-c}(x, t; \cdot) \in L_2(E_2)$ $(y, x \in E_2;\ t \in [0, \infty))$.

The inequality (2.80) is obtained by integrating (2.77). The lemma follows.

With this lemma it is possible to prove

Theorem 2.9. *Consider the two-dimensional, semi-bounded below Schrödinger expression* (2.43) *on* $C_0^\infty(E_2)$ *with* $c(x) \in C^2(E_2)$. *As shown in subsection* 8, b), *there exists a minimal operator* Λ *which is semi-bounded below and selfadjoint.*

For each $t \geq 0$ *the operator* $2\Lambda^{-1}\sin^2(\frac{1}{2}\sqrt{\Lambda}\, t)$ [1] *exists as an integral operator with the Carleman kernel* $C_t(x, y) = W_{-c}(x, t; y)$ $(x, y \in E_2)$. *This kernel is a continuous function of* $(x, t, y) \in E_2 \times [0, \infty) \times E_2$ *in the region* $|x - y| > 0$ *and vanishes for* $|x - y| \geq t$. *The estimate*

$$|C_t(x, y)| \leqslant \frac{3}{2\pi} e^{t\sqrt{c_-(x) + \omega(x, t)}} \log \frac{2t}{|x - y|}$$

$$(x, y \in E_2;\ |x - y| \leqslant t;\quad 0 \leqslant t < \infty) \tag{2.82}$$

holds (here $c_-(x) = \max(-c(x), 0)$ *and* $\omega(x, \delta)$ *is the modulus of continuity of the function* c *at the point* x). [2]

As a preliminary, we make one basic remark. We use the notation of §1.7 and consider weak solutions of the Cauchy problem for the equation

$$\frac{d^2u}{dt^2} + S^*u = g(t) \ (0 \leqslant t < \infty), \tag{2.83}$$

where $g(t)$ is a vector-function with values in H which is strongly continuous for $t \in [0, \infty)$ (the definition of a weak solution for (2.83) differs from the definition (1.18) in that in this equation $(g(t), f)$ must replace 0 on the right, and S is replaced by $-S$). Let S be an Hermitian operator, semi-bounded below by the number C (i.e., $(Sf, f) \geq C\|f\|^2$, $f \in \mathfrak{D}(S)$) and let E_λ be the spectral resolution corresponding to one of its selfadjoint extensions A, which is also semi-bounded from below by C. Let $g(t) \in \mathfrak{D}(\sqrt{A})$ for each $t \in [0, \infty)$. As on p. 393 it is easy to verify that the vector-function

$$u(t) = \int_0^t \left(\int_C^\infty \frac{1}{\sqrt{\lambda}} \sin \sqrt{\lambda}(t - \tau)\, dE_\lambda \right) g(\tau)\, d\tau \ (0 \leqslant t < \infty) \tag{2.84}$$

is a weak solution of the equation (2.83) which satisfies the conditions $u(0) = (du/dt)(0) = 0$. If $g(t) = g$, independent of t, then (2.84) is rewritten in the form

---

1) This is the notation for the operator $F(\Lambda)$ corresponding to the entire function $F(\lambda) = 2\lambda^{-1}\sin^2(\frac{1}{2}\sqrt{\lambda}\, t)$.

2) Semi-boundedness from below of the expression (2.43) may not actually be necessary. Without it, some complications arise in the arguments used to prove that the unbounded operator $2A^{-1}\sin^2(\frac{1}{2}\sqrt{A}\, t)$ (A is a selfadjoint extension of Λ) is an integral operator with Carleman kernel satisfying the estimate (2.82). The verification of the inclusion $C_0^\infty(E_2) \subset \mathfrak{D}(2A^{-1}\sin^2(\frac{1}{2}\sqrt{A}\, t))$ is basic here.

$$u(t) = \int_C^\infty \left(\int_0^t \frac{1}{\sqrt{\lambda}} \sin \sqrt{\lambda}(t-\tau)\, d\tau \right) dE_\lambda g = \int_C^\infty \frac{2}{\lambda} \sin^2 \frac{\sqrt{\lambda}}{2} t\, dE_\lambda g$$

$$= \left(2A^{-1} \sin^2 \frac{\sqrt{A}}{2} t \right) g \quad (0 \leqslant t < \infty). \tag{2.85}$$

If the closure $\overline{S}$ of S is selfadjoint then by Theorem 1.7, 2) the weak solution of equation (2.83) is uniquely defined and therefore has the form (2.84) or (2.85) where $A = \overline{S}$.

Proof of the theorem. Let $g(x) \in C_0^\infty(E_2) \subset \mathfrak{D}(\Lambda) \subseteq \mathfrak{D}(\sqrt{\Lambda})$. Then by (2.76) the solution $u(x, t)$ of the Cauchy problem (2.75) will be finite in x for each t. Consequently $u(x, t)$ may be considered as a vector-function $u(t)$ with values in $L_2(E_2)$, satisfying the equation $d^2u/dt^2 + \Lambda u = g$ in the strong and, therefore, the weak sense. Moreover, $u(0) = (du/dt)(0) = 0$. By using formula (2.85) for $u(t)$, we obtain

$$\int_{E_2} W_{-c}(x, t;\, y)\, g(y)\, dy = u(x, t) = \left(2\Lambda^{-1} \sin^2 \frac{\sqrt{\Lambda}}{2} t \right) g$$
$$(g \in C_0^\infty(E_2),\ (0 \leqslant t < \infty).$$

By passing to a limit, this equation may be extended to an arbitrary $g \in L_2(E_2)$. It shows that the operator $2\Lambda^{-1} \sin^2(\tfrac{1}{2}\sqrt{\Lambda}\, t)$ has the kernel $C_t(x, y) = W_{-c}(x, t;\, y)$.

The series properties of the kernel C_t were established in Lemma 2.8. We now prove the estimate (2.82). From (2.80) and (2.81) we obtain

$$|C_t(x_0, y)| \leqslant |W_{-c(x_0)}(x_0, t_0;\, y)| + W_{c_-(x_0)+\omega(x_0,t_0)}(x_0, t_0;\, y) + W_{c_-(x_0)}(x_0, t_0;\, y)$$

$$\leqslant \frac{3}{2\pi} \int_0^{t_0-|x_0-y|} \frac{\operatorname{ch}\left(\sqrt{c_-(x_0)+\omega(x_0, t_0)}\,\Gamma((x_0, t_0), (y, \tau))\right)}{\Gamma((x_0, t_0), (y, \tau))}\, d\tau$$

$$\leqslant \frac{3}{2\pi} \int_0^{t_0-|x_0-y|} \frac{\exp\left(\sqrt{c_-(x_0)+\omega(x_0, t_0)} \cdot \sqrt{(t_0-\tau)^2 - |x_0-y|^2}\right)}{\sqrt{(t_0-\tau)^2 - |x_0-y|^2}}\, d\tau$$

$$\leqslant \frac{3}{2\pi} e^{t_0\sqrt{c_-(x_0)+\omega(x_0,t_0)}} \int_0^{t_0-|x_0-y|} \frac{d\tau}{\sqrt{(t_0-\tau)^2 - |x_0-y|^2}} =$$

$$= \frac{3}{2\pi} e^{t_0\sqrt{c_-(x_0)+\omega(x_0,t_0)}} \log \frac{t_0 + \sqrt{t_0^2 - |x_0 - y|^2}}{|x_0 - y|}$$

$$\leqslant \frac{3}{2\pi} e^{t_0\sqrt{c_-(x_0)+\omega(x_0,t_0)}} \log \frac{2t_0}{|x_0 - y|}$$

for $|x_0 - y| \le t_0$, i.e., (2.82). We have already discussed the square summability of the kernel $C_t(x, y)$ in each of the variables x and y, in Lemma 2.8. The theorem is proved.

For $n = 3$ analogous results may be established. By Theorem 2.8 the solution of a problem of the type (2.75) with $-c = a(x, t)$ and $g = g(x, t)$ takes the form

$$u(x, t) = \frac{1}{4\pi} \int\limits_{|x-y|<t} \frac{g(y, t - |x - y|)}{|x - y|} dy + \int\limits_{q \prec p} T_{\text{reg}}(p, q)\, g(q)\, dq$$

$$= \frac{1}{4\pi} \int\limits_{|x-y|<t} \frac{g(y, t - |x - y|)}{|x - y|} dy + \int\limits_{E_3\times[0,\infty)} T_a(p, q)\, g(q)\, dq \quad (p = (x, t), q = (y, \tau)), \tag{2.86}$$

where $T_{a+\alpha}(p, q)$ is defined from the kernel $T_{\text{reg}}(p, q)$, which appears in Theorem 2.8, by means of (2.65). If in equation (2.75) the coefficients and g are independent of t, then formula (2.86) may be rewritten

$$u(x, t) = \int\limits_{E_3} W_{-c}(x, t; y)\, g(y) dy; \tag{2.87}$$

$$W_{-c}(x, t; y) = \frac{1}{4\pi} \frac{1}{|x-y|} + \int\limits_0^{t-|x-y|} T_{-c}((x,t), (y,\tau))\, d\tau \text{ if } |x-y| \leqslant t, \; W_{-c}(x, t; y) = 0$$

if $|x - y| > t$

$$(x, y \in E_3;\; t \in [0, \infty)).$$

The analog of (2.78) has the form

$$T_a(p, q) = \frac{i\sqrt{a}}{4\pi\Gamma(p, q)} J_{-1}(i\sqrt{a}\Gamma(p, q)) = \frac{1}{2\pi} \sum_{j=1}^{\infty} \left(\frac{a}{4}\right)^j \frac{\Gamma^{2(j-1)}(p, q)}{(j-1)!\,j!} \tag{2.88}$$

$$(q \prec p; \quad a = \text{const}).$$

Now, in addition, we may prove lemmas analogous to Lemmas 2.7 and 2.8. For this, it is convenient to apply the approach mentioned near the end of subsection 9 on page 430: instead of the kernel $T(p, q)$ of the operator $\sum_{j=0}^{\infty} I^2 (AI^2)^j$ the kernel $T(p, q; \beta_0, \beta_1, \cdots)$ of the operator $\sum_{j=0}^{\infty} I^{\beta_0} (AI^{\beta_1} \ldots AI^{\beta_j})$ $(\beta_0, \beta_1, \cdots > 2)$

is considered. It may be represented as a sum of a nicely converging series as in (2.63). For $A(p) = a = \text{const} < 0$ this is an alternating series and the terms are monotone decreasing in absolute value. Therefore the inequality

$$|T_{\alpha}(p_0, q; \beta_0, \beta_1, \ldots)| \leqslant |T_0(p_0, q; \beta_0, \beta_1, \ldots)| \qquad (q \prec p_0) \tag{2.89}$$

is now correct (T_{α} is defined as in (2.65)). It is possible to establish an estimate of the type (2.77) replacing the kernel $T_{-c}(p_0, q)$ by the kernel $T_{-c}(p_0, q; \beta_0, \beta_1, \cdots)$; we use (2.89) and proceed exactly as in the proof of Lemma 2.7. After this the remaining facts presented on pp. 432–434 may be established as before but with kernels such that $\beta_0, \beta_1, \cdots > 2$. We then pass to the limit as $\beta_0, \beta_1, \cdots \longrightarrow 2$. Using this procedure the following estimate is obtained in place of (2.82):

$$|W_{-c}(x_0, t_0; y)| \leqslant \frac{3}{4\pi}\frac{1}{|x_0 - y|} + 3\int_0^{t_0 - |x_0 - y|} T_{c_-(x_0)+\omega(x_0,t_0)}((x_0, t_0), (y, \tau))\, d\tau$$

$$= \frac{3}{4\pi}\Bigg(\frac{1}{|x_0 - y|} + i\sqrt{c_-(x_0) + \omega(x_0, t_0)}$$

$$\times \int_0^{t_0 - |x_0 - y|} \frac{J_{-1}(i\sqrt{c_-(x_0) + \omega(x_0, t_0)}\cdot\sqrt{(t_0 - \tau)^2 - |x_0 - y|^2})}{\sqrt{(t_0 - \tau)^2 - |x_0 - y|^2}}\, d\tau\Bigg)$$

$$\leqslant \frac{3}{4\pi}\Bigg(\frac{1}{|x_0 - y|} + i\sqrt{c_-(x_0) + \omega(x_0, t_0)}\, J_{-1}(it_0\sqrt{c_-(x_0) + \omega(x_0, t_0)})$$

$$\times \int_0^{t_0 - |x_0 - y|} \frac{d\tau}{\sqrt{(t_0 - \tau)^2 - |x_0 - y|^2}}\Bigg) \leqslant \frac{3}{4\pi}\Bigg(\frac{1}{|x_0 - y|}$$

$$+ \sqrt{c_-(x_0) + \omega(x_0, t_0)}\, e^{t_0\sqrt{c_-(x_0)+\omega(x_0,t_0)}} \log\frac{2t_0}{|x_0 - y|}\Bigg)$$

$$(|x_0 - y| \leqslant t_0)$$

(we use the inequality $|J_{-1}(is)| \leq e^s$ $(s \geq 0)$ and notation analogous to that used in Lemma 2.7). We have proved

Theorem 2.10. *Theorem 2.9 is valid in its entirety for the three-dimensional Schrödinger expression, with E_2 replaced by E_3 and the estimate (2.82) by the estimate*

$$|C_t(x, y)| \leqslant \frac{3}{4\pi}\left(\frac{1}{|x - y|} + \sqrt{c_-(x) + \omega(x, t)}\, e^{t\sqrt{c_-(x)+\omega(x,t)}} \log\frac{2t}{|x - y|}\right)$$

$$(x, y \in E_3;\ |x - y| \leqslant t;\ 0 \leqslant t < \infty). \tag{2.90}$$

An analog of Theorem 2.9 exists in the n-dimensional case $(n > 3)$ but it is more complicated; we omit its formulation.

We proceed to some applications of Theorems 2.9 and 2.10 to spectral theory; in what follows below, we take $n = 2, 3$ and consider the semi-bounded below Schrödinger expression. For fixed $t > 0$ the function

$$\gamma(\lambda) = \frac{2}{\lambda} \sin^2 \frac{\sqrt{\lambda}}{2} t \; (-\infty < \lambda < \infty)$$

vanishes at the points $\lambda_m = (2\pi m/t)^2$ $(m = 1, 2, \cdots)$ and therefore is not immediately applicable for the constructions of §§4–5, Chapter V, and §2 of this chapter. But if we set

$$\gamma(\lambda) = \gamma_{t,\tau}(\lambda) = \frac{2}{\lambda}\left[\sin^2 \frac{\sqrt{\lambda}}{2}(t-\tau) + \sin^2 \frac{\sqrt{\lambda}}{2} t\right] \quad (-\infty < \lambda < \infty), \tag{2.91}$$

where $\tau \in (0, t)$ is sufficiently small, then $\gamma(\lambda)$ will be bounded on the spectrum of Λ and different from zero, therefore suitable for our purposes.

It follows from Theorems 2.9 and 2.10 that $\gamma(\Lambda)$ is an integral operator, the kernel of which, $C(x, y) = C_{t,\tau}(x, y)$, vanishes for $|x - y| \geq t$ and satisfies the estimates (2.82) and (2.90) (the right sides must be multiplied by 2). The function $\gamma(\lambda)$ is real, so the operator $\gamma(\Lambda)$ is selfadjoint and the kernel $C(x, y)$ is Hermitian. Consequently we have the estimates

$$|C(x, y)| \leqslant \frac{3}{\pi} e^{t\sqrt{c_-(y)+\omega(y,t)}} \log \frac{2t}{|x-y|} \quad (n = 2; |x - y| \leqslant t),$$

$$|C(x, y)| \leqslant \frac{3}{2\pi}\left(\frac{1}{|x-y|} + \sqrt{c_-(y) + \omega(y, t)}\, e^{t\sqrt{c_-(y)+\omega(y,t)}} \log \frac{2t}{|x-y|}\right)$$
$$(n = 3; |x - y| \leqslant t). \tag{2.92}$$

Squaring both sides of (2.92) and integrating over x, we find that

$$\int_{E_n} |C(x, y)|^2 dx \leqslant \begin{cases} Ce^{2t\sqrt{c_-(y)+\omega(y,t)}} & (n = 2;\; y \in E_2), \\ C(c_-(y) + \omega(y, t))\, e^{2t\sqrt{c_-(y)+\omega(y,t)}} & (n = 3;\; y \in E_3). \end{cases}$$

Thus for arbitrary $\kappa > 0$ a function $\gamma(\lambda)$ of the form (2.91) may be chosen, i.e., for $t > 0$ sufficiently small, there is some $C_\kappa > 0$ for which

$$C(y) = \int_{E_n} |C(x, y)|^2 dx \leqslant C_\varkappa e^{\varkappa \sqrt{c_-(y)+\omega(y,\varkappa)}} \qquad (y \in E_n;\ n = 2, 3). \tag{2.93}$$

Thus for the function $p(x)$ satisfying condition (4.2) of Chapter V, we may choose

$$p(x) = (1 + |x|)^{n+\varepsilon} e^{\varkappa \sqrt{c_-(x)+\omega(x,\varkappa)}} \qquad (\varepsilon > 0;\ x \in E_n;\ n = 2, 3). \tag{2.94}$$

It is now easy to estimate the function $V(x)$ of Theorem 5.5, Chapter V. In fact, choosing $t \in (0, \kappa)$ sufficiently small, by (2.92), we have for example, in the case $n = 2$:

$$B(x) = \int_{E_2} |C(x, y)|^2 p(y)\, dy \leqslant C \int_{|x-y|<t} e^{3\varkappa \sqrt{c_-(y)+\omega(y,\varkappa)}} \left(\log \frac{1}{|x-y|}\right)^2$$

$$\times (1+|y|)^{n+\varepsilon} dy \leqslant C e^{3\varkappa \sqrt{c_-(x)+2\omega(x,\, 2\varkappa)}} (1 + |x| + t)^{n+\varepsilon} \int_{|x-y|<t} \left(\log \frac{1}{|x-y|}\right)^2 dy$$

$$\leqslant C_1 e^{3\sqrt{2}\, \varkappa \sqrt{c_-(x)+\omega(x,2\varkappa)}} (1 + |x|)^{n+\varepsilon} \qquad (x \in E_n)$$

(estimating c_- near the point x by $c_-(x) + \omega(x, \kappa)$ and using the relation $\sup_{|x-y| \leq \kappa} \omega(y, \kappa) \leq \omega(x, 2\kappa)$). This estimate also holds for $n = 3$. Consequently it is easy to show that for arbitrary $\epsilon, \kappa > 0$ one may choose a function $\gamma(\lambda)$ as in (2.91) so that for some $C_{\epsilon,\kappa} > 0$

$$B(x) \leqslant C_{\varepsilon,\varkappa} (1 + |x|)^{n+\varepsilon} e^{\varkappa \sqrt{c_-(x)+\omega(x,\varkappa)}} \qquad (x \in E_n;\ n = 2, 3). \tag{2.95}$$

Recalling that the spectral kernel $\Phi(x, y;\ \lambda)$ does not depend on the choice of $\gamma(\lambda)$ (see p. 354) and applying Theorem 5.5 of Chapter V, we obtain

Theorem 2.11. *Consider the Schrödinger expression (2.43) on all of* E_n $(n = 2, 3)$, *which is, in addition, semi-bounded below on* $C_0^\infty(E_n)$; $c(x) \in C^2(E_n)$. *The minimal operator* Λ, *constructed from* L *on* $G = E_n$, *will be selfadjoint. Let* $\Phi(x, y;\ \lambda)$ *be the spectral kernel corresponding to* Λ, *let* $\phi_\alpha(x;\ \lambda)$ $(\alpha = 1, \cdots, N_\lambda)$ *be the individual eigenfunctions, and let* $d\rho(\lambda)$ *be the spectral density. Then for arbitrary* $\epsilon, \kappa > 0$ *the following estimate is valid for* ρ*-almost all* λ:

$$\begin{aligned} \Phi(x, y;\ \lambda) &= \underset{|x|,|y|\to\infty}{O} \left(|x|^{\frac{n}{2}+\varepsilon} |y|^{\frac{n}{2}+\varepsilon} e^{\varkappa \sqrt{c_-(x)+\omega(x,\varkappa)+c_-(y)+\omega(y,\varkappa)}}\right), \\ \varphi_\alpha(x;\ \lambda) &= \underset{|x|\to\infty}{O} \left(|x|^{\frac{n}{2}+\varepsilon} e^{\varkappa \sqrt{c_-(x)+\omega(x,\varkappa)}}\right) \quad (\alpha = 1, \ldots, N_\lambda;\ n = 2, 3), \end{aligned} \tag{2.96}$$

where $c_-(x) = \max(-c(x), 0)$ *and* $\omega(x, \delta)$ *is the modulus of continuity of the function* c *at the point* x.

If the coefficient $c(x)$ *is semi-bounded below* ($c(x) \geq C > -\infty$, $x \in E_n$) *and uniformly continuous, then the right sides of* (2.96) *may be replaced by*

$$O(|x|^{\frac{n}{2}+\varepsilon}|y|^{\frac{n}{2}+\varepsilon}) \text{ and } O(|x|^{\frac{n}{2}+\varepsilon}).\text{ 1)}$$

Physical considerations demand that in the case where $c(x)$ is bounded below all of the eigenfunctions of the Schrödinger operator must be bounded almost everywhere with respect to ρ at ∞. Theorem 2.11 claims a close result. But in general it is impossible to obtain the boundedness of $\Phi(x, y; \lambda)$ and $\phi_\alpha(x, \lambda)$ at ∞ from (2.96) alone. (One can construct an example of a one-dimensional Schrödinger operator with bounded smooth $c(x)$ for which this boundedness does not occur.)

In connection with this theorem, it is useful to show that there exists a semi-bounded below Schrödinger expression on $C_0^\infty(E_n)$ for which $\inf_{x\in E_n} c(x) = -\infty$. We limit ourselves to the case $n = 2$ and introduce polar coordinates ($\rho = |x|$, ϕ) on E_2. Considering that

$$\Delta = \frac{1}{\varrho}\frac{\partial}{\partial\varrho}\left(\varrho\frac{\partial}{\partial\varrho}\right) + \frac{1}{\varrho^2}\frac{\partial^2}{\partial\varphi^2}$$

and integrating by parts, we have

$$(Lu, u)_0 = \int_0^{2\pi}\int_0^{\infty}\left(\left|\frac{\partial u}{\partial\varrho}\right|^2 + \frac{1}{\varrho^2}\left|\frac{\partial u}{\partial\varphi}\right|^2 + c(x)|u|^2\right)\varrho\, d\varrho\, d\varphi = I_{c(x)}(u, u) \quad (u \in C_0^2(E_2)). \tag{2.97}$$

We set $I_1(u, u) = I_{c(x)\equiv 1}(u, u)$ $u(x) = f(\rho)v(x)$ in the integral, where $v \in C_0^2(E_2)$ and $f \in C^4([0, \infty))$ is real and bounded by a constant $C < \infty$. Integrating by parts in (2.97) we obtain

$$0 < I_1(fv, fv) = \int_0^{2\pi}\int_0^{\infty}\left(f^2\left|\frac{\partial v}{\partial\varrho}\right|^2 + \frac{f^2}{\varrho^2}\left|\frac{\partial v}{\partial\varphi}\right|^2 + (f^2 + f'^2)|v|^2 + ff'\frac{\partial}{\partial\varrho}|v|^2\right)\varrho\, d\varrho\, d\varphi =$$

---

1) As in the case of Theorems 2.9 and 2.10 it is not necessary to require the hypothesis of semi-boundedness below of the expression 2.43 (see the previous footnote), in order to obtain the estimates (2.96) for some selfadjoint $A \supseteq \Lambda$. The arguments given above remain as before, if one only notes that the necessary results of §§4–5, Chapter V remain valid for unbounded $\gamma(A)$.

$$= \int_0^{2\pi}\int_0^{\infty}\left(f^2\left|\frac{\partial v}{\partial \varrho}\right|^2 + \frac{f^2}{\varrho^2}\left|\frac{\partial v}{\partial \varphi}\right|^2 + \left(-ff'' - \frac{ff'}{\varrho} + f^2\right)|v|^2\right)\varrho\, d\varrho\, d\varphi \leqslant C^2 \int_0^{2\pi}\int_0^{\infty}\left(\left|\frac{\partial v}{\partial \varrho}\right|^2\right.$$

$$\left. + \frac{1}{\varrho^2}\left|\frac{\partial v}{\partial \varphi}\right|^2 + \frac{f}{C^2}\left(-f'' - \frac{f'}{\varrho} + f\right)|v|^2\right)\varrho\, d\varrho\, d\varphi = l_{c(x)}(v, v) = (Lv, v)_0,$$

$$c(x) = \frac{f}{C^2}\left(-f'' - \frac{f'}{\varrho} + f\right).$$

It then follows that the required example will be complete if a function $f(\rho)$ can be chosen such that $\inf_{\rho \in [0,\infty)} f(-f'' - f'/\rho + f) = -\infty$. For such an example, we set $f(\rho) = 2 + \sin \rho^3$. Then for $\rho_n = (2\pi n)^{1/3}$ $(n = 1, 2, \cdots)$,

$$\left(f\left(-f'' - \frac{f'}{\varrho} + f\right)\right)(\varrho_n) = -18\,(2\pi n)^{\frac{1}{3}} + 4 \to -\infty,$$

as required.

As in Theorems 2.9–2.10, estimates of the type of (2.96) are valid for the case $n \geq 3$. Thus it is possible to establish the following result (see for example, Gel'fand and Šilov [3], Chapter 4, §9, Russian pp. 249–261). We consider the formally elliptic selfadjoint differential expression of order r with coefficients $a_\alpha(x)$, which, aside from the general smoothness conditions of Theorem 2.1, satisfy the following condition: *the derivatives* $D^\beta(a_\alpha)$, $|\beta| \leq r$, *and* $(D^\beta a_\alpha)(x)$, $|\beta| \leq 1$ *are bounded on all of* E_n *for* $|\alpha| = r$ *and* $|\alpha| \leq r$ *respectively*. The assertion is that for $N = [n/2r] + 1$ and $z \neq \bar{z}$, the resolvent R_z of the operator Λ (it is selfadjoint – see p. 386) is such that R_z^N is an integral operator with kernel $C(x, y)$ satisfying the estimate

$$|C(x, y)| \leqslant \frac{A}{|x - y|^{n - Nr}} e^{-B|x-y|} \quad (A, B > 0;\ x, y \in E_n,\ x \neq y). \tag{2.98}$$

Since $Nr > n/2$, then $n - Nr < n/2$. This allows us to conclude that

$$C(y) = \int_{E_n} |C(x, y)|^2 dx \leqslant C < \infty \quad (y \in E_n). \tag{2.99}$$

By using Theorem 5.5 of Chapter V the following assertion follows from the estimates (2.98) and (2.99) in a manner similar to the above: estimate (2.96), with the exponent replaced by one, holds for the spectral kernel $\Phi(x, y; \lambda)$ and the eigenfunctions $\phi_\alpha(x; \lambda)$ of the elliptic expression in question.

We note that an estimate of the type (2.98) may be established for a Schrödinger expression with a semi-bounded below coefficient $c(x)$, (but not bounded) by using the maximum principle. This, in combination with Theorem 5.5, Chapter V, yields another way of obtaining the last part of Theorem 2.11 (which does not require the uniform continuity of $c(x)$).

§3. SPECTRAL THEORY OF GENERAL SELFADJOINT DIFFERENTIAL OPERATORS

Here we will consider generalized eigenfunction expansions in $H_0 = L_2(G)$ ($G \subseteq E_n$, bounded or not) of operators induced by formally selfadjoint L and (bd). Aside from some details, L will be considered as a special case of the general remarks of §3, Chapter V.

1. Construction of the generalized eigenfunction expansion. Let L be a formally selfadjoint differential operator on G with the usual assumptions made on the smoothness of the coefficients, and let formally selfadjoint (bd) be given on Γ. We construct the strong operator Λ (bd) on $L_2(G)$; it is obviously Hermitian and closed. As in §2.1, we denote by A one of its selfadjoint extensions either on $L_2(G)$ or some larger space, and by $E(\Delta)$ the corresponding (generalized or not) resolution of the identity.

Then the general construction of §3 applies to A where for $H_- \supseteq H_0 \supseteq H_+$ any of the chains a)–c) of Chapter V, §3.1 may be chosen. In case c) the Parseval equality takes the form

$$(E(\Delta)u, v)_0 = \int_\Delta \left\{ \int_G \int_G \Psi(x, y; \lambda)\,(\mathrm{D}u)(y)\overline{(\mathrm{D}v)(x)}\,dx\,dy \right\} d\varrho(\lambda)$$

$$= \int_\Delta (\Phi_\lambda, v(x)\overline{u(y)})_0\, d\varrho(\lambda) \quad (u, v \in C_0^\infty(G);\ \mathrm{D} = D_1 \ldots D_n), \tag{3.1}$$

where Φ_λ is a generalized kernel, in the sense of L. Schwartz, equal to $\mathrm{D}_x \mathrm{D}_y \Psi(x, y; \lambda)$. We have called this kernel the (generalized) spectral kernel. The ordinary positive definite kernel $\Psi(x, y; \lambda)$, an integral spectral kernel, satisfies the relations (3.7) of Chapter V for ρ-almost all λ.

As earlier we introduce the integral eigenfunctions $\psi_\alpha(x; \lambda)$ and the generalized (in the sense of L. Schwartz) eigenfunctions $\phi_\alpha(\lambda) = (-1)^n \mathrm{D}\, \psi_\alpha(x; \lambda)$.

What is new in comparison with the results of §3, Chapter V, is the fact that Φ_λ in each of the variables x, y, and $\phi_\alpha(x)$ are generalized solutions of a differential operator of the type $Lu - \lambda u = 0$ inside G. More precisely this means that the equations

$$\int_G \psi_\alpha(x;\lambda)\overline{(\mathrm{D}(Lu-\lambda u))(x)}\,dx = 0.\ \int_G \Psi(x,y;\lambda)\overline{(\mathrm{D}(Lu-\lambda u))(x)}\,dx = 0$$
$$(u\in C_0^\infty(G);\ \alpha = 1,\ldots,N_\lambda;\ y\in G) \tag{3.2}$$

are satisfied and that the second equation is symmetric with respect to y (we make the additional assumption that the coefficients $a_\alpha(x)$ of the expression L are each in $C^n(G)$. The equations in (3.2) follow without difficulty from equations (1.14) and (1.18) of Chapter V.

It is clear that the construction using the chain c) does not catch the behavior of the generalized eigenfunctions near Γ. The chain a) must be used to show that these functions satisfy (bd) up to Γ. We will not repeat the verification of this, since it was covered in §2.5 (all that was said there, with the exception mentioned above, is true for general L).

2. Differential expressions with constant coefficients in the space $L_2(E_n)$.[1] We consider the expression

$$Lu = \sum_{|\alpha|\leq r} a_\alpha \partial^\alpha u,\ \partial^\alpha = \partial_1^{\alpha_1}\ldots\partial_n^{\alpha_n},\ \partial_j = \frac{1}{i}D_j\ (j=1,\ldots,n) \tag{3.3}$$

with real constant coefficients. As we know (see §1.5), the corresponding minimal operator Λ is selfadjoint on the space $L_2(E_n)$. We describe the form of the expansion of subsection 1 for this operator, first considering the similar questions for the Fourier-image $\widetilde{\Lambda}$, which coincides with the closure of the operator of multiplication by $L(\xi) = \Sigma_{|\alpha|\leq r}\, a_\alpha \xi^{\alpha}$, $(\xi\in E_{nj})$ on $L^2(E_n)$.

Thus, in the space $L^2(E_n)$ of functions $\widetilde{f}(\xi)$, the Hermitian operator $\widetilde{u}(\xi)\longrightarrow L(\xi)\widetilde{u}(\xi)$, $(u\in S)$ is considered. Its closure is denoted $\widetilde{\Lambda}$ (since $C_0^\infty(E_n)$ is dense in S, it follows that $\widetilde{\Lambda}$ coincides with the closure of the more restricted operator $\widetilde{u}(\xi)\longrightarrow L(\xi)\widetilde{u}(\xi)$, $\widetilde{u}\in C_0^\infty(E_n)$). The operator $\widetilde{\Lambda}$ is selfadjoint, its spectrum coincides with the set of values of the polynomial $L(\xi)$ $(\xi\in E_n)$ and the resolvents $\widetilde{R}_z = (\widetilde{\Lambda} - zE)^{-1}$ are the operators of multiplication by $1/(L(\xi) - z)$. Let $\widetilde{E}(\Delta)$ be the resolution of the identity corresponding to the operator $\widetilde{\Lambda}$. Obviously $\widetilde{E}(\Delta)$ is the operator of multiplication by the characteristic function $e_\Delta(\xi)$ of the preimage of the set Δ under the mapping $\xi\longrightarrow L(\xi)$ of the space E_n into E_1.

The role of the generalized projection operator $\widetilde{P}(\lambda)$ is naturally played by

---

1) One such example has already been considered; see example a), §2.8.

the operator "multiplication by the δ-function concentrated on the surface L_λ with the equation $L(\xi) = \lambda$" i.e., the operator which takes $\tilde{f}(\xi) \in L_2(E_n)$ into the function

$$(\tilde{P}(\lambda)\tilde{f})(\xi) = \begin{cases} \tilde{f}(\xi) & \text{for } \xi \in L_\lambda, \\ 0 & \text{for } \xi \overline{\in} L_\lambda. \end{cases}$$

To obtain a complete system of generalized eigenfunctions corresponding to λ, choose a complete system of functions on the surface L_λ and then extend each to zero on the rest of E_n. It is clear that the above is just an intuitive argument. For the actual proofs we must introduce the basic chain $H_- \supseteq H_0 = L_2(E_n) \supseteq H_+$. We do this later since the construction of such a chain is connected with the chain of subsection 1, arising in the study of the original operator Λ. With this aim we recall some facts on Fourier images of generalized functions in the basic space S. (See, for example, Gel'fand and Šilov [2] Chapter III, §§1–3).

We let S, with the convergence introduced in §1.5, be the fundamental space of functions; the space S' of anti-linear functionals on S, $l(u) = (l, u)_0$ forms the space of generalized functions. As already mentioned, S is invariant under the Fourier transformation: $\tilde{S} = S$. This allows us to define the Fourier transform of a generalized function by means of the "Parseval equation" $(\tilde{l}, \tilde{u})_0 = (l, u)_0$ as a functional on the space S. In the case where l is an ordinary summable function, i.e., more precisely, where $(l, u)_0 = \int_{E_n} l(x)\overline{u(x)}\,dx$ $(u \in S)$, for $l(x) \in L_1(E_n)$, then $\tilde{l}$ is its ordinary Fourier transform $\tilde{l}(x)$ i.e., $(\tilde{l}, \tilde{u})_0 = \int_{E_n} \tilde{l}(x)\overline{\tilde{u}(x)}\,dx$ $(\tilde{u} \in S)$. The inverse Fourier transform $\backsim$ is naturally defined so that $\tilde{\tilde{l}} = l$. We denote by $\tilde{A}$ the continuous operator of multiplication by some bounded function $\tilde{a}(\xi) : (\tilde{A}\tilde{f})(\xi) = \tilde{a}(\xi)\tilde{f}(\xi)$ $(\tilde{f} \in L_2(E_n))$. Its Fourier preimage $Af = \widetilde{\tilde{A}\tilde{f}}$, obviously coincides with the operator, convolution with the generalized function $a = \tilde{\tilde{a}}$, which is the Fourier preimage of the function $\tilde{a}$. If $\tilde{a}$ is sufficiently "nice", then a will be an ordinary function and the convolution operator will have the form

$$(Af)(x) = \frac{1}{\sqrt{(2\pi)^n}} \int_{E_n} a(x-y) f(y)\,dy = \frac{1}{\sqrt{(2\pi)^n}} \int_{E_n} a(y) f(x-y)\,dy. \qquad (3.4)$$

In the general case, in connection with the second of the integrals (3.4), it is necessary to put, for $u \in S$, $(Au)(x) = (1/\sqrt{(2\pi)^n})\,(a, \overline{u(x-\cdot)})_0$ $(x \in E_n)$, and then extend A to all of $L_2(E_n)$ by continuity (we note that if $u(.) \in S$, then $u(x-\cdot) \in S$ for arbitrary $x \in E_n$).

Using the Fourier transform and the above discussion on $\tilde{\Lambda}$, we conclude that the resolvents R_z and the resolution of the identity $E(\Delta)$ of the operator Λ have the form

$$(R_z u)(x) = \frac{1}{\sqrt{(2\pi)^n}} \left(\widetilde{\frac{1}{L(\cdot) - z}}, \overline{u(x - \cdot)} \right)_0,$$

$$(E(\Delta) u(x)) = \frac{1}{\sqrt{(2\pi)^n}} (\tilde{e}_\Delta, \overline{u(x - \cdot)})_0 \quad (x \in E_n, u \in S). \tag{3.5}$$

In the case where the above exists in terms of integrals, we conclude that R_z and $E(\Delta)$ are integral operators with kernels depending on the difference $x - y$:

$$R(x, y; z) = R(x - y; z) = \frac{1}{(2\pi)^n} \int_{E_n} \frac{e^{i\langle x-y, \xi\rangle}}{L(\xi) - z} d\xi,$$

$$\Xi(x, y; \Delta) = \Xi(x - y; \Delta) = \frac{1}{(2\pi)^n} \int_{L(\xi)\in\Delta} e^{i\langle x-y,\xi\rangle} d\xi \quad (x, y \in E_n). \tag{3.6}$$

We proceed to the construction of generalized eigenfunctions for Λ. We will consider both schemes a) and c) of subsection 1. As a preliminary we make some general remarks about expansions of the type (3.1), which are close to those discussed at the end of §3.2 of Chapter V. We have

Lemma 3.1. *Let $\rho_1(\Delta)$ be a nonnegative measure concentrated on the spectrum of A and such that the measures $\Theta(x, y; \Delta) = (E(\Delta)\,\omega(y, \cdot), \omega(x, \cdot))_0$ $(x, y \in G)$ are each absolutely continuous with respect to ρ. Then $\rho_1(\Delta)$ may be taken as the spectral measure and $\Psi_1(x, y; \lambda) = d\Theta(x, y; \lambda)/d\rho_1(\lambda)$ as the integral spectral kernel.*

Proof. We verify that

$$\int_\Delta \Psi(x, y; \lambda)\, d\rho(\lambda) = \Theta(x, y; \Delta) \qquad (x, y \in G) \tag{3.7}$$

for the kernel $\Psi(x, y; \lambda)$ of (3.1). For this, note that $\Psi(x, y; \lambda) = q(x)\, q(y)\, \hat{\Psi}(x, y; \lambda)$ by subsections 1–2 of §3, Chapter V, where $\hat{\Psi}(x, y; \lambda)$ is the kernel of the operator $\Psi(\lambda) = (d/d\rho(\lambda))\, T^{-1*} E_\lambda T^{-1}$; the operator T^{-1} has the form (3.5) in Chapter V. Let $u, v \in C_0^\infty(G)$. Then

$$(T^{-1^*}E(\Delta)T^{-1}u,v)_0=(E(\Delta)T^{-1}u,T^{-1}v)_0=\Big(E(\Delta)\int_G\frac{1}{q(y)}\omega(y,\cdot)u(y)dy,$$
$$\int_G\frac{1}{q(x)}\omega(x,\cdot)v(x)\,dx\Big)_0=\int_G\int_G(E(\Delta)\omega(y,\cdot),\omega(x,\cdot))_0\frac{u(y)\overline{v(x)}}{q(y)\,q(x)}dxdy. \qquad (3.8)$$

On the other hand,

$$(T^{-1^*}E(\Delta)T^{-1}u,v)_0=\Big(\int_\Delta\Psi(\lambda)\,d\varrho(\lambda)\,u,v\Big)_0$$
$$=\int_G\int_G\Big(\int_\Delta\frac{\Psi(x,y;\lambda)}{q(x)q(y)}\,d\varrho(\lambda)\Big)\,u(y)\overline{v(x)}\,dxdy. \qquad (3.9)$$

Equating (3.8) and (3.9) we arrive at (3.7).

Differentiating $\Theta(x, y;\ \Delta)$ with respect to $\rho_1(\Delta)$ in (3.7), we have,

$$\int_\Delta\Psi(x,y;\lambda)\,d\varrho(\lambda)=\int_\Delta\Psi_1(x,y;\lambda)\,d\varrho_1(\lambda) \qquad (x,y\in G). \qquad (3.10)$$

The lemma follows easily from this and the remarks on pp. 336–337. (The spectral measure $\rho_1(\Delta)$ may not be absolutely continuous with respect to $\rho(\Delta) = \operatorname{tr}(T^{-1*}E(\Delta)T^{-1})$.)

We may now find $\Psi(x, y;\ \lambda)$ and $d\rho(\lambda)$ for the operator Λ. Since here $G = E_n$,

$$\omega(x,t)=(-1)^n\operatorname{sign}(x_1\ldots x_n)\prod_{j=1}^n\varkappa_{(0,x_j)}(t_j) \qquad (x,t\in E_n), \qquad (3.11)$$

where $\kappa_{(a,b)}$ is the characteristic function of the interval (a, b). Taking the Fourier transform with respect to t in (3.11), we obtain

$$\widetilde{(\omega(x,.))}(\xi)=\frac{i^n}{\sqrt{(2\pi)^n}}\operatorname{sign}(x_1\ldots x_n)\prod_{j=1}^n\frac{1-e^{-ix_j\xi_j}}{\xi_j} \qquad (x,\xi\in E_n). \qquad (3.12)$$

Using the form of the operator $\widetilde{E}(\Delta)$ and (3.12), we obtain with the help of the Parseval equality,

$$\Theta(x,y;\Delta)=(E(\Delta)\omega(y,.),\omega(x,.))_0=(\widetilde{E}(\Delta)\widetilde{\omega}(y,.),\widetilde{\omega}(x,.))_0$$
$$=\frac{\operatorname{sign}(x_1,\ldots x_ny_1\ldots y_n)}{(2\pi)^n}\int_{L(\xi)\in\Delta}\prod_{j=1}^n\frac{1}{\xi_j^2}(1-e^{ix_j\xi_j})(1-e^{-iy_j\xi_j})d\xi\ (x,y\in E_n). \qquad (3.13)$$

Below (see Lemma 3.2) we will show that the measure defining the last integral is absolutely continuous with respect to Lebesgue measure ($L(\xi) \not\equiv$ const). Applying Lemma 3.1, we obtain

$$\Psi(x, y; \lambda) =$$

$$= \frac{\operatorname{sign}(x_1 \ldots x_n y_1 \ldots y_n)}{(2\pi)^n} \frac{d}{d\lambda} \int\limits_{L(\xi)<\lambda} \prod_{j=1}^{n} \frac{1}{\xi_j^2} (1 - e^{ix_j\xi_j})(1 - e^{-iy_j\xi_j})\, d\xi$$

$$(x, y \in E_n). \tag{3.14}$$

If the surface $L(\xi) = \lambda$ does not have a singular point, i.e. if on it $(\operatorname{grad} L)(\xi) = ((D_1 L)(\xi), \cdots, (D_n L)(\xi)) \neq 0$, then it is known that (see for example, Gel'fand and Šilov [1], Chapter 3, §1, Russian pp. 272–274) the differential expression of order $n - 1$,

$$\sigma_\lambda = \Sigma\, a_{j_1, \ldots, j_{n-1}}\, d\xi_{j_1} \wedge \cdots \wedge d\xi_{j_{n-1}}$$

exists and is such that $dL \wedge \sigma_\lambda = d\xi_1 \wedge \cdots \wedge d\xi_n$ where dL is the differential of the function $L(\xi)$, $\wedge$ denotes the exterior product, and $d\xi_1 \wedge \cdots \wedge d\xi_n$ is the volume element. Now, differentiating, (3.14) is written in the form of an $(n-1)$-dimensional integral:

$$\Psi(x, y; \lambda) =$$

$$= \frac{\operatorname{sign}(x_1 \ldots x_n y_1 \ldots y_n)}{(2\pi)^n} \int\limits_{L(\xi)=\lambda} \prod_{j=1}^{n} \frac{1}{\xi_j^2} (1 - e^{ix_j\xi_j})(1 - e^{-iy_j\xi_j})\, \sigma_\lambda$$

$$(x, y \in E_n). \tag{3.15}$$

It would not make sense to consider the case of a singular point on the surface $L(\xi) = \lambda$ since it is not difficult to show that such an occurrence can take place only on a set of zero Lebesgue measure (see Lemma 3.3) and $\Psi(x, y; \lambda)$ is defined almost everywhere. We have proved

Theorem 3.1. *The spectral measure of the operator Λ, induced on $L_2(E_n)$ by the expression* (3.3) *of order $n \geq 1$, coincides with Lebesgue measure on the spectrum of Λ (i.e., as the set of values of the polynomial $L(\xi)$, $(\xi \in E_n)$). The integral spectral kernel $\Psi(x, y; \lambda)$ has the form* (3.15) *where the $(n-1)$-dimensional integral is defined for almost all λ in the sense of this measure.*

In the case of separation of variables in the following section, a simple method of calculation for $\Psi(x, y; \lambda)$ will be indicated. To obtain corresponding formulas for the operator $\widetilde{\Lambda}$ from formulas (3.14) amd (3.15), one may consider the kernel $\hat{\Psi}(x, y; \lambda) = (1/q(x)\, q(y))\, \Psi(x, y; \lambda)$ and take its Fourier transform; here $q(x) = (1 + |x_1|)^{1+\epsilon} \cdots (1 + |x_n|)^{1+\epsilon}$ $(\epsilon > 0)$ (or some other suitable function for the constructions in §3, Chapter V). We fill in two results that we omitted earlier.

Lemma 3.2. *Let* $f(\xi) \in L_1(E_n)$, *and* $Q(\xi) \not\equiv \text{const}$ *be some polynomial with real coefficients. Then the measure*

$$\theta(\Delta) = \int_{Q(\xi)\in\Delta} f(\xi)\, d\xi \tag{3.16}$$

defined on the Borel sets of the real line, is absolutely continuous with respect to Lebesgue measure.

Proof. Since $f(\xi)$ is summable on all of E_n, it follows that the integral (3.16) exists and defines a measure. If Δ_0 is a set of Lebesgue measure 0, we must show that $\theta(\Delta_0) = 0$. For this it is sufficient to verify that the preimage Ξ_n of the set Δ_0 under the transformation $\xi \longrightarrow Q(\xi)$ from E_n into E_1 is a set of μ_n measure (i.e. n-dimensional Lebesgue measure) zero. The assertion is obvious in the one-dimensional case, and the proof for the general case will be by induction on the dimension n.

Suppose the assertion is true for polynomials in $\eta \in E_{n-1}$. We consider the polynomial $Q(\xi) \not\equiv \text{const}$, where $\xi \in E_n$. Set $\xi = (\eta, \xi_n)$, $\eta = (\xi_1, \cdots, \xi_{n-1}) \in E_{n-1}$. If $Q(\xi)$ does not depend on ξ_n, i.e., $Q(\xi) = P(\eta)$, where P is a polynomial in $n-1$ variables, then $\Xi_n = \Xi_{n-1} \times E_1$, where Ξ_{n-1} is the preimage of Δ_0 under the transformation $\eta \longrightarrow P(\eta)$ of the space E_{n-1} into E_1. Since $\mu_{n-1}(\Xi'_{n-1}) = 0$ by the induction hypothesis, then $\mu_n(\Xi_n) = 0$.

Now suppose $Q(\xi)$ depends on ξ_n. We show that one may pick a number $j = n,\ n-1$, such that there is only a finite number of values of the variable ξ_j, for which $Q(\xi)$ as a polynomial in $\eta = (\xi_1, \cdots, \xi_{n-1})$ or in $\eta = (\xi_1, \cdots, \xi_{n-2}, \xi_n)$ is identically equal to some constant. For this, we assume that there there is an infinite set $\xi_n^{(\alpha)}$ $(\alpha = 1, 2, \cdots)$ of values ξ_n, such that $Q(\eta, \xi_n^{(\alpha)}) = C^{(\alpha)}$ $(\alpha = 1, 2, \cdots)$ for all $\eta \in E_{n-1}$. In this case, for each fixed ξ_{n-1}, $Q(\xi)$ as a polynomial in $(\xi_1, \cdots, \xi_{n-2}, \xi_n)$ is not identically constant, i.e., we may take $j = n-1$. In fact if for some $\xi_{n-1} = t$, $Q(\xi_1, \cdots, \xi_{n-2}, t, \xi_n)$ is constant, then letting $\xi_n = \xi_n^{(\alpha)}$ $(\alpha = 1, 2, \cdots)$, we find that all of the $C^{(\alpha)}$ are equal. But then for each fixed η, the polynomial $Q(\eta, \xi_n)$ of one variable ξ_n, takes an infinite number of equal values, i.e., they do not depend on ξ_n, contrary to our hypothesis. Thus the possibility of choosing j is established. Let, for example, $j = n$.

We fix $\xi_n = t$ and consider the corresponding section of the set Ξ_n, i.e. the set such that $\eta \in E_{n-1}$, $(\eta, t) \in \Xi_n$. This section is the preimage of Δ_0 under the transformation $\eta \longrightarrow Q(\eta, t)$ of the space E_{n-1} into E_1. Since the polynomial $Q(\eta, t) \not\equiv$ const for almost all t, it follows by the induction hypothesis that the measure μ_{n-1} of the corresponding section is equal to zero. But it is known that if the measure of almost all sections of a set is equal to zero, then the measure of the set itself is equal to zero. Thus $\mu_n(\Xi_n) = 0$ and the lemma is proved.

Lemma 3.3. *Let* $Q(\xi) \neq$ const *be a polynomial with real coefficients, and let* λ *be some point of the set* $Q(\xi)$ $(\xi \in E_n)$. *Then for almost all* λ *in the sense of Lebesgue measure, the surface* $Q(\xi) = \lambda$ *does not contain a singular point.*

Proof. For fixed λ, the set of singular points of the surface $Q(\xi) = \lambda$ coincides with the set of real solutions $\xi = (\xi_1, \cdots, \xi_n)$ of the system of $n + 1$ equations

$$Q(\xi) = \lambda, (D_1Q)(\xi) = 0, \ldots, (D_nQ)(\xi) = 0. \tag{3.17}$$

We denote by N the set of solutions in E_n of the system $(D_1Q)(\xi) = 0, \cdots, (D_nQ)(\xi) = 0$ or, what is equivalent, of the equation $P(\xi) = (D_1Q)^2(\xi) + \cdots + (D_nQ)^2(\xi) = 0$. It is easy to see that the set of real zeros of an arbitrary polynomial $P(\xi)$ with real coefficients consists of at most a countable (and even finite) number of connected components, where any two points in a given component may be joined by a smooth curve in the component. Therefore $N = \bigcup_{j=1}^m N_j$, $m \leq \infty$, where N_j is a connected component of the solutions in E_n of the system $(D_1Q)(\xi) = 0, \cdots, (D_nQ)(\xi) = 0$.

It is easy to see that $Q(\xi)$ takes a constant value on each N_j. In fact, let $\xi, \eta \in N_j$ and $\phi(t) \in E_n$ $(t \in [0, 1];\ \phi(0) = \xi, \phi(1) = \eta)$ and join these points by a one time continuously differentiable curve in N_j. Let $f(t) = Q(\phi(t))$ $(t \in [0, 1])$. Then for each $t \in [0, 1]$ which is not a discontinuity of $\phi(t)$,

$$\frac{df(t)}{dt} = \sum_{j=1}^{n} (D_jQ)(\varphi(t)) \frac{d\varphi(t)}{dt} = 0.$$

It then follows that $f(t) \equiv$ const, i.e. $Q(\xi) = Q(\eta)$.

From the above, it now follows that the polynomial $Q(\xi)$ takes on at most a countable number of values $\lambda_1, \lambda_2, \cdots$ for $\xi \in N$. Therefore if $\lambda \neq \lambda_j$ $(j = 1, 2, \cdots)$ the system of equations (3.17) will not have a solution. The lemma follows.

We now proceed with the generalized eigenfunction expansion of the operator

Λ, using the chain a). By what was said in §3.1, Chapter V, it is possible to choose $H_+ = W_2^{(l,1+|x|^{l+\epsilon})}(E_n)$ $(\epsilon > 0)$, where $l > n/2$. Later on it will be convenient to interpret the elements of H_- as generalized functions in the space S'. This may be done since the inclusion $W_2^{(l,1+|x|^m)}(E_n) \supset S$ $(l = 0, 1, \cdots; m \geq 0)$ is always topological, and S is dense in $W_2^{(l,1+|x|^m)}(E_n)$. Thus

$$S' \supset H_- \supset H_0 = L_2(E_n) \supset H_+ \supset S. \tag{3.18}$$

We consider the Fourier transform of a generalized function in S'. Since $\widetilde{S}' = S'$, $\widetilde{H}_0 = H_0$ and $\widetilde{S} = S$, it follows that under the action of this transformation, the chain (3.18) becomes

$$S' \supset \widetilde{H}_- \supset H_0 = L_2(E_n) \supset \widetilde{H}_+ \supset S. \tag{3.19}$$

The inclusion $\widetilde{H}_+ \longrightarrow H_0$ is obviously quasi-nuclear so that the chain (3.19) is suitable for the construction of a generalized eigenfunction expansion of the operator $\widetilde{\Lambda}$. We first construct the expansion for $\widetilde{\Lambda}$ $(L(\xi) \not\equiv \text{const})$. Since the spectral measure essentially does not depend on the choice of $H_- \supseteq H_0 \supseteq H_+$ then by Theorem 3.1, we may assume that $d\rho(\lambda) = d\lambda$. We consider the operator $\widetilde{E}(\Delta)$ as acting from $\widetilde{H}_+$ into $\widetilde{H}_-$. Then by the remarks at the end of §2.3, Chapter V, the derivative $d\widetilde{E}_\lambda/d\lambda = \widetilde{P}(\lambda)$ exists in the sense of the Hilbert-Schmidt norm of operators from $\widetilde{H}_+$ into $\widetilde{H}_-$. It then follows from (3.19) that for $u \in S$, the derivative $d\widetilde{E}_\lambda u/d\lambda = \widetilde{P}(\lambda)$ exists as a generalized function in S' and is equal to $\widetilde{P}(\lambda)u \in \widetilde{H}_- \subset S'$, i.e. for arbitrary $v \in S$, $(d/d\lambda)/(\widetilde{E}_\lambda u, v)_0 = (\widetilde{P}(\lambda)u, v)_0$. Using the form $\widetilde{E}_\lambda$, we rewrite this equation

$$(\widetilde{P}(\lambda)\, u, v)_0 = \frac{d}{d\lambda} \int\limits_{L(\xi)<\lambda} u(\xi)\, \overline{v(\xi)}\, d\xi \qquad (u, v \in S). \tag{3.20}$$

If the surface L_λ with equation $L(\xi) = \lambda$ does not have a singular point, then, similarly to 3.15, equation (3.20) may be written as

$$(\widetilde{P}(\lambda)\, u, v)_0 = \int\limits_{L(\xi)=\lambda} u(\xi)\, \overline{v(\xi)}\, \sigma_\lambda \qquad (u, v \in S). \tag{3.21}$$

In connection with (3.15) and (3.21), we recall the notion of a δ-function, concentrated on a surface. Let $L(\xi) \in C^\infty(E_n)$ be fixed. We assume that the derivative $(d/d\lambda) \int_{L(\xi)<\lambda} u(\xi)\, d\xi$ exists in the weak sense for every $u \in S$, thus defining an anti-linear functional on S, i.e. an element of S'. For now, we denote it $\delta(L_\lambda)$:

$$(\delta(L_\lambda), u)_0 = \frac{d}{d\lambda} \int_{L(\xi)<\lambda} \overline{u(\xi)}\, d\xi \qquad (u \in S). \tag{3.22}$$

In the case where the surface L_λ $(L(\xi) = \lambda)$ does not have a singular point $((\operatorname{grad} L)(\xi) \neq 0$ on $L_\lambda)$, the derivative in (3.22) may be computed and the definition takes the form

$$(\delta(L_\lambda), u)_0 = \int_{L(\xi)=\lambda} \overline{u(\xi)}\, \sigma_\lambda \qquad (u \in S), \tag{3.23}$$

where σ_λ is an $n-1$ order differential form such that $dL \wedge \sigma_\lambda = d\xi_1 \wedge \cdots \wedge d\xi_n$. The functional $\delta(L_\lambda) \in S'$, defined by equation (3.23), is called the δ-function concentrated on the surface L_λ.

Thus the following theorem is established.

Theorem 3.2. *Let $P(\lambda)$ and $\widetilde{P}(\lambda)$ be generalized projection operators constructed as in Theorem 3.1 corresponding to the operator Λ and its Fourier image Λ. Let L_γ denote the surface with the equation $L(\xi) = \lambda$. Then for all almost all λ, in the sense of Lebesgue measure, the δ-functions $\delta(L_\lambda)$ exist and*

$$(\widetilde{P}(\lambda)\, u, v)_0 = (\delta(L_\lambda), \bar{u}v)_0.$$

$$(P(\lambda)\, u, v)_0 = (\widetilde{P}(\lambda)\, \tilde{u}, \tilde{v})_0 = (\delta(L_\lambda), \overline{\tilde{u}}\, \tilde{v})_0 \qquad (u, v \in S). \tag{3.24}$$

It follows from the equation $(P(\lambda)u, v)_0 = (\delta(L_\lambda), \overline{\tilde{u}}\,\tilde{v}_0)$ that in the case above where $(\delta(L_\lambda), u)_0$ can be written out, $P(\lambda)$ is an integral operator depending on a difference kernel, namely the spectral kernel

$$\Phi(x, y; \lambda) = \Phi(x - y; \lambda) = \frac{1}{(2\pi)^n} \frac{d}{d\lambda} \int_{L(\xi)<\lambda} e^{i\langle x-y, \xi\rangle}\, d\xi = \frac{1}{(2\pi)^n} \int_{L(\xi)=\lambda} e^{i\langle x-y, \xi\rangle}\, \sigma_\lambda. \tag{3.25}$$

$$(x, y \in E_n).$$

In conclusion, we note that in terms of δ-functions $\delta(L_\lambda)$, formula (3.15) for the integral spectral kernel may be rewritten in the form

$$\Psi(x, y; \lambda) = \frac{\operatorname{sign}(x_1 \cdots x_n y_1 \cdots y_n)}{(2\pi)^n} \Big(\delta(L_\lambda), \prod_{j=1}^{n} \frac{1}{\xi_j^2} (1 - e^{-ix_j\xi_j})(1 - e^{iy_j\xi_j})\Big)_0$$

$$(x, y \in E_n).$$

3. The case of a Carleman operator. It is not difficult to write the Carleman condition of an operator in an equivalent form involving $L(\xi)$ of the last subsection. Namely, for the operator Λ to be a Carleman operator it is necessary and sufficient that there exist a nonvanishing, bounded, continuous function $\gamma(\lambda)$ on the value set of $L(\xi)$ $(\lambda \in E_n)$ such that

$$\int_{E_n} |\gamma(L(\xi))|^2 d\xi < \infty. \tag{3.26}$$

For if $F(\lambda)$ is bounded on $\{L(\xi),\ \xi \in E_n\}$, then $F(\widetilde{\Lambda})$ is obviously equal to the operator of multiplication by $F(L(\xi))$. Therefore $F(\Lambda)$ coincides with the convolution operator with the generalized function $(1/\sqrt{(2\pi)^n})\, \widetilde{(F(L(\xi)))}\,(x)$. If $\gamma(\lambda)$ is such that (3.26) holds then $(1/\sqrt{(2\pi)^n})\, \widetilde{(\gamma(L(\xi)))}\,(x) \in L_2(E_n)$ and the indicated convolution operator will be an integral operator with kernel

$$K(x, y) = K(x - y) = \frac{1}{\sqrt{(2\pi)^n}} \widetilde{(\gamma(L(\xi)))}\,(x - y)$$
$$(x, y \in E_n). \tag{3.27}$$

We have

$$\int_{E_n} |K(x, y)|^2 dx = \int_{E_n} |K(x)|^2 dx = \frac{1}{(2\pi)^n} \int_{E_n} |\widetilde{(\gamma(L(\xi)))}\,(x)|^2 dx$$
$$= \frac{1}{(2\pi)^n} \int_{E_n} |\gamma(L(\xi))|^2 d\xi = C < \infty \qquad (y \in E_n), \tag{3.28}$$

i.e. Λ is Carleman. Inverting the argument we obtain that if Λ is Carleman, then (3.26) holds.

The general facts established in §4, Chapter V of course extend to Carleman operators; in particular the spectral function will now be an ordinary function. In addition, by (3.28) it must be in such a form that $\int_{E_n} |K(x, y)^2|\, dx = C$ $(y \in E_n)$ so for $p(x)$ we may choose, for example, $(1 + |x|)^{n+\epsilon}$ $(\epsilon > 0)$.

The kernel (3.27) of the operator $\gamma(\Lambda)$ is, in general, not continuous in $(x, y) \in E_n \times E_n$. However, *the kernel of the operator* $(\gamma(\Lambda))^* \gamma(\Lambda) = |\gamma|^2(\Lambda)$ *is in* $C(E_n \times E_n)$: we put $\gamma_1(\lambda) = |\gamma(\lambda)|^2$, so that, since $\gamma(\lambda)$ is bounded, the estimate (3.26) follows with γ replaced by γ_1. This allows us to write the kernel $K_1(x, y)$ of the operator $\gamma_1(\Lambda) = (\gamma(\Lambda))^* \gamma(\Lambda)$ by means of a representation of the type (3.27): $K_1(x, y) = (1/\sqrt{(2\pi)^n})\,(\widetilde{\gamma_1(L(\xi))})\,(x - y)$ $(x, y \in E_n)$. But $\gamma_1(L(\xi)) = |\gamma(L(\xi))|^2 \in L_1(E_n)$ (see (3.26)), and therefore $(\widetilde{\gamma_1(L(\xi))})(x)$ $(x \in E_n)$ is continuous. The assertion is proved.

It follows in particular that if L is such that condition (3.26) is fulfilled for some γ, then a new γ may always be chosen so that $\gamma(\Lambda)$ will be an integral operator with kernel in $C(E_n \times E_n)$.

An expression L of the form (3.3) with real constant coefficients will be called strongly Carleman if $|L(\xi)| \longrightarrow \infty$ as $|\xi| \longrightarrow \infty$. The following theorem holds.

Theorem 3.3. *Let L be a strongly Carleman expression, and $F(\lambda)$ $(\lambda \in (-\infty, \infty))$ a bounded nonincreasing function on the spectrum of Λ such that $|\lambda^N F(\lambda)| \leq C_N < \infty$ (on the spectrum for $N = 0, 1, 2, \cdots$). Then $F(\Lambda)$ is an integral operator with kernel $K(x, y) = K(x - y)$ $(x, y \in E_n)$, where $K(\cdot) \in C^\infty(E_n)$, and $(D^\alpha K)(\cdot) \in L_2(E_n)$ for all α.*

The Λ is a Carleman operator. Moreover, its spectral kernel has the property $\Phi(x, y; \lambda) \in C^\infty(E_n \times E_n)$ for almost all λ (with respect to Lebesgue measure) and is of the form (3.25).

Proof. We use the following assertion (see E. A. Gorin [1], §3): Let $Q(\xi)$ be a polynomial with real coefficients $\xi \in E_n$. Then as $r \longrightarrow \infty$

$$\min_{|\xi|=r} |Q(\xi)| = ar^b(1 + o(1)),$$

where $a \geq 0$ and $b \in (-\infty, \infty)$ are numbers and b is rational. We then conclude that for the strongly Carleman expression L, there exist R, C_1, $b > 0$ such that

$$|L(\xi)| \geqslant C_1 |\xi|^b, \quad |\xi| \geqslant R. \tag{3.29}$$

By the form of $F(\lambda)$, for arbitrary $N \geq 0$ there is a $C_2 > 0$ such that $|F(\lambda)| \leq C_2(1 + |\lambda|^N)^{-1}$ on the spectrum of Λ. It then follows from (3.29) that for some $C_3 > 0$,

$$|F(L(\xi))| \leqslant C_3(1 + |\xi|^{bN})^{-1} \quad (\xi \in E_n).$$

Choosing N sufficiently large, we prove the convergence of the integrals

$$\int_{E_n} |\xi^\alpha F(L(\xi))|\, d\xi, \quad \int_{E_n} |\xi^\alpha F(L(\xi))|^2 d\xi$$

$$(\alpha = (\alpha_1, \ldots, \alpha_n);\ \alpha_1, \ldots, \alpha_n = 0, 1, \ldots).$$

As already indicated, $F(\Lambda)$ is the convolution operator with the function

$$K(x) = \frac{1}{\sqrt{(2\pi)^n}} \widetilde{(F(L(\xi)))}(x) \quad (x \in E_n).$$

The convergence of the first of the indicated integrals implies the inclusion, $K(x) \in C^\infty(E_n)$ and the second, the inclusion $(D^\alpha K)(x) \in L_2(E_n)$.

For the proof of the second part of the theorem, we note that the condition $|L(\xi)| \longrightarrow \infty$ as $|\xi| \longrightarrow \infty$ implies that each of the surfaces $L(\xi) = \lambda$ is bounded in E_n. By Lemma 3.3, we conclude that the integrals $\int_{L(\xi)=\lambda} e^{i<x-y,\xi>} \sigma_\lambda$ make sense and exist for almost all λ; they lie in $C^\infty(E_n \times E_n)$ as a function of (x, y). The theorem now follows from an application of formula (3.25).

Remark. From the proof of the theorem, it is clear that if $F(\lambda)$ is bounded on the spectrum of Λ and decreases no slower as $|\lambda| \longrightarrow \infty$ than sufficiently large powers $1/|\lambda|^N$ $(N \geq 0)$, then $F(\Lambda)$ will be an integral operator with kernel $K(x) \in C^{l(N)}(E_n)$ and $(D^\alpha K)(x) \in L_2(E_n)$ $(|\alpha| \leq l(N))$ where $l(N) = 0, 1, \cdots$ depends on N and $l(N) \longrightarrow \infty$ as $N \longrightarrow \infty$.

Theorem 3.3 shows that all of the theorems of §4, Chapter V apply to the operator Λ, constructed from a strongly Carleman expression L. Moreover, by Lemma 2.3 above we conclude that the individual eigenfunctions $\phi_\alpha(x; \lambda)$ lie in $C^\infty(E_n)$ and the expansion $\Phi(x, y; \lambda) = \sum_{\alpha=1}^{N\lambda} \phi_\alpha(x; \lambda) \phi_\alpha(y; \lambda)$ $(x, y \in E_n)$ may be differentiated in x and y.

In conclusion, we note that if L is a strongly Carleman expression, then the operator Λ is semi-bounded from above or below (with the exclusion of the case $n = 1$ and odd order L). In fact, let $n \geq 2$. In this case the complement of the sphere $|\xi| < R$ is connected in E_n and therefore if the polynomial takes both a positive and a negative value for large $|\xi|$ then it has a zero ξ with $|\xi|$ as large as we please. But this contradicts the hypothesis that $L(\xi) \longrightarrow \infty$ as $|\xi| \longrightarrow \infty$. Thus there exists $R > 0$ such that for $|\xi| \geq R$, for example, $L(\xi) > 0$. Then, there is a $C > -\infty$ such that $L(\xi) \geq C$ $(\xi \in E_n)$. Applying the Parseval equation, we obtain

$$(\Lambda u, u)_0 = (Lu, u)_0 = \int_{E_n} L(\xi) |\tilde{u}(\xi)|^2 d\xi \geqslant C \int_{E_n} |\tilde{u}(\xi)|^2 d\xi = C \| u \|_0^2$$

$$(u \in C_0^\infty(E_n)),$$

which is what was required. The case $n = 1$ is considered analogously.

4. **Hypoelliptic expressions.** The results of the preceding subsection

concerned the operator Λ constructed from the expression L on $L_2(G)$, where $G = E_n$. We will now consider an important class of expressions with constant coefficients for which similar results are valid for arbitrary $G \subseteq E_n$. This class is introduced independently of spectral theory; we cite the required definitions.

We consider the space $D'(G)$ $(G \subseteq E_n)$ of generalized functions of L. Schwartz, namely anti-linear functionals $(\alpha, u)_0$ on the space $D(G) = C_0^\infty(G)$, where convergence is introduced in the necessary way ($u_n \longrightarrow 0$ if the supports of u_n are contained in a single compact subset of G and these functions and all of their derivatives converge uniformly to zero). Let L be some expression of the form (3.3) with constant, in general, complex coefficients; $\phi \in D'(G)$ is called a generalized solution (inside G) of the equation $Lu = f \in D'(G)$ if $(\phi, L^+v)_0 = (f, v)_0$, $(v \in D(G))$.

The expression L is called hypoelliptic if each solution $\phi \in D'(G)$ of the equation $Lu = 0$ is an infinitely differentiable function, i.e., $(\phi, v)_0 = (h, v)_0 = \int_G h(x)\, \overline{v(x)}\, dx$ $(v \in D(G))$, where $h(x) \in C^\infty(G)$. It turns out that the notion of hypoellipticity of L does not depend on the region G and may be expressed in terms of the polynomial $L(\xi)$.[1] We introduce some necessary and sufficient conditions for the hypoellipticity of L.

a) For arbitrary $\theta \in E_n$

$$\lim_{|\xi| \to \infty} \frac{L(\xi + \theta)}{L(\xi)} = 1.$$

b) For an arbitrary derivative D^α, $\alpha \neq 0$,

$$\lim_{|\xi| \to \infty} \frac{(D^\alpha L)(\xi)}{L(\xi)} = 0. \tag{3.30}$$

In this connection, it is sufficient for the hypoellipticity of L, that (3.30) hold only for $|\alpha| = 1$.

c) If $\xi + i\eta \in C_n$, then $|L(\xi + i\eta)| \longrightarrow \infty$ as $|\xi| \longrightarrow \infty$, where the convergence is uniform in η for $|\eta| \leq C$.

---

1) For proofs of the facts cited below, see L. Hörmander [1], Chapter 3, 3.3–3.6, and G. E. Šilov [1]. In what follows we will only need a part of these results. Namely, criterion b) of hypoellipticity which is used to study the smoothness of the spectral kernel $\Phi(x, y; \lambda)$ as a function of the point (x, y), is a characterization of hypoellipticity in terms of $\mathfrak{D}(Л)$. The remaining results are introduced only for completeness. In addition, we note that the formal notion of hypoellipticity applies in the case of an expression with infinitely differentiable, variable coefficients, but we will not present the corresponding results.

d) The complex zeros $\zeta = \xi + i\eta$ of the polynomial $L(\zeta)$ are scattered in a region of C_n such that $|\xi| \longrightarrow \infty$ and $|\eta| \longrightarrow \infty$. If L is hypoelliptic, then this region necessarily has the form $|\eta| \geq C_1 |\xi|^h + C_2$, where $C_1 h > 0$ and $C_2 \in (-\infty, \infty)$ are constants.

Let us make some further remarks. For the hypoellipticity of L it is sufficient that only the generalized solutions of $Lu = 0$ that enter G in L_2 be infinitely differentiable.

Hypoellipticity is closely connected with the behavior of the fundamental solution e_ξ, with a singularity at the point ξ, of the expression L (for the definition of e_ξ, see §4.1, Chapter III; for its existence for expressions with constant coefficients see §1.1, Chapter IV, Corollary 5, Theorem 1.1). It turns out that a necessary and sufficient condition for the hypoellipticity of L is that the solution e_ξ be an ordinary function in C^∞ on the complement of the point $\xi \in G$. (Since L has constant coefficients, it is sufficient to satisfy this condition for only one $\xi \in G$; necessity follows trivially from the definition, and sufficiency is established by an argument close to that used to prove Theorem 4.1 of Chapter III.) We note that the summability of e_ξ in a neighborhood of the point ξ is not clear for the general case of hypoelliptic L.

Finally, hypoellipticity is naturally connected with the structure of the domain $\mathfrak{D}(\Pi)$ of the maximal operator Π, constructed from L on $L_2(G)$, ($G \subseteq E_n$, bounded or not). Namely, we will only consider complete polynomials $L(\xi)$ (see page 277; in view of the relation $|L(\xi)| \longrightarrow \infty$ as $|\xi| \longrightarrow \infty$, $L(\xi)$ is trivially complete in the hypoelliptic case). Then a necessary and sufficient condition for L to be hypoelliptic, is the following: for arbitrary $f(x) \in \mathfrak{D}(\Pi)$ and $\chi(x) \in C_0^\infty(G)$, the function $\chi(x) f(x) \in \mathfrak{D}(\Pi)$ and thus is in $\mathfrak{D}(\Lambda)$ by Theorem 1.3, Chapter IV. This property shows that the local structure of the minimal and maximal operators is obviously the same (hypoelliptic operators were originally called local).

We proceed to the spectral theory of selfadjoint operators arising from formally selfadjoint hypoelliptic expressions L of type (3.3) on the space $L_2(G)$, $G \subseteq E_n$. From c) (or b)) it follows that for such an expression $|L(\xi)| \longrightarrow \infty$ as $|\xi| \longrightarrow \infty$, i.e., that it is strongly Carleman, [1] and therefore that of all the results

---

1) We note that there are strongly Carleman expressions which are not hypoelliptic. For example, let $L = D_1^4 D_2^4 - D_1^2 - D_2^2$. Then $L(\xi) = \xi_1^4 \xi_2^4 + \xi_1^2 + \xi_2^2 \longrightarrow \infty$ as $|\xi| \longrightarrow \infty$. More-

of subsection 3 related to the operator Λ on the space $L_2(E_n)$ apply.

Thus, let $G \subset E_n$ be bounded, let Γ be its smooth boundary and Λ the minimal operator on $L_2(G)$ corresponding to L. We assume that $n \geq 2$. Exactly as at the end of the preceding subsection we show that Λ is a semi-bounded (above or below) operator. Consequently, it has equal deficiency indices and therefore it has selfadjoint extensions on $L_2(G)$. Let A be one of these and $E(\Delta)$ a corresponding resolution of the identity. We will construct an eigenfunction expansion from $E(\Delta)$ (some modifications may be necessary, considering that we may want selfadjoint extensions of Λ in some larger space). The scheme of the construction will now naturally be different from those of subsections 2 and 3, but rather, close to the presentations of subsections 1 and 4 of §2. Since boundary value theory for hypoelliptic equations is not sufficiently developed we will limit ourselves to the spectral theory inside the region.

Lemma 3.4. *The operator A just constructed is a Carleman operator. In particular: let R_z $(\operatorname{Im} z \neq 0)$ denote a typical resolvent of A, and let $N = 0, 1, \cdots$ be sufficiently large. Then the operator $R = R_z^N$ is an integral operator with a kernel $R(x, y)$ $(x, y \in G)$ for which the integrals*

$$\int_G |R(x, y)|^2 dy, \quad \int_G |R(x, y)|^2 dx \tag{3.31}$$

are bounded for x, y varying strictly inside G and bounded. The vector-function $R(x, \cdot)$, $R(\cdot, y)$ $(x, y \in G)$ with values in the space $L_2(G)$ is weakly continuously differentiable of order $l(N) = 0, 1, \cdots$, where $l(N) \longrightarrow \infty$ as $N \longrightarrow \infty$.

Proof. We construct the minimal operator corresponding to L on the space $L_2(E_n)$ and denote it by Λ_0; we let $J = (\Lambda_0 - zE)^{-N}$. By the remark at the end of Theorem 3.3, the operator J will be an integral operator for sufficiently large $N = 0, 1, \cdots$. We choose N so, and let $J(x, y) = J(x - y)$ $(x, y \in E_n)$ be its kernel; $J(x) \in C^{l(N)}(E_n)$, $(D^\alpha J)(x) \in L_2(E_n)$ $(|\alpha| \leq l(N))$ for some $l(N) = 0, 1, \cdots$. This will be the $l(N)$ used for the theorem.

---

over,

$$\frac{(D_1 L)(\xi)}{L(\xi)} = \frac{4\xi_1^3\xi_2^4 + 2\xi_1}{\xi_1^4\xi_2^4 + \xi_1^2 + \xi_2^2},$$

and putting $\xi_1 = 1$, we see that this quotient does not tend to zero as $|\xi| \longrightarrow \infty$. Then, according to b), L is not hypoelliptic.

Let $f \in L_2(G)$ be considered as a function of $L_2(E_n)$ by extending it to be zero outside G. Then the operator $(Sf)(x) = (Rf)(x) - (Jf)(x)$ $(x \in G)$ is obviously continuous on $L_2(G)$. It is easy to see that Sf is a generalized solution of the equation $(L - zE)^N u = 0$, inside G: for $v \in C_0^\infty$, we have

$$(Sf, (L - \bar{z}E)^N v)_0 = (R_z^N f, (A - \bar{z}E)^N v)_0 - ((\Lambda_0 - zE)^{-N} f, (\Lambda_0 - \bar{z}E)^N v)_{L_2(E_n)}$$
$$= (f, v)_0 - (f, v)_{L_2(E_n)} = 0.$$

Using criterion b) it is easy to check that the hypoellipticity of $(L - zE)^N$ follows from that of L. Thereofre $Sf \in C^\infty(G)$. It further follows from the properties of the kernel $J(x - y)$, that the derivatives $D^\alpha Jf$ $(|\alpha| \leq l(N))$ exist and are in $C(E_n)$, and consequently that $Rf = Jf + Sf \in C^{l(N)}(G)$.

We now use an argument similar to that of Lemma 5.2, Chapter III. Namely, let $\tilde{G}$ be a bounded subregion strictly contained in G. We consider the transformation $f \rightarrow (Rf)(x)$ $(x \in \bar{\tilde{G}})$ of the entire space $L_2(G)$ into the space $C^{l(N)}(\bar{\tilde{G}})$. It follows from the continuity of R in $L_2(G)$ that this transformation is closed, which in turn implies that it is continuous. Therefore

$$\| Rf \|_{C^{l(N)}(\bar{\tilde{G}})} \leqslant C \| f \|_{L_2(G)} \quad (f \in L_2(G)). \tag{3.32}$$

The proof of the lemma is now completed in the usual way (cf. the proofs of Theorems 5.5 and 5.7 of Chapter III). We consider the homogeneous, additive functional l_x on $L_2(G)$ given by $L_2(G)\ l_x(f) = (Rf)(x)$ $(x \in \bar{\tilde{G}})$. By (3.32) it is continuous and therefore admits a representation $(Rf)(x) = l_x(f) = \int_G h_x(y) f(y) dy$, where $h_x(\cdot) \in L_2(G)$. If we set $R(x, y) = h_x(y)$ $(x \in \bar{\tilde{G}}, y \in G)$, then the required estimate on the first of the integrals in (3.31) follows from (3.32). The smoothness of the vector-function $R(x, \cdot)$ follows from that of $(Rf)(x) = l_x(f) = (R(x, \cdot), f)_0$ $(f \in L_2(G))$.

The boundedness of the second of the integrals in (3.31) and the properties of the function $R(\cdot, y)$ reduce to what has already been established, since $R^* = (R_z^N)^* = R_{\bar{z}}^N$. The lemma follows.

Consequently, the results of §4, Chapter V on general Carleman operators apply to the operator A, above. In particular, the spectral kernel $\Phi(x, y; \lambda)$ $(x, y \in G)$ will behave as usual. For fixed y, $\Phi(\cdot, y; \lambda) \in C^\infty(G)$ since this function is a generalized solution of the singular elliptic equation $(L - \lambda E) u = 0$; analogously $\Phi(x, \cdot; \lambda) \in C^\infty(G)$.

We now consider the behavior of $\Phi(x, y; \lambda)$ as a function of the point (x, y).

For this it is convenient to make use of the approach of §4.2 on the smoothness of the kernel of an elliptic operator up to the boundary. Since we are now interested only in smoothness inside the region, the presentation will be somewhat less difficult. First of all, we note the following lemma.

Lemma 3.5. *The kernel* $R(x, y)$ $(x, y \in G)$ *constructed in Lemma* 3.4 *is infinitely differentiable in each of the variables for* $x \neq y$, *and*

$$((L - zE)_x^N R)(x, y) = \delta_y, \quad ((L\otimes - zE)_y^N R)(x, y) = \delta_x. \tag{3.33}$$

Proof. The first equation in (3.33) means that for $v \in C_0^\infty(G)$,

$$(R(\cdot, y), (L - \bar{z}E)^N v)_0 = \overline{v(y)} \quad (y \in G), \tag{3.34}$$

or, what is the same,

$$\int_G (R(\cdot, y), (L - \bar{z}E)^N v)_0 \, u(y)\, dy = \int_G u(y)\, \overline{v(y)}\, dy. \tag{3.35}$$

for arbitrary $u, v \in C_0^\infty(G)$. Interchanging the order of integration (this is possible by Lemma 3.4), we obtain from (3.35):

$$\int_G (R(\cdot, y), (L - \bar{z}E)^N v)_0 \, u(y)\, dy = (R_z^N u, (A - \bar{z}E)^N v)_0 = (u, v)_0.$$

Thus (3.34) is proved. Choosing $v \in C_0^\infty(G)$ in this relation and such that v vanishes in a neighborhood of the point y, we find that $R(x, y)$ satisfies the singular elliptic equation $(L - zE)^N = 0$ for $x \in G\setminus\{y\}$, and therefore is an element of $C^\infty(G\setminus\{y\})$.

The properties of $R(x, y)$ relative to y are established analogously. The lemma follows.

In particular, this lemma shows that the singularities of $R(x, y)$ are concentrated on the diagonal $y = x$.

We consider a bounded subregion U strictly contained in G and select a region V strictly in G such that $U \subset V \subset G$. Then let $h(x) \in C_0^\infty(G)$ be equal to 1 on U and vanish off V. For each function $u \in C_0(U)$ (extended to zero on all of G) the representation of type (2.16)

$$u(x) = \int_G (L - zE)_x^N [R(x, y)(1 - h(x))]\, u(y)\, dy$$
$$+ M\left(\int_G R(x, y)\, h(x)\, u(y)\, dy\right) \quad (x \in G) \tag{3.36}$$

holds where M is the minimal operator induced on $L_2(G)$ by the expression $M = (L - zE)^N$ (it is clear that $\int_G R(x, y) u(y)\, dy$ is only in $C^{l(N)}(G)$ and therefore it is not immediately possible to apply the expression $(L - zE)^N$ to this integral, as in (2.16) with $l(N) < Nr$).

We verify (3.36). First of all we note that the first integral of (3.36) makes sense since the singularities of $R(x, y)$ are excluded. The second term also makes sense: $\int_G R(x, y) u(y) dy = (R_z^N u)(x) \in \mathfrak{D}((A - zE)^N) \subseteq \mathfrak{D}(\mathrm{M})$ (M is the maximal operator on $L_2(G)$ constructed from M), and therefore by the hypoellipticity of $(L - zE)^N$, the product of these two functions is in $\mathfrak{D}(\mathrm{M})$.

Since $R_z^N u \in \mathfrak{D}((A - zE)^N)$, $hR_z^N u \in \mathfrak{D}(\mathrm{M}) \subseteq \mathfrak{D}((A - zE)^N)$, then $f = (1 - h) R_z^N u \in \mathfrak{D}((A - zE)^N)$. But the function f is in $C^\infty(G)$, so the operator $(A - zE)^N$, a restriction of M, is such that $\mathrm{M}f = (L - zE)^N f$. Thus

$$u = (A - zE)^N R_z^N u = (A - zE)^N ((1 - h) R_z^N u) + (A - zE)^N (hR_z^N u)$$
$$= (L - zE)^N ((1 - h) R_z^N u) + \mathrm{M}(hR_z^N u),$$

i.e., equation (3.36) is established.

We show (cf. (2.17)) that

$$A_1(x, y) = (L - zE)_x^N [R(x, y)(1 - h(x))], \quad A_2(x, y) = R(x, y) h(x)$$
$$(x \in G, y \in U); \tag{3.37}$$

these functions vanish for $x \in G \setminus V$. Let $\phi \in C^\infty(G)$ be such that $(L\phi)(x) = \lambda\phi(x)$ $(x \in G)$. Then

$$\varphi(y) = \int_V \overline{(A_1(x, y) + (\lambda - \bar{z})^N A_2(x, y))}\, \varphi(x)\, dx \quad (y \in U). \tag{3.38}$$

In fact, let $u \in C_0(U)$. Using (3.36), we obtain

$$\int_G \int_G A_1(x, y) \overline{\varphi(x)} u(y)\, dxdy + (\lambda - z)^N \int_G \int_G A_2(x, y) \overline{\varphi(x)} u(y)\, dxdy$$
$$= \int_G \int_G A_1 \ldots + \int_G \left(\int_G A_2(x, y) u(y)\, dy \right) \overline{((L - \bar{z}E)^N \varphi)(x)}\, dx \tag{3.39}$$
$$= \int_G \left(\int_G A_1(x, y) u(y)\, dy + \mathrm{M} \int_G A_2(x, y) u(y)\, dy \right) \overline{\varphi(x)}\, dx = \int_G u(x) \overline{\varphi(x)}\, dx$$

(it is not difficult to justify the differentiation by parts). We conclude from the arbitrariness of u and (3.39) that (3.38) is correct.

Now, in analogy with (2.21), we make use of (3.38) to obtain the following representation of the spectral kernel:

$$\Phi(x, y; \lambda) = \int_V \int_V \overline{(A_1(\xi, x) + (\lambda - \bar{z})^N A_2(\xi, x))} (A_1(\eta, y) + (\lambda - z)^N A_2(\eta, y)) \, \Phi(\xi, \eta; \lambda) \, d\xi d\eta \qquad (x, y \in U). \tag{3.40}$$

This representation provides the possibility of investigating the smoothness of the kernel $\Phi(x, y; \lambda)$ with respect to $(x, y) \in U \times U$. The scheme is exactly the same as in §2.4 and we only sketch it. From Lemma 3.4 and (3.37) it follows that the vector-function $A_2(\cdot, y)$ $(y \in U)$ with values in the space $L_2(V)$ is weakly continuously differentiable of order $l(N)$. It is possible to show that the analogous vector-function $A_1(\cdot, y)$ $(y \in U)$ is infinitely differentiable. If we form $g_y = A_1(\cdot, y) + (\lambda - z)^N A_2(\cdot, y)$ and $f_x = \overline{g}_x$ and consider that $\Phi(\cdot, \cdot; \lambda) \in L_2(V \times V) = L_2(V) \otimes L_2(V)$, we conclude with the help of Lemma 2.5 that the derivatives $(D_x^\alpha D_y^\beta \Phi)$ $(x, y; \lambda)$ $(|\alpha|, |\beta| \le l(N))$ exist and are continuous as functions of $(x, y) \in U \times U$.

We clarify why $A_1(x, y)$ may be regarded as a continuous vector-function $A_1(\cdot, y)$ with values in $L_2(V)$. For each $y \in U$, $A_1(\cdot, y) \in C_0^\infty(G)$ and therefore $A_1(\cdot, y) \in L_2(V)$. Letting $g \in L_2(V)$ it is easy to see that $\int_V \overline{A_1(x, y)}\, g(x)\, dx$ $(y \in U)$ is a generalized solution of the hypoelliptic equation $(L - \bar{z}E)^N u = 0$ in U (see the calculations in §2.4). The smoothness of the integral follows from this, i.e., the weak smoothness of $A_1(\cdot, y)$.

So the derivatives $(D_x^\alpha D_y^\beta \Phi)$ $(x, y; \lambda)$ $(|\alpha|, |\beta| \le l(N))$ exist and are continuous with respect to $(x, y) \in U \times U$. Since $l(N) \longrightarrow \infty$ as $N \longrightarrow \infty$ and U is an arbitrary bounded subregion in G, it follows that $\Phi(\cdot, \cdot; \lambda) \in C^\infty(G \times G)$. We have obtained the following theorem.

Theorem 3.4. *Let G be a (generally unbounded) region, and consider the hypoelliptic expression* (3.3) *with real constant coefficients on G. Let Λ be the corresponding minimal operator and let A be one of its selfadjoint extensions on $L_2(G)$ and E_λ the corresponding resolution of the identity.*

Then all of the conclusions of Theorem 2.1 *are valid for this E_λ with the following additions:* a) *the spectral kernel and eigenfunctions are infinitely differentiable, i.e.* $\Phi(\cdot, \cdot; \lambda) \in C^\infty(G \times G)$, $\phi_\alpha(\cdot; \lambda) \in C^\infty(G)$; b) *the expansion* (2.10) *may be infinitely differentiated with respect to $x, y \in G$ without altering the convergence;* c) *the function $F(\lambda)$ on the spectrum of A must be bounded and nonincreasing as $|\lambda| \longrightarrow \infty$ faster than any power (more precisely, not more* *slowly than some fixed sufficiently large power* $1/|\lambda|^N$ $(N \geq 0)$ *as indicated in the remark to Theorem* 3.3).

As in the elliptic case, the representation in (3.40) provides the possibility of studying the smoothness of the kernel $K(x, y)$ of the operator $F(A)$ relative to $(x, y) \in G \times G$. In this connection, see the end of §2.4.

5. **On examples of expansions.** The formulas presented in subsection 2 provide the possibility of computing the resolvents, resolution of the identity, integral spectral kernel and spectral kernel (generalized or not) for concrete examples of differential operators with constant coefficients on $L_2(E_n)$. Formulas (3.6), (3.15), (3.24)–(3.23) and (3.25) are such formulas. We will not cite the similarly laborious computations (one of these was presented in §2.8, example a)); instead, we will demonstrate the method of separation of variables, for this purpose, in the next section.

In conclusion we note that one example of a generalized eigenfunction expansion of a nonelliptic operator on a bounded region, was presented in §2.3 of Chapter IV.

§4. SEPARATION OF VARIABLES

Often the method of separation of variables may be applied to eigenvalue problems. The main problem is to construct an eigenfunction expansion of a given operator if the expansions for the operators obtained after separation of variables are known. It will be convenient for this purpose to work in an abstract Hilbert space.

1. **Separation of variables for operators on an abstract Hilbert space.** We consider two Hilbert spaces H' and H'' and their tensor product $H' \otimes H''$. Let A' and A'' be operators on H' and H'' with domains $\mathfrak{D}(A')$ and $\mathfrak{D}(A'')$. We construct an operator A on $H' \otimes H''$ by setting

$$A = A' \otimes E'' + E' \otimes A'', \quad \mathfrak{D}(A) = \mathfrak{D}(A') \otimes \mathfrak{D}(A''), \tag{4.1}$$

where E' and E'' are the identity operators in the spaces H' and H'' respectively. As usual, we require that $\mathfrak{D}(A')$ and $\mathfrak{D}(A'')$ are dense in H' and H'' so that $\mathfrak{D}(A)$ is dense on $H' \otimes H''$. We say that the operator A admits a separation of variables. It is clear that this notion is connected with differential operators induced by expressions of the form

$$(Lu)(x) = (L'_{x_1,\ldots,x_m}u)(x) + (L''_{x_{m+1},\ldots,x_n}u)(x)$$

$$(x = (x_1, \ldots, x_m, x_{m+1}, \ldots, x_n),$$

where L' and L'' are expressions respectively on the variables $x_1, \cdots, x_m$, and $x_{m+1}, \cdots, x_n$.

If A' and A'' are Hermitian, then $A' \otimes E''$ and $E' \otimes A''$ are, so that A is Hermitian ($\mathfrak{D}(A' \otimes E'') = \mathfrak{D}(A') \otimes H''$, $\mathfrak{D}(E' \otimes A'') = H' \otimes \mathfrak{D}(A'')$). For example we consider the operator $A' \otimes E''$. For $f, g \in \mathfrak{D}(A' \otimes E'') = \mathfrak{D}(A') \otimes H''$, i.e. for

$$f = \sum_j f'_j \otimes f''_j, \quad g = \sum_k g'_k \otimes g''_k \quad (f'_j,\ g'_k \in \mathfrak{D}(A');\quad f''_j,\ g''_k \in H'')$$

(here and below in subsections 1 and 2 the similar sums are finite) we have

$$((A' \otimes E'')f, g) = \left(\sum_j (A'f'_j) \otimes f''_j,\ \sum_k g'_k \otimes g''_k\right)$$

$$= \sum_{j,k} (A'f'_j,\ g'_k)(f''_j,\ g''_k) = \sum_{j,k} (f'_j,\ A'g'_k)(f''_j,\ g''_k) = (f, (A' \otimes E'')g),\ ^{1)}$$

as required.

Theorem 4.1. *Let A' and A'' be Hermitian operators and let E'_λ and E''_λ be ordinary resolutions of the identity corresponding to them. Then the family of operators $E_\lambda (-\infty < \lambda < \infty)$ on $H' \otimes H''$ defined by the formula*

$$(E_\lambda (f' \otimes f''),\ g' \otimes g'') = \int_{-\infty}^{\infty} (E'_{\lambda-\mu} f', g')\, d_\mu (E''_\mu f'', g'') \tag{4.2}$$

$$(f',\ g' \in H';\quad f'',\ g'' \in H''),$$

is one of the ordinary resolutions of the identity for the Hermitian operator A. (We clarify that E_λ is defined by extending (4.2) to a bilinear form and then noting that this form is continuous on $H' \otimes H''$.)

Proof. We define, on the linear span L of the formal products $f' \otimes f''$, the bilinear form $B_\lambda (-\infty < \lambda < \infty)$, putting

$$B_\lambda (f, g) = B_\lambda \left(\sum_j f'_j \otimes f''_j,\ \sum_k g'_k \otimes g''_k\right) = \sum_{j,k} B_\lambda (f'_j \otimes f''_j,\ g'_k \otimes g''_k) =$$

---

1) In subsection 1 we omit the indices of the spaces in the notation of the scalar products and norms.

$$= \sum_{j,k} \int_{-\infty}^{\infty} (E'_{\lambda-\mu} f'_j, g'_k) d_\mu (E''_\mu f''_j, g''_k)$$

$$\left(f = \sum_j f'_j \otimes f''_j, \; g = \sum_k g'_k \otimes g''_k \in L \right);$$

it is not difficult to see (cf. pp. 40–42) that B_λ is well defined.

For $\lambda_1 < \lambda_2$

$$B_{\lambda_1}(f, f) \le B_{\lambda_2}(f, f) \quad (f \in L). \tag{4.3}$$

In fact, if we denote $[\lambda_1 - \mu, \lambda_2 - \mu) = \delta_\mu$, then

$$B_{\lambda_2}(f, f) - B_{\lambda_1}(f, f) = \sum_{j,k} \int_{-\infty}^{\infty} (E'(\delta_\mu) f'_j, f'_k) d_\mu (E''_\mu f''_j, f''_k) \quad \left(f = \sum_j f'_j \otimes f''_j\right).$$

In order to establish the nonnegativity of the last sum it is sufficient to verify that the similar expression with the integrals replaced by partial sums is nonnegative, i.e., it is sufficient to establish the nonnegativity of sums of the form

$$\sum_{j,k} \sum_{l=1}^{N} (E'(\delta_{\mu_l}) f'_j, f'_k)(E''(\Delta_l) f''_j, f''_k)$$

$$= \sum_{l=1}^{N} \left[\sum_{j,k} (E'(\delta_{\mu_l}) f'_j, f'_k)(E''(\Delta_l) f''_j, f''_k) \right],$$

where $(-\infty, \infty) = \bigcup_{l=1}^{N} \Delta_l$ is some partition of the line into half-closed intervals Δ_l; $\mu_l \in \Delta_l$. But each expression in the square brackets is nonnegative, since the finite-dimensional matrices $\|a_{jk}\| = \|(E'(\delta_{\mu_l}) f'_j, f'_k)\|$ and $\|b_{jk}\| = \|(E''(\Delta_l) f''_j, f''_k)\|$ are positive definite, so by a well-known theorem the matrix $\|a_{jk} b_{jk}\|$ is positive definite. Thus the inequality (4.3) is established.

It is not difficult to see that

$$\lim_{\lambda \to +\infty} B_\lambda(f, f) = (f, f) \quad (f \in L). \tag{4.4}$$

In fact, since $\|E'_\nu\| = 1$, we may take the limit under the integral sign and obtain

$$\lim_{\lambda \to +\infty} B_\lambda (f' \otimes f'', g' \otimes g'') = \lim_{\lambda \to +\infty} \int_{-\infty}^{\infty} (E'_{\lambda-\mu} f', g') d_\mu (E''_\mu f'', g'')$$

$$= (f', g')(f'', g'') = (f' \otimes f'', g' \otimes g'')$$

$$(f', g' \in H'; \quad f'', g'' \in H''), \tag{4.5}$$

which proves (4.4).

It follows from (4.3) and (4.4) that $B_\lambda(f, f) \le (f, f)$ $(f \in L)$. Also, the definition of B_λ implies that this form is Hermitian and therefore the last inequality implies that B_λ is bounded. Consequently there exist bounded Hermitian operators E_λ on $H' \otimes H''$ such that $(E_\lambda f, g) = B_\lambda(f, g)$ $(f, g \in L)$.

To prove the theorem we must verify that the family E_λ $(-\infty < \lambda < \infty)$ is a resolution of the identity for the operator A. First, we show that the operator E_λ is an orthogonal projector; for this purpose it is sufficient to verify the equation $E_\lambda^2 = E_\lambda$. We construct a sequence of partitions of the line $(-\infty, \infty)$ into a finite number of intervals $\Delta_l^{(N)}$ of type $[a, b)$ (there are N intervals in the Nth partition). Then

$$(E_\lambda (f' \otimes f''), g' \otimes g'') = \int_{-\infty}^{\infty} (E'_{\lambda-\mu} f', g')\, d_\mu (E''_\mu f'', g'')$$

$$= \lim (E_\lambda^{(N)} (f' \otimes f''), g' \otimes g''),$$

$$E_\lambda^{(N)} (f' \otimes f'') = \sum_{l=1}^{N} (E'_{\lambda-\mu_l^{(N)}} f') \otimes (E''(\Delta_l^{(N)}) f''), \tag{4.6}$$

where $\mu_l^{(N)}$ is the left end of the interval $\Delta_l^{(N)}$, and $f', g' \in H'$ and $f'', g'' \in H''$ are arbitrary. Each operator $E_\lambda^{(N)}$ is a projection since it is obviously Hermitian and satisfies the relation

$$E_\lambda^{(N)2} (f' \otimes f'') = \sum_{l=1}^{N} E_\lambda^{(N)} ((E'_{\lambda-\mu_l^{(N)}} f') \otimes (E''(\Delta_l^{(N)}) f''))$$

$$= \sum_{l, k=1}^{N} (E'_{\lambda-\mu_k^{(N)}} E'_{\lambda-\mu_l^{(N)}} f') \otimes (E''(\Delta_k^{(N)}) E''(\Delta_l^{(N)}) f'') = E_\lambda^{(N)} (f' \otimes f''),$$

i.e., $E_\lambda^{(N)2} = E_\lambda^{(N)}$. So $\|E_\lambda^{(N)}\| = 1$ (if $E_\lambda^{(N)} \ne 0$). Further, from (4.6) we obtain that by refining the partitions sequentially $(E_\lambda^{(N)} f, g) \to (E_\lambda f, g)$ $(f, g \in L)$. Since $\|E_\lambda^{(N)}\| \le 1$, then $E_\lambda^{(N)} \to E_\lambda$ weakly. Moreover,

$$(E_\lambda E_\lambda^{(N)} (f' \otimes f''), g' \otimes g'') = \sum_{l=1}^{N} \int_{-\infty}^{\infty} (E'_{\lambda-\mu} E'_{\lambda-\mu_l^{(N)}} f',$$

$$g')\, d_\mu (E''_\mu E''(\Delta_l^{(N)}) f'', g'') = \sum_{l=1}^{N} \int_{\Delta_l^{(N)}} (E'_{\lambda-\mu} E'_{\lambda-\mu_l^{(N)}} f', g')\, d_\mu (E''_\mu f'', g'') =$$

$$= \sum_{l=1}^{N} \int_{\Delta_l^{(N)}} (E'_{\lambda-\mu} f', g')\, d_\mu (E''_\mu f'', g'') = (E_\lambda (f' \otimes f''), g' \otimes g''),$$

i.e., $E_\lambda E_\lambda^{(N)} = E_\lambda$. Since $E_\lambda^{(N)}$ converges weakly to E_λ, then we conclude that $E_\lambda^2 = E_\lambda$, i.e. E_λ is an orthogonal projection.

It follows from (4.3) that $E_{\lambda_1} \leq E_{\lambda_2}$ for $\lambda_1 < \lambda_2$. From this fact and the fact that the E_λ are projections, we obtain the equation $E_{\lambda_1} E_{\lambda_2} = E_{\min(\lambda_1, \lambda_2)}$. For the proof that E_λ is a resolution of the identity, we note that it satisfies the normalization condition. It follows from (4.5) that $E_{+\infty} = E$; similarly, it is easy to conclude from (4.5) that $E_{-\infty} = 0$ and $E_{\lambda-0} = E_\lambda$.

It remains to show that the resolution of the identity E_λ is a resolution of the identity for the operator A. For this it is sufficient to verify the equations

$$(A (f' \otimes f''), g' \otimes g'') = \int_{-\infty}^{\infty} \lambda d_\lambda (E_\lambda (f' \otimes f''), g' \otimes g'')$$

$$(f', g' \in H'; \quad f'', g'' \in H'').$$

We have

$$\int_{-\infty}^{\infty} \lambda d_\lambda (E_\lambda (f' \otimes f''), g' \otimes g'') = \int_{-\infty}^{\infty} \lambda d_\lambda \left\{ \int_{-\infty}^{\infty} (E'_{\lambda-\mu} f', g')\, d_\mu (E''_\mu f'', g'') \right\}$$

$$= \int_{-\infty}^{\infty} \left\{ \int_{-\infty}^{\infty} \lambda d_\lambda (E'_{\lambda-\mu} f', g') \right\} d_\mu (E''_\mu f'', g'')$$

$$= \int_{-\infty}^{\infty} \left\{ \int_{-\infty}^{\infty} (\mu + \nu)\, d_\nu\, (E'_\nu f', g') \right\} d_\mu\, (E''_\mu f'', g'')$$

$$= \int_{-\infty}^{\infty} \mu \left\{ \int_{-\infty}^{\infty} d_\nu (E'_\nu f', g') \right\} d_\mu (E''_\mu f'', g'')$$

$$+ \int_{-\infty}^{\infty} \left\{ \int_{-\infty}^{\infty} \nu d_\nu (E'_\nu f', g') \right\} d_\mu (E''_\mu f'', g'')$$

$$= (f', g') (A'' f'', g'') + (A' f', g') (f'', g'')$$

$$= ([(A' f') \otimes f'' + f' \otimes (A'' f'')], g' \otimes g'') = (A (f' \otimes f''), g' \otimes g''),$$

as required. The theorem is proved.

We note that is is easy to write a resolution of the identity which corresponds to the Hermitian operators $A' \otimes E''$ and $E' \otimes A''$. Namely the operators

$E'_\lambda \otimes E''$ and $E' \otimes E''_\lambda$ are such resolutions (we are using the notation of Theorem 4.1). The proof of this fact is not difficult to obtain by considering the class of tensor products of operators. (See formula (2.7), Chapter I.) By using the resolutions of the identity $E'_\lambda \otimes E''$ and $E' \otimes E''_\lambda$, formula (4.2) may be written as a weak integral

$$E_\lambda = \int_{-\infty}^{\infty} (E'_{\lambda-\mu} \otimes E'')\, d_\mu (E' \otimes E''_\mu) \tag{4.7}$$

(the definition of such an integral is similar to that of §2.3, Chapter VII).

Let B', B be selfadjoint operators which are respectively defined on H' and $H' \otimes H''$, with corresponding resolutions of the identity E'_λ and E_λ. Let $F(\lambda)$ be some bounded Borel measurable function. Then by (4.7) we have

$$F(B) = \int_{-\infty}^{\infty} F(\lambda)\, dE_\lambda = \int_{-\infty}^{\infty} F(\lambda)\, d_\lambda \left\{ \int_{-\infty}^{\infty} (E'_{\lambda-\mu} \otimes E'')\, d_\mu (E' \otimes E''_\mu) \right\}$$

$$= \int_{-\infty}^{\infty} \left(\left(\int_{-\infty}^{\infty} F(\lambda)\, d_\lambda E'_{\lambda-\mu} \right) \otimes E'' \right) d_\mu (E' \otimes E''_\mu) .$$

But $\int_{-\infty}^{\infty} F(\lambda) dE'_{\lambda-\mu} = F(B' + \mu E')$ since, generally, if E_λ is a resolution of the identity for some operator A, then $E_{\lambda-\lambda_0}$ is a resolution of the identity for the operator $A + \lambda_0 E$. Therefore we obtain

$$F(B) = \int_{-\infty}^{\infty} (F(B' + \mu E') \otimes E'')\, d_\mu (E' \otimes E''_\mu) . \tag{4.8}$$

The integrals in (4.7) and (4.8) converge in some weak sense. We clarify this only for the integral (4.8) in the case of continuous $F(\lambda)$. In this case, if $f \in H' \otimes H''$,

$$\int_{-\infty}^{\infty} (F(B' + \mu E') \otimes E'')\, d_\mu (E' \otimes E''_\mu) f$$

$$= \lim \sum_{l=1}^{N} (F(B' + \mu_l E') \otimes E'')(E' \otimes E''(\Delta_i)) f$$

$$= \lim \sum_{l=1}^{N} (F(B' + \mu_l E') \otimes E''(\Delta_l)) f \tag{4.9}$$

in the sense of convergence in $H' \otimes H''$, where $\{\Delta_1, \cdots, \Delta_N\}$ is a partition of the line $(-\infty, \infty)$ into intervals of the form $[a, b)$, $\mu_l \in \Delta_l$; the limit is taken by refining the partition. The relation (4.9) is easily verified by the usual argument for convergence of integrals of the form $\int_{-\infty}^{\infty} G(\mu) dE_\mu$ where E_λ is some resolution of the identity and $G(\mu)$ is a scalar function. The presence of an operator-valued function $F(B' + \mu E') \otimes E''$, instead of the scalar function $G(\mu)$, does not change the argument, since this function commutes with the operator-valued measure $E' \times E''(\Delta)$.

In particular, denoting the resolvents of B' and B by R'_z and R_z we obtain the formula

$$R_z = \int_{-\infty}^{\infty} (R'_{z-\mu} \otimes E'')\, d_\mu (E' \otimes E''_\mu) \quad (\operatorname{Im} z \neq 0) \tag{4.10}$$

in the sense of weak convergence.

We assume that the operators A' and A'' are selfadjoint. It is easy to see that the closures of $A' \otimes E''$ and $E' \otimes A''$ are then selfadjoint. So for $\operatorname{Im} z \neq 0$

$$\begin{aligned}(A' \otimes E'' - zE)(f' \otimes f'') &= ((A' - zE') \otimes E'')(f' \otimes f'') \\ &= ((A' - zE')f') \otimes f'' \qquad (f' \in \mathfrak{D}(A'),\ f'' \in \mathfrak{D}(A''))\end{aligned}$$

and therefore $\Re(A' \otimes E'' - zE)$ is dense in $H' \times H''$, i.e. $\overline{A' \otimes E''}$ is selfadjoint.

The following less trivial lemma is true.

Lemma 4.1. *If the operators A' and A'' are selfadjoint, then the closure of A is selfadjoint.*

Proof. Let B be the selfadjoint extension in question in the above, and R_z its resolvent. For the proof of the lemma, it is sufficient to verify that for $\operatorname{Im} z \neq 0$, $R_z(f' \otimes f'')$ $(f' \in \mathfrak{D}(A'),\ f'' \in \mathfrak{D}(A''))$, lies in the domain of the closure of A. Replacing the integral in (4.10) by a partial sum, we obtain from (4.9)

$$\begin{aligned}R_z(f' \otimes f'') &= \lim \sum_{l=1}^{N} (R'_{z-\mu_l} \otimes E''(\Delta_l))(f' \otimes f'') \\ &= \lim \sum_{l=1}^{N} (R'_{z-\mu_l} f') \otimes (E''(\Delta_l) f''),\end{aligned}$$

where

$$\sum_{l=1}^{N} (R'_{z-\mu_l} f') \otimes (E''(\Delta_l) f'') \in \mathfrak{D}(A') \otimes \mathfrak{D}(A'') = \mathfrak{D}(\dot{A}).$$

Moreover,

$$A\Big(\sum_{l=1}^{N} (R'_{z-\mu_l} f') \otimes (E''(\Delta_l) f'')\Big) = \sum_{l=1}^{N} (R'_{z-\mu_l} \otimes E''(\Delta_l))\, A(f' \otimes f''),$$

and therefore by (4.9) the last expression converges (to $R_z A(f' \otimes f'')$) in $H' \otimes H''$. Thus $R_z(f' \otimes f'') \in \mathfrak{D}(\bar{A})$. The lemma follows.

From this lemma and Theorem 4.1, we obtain

Theorem 4.2. *If A' and A'' are selfadjoint, then the selfadjoint closure of A and the resolution of the identity of this operator, functions of it, and its resolvents, are written according to formulas* (4.7) *(i.e.* (4.2)), (4.8) *and* (4.10).

It is clear that all that is necessary for Lemma 4.1 and Theorem 4.2 is the selfadjointness of the closures of A' and A''. If at least one of these closures is not selfadjoint, then the selfadjoint extension B of the operator A constructed from the resolution of the identity (4.7) will be said to be separated. Suppose the operators A', A'' have equal deficiency indices. Then by running through all possible E'_λ and E''_λ we obtain all possible separated selfadjoint extensions of A. It may be shown that the set of all separated selfadjoint extensions of A is smaller than the set of all selfadjoint extensions of A in $H' \otimes H''$. An example of this sort was constructed in §4.6 of Chapter III: the spectral matrix (4.33), in Chapter VII, corresponding to the separated extension of L, depends on a smaller number of defining parameters than the spectral matrix of a general selfadjoint extension of L in $l_2(\Pi)$, which may depend on an arbitrary operator on the operator circumference (see page 580).

We show further that *the spectrum of a separated extension of the operator A coincides with the closure of the algebraic sums of the spectra $S(B')$ and $S(B'')$ of the selfadjoint operators B' and B'' corresponding to E'_λ and E''_λ: $S(B) = \overline{S(B') + S(B'')}$ (i.e., $\lambda \in S(B)$ if and only if λ is a limit point of the set $\lambda' + \lambda''$ where $\lambda' \in S(B')$ and $\lambda'' \in S(B'')$).*

The proof follows from the following easily established remark: if $\sigma'(\lambda)$ and $\sigma''(\lambda)$ are bounded nondecreasing functions, then the set of points of growth of the nondecreasing bounded function

$$\sigma(\lambda) = \int_{-\infty}^{\infty} \sigma'(\lambda - \mu)\, d\sigma''(\mu) \qquad (-\infty < \lambda < \infty) \tag{4.11}$$

coincides with the closure of the algebraic sum of the sets of points of growth of the functions $\sigma'(\lambda)$ and $\sigma''(\lambda)$. For if we let $S(B', f')$, $S(B'', f'')$ and $S(B, f'\otimes f'')$ denote the sets of points of growth of the functions $(E'_\lambda f', f')$, $(E''_\lambda f'', f'')$ and $(E_\lambda(f'\otimes f''), f'\otimes f'')$, $(f'\in H', f''\in H'')$, then obviously,

$$S(B') = \bigcup_{f'\in H'} S(B', f'), \quad S(B'') = \bigcup_{f''\in H''} S(B'', f''),$$
$$S(B) = \bigcup_{f'\in H',\, f''\in H''} S(B, f'\otimes f'')$$

(recall that the linear span of the vectors $f'\otimes f''$ is dense in $H'\otimes H''$). Setting $g' = f'$ and $g'' = f''$ in (4.2) and comparing the equation obtained with (4.11) we conclude by the above remark that $S(B, f'\otimes f'') = \overline{S(B', f') + S(B'', f'')}$ for arbitrary $f'\in H'$, $f''\in H''$. It is now easy to obtain that $S(B) = \overline{S(B') + S(B'')}$ as required.

In particular it follows from what has been said that *formula* (4.10) *holds for any regular point* z *of the operator* B, since if $z \,\overline{\in}\, S(B)$, then $z-\mu \,\overline{\in}\, S(B')$ if $\mu\in S(B'')$.

We make one last remark. In the above we considered only ordinary resolutions of the identity and selfadjoint extensions in H', H'' and $H'\otimes H''$. At the same time, it is not difficult to draw conclusions from the above facts about the connections between the generalized resolutions of the identity of the operators A', A'' and A.

2. **Expansions in generalized eigenvectors.** We will construct here expansions for operators A as in (4.1), where A' and A'' are Hermitian operators acting on separable Hilbert spaces H'_0 and H''_0. By subsection 1 and Chapter V it is clear that in fact we need consider only the case where A' and A'', and consequently $\overline{A}$, are selfadjoint; we will assume this hypothesis below.

It is especially convenient at this time to make a special choice of the equipment of the space $H'_0\otimes H''_0$. We consider the chains

$$H'_- \supseteq H'_0 \supseteq H'_+, \quad H''_- \supseteq H''_0 \supseteq H''_+ \tag{4.12}$$

with quasi-nuclear inclusions $H'_+ \to H'_0$ and $H''_+ \to H''_0$. Taking the tensor product in (4.12) we obtain the chain (see §2.2, Chapter I)

$$H'_-\otimes H''_- \supseteq H'_0\otimes H''_0 \supseteq H'_+\otimes H''_+. \tag{4.13}$$

Obviously the tensor product of two Hilbert-Schmidt operators is again Hilbert-Schmidt. Since the inclusion operator $H'_+ \otimes H''_+ \longrightarrow H'_0 \otimes H''_0$ is equal to the tensor product of the inclusion operators $H'_+ \longrightarrow H'_0$ and $H''_+ \longrightarrow H''_0$, the inclusion $H'_+ \otimes H''_+ \longrightarrow H'_0 \otimes H''_0$ is quasi-nuclear. We will use the chain (4.13) to construct a generalized eigenvector expansion for $\overline{A}$.

It is well known that the choice of the spectral measure does not play any particular role. In all cases here it is convenient to construct them in the usual way, involving trace class operators as in (1.10), Chapter V. If the spectral measures of the operators A', A'' and $\overline{A}$ thus chosen are denoted $d\rho'(\lambda)$, $d\rho''(\lambda)$ and $d\rho(\lambda)$, it is not difficult to verify that ρ will be equal to the convolution of ρ' with ρ'':

$$\varrho(\lambda) = \int_{-\infty}^{\infty} \varrho'(\lambda - \mu)\, d\varrho''(\mu) = (\varrho' * \varrho'')(\lambda).\ ^{1)} \tag{4.14}$$

In fact, let J', J'' and J be operators of the type J connected respectively with the chains (4.12) and (4.13). Then (see Theorem 2.1, Chapter I) $J = J' \otimes J''$. We consider the operators $\hat{J}'$, $\hat{J}''$ and $\hat{J}$ acting on the spaces H'_0, H''_0 and $H'_0 \otimes H''_0$. By the general scheme of §2.1, Chapter V, we have $\rho'(\Delta) = \operatorname{tr}(\hat{J}'E'(\Delta)\hat{J}')$, $\rho''(\Delta) = \operatorname{tr}(\hat{J}''E''(\Delta)\hat{J}'')$, $\rho(\Delta) = \operatorname{tr}(\hat{J}E(\Delta)\hat{J})$. We chóose orthonormal bases $e'_1, e'_2, \cdots$ and $e''_1, e''_2, \cdots$ for H'_0 and H''_0, so that $e'_j \otimes e''_k$ $(j, k = 1, 2, \cdots)$ is an orthonormal basis for $H'_0 \otimes H''_0$. Using (4.2) we obtain

$$\begin{aligned}
\varrho(\lambda) = \operatorname{tr}(\hat{J}E_\lambda\hat{J}) &= \sum_{j,k=1}^{\infty} ((\hat{J}' \otimes \hat{J}'')E_\lambda(\hat{J}' \otimes \hat{J}'')(e'_j \otimes e''_k), e'_j \otimes e''_k)_{H'_0 \otimes H''_0} \\
&= \sum_{j,k=1}^{\infty} (E_\lambda((\hat{J}'e'_j) \otimes (\hat{J}''e''_k)), (\hat{J}'e'_j) \otimes (\hat{J}''e''_k))_{H'_0 \otimes H''_0} \\
&= \sum_{j,k=1}^{\infty} \int_{-\infty}^{\infty} (E'_{\lambda-\mu}\hat{J}'e'_j, \hat{J}'e'_j)_{H'_0}\, d_\mu (E''_\mu\hat{J}''e''_k, \hat{J}''e''_k)_{H''_0} \\
&= \sum_{k=1}^{\infty} \int_{-\infty}^{\infty} \varrho'(\lambda - \mu)\, d_\mu (E''_\mu\hat{J}''e''_k, \hat{J}''e''_k)_{H''_0} = \int_{-\infty}^{\infty} \varrho'(\lambda - \mu)\, d\varrho''(\mu),
\end{aligned}$$

as required.

We let $P'(\lambda)$ and $P''(\lambda)$ denote generalized projection operators

---

1) The equation $S(B) = \overline{S(B') + S(B'')}$, established at the end of subsection 1, follows again from these formulas.

corresponding to A' and A''; these are Hilbert-Schmidt operators (in fact they are trace class) respectively from H'_+ into H'_- and from H''_+ into H''_-. It is not difficult to show that

$$E_\lambda = \int_{-\infty}^{\infty}\int_{-\infty}^{\lambda-\mu} P'(\nu)\otimes P''(\mu)\,d\varrho'(\nu)\,d\varrho''(\mu)$$
$$= \int_{\nu+\mu<\lambda} P'(\nu)\otimes P''(\mu)\,d\varrho'(\nu)\,d\varrho''(\mu)\,, \tag{4.15}$$

where the integral converges in the Hilbert norm of the operators, defined from $H'_+\otimes H''_+$ into $H'_-\otimes H''_-$.

For obviously $|A\otimes B| = |A|\,|B|$ and therefore $|P'(\nu)\otimes P''(\mu)| = |P'(\nu)|\,|P''(\mu)| \le 1$. Then, since the measure $d\rho'(\nu)\,d\rho''(\mu)$ is finite, the integral (4.15) converges in the indicated sense. Further, by (4.2) and (2.15), Chapter V, we have, for $u', v' \in H'_+$ and $u'', v'' \in H''_+$,

$$(E_\lambda(u'\otimes u''), v'\otimes v'')_{H'_0\otimes H''_0} = \int_{-\infty}^{\infty} (E'_{\lambda-\mu}u', v')_{H'_0}\,d_\mu (E''_\mu u'', v'')_{H''_0}$$
$$= \int_{-\infty}^{\infty}\int_{-\infty}^{\lambda-\mu} (P'(\nu)u', v')_{H'_0}(P''(\mu)u'', v'')_{H''_0}\,d\varrho'(\nu)\,d\varrho''(\mu)$$
$$= \left(\left(\int_{-\infty}^{\infty}\int_{-\infty}^{\lambda-\mu} P'(\nu)\otimes P''(\mu)\,d\varrho'(\nu)\,d\varrho''(\mu)\right)(u'\otimes u''),\ v'\otimes v''\right)_{H'_0\otimes H''_0},$$

from which follows equation (4.15).

We will consider E_λ as an operator acting from $H'_+\otimes H''_+$ into $H'_-\otimes H''_-$, so that by the remark at the end of §2.3 of Chapter V, the derivative $dE_\lambda/d\rho(\lambda)$ exists for ρ-almost all λ, and is equal to the generalized projection operator $P(\lambda)$ corresponding to $\bar{A}$. Thus we have

$$P(\lambda) = \frac{d}{d\varrho(\lambda)} \int_{\nu+\mu<\lambda} P'(\nu)\otimes P''(\mu)\,d\varrho'(\nu)\,d\varrho''(\mu)\,. \tag{4.16}$$

Formulas (4.8) and (4.10) are also useful when rewritten in terms of generalized projection operators. For this we must note that if a continuous operator C on H'_0 is considered as an operator from H'_+ into H'_-, it will be a Hilbert-Schmidt operator (by the quasi-nuclearity of the inclusions $H'_+ \to H'_0$ and $H'_0 \to H'_-$). Therefore $F(A' + \mu E')\otimes P''(\mu)$ is a Hilbert-Schmidt operator from $H'_+\otimes H''_+$ into $H'_-\otimes H''_-$, where

$$|F(A'+\mu E')\otimes P''(\mu)| = |F(A'+\mu E')||P''(\mu)| \leqslant |F(A'+\mu E')|$$
$$= |S'F(A'+\mu E')O'| \leqslant \| S'F(A'+\mu E')\| |O'| \leqslant$$
$$\leqslant |S'F(A'+\mu E')||O'| \leqslant |S'| \| F(A'+\mu E')\| |O'| \leqslant C < \infty$$

uniformly for $\mu \in (-\infty, \infty)$ (we used the properties of the Hilbert norm introduced in Chapter V, §1.1; O', S' are corresponding inclusion operators). Now by an approach similar to that used to obtain (4.15) we easily conclude from (4.8) and (4.10) that

$$\begin{aligned} F(\bar{A}) &= \int_{-\infty}^{\infty} F(A'+\mu E')\otimes P''(\mu)\,d\varrho''(\mu), \\ R_z &= \int_{-\infty}^{\infty} R'_{z-\mu}\otimes P''(\mu)\,d\varrho''(\mu) \quad (z \bar{\in} S(\bar{A})) \end{aligned} \tag{4.17}$$

(the integrals converge in the sense of the Hilbert norm of the operators, acting from $H'_+\otimes H''_+$ into $H'_-\otimes H''_-$).

Finally, using (2.16) of Chapter V, it is possible to write (4.17) as (the convergence is as before)

$$\begin{aligned} F(\bar{A}) &= \int_{-\infty}^{\infty}\int_{-\infty}^{\infty} F(\nu+\mu)P'(\nu)\otimes P''(\mu)\,d\varrho'(\nu)\,d\varrho''(\mu), \\ R_z &= \int_{-\infty}^{\infty}\int_{-\infty}^{\infty} \frac{1}{\nu+\mu-z}P'(\nu)\otimes P''(\mu)\,d\varrho'(\nu)\,d\varrho''(\mu) \quad (z \bar{\in} S(\bar{A})). \end{aligned} \tag{4.18}$$

We summarize this subsection in the following theorem.

Theorem 4.3. *Let A' and A'' be selfadjoint operators on the spaces H'_0 and H''_0 such that the closure of A is selfadjoint on the space $H'_0\otimes H''_0$. Consider generalized eigenvector expansions of the operators A', A'' and $\bar{A}$, using the chains* (4.12) *and* (4.13), *where the inclusions $H'_+\to H'_0$ and $H''_+\to H''_0$ are quasi-nuclear. Let E'_λ, E''_λ, E_λ and $d\rho'(\lambda)$, $d\rho''(\lambda)$, $d\rho(\lambda)$ be resolutions of the identity and spectral measures (constructed from a trace class operator) of the operators A', A'', $\bar{A}$, and let $P'(\lambda)$, $P''(\lambda)$ and $P(\lambda)$ be corresponding generalized projection operators.*

Then formulas (4.14)–(4.18) *are valid, where the integrals in* (4.15)–(4.18) *converge in the Hilbert norm of the operators (from $H'_+\otimes H''_+$ into $H'_-\otimes H''_-$) and* *the derivative in* (4.16) *exists for* ρ*-almost all* λ *in the sense of this norm. In* (4.17)–(4.18), $F(\lambda)$ *is an arbitrary bounded Borel measurable function and* R'_z *and* R_z *are the resolvents of the operators* A' *and* $\bar{A}$.

We now establish an interesting formula connected with the construction of the derivative (4.16). The approach will be to use arguments of the type applied on pp. 446–447 in connection with the forms σ_λ (here $L(\nu, \mu) = \nu + \mu$). Now, however, the abstract measure $d\rho'(\nu)\, d\rho''(\mu)$ replaces Lebesgue measure $d\xi_1 \cdots$ $\cdots d\xi_n$, so that the situation is somewhat more complicated. We first recall some facts on integration theory (see N. Bourbaki [1], pp. 57–63).

We consider two locally compact separable spaces Q and Λ and let $\lambda = L(x)$ ($x \in Q$, $\lambda \in \Lambda$) be a continuous transformation of Q onto Λ. Suppose $\sigma(\Delta)$ is a finite measure on the Borel sets of the space Q. Given L, the L-image $(L\sigma)(\Delta)$ of this measure, is the finite measure $L\sigma$ defined on the Borel sets of the space Λ by the equation

$$\int_\Lambda f(\lambda)\, d(L\sigma)(\lambda) = \int_Q f(L(x))\, d\sigma(x), \tag{4.19}$$

where $f(\lambda)$ is an arbitrary continuous function of λ with a finite limit at ∞. The existence of the measure $L\sigma$ follows immediately from the theorem on the general form of a continuous linear functional on the space of continuous functions on compacta: the right-hand side of (4.19) defines such a functional on $C(\Lambda \cup \infty)$, where $\Lambda \cup \infty$ is the compactification of Λ by formally adjoining the point at infinity ∞.

We establish the following useful facts. Let L_λ denote the preimage of the point λ under the transformation $x \longrightarrow L(x)$ (the "surface" of the equation $L(x) = \lambda$). We assert that there is a collection of finite measures $\sigma_\lambda(\Delta)$ ($\lambda \in \Lambda$) on the Borel sets of Q, with the following properties: a) each measure $\sigma_\lambda(\Delta)$ is concentrated on L_λ; b) the equation

$$\int_Q g(x)\, d\sigma(x) = \int_\Lambda \left(\int_{L_\lambda} g(x)\, d\sigma_\lambda(x) \right) d(L\sigma)(\lambda) \tag{4.20}$$

is valid for all $g(x) \in L_1(Q, d\sigma(x))$.

We assume that $\Lambda = (-\infty, \infty)$ and in (4.20) we replace $g(x)$ by the summable function with respect to $d\sigma(x)$, $\kappa_{(-\infty,\lambda)}(L(x))\, g(x)$, where $\kappa_{(-\infty,\lambda)}$ is the characteristic function of the interval $(-\infty, \lambda)$ and $g \in L_1(Q, d\sigma(x))$. We obtain

$$\int_{L(x)<\lambda} g(x)\,d\sigma(x) = \int_{-\infty}^{\lambda}\left(\int_{L_\mu} g(x)\,d\sigma_\mu(x)\right) d(L\sigma)(\mu).$$

We then conclude that for $L\sigma$-almost all λ the formula

$$\frac{d}{d(L\sigma)(\lambda)}\int_{L(x)<\lambda} g(x)\,d\sigma(x) = \int_{L_\lambda} g(x)\,d\sigma_\lambda(x) \quad (g \in L_1(Q,\ d\sigma(x))) \tag{4.21}$$

holds.

We use this formula to compute the derivative (4.16). For this purpose we set $Q = E_2$, $x = (\nu, \mu)$, $L(x) = \nu + \mu$, $d\sigma(x) = d\rho'(\nu)\,d\rho''(\mu)$. We shall find $L\sigma$. By (4.19) we have

$$\int_{-\infty}^{\infty} f(\lambda)\,d(L\sigma)(\lambda) = \int_{-\infty}^{\infty}\int_{-\infty}^{\infty} f(\nu+\mu)\,d\varrho'(\nu)\,d\varrho''(\mu)$$

$$= \int_{-\infty}^{\infty} f(\lambda)\,d_\lambda\left(\int_{-\infty}^{\infty} \varrho'(\lambda-\mu)\,d\varrho''(\mu)\right) = \int_{-\infty}^{\infty} f(\lambda)\,d(\varrho' * \varrho'')(\lambda),$$

so by the arbitrariness of $f(\lambda)$, it follows that $L\sigma = \rho' * \rho''$. Finally by (4.14) we find $L\sigma = \rho$.

Let $U, V \in H'_+ \otimes H''_+$. Then by (4.16) and (4.21) we obtain

$$(P(\lambda)U,\ V)_{H'_0\otimes H''_0} = \frac{d}{d\varrho(\lambda)}\int_{\nu+\mu<\lambda} ((P'(\nu)\otimes P''(\mu))\,U,$$

$$V)_{H'_0\otimes H''_0}\,d\varrho'(\nu)\,d\varrho''(\mu) = \int_{\nu+\mu=\lambda} ((P'(\nu)\otimes P''(\mu)\,U,\ V)_{H'_0\otimes H''_0}\,d\varrho_\lambda(\nu,\ \mu), \tag{4.22}$$

where $d\rho_\lambda(\nu, \mu)$ denotes the finite measure $d\sigma_\lambda(\nu, \mu)$. Equation (4.22) may be rewritten in the form

$$P(\lambda) = \int_{\nu+\mu=\lambda} P'(\nu)\otimes P''(\mu)\,d\varrho_\lambda(\nu,\ \mu), \tag{4.23}$$

where, by the finiteness of the measure $d\rho_\lambda(\nu, \mu)$, this integral converges not only weakly but also in the Hilbert norm. Thus we have proved

Theorem 4.4. *For almost all $\lambda \in (-\infty, \infty)$, there is a finite measure $d\rho_\lambda(\nu, \mu)$ on the Borel sets of the plane (ν, μ), concentrated on the line $\nu + \mu = \lambda$ and such that the representation (4.23) is valid. The integral converges in the Hilbert norm of the operators from $H'_+ \otimes H''_+$ into $H'_- \otimes H''_-$.*

It often happens that the spectral measure is not given as the trace of some operator as in (1.10) of Chapter V (or that this is not known). We consider here some of the questions which then arise. First of all, may we now use formula (4.14) to compute $d\rho(\lambda)$? It turns out that *if* $d\rho'(\lambda)$ *and* $d\rho''(\lambda)$ *are arbitrarily defined spectral measures for the operators* A' *and* A'' *which are finite, then formula* (4.14) *yields a spectral measure for* $\overline{A}$. It is clear from the definition of the spectral measure that to verify this assertion it is necessary and sufficient to establish the following: let finite measures ρ'_1, ρ''_1 and ρ', ρ'' be given on the Borel sets of the line where ρ'_1 (ρ''_1) is absolutely continuous with respect to ρ' (ρ''). Then $\rho'_1 * \rho''_1$ is absolutely continuous with respect to $\rho' * \rho''$. This fact follows from formula (4.21). In particular we denote $M'(\lambda) = (d\rho'_1(\lambda)/d\rho'(\lambda))$, $M''(\lambda) = (d\rho''_1(\lambda)/d\rho''(\lambda))$ and put $Q = E_2$, $x = (\nu, \mu)$, $L(x) = \nu + \mu$, $d\sigma(x) = d\rho'(\nu)d\rho''(\mu)$, $g(x) = M'(\nu)M''(\mu)$ in (4.21). We already know that $L\sigma = \rho' * \rho''$. The existence of the derivative in (4.21) means that the nondecreasing function of λ,

$$\int\limits_{\nu+\mu<\lambda} M'(\nu)M''(\mu)\, d\varrho'(\nu)\, d\varrho''(\mu) = \int\limits_{\nu+\mu<\lambda} d\varrho'_1(\nu)\, d\varrho''_1(\mu)$$
$$= \int\limits_{-\infty}^{\infty} \varrho'_1(\lambda-\mu)\, d\varrho''_1(\mu) = (\varrho'_1 * \varrho''_1)(\lambda),$$

defines an absolutely continuous measure with respect to $\rho' * \rho''$ as was required.

Thus in calculating the spectral measure $d\rho(\lambda)$ of the operator $\overline{A}$ we can proceed as follows. The given spectral measures $d\rho'(\lambda)$ and $d\rho''(\lambda)$ are transformed into the finite spectral measures $d\rho'_1(\lambda)$ and $d\rho''_1(\lambda)$. Then we may construct the convolution $\rho'_1 * \rho''_1$ and for $d\rho(\lambda)$ choose an arbitrary measure equivalent to $d(\rho'_1 * \rho''_1)$.

In equations (4.15)–(4.18) we may substitute any spectral measure for those used previously. This is obvious since only the products $P'(\lambda)d\rho'(\lambda)$, $P''(\lambda)d\rho''(\lambda)$ and $P(\lambda)\,d\rho(\lambda)$ enter in these formulas, and they are invariant with respect to transformations of the spectral measures. Equation (4.23) is also invariant under these transformed generalized projection operators, where the new measure $d\rho_\lambda(\nu, \mu)$ which arises is possibly infinite but has the previous properties. In fact, let $P'_1(\lambda) = (1/M'(\lambda))\,P'(\lambda)$, $P''_1(\lambda) = (1/M''(\lambda))\,P''(\lambda)$ and $P_1(\lambda) = (1/M(\lambda))\,P(\lambda)$ be the transformed projection operators. Expressing $P'(\lambda)$, $P''(\lambda)$ and $P(\lambda)$ in terms of $P'_1(\lambda)$, $P''_1(\lambda)$ and $P_1(\lambda)$ and entering them in (4.23) we obtain the same kind of equation relative to $P'_1(\lambda)$, $P''_1(\lambda)$ and $P_1(\lambda)$, where

$$\frac{M'(\nu)M''(\mu)}{M(\lambda)}\,d\varrho_\lambda(\nu,\ \mu) \tag{4.24}$$

takes the place of $d\rho_\lambda(\nu, \mu)$.

In order to apply the theory just developed one must know how to compute the measure $d\rho_\lambda(\nu, \mu)$ in (4.23). Of course, it is possible simply to differentiate the spectral measure $d\rho(\lambda)$ of the operator $\overline{A}$, but the technicalities are usually difficult. We proceed in the following way. First of all, we note that the formula

$$\frac{d}{d\varrho(\lambda)}\int\limits_{\nu+\mu<\lambda} g(\nu,\ \mu)\,d\varrho'(\nu)\,d\varrho''(\mu) = \int\limits_{\nu+\mu=\lambda} g(\nu,\ \mu)\,d\varrho_\lambda(\nu,\ \mu)$$
$$(g\in L_1(E_2,\ d\varrho'(\nu)\,d\varrho''(\mu))) \tag{4.25}$$

is valid for an arbitrary choice of spectral measures.

Indeed, if we first let the spectral measure be the trace measure, then (4.25) follows immediately from (4.21) if we use Q, L, etc. as indicated in the approach to (4.23). For the general case we substitute $d\rho'(\nu) = (1/M'(\nu))\,d\rho'_1(\nu)$, $d\rho''(\mu) = (1/M''(\mu))\,d\rho''_1(\mu)$ and $d\rho(\lambda) = (1/M(\lambda))\,d\rho_1(\lambda)$ in (4.25) and use (4.24) for $d\rho_\lambda(\nu, \mu)$.

The integral on the right side of (4.25) may be rewritten in the form $\int_{-\infty}^{\infty} g(\lambda-\mu, \mu)d_\mu\rho_\lambda\ (\lambda-\mu, \mu)$. Setting $g(\nu, \mu) = \operatorname{sign}\tau\cdot\kappa_{[0,\tau)}(\mu)\ (\tau\in(-\infty, \infty))$ in (4.25), where for $\tau<0$, $[0, \tau)$ is understood to mean $[\tau, 0)$, we obtain

$$\varrho_\lambda(\lambda-\tau,\ \tau)-\varrho_\lambda(\lambda,\ 0) = \operatorname{sign}\tau\cdot\frac{d}{d\varrho(\lambda)}\int\limits_{\substack{\nu+\mu<\lambda,\\ \mu\in[0,\tau)}} d\varrho'(\nu)d\varrho''(\mu)$$
$$(\lambda,\ \tau\in(-\infty,\ \infty)). \tag{4.26}$$

Thus the representation (4.23) is valid for arbitrary spectral measures. We write it in the form

$$P(\lambda) = \int_{-\infty}^{\infty} P'(\lambda-\mu)\otimes P''(\mu)\,d_\mu\varrho_\lambda(\lambda-\mu,\ \mu): \tag{4.27}$$

The measure $d_\mu\rho_\lambda\ (\lambda-\mu, \mu)$ is defined for ρ-almost all λ by formula (4.26).

We make still another remark.

It is possible to write formulas (4.15)–(4.18), (4.23) and (4.27) in terms of individual eigenvectors and Fourier transforms of these, by applying representations of the type (2.20) of Chapter V. We leave the statements and proofs of the corresponding formulas to the reader. We note that equation (4.23) extends a fact that is well known in the case of a discrete spectrum, that linear combinations of tensor products of eigenvectors of A' and A'' may be used to construct a complete system of eigenvectors for $\bar{A}$.

In addition, we have not mentioned the linear topological space $Д$ for $\bar{A}$ in the case where an extension of the equipment is possible. It is clear that if this is the case for A' and A'' with corresponding spaces $Д'$ and $Д''$, then it will also be so for $\bar{A}$ with $Д = Д' \otimes Д''$.

Finally we note that it is possible to develop the theory of subsections 1 and 2 by considering other constructions of the operator A from A' and A''. For example, $A = A' \otimes A''$ may be constructed from a large number of operators A', A'', ..., "acting on distinct variables" etc. For this, analogs of the constructions of §3.2 follow naturally.

3. Separation of variables in the space L_2. Separation of variables is often used for the case $H'_0 = L_2(Q', dx')$, $H''_0 = L_2(Q'', dx'')$. Here Q' is a locally compact separable space, dx' a nonnegative measure on the Borel sets of Q', finite on the compact sets and positive on open sets; Q'' and dx'' are defined analogously. Now $H'_0 \otimes H''_0 = L_2(Q' \times Q'', dx'dx'')$. As before, we assume that A' and A'' are selfadjoint.

The general situation is where A' and A'' are Carleman operators but $\bar{A}$ is not. With the natural notation for the spectral kernel we obtain from (4.16), (4.23) and (4.27):

$$\Phi((x', x''), (y', y''); \lambda) = \frac{d}{d\varrho(\lambda)} \int_{\nu+\mu<\lambda} \Phi'(x', y'; \nu)\, \Phi''(x'', y''; \mu)$$

$$\times\, d\varrho'(\nu)\, d\varrho''(\mu) = \int_{\nu+\mu=\lambda} \Phi'(x', y'; \nu)\, \Phi''(x'', y''; \mu)\, d\varrho_\lambda(\nu, \mu)$$

$$= \int_{-\infty}^{\infty} \Phi'(x', y'; \lambda-\mu)\, \Phi''(x'', y''; \mu)\, d_\mu \varrho_\lambda(\lambda-\mu, \mu)$$

$$(x', y' \in Q'; \; x'', y'' \in Q''). \tag{4.28}$$

We note that the integrals here converge in some generalized sense, and therefore the $\Phi((x', x''), (y', y''); \lambda)$ are possibly generalized functions. Similar representations are obtained from formulas (4.15), (4.17) and (4.18).

In the case of L_2 with respect to Lebesgue measure ($H'_0 = L_2(G', dx')$, $H''_0 = L_2(G'', dx'')$), the kernel is written $\Theta(x, y; \lambda)$ (see p. 348). Then by (4.2), in the natural notation,

$$\Theta((x', x''), (y', y''); \lambda) = \int_{-\infty}^{\infty} \Theta'(x', y'; \lambda - \mu)\, d_\mu \Theta''(x'', y''; \mu)$$

$$(x', y' \in G';\ x'', y'' \in G''). \tag{4.29}$$

Further details of this sort for the formulas of subsections 1 and 2 will be indicated in the examples of the following two subsections.

4. **Examples. Elliptic expressions.** We limit ourselves to the less well known cases of problems in unbounded regions.

a) **Laplace equation in the half-plane.** Let G be the half-plane $\xi > 0$ of the space E_{n+1} of points $(x, \xi) = (x_1, \cdots, x_n, \xi)$, and consider the $(n+1)$-dimensional Laplace expression (2.29) with boundary conditions $(\partial u/\partial \xi)\ (x, 0) = 0\ (x \in E_n)$. It is clear that the corresponding strong operator $\Lambda(\mathrm{bd})$ is Hermitian on $L_2(G)$. We may regard it as being obtained by separation of variables. For this purpose let $A' = \Lambda_n$ be the minimal operator induced on $H'_0 = L_2(E_n)$ by the n-dimensional Laplace equation, and $A'' = \Lambda_1(\mathrm{bd})$ the strong operator induced by the expression $-d^2/d\xi^2$ and the boundary conditions $(du/d\xi)\,(0) = 0$ on the space $L_2((0, \infty))$ of functions $f(\xi)$. Then $L_2(G) = L_2(E_n) \otimes L_2((0, \infty)) = H'_0 \otimes H''_0$ and $\Lambda(\mathrm{bd})$ is the operator $\bar{A}$.

As indicated in §2.8, the operator Λ_n is selfadjoint; it is not difficult to show in addition (see §5.3) that $\Lambda_1(\mathrm{bd})$ is also selfadjoint. So $\Lambda(\mathrm{bd})$ is selfadjoint: Its spectral characteristics may be found by using Theorems 4.3–4.4 since Λ_n is sufficiently known and the spectral kernel of $\Lambda_1(\mathrm{bd})$ has the form (see §5.3):

$$\Phi''(\xi, \eta; \lambda)\, d\varrho''(\lambda) = \begin{cases} \dfrac{1}{\pi} \cos\sqrt{\lambda}\xi \cdot \cos\sqrt{\lambda}\eta \,\dfrac{d\lambda}{\sqrt{\lambda}}, & \lambda > 0, \\ & (\xi, \eta \in (0, \infty)). \\ 0, & \lambda \leqslant 0 \end{cases} \tag{4.30}$$

By subsection 1, the spectrum of $\Lambda(\mathrm{bd})$ coincides with the interval $[0, \infty)$. Further, its spectral measure has the form

$$d\varrho(\lambda) = \begin{cases} d\lambda, & \lambda > 0, \\ 0, & \lambda \leqslant 0. \end{cases} \tag{4.31}$$

In fact, we shall assume that $d\rho'(\lambda) = d\rho''(\lambda) = M(\lambda)\, d\lambda$ where $M(\lambda) \in C((-\infty, \infty)) \cap L_1((-\infty, \infty), d\lambda)$ vanishes for $\lambda \le 0$ and is positive for $\lambda > 0$. Computing $d\rho(\lambda)$, with the help of (4.14), we find that $d\rho(\lambda) = N(\lambda)\, d\lambda$, where $N(\lambda)$ is of the same form as $M(\lambda)$.

Therefore we take $d\rho'(\lambda) = d\rho''(\lambda) = d\rho(\lambda)$ to be defined as in (4.31). We compute $d_\tau \rho_\lambda(\lambda - \tau, \tau)$ by using (4.26). Obviously the integral in it vanishes for $\lambda < 0$ and for $\lambda \ge 0$

$$\int\limits_{\substack{\nu+\mu<\lambda,\\ \mu\in[0,\tau)}} d\varrho'(\nu)\, d\varrho''(\mu) = \begin{cases} \dfrac{\lambda^2}{2}, & \tau\in[\lambda, \infty), \\ \lambda\tau - \dfrac{\tau^2}{2}, & \tau\in[0, \lambda), \\ 0, & \tau\in(-\infty, 0); \end{cases}$$

$$d_\tau \varrho_\lambda(\lambda - \tau, \tau) = \begin{cases} d\tau, & \tau\in(0, \lambda), \\ 0, & \tau\bar{\in}(0, \lambda). \end{cases} \tag{4.32}$$

By using formula (4.28), and considering the forms (2.41) and (4.30) of the spectral kernels of the operators $A' = \Lambda(\mathrm{bd})$, we obtain the following expression for the spectral kernel of the operator $\Lambda(\mathrm{bd})$:

$$\Phi((x, \xi), (y, \eta); \lambda)$$

$$= \frac{1}{(2\pi)^{\frac{n}{2}+1} |x - y|^{\frac{n}{2}-1}} \int\limits_0^\lambda \frac{(\sqrt{\lambda - \mu})^{\frac{n}{2}-1}}{\sqrt{\mu}} J_{\frac{n}{2}-1}(\sqrt{\lambda - \mu}\, |x - y|)$$

$$\times \cos\sqrt{\mu}\xi \cdot \cos\sqrt{\mu}\eta \;\; d\eta$$

$$(x, y\in E_n;\ \xi, \eta\in(0, \infty);\ \lambda > 0). \tag{4.33}$$

To compute the kernel of the resolvent $R((x, \xi), (y, \eta); z)$ of the operator $\Lambda(\mathrm{bd})$, one may use formula (4.17), which here takes the form

$$R((x', x''), (y', y''); z) = \int\limits_{-\infty}^{\infty} R'(x', y'; z - \mu)\, \Phi''(x'', y''; \mu)\, d\varrho''(\mu) \tag{4.34}$$

$$(z\bar{\in} S(\bar{A})).$$

Now, by substituting (2.35) and (4.30) and considering the form of $d\rho''(\lambda)$, we obtain

$$R((x, \xi), (y, \eta); z) = \frac{1}{2^{\frac{n}{2}}\pi^{\frac{n}{2}+1}|x-y|^{\frac{n}{2}-1}} \int_0^\infty \frac{(-i\sqrt{z-\mu})^{\frac{n}{2}-1}}{\sqrt{\mu}}$$

$$\times K_{\frac{n}{2}-1}(-i\sqrt{z-\mu}\,|x-y|)\cos\sqrt{\mu}\,\xi\cdot\cos\sqrt{\mu}\,\eta\,d\mu$$

$$(x, y\in E_n;\ \xi, \eta\in(0, \infty);\ z\overline{\in}[0, \infty)). \tag{4.35}$$

The expression for an arbitrary bounded function $F(\Lambda(\text{bd}))$ of the operator $\Lambda(\text{bd})$ may be written by using (4.17) and (4.30) (or (4.18) and (4.33)). It is useful to remark that if the function $F(\Lambda_n + \mu E')$ is sufficiently well known, for example as an integral operator with a known kernel, then (4.17) yields a simple representation of the (possibly generalized) kernel of the operator $F(\Lambda(bd))$ by means of this kernel (a similar example occurs for the function $F(\lambda) = (2/\lambda)\sin^2(\sqrt{\lambda}/2)\,t$ of §2.10). It is clear that in this way it is possible to obtain formulas for solutions of the mixed boundary value problem of the wave equation

$$\frac{\partial^2 u}{\partial t^2} - D_1^2 u - \ldots - D_n^2 u - \frac{\partial^2 u}{\partial \xi^2} = g(x, \xi, t), \tag{4.36}$$

$$u(x, \xi, 0) = \left(\frac{\partial u}{\partial t}\right)(x, \xi, 0) = 0, \quad \left(\frac{\partial u}{\partial \xi}\right)(x, 0, t) = 0$$

$$(x\in E_n,\ \xi\in(0, \infty),\ t\in[0, \infty))$$

(with the use of representation (2.84)). We limit ourselves to these general remarks.

Above, we studied only the case of the boundary condition $(\partial u/\partial\xi)(x, 0) = 0$ $(x \in E_n)$. But of course, it would be possible to consider the more general conditions

$$\alpha\left(\frac{\partial u}{\partial \xi}\right)(x, 0) + \beta u(x, 0) = 0 \quad (x\in E_n;\ \operatorname{Im}\alpha = \operatorname{Im}\beta = 0;\ \alpha^2 + \beta^2 > 0); \tag{4.37}$$

representations (4.33) and (4.35) are somewhat complicated because the form of $\Phi''(\xi, \eta; \lambda)$ is more complicated than (4.30).

Finally we note that in formula (4.34) and for the computation of $F(\Lambda(\text{bd}))$, it is possible to interchange the roles of the operators Λ_n and $\Lambda_1(\text{bd})$.

b) Laplace expression in a plane layer. Let G be the layer $0 < \xi < l < \infty$ in the space E_{n+1} of points $(x, \xi) = (x_1, \cdots, x_n, \xi)$. We consider the $(n+1)$-dimensional Laplace expression with boundary conditions $u(x, 0) = u(x, l) = 0$ $(x \in E_n)$ with $\Lambda(\text{bd})$, the corresponding strong operator. Now $\Lambda(\text{bd}) = \overline{A}$ where $A' = \Lambda_n$ is the previous operator acting on $H'_0 = L_2(E_n)$, and $A'' = \Lambda_1(\text{bd})$ is the strong operator as the space $H''_0 = L_2((0, l))$ of functions of ξ, induced by the expression $-d^2/d\xi^2$ with the boundary conditions $u(0) = u(l) = 0$; $H'_0 \otimes H''_0 = L_2(G)$. This example is interesting in that the operator A' is singular and A'' is regular.

We proceed to develop the spectral theory for this case analogously to example a) by using the following elementary calculation in place of formula (4.30):

$$\Phi''(\xi, \eta; \lambda)\, d\varrho''(\lambda) = \begin{cases} \dfrac{2}{l} \sin \dfrac{j\pi}{l}\xi \cdot \sin \dfrac{j\pi}{l}\eta, & \lambda = \lambda_j = \left(\dfrac{j\pi}{l}\right)^2, \\ 0, & \lambda \neq \lambda_j \ (j = 1, 2, \ldots). \end{cases} \tag{4.38}$$

According to subsection 1, the spectrum of the operator $\Lambda(\text{bd})$ coincides with $[(\pi/l)^2, \infty)$, so that, unlike in a), the operator $(\Lambda(\text{bd}))^{-1}$ exists.

For $\rho''(\lambda)$ we may take any piecewise constant nondecreasing function of λ with jumps at the points $\lambda_j = (j\pi/l)^2$ $(j = 1, 2, \cdots)$. We will assume that each of these jumps is equal to 1. By using the procedure outlined in subsection 2, it is easy to see that one may put

$$d\varrho(\lambda) = \begin{cases} d\lambda, & \lambda > \left(\dfrac{\pi}{l}\right)^2, \\ 0, & \lambda \leqslant \left(\dfrac{\pi}{l}\right)^2. \end{cases} \tag{4.39}$$

We find $d_\tau \rho_\lambda(\lambda - \tau, \tau)$. Evaluating the integral in (4.26), we find that it vanishes for $\lambda < (\pi/l)^2$ and that

$$\int\limits_{\substack{\nu+\mu<\lambda,\\ \mu\in[0,\tau)}} d\varrho'(\nu)\, d\varrho''(\mu) = \begin{cases} \displaystyle\sum_{\left(\frac{\pi}{l}\right)^2 \leqslant \left(\frac{j\pi}{l}\right)^2 < \lambda} \left(\lambda - \left(\frac{j\pi}{l}\right)^2\right), & \tau \in [\lambda, \infty), \\ \displaystyle\sum_{\left(\frac{\pi}{l}\right)^2 \leqslant \left(\frac{j\pi}{l}\right)^2 < \tau} \left(\lambda - \left(\frac{j\pi}{l}\right)^2\right), & \tau \in \left[\left(\frac{\pi}{l}\right)^2, \lambda\right), \\ 0, & \tau \in \left(-\infty, \left(\frac{\pi}{l}\right)^2\right) \end{cases}$$

for $\lambda \geq (\pi/l)^2$. Taking the derivative $d/d\lambda$ we see that the measure $d_\tau\rho_\lambda(\lambda-\tau, \tau)$ is discrete and is concentrated at the points $(j\pi/l)^2$ $(j = 1, 2, \cdots)$ on the interval $[(\pi/l)^2, \lambda)$. Its value is equal to one at each of these points. So with the help of (4.28), (2.41) and (4.38) we now obtain

$$\Phi((x, \xi), (y, \eta); \lambda) =$$

$$= \frac{1}{l(2\pi)^{\frac{n}{2}} |x-y|^{\frac{n}{2}-1}} \sum_{\left(\frac{\pi}{l}\right)^2 \leqslant \left(\frac{j\pi}{l}\right)^2 < \lambda} \left(\sqrt{\lambda - \left(\frac{j\pi}{l}\right)^2}\right)^{\frac{n}{2}-1}$$

$$\times J_{\frac{n}{2}-1}\left(\sqrt{\lambda - \left(\frac{j\pi}{l}\right)^2}\, |x-y|\right) \sin\frac{j\pi}{l}\xi \cdot \sin\frac{j\pi}{l}\eta$$

$$(x, y \in E_n;\ \xi, \eta \in (0, l);\ \lambda > 0). \tag{4.40}$$

Analogously to (4.35) we have

$$R((x, \xi), (y, \eta); z) =$$

$$= \frac{1}{l 2^{\frac{n}{2}-1} \pi^{\frac{n}{2}} |x-y|^{\frac{n}{2}-1}} \sum_{j=1}^{\infty} \left(-i\sqrt{z - \left(\frac{j\pi}{l}\right)^2}\right)^{\frac{n}{2}-1}$$

$$\times K_{\frac{n}{2}-1}\left(-i\sqrt{z - \left(\frac{j\pi}{l}\right)^2}\, |x-y|\right) \sin\frac{j\pi}{l}\xi \cdot \sin\frac{j\pi}{l}\eta \tag{4.41}$$

$$\left(x, y \in E_n;\ \xi, \eta \in (0, l);\ z \overline{\in} \left[\left(\frac{\pi}{l}\right)^2, \infty\right)\right).$$

It is clear that all that was said at the end of example a) with respect to the computation of $F(\Lambda(\text{bd}))$ and the solution of the mixed boundary problem of type (4.36) is now applicable (but with boundary conditions $u(x, 0, t) = u(x, l, t) = 0$ $(x \in E_n,\ t \in [0, \infty))$). It might be possible to consider more general conditions on the points $\xi = 0, l$, namely conditions of the form (4.37).

c) It is clear from examples a) and b) that examples of eigenfunction expansions of the Laplace operator on the region $G = G' \times G'' \times G'''$ may be constructed, where G' is a product of a finite number of intervals, G'' a product of a finite number of half-lines and G''' is an m-dimensional space. "Reduced" boundary conditions of the type (4.37) must be given on the boundary of G. We omit the formulation of these.

If a separation of variables is introduced for the Laplace expression on all of E_n, where $E_n = E_{n'} \times E_{n''}$ $(n' + n'' = n)$, then formulas of type (4.28) and (4.34) are transformed into some relation involving cylindrical functions. The reasoning used for the solution of the mixed boundary value problems in a) and b) is useful for the construction of solutions of the Cauchy problem for equations with constant coefficients. This is illustrated for the problem

$$\frac{\partial^2 u}{\partial t^2} - D_1^2 u - \dots - D_n^2 u + cu = g(x, t),$$

$$u(x, 0) = \left(\frac{\partial u}{\partial t}\right)(x, 0) = 0 \quad (x \in E_n;\ t \in [0, \infty)) \tag{4.42}$$

$(c \in (-\infty, \infty)$ is a constant). We sketch a formal scheme. In particular we show how the solution of (4.42) for $n + 1$ dimensions may be obtained from the n-dimensional one.

As before we will denote $(x, \xi) \in E_{n+1}$, $x \in E_n$, $\xi \in E_1$; we put $H'_0 = L_2(E_n)$, $H''_0 = L_2(E_1)$, $H'_0 \otimes H''_0 = L_2(E_{n+1})$. Let Λ_n, Λ_1 and Λ_{n+1} be minimal operators induced on the spaces of dimension n, 1, and $n + 1$, by the negative of the Laplace expression. Then, by (2.84), the solution $u(x, \xi, t)$ of the $(n + 1)$-dimensional problem (4.42) with $g(x, \xi, t)$ on the right side takes the form

$$u(x, \xi, t) = \int_0^t (\sqrt{\Lambda_{n+1} + cE})^{-1} \sin \sqrt{\Lambda_{n+1} + cE}\,(t - \tau)\, g(\cdot, \cdot, \tau)\, d\tau. \tag{4.43}$$

We assume that analogous n-dimensional formulas are possible, written in the form

$$u(x, t) = \int_0^t (\sqrt{\Lambda_n + cE'})^{-1} \sin \sqrt{\Lambda_n + cE'}\,(t - \tau)\, g(\cdot, \tau)\, d\tau$$

$$= (T_c^{(n)}(x, t; \cdot, \cdot), g(\cdot, \cdot))_{L_2(E_n \times (0, \infty))}, \tag{4.44}$$

where $T_c^{(n)}(x, t; y, \tau)$ is a generalized kernel of the type which figured in Theorems 2.7 and 2.8. It follows from the first of the formulas in (4.17), that

$$(\sqrt{\Lambda_{n+1} + cE})^{-1} \sin \sqrt{\Lambda_{n+1} + cE}\,(t - \tau) = \int_{-\infty}^{\infty} ((\sqrt{\Lambda_n + (c + \mu)E'})^{-1}$$

$$\times \sin \sqrt{\Lambda_n + (c + \mu) E'}\,(t - \tau)) \otimes P''(\mu)\, d\varrho''(\mu).$$

Applying this equation to $g(y, \eta, \tau)$, integrating over τ from 0 to t and changing the order of integration, we obtain from (4.43) and (4.44):

$$u(x,\xi,t)=\int_{-\infty}^{\infty}\Big(\int_0^t\big((\sqrt{\Lambda_n+(c+\mu)E'})^{-1}\sin\sqrt{\Lambda_n+(c+\mu)\,E'}\,(t-\tau)\big)_y$$

$$\times(P''_\eta(\mu)\,g(y,\eta,\tau))\,d\tau d\varrho''(\mu) \qquad (4.45)$$

$$=\int_{-\infty}^{\infty}\big(T^{(n)}_{c+\mu}(x,t;y,\tau),P''_\eta(\mu)\,g(y,\eta,\tau)\big)_{L_2(E_n\times(0,\infty))}d\varrho''(\mu).$$

The spectral kernel and measure for Λ_1, the minimal operator induced by $-d^2/d\xi^2$ in $L_2(E_1)$, is given by the equation

$$\Phi''(\xi,\eta;\lambda)\,d\varrho''(\lambda)=\begin{cases}\dfrac{1}{2\pi}\cos\sqrt{\lambda}\,(\xi-\eta)\,\dfrac{d\lambda}{\sqrt{\lambda}}, & \lambda>0,\\ 0 & \lambda\leqslant 0\end{cases}\qquad (\xi,\eta\in E_1), \qquad (4.46)$$

(this is (2.41) with $n=1$; see the end of this chapter). We therefore see by considering the kernels in (4.45) that the solution (4.43) may be written similarly to (4.44) in terms of the generalized kernel $T^{(n+1)}_c(x,\xi,t;y,\eta,\tau)$ having the form

$$T^{(n+1)}_c(x,\xi,t;y,\eta,\tau)=\frac{1}{2\pi}\int_0^{\infty}T^{(n)}_{c+\mu}(x,t;y,\tau)\cos\sqrt{\mu}\,(\xi-\eta)\,\frac{d\mu}{\sqrt{\mu}}. \qquad (4.47)$$

This, however, is the required formula. Setting $n=2$ and considering that by (2.78) the kernel $T^{(2)}_c(x,t;y,\tau)$ is equal to $T_{-c}((x,t),(y,\tau))$ for $(y,\tau)<(x,t)$ and zero otherwise, it is easy to obtain that $T^{(3)}_c=T_{\rm sing}+T_{\rm reg}$, where the singular kernel $T_{\rm sing}$ is indicated in Theorem 2.8 and the regular one $T_{\rm reg}$ has the form (2.88). Then (4.47) is sequentially applied to yield generalized kernels for given solutions of (4.42) with $n=4,5,\cdots$, which are constructed by means of the analytic continuation mentioned on pp. 429–430. Thus for higher dimensional spaces, everything reduces to the sequential computation of a one-dimensional Fourier cosine transformation with respect to μ, of some generalized functions which depend on μ as a parameter. The scheme just outlined is then a scheme for the solution of the Cauchy problem for (4.42) by using expansions in (and moreover, by developing a method for the computation of) ordinary n-fold Fourier integrals.

d) The Schrödinger expression in the case of radial symmetry. The usual separation of variables in expression (2.43) with $c(x)$ depending only on $|x|$ results in a more complicated operator than (4.1).

Namely, let H'_0 and H''_0 be Hilbert spaces, let A' and C' be Hermitian operators on H'_0 with common domain $\mathfrak{D}(A')$, and let A'' be a Hermitian operator on H''_0. By separating variables we obtain the operator

$$A = A' \otimes E'' + C' \otimes A'', \quad \mathfrak{D}(A) = \mathfrak{D}(A') \otimes \mathfrak{D}(A'') \tag{4.48}$$

on $H'_0 \otimes H''_0$. A is then obviously Hermitian. It will be sufficient for our purposes to limit ourselves to the construction of the spectral theory for A in the most elementary case. In particular, we will assume that A'' is selfadjoint and has a discrete spectrum $\mu_0, \mu_1, \cdots$, where each of the eigenmanifolds $H''^{(l)}_0$ corresponding to μ_l $(l = 0, 1, 2, \cdots)$ is finite-dimensional. If we let $P''(\mu_l)$ denote the orthogonal projection onto $H''^{(l)}_0$, then

$$E'' = \oplus \sum_{l=0}^{\infty} P''(\mu_l), \quad H''_0 = \oplus \sum_{l=0}^{\infty} H''^{(l)}_0, \quad H'_0 \otimes H''_0 = \oplus \sum_{l=0}^{\infty} H_0 \otimes H''^{(l)}_0 \tag{4.49}$$

(all the sums are orthogonal). Let $A^{(l)}$ be the restriction of the operator A to $\mathfrak{D}(A^{(l)}) = \mathfrak{D}(A') \otimes H''^{(l)}_0 \subseteq \mathfrak{D}(A)$; $A^{(l)}$ is an Hermitian operator on the space $H'_0 \otimes H''^{(l)}_0$. We will assume that for $l = 1, 2, \cdots$, each of the operators $A^{(l)}$ has equal deficiency indices and will let $E^{(l)}_\lambda$ denote one of its resolutions of the identity. By the last equation in (4.49), the operators

$$E_\lambda = \oplus \sum_{l=0}^{\infty} E^{(l)}_\lambda (E' \otimes P''(\mu_l)) \tag{4.50}$$

will comprise a resolution of the identity for A; the spectrum of a selfadjoint extension of A coincides with the closure of the spectra of the $A^{(l)}$, and the resolvents R_z have the form

$$R_z = \oplus \sum_{l=0}^{\infty} R^{(l)}_z (E' \otimes P''(\mu_l)). \tag{4.51}$$

We give a more detailed form of the operators $A^{(l)}$, $E^{(l)}_\lambda$ and $R^{(l)}_z$. Since $A''P''(\mu_l) = \mu_l P''(\mu_l)$, then by (4.48)

$$A^{(l)} = A' \otimes P''(\mu_l) + C' \otimes (\mu_l P''(\mu_l)) = (A' + \mu_l C') \otimes P''(\mu_l). \tag{4.52}$$

Considering the remark after the proof of Theorem 4.1 and formula (2.7) of Chapter I, we obtain

$$E^{(l)}_\lambda = E'^{(l)}_\lambda \otimes P''(\mu_l), \quad R^{(l)}_z = R'^{(l)}_z \otimes P''(\mu_l), \tag{4.53}$$

where $E'^{(l)}_\lambda$ and $R'^{(l)}_z$ are the resolutions of the identity and the resolvents of the Hermitian operators $A' + \mu_l C'$ on the space H'_0. If the closure of the operator $A' + \mu_l C'$ is selfadjoint, then by (4.52), the closure of the operator $A^{(l)}$ is also selfadjoint on $H'_0 \otimes H''^{(l)}_0$. If $A^{(l)}$ is selfadjoint, for each $l = 0, 1, \cdots$ then by (4.51) the closure of A is selfadjoint. Also, it is not difficult to reverse this argument: if, indeed, $\overline{A' + \mu_l C'}$ is not selfadjoint for some l, then $\bar{A}$ is also nonselfadjoint.

Let $H'_- \supseteq H'_0 \supseteq H'_+$ be some chain for which the inclusion $H'_+ \longrightarrow H'_0$ is quasi-nuclear. It is possible to use it for a generalized eigenvector expansion for the operator $A' + \mu_l C'$: $dE'^{(l)}_\lambda = P'^{(l)}(\lambda)\, d\rho'^{(l)}(\lambda)$. To obtain an expansion for the operator $A^{(l)}$, by the finite dimensionality of $H''^{(l)}_0$, the chain $H'_- \otimes H''^{(l)}_0 \supseteq H'_0 \otimes H''^{(l)}_0 \supseteq H'_+ \otimes H''^{(l)}_0$ may be used. Then

$$P^{(l)}(\lambda)\, d\varrho(\lambda) = P'^{(l)}(\lambda) \otimes P''(\mu_l)\, d\varrho(\lambda),$$

where $d\rho(\lambda)$ is a spectral measure for $A' + \mu_l C'$ chosen independently of $l = 0, 1, \cdots$ (this is obviously possible). Now the generalized eigenvector expansion of the operator A which corresponds to (4.50) takes the form

$$P(\lambda)\, d\varrho(\lambda) = \left(\sum_{l=0}^{\infty} P'^{(l)}(\lambda) \otimes P''(\mu_l)\right) d\varrho(\lambda). \tag{4.54}$$

The series converges in the Hilbert norm of the operators acting from $H'_+ \otimes H''_+$ to $H'_- \otimes H''_-$ where the chain $H''_- \supseteq H''_0 \supseteq H''_+$ is similarly such that $H''_+ \longrightarrow H''_0$ is quasi-nuclear.

With this we conclude the general remarks associated with the operator (4.48) and proceed to the example itself. We limit ourselves to the three-dimensional case.

We introduce the spherical coordinates $\rho = |x|$, θ, ϕ in E_3. Then, considered on all of E_3, the Schrödinger expression has the form

$$Lu = -\Delta u + c(\varrho)\, u \quad (c \in C^2([0, \infty))) \tag{4.55}$$

which is spherical coordinates becomes

$$(Lu)(\varrho, \theta, \varphi)$$

$$= -\frac{1}{\varrho^2}\frac{\partial}{\partial\varrho}\left(\varrho^2 \frac{\partial u}{\partial \varrho}\right) + c(\varrho)\, u + \frac{1}{\varrho^2}\left[-\frac{1}{\sin\theta}\frac{\partial}{\partial\theta}\left(\sin\theta\,\frac{\partial u}{\partial\theta}\right) - \frac{1}{\sin^2\theta}\frac{\partial^2 u}{\partial\varphi^2}\right]. \tag{4.56}$$

We construct the minimal operator Λ for (4.55)–(4.56) on $L_2(E_3)$ and we show that its "negligible" restriction may be written in the form of (4.48).

For this, we have

$$(f, g)_{L_2(E_3)} = \int_0^{\infty}\int_0^{\pi}\int_0^{2\pi} f(\varrho, \theta, \varphi)\, \overline{g(\varrho, \theta, \varphi)}\, \varrho^2 \sin\theta\, d\varrho\, d\theta\, d\varphi,$$

and therefore $L_2(E_3) = L_2((0, \infty), \rho^2\, d\rho) \otimes L_2(K)$, where $L_2(K)$ is the space of functions $f(\theta, \phi)$ on the unit sphere K, which are square summable with respect to Lebesgue measure $\sin\theta\, d\theta\, d\phi$. We let $H'_0 = L_2((0, \infty), \rho^2 d\rho)$, $H''_0 = L_2(K)$, $H'_0 \otimes H''_0 = L_2(E_3)$, and introduce the Hermitian operators A' and C' on H'_0 respectively equal to $u \longrightarrow -(1/\rho^2)(\partial/\partial\rho)(\rho^2\, \partial u/\partial\rho) + c(\rho) u$ and $u \longrightarrow (1/\rho^2) u$ $(u \in \mathfrak{D}(A') = \mathfrak{D}(C') = C_0^\infty((0, \infty)))$.

We proceed to construct A''. For this we consider the operator

$$u \rightarrow -\frac{1}{\sin\theta}\frac{\partial}{\partial\theta}\left(\sin\theta\,\frac{\partial u}{\partial\theta}\right) - \frac{1}{\sin^2\theta}\frac{\partial^2 u}{\partial\varphi^2}$$

acting on the set of twice continuously differentiable functions $u(\theta, \phi)$ in the space $L^2(k)$. It is obviously Hermitian, and we denote its closure by A''. Now, with A', C' and A'' so constructed, the corresponding operator A may be constructed by (4.48). Then by (4.56) A will be some restriction of Λ as required.

It is well known that the operator A'' is selfadjoint and has a discrete spectrum with finite-dimensional eigenmanifolds (see, for example, A. N. Tihonov, A. A. Samarskiĭ [1], Appendix 2, §2). For each of the eigenvalues $\mu_l = l(l+1)$ $(l = 0, 1, \cdots)$, the corresponding eigenmanifolds $H''^{(l)}_0$ are $(2l+1)$-dimensional. For each of these spaces $H''^{(l)}_0$, it is possible to pick an orthonormal basis consisting of the $2l+1$ spherical functions

$$Y_l^{(k)}(\theta, \varphi) = \sqrt{\frac{2l+1}{2\pi\varepsilon_k}\cdot\frac{(l-k)!}{(l+k)!}}\; P_l^{(k)}(\cos\theta) \begin{cases} \cos k\varphi, & k = -l, \dots, 0, \\ \sin k\varphi, & k = 1, \dots, l \end{cases} \tag{4.57}$$

$$(0 \leqslant \theta < \pi,\; 0 \leqslant \varphi < 2\pi),$$

where $\epsilon_0 = 2$, $\epsilon_k = 1$ for $k \neq 0$, and $P_l^{(k)}(s)$ is the associated Legendre function. Thus, for the orthogonal projection operators of $L_2(K)$ onto $H''^{(l)}_0$, we may use the integral operators with the kernel

$$K^{(l)}((\theta, \varphi), (\theta', \varphi')) = \sum_{k=-l}^{l} Y_l^{(k)}(\theta, \varphi)\, Y_l^{(k)}(\theta', \varphi') \quad ((\theta, \varphi), (\theta', \varphi') \in K). \tag{4.58}$$

$A' + \mu_l C'$ now takes the form of an operator on $H'_0 = L_2((0, \infty), \rho^2 d\rho)$ defined on $C_0^\infty((0, \infty))$ by

$$(A' + \mu_l C')\,u = -\frac{1}{\varrho^2}\frac{d}{d\varrho}\left(\varrho^2 \frac{du}{d\varrho}\right) + c(\varrho)\,u + \frac{l(l+1)}{\varrho^2}u \tag{4.59}$$

$$(l = 0, 1, \ldots).$$

For simplicity, we will assume that $c(\rho)$ is bounded on $[0, \infty)$. Then by Lemma 1.2, the selfadjointness of $\overline{A' + \mu_l C'}$ is equivalent to the selfadjointness of the closure of the operator (4.59) with $c(\rho) \equiv 0$. It is known (M. A. Naĭmark [2], Chapter 7, § 24) that this will occur for $l \geq 1$. In the case $l = 0$, $\overline{A' + \mu_0 C'}$ is not selfadjoint (if it were, the closure of the operator $u \longrightarrow Lu$ in $L_2(E_3)$, defined for $u \in C_0^\infty(E_3)$ and vanishing in some neighborhood of 0, would be selfadjoint). But if $A' + \mu_0 C'$ is extended by means of (4.59) to all of the functions of $C^\infty([0, \infty))$ which are finite at infinity, and then if the closure is constructed, the operator obtained has been shown to be selfadjoint. So in what follows we assume that $A' + \mu_0 C'$ is defined exactly as in formula (4.59) with $l = 0$ but on the space $C^\infty([0, \infty)) \cap C_0^\infty((-\infty, \infty))$.

Now using formulas (4.51) and (4.53) it is easy to write the expression for the kernel $R((\rho, \theta, \phi), (\rho', \theta', \phi'); z)$ of the resolvents of the operator Λ by means of the kernel $R^{(l)}(\rho, \rho'; z)$ of the resolvents of the operator (4.59). In fact we have from (4.51) and (4.53) that $R_z = \oplus \sum_{l=0}^\infty R_z'^{(l)} \otimes P''(\mu_l)$, so by passing to the kernels here and using (4.58) we find that

$$R((\varrho, \theta, \varphi), (\varrho', \theta', \varphi'); z) = \sum_{l=0}^{\infty} R'^{(l)}(\varrho, \varrho'; z) \sum_{k=-l}^{l} Y_l^{(k)}(\theta, \varphi)\, Y_l^{(k)}(\theta', \varphi').$$

Changing the order of integration, using form (4.57) of the function $Y_l^{(k)}$ and applying the formula for the addition of Legendre polynomials $P_l(s)$ (see for example Ryžik and Gradšteĭn [1], formula 6.794), we obtain after some simple calculations

$$R((\varrho, \theta, \varphi), (\varrho', \theta', \varphi'); z)$$

$$= \frac{1}{2\pi}\sum_{l=0}^{\infty}\left(l + \frac{1}{2}\right) R'^{(l)}(\varrho, \varrho'; z)\, P_l(\cos\theta\cdot\cos\theta' - \sin\theta\cdot\sin\theta'\cdot\cos(\varphi - \varphi')) \tag{4.60}$$

$$((\varrho, \theta, \varphi), (\varrho', \theta', \varphi') \in E_3;\quad (\varrho, \theta, \varphi) \neq (\varrho', \theta', \varphi');\quad \operatorname{Im} z \neq 0).$$

This may be rewritten in terms of the resolvent kernel of an operator of the form (4.59) but acting on the space $L_2((0, \infty), d\rho)$ instead of $L_2((0, \infty)\,\rho^2 d\rho)$. With this purpose we note that the transformation $f(\rho) \longrightarrow \rho f(\rho)$ defines an isometric operator taking all of $L_2((0, \infty), \rho^2\, d\rho)$ onto all of $L_2((0, \infty), d\rho)$. The operator (4.59) is transformed into the operator

$$u \to -\frac{d^2u}{d\varrho^2} + c(\varrho)\,u + \frac{l(l+1)}{\varrho^2}u \quad (l = 0, 1, \ldots), \tag{4.61}$$

on $L_2((0, \infty), d\rho)$ defined for $l \geq 1$ on $C_0^\infty((0, \infty))$, and for $l = 0$ on $C^\infty([0, \infty)) \cap C_0^\infty((-\infty, \infty))$. If instead of $R'^{(l)}(\rho, \rho'; z)$, the resolvent kernel of the operator (4.61) is used in (4.60), then (4.60) is valid if the term $1/\rho\rho'$ is placed before the sum.

We will omit the conclusion of the analogous results which use (4.54) to represent the kernel $\Phi((\rho, \theta, \phi), (\rho', \theta', \phi'); \lambda)$.

5. Examples. Nonelliptic expressions. As already mentioned, one example similar to those involving separation of variables has been introduced in §2.3, Chapter IV. At this time we give three such examples on an unbounded region, namely all of E_n. Where convenient they may be interpreted as a method of computation of the integrals (3.25) and (3.26) for special L.

a) Ultra-hyperbolic expressions on E_n. Let $n = n' + n''$ $(n', n'' \geq 1)$, so that $E_n = E_{n'} \times E_{n''}$, $L_2(E_n) = L_2(E_{n'}) \otimes L_2(E_{n''})$. A point $x \in E_n$ will be denoted by $x = (x', x'') = (x'_1, \cdots, x'_{n'}, x''_1, \cdots, x''_{n''})$. We consider the minimal operator Λ on $L_2(E_n)$ induced by the ultra-hyperbolic expression

$$Lu = -\frac{\partial^2 u}{\partial x_1'^2} - \cdots - \frac{\partial^2 u}{\partial x_{n'}'^2} + \frac{\partial^2 u}{\partial x_1''^2} + \cdots + \frac{\partial^2 u}{\partial x_{n''}''^2}.$$

We set $H'_0 = L_2(E_{n'})$, $H''_0 = L_2(E_{n''})$ and define the operator A' on H'_0 as the minimal operator Λ' induced by the n'-dimensional expression $-\Delta$ and similarly $A'' = -\Lambda''$ on H''_0, with Λ'' induced by the n''-dimensional expression $-\Delta$. Obviously $\Lambda = \bar{A}$ where A is constructed from A' and A'' according to (4.1). All of the operators A', A'' and Λ are selfadjoint.

The spectral kernel and measure of the operator A' are given by formula (2.41). The spectral measure for A'' is $d\rho''(\lambda) = d\lambda$ for $\lambda < 0$ and $d\rho''(\lambda) = 0$ for $\lambda \geq 0$; the spectral kernel is that of (2.41) where λ is replaced by $-\lambda$.

The equality $S(\bar{A}) = \overline{S(A') + S(A'')}$ implies that the spectrum of Λ is the whole real line. By Theorem 3.1, the measure $d\rho(\lambda) = d\lambda$ $(-\infty < \lambda < \infty)$ may be taken as the spectral measure for Λ.

We will compute the spectral kernel of the operator Λ by using (4.28). As a preliminary, we compute the measure $d_\tau\rho_\lambda(\lambda - \tau, \tau)$ with the help of (4.26). For $\lambda < 0$ we have

$$\text{for } \lambda < 0 \quad \int\limits_{\substack{\nu+\mu<\lambda,\\ \mu\in[0,\tau)}} d\varrho'(\nu)\, d\varrho''(\mu) = \begin{cases} 0, & \tau \in [\lambda, \infty), \\ \dfrac{(-\tau+\lambda)^2}{2}, & \tau \in (-\infty, \lambda); \end{cases} \tag{4.61}$$

$$\text{and for } \lambda \geqslant 0 \quad \int\limits_{\substack{\nu+\mu<\lambda,\\ \mu\in[0,\tau)}} d\varrho'(\nu)\, d\varrho''(\mu) = \begin{cases} 0, & \tau \in [0, \infty), \\ -\lambda\tau + \dfrac{\tau^2}{2}, & \tau \in (-\infty, 0). \end{cases}$$

From this it is easy to conclude that $d_\tau \rho_\lambda (\lambda - \tau, \tau) = d\tau$ for $\tau \in (-\infty, \min(\lambda, 0))$ and equal to zero for $\tau \in [\min(\lambda, 0), \infty)$. We now obtain the required expression

$$\Phi((x', x''), (y', y''); \lambda)$$

$$= \frac{1}{2^{\frac{n}{2}+2} \pi^{\frac{n}{2}} |x' - y'|^{\frac{n'}{2}-1} |x'' - y''|^{\frac{n''}{2}-1}} \int\limits_{-\infty}^{\min(\lambda, 0)} (\sqrt{\lambda - \mu})^{\frac{n'}{2}-1}$$

$$\times (\sqrt{-\mu})^{\frac{n''}{2}-1} J_{\frac{n'}{2}-1} (\sqrt{\lambda - \mu}\, |x' - y'|)\, J_{\frac{n''}{2}-1} (\sqrt{-\mu}\, |x'' - y''|)\, d\mu. \tag{4.62}$$

The integral here converges in the usual sense, namely in the same sense as in formula (4.23) (see Theorem 4.4). In each case it converges in the sense of the Schwartz generalized functions of the variable $(x, y) \in E_{2n}$. Therefore, the spectral kernel (4.62) will be a generalized kernel.

By using (4.34), (2.35) and the expression for $\Phi''(x'', y''; \lambda)$, it is easy to write the formula for the resolvent kernel of the operator Λ. We note also that it is now convenient to apply formula (4.29), which expresses an equation which is essentially equivalent to (4.62).

b) The wave equation on E_2. We consider the minimal operator Λ induced on $L_2(E_2)$ by the expression

$$Lu = -\frac{\partial^2 u}{\partial x_1^2} + \frac{\partial^2 u}{\partial x_2^2}.$$

This is a particular case of example a) with $n' = n'' = 1$. We will make some rather detailed calculations. Since (4.46) is a particular case of (2.41) with $n = 1$, we may set $n' = n'' = 1$. We obtain

$$\Phi(x, y; \lambda) = \frac{1}{4\pi^2} \int_{-\infty}^{\min(\lambda, 0)} \frac{1}{\sqrt{-\mu(\lambda-\mu)}} \cos\sqrt{\lambda-\mu}$$

$$\times (x_1 - y_1) \cdot \cos\sqrt{-\mu}\,(x_2 - y_2)\, d\mu,$$

where the integrals converge, for example, in the sense of L. Schwartz on E_4.

To obtain the resolvent kernel $R'(x_1, y_1; z)$ of the minimal operator induced on $L_2(E_1)$ by the expression $-d^2/dx_1^2$, let $n = 1$ in (2.35) (see §5.3):

$$R'(x_1, y_1; z) = R'(x_1 - y_1; z) = \frac{i}{2\sqrt{z}} e^{i\sqrt{z}|x_1 - y_1|} \quad (x_1, y_1 \in E_1;\ z \overline{\in} [0, \infty)). \tag{4.63}$$

By using (4.34), (4.63) and (4.46) we find a representation for the resolvent kernel $R(x, y; z)$ of our operator Λ:

$$R(x, y; z) = \frac{i}{4\pi} \int_{-\infty}^{0} \frac{1}{\sqrt{-\mu(z-\mu)}} e^{i\sqrt{z-\mu}|x_1 - y_1|} \cos\sqrt{-\mu}\,(x_2 - y_2)\, d\mu$$

$$(x, y \in E_2;\ x \neq y;\ \operatorname{Im} z \neq 0). \tag{4.64}$$

Here the integral converges; hence the kernel $R(x, y; z)$ is an ordinary one. The integral in (4.64) may be expressed in terms of cylindrical functions corresponding to the hyperbolic metric $\Gamma(x, y) = \sqrt{(x_1 - y_1)^2 - (x_2 - y_2)^2}$ (see, for example, I. M. Ryžik, I. C. Gradšteĭn [1], formula 4.419,8). However, we will omit this.

We note that in view of the relation $S(\Lambda) = S(A') + S(A'')$, the spectrum of the operator Λ as a rule coincides with the point zero in the case of separation of variables for the ultra-hyperbolic expression L: $S(A')$ is nonnegative and $S(A'')$ is nonpositive. It is easy to see that if one of the operators A' or A'' is considered on the whole space E_n, then necessarily, $0 \overline{\in} S(\Lambda)$ (see §2.3, Chapter IV), but it will not be stable under changes in the region. To obtain a more stable relation $0 \overline{\in} S(\Lambda)$, the operator A' is taken to be nonselfadjoint, with nonreal spectrum (by changing L or (bd)).

c) The nonstationary Schrödinger equation on E_2. The minimal operator Λ induced on $L_2(E_2)$ by the expression

$$Lu = -\frac{\partial^2 u}{\partial x_1^2} + i\frac{\partial u}{\partial x_2}$$

may be considered analogously to examples a) and b). Here a separation of variables is possible where the operator A' is exactly as in b) and A'' coincides with the minimal operator on $L_2(E_1)$, induced by the expression $i\, d/dx_2$, i.e. with the operator which induces the usual Fourier transform (see §5.3). It is possible to study Λ by using a spectral analysis of the operators A' and A''.

§5. SPECTRAL THEORY OF ORDINARY SELFADJOINT DIFFERENTIAL OPERATORS

In this section we will only discuss the way in which the spectral theory of such operators fits into the general scheme constructed in Chapters V and VI. We do not claim any measure of completeness, but refer the reader to M. A. Naĭmark [2], Ahiezer and Glazman [1], E. C. Titchmarsh [1], B. M. Levitan [1], Dunford and Schwartz [2]. With only a few exceptions we will not present exact formulations and proofs.

1. **Construction of the spectral kernel.** We will consider the ordinary differential expression

$$Lu = \sum_{\alpha \leqslant r} a_\alpha(x) D^\alpha u \quad \left(Du = \frac{du}{dx}\right) \tag{5.1}$$

on the interval $G = (a, b) \subseteq (-\infty, \infty)$; the coefficients $a_\alpha(x)$ are assumed to be sufficiently smooth.

It is possible to establish smoothness theorems (inside G) similar to Theorems 4.1–4.4 of Chapter III for the generalized solutions of the equation $Lu = f$. This is connected with the fact that it is easy to construct fundamental solutions $e(x, \xi)$ $(x, \xi \in G)$ of the expression (5.1) from the solution of the Cauchy problem; these solutions possess properties analogous to properties 1)–3) of Chapter III, §4.1. If $a_\alpha \in C^{\alpha+p}(G)$ with $p \geq 0$, then property 1) is interpreted exactly as before, and 2) and 3) take the following form:

For $x \neq \xi$, the derivatives $(D_x^\alpha D_\xi^\beta e)(x, \xi)$ $(\alpha, \beta \leq r + p)$ exist and are continuous. Each of these derivatives is bounded for $x = \xi$.

If $f \in C^q(\overline{V})$ $(\overline{V} \subset G)$ for $q \geq 0$, $p \geq 0$ then the integrals in (4.4), Chapter III, are in $C^{q+r}(\overline{V})$ and satisfy the indicated equation.

The results on smoothness up to the boundary are also valid for the generalized solutions of equation (5.1). The situation here will be significantly more simple than that for elliptic expressions. In fact, for f sufficiently regular the generalized solutions of the equation $Lu = f$ will be smooth inside $G = (a, b)$. Moreover, every solution of the Cauchy problem for the equation $Lu = f$ may be uniquely extended to a smooth solution on $\overline{G}$, if the coefficients $a_\alpha(x)$ are sufficiently smooth in $\overline{G}$. Therefore in the case under consideration every generalized solution inside G will be smooth up to the boundary. A consequence is that all the complicated techniques used for studying the smoothness of generalized solutions up to the boundary are here eliminated. The presentation of these facts is based on the possibility of solving the Cauchy problem at least formally without using fundamental solutions. For this see M. A. Naĭmark [2], Chapter 5, §17.

It is clear at this point that by using the type of construction introduced in §2, it is easy to develop the spectral theory for the formally selfadjoint expression (5.1). The approach of §2, subsections 1, 2, and 5 is possible here. The spectral kernel $\Phi(x, y; \lambda)$ turns out to be sufficiently smooth in the variable (x, y) for ρ-almost all λ and satisfies the given boundary conditions as a function of each of the variables. The expansion theorems may be formulated in the form of Theorems 2.1 and 2.3 with $n = 1$.

2. The notion of the spectral matrix. The eigenfunction expansion of an ordinary differential operator is usually written in a form other than that just mentioned. Namely, we let $\chi_0(x; \lambda), \cdots, \chi_{r-1}(x; \lambda)$ denote a fundamental system of solutions of the equation $Lu - \lambda u = 0$ $(x \in G)$, which satisfies the initial condition

$$\left(\frac{d^k}{dx^k}\chi_j\right)(x; \lambda)\bigg|_{x=c} = \delta_{jk} \qquad (j, k = 0, \ldots, r-1), \tag{5.2}$$

where c is some point of G. Each solution u of the equation $Lu - \lambda u = 0$ is expressed in the $\chi_j(x; \lambda)$ by the formula

$$u(x) = \sum_{j=0}^{r-1}\left(\frac{d^j u}{dx^j}\right)(c)\,\chi_j(x; \lambda) \quad (x \in G).$$

The spectral kernel $\Phi(x, y; \lambda)$ satisfies the equation

$$L_x\Phi(x, y; \lambda) = \lambda\Phi(x, y; \lambda), \qquad \overline{L}_y\Phi(x, y; \lambda) = \lambda\Phi(x, y; \lambda) \ (x, y \in G). \tag{5.3}$$

Applying this formula twice we obtain the representation

$$\Phi(x, y; \lambda) = \sum_{j=0}^{r-1}\left(\frac{\partial^j\Phi}{\partial x^j}\right)(c, y; \lambda)\,\chi_j(x; \lambda) =$$

$$= \sum_{j,k=0}^{r-1} \left(\frac{\partial^{j+k}\Phi}{\partial x^j \partial y^k} \right)(c, c; \lambda)\, \chi_j(x; \lambda)\, \overline{\chi_k(y; \lambda)} \qquad (x, y \in G). \tag{5.4}$$

Inserting this in the equation

$$(E(\Delta)u, v)_0 = \int_\Delta (P(\lambda)u, v)_0\, d\varrho(\lambda) = \int_\Delta \left\{ \int_G \int_G \Phi(x, y; \lambda)\, u(y) \overline{v(x)} dx dy \right\} d\varrho(\lambda)$$

$$(u, v \in C_0(G)),$$

we obtain

$$(E(\Delta)u, v)_0$$

$$= \int_\Delta \left\{ \sum_{j,k=0}^{r-1} \left(\frac{\partial^{j+k}\Phi}{\partial x^j \partial y^k} \right)(c, c; \lambda) \int_G u(y) \overline{\chi_k(y; \lambda)} dy\, \overline{\int_G v(x) \overline{\chi_j(x; \lambda)}\, dx} \right\} d\varrho(\lambda)$$

$$= \int_\Delta \left\{ \sum_{j,k=0}^{r-1} \widetilde{u}_k(\lambda) \overline{\widetilde{v}_j(\lambda)} d\sigma_{jk}(\lambda) \right\}, \tag{5.5}$$

$$\widetilde{u}_k(\lambda) = \int_G u(x) \overline{\chi_k(x; \lambda)} dx, \qquad d\sigma_{jk}(\lambda) = \left(\frac{\partial^{j+k}\Phi}{\partial x^j \partial y^k} \right)(c, c; \lambda)\, d\varrho(\lambda)$$

$$(j,\ k = 0, \ldots, r-1).$$

Therefore, each function $u \in C_0(G)$ may be put into correspondence with its Fourier transform, i.e. the r-dimensional vector-function

$$\widetilde{u}(\lambda) = (\widetilde{u}_0(\lambda), \ldots, \widetilde{u}_{r-1}(\lambda)),\ \widetilde{u}_k(\lambda) = \int_G u(x) \overline{\chi_k(x; \lambda)}\, dx$$

$$(k = 0, \ldots, r-1), \tag{5.6}$$

where the Parseval equation takes the form

$$(E(\Delta)u, v)_0 = \int_\Delta \left\{ \sum_{j,k=0}^{r-1} \widetilde{u}_k(\lambda) \overline{\widetilde{v}_j(\lambda)}\, d\sigma_{jk}(\lambda) \right\} (u, v \in C_0(G)).\ ^{1)} \tag{5.7}$$

---

1) The Fourier transform (5.6) is of course different from the Fourier transform (2.19) of Chapter V. The difference is that each function $\widetilde{u}_k(\lambda)$ $(k = 0, \cdots, r-1)$ is an entire function of λ since the solutions $\chi_k(x; \lambda)$ are known to be such functions. Analyticity in λ of the vector $\widetilde{u}(\lambda)$ is an important advantage of the transformation (5.6) over (2.19) of Chapter V.

The matrix $\|d\sigma_{jk}(\lambda)\|_0^{r-1}$ is called the spectral matrix. It is expressed by means of the values of the derivatives at the point c of the kernel $\Xi(x, y;\ \lambda)$ of the operator E_λ, i.e. of the corresponding spectral function

$$d\sigma_{jk}(\lambda) = \left(\frac{\partial^{j+k}\Phi}{\partial x^j \partial y^k}\right)(c, c; \lambda)\, d\varrho(\lambda) = \frac{\partial^{j+k}}{\partial x^j \partial y^k} d_\lambda \Xi(c, c; \lambda). \tag{5.8}$$

The matrix $\|d\sigma_{jk}(\lambda)\|_0^{r-1}$, more precisely $\|\sigma_{jk}(\Delta)\|_0^{r-1}$, is positive definite. This is a consequence of the following general lemma, which we will use in the sequel.

Lemma 5.1. *Consider the kernel $\Phi(x, y;\ \lambda)$ $(x, y \in G)$ for some fixed λ. Assume that the derivatives $(\partial^{j+k}\Phi/\partial x^j \partial y^k)(x, y;\ \lambda)$ $(j, k = 0, \cdots, r)$ exist and are continuous relative to $(x, y) \in G \times G$, and that equation (5.3) is satisfied. If $\Phi(x, y;\ \lambda)$ is positive definite $(x, y \in G)$ then for arbitrary $c \in G$ the matrix*

$$\left\| \left(\frac{\partial^{j+k}\Phi}{\partial x^j \partial y^k}\right)(c, c; \lambda) \right\|_{j,k=0}^{r-1}$$

is also positive definite.

Proof. First we note that representation (5.4) is valid for the kernel Φ, where the fundamental system of solutions $\chi_j(x;\ \lambda)$ satisfies the conditions of (5.2). We now find r points $x_\alpha \in G$ $(\alpha = 0, \cdots, r-1)$ such that the matrix $\|\chi_j(x_\alpha;\ \lambda)\|_{j,\alpha=0}^{r-1}$ is nonsingular. Then each vector $\xi = (\xi_0, \cdots, \xi_{r-1}) \in C_0$ may be written in the form $\xi_j = \Sigma_{\alpha=0}^{r-1} c_\alpha \chi_j (x_\alpha;\ \lambda)$ $(j = 0, \cdots, r-1)$. Using this representation in equation (5.4) we obtain

$$\sum_{j,k=0}^{r-1} \left(\frac{\partial^{j+k}\Phi}{\partial x^j \partial y^k}\right)(c, c; \lambda)\, \xi_k \xi_j = \sum_{j,k=0}^{r-1} \left(\frac{\partial^{j+k}\Phi}{\partial x^j \partial y^k}\right)(c, c; \lambda)$$

$$\times \left\{ \sum_{\alpha,\beta=0}^{r-1} c_\beta c_\alpha \chi_k(x_\beta; \lambda)\, \overline{\chi_j(x_\alpha; \lambda)} \right\} = \sum_{\alpha,\beta=0}^{r-1} c_\beta \bar{c}_\alpha \left\{ \sum_{j,k=0}^{r-1} \left(\frac{\partial^{j+k}\Phi}{\partial x^j \partial y^k}\right)(c, c; \lambda) \right.$$

$$\left. \times\, \chi_k(x_\beta; \lambda)\, \overline{\chi_j(x_\alpha; \lambda)} \right\} = \sum_{\alpha,\beta=0}^{r-1} \Phi(x_\beta, x_\alpha; \lambda)\, c_\beta \bar{c}_\alpha \geqslant 0,$$

as required. The lemma is proved.

So far we have interpreted the integral in (5.7) as a formal statement of the transformation described in (5.5). However, after the proof of the positive definiteness of the matrix $\| d\sigma_{jk}(\lambda) \|_0^{r-1}$, this integral may be interpreted as an integral with respect to a nonnegative operator-valued measure. The definition and properties of such integrals will be presented in §2.3 of Chapter VII. This provides the possibility of passing to arbitrary functions $u, v \in L_2(G)$ in equation (5.7) as in the indicated place in Chapter VII. In addition to the term "spectral matrix" we sometimes use the term "operator-valued spectral measure".

In general, it is impossible to give a more detailed form of the Parseval equation (5.7). However, if we know an eigenfunction expansion for some selfadjoint extension induced by some given boundary conditions (bd), then the following simplification is possible. The solutions of the equation $Lu - \lambda u = 0$ $(x \in G)$ which satisfy the conditions (bd) (or part of them) may be used in the capacity of the system of functions $\chi_j(x; \lambda)$, so that we obtain by this system only those solutions of our equation which satisfy the considered boundary conditions. Therefore the number of functions $\chi_j(x; \lambda)$ will now be less than r. The spectral kernel $\Phi(x, y; \lambda)$ satisfies the conditions (bd) for x and y, so that similarly to (5.4) it may be expressed as a bilinear form on the obtained system of solutions. Thus in this case the Parseval equation is written in the form of (5.7), but the spectral matrix will be of order less than r.

We consider one more question. We have already said that analogs of Theorems 4.2 and 4.4 on the smoothness of the generalized kernels may be established; the arguments remain as earlier, but are considerably simpler. Since we will need the following result in Chapter VIII, we state it precisely here.

Theorem 5.1. *Let L' be an expression of order r' of the form* (5.1) *on an interval G' with coefficients $a'_\alpha(x') \in C^{\alpha+p'}(G')$, $p' \geq \sigma' \geq 0$. Let L'' be defined analogously on G''. Assume that $\Phi \in W_2^{-\sigma'}(G') \otimes W_2^{-\sigma''}(G'')$ satisfies the system of equations*

$$L'_{x'} U = F, \quad L''_{x''} U = F \tag{5.9}$$

inside $O \subseteq G' \times G''$, where $F(x', x'')$ $((x', x'') \in O)$ is such that the derivatives $D_{x'}^{\alpha'} D_{x''}^{\alpha''} F$ exist and are continuous for $\alpha' \leq q'$ and $\alpha'' \leq q''$. In other words, the relations (4.30) *of Chapter* III *are satisfied.*

Then Φ coincides with the ordinary kernel $H(x', x'')$ on O and in addition satisfies the following conditions of smoothness: if $F = 0$, then the derivatives $D_{x'}^{\alpha'} D_{x''}^{\alpha''} H$ $(\alpha' \leq r' + p', \alpha'' \leq r'' + p'')$ exist and are continuous relative to $(x', x'') \in O$; if $F \neq 0$ then the similar derivatives exist for

$\alpha' \leq r' + \min(p', q'), \quad \alpha'' \leq r'' + \min(p'', q'')$.

We note that this theorem is easily generalized to the case of more than two differential expressions of the form (5.1).

3. **Further results and examples.** The remaining results on spectral analysis, investigated in the previous sections of this chapter, carry over to ordinary differential expressions. The arguments go through in the same way but in general are considerably simpler. Among these are the theorems on the structure of the differential operators induced by (5.1), and the selfadjointness of these. Also, the theorems in §5, Chapter V on the behavior of the eigenfunctions at ∞, mentioned in §2.7, apply. In the one-dimensional case, even the theorems of §2.10 on the Schrödinger equation, now called a Sturm-Liouville equation, are valid. We note here that in the case $n = 1$ Theorem 2.11 may be proved differently, including the assumption of semi-boundedness below of $c(x)$ but not that of uniform continuity.[1] The facts in §4 are also well known for operators induced by (5.1).

We now again mention some examples of eigenfunction expansions for the expression (5.1) which we have already used in §§4.4–4.5.

a) The expression $-i\, d/dx$ in E_1. The minimal operator Λ (on $L_2(E_1)$) corresponding to this expression is suitable for the construction of an example of a singular selfadjoint differential operator. The eigenfunction expansion leads to the classical one-dimensional Fourier transformation. We construct such an expansion not relying on the Fourier transformation.

The operator Λ is selfadjoint: let $\phi \in L_2(E_1)$ be such that $\Lambda^* \phi = \bar{z}\phi$ ($\operatorname{Im} z \neq 0$). Then, for $v \in C_0^\infty(E_1)$ $(-iv' - zv, \phi)_0 = 0$, i.e. ϕ is a generalized, and hence a smooth solution of the equation $iu' - \bar{z}u = 0$. Therefore $\phi(x) = Ce^{-i\bar{z}x} \in L_2(E_1)$ is possible only for $C = 0$. So $\phi = 0$ and $\Lambda^* = \Lambda$.

We find the resolvent R_z of the operator Λ. Let $\operatorname{Im} z > 0$, and $f \in C_0^\infty(E_1)$. The solution of the equation $(\Lambda - zE)u = f$ is equivalent to the solution of the differential $-iu' - zu = f$ on $L_2(E_1)$. Finding this solution we obtain

$$(R_z f)(x) = u(x) = ie^{izx} \int_{-\infty}^{x} e^{-izy} f(y)\, dy = \int_{-\infty}^{\infty} i\varkappa_{(-\infty,x)}(y)\, e^{iz(x-y)} f(y)\, dy \quad (x \in E_1),$$

1) Recently, this was successfully done for the case of arbitrary n. (See the Literature notes.)

where $\kappa_{(a,b)}$ is the characteristic function of the interval (a, b). Thus the resolvent kernel has the form

$$R(x, y; z) = R(x - y; z) = \begin{cases} i\kappa_{(-\infty,x)}(y)\, e^{iz(x-y)}, & \operatorname{Im} z > 0, \\ -i\kappa_{(x,+\infty)}(y)\, e^{iz(x-y)}, & \operatorname{Im} z < 0 \end{cases}$$

$$(x, y \in E_1)^{1)} \tag{5.10}$$

(the formula for $\operatorname{Im} z < 0$ follows from the relation $R_z = R^*_{\bar z}$).

To find the spectral kernel the first two equations of (2.39) are used (the third is now not true). Calculating the integral $(1/2\pi i) \int_{\Delta + i\epsilon} ((R_z - R^*_z)f, g)_0\, dz$ with the help of (5.10), and then passing to the limit as $\epsilon \longrightarrow +0$, we obtain

$$\Phi(x, y; \lambda)\, d\varrho(\lambda) = \Phi(x - y; \lambda)\, d\varrho(\lambda) = \frac{1}{2\pi} e^{i\lambda(x-y)}\, d\lambda$$
$$(-\infty < \lambda < \infty;\ x, y \in E_1).$$

Thus we may consider this as the construction of the usual one-dimensional Fourier integral. To construct the n-dimensional Fourier integral, Theorem 2.5 of Chapter V on the generalized eigenvector expansion of a system of commuting selfadjoint operators may be used. The operators used must be the minimal operators on $L_2(E_n)$ induced by the expressions $-iD_1, \cdots, -iD_n$.

b) The expression $-d^2/dx^2$ on E_1. The generalized eigenfunction expansion for the minimal operator induced by this expression on $L_2(E_1)$ is constructed exactly as in example a) §2.8, only the computations here will be more elementary. As a result we obtain formulas which are identical to (2.35) and (2.41) with $n = 1$. Namely

$$R(x, y; z) = R(x - y; z) = \frac{i}{2\sqrt{z}} e^{i\sqrt{z}|x-y|} \qquad (x, y \in E_1;\ z \,\overline{\in}\, [0, \infty)),$$

$$\Phi(x, y; \lambda)\, d\varrho(\lambda) = \Phi(x - y; \lambda)\, d\varrho(\lambda)$$
$$= \begin{cases} \dfrac{1}{2\pi} \cos\sqrt{\lambda}(x - y) \dfrac{d\lambda}{\sqrt{\lambda}}, & \lambda > 0, \\ 0, & \lambda \leqslant 0 \end{cases} \quad (x, y \in E_1).$$

We write the spectral matrix, putting $c = 0$ in the formulas of subsection 2. Now $\chi_0(x; \lambda) = \cos\sqrt{\lambda}x$, $\chi_1(x; \lambda) = \sin\sqrt{\lambda}x/\sqrt{\lambda}$ $(\lambda > 0;\ x \in E_1)$. By (5.8), for $\lambda > 0$ we have

1) We note also that $R(x-y;\ z) = (1/2\pi) \int_{-\infty}^{\infty} (e^{i(x-y)\xi}/(\xi - z))\, d\xi$ corresponds to (3.6).

$$\| d\sigma_{jk}(\lambda) \|_0^1 = \frac{1}{2\pi} \left\| \begin{matrix} \frac{1}{\sqrt{\lambda}} & 0 \\ 0 & \sqrt{\lambda} \end{matrix} \right\| d\lambda.$$

c) The expression $-d^2/dx^2$ on $(0, \infty)$. We must impose some boundary conditions at zero here which along with the condition $u = 0$ at ∞ would be formally selfadjoint. The general form will be: $\alpha u'(0) + \beta u(0) = 0$ ($\operatorname{Im} \alpha = \operatorname{Im} \beta = 0$, $\alpha^2 + \beta^2 > 0$). We construct the corresponding strong operator Λ(bd), and note that it is not difficult to show, similarly to a) for example, that it is selfadjoint. We will not consider $R(x, y; z)$ or $\Phi(x, y; \lambda)$ for these but limit ourselves to the fact that, for the boundary condition $u'(0) = 0$, Φ has the form

$$\Phi(x, y; \lambda)\, d\varrho(\lambda) = \begin{cases} \frac{1}{\pi} \cos \sqrt{\lambda} x \cdot \cos \sqrt{\lambda} y \frac{d\lambda}{\sqrt{\lambda}}, & \lambda > 0, \\ 0, & \lambda \leqslant 0 \end{cases}$$

$$(x, y \in (0, \infty)).$$

This formula may be obtained from the Parseval equation in example b) if only even functions are considered in it.

This example illustrates what was said in subsection 2 about the decrease in the order of the spectral matrix. Namely, we may now set $\chi_0(x; \lambda) = \cos \sqrt{\lambda}\, x$ ($\lambda > 0$; $x \in (0, \infty)$); the spectral matrix will be one-dimensional: $d\sigma_{00}(\lambda) = d\lambda / \pi\sqrt{\lambda}$ for $\lambda > 0$.

CHAPTER VII

SPECTRAL THEORY OF SELFADJOINT DIFFERENCE OPERATORS

In this chapter we examine the spectral theory of the simplest unbounded selfadjoint operators, namely difference operators. Both the classical results in the theory of Jacobi matrices, and the spectral theory of partial difference operators are presented. The latter is conveniently based on the spectral theory of Jacobi matrices with operator coefficients; this theory is presented in §2. The results of the chapter are closely connected with the results of §5, Chapter VIII.

§1. SECOND ORDER DIFFERENCE OPERATORS ON THE SEMI-AXIS (JACOBI MATRICES)

1. **Difference expressions and operators.** In this section we will consider the difference analogue of the Sturm-Liouville differential expression. Without loss of generality, we can assume that the coefficients of the expression L are defined for all integral values of the index j. This expression has the form

$$(Lu)_j = a_{j-1}u_{j-1} + a_j u_{j+1} + b_j u_j \quad (j = \ldots, -1, 0, 1, \ldots), \tag{1.1}$$

where a_j, b_j are the given coefficients, and $u = (u_j) = (\cdots, u_{-1}, u_0, u_1, \cdots)$ is a sequence on which L acts. It is assumed that $a_j > 0$ and $\operatorname{Im} b_j = 0$ (for all j). We show that (1.1) is in fact the difference analogue of the Sturm-Liouville expression of the form $d(a(x)\,du/dx)/dx + q(x)\,u(x)$. For this purpose we introduce the left and right differences of the first order

$$(\Delta_\ell u)_j = u_j - u_{j-1}, \quad (\Delta_r u)_j = u_{j+1} - u_j \quad (j = \ldots, -1, 0, 1, \ldots). \tag{1.2}$$

Then the desired analogue has the form

$$(\Delta_\ell[a(\Delta_\pi u)])_j + q_j u_j = a_j(u_{j+1} - u_j) - a_{j-1}(u_j - u_{j-1}) + q_j u_j$$
$$= a_{j-1}u_{j-1} + a_j u_{j+1} + b_j u_j, \quad b_j = -a_{j-1} - a_j + q_j$$
$$(j = \ldots, -1, 0, 1, \ldots). \tag{1.3}$$

We will sometimes write (1.1) in the form (1.3).

A simple calculation shows that Green's formula is valid:

$$\sum_{j=k}^{l} [(Lu)_j\bar{v}_j - u_j\overline{(Lv)_j}] = a_l(u_{l+1}\bar{v}_l - u_l\bar{v}_{l+1})$$
$$- a_{k-1}(u_k\bar{v}_{k-1} - u_{k-1}\bar{v}_k) \quad (k, l = \ldots, -1, 0, 1, \ldots; \quad k < l). \tag{1.4}$$

We will now construct operators which are connected with the expression L. In this section (with the exception of the last subsection) we will restrict ourselves to the case which appears in the classical power moment problem; it is analogous to the problem for the Sturm-Liouville equation on the semi-axis $(0, \infty)$ with boundary condition $u(0) = 0$. The examination will be made in the Hilbert space $l_2([0, \infty)) = H_0$, which consists of sequences $u = (u_0, u_1, \cdots)$, $(u, v) = \sum_{j=0}^{\infty} u_j\bar{v}_j$. We define the operator L' on the set $l_{2,0}([0, \infty))$ of sequences u which are finite at ∞ by setting $(\mathrm{L}'u)_j = (Lu)_j$, where for the calculation of $(Lu)_0$ we set $u_{-1} = 0$ (this condition plays the role of the boundary condition $u(0) = 0$). It is easy to show with the help of Green's formula that L' is Hermitian. Let L denote the closure of the operator L'; we will call L the operator induced by L.

It is easy to show that *the domain of the adjoint operator* L^* *consists of those* $v \in l_2([0, \infty))$ *for which* $Lv \in l_2([0, \infty))$; *moreover,* $(\mathrm{L}^*v)_j = (Lv)_j$ *(as before, for the calculation of* $(Lv)_0$ *we set* $v_{-1} = 0$). In fact, let $v \in \mathfrak{D}(\mathrm{L}^*)$; then $(Lu, v)_0 = (u, \mathrm{L}^*v)_0$ for all $u \in l_{2,0}([0, \infty))$. In other words, by (1.4), $(Lu, v)_0 = (u, Lv)_0$. Therefore

$$(u, \mathrm{L}^*v)_0 = (u, Lv)_0 \ (u \in l_{2,0}([0, \infty))),$$

whence $Lv = \mathrm{L}^*v \in l_2([0, \infty))$. Thus, if $v \in \mathfrak{D}(\mathrm{L}^*)$, then $Lv \in l_2([0, \infty))$ and $\mathrm{L}^*v = Lv$. The converse relation follows from Green's formula.

In general, $\mathrm{L}^* \neq \mathrm{L}$. Later, we will study in detail the question of selfadjointness of the operator L. We remark now only that the deficiency indices of L are equal, as follows from the fact that L is real (because the coefficients of L are real) with respect to the involution $u = (u_j) \to \bar{u} = (\bar{u}_j)$.

In all of §1, we assume in the calculation of $(Lu)_0$ that $u_{-1} = 0$. Then the passage from u to Lu can be represented as the image of the vector

$u = (u_0, u_1, \cdots)$ under the matrix

$$J = \begin{Vmatrix} b_0 & a_0 & 0 & 0 & 0 & \cdots \\ a_0 & b_1 & a_1 & 0 & 0 & \cdots \\ 0 & a_1 & b_2 & a_2 & 0 & \cdots \\ \cdot & \cdot & \cdot & \cdot & \cdot & \cdots \end{Vmatrix} \quad (a_j > 0,\ \operatorname{Im} b_j = 0;\quad j = 0, 1, \ldots). \tag{1.5}$$

Matrices of this form are called Jacobi matrices. The results of this section can be regarded as a theory of such matrices.

2. **Polynomials of the first kind. Criteria for selfadjointness of the operator L.** First of all, we introduce an important concept. Consider the equation

$$(Lu)_j = a_{j-1}u_{j-1} + a_j u_{j+1} + b_j u_j = zu_j \quad (j = 0, 1, \ldots), \tag{1.6}$$

where z is some complex number. It can be considered as a recursion relation for the determination of u_{j+1} from u_j and u_{j-1}; since $a_j \neq 0$, this relation is always solvable. Put $u_{-1} = 0$, $u_0 = 1$, and define u_j for $j \geq 1$ by (1.6). Clearly, u_j is a polynomial of degree j in z (as, for example, $u_1 = (z - b_0)/a_0$); write $u_j = P_j(z)$. These polynomials are called polynomials of the first kind, generated by L. Thus

$$(LP(z))_j = zP_j(z) \quad (j = 0, 1, \ldots); \quad P_{-1}(z) = 0, \quad P_0(z) = 1. \tag{1.7}$$

Since a_j and b_j are real, the coefficients of the polynomials $P_j(z)$ are real; as is easily seen, the positivity of a_j implies that the coefficient of z^j in $P_j(z)$ is always positive. Since the difference equation (1.6) is of second order, it has two linearly independent solutions. The second solution, normalized in a specific way, will be introduced later.

Let $\operatorname{Im} z \neq 0$, and denote by $N_{\bar z}$ the orthogonal complement of $\Re(L - \bar z E)$, i.e. the deficiency subspace of the operator L. This subspace coincides with the subspace of solutions of the equation $L^*\phi = z\phi$ or, because of the form of L^*, with the subspace of solutions of the difference equation $(Lu)_j = zu_j$, $u_{-1} = 0$, which belong to $l_2([0, \infty))$. Each solution of this equation is representable in the form $u_j = u_0 P_j(z)$, and therefore the deficiency subspace is at most one-dimensional; moreover, it is nonzero if and only if $(u_j) = (u_0 P_j(z)) \in l_2([0, \infty))$, i.e. if $\sum_{j=0}^{\infty} |P_j(z)|^2 < \infty$.

Taking into account these remarks, the invariance of the deficiency numbers and their equality for the operator under consideration, we obtain

Theorem 1.1. *The operator* L *has deficiency index* $(0, 0)$ *or* $(1, 1)$. *The first case is characterized by the divergence of the series* $\sum_{j=0}^{\infty} |P_j(z)|^2$ *for all*

nonreal z, *and the second case by the convergence of this series.*

In the second case, the deficiency subspace $N_{\bar{z}}$ *is orthogonal to* $\Re(L - \bar{z}E)$, *and is spanned by the vector* $(P_0(z), P_1(z), \cdots)$.

It follows from the theorem that a necessary condition that L be selfadjoint is that the series $\Sigma_{j=0}^{\infty} |P_j(z)|^2$ diverge for all nonreal z, while a sufficient condition is that the series diverge for only one such z. Sufficient conditions for the divergence or convergence of the series, i.e. conditions for the selfadjointness or nonselfadjointness of L, can be given in terms of the coefficients a_j, b_j. Some of these conditions will be mentioned now. First of all, we establish an elementary theorem.

Theorem 1.2. *If the coefficients* a_j *and* b_j *are bounded, then the operator* L *is bounded, and consequently is selfadjoint.*

Proof. Let $|a_j|, |b_j| \le C$ $(j = 0, 1, \cdots)$; then by the triangle inequality

$$\| \mathrm{L}u \|_0 = \| Lu \|_0 = \Big(\sum_{j=0}^{\infty} | a_{j-1}u_{j-1} + a_j u_{j+1} + b_j u_j |^2 \Big)^{\frac{1}{2}}$$

$$\leqslant \Big(\sum_{j=0}^{\infty} | a_{j-1}u_{j-1} |^2 \Big)^{\frac{1}{2}} + \Big(\sum_{j=0}^{\infty} | a_j u_{j+1} |^2 \Big)^{\frac{1}{2}} + \Big(\sum_{j=0}^{\infty} | b_j u_j |^2 \Big)^{\frac{1}{2}}$$

$$\leqslant C \Big(\Big(\sum_{j=0}^{\infty} | u_{j-1} |^2 \Big)^{\frac{1}{2}} + \Big(\sum_{j=0}^{\infty} | u_{j+1} |^2 \Big)^{\frac{1}{2}} + \| u \|_0 \Big) \leqslant 3C \| u \|_0 ,$$

as required. The theorem is proved.

Theorem 1.3. *If* b_j *is arbitrary and* a_j *is such that*

$$\sum_{j=0}^{\infty} \frac{1}{a_j} = \infty, \tag{1.8}$$

then the operator L *is selfadjoint.*

Proof. It is sufficient to show that (1.8) implies divergence of the series $\Sigma_{j=0}^{\infty} |P_j(z)|^2$ for some nonreal z. Using Green's formula (1.4), we find that

$$(z - \bar{z}) \sum_{j=0}^{n} P_j(z) \overline{P_j(z)} = \sum_{j=0}^{n} \{ (L[P(z)])_j \overline{P_j(z)} - P_j(z) \overline{(L[P(z)])_j} \}$$

$$= a_n \big(P_{n+1}(z) \overline{P_n(z)} - P_n(z) \overline{P_{n+1}(z)}\big) \quad (n = 0, 1, \ldots).$$

Hence

$$\sum_{j=0}^{n} |P_j(z)|^2 = \frac{a_n}{z-\bar{z}}(P_{n+1}(z)\overline{P_n(z)} - P_n(z)\overline{P_{n+1}(z)}) \tag{1.9}$$

$$(n = 0, 1, \ldots).$$

Since $P_0(z) = 1$, then by estimating the absolute value of (1.9) we obtain

$$1 \leqslant \frac{a_n}{|z-\bar{z}|}(|P_{n+1}(z)||P_n(z)| + |P_n(z)||P_{n+1}(z)|)$$

$$= \frac{2a_n}{|z-\bar{z}|}|P_n(z)||P_{n+1}(z)|,$$

and hence $1/a_n \leq C|P_n(z)||P_{n+1}(z)|$. Furthermore

$$\infty = \sum_{n=0}^{\infty}\frac{1}{a_n} \leqslant C\sum_{n=0}^{\infty}|P_n(z)||P_{n+1}(z)|$$

$$\leqslant C\left(\sum_{n=0}^{\infty}|P_n(z)|^2 \cdot \sum_{n=0}^{\infty}|P_{n+1}(z)|^2\right)^{\frac{1}{2}} < C\sum_{n=0}^{\infty}|P_n(z)|^2,$$

i.e. $\Sigma_{n=0}^{\infty}|P_n(z)|^2 = \infty$. The theorem is proved.

Theorem 1.4. *If* $a_{j-1} + a_j + b_j \leq C < \infty$ $(j = 0, 1, \cdots)$, *then the operator* L *is semi-bounded above on finite sequences (i.e.* $(\mathrm{L}u, u)_0 \leq C(u, u)_0$, $u \in l_{2,0}([0,\infty))$) *and is selfadjoint.*

Proof. We will use the following easily proved formula on "summation by parts":

$$\sum_{j=k}^{l}(\Delta_\varrho u)_j v_j = -u_{k-1}v_k + u_l v_{l+1} - \sum_{j=k}^{l} u_j(\Delta_\pi v)_j$$

$$(k, l = \ldots, -1, 0, 1, \ldots; \quad k < l). \tag{1.10}$$

Let $u \in l_{2,0}([0,\infty))$. Then by taking N sufficiently large we find from (1.10) that $(u_{-1} = 0)$

$$(\Delta_\varrho[a.(\Delta_\pi u).], u)_0 = \sum_{j=0}^{N}(\Delta_\varrho[a.(\Delta_\pi u).])_j\bar{u}_j =$$

$$= -a_{-1}(u_0 - u_{-1})\bar{u}_0 - \sum_{j=0}^{N} a_j(\Delta_n u)_j\overline{(\Delta_n u)_j}$$

$$= -a_{-1}|u_0|^2 - \sum_{j=0}^{N} a_j|(\Delta_n u)_j|^2 \leqslant 0. \tag{1.11}$$

We will use the expression L in the form (1.3). Since $q_j = a_{j-1} + a_j + b_j \le C$, then by (1.11) we have for $u \in l_{2,0}([0, \infty))$:

$$(Lu, u)_0 = (\Delta_\ell[a_.(\Delta_n u)_.], u)_0 + \sum_{j=0}^{\infty} q_j|u_j|^2 \leqslant C\sum_{j=0}^{\infty}|u_j|^2 = C(u, u)_0.$$

This establishes the semi-boundedness of L.

To prove the theorem, it must be shown that $\Sigma_{j=0}^{\infty}|P_j(z)|^2 = \infty$ for some non-real z. In subsection 6 we show independently that the polynomials $P_j(z)$ satisfy the inequality $|P_j(x+iy)| \ge |P_j(x)|$ $(-\infty < x, y < \infty)$, so the divergence of the required series will be proven if it is shown that $\Sigma_{j=0}^{\infty}|P_j(x)|^2 = \infty$ for some real x. We use the following simple fact: the solutions of the difference equations $(\Delta_\ell u)_j = f_j$, $(\Delta_n u)_j = f_j$, $(j = 0, 1, \cdots)$ have the respective forms

$$u_n = u_0 + \sum_{j=1}^{n} f_j, \quad v_n = v_0 + \sum_{j=0}^{n-1} f_j \quad (n = 1, 2, \ldots). \tag{1.12}$$

If we apply the first of the formulas (1.12) to the relation $(\Delta_\ell[a_0(\Delta_n P(z))])_j = (z - a_{j-1} - a_j - b_j)P_j(z)$ $(j = 0, 1, \cdots;\ P_0(z) = 1)$ (see (1.7) and (1.3)), we obtain $a_k(\Delta_n P(z))_k = a_0(\Delta_n P(z))_0 + \Sigma_{j=1}^{k}(z - a_{j-1} - a_j - b_j)P_j(z)$ $(k = 1, 2, \cdots)$. Since $a_0(\Delta_n P(z))_0 = z - a_0 - b_0$, then the equation obtained may be rewritten in the form $a_k(\Delta_n P(z))_k = \Sigma_{j=0}^{k}(z - a_{j-1} - a_j - b_j)P_j(z)$ $(k = 0, 1, \cdots)$, if it is only assumed that $a_{-1} = 0$. Hence by the second of the formulas (1.12) we obtain

$$P_n(z) = 1 + \sum_{k=0}^{n-1}\frac{1}{a_k}\sum_{j=0}^{k}(z - a_{j-1} - a_j - b_j)P_j(z) \quad (n = 1, 2, \ldots). \tag{1.13}$$

We now take $z = x$ real $\ge C$. Then $z - a_{j-1} - a_j - b_j \ge 0$ and from (1.13) in turn we find that $P_0(x) = 1$, $P_1(x) \ge 1$, $P_2(x) \ge 1, \cdots$. Thus $\Sigma_{j=0}^{\infty}|P_j(x)|^2 = \infty$ as required. The theorem is proved.

Corollary. *If* $a_{j-1} + a_j - b_j \le C < \infty$ $(j = 0, 1, \cdots)$, *then the operator* L *is selfadjoint.*

In fact, the polynomials $\hat{P}_j(z) = (-1)^{j-1}P_j(-z)$ $(j = 0, 1, \cdots)$ satisfy the relation $a_{j-1}\hat{P}_{j-1}(z) + a_j\hat{P}_{j+1}(z) - b_j\hat{P}_j(z) = z\hat{P}_j(z)$ $(j = 0, 1, \cdots;\ \hat{P}_0(z) = 1)$

i.e. are polynomials of the first kind for the expression $(\hat{L}u)_j = a_{j-1}u_{j-1} + a_j u_{j+1} - b_j u_j$. By Theorem 1.4 the condition $a_{j-1} + a_j - b_j \leq C$ implies divergence of the series $\Sigma_{j=0}^{\infty} |\hat{P}_j(z)|^2$, that is, $\Sigma_{j=0}^{\infty} |P_j(-z)|^2 = \infty$, which in turn implies that L is selfadjoint.

The condition $a_{j-1} + a_j + b_j \leq C < \infty$ $(j = 0, 1, \cdots)$ is not necessary for L to be semi-bounded above. In addition, semi-boundedness of L does not, in general, imply that it is selfadjoint,[1] This is clarified by the following example. Let L be an expression of the form (1.1), which is nonpositive on $l_{2,0}([0, \infty))$ (i.e. $(Lu, u)_0 \leq 0$, $u \in l_{2,0}([0, \infty))$). Denote by $(P_0(z), P_1(z), \cdots)$ the corresponding sequence of polynomials of the first kind; the solution of the equation $(Lu)_j = zu_j$ $(j = 1, 2, \cdots)$ with initial conditions $u_0 = 0$, $u_1 = 1/a_0$ we denote by $(Q_0(z) = 0,\ Q_1(z) = 1/a_0,\ Q_2(z), \cdots)$ ($Q_j(z)$ are the so-called polynomials of the second kind; see subsection 6). Let $d_0 = d_1 = 1$, $d_2, d_3, \cdots \geq 1$ be a rapidly increasing sequence so that $(P_0(z)/d_0, P_1(z)/d_1, \cdots)$ and $(Q_0(z)/d_0, Q_1(z)/d_1, \cdots)$ for $z = 0$ belong to $l_2([0, \infty))$. Let D be the diagonal matrix with the elements $d_0, d_1, \cdots$ on the diagonal; let $M = DLD$. The expression M has the form (1.1); it, obviously, is not positive on $l_{2,0}([0, \infty))$. Moreover, the polynomials $P_j(z)/d_j$ and $Q_j(z)/d_j$ $(j = 0, 1, \cdots)$ are polynomials of the first and second kinds for M, where at the point $z = 0$ they form sequences, which belong to $l_2([0, \infty))$ by construction. It will be shown below (see p. 539) that such a situation implies that the operator corresponding to the difference expression M is not selfadjoint.

We now prove a theorem in contrast to the nature of the previous theorems: it gives a condition for which L will not be selfadjoint.

Theorem 1.5. *Assume that* $|b_j| \leq C$ $(j = 0, 1, \cdots)$, $a_{j-1}a_{j+1} \leq a_j^2$ *beginning with some* j, *and*

$$\sum_{j=0}^{\infty} \frac{1}{a_j} < \infty. \tag{1.14}$$

Then the operator L *is not selfadjoint.*

Proof. Fix z not real. Because of (1.14), for the proof of the condition $\Sigma_{j=0}^{\infty} |P_j(z)|^2 < \infty$, and hence of the theorem, it is sufficient to establish the estimate

---

[1] C.f. Theorems 1.7 and 1.8, Chapter VI.

$$\sqrt{a_j}\,|P_j(z)| \leqslant A < \infty \quad (j = 0, 1, \ldots). \tag{1.15}$$

We assume that the inequalities $\sqrt{a_j}\,|P_j(z)| \leq A_n$ $(j = 0, \cdots, n)$ hold and we will choose a constant A_{n+1} on the basis of A_n; in this connection we assume that $n \geq n_0$, where $a_{j-1}a_{j+1} \leq a_j^2$ $(j = n_0, n_0 + 1, \cdots)$. Since $P_{n+1}(z) = (1/a_n)(z - b_n)P_n(z) - (a_{n-1}/a_n)P_{n-1}(z)$, then $(C_1 = C + |z|)$

$$\sqrt{a_{n+1}}\,|P_{n+1}(z)| \leqslant \frac{\sqrt{a_{n+1}}}{a_n}|z - b_n|\,|P_n(z)| + \frac{\sqrt{a_{n+1}a_{n-1}}}{a_n}|P_{n-1}(z)|$$

$$\leqslant C_1\frac{\sqrt{a_{n+1}a_{n-1}}}{a_n}\frac{1}{\sqrt{a_{n-1}a_n}}\sqrt{a_n}\,|P_n(z)| + \frac{\sqrt{a_{n+1}a_{n-1}}}{a_n}\sqrt{a_{n-1}}|P_{n-1}(z)|$$

$$\leqslant A_n\left(1 + \frac{C_1}{\sqrt{a_{n-1}a_n}}\right).$$

Set $A_{n+1} = A_n(1 + C_1/\sqrt{a_{n-1}a_n})$. Thus we have

$$A_n = A_{n_0}\prod_{j=n_0}^{n-1}\left(1 + \frac{C_1}{\sqrt{a_{j-1}a_j}}\right) \leqslant A_{n_0}\prod_{j=1}^{\infty}\left(1 + \frac{C_1}{\sqrt{a_{j-1}a_j}}\right) = A(n > n_0).$$

If the latter product converges, then $A < \infty$ and (1.15) is proved. But convergence must hold, since in view of (1.14)

$$\sum_{j=1}^{\infty}\frac{1}{\sqrt{a_{j-1}a_j}} \leqslant \left(\sum_{j=1}^{\infty}\frac{1}{a_{j-1}}\cdot\sum_{j=1}^{\infty}\frac{1}{a_j}\right)^{\frac{1}{2}} < \infty.$$

The theorem is proved.

3. **The eigenfunction expansion.** We will now construct such an expansion for a selfadjoint extension (in $l_2([0, \infty))$ or a larger space) of the operator L. Three approaches to the problem will be mentioned. First of all, we consider a construction which arises from the general results of Chapter V and is analogous to that traced in Chapter VI, §5.2. Let $E(\Delta)$, generally speaking, be the resolution of the identity corresponding to L. Since L acts in $l_2([0, \infty))$, the results of Chapter V, §4.4 can be applied to this operator. We have

$$E(\Delta) = \int_{\Delta} P(\lambda)\,d\varrho(\lambda), \tag{1.16}$$

where $P(\lambda)$ is a generalized projection operator acting from the space $l_2([0, \infty), p_j)$ to $l_2([0, \infty), 1/p_j)$; here $p_j \geq 1$ is such that $\Sigma_{j=0}^{\infty} 1/p_j < \infty$. The operator $P(\lambda)$ is represented by the matrix $\|\Phi_{jk}(\lambda)\|_0^\infty$, which is positive definite and satisfies the condition

$$\sum_{j,\,k=0}^{\infty} \frac{|\Phi_{jk}(\lambda)|^2}{p_j p_k} \leqslant 1 \tag{1.17}$$

for almost every λ with respect to ρ.

Lemma 1.1. *The representation*

$$\Phi_{jk}(\lambda) = P_j(\lambda) P_k(\lambda) \Phi_{00}(\lambda) \quad (j,\ k = 0,\ 1, \ldots) \tag{1.18}$$

holds.

Proof. Each vector $\phi \in \Re(P(\lambda))$ is a generalized eigenvector, corresponding to the eigenvalue λ. This means (see Chapter V, §2.2) that $(\phi, (L^* - \lambda E)u)_0 = 0$ for all $u \in l_{2,0}([0, \infty))$; in other words $(\phi, (L - \lambda E)u)_0 = 0$ $(u \in l_{2,0}([0, \infty))$, $u_{-1} = 0)$. Using Green's formula (1.4), we obtain $0 = (\phi, (L - \lambda E)u)_0 = ((L - \lambda E)\phi, u)_0 - a_{-1}\phi_{-1}u_0$, i.e. $a_{-1}\phi_{-1}u_0 = ((L - \lambda E)\phi, u)_0$. Because u is arbitrary, the latter relation is possible only if $((L - \lambda E)\phi)_j = 0$ $(j = 1, 2, \cdots)$ and $a_0\phi_1 + (b_0 - \lambda)\phi_0 = 0$. In other words it may be assumed that $((L - \lambda E)\phi)_j = 0$ $(j = 0, 1, \cdots)$ and $\phi_{-1} = 0$. Therefore $\phi_j = \phi_0 P_j(\lambda)$ $(j = 0, 1, \cdots)$.

In particular, for fixed k the vector $(\Phi_{0k}(\lambda), \Phi_{1k}(\lambda), \cdots) = P(\lambda)\delta_k \in \Re(P(\lambda))$ $(\delta_k = (\delta_{0k}, \delta_{1k}, \cdots))$, and therefore $\Phi_{jk}(\lambda) = \Phi_{0k}(\lambda)P_j(\lambda)$ $(j = 0, 1, \cdots)$. Furthermore $\overline{\Phi_{0k}(\lambda)} = \Phi_{k0}(\lambda) \in \Re(P(\lambda))$, hence $\overline{\Phi_{0k}(\lambda)} = \overline{\Phi_{00}(\lambda)P_k}(\lambda)$. Since $P_k(\lambda)$ is real $\Phi_{0k}(\lambda) = \Phi_{00}(\lambda)P_k(\lambda)$ $(k = 0, 1, \cdots)$. Substituting this equation in the expression obtained for $\Phi_{jk}(\lambda)$, yields (1.18). The lemma is proved.

If we let $d\sigma(\lambda) = \Phi_{00}(\lambda)\,d\rho(\lambda)$, then since $\Phi_{00}(\lambda) \geq 0$, $d\sigma(\lambda)$ is a nonnegative measure. If we substitute (1.18) in (1.16), we obtain the basic formula

$$E(\Delta)_{jk} = (E(\Delta)\delta_k,\ \delta_j)_0 = \int_\Delta P_j(\lambda) P_k(\lambda)\, d\sigma(\lambda) \qquad (j,\ k = 0,\ 1, \ldots). \tag{1.19}$$

Here, as before, $\delta_k = (\delta_{0k}, \delta_{1k}, \cdots)$ $(k = 0, 1, \ldots)$: we will retain such notation of the "δ-sequence" in all that follows. It follows from (1.19) that

$$\sigma(\Delta) = (E(\Delta)\delta_0,\ \delta_0)_0. \tag{1.20}$$

In this section it is convenient to call $d\sigma(\lambda)$ the spectral measure, rather than $d\rho(\lambda)$. Clearly, each of these two measures is absolutely continuous with respect to the other. It follows from (1.19) that the polynomials $P_j(\lambda)$ form an orthonormal system with respect to $d\sigma(\lambda)$:

$$\int_{-\infty}^{\infty} P_j(\lambda)\, P_k(\lambda)\, d\sigma(\lambda) = \delta_{jk} \quad (j,\ k = 0,\ 1, \ldots). \tag{1.21}$$

We will write down Parseval's equation. To this end, we introduce the Fourier transform for finite sequences u by

$$\tilde{u}(z) = \sum_{j=0}^{\infty} u_j P_j(z) \quad (u \in l_{2,0}([0,\ \infty))). \tag{1.22}$$

Using formula (1.19), we obtain the required equation

$$(E(\Delta)\, u,\ v)_0 = \int_{\Delta} \tilde{u}(\lambda)\, \overline{\tilde{v}(\lambda)}\, d\sigma(\lambda) \quad (u,\ v \in l_{2,0}([0,\ \infty)))\,. \tag{1.23}$$

We note that, as in the case of differential equations, it is essential to distinguish between the Fourier transform introduced here and the analogous concepts on page 338: here $\tilde{u}(\lambda)$ is an analytic function (even a polynomial) of λ. It is obvious from (1.22) and (1.23) that the spectrum in our case is simple. We sum up these results in the form of a theorem.

Theorem 1.6. *Let $E(\Delta)$ be a resolution of the identity (ordinary or generalized) corresponding to the operator* L. *Construct the measure $\sigma(\Delta) = (E(\Delta)\,\delta_0,\ \delta_0)_0$, namely the spectral measure; with respect to this measure, the polynomials $P_j(\lambda)$ $(j = 0, 1, \cdots)$ form an orthonormal system. The eigenfunction expansion corresponding to $E(\Delta)$ is expressed by formulas* (1.23) *and* (1.22).

Thus, from the solutions $P_j(\lambda)$ of the difference equation $(LP(\lambda))_j = \lambda P_j(\lambda)$ $(j = 0, 1, \cdots;\ P_{-1}(\lambda) = 0)$ as eigenfunctions (more precisely, sequences), those solutions are chosen for which λ belongs to the spectrum of the corresponding extension. It follows from (1.17) and (1.18) that for almost all λ with respect to σ, such sequences $(P_0(\lambda),\ P_1(\lambda), \cdots)$ satisfy the growth estimate

$$\sum_{j=0}^{\infty} \frac{|P_j(\lambda)|^2}{p_j} < \infty, \tag{1.24}$$

where $p_j \geq 0$, $\Sigma_{j=0}^{\infty} 1/p_j < \infty$ (the set of λ for which (1.24) holds depends on the choice of p_j). However, the estimate (1.24) can be obtained directly by means of a simple argument, using the orthogonality relations (1.21).

We now give two proofs of Theorem 1.6, which do not make use of the general theory of expansions in eigenvectors. The first of these is based on the following lemma.

Lemma 1.2. *Suppose that* $f(\lambda) = (f_0(\lambda), f_1(\lambda), \cdots)$ $(-\infty < \lambda < \infty)$, *is a sequence of functions of bounded variation such that*

$$\int_{-\infty}^{\infty} |\lambda|^m |df_j(\lambda)| < \infty \quad (m, j = 0, 1, \ldots), \quad (Lf(\lambda))_j = \int_{-\infty}^{\lambda} \mu df_j(\mu)$$

$$(j = 0, 1, \ldots; \; f_{-1}(\lambda) = 0).$$

Then

$$f_j(\lambda) = \int_{-\infty}^{\lambda} P_j(\mu)\, df_0(\mu) \quad (j = 0, 1, \ldots). \tag{1.25}$$

Proof. Form the sequence

$$g_j(\lambda) = \int_{-\infty}^{\lambda} P_j(\mu)\, df_0(\mu) \quad (j = 0, 1, \ldots; \; g_0(\lambda) = f_0(\lambda)).$$

Then

$$(Lg(\lambda))_j = \int_{-\infty}^{\lambda} (LP(\mu))_j df_0(\mu) = \int_{-\infty}^{\lambda} \mu P_j(\mu)\, df_0(\mu)$$

$$= \int_{-\infty}^{\lambda} \mu d\Big(\int_{-\infty}^{\mu} P_j(\nu)\, df_0(\nu)\Big) = \int_{-\infty}^{\lambda} \mu dg_j(\mu) \quad (j = 0, 1, \ldots; \; g_{-1}(\lambda) = 0).$$

Thus the difference $h_j(\lambda) = f_j(\lambda) - g_j(\lambda)$ satisfies the equation

$$(Lh(\lambda))_j = \int_{-\infty}^{\lambda} \mu dh_j(\mu) \quad (j = 0, 1, \ldots)$$

and the conditions $h_{-1}(\lambda) = h_0(\lambda) = 0$; hence in turn we find that $0 = h_1(\lambda) = h_2(\lambda) = \cdots$. Thus $f_j(\lambda) = g_j(\lambda)$ $(j = 0, 1, \cdots)$, and the lemma is proved.

To prove the theorem, it suffices to establish equation (1.19). Note that for fixed k the function $f_j(\lambda) = (E_\lambda \delta_k, \delta_j)_0 = (E_\lambda \delta_k)_j$ satisfies the conditions of the lemma since

$$(Lf(\lambda))_j = (L[E_\lambda \delta_k])_j = (\mathrm{L}E_\lambda \delta_k)_j$$

$$= \int_{-\infty}^{\lambda} \mu d(E_\mu \delta_k)_j = \int_{-\infty}^{\lambda} \mu df_j(\mu) \quad (j = 0, 1, \ldots).$$

Therefore

$$(E_\lambda \delta_k,\ \delta_j)_0 = \int_{-\infty}^{\lambda} P_j(\mu)\, d_\mu (E_\mu \delta_k,\ \delta_0)_0 \quad (j,\ k = 0,\ 1, \ldots). \tag{1.26}$$

Furthermore

$$(E_\mu \delta_k,\ \delta_0)_0 = (\delta_k,\ E_\mu \delta_0)_0 = \overline{(E_\mu \delta_0,\ \delta_k)_0} = \overline{\int_{-\infty}^{\mu} P_k(\nu)\, d_\nu (E_\nu \delta_0,\ \delta_0)_0}$$

$$= \int_{-\infty}^{\mu} P_k(\nu)\, d_\nu (E_\nu \delta_0,\ \delta_0)_0 \quad (k = 0,\ 1, \ldots).$$

On substituting this expression in (1.26), we obtain

$$(E_\lambda \delta_k,\ \delta_j)_0 = \int_{-\infty}^{\lambda} P_j(\mu) P_k(\mu)\, d_\mu (E_\mu \delta_0,\ \delta_0)_0 \quad (j,\ k = 0,\ 1, \ldots).$$

The equation (1.19), and hence the theorem, is established.

We will introduce still another direct proof of Theorem 1.6. We will clarify, first of all, how the operator L acts on the vectors δ_j. For arbitrary $u \in l_{2,0}([0,\ \infty))$ we have

$$(u,\ \mathrm{L}\delta_j)_0 = (\mathrm{L}u,\ \delta_j)_0 = (\mathrm{L}u)_j = (Lu)_j = a_{j-1}u_{j-1} + a_j u_{j+1}$$
$$+ b_j u_j = (u,\ a_{j-1}\delta_{j-1} + a_j \delta_{j+1} + b_j \delta_j)_0.$$

It follows that

$$\mathrm{L}\delta_j = a_{j-1}\delta_{j-1} + a_j \delta_{j+1} + b_j \delta_j \quad (j = 0,\ 1, \ldots), \tag{1.27}$$

where here we must assume that $\delta_{-1} = 0$. Formula (1.27) shows that $\mathrm{L}\delta_j$ is again finite,and, consequently, belongs to $\mathfrak{D}(\mathrm{L})$. Thus, δ_j belongs to the domain of definition of any power L^n $(n = 0, 1, \cdots)$.

The equation (1.27) may be regarded as a recursion relation for the determination of δ_j. So, for $j = 0$ we obtain $a_0 \delta_1 + b_0 \delta_0 = \mathrm{L}\delta_0$ $(\delta_{-1} = 0)$, and hence $\delta_1 = (1/a_0)(\mathrm{L} - b_0 E)\delta_0 = P_1(\mathrm{L})\delta_0$. Next, obviously, we find $\delta_2 = P_2(\mathrm{L})\delta_0$, etc. Thus

$$\delta_j = P_j(\mathrm{L})\delta_0 \quad (j = 0, 1, \cdots). \tag{1.28}$$

Now it is easy to establish (1.19):

$$(E(\Delta)\delta_k, \delta_j)_0 = (E(\Delta) P_k(\mathrm{L})\delta_0,\ P_j(\mathrm{L})\delta_0)_0 = (P_j(\mathrm{L}) E(\Delta) P_k(\mathrm{L})\delta_0, \delta_0)_0$$
$$= \int_{\Delta} P_j(\lambda) P_k(\lambda)\, d(E_\lambda \delta_0, \delta_0)_0 \quad (j, k = 0, 1, \ldots).$$

The theorem is proved.

4. **Study of Fourier transforms.** The polynomials $P_j(\lambda)$ $(j = 0, 1, \cdots)$ are orthonormal and therefore linearly independent, and, in addition, each of these has degree exactly j. This shows that they form a basis in the space of polynomials, i.e. any polynomial in λ can be expressed as a finite linear combination of $P_j(\lambda)$. Thus it follows from (1.22) that the set of Fourier transforms of all finite sequences is the set of all polynomials in λ.

Since $P_j(\lambda) \in L_2((-\infty, \infty), d\sigma(\lambda))$ (see (1.21)), any polynomial belongs to $L_2((-\infty, \infty), d\sigma(\lambda))$; in other words, the spectral measure is always such that

$$\int_{-\infty}^{\infty} |\lambda|^m \, d\sigma(\lambda) < \infty \quad (m = 0, 1, \ldots). \tag{1.29}$$

At the same time, the set of all polynomials is not necessarily dense in $L_2((-\infty, \infty), d\sigma(\lambda))$; criteria for denseness will be given below.

We point out still another important property of the spectral measure: *the set of points of increase of the function $\sigma(\lambda)$ is infinite.* For assume the contrary, and construct a polynomial $P(\lambda)$ which does not vanish identically and has degree sufficiently large so that it vanishes at each point of Λ. Represent $P(\lambda)$ with respect to the system $P_j(\lambda)$: $P(\lambda) = \Sigma_{j=0}^{N} c_j P_j(\lambda)$; then $c_j = \int_{-\infty}^{\infty} P(\lambda) P_j(\lambda)\, d\sigma(\lambda) = 0$ $(j = 0, \cdots, N)$, i.e. $P(\lambda) \equiv 0$, which is absurd. The property just proved may also be formulated in the following way: *if the polynomial $P(\lambda)$ is such that $\int_{-\infty}^{\infty} |P(\lambda)|^2 d\sigma(\lambda) = 0$, then $P(\lambda) \equiv 0$.*

The correspondence $u \to \tilde{u}(\lambda)$ is a one-to-one correspondence between finite sequences and Fourier transforms, certain polynomials in λ understood as elements of the space $L_2((-\infty, \infty), d\sigma(\lambda))$. By virtue of Parseval's equation

$$(u, v)_0 = \int_{-\infty}^{\infty} \tilde{u}(\lambda) \overline{\tilde{v}(\lambda)} \, d\sigma(\lambda) \tag{1.30}$$

(see (1.23), $\hat{\Delta} = (-\infty, \infty)$), this correspondence is an isometry between parts of $l_2([0, \infty))$ and $L_2((-\infty, \infty), d\sigma(\lambda))$. Extending it by continuity, we obtain an isometry between all of $l_2([0, \infty))$ and, in general, that part of $L_2((-\infty, \infty), d\sigma(\lambda))$, coinciding with the closure in this space of the set of all polynomials. We denote this closure by $\widetilde{l_2([0, \infty))}$. Let $u \in l_2([0, \infty))$ correspond to some $\tilde{u}(\lambda) \in \widetilde{l_2([0, \infty))}$; clearly, $\tilde{u}(\lambda)$ is computed from u by the same formula (1.22), only the series is now infinite and converges in the sense of $L_2((-\infty, \infty), d\sigma(\lambda))$. Thus, we have extended the concept of the Fourier transform to the case of arbitrary sequences $u \in l_2([0, \infty))$.

The operator L in $l_2([0, \infty))$ is transformed by the Fourier transform into the operator of multiplication by λ in $L_2((-\infty, \infty), d\sigma(\lambda))$. More precisely, the operator L is always defined on $l_{2,0}([0, \infty))$; its image $\tilde{\mathrm{L}}$ acts on the image of this set (the set of all polynomials) as multiplication by λ: by (1.4)

$$\widetilde{(\mathrm{L}u)}(\lambda) = \sum_{j=0}^{\infty} (Lu)_j P_j(\lambda) = \sum_{j=0}^{\infty} u_j (LP(\lambda))_j = \lambda \sum_{j=0}^{\infty} u_j P_j(\lambda) = \lambda \tilde{u}(\lambda)$$

$$(u \in l_{2,0}([0, \infty)); u_{-1} = 0).$$

Since L is the closure of L restricted to $l_{2,0}([0, \infty))$, it follows that $\tilde{\mathrm{L}}$ is the closure of the operator of multiplication by λ, defined at first on the set of polynomials.

Theorem 1.7. *A necessary and sufficient condition that the set of all polynomials in λ be dense in the space $L_2((-\infty, \infty), d\sigma(\lambda))$ is that $d\sigma(\lambda)$ be generated by an ordinary resolution of the identity. Such spectral measures will be called orthogonal.*

Proof. Let $\sigma(\Delta) = (E(\Delta)\delta_0, \delta_0)_0$, where $E(\Delta)$ is an ordinary resolution of the identity; we will show that the polynomials are dense in $L_2((-\infty, \infty), d\sigma(\lambda))$. Let $A \supseteq \mathrm{L}$ be the selfadjoint extension of the operator L, corresponding to $E(\Delta)$; R_z ($\mathrm{Im}\, z \neq 0$) its resolvent. Let $u \in l_{2,0}([0, \infty))$; since $R_z u \in \mathfrak{D}(A) \subseteq l_2([0, \infty))$, then (for fixed z) there is a $v \in l_{2,0}([0, \infty))$, such that $\|R_z u - v\|_0 < \epsilon$. Transforming via the isometry from the space $l_2([0, \infty))$ to the space $L_2((-\infty, \infty), d\sigma(\lambda))$, we find that for each polynomial $\tilde{u}(\lambda)$ there is a polynomial $\tilde{v}(\lambda)$ such that

$$\left\| \frac{\tilde{u}(\lambda)}{\lambda - z} - \tilde{v}(\lambda) \right\|_{L_2((-\infty, \infty), d\sigma(\lambda))} < \varepsilon.$$

Since ϵ is arbitrary, this means that any function $\tilde{u}(\lambda)/(\lambda - z)$ can be approximated by a polynomial, i.e. $\tilde{u}(\lambda)/(\lambda - z) \in \widetilde{l_2([0, \infty))}$ for any polynomial $\tilde{u}(\lambda)$.

Now it is easy to complete the proof of the sufficiency. Let $h(\lambda) \in L_2((-\infty, \infty), d\sigma(\lambda))$ be orthogonal to $\widetilde{l_2([0, \infty))}$. Then for any nonreal z $\int_{-\infty}^{\infty} (1/(\lambda - z)) h(\lambda)\, d\sigma(\lambda) = 0$ ($u = \delta_0$, $\tilde{u}(\lambda) = 1$). As is well known from the theory of Stieltjes transforms, this means that the measure $\eta(\Delta) = \int_\Delta h(\lambda)\, d\sigma(\lambda) = 0$, i.e. $h(\lambda) = 0$ almost everywhere. Thus $\widetilde{l_2([0, \infty))} = L_2((-\infty, \infty), d\sigma(\lambda))$, as required.

We establish the necessity. Let $\widetilde{l_2([0, \infty))} = L_2((-\infty, \infty), d\sigma(\lambda))$; we must show that $d\sigma(\lambda)$ is generated by some selfadjoint extension A of the operator L in $l_2([0, \infty))$. The operator L is transformed by the isometry of $l_2([0, \infty))$ onto $L_2((-\infty, \infty), d\sigma(\lambda))$ into the operator $\widetilde{\mathrm{L}}$ of multiplication by λ, defined first on polynomials and then extended by taking the closure. Denote by $\widetilde{A}$ the usual operator of multiplication by λ in the space $L_2((-\infty, \infty), d\sigma(\lambda))$; it is selfadjoint, $\widetilde{\mathrm{L}} \subseteq \widetilde{A}$, and $\sigma(\Delta) = (\widetilde{E}(\Delta)1, 1)_{L_2((-\infty, \infty), d\sigma(\lambda))}$, where $\widetilde{E}(\Delta)$ is the resolution of the identity corresponding to $\widetilde{A}$ and coinciding with the operation of multiplication by the characteristic function. Since $L_2((-\infty, \infty), d\sigma(\lambda)) = \widetilde{l_2([0, \infty))}$ then, by means of the inverse isometry, we can pass from $\widetilde{A}$ to an operator A in the space $l_2([0, \infty))$. Obviously this will be a selfadjoint operator which is an extension of L and which generates $d\sigma(\lambda)$. The theorem is proved.

With the help of this theorem, we can prove

Theorem 1.8. *Assume that the spectral measure is such that*

$$\int_{-\infty}^{\infty} \frac{\log \sigma'(\lambda)}{1+\lambda^2} d\lambda > -\infty. \tag{1.31}$$

Then it is generated by a generalized resolution of the identity, i.e. it is nonorthogonal.

Proof. We make use of the following theorem (see, for example, N. I. Ahiezer [2], Chapter 2, Russian p. 112): a necessary and sufficient condition that the linear span of the functions $e^{i\alpha\lambda}$ $(0 \le \alpha < \infty)$ be dense in $L_p((-\infty, \infty), d\sigma(\lambda))$ is that $\int_{-\infty}^{\infty} \log \sigma'(\lambda) \cdot (1+\lambda^2)^{-1} d\lambda = -\infty$ (here $d\sigma(\lambda)$ is an arbitrary nonnegative finite measure on the real axis). Because of this theorem, (1.31) implies that there exists a function $0 \neq h(\lambda) \in L_2((-\infty, \infty), d\sigma(\lambda))$ such that $\int_{-\infty}^{\infty} h(\lambda) e^{i\alpha\lambda} d\sigma(\lambda) = 0$ $(0 \le \alpha < \infty)$. If we differentiate this with respect to α and then put $\alpha = 0$, we find that $\int_{-\infty}^{\infty} h(\lambda) \lambda^j d\sigma(\lambda) = 0$ $(j = 0, 1, \cdots)$. This shows that the polynomials are not dense in $L_2((-\infty, \infty), d\sigma(\lambda))$ and therefore, by Theorem 1.7, that $d\sigma(\lambda)$ is generated by a generalized resolution of the identity. The theorem is proved.

So far we have defined the spectral measure as the measure $\sigma(\Delta) = (E(\Delta)\delta_0, \delta_0)_0$. We will show that it can be described intrinsically.

Theorem 1.9. *Let $d\sigma(\lambda)$ be a nonnegative finite measure on $(-\infty, \infty)$ such* *that the integrals* (1.29) *exist. If Parseval's formula* (1.30) *holds for any finite sequences* u, v *and their Fourier transforms (defined by* (1.22)) *(or equivalently if the orthogonality relations* (1.21) *hold), then* $d\sigma(\lambda)$ *is a spectral measure, i.e. there exists, generally speaking, a generalized resolution of the identity* $E(\Delta)$, *constructed from a selfadjoint extension of* L, *such that* $\sigma(\Delta) = (E(\Delta)\delta_0, \delta_0)_0$.

The proof of the theorem is almost obvious: as before, we use Parseval's formula to establish an isometry between $l_2([0,\infty))$ and $\widetilde{l_2([0,\infty))} \subseteq L_2((-\infty,\infty), d\sigma(\lambda))$, by which the operator L is transformed into the operator $\widetilde{\mathrm{L}}$ of multiplication by λ, equal to the closure of the operator of multiplication by λ on polynomials. Using this isomorphism, we reduce the original problem to the problem of constructing a selfadjoint extension $\widetilde{A}$ of the operator $\widetilde{\mathrm{L}}$ such that $\sigma(\Delta) = (\widetilde{E}(\Delta)1, 1)_{L_2((-\infty,\infty), d\sigma(\lambda))}$, where $\widetilde{E}(\Delta)$ is the resolution of the identity for $\widetilde{A}$. However, the usual selfadjoint operator of multiplication by λ in $L_2((-\infty,\infty), d\sigma(\lambda))$ may be taken for $\widetilde{A}$. If $\widetilde{l_2([0,\infty))} = L_2((-\infty,\infty), d\sigma(\lambda))$, then the extension of L will act in $l_2([0,\infty))$, while for $\widetilde{l_2([0,\infty))} \subset L_2((-\infty,\infty), d\sigma(\lambda))$ the extension will act in a larger space. The theorem is proved.

Since we can now define spectral measure by means of Parseval's equation (1.30), independently of the theory of operators, then following corollary of the theorem is meaningful.

Corollary. *There exists a unique spectral measure for the difference expression if and only if the operator* L *is selfadjoint.*

In fact, by equation (1.23), we have a one-to-one correspondence between spectral measures and generalized resolutions of the identity.

In what follows, let us agree to say that the difference expression (or Jacobi matrix) is determinate or not, if the operator L is selfadjoint or not.

Fix the difference expression L and consider the set Σ of all spectral measures corresponding to this expression. In the indeterminate case Σ consists of more than one point. It is not difficult to see that Σ is convex, i.e. that if $\sigma_1, \sigma_2 \in \Sigma$, then $\sigma(\Delta) = \mu_1\sigma_1(\Delta) + \mu_2\sigma_2(\Delta)$ $(\mu_1 + \mu_2 = 1;\ \mu_1, \mu_2 \geq 0)$ also belongs to Σ. In fact, if σ_1 and σ_2 satisfy Parseval's equation (1.30), then so does σ. Extreme points of the set Σ, i.e. measures $\sigma \in \Sigma$ which cannot be expressed in the form $\sigma(\Delta) = \mu_1\sigma_1(\Delta) + \mu_2\sigma_2(\Delta)$ $(\sigma_1, \sigma_2 \in \Sigma;\ \mu_1 + \mu_2 = 1;\ \mu_1, \mu_2 > 0)$ are called extreme spectral measures. If the expression L under consideration is determinate, then the unique spectral measure is extreme. In subsection 9 we will show that each orthogonal spectral measure is extreme (however these are not all of the extreme spectral measures).

Theorem 1.10. *A necessary and sufficient condition that the set of all polynomials be dense in the space* $L_1((-\infty, \infty), d\sigma(\lambda))$ *is that* $d\sigma(\lambda)$ *be an extreme spectral measure.*

First we establish the following general lemma.

Lemma 1.3. *Two nonnegative measures* $d\sigma_1(\lambda)$ *and* $d\sigma_2(\lambda)$ *on the real line, which satisfy the condition* (1.29), *belong to the same class* Σ *if and only if for any polynomial* $P(\lambda)$

$$\int_{-\infty}^{\infty} P(\lambda)\, d\sigma_1(\lambda) = \int_{-\infty}^{\infty} P(\lambda)\, d\sigma_2(\lambda). \tag{1.32}$$

Proof. If (1.32) holds and if Parseval's equation (1.30) holds for $d\sigma_1(\lambda)$, then it holds for $d\sigma_2(\lambda)$ since $\widetilde{u}(\lambda)\overline{\widetilde{v}(\lambda)}$ $(u, v \in l_{2,0}([0, \infty)))$ is a polynomial. Conversely, suppose that $d\sigma_1(\lambda)$ and $d\sigma_2(\lambda)$ satisfy (1.30) with the same L. Then the $P_j(\lambda)$ are orthonormal in each of the spaces $L_2((-\infty, \infty), d\sigma_1(\lambda))$ and $L_2((-\infty, \infty), d\sigma_2(\lambda))$. Decomposing $P(\lambda)$ with respect to $P_j(\lambda)$, we obtain

$$\int_{-\infty}^{\infty} P(\lambda)\, d\sigma_1(\lambda) = \int_{-\infty}^{\infty} \left(\sum_{j=0}^{N} c_j P_j(\lambda) \right) d\sigma_1(\lambda) = c_0 = \int_{-\infty}^{\infty} P(\lambda)\, d\sigma_2(\lambda).$$

The lemma is proved.

Proof of the theorem. We will show first of all that if $d\sigma(\lambda)$ is not extreme, the set of polynomials is not dense in $L_1((-\infty, \infty), d\sigma(\lambda))$. Indeed, let $\sigma(\Delta) = \mu_1\sigma_1(\Delta) + \mu_2\sigma_2(\Delta)$ $(\sigma_1, \sigma_2 \in \Sigma;\ \mu_1 + \mu_2 = 1;\ \mu_1, \mu_2 > 0)$. Since $\sigma_j(\Delta) \le (1/\mu_j)\sigma(\Delta)$, $d\sigma_j(\lambda)$ is absolutely continuous with respect to $d\sigma(\lambda)$ and $\phi_j(\lambda) = d\sigma_j(\lambda)/d\sigma(\lambda) \le \mu_j$ $(j = 1, 2)$. By Lemma 1.3, for any polynomial $P(\lambda)$

$$\int_{-\infty}^{\infty} P(\lambda)\varphi_1(\lambda)\, d\sigma(\lambda) = \int_{-\infty}^{\infty} P(\lambda)\, d\sigma_1(\lambda) = \int_{-\infty}^{\infty} P(\lambda)\, d\sigma_2(\lambda) = \int_{-\infty}^{\infty} P(\lambda)\varphi_2(\lambda)\, d\sigma(\lambda),$$

i.e. the bounded function $\psi(\lambda) = \phi_1(\lambda) - \phi_2(\lambda)$ is not equal to zero almost everywhere with respect to σ and is such that $\int_{-\infty}^{\infty} P(\lambda)\psi(\lambda)\, d\sigma(\lambda) = 0$ for any $P(\lambda)$. This means that there exists a nonzero functional on $L_1((-\infty, \infty), d\sigma(\lambda))$ which annihilates all polynomials, i.e. the set of all polynomials is not dense in $L_1((-\infty, \infty), d\sigma(\lambda))$.

Conversely, if the polynomials are not dense in $L_1((-\infty, \infty), d\sigma(\lambda))$, then there exists a bounded function $\psi(\lambda)$, which is not equal to zero σ-almost everywhere, such that $\int_{-\infty}^{\infty} P(\lambda)\psi(\lambda)\,d\sigma(\lambda) = 0$ for any polynomial $P(\lambda)$. Construct nonnegative measures $d\sigma_1(\lambda) = (1 + \psi(\lambda))\,d\sigma(\lambda)$, $d\sigma_2(\lambda) = (1 - \psi(\lambda))\,d\sigma(\lambda)$; they obviously satisfy (1.29) and are such that

$$\int_{-\infty}^{\infty} P(\lambda)\,d\sigma(\lambda) = \int_{-\infty}^{\infty} P(\lambda)\,d\sigma_1(\lambda) = \int_{-\infty}^{\infty} P(\lambda)\,d\sigma_2(\lambda)$$

for any $P(\lambda)$. By Lemma 1.3, $\sigma_1, \sigma_2 \in \Sigma$, where Σ is the convex set of measures corresponding to L. Moreover $\sigma_1 \neq \sigma_2$ and $\sigma = \sigma_1/2 + \sigma_2/2$, i.e. σ is not an extreme spectral measure. The theorem is proved.

5. **The inverse problem of spectral analysis.** So far we have considered a straightforward problem: for a given expression L we constructed a spectral decomposition. However, it is natural to consider the inverse problem: whether we can recover L from the spectral data. We will show that such a recovery is possible, when the spectral data consists of a spectral measure. And even more so, it will be shown that the set of all possible spectral measures is easily described.

We need to express the coefficients of the difference expression in terms of the polynomials $P_j(\lambda)$. Since $a_{j-1}P_{j-1}(\lambda) + a_j P_{j+1}(\lambda) + b_j P_j(\lambda) = \lambda P_j(\lambda)$ $(j = 0, 1, \cdots; P_{-1}(\lambda) = 0)$, then taking the scalar product in $L_2((-\infty, \infty), d\sigma(\lambda))$ of each side of this equation with $P_k(\lambda)$ and using the orthogonality relations (1.21), we obtain

$$a_j = \int_{-\infty}^{\infty} \lambda P_j(\lambda) P_{j+1}(\lambda)\,d\sigma(\lambda),\ b_j = \int_{-\infty}^{\infty} \lambda P_j^2(\lambda)\,d\sigma(\lambda) \qquad (1.33)$$
$$(j = 0, 1, \ldots).$$

Suppose now that $d\sigma(\lambda)$ is a given nonnegative measure on $(-\infty, \infty)$ such that the integrals (1.29) converge, $\sigma((-\infty, \infty)) = 1$, and $\sigma(\lambda)$ has an infinite number of points of increase. We will show that it is a spectral measure of some difference expression L. To this end consider the space $L_2((-\infty, \infty), d\sigma(\lambda))$ and in it the system of functions $1, \lambda, \lambda^2, \cdots$. Orthogonalize this sequence by the usual procedure: take $P_0(\lambda) \equiv 1$; among the vectors $c_1 \cdot 1 + c_2\lambda$ we choose the unit vector orthogonal to the subspace spanned by 1; among the vectors $c_1 \cdot 1 + c_2\lambda + c_3\lambda^2$ we choose the unit vector orthogonal to the subspace spanned by 1 and λ, etc. This process of choosing unit vectors is not unique, but if we restrict ourselves to real scalars c_j and require that for each vector, which is a polynomial of specific degree, the leading coefficient be positive, then it is obviously unique. The process will be infinite, since if a polynomial is zero in the norm of

$L_2((-\infty, \infty), d\sigma(\lambda))$, it is identically zero because of the infinite number of points of increase of $\sigma(\lambda)$. Thus in the end we obtain an orthonormal sequence of real polynomials $P_0(\lambda) = 1$, $P_1(\lambda), \cdots$, where each $P_j(\lambda)$ has degree j and its leading coefficient is positive.

Define numbers a_j, b_j by means of the equations (1.33) for the polynomials $P_j(\lambda)$. It is easy to see that $a_j > 0$ $(j = 0, 1, \cdots)$. In fact, $\lambda P_j(\lambda)$ is a polynomial of degree $j+1$ whose leading coefficient is positive, and therefore in the representation $\lambda P_j(\lambda) = c_{j+1}P_{j+1}(\lambda) + \cdots + c_0 P_0(\lambda)$, $c_{j+1} > 0$, but obviously, $c_{j+1} = a_j$. Thus the numbers a_j, b_j $(j = 0, 1, \cdots)$ may be taken as the coefficients of some difference expression L.

We will show that the $P_j(\lambda)$ are polynomials of the first kind for the expression L just constructed, i.e. we will show that $\lambda P_j(\lambda) = a_{j-1}P_{j-1}(\lambda) + a_j P_{j+1}(\lambda) + b_j P_j(\lambda)$ $(j = 0, 1, \cdots; P_{-1}(\lambda) = 0, P_0(\lambda) = 1)$. For the proof, it is sufficient to show that in the decomposition of the polynomial $\lambda P_j(\lambda)$ of degree $j+1$ with respect to $P_0(\lambda), \cdots, P_{j+1}(\lambda)$, the coefficients of $P_0(\lambda), \cdots, P_{j-2}(\lambda)$ are zero, i.e. $\int_{-\infty}^{\infty} \lambda P_j(\lambda) P_k(\lambda)\, d\sigma(\lambda) = 0$ for $0 \le k \le j-2$. But $\lambda P_k(\lambda)$ is a polynomial of degree at most $j-1$, so $P_j(\lambda)$ is orthogonal to it, as required.

Thus the measure $d\sigma(\lambda)$ has the property that the polynomials of the first kind corresponding to the expression L are orthonormal with respect to it. Hence Parseval's equation (1.30) follows for finite u and v, i.e. $d\sigma(\lambda)$ is a spectral measure for L. Thus we have proved

Theorem 1.11. *Let $d\sigma(\lambda)$ be a nonnegative measure on the real line $(-\infty, \infty)$, for which $\sigma(\lambda)$ has an infinite number of points of increase, and such that*

$$\int_{-\infty}^{\infty} d\sigma(\lambda) = 1, \quad \int_{-\infty}^{\infty} |\lambda|^n \, d\sigma(\lambda) < \infty \qquad (n = 1, 2, \ldots). \tag{1.34}$$

Then this measure is necessarily a spectral measure for some difference expression. The coefficients of this expression are uniquely determined by $d\sigma(\lambda)$ by formula (1.33), where $P_0(\lambda)$, $P_1(\lambda), \cdots$ is an orthonormal system of polynomials constructed by orthogonalization in the space $L_2((-\infty, \infty), d\sigma(\lambda))$ of the system of powers $1, \lambda, \lambda^2, \cdots$.

This theorem shows that the results of this section can be interpreted as certain facts concerning orthonormal polynomials, constructed with respect to the measure $d\sigma(\lambda)$ just described.

6. Polynomials of the second kind. Resolvents. Consider the difference equation $(Lu)_j = zu_j$ $(j = 1, 2, \cdots)$ with initial data $u_0 = 0$, $u_1 = 1/a_0$. Let $(Q_1(z) = 1/a_0, Q_2(z), \cdots)$ be a solution of this Cauchy problem: it is easy to see that $Q_j(z)$ is a polynomial of degree $j - 1$ with real coefficients and whose leading coefficient is positive. The polynomials $Q_j(z)$ $(j = 0, 1, \cdots; Q_0(z) = 0)$ are called polynomials of the second kind, generated by L. Clearly, $P(z) = (P_1(z), P_2(z), \cdots)$ and $Q(z) = (Q_1(z), Q_2(z), \cdots)$ form a linearly independent system of solutions of the equation $(Lu)_j = zu_j$ $(j = 1, 2, \cdots)$.

The polynomials $Q_j(z)$ and $P_j(z)$ are connected by an interesting relation. We show that

$$Q_j(z) = \int_{-\infty}^{\infty} \frac{P_j(\lambda) - P_j(z)}{\lambda - z}\, d\sigma(\lambda) \qquad (j = 0, 1, \dots). \tag{1.35}$$

In fact, the sequence $u_j = \int_{-\infty}^{\infty} (P_j(\lambda) - P_j(z))(\lambda - z)^{-1} d\sigma(\lambda)$ satisfies the equation

$$(Lu)_j = \int_{-\infty}^{\infty} \frac{(LP(\lambda))_j - (LP(z))_j}{\lambda - z}\, d\sigma(\lambda) = z \int_{-\infty}^{\infty} \frac{P_j(\lambda) - P_j(z)}{\lambda - z}\, d\sigma(\lambda)$$

$$+ \int_{-\infty}^{\infty} P_j(\lambda)\, d\sigma(\lambda) = zu_j \qquad (j = 1, 2, \dots)$$

(the last integral vanishes by (1.21)). In addition, $u_0 = 0$ and

$$u_1 = \int_{-\infty}^{\infty} \left(\frac{1}{a_0}(\lambda - b_0) - \frac{1}{a_0}(z - b_0) \right) (\lambda - z)^{-1}\, d\sigma(\lambda) = \frac{1}{a_0};$$

therefore $u_j = Q_j(z)$ $(j = 1, 2, \cdots)$. The relation (1.35) is established.

Observe that the polynomials $Q_j(\lambda)$ are also orthogonal with respect to some new measure $d\hat{\sigma}(\lambda)$ on $(-\infty, \infty)$. In fact, $a_0 Q_j(z)$ may be regarded as a polynomial of the first kind of the shifted difference expression $\hat{L}$ with coefficients $\hat{a}_j = a_{j+1}$, $\hat{b}_j = b_{j+1}$ $(j = -1, 0, \cdots)$; therefore a spectral measure corresponding to $\hat{L}$ can be taken for $d\hat{\sigma}(\lambda)$.

We need the following general lemma.

Lemma 1.4. *Let $R_0(\lambda), R_1(\lambda), \cdots$ be an arbitrary sequence of real polynomials of degrees $0, 1, \cdots$, which are orthogonal on $(-\infty, \infty)$ with respect to some* *measure $d\sigma(\lambda)$ which satisfies the requirements of Theorem* 1.11. *Then all the zeros of these polynomials are real and distinct.*

Proof. Suppose that some polynomial $R_n(\lambda)$ has less than n real, distinct zeros. Let $\lambda_1 < \cdots < \lambda_m$ be these real zeros for which $R_n(\lambda)$ changes sign under passage through a zero. Construct a polynomial $P(\lambda)$ of degree m with zeros $\lambda_1, \cdots, \lambda_m$, such that $\operatorname{sign}(P(\lambda)) = \operatorname{sign}(R_n(\lambda))$ $(-\infty < \lambda < \infty)$. Then, on the one hand, $P(\lambda)$ can be represented in the form of a linear combination $\Sigma_{j=0}^m c_j R_j(\lambda)$ and therefore $\int_{-\infty}^{\infty} P(\lambda) R_n(\lambda)\, d\sigma(\lambda) = 0$, but on the other, this equality is impossible by the construction of $P(\lambda)$. We have arrived at a contradiction. This proves the lemma.

Corollary. *The polynomial $R_j(z)$ satisfies the inequality*

$$|R_j(x+iy')| \leqslant |R_j(x+iy'')|, \ |y'| \leqslant |y''| \qquad (j = 0, 1, \ldots). \tag{1.36}$$

This inequality follows immediately from the representation $R_j(z) = a\Pi_{\alpha=1}^j (z - \lambda_\alpha)$, where λ_α are the real zeros of the polynomial $R_j(z)$.

In particular, the zeros of polynomials of the first and second kinds are all real; the inequalities (1.36) hold for these polynomials.

We turn to the examination of resolvents connected with L. Let A be a self-adjoint extension of the operator L, in general, acting in a larger space $\widetilde{H}_0$ than $l_2([0, \infty))$. Denote by $\widetilde{E}_\lambda$ and $\widetilde{R}_z$ the corresponding resolution of the identity and resolvent of the operator A in $\widetilde{H}_0$, and by E_λ and R_z the generalized resolution of the identity and resolvent. If P is the projection operator of $\widetilde{H}_0$ onto $l_2([0, \infty))$, then $E_\lambda = P\widetilde{E}_\lambda P$ and $R_z = P\widetilde{R}_z P$. Since $R_z = \int_{-\infty}^{\infty} (\lambda - z)^{-1} dE_\lambda$, then in view of (1.19) the matrix of the operator R_z in the basis $\delta_0, \delta_1, \cdots$ has the form

$$R_{z;jk} = (R_z\delta_k, \delta_j)_0 = \int_{-\infty}^{\infty} \frac{P_j(\lambda) P_k(\lambda)}{\lambda - z}\, d\sigma(\lambda) \qquad (j, k = 0, 1, \ldots). \tag{1.37}$$

The function

$$m(z) = R_{z;00} = (R_z\delta_0, \delta_0)_0 = \int_{-\infty}^{\infty} \frac{d\sigma(\lambda)}{\lambda - z}, \tag{1.38}$$

the Stieltjes transform of the spectral measure, plays an essential part in what follows. The function is holomorphic outside the spectrum of A. As is well known, $\sigma(\Delta)$ is uniquely regenerated by the inversion formula for $m(z)$. We deduce an important relation in the case when $d\sigma(\lambda)$ is orthogonal, i.e. is constructed with respect to an ordinary resolution of the identity. By (1.37) and (1.35),

$$(R_z\delta_0)_j = \int_{-\infty}^{\infty} \frac{P_j(\lambda)}{\lambda - z}\, d\sigma(\lambda) = \int_{-\infty}^{\infty} \frac{P_j(\lambda) - P_j(z)}{\lambda - z}\, d\sigma(\lambda)$$

$$+ P_j(z) \int_{-\infty}^{\infty} \frac{d\sigma(\lambda)}{\lambda - z} = Q_j(z) + m(z) P_j(z) \qquad (j = 0, 1, \ldots). \tag{1.39}$$

Since R_z is an ordinary resolvent here, Hilbert's identity $R_\mu - R_\lambda = (\mu - \lambda) R_\mu R_\lambda$ is valid. By this and (1.39) we find that

$$\frac{\overline{m(\zeta)} - m(z)}{\bar{\zeta} - z} = \left(\frac{R_{\bar{\zeta}} - R_z}{\bar{\zeta} - z}\, \delta_0, \delta_0\right)_0 = (R_{\bar{\zeta}} R_z \delta_0, \delta_0)_0 = (R_\zeta^* R_z \delta_0, \delta_0)_0$$

$$= (R_z\delta_0, R_\zeta\delta_0)_0 = \sum_{j=0}^{\infty} (R_z\delta_0)_j \overline{(R_\zeta\delta_0)_j}$$

$$= \sum_{j=0}^{\infty} (Q_j(z) + m(z) P_j(z)) \overline{(Q_j(\zeta) + m(\zeta) P_j(\zeta))}.$$

Thus, for any regular ζ and z

$$\frac{\overline{m(\zeta)} - m(z)}{\bar{\zeta} - z} = \sum_{j=0}^{\infty} (Q_j(z) + m(z) P_j(z)) \overline{(Q_j(\zeta) + m(\zeta) P_j(\zeta))} \qquad (\bar{\zeta} \neq z). \tag{1.40}$$

On setting $\zeta = z$ here, we obtain

$$\frac{\overline{m(z)} - m(z)}{\bar{z} - z} = \sum_{j=0}^{\infty} |Q_j(z) + m(z) P_j(z)|^2 \qquad (\operatorname{Im} z \neq 0). \tag{1.41}$$

Let us see how a relation of the type (1.41) appears in the case when $d\sigma(\lambda)$ is constructed with respect to a generalized resolution of the identity. Now we use Hilbert's identity $\widetilde{R}_\mu - \widetilde{R}_\lambda = (\mu - \lambda)\widetilde{R}_\mu \widetilde{R}_\lambda$ and set $\zeta = z$. Then

$$\frac{\overline{m(z)} - m(z)}{\bar{z} - z} = \left(\frac{R_{\bar{z}} - R_z}{\bar{z} - z}\, \delta_0, \delta_0\right)_0 = \left(\frac{\widetilde{R}_{\bar{z}} - \widetilde{R}_z}{\bar{z} - z}\, \delta_0, \delta_0\right)_0$$

$$= (\widetilde{R}_{\bar{z}} \widetilde{R}_z \delta_0, \delta_0)_0 = (\widetilde{R}_z^* \widetilde{R}_z \delta_0, \delta_0)_{\widetilde{H}_0} = (\widetilde{R}_z\delta_0, \widetilde{R}_z\delta_0)_{\widetilde{H}_0} \geqslant (P\widetilde{R}_z\delta_0, P\widetilde{R}_z\delta_0)_0$$

$$= (R_z\delta_0, R_z\delta_0)_0 = \sum_{j=0}^{\infty} |Q_j(z) + m(z) P_j(z)|^2.$$

Thus, *if* $d\sigma(\lambda)$ *is orthogonal, then the relation* (1.41) *holds. If* $d\sigma(\lambda)$ *is not orthogonal, then* (1.41) *is valid with the equal sign replaced by* $\geq$.

The relation (1.41) sometimes makes it possible to find $m(z)$, and hence $d\sigma(\lambda)$, for given L. In fact, suppose we have the determinate case; suppose that we have found a function $f(z)$ ($\operatorname{Im} z \neq 0$) such that the sequence $Q_j(z) + f(z)P_j(z) \in l_2([0, \infty))$ for each nonreal z. Then $m(z) = f(z)$. Indeed, suppose $m(z_0) \neq f(z_0)$. Since $Q_j(z_0) + m(z_0)P_j(z_0) \in l_2([0, \infty))$ by (1.41), and since $Q_j(z_0) + f(z_0)P_j(z_0) \in l_2([0, \infty))$, then the difference of these sequences $(m(z_0) - f(z_0))P_j(z_0) \in l_2([0, \infty))$, i.e. $P_j(z_0) \in l_2([0, \infty))$, and this is impossible because of the assumption that L is determinate. A similar result for the problem on the whole axis will be given in §3.2.

7. **The indeterminate case. Description of orthogonal spectral measures.** We will assume that the expression L is indeterminate. It turns out that the set of all spectral measures can be described; now we will describe only those measures mentioned in the subsection heading. As a preliminary, we establish some auxiliary facts.

As has been already mentioned, the series $\sum_{j=0}^{\infty} |P_j(z)|^2$ converges for nonreal z. Actually, a stronger result is valid.

Lemma 1.5. *In the indeterminate case the series* $\sum_{j=0}^{\infty} |P_j(z)|^2$ *and* $\sum_{j=0}^{\infty} |Q_j(z)|^2$ *converge for any* z; *the convergence is uniform on each bounded region in the complex plane.*

Proof. Consider $m(z) = \int_{-\infty}^{\infty} (\lambda - z)^{-1} d\sigma(\lambda)$, corresponding to an ordinary resolution of the identity; $m(z)$ satisfies (1.41), Since the left-hand side of this equation is continuous everywhere outside the real axis $(-\infty, \infty)$, by the theorem of Dini the series $\sum_{j=0}^{\infty} |Q_j(z) + m(z)P_j(z)|^2$ converges uniformly in each bounded region which is at a positive distance from $(-\infty, \infty)$.

Let $d\sigma_1(\lambda)$ be a spectral measure for L which is distinct from $d\sigma(\lambda)$, and let $m_1(z)$ be the function corresponding to it in (1.38). Since $m_1(z) \not\equiv m(z)$, the equality $m_1(z) = m(z)$ is possible only on a sequence $z_1, z_2, \cdots$ of points, the limit points of which can lie only on the real axis. We will show that in each bounded region G in the complex plane at a positive distance from $(-\infty, \infty)$ and the points z_j, the series $\sum_{j=0}^{\infty} |P_j(z)|^2$ converges uniformly.

In fact, both series $\sum_{j=0}^{\infty} |Q_j(z) + m(z)P_j(z)|^2$ and $\sum_{j=0}^{\infty} |Q_j(z) + m_1(z)P_j(z)|^2$ converge uniformly in G, but then

$$|m(z) - m_1(z)|^2 \sum_{j=0}^{\infty} |P_j(z)|^2 = \sum_{j=0}^{\infty} |(Q_j(z) + m(z)P_j(z)) - (Q_j(z) + m_1(z)P_j(z))|^2,$$

also converges uniformly in G, and the required result follows.

Since by the inequality (1.36) the series $\sum_{j=0}^{\infty} |P_j(x+iy')|^2$ is majorized by the series $\sum_{j=0}^{\infty} |P_j(x+iy'')|^2$ where $|y''| \geq |y'|$, it follows from the uniform convergence of the series $\sum_{j=0}^{\infty} |P_j(z)|^2$ in the region G that this series converges uniformly in any bounded region, as asserted in the lemma. Finally, it follows from the uniform convergence of the series $\sum_{j=0}^{\infty} |Q_j(z) + m(z)P_j(z)|^2$ and $\sum_{j=0}^{\infty} |P_j(z)|^2$ in bounded regions at a positive distance from $(-\infty, \infty)$, that the series $\sum_{j=0}^{\infty} |Q_j(z)|^2$ converges in such regions. Taking (1.36) into account, we obtain such convergence of this series in the domains asserted in the lemma. The lemma is proved.

Fix z not real and consider the points $m(z)$ for all possible $d\sigma(\lambda)$ corresponding to ordinary resolutions of the identity. It turns out that as in the case of the Sturm-Liouville equation, all of these points lie on some circle, the so-called Weyl-Hamburger circle. For the proof, recall that the equation

$$a|w|^2 + b\bar{w} + \bar{b}w + c = 0 \quad (a > 0, \ \operatorname{Im} c = 0, \ |b|^2 - ac > 0) \tag{1.42}$$

for the complex variable w represents a circle, with center O and radius R given by the formulas

$$O = -\frac{b}{a}, \quad R^2 = \frac{1}{a^2}(|b|^2 - ac). \tag{1.43}$$

In view of Lemma 1.5, by simple manipulations (1.41) can be rewritten in the form

$$\left(\sum_{j=0}^{\infty} |P_j(z)|^2\right)|m(z)|^2 + \overline{\left(\frac{1}{z-\bar{z}} + \sum_{j=0}^{\infty} \overline{P_j(z)}\,Q_j(z)\right)}\,\overline{m(z)}$$

$$+ \left(\frac{1}{z-\bar{z}} + \sum_{j=0}^{\infty} \overline{P_j(z)}\,Q_j(z)\right) m(z) + \sum_{j=0}^{\infty} |Q_j(z)|^2 = 0. \tag{1.44}$$

This is a relation of the type (1.42) (note that the inequality $|b|^2 - ac > 0$ holds automatically if it is known that there exists a point w which satisfies equation (1.42)). Thus, all the values $m(z)$ actually lie on some circle. We now show that they fill the whole circle.

Consider the Cayley transform of the operator L: $U_z = (\mathrm{L} - \bar{z}E)(\mathrm{L} - zE)^{-1}$. This operator is isometric and maps $\Re(\mathrm{L} - zE)$ onto all of $\Re(\mathrm{L} - \bar{z}E)$. Construct an isometric operator X mapping all of the deficiency subspace N_z onto all of $N_{\bar{z}}$. The orthogonal sum $V_z = U_z \oplus X$ defines, by the Cayley transform, a self-adjoint extension A of the operator L; by taking all possible X we obtain all such extensions. Recall that the deficiency subspace N_z is one-dimensional and is spanned by the vector $(P_0(\bar{z}), P_1(\bar{z}), \cdots)$.

Decompose the vector δ_0 with respect to the orthogonal components $\Re(\mathrm{L} - zE)$ and N_z:

$$\delta_0 = e_z + \iota_z \quad (e_z \in \Re(\mathrm{L} - zE), \ \iota_z \in N_z). \tag{1.45}$$

We compute $\|i_z\|_0$. If ρ denotes distance, we can write $\|i_z\|_0^2 = \rho^2(\delta_0, \Re(\mathrm{L} - zE)) = \rho^2(\delta_0, (L - zE)\, l_{2,0}([0, \infty)))$. The last equation is written on the basis that the set $(L - zE)\, l_{2,0}([0, \infty))$ is dense in $\Re(\mathrm{L} - zE)$. We now pass to the Fourier transform. Since $\tilde{\delta}_0 = 1$, and $\widetilde{(L - zE)\, l_{2,0}([0, \infty))}$ consists of all polynomials of the form $(\lambda - z) P(\lambda)$, where $P(\lambda)$ is an arbitrary polynomial, we have

$$\begin{aligned} \|i_z\|_0^2 &= \varrho^2(\delta_0, (L - zE)\, l_{2,0}([0, \infty))) = \varrho^2(\tilde{\delta}_0, \widetilde{(L - zE)\, l_{2,0}([0, \infty))}) \\ &= \varrho^2_{P(z)=0}(1, P(\lambda)) = \inf_{P(z)=0} \| 1 - P(\lambda) \|^2_{L_2((-\infty,\infty), d\sigma(\lambda))} \\ &= \inf_{P(z)=1} \| P(\lambda) \|^2_{L((-\infty,\infty) d\sigma(\lambda))}. \end{aligned}$$

We compute the last inf. An arbitrary polynomial $P(\lambda)$ with the property $P(z) = 1$ has the form

$$P(\lambda) = \sum_{j=0}^{\infty} c_j P_j(\lambda) \left(\sum_{j=0}^{\infty} c_j P_j(z) \right)^{-1},$$

where the sequence of coefficients c_j is finite. Therefore, by means of the Cauchy-Bunjakovskiĭ inequality, we obtain

$$\| P(\lambda) \|^2_{L_2((-\infty,\infty), d\sigma(\lambda))}$$

$$= \int_{-\infty}^{\infty} \left| \frac{\sum_{j=0}^{\infty} c_j P_j(\lambda)}{\sum_{j=0}^{\infty} c_j P_j(z)} \right|^2 d\sigma(\lambda) = \frac{\sum_{j=0}^{\infty} |c_j|^2}{\left| \sum_{j=0}^{\infty} c_j P_j(z) \right|^2} \geqslant \frac{1}{\sum_{j=0}^{\infty} |P_j(z)|^2}.$$

In other words, if we set $c_j = \overline{P_j(z)}$ $(j = 0, \cdots, N)$, $c_j = 0$ $(j \geq N+1)$, we have $\|P(\lambda)\|^2_{L_2((-\infty,\infty), d\sigma(\lambda))} = (\Sigma_{j=0}^N |P_j(z)|^2)^{-1}$. Thus

$$\| i_z \|_0^2 = \inf_{P(z)=1} \| P(\lambda) \|^2_{L_2((-\infty,\infty),d\sigma(\lambda))} = \frac{1}{\sum_{i=0}^{\infty} |P_i(z)|^2} \tag{1.46}$$

In particular, (1.46) shows that $\|i_z\|_0 \neq 0$. If $\delta_0 = l_{\bar{z}} + i_{\bar{z}}$ is the decomposi- with respect to the representation $l_2([0, \infty)) = \Re(\mathrm{L} - \bar{z}E) \oplus N_{\bar{z}}$, then $\|i_{\bar{z}}\|_0 = \|i_z\|_0$.

Let A^0 be a fixed selfadjoint extension of the operator L in $l_2([0, \infty))$, and let A be an arbitrary extension of the same type. Denote their Cayley transforms by V_z^0 and V_z respectively. Since V_z^0 and V_z act equally on $\Re(\mathrm{L} - zE)$, for some $\phi \in [0, 2\pi)$,

$$V_z\delta_0 = V_z e_z + V_z i_z = V_z^0 e_z + e^{i\varphi} V_z^0 i_z;$$

$$(V_z\delta_0, \delta_0)_0 = (V_z^0 e_z + e^{i\varphi} V_z^0 i_z, e_{\bar{z}} + i_{\bar{z}})_0 = (V_z^0 e_z, e_{\bar{z}})_0 + e^{i\varphi} (V_z^0 i_z, i_{\bar{z}})_0. \tag{1.47}$$

We now make a special choice of an isometric operator, which maps N_z onto $N_{\bar{z}}$ and defines the operator V_z^0: set $V_z^0 i_z = i_{\bar{z}}$. Then (1.47) takes the form $(V_z \delta_0, \delta_0)_0 = (V_z^0 e_z, e_{\bar{z}})_0 + e^{i\phi} \|i_{\bar{z}}\|_0^2 = (V_z^0 e_z, e_{\bar{z}})_0 + e^{i\phi} \|i_z\|_0^2$. But $V_z = (A - \bar{z}E)(A - zE)^{-1} = E + (z - \bar{z}) R_z$; therefore $(V_z \delta_0, \delta_0)_0 = 1 + (z - \bar{z}) m(z)$. Thus $1 + (z - \bar{z}) m(z) = (V_z^0 e_z, e_{\bar{z}})_0 + e^{i\phi} \|i_z\|_0^2$, whence

$$m(z) = \frac{1}{z - \bar{z}} [(V_z^0 e_z, e_{\bar{z}})_0 - 1 + e^{i\varphi} \| i_z \|_0^2]. \tag{1.48}$$

By letting ϕ vary in $[0, 2\pi)$, we obtain all possible isometric operators mapping N_z onto $N_{\bar{z}}$; the operator A then runs through all the selfadjoint extensions of L in $l_2([0, \infty))$. According to (1.48) the points $m(z)$ will, in this connection, describe a circle, which, obviously, coincides with the circle (1.44). Its center and radius can be calculated by formula (1.43); however, the expression for the radius is obtained more conveniently from (1.48) and (1.46):

$$R = \frac{\| i_z \|_0^2}{|z - \bar{z}|} = \left(|z - \bar{z}| \sum_{i=0}^{\infty} |P_i(z)|^2 \right)^{-1}.$$

We have arrived at the first part of the following theorem.

Theorem. 1.12. *Assume that the expression L is indeterminate. For fixed nonreal z consider the point* $m(z) = \int_{-\infty}^{\infty}(1/(\lambda - z))\, d\sigma(\lambda)$, *where* $d\sigma(\lambda)$ *is an orthogonal spectral measure. If* $d\sigma(\lambda)$ *runs through all such measures, then the points* $m(z)$ *describe a circle* K_z, *the so-called Weyl-Hamburger circle, whose center and radius are given by*

$$O(z) = -\frac{1}{\sum_{i=0}^{\infty}|P_i(z)|^2}\left(\frac{1}{z-\bar{z}} + \sum_{i=0}^{\infty}\overline{P_i(z)}\,Q_i(z)\right),$$

$$R(z) = \frac{1}{|z-\bar{z}|\sum_{i=0}^{\infty}|P_i(z)|^2}. \tag{1.49}$$

If L is determinate, then the circle (1.49) *degenerates into the Weyl-Hamburger point.*

The points w of the Weyl-Hamburger circle are in one-to-one correspondence with the orthogonal spectral measures $d\sigma(\lambda)$ *(and hence, in view of* (1.19), *with the corresponding resolutions of the identity). Namely, to each* $d\sigma(\lambda)$ *there corresponds the point* $w_\sigma = m(z) = \int_{-\infty}^{\infty}(1/(\lambda - z))\, d\sigma(\lambda)$. *Conversely, to each* $w \in K_z$ *there corresponds the measure* $d\sigma(\lambda)$, *whose Stieltjes transform is calculated by the formula*

$$m(\zeta) = \frac{E_0(\zeta, z)\,w + E_1(\zeta, z)}{D_0(\zeta, z)\,w + D_1(\zeta, z)}, \tag{1.50}$$

where $E_0(\zeta, z)$, $E_1(\zeta, z)$, $D_0(\zeta, z)$, *and* $D_1(\zeta, z)$ *are entire functions of each variable separately, expressed by the series*

$$E_0(\zeta, z) = 1 + (\zeta - z)\sum_{i=0}^{\infty} Q_i(\zeta)P_i(z),\quad E_1(\zeta, z) = (\zeta - z)\sum_{i=0}^{\infty} Q_i(\zeta)Q_i(z),$$

$$D_0(\zeta, z) = -(\zeta - z)\sum_{i=0}^{\infty} P_i(\zeta)P_i(z),\quad D_1(\zeta, z) = 1 - (\zeta - z)\sum_{i=0}^{\infty} P_i(\zeta)Q_i(z). \tag{1.51}$$

Proof of the second part of the Theorem. The equation for $m(\zeta)$ is obtained by replacing ζ by $\bar{\zeta}$ in (1.40). We have

$$m(\zeta) = \frac{E_0(\zeta, z)\,m(z) + E_1(\zeta, z)}{D_0(\zeta, z)\,m(z) + D_1(\zeta, z)} \tag{1.52}$$

where E_0, E_1, D_0, and D_1 have the form (1.51) (convergence of the series in (1.51) and the analyticity properties follow from Lemma 1.5). The relation (1.52) shows that if $m(z)$ is known at one point, it is known everywhere; the theorem now follows in the obvious way.

Remark. The Weyl-Hamburger circle lies entirely in the interior of the upper half-plane if $\operatorname{Im} z > 0$, and in the lower half-plane if $\operatorname{Im} z < 0$. This follows from the fact that the points $m(z)$, corresponding to all orthogonal spectral measures, represent K_z, and moreover

$$\operatorname{Im} m(z) = \operatorname{Im} \int_{-\infty}^{\infty} \frac{d\sigma(\lambda)}{\lambda - z} = y \int_{-\infty}^{\infty} \frac{d\sigma(\lambda)}{(\lambda - x)^2 + y^2} \quad (z = x + iy).$$

Corollary. *In the indeterminate case, the spectrum of a selfadjoint extension of the operator* L *in the space* $l_2([0, \infty))$ *is always discrete and has no finite limit points.*

In fact, it follows from (1.50) that $m(\zeta)$ is a meromorphic function, and this is equivalent to the asserted character of the spectrum.

Formula (1.50), giving an expression of the functions $m(\zeta)$ in terms of points on the Weyl-Hamburger circle, can be simplified by passing to a limit as z approaches the real axis. First of all, we establish some properties of the functions (1.51).

Lemma 1.6. *The relations*

$$E_0(z, \zeta) = D_1(\zeta, z),\ E_1(z, \zeta) = - E_1(\zeta, z),\ D_0(z, \zeta) = - D_0(\zeta, z); \qquad (1.53)$$

$$E_0(\zeta, z) D_1(\zeta, z) - E_1(\zeta, z) D_0(\zeta, z) = 1 \qquad (1.54)$$

hold for all complex ζ *and* z.

Proof. (1.53) follows from (1.51). We prove (1.54). To this end, consider the functions $E_0^{(N)}(\zeta, z)$, $E_1^{(N)}(\zeta, z)$, $D_0^{(N)}(\zeta, z)$, and $D_1^{(N)}(\zeta, z)$, which are defined as in (1.51), except that the summations are extended only up to N, and not ∞. It is not difficult to show that by means of Green's formula,

$$\begin{aligned} E_0^{(N)}(\zeta, z) &= a_N (Q_{N+1}(\zeta) P_N(z) - Q_N(\zeta) P_{N+1}(z)), \\ E_1^{(N)}(\zeta, z) &= a_N (Q_{N+1}(\zeta) Q_N(z) - Q_N(\zeta) Q_{N+1}(z)), \\ D_0^{(N)}(\zeta, z) &= a_N (P_N(\zeta) P_{N+1}(z) - P_{N+1}(\zeta) P_N(z)), \\ D_1^{(N)}(\zeta, z) &= a_N (P_N(\zeta) Q_{N+1}(z) - P_{N+1}(\zeta) Q_N(z)). \end{aligned} \qquad (1.55)$$

In fact, for example,

$$E_0^{(N)}(\zeta, z) = 1 + (\zeta - z)\sum_{j=0}^{N} Q_j(\zeta) P_j(z) = 1 + \sum_{j=0}^{N} [(LQ(\zeta))_j P_j(z)$$
$$- Q_j(\zeta)(LP(z))_j] = a_N (Q_{N+1}(\zeta) P_N(z) - Q_N(\zeta) P_{N+1}(z)).$$

If we set $\zeta = z$ in the first of the equations (1.55), we obtain the following difference analogue of the Liouville-Ostrogradskiĭ formula:

$$P_N(z) Q_{N+1}(z) - P_{N+1}(z) Q_N(z) = \frac{1}{a_N} \quad (N = 0, 1, \ldots). \tag{1.56}$$

Using the relations (1.55) and the identity (1.56), it is not difficult to compute that

$$E_0^{(N)}(\zeta, z) D_1^{(N)}(\zeta, z) - E_1^{(N)}(\zeta, z) D_0^{(N)}(\zeta, z) = 1 \quad (N = 0, 1, \ldots). \tag{1.57}$$

On passing to the limit here as $N \to \infty$, we obtain (1.54). The lemma is proved.

By virtue of (1.54), the linear fractional transformation $w \to v$

$$v = \frac{E_0(\zeta, z) w + E_1(\zeta, z)}{D_0(\zeta, z) w + D_1(\zeta, z)} \tag{1.58}$$

(ζ and z fixed) is nondegenerate. We will show that it transforms: 1) K_z into K_ζ if $\operatorname{Im}\zeta$, $\operatorname{Im} z \neq 0$; 2) K_z into the axis $[-\infty, \infty]$ if $\operatorname{Im}\zeta = 0$, $\operatorname{Im} z \neq 0$; 3) $[-\infty, \infty]$ into K_ζ if $\operatorname{Im}\zeta \neq 0$, $\operatorname{Im} z = 0$; 4) $[-\infty, \infty]$ into $[-\infty, \infty]$ if $\operatorname{Im}\zeta = \operatorname{Im} z = 0$.

In fact, case 1) follows from (1.52) and the fact that $m(p)$ describes the whole circle K_p as $d\sigma(\lambda)$ is varied. Consider case 2). First of all, note that since $m(z)$ is a meromorphic function, it either has a finite real limit, or it tends to ∞ as z approaches the real axis. Now pass to the limit in (1.52) as ζ approaches the real axis ($\zeta \to \xi$); do this for three distinct $d\sigma(\lambda)$. As a result we obtain three distinct points on K_z of the form $m(z)$ which are mapped by (1.58) (where ζ is replaced by ξ) into points on $[-\infty, \infty]$. Consequently, this mapping transforms K_z into $[-\infty, \infty]$. In case 3) (when $z = x \in (-\infty, \infty)$) invert the transformation (1.58) and use (1.53): we find that it has the form $w = (E_0(x, \zeta) v + E_1(x, \zeta))/(D_0(x, \zeta) v + D_1(x, \zeta))$ and therefore by 2) it transforms K_ζ into $[-\infty, \infty]$. But then the original transformation transforms $[-\infty, \infty]$ into K_z. Finally, in case 4) $[-\infty, \infty]$ is transformed into $[-\infty, \infty]$ because of the realness of the coefficients.

Now it is easy to prove the following theorem.

Theorem 1.13. *Let x, real, be fixed. The orthogonal spectral measures are in one-to-one correspondence with the points t of the real axis (including $t = \infty$). The correspondence is established by the formula*

$$m(\zeta) = \frac{E_0(\zeta, x)t + E_1(\zeta, x)}{D_0(\zeta, x)t + D_1(\zeta, x)} \quad (\operatorname{Im}\zeta \neq 0). \tag{1.59}$$

Proof. Pass to the limit in (1.52) as $z \to x \in (-\infty, \infty)$. Then $m(z) \to t$; as a result we obtain (1.59). In addition, the various values of t run through all of $[-\infty, \infty]$. This follows from the proof of Lemma 1.6 (case 2)), on letting $\zeta \to x$ in (1.52). Each t in (1.59) is uniquely determined by $m(\zeta)$ by means of the inverse transformation. The theorem is proved.

8. The indeterminate case. Description of nonorthogonal spectral measures. For the analysis of these measures, we must augment Theorems 1.12 and 1.13 in the following way.

Theorem 1.14. *Let z not real be fixed and consider all holomorphic functions $w(\zeta)$ in the upper half-plane* $\operatorname{Im}\zeta > 0$, *which map the half-plane into the interior of the circle K_z. The nonorthogonal spectral measures are in one-to-one correspondence with the functions $w(\zeta)$. The correspondence is established by formula* (1.50), *where the number w is replaced by $w(\zeta)$; ζ is taken from the upper half-plane.*[1)]

Another description of these measures can be given. Let x, real, be held fixed and consider all holomorphic functions $t(\zeta)$ in the upper half-plane, which map the half-plane into itself. The measures under consideration are in one-to-one correspondence with the functions $t(\zeta)$. The correspondence is established by (1.59), *where t is replaced by $t(\zeta)$*: $\operatorname{Im}\zeta > 0$.

The proof requires constructions of the kind previously considered, but in connection with extensions which act in a larger space than $l_2([0, \infty))$. We confine ourselves to the simplest part of the theorem – the proof of the existence of the functions $w(\zeta)$ and $t(\zeta)$, if $m(\zeta)$ is given.

We show that *the mapping* (1.58) *in case* 1) *maps the interior of the Weyl-Hamburger circle into the interior, if* $\operatorname{Im}\zeta \cdot \operatorname{Im} z > 0$, *and into the exterior, if* $\operatorname{Im}\zeta \cdot \operatorname{Im} z < 0$; *in cases* 2) *and* 3) *the interior of the Weyl-Hamburger circle and*

1) Because of the realness of $d\sigma(\lambda)$ this measure is determined by $m(\zeta) = \int_{-\infty}^{\infty} (\lambda - \zeta)^{-1} d\sigma(\lambda)$, considered in one of the half-planes $\operatorname{Im}\zeta > 0$ or $\operatorname{Im}\zeta < 0$.

the half-plane in which it lies are transformed into each other; in case 4) the upper half-plane is mapped into itself, and the lower half-plane is mapped into itself.

In fact, for $\zeta = z$ the transformation (1.58) is the identity, and therefore is orientation preserving. It preserves orientation by continuity as z moves away from ζ. But if z becomes real, then K_z degenerates into a half-plane, and therefore if z crosses the real axis the transformation (1.58) reverses orientation. The stated assertions obviously follow from these considerations.

If $m(\zeta)$ ($\operatorname{Im}\zeta > 0$) is constructed with respect to a generalized resolution of the identity, then it satisfies the relation (1.41) with the equal sign replaced by $\geq$. The condition on w, $(\bar{w} - w)/(\bar{\zeta} - \zeta) \geq \sum_{j=0}^{\infty} |Q_j(\zeta) + wP_j(\zeta)|^2$, characterizes the interior of K_ζ. Thus $m(\zeta)$ lies in K_ζ. Therefore $w(\zeta)$, defined by the equation

$$m(\zeta) = \frac{E_0(\zeta, z)w(\zeta) + E_1(\zeta, z)}{D_0(\zeta, z)w(\zeta) + D_1(\zeta, z)}, \tag{1.60}$$

lies inside K_z. Clearly, $w(\zeta)$ is holomorphic for $\operatorname{Im}\zeta > 0$. Thus we have obtained the function $w(\zeta)$ of the required form, connected with $m(\zeta)$ by (1.60) for $\operatorname{Im}\zeta > 0$.

The existence of the function $t(\zeta)$ is proved analogously.

9. **Some further theorems.** We will now establish several interesting consequences of the theory of the previous three subsections. First of all, we will clarify the assertion that *each orthogonal measure is extreme* (an extreme point of the convex set Σ of all spectral measures of the expression L). In fact, suppose that such a measure σ is represented in the form $\sigma(\Delta) = \mu_1\sigma_1(\Delta) + \mu_2\sigma_2(\Delta)$, where $\mu_1, \mu_2 > 0$, $\mu_1 + \mu_2 = 1$; σ_1 and σ_2 are some spectral measures. If z nonreal is fixed, then for the corresponding Stieltjes transforms we have: $m(z) = \mu_1 m_1(z) + \mu_2 m_2(z)$. Since the points $m_1(z)$ and $m_2(z)$ lie interior to or on the boundary of the Weyl-Hamburger circle K_z, $m(z)$ lies in the interior of K_z, which is impossible (see Theorem 1.12).

We topologize Σ in the following way. Extend the axis $(-\infty, \infty)$ to the compactum $Q = [-\infty, \infty]$, by adjoining the point ∞, and consider the space $C(Q)$ of continuous complex-valued functions on Q. In other words, the elements of $C(Q)$ are the continuous functions $u(\lambda)$ $(\lambda \in (-\infty, \infty))$ which have a finite limit $u(\infty)$ as $\lambda \to \infty$. The continuous linear functionals on $C(Q)$ have the form $l(u) = \int_{-\infty}^{\infty} u(\lambda)\, d\omega(\lambda) + u(\infty)\,\omega_\infty$, where $\omega(\lambda)$ is a function of bounded variation, and

ω_∞ is a certain constant ("the measure of infinity"); $\|l\| = \mathrm{Var}\,\omega_{(-\infty,\infty)} + |\omega_\infty|$. Thus each measure in Σ may be identified with a functional on $C(Q)$ and we may write $\Sigma \subset (C(Q))'$.

Theorem 1.15. *The set Σ of spectral measures corresponding to N is a convex compactum in the sense of the weak topology on $(C(Q))'$.*

Proof. As has already been shown, Σ is convex. It is precompact because of the weak compactness of the sphere in the conjugate space of the separable space $C(Q)$. It remains to show that Σ is closed in the sense of weak convergence. Let $\sigma_n \in \Sigma$ and $\sigma_n \to l \in (C(Q))'$ weakly, where l induces a function $\omega(\lambda)$ and a number ω_∞. Since $d\sigma_n(\lambda)$ is nonnegative, the measure $d\omega(\lambda) = d\sigma(\lambda)$ is also nonnegative and therefore is an ordinary measure; we will show the existence of the integrals (1.29). First of all, we point out a simple property, which is used everywhere below: for any $m = 0, 1, \cdots$ the integrals $\int_{-\infty}^{\infty} \lambda^m \, d\sigma_n(\lambda)$ do not depend on n. In fact, let $\lambda^m = \sum_{j-0}^{m} c_j^{(m)} P_j(\lambda)$ be the decomposition of λ^m with respect to the polynomials $P_j(\lambda)$, corresponding to L. Then by orthogonality $\int_{-\infty}^{\infty} \lambda^m \, d\sigma_n(\lambda) = \sum_{j=0}^{m} c_j^{(m)} \times \int_{-\infty}^{\infty} P_j(\lambda)\, d\sigma_n(\lambda) = c_0^{(m)}$ is independent of n.

To prove (1.29) it is sufficient to show that for m even, $\int_{-\infty}^{\infty} \lambda^m \, d\sigma(\lambda) < \infty$. Let $N > 0$ and construct the partition of unity $1 = \chi_1^{(N)}(\lambda) + \chi_2^{(N)}(\lambda)$, where $\chi_1^{(N)}(\lambda)$ vanishes for $|\lambda| \geq N + 1$ and $\chi_2^{(N)}(\lambda)$ vanishes for $|\lambda| \leq N$. Since $\chi_1^{(N)}(\lambda)\, \lambda^m \in C(Q)$,

$$\int_{-\infty}^{\infty} \chi_1^{(N)}(\lambda)\, \lambda^m d\sigma_n(\lambda) \underset{n\to\infty}{\longrightarrow} l\,(\chi_1^{(N)}(\lambda)\, \lambda^m) = \int_{-\infty}^{\infty} \chi_1^{(N)}(\lambda)\, \lambda^m d\sigma(\lambda). \tag{1.61}$$

But $\int_{-\infty}^{\infty} \chi_1^{(N)}(\lambda)\, \lambda^m \, d\sigma_n(\lambda) \leq \int_{-\infty}^{\infty} \lambda^m \, d\sigma_n(\lambda) = c_0^{(m)}$, and hence for any N $\int_{-\infty}^{\infty} \chi_1^{(N)}(\lambda)\, \lambda^m \, d\sigma(\lambda) \leq c_0^{(m)}$. On taking the limit as $N \to \infty$, we obtain $\int_{-\infty}^{\infty} \lambda^m \, d\sigma(\lambda) \leq c_0^{(m)} < \infty$, as required.

We now show that $\omega_\infty = 0$. Since $\chi_2^{(N)} \in C(Q)$ and $\chi_2^{(N)}(\infty) = 1$,

$$\int_{-\infty}^{\infty} \chi_2^{(N)}(\lambda)\, d\sigma_n(\lambda) \underset{n\to\infty}{\longrightarrow} l\,(\chi_2^{(N)}) = \int_{-\infty}^{\infty} \chi_2^{(N)}(\lambda)\, d\sigma(\lambda) + \omega_\infty. \tag{1.62}$$

Let $\epsilon > 0$ be given and choose N so large that $\int_{-\infty}^{\infty} \chi_2^{(N)}(\lambda)\, d\sigma(\lambda) < \epsilon$. Furthermore, denoting $Q = (-\infty, \infty) \setminus [-N, N]$ we have

$$\int_{-\infty}^{\infty} \chi_2^{(N)}(\lambda)\, d\sigma_n(\lambda) \leqslant \int_{(-\infty,\infty)\setminus[-N,N]} d\sigma_n(\lambda) = \int_{(-\infty,\infty)\setminus[-N,N]} \frac{1}{\lambda^2}\, \lambda^2 d\sigma_n(\lambda)$$

$$\leqslant \frac{1}{N^2} \int_{-\infty}^{\infty} \lambda^2 d\sigma_n(\lambda) = \frac{c_0^{(2)}}{N^2} < \varepsilon$$

for N sufficiently large. On comparing these estimates with (1.62), we find that $|\omega_\infty| < 2\epsilon$, i.e. $\omega_\infty = 0$.

Thus we have shown that the limit functional l induced by the measure $d\sigma(\lambda)$ satisfies (1.29). It remains to verify that $d\sigma(\lambda)$ is a spectral measure for the expression L. By Theorem 1.9, it is sufficient to show that Parseval's equation (1.30) holds for σ with $u, v \in l_{2,0}([0,\infty))$. Since it holds for σ_n, we must show that we can pass to a limit in (1.30) under the integral sign. This will be proved if we can show that for any $m = 0, 1, \cdots$ $\int_{-\infty}^{\infty} \lambda^m\, d\sigma_n(\lambda) \underset{n\to\infty}{\longrightarrow} \int_{-\infty}^{\infty} \lambda^m\, d\sigma(\lambda)$. But $1 = \chi_1^{(N)}(\lambda) + \chi_2^{(N)}(\lambda)$, and so by (1.61) it is sufficient to show that for any $\epsilon > 0$ there exists a choice of N such that $|\int_{-\infty}^{\infty} \chi_2^{(N)}(\lambda)\, \lambda^m d\sigma(\lambda)| < \epsilon$ and $|\int_{-\infty}^{\infty} \chi_2^{(N)}(\lambda)\, \lambda^m d\sigma_n(\lambda)| < \epsilon$ uniformly in n. The first inequality is possible by the convergence of the integral $\int_{-\infty}^{\infty} |\lambda|^m\, d\sigma(\lambda)$. The second inequality for $m > 0$ follows from the estimate

$$\left|\int_{-\infty}^{\infty} \chi_2^{(N)}(\lambda)\, \lambda^m d\sigma_n(\lambda)\right| \leqslant \int_{(-\infty,\infty)\setminus[-N,N]} \lambda^m d\sigma_n(\lambda) = \int_{(-\infty,\infty)\setminus[-N,N]} \frac{1}{\lambda^m}\, \lambda^{2m} d\sigma_n(\lambda)$$

$$\leqslant \frac{1}{N^m} \int_{-\infty}^{\infty} \lambda^{2m} d\sigma_n(\lambda) = \frac{c_0^{(2m)}}{N^m} \quad (n = 1, 2, \ldots).$$

The case $m = 0$ was considered earlier. The theorem is proved.

As is already known (Theorems 1.13 and 1.14), the formula

$$m(\zeta) = \frac{E_0(\zeta, x)\, t(\zeta) + E_1(\zeta, x)}{D_0(\zeta, x)\, t(\zeta) + D_1(\zeta, x)} \quad (\operatorname{Im} \zeta \neq 0) \tag{1.63}$$

(x is a fixed real number) gives the Stieltjes transform of an orthogonal spectral measure $d\sigma(\lambda)$, if in this formula the arbitrary holomorphic function $t(\zeta)$ of $\operatorname{Im}\zeta > 0$ such that $\operatorname{Im} t(\zeta) \geq 0$ is replaced by a real constant (possibly equal to ∞). It turns out that the measure $d\sigma(\lambda)$ which belongs to the closed convex hull of the orthogonal measures can be described in terms of $t(\zeta)$.

Theorem 1.16. *Denote by* $\Sigma_0 \subseteq \Sigma$ *the closed convex hull of the orthogonal spectral measures, corresponding to* L, *i.e. the closure in the sense of weak convergence in* $(C(Q))'$ *of the measures*

$$\sigma(\Delta) = \sum_{\alpha=1}^{N} \mu_\alpha \sigma_\alpha(\Delta) \quad \left(\mu_\alpha \geqslant 0, \ \alpha = 1, \ldots, N; \ \sum_{\alpha=1}^{N} \mu_\alpha = 1 \right) \tag{1.64}$$

where $d\sigma_\alpha(\lambda)$ *are orthogonal measures. A necessary and sufficient condition that* $\sigma \in \Sigma_0$ *is that the function* $t(\zeta)$ *in* (1.63) *has the form*

$$t(\zeta) = t^*(w(\zeta)), \quad w(\zeta) = \frac{D_1(\zeta, x)}{D_0(\zeta, x)}, \tag{1.65}$$

where $t^*(w)$ *is an arbitrary function, holomorphic for* $\operatorname{Im} w > 0$, *such that* $\operatorname{Im} t^*(w) \geq 0$ *(in particular,* $t^*(w)$ *may coincide with a real constant, possibly* ∞*).*

Before proving the theorem, we examine in more detail functions $f(z)$ which are holomorphic for $\operatorname{Im} z > 0$ and satisfy $\operatorname{Im} f(z) \geq 0$. We denote the collection of these so-called Nevanlinna functions by N.[1] Obviously, the class N is additive (i.e. if $f, g \in N$ then $f + g \in N$) and is closed with respect to composition (i.e. if $f, g \in N$ then $f(g(z)) \in N$). Since $1/z \in N$, then if $f \in N$, $-1/f(z) \in N$ also. The functions of class N have a well-known representation – this class coincides with the functions of the form

$$f(z) = \alpha + \beta z + \int_{-\infty}^{\infty} \frac{1 + \lambda z}{\lambda - z} d\varrho(\lambda) \quad (\operatorname{Im} z > 0) \tag{1.66}$$

where $\alpha \in (-\infty, \infty)$ and $\beta \in [0, \infty)$ are constants, and $d\sigma(\lambda)$ is a nonnegative finite measure on the real line $(-\infty, \infty)$. It follows from (1.66) that for each $f \in N$, $\lim_{y \to +\infty} f(iy)/y = i\beta$ $(z = x + iy)$.

Let $F \in N$ and assume that $\overline{\lim}_{y \to +\infty} |yF(iy)| < \infty$; such functions are described by the formula

$$F(z) = \int_{-\infty}^{\infty} \frac{d\tau(\lambda)}{\lambda - z} \quad (\operatorname{Im} z > 0), \tag{1.67}$$

where $d\tau(\lambda)$ is a nonnegative finite measure on $(-\infty, \infty)$. It follows from (1.67) that if $\overline{\lim}_{y \to +\infty} |yF(iy)| < \infty$, then in fact $\lim_{y \to +\infty} yF(iy) = i\tau((-\infty, \infty))$.

Lemma 1.7. *The class* N *coincides with the class of functions* $f(z) = -z - 1/F(z)$ $(\operatorname{Im} z > 0)$, *where* $F(z)$ *has the form* (1.67), *where* $0 < \tau((-\infty, \infty)) < 1$.

---

[1] The facts presented below concerning these functions can be found, for example in the book by N. I. Ahiezer and I. M. Glazman [1], Chapter 6, § 59, pp. 206–213; English transl. Vol. II pp. 7–11.

Proof. If $f \in N$ then $f(z) + z \in N$ and thus $-1/(f(z)+z) = F(z)$. But $\lim_{y\to+\infty} yF(iy) = -\lim_{y\to+\infty}(f(iy)/y + i)^{-1} = i(\beta+1)^{-1}((\beta \in [0,\infty), (\beta+1)^{-1} \in [0,1])$, so F has a representation of the form (1.67), where $0 < \tau((-\infty,\infty)) \le 1$. Conversely, if F has the form (1.67) $(0 < \tau((-\infty,\infty)) \le 1)$, then $f(z) = -z - 1/F(z)$ is holomorphic for $\operatorname{Im} z > 0$; we show that $\operatorname{Im} f(z) \ge 0$. By the Cauchy-Bunjakovskiĭ inequality we have

$$\operatorname{Im} f(z) = \operatorname{Im}\left\{-z - \frac{1}{F(z)}\right\} = -y$$

$$+ \frac{y\int\limits_{-\infty}^{\infty}\frac{d\tau(\lambda)}{(\lambda-x)^2+y^2}}{\left(\int\limits_{-\infty}^{\infty}\frac{(\lambda-x)\,d\tau(\lambda)}{(\lambda-x)^2+y^2}\right)^2 + y^2\left(\int\limits_{-\infty}^{\infty}\frac{d\tau(\lambda)}{(\lambda-x)^2+y^2}\right)^2}$$

$$\geqslant -y + \frac{y}{\int\limits_{-\infty}^{\infty}\frac{(\lambda-x)^2 d\tau(\lambda)}{(\lambda-x)^2+y^2} + y^2\int\limits_{-\infty}^{\infty}\frac{d\tau(\lambda)}{(\lambda-x)^2+y^2}}$$

$$= -y + \frac{y}{\tau((-\infty,\infty))} \geqslant 0 \quad (\operatorname{Im} z > 0).$$

The lemma is proved.

We make one more remark. We assert that *for fixed real* x *the function* $w(\zeta) = D_1(\zeta,x)/D_0(\zeta,x)$ $(\operatorname{Im}\zeta > 0)$ *belongs to the class* N. In fact, for $z = x$ the function (1.58) maps the upper half-plane into the interior of the circle K_ζ (see proof of Lemma 1.6, case 3) and the proof and remark to Theorem 1.12) and is therefore finite for $\operatorname{Im} w > 0$. Thus a zero of the denominator in (1.58) $w = -D_1(\zeta,x)/D_0(\zeta,x)$ can lie only in the lower half-plane (by (1.54) this zero cannot be a zero of the numerator). Thus, for $\operatorname{Im}\zeta > 0$, $\operatorname{Im}\{-D_1(\zeta,x)/D_0(\zeta,x)\} \le 0$, as required.

It follows, in particular, from this result that a function $t(\zeta)$ of the form (1.65) is always of class N.

Proof of the theorem. Since $(az+b)/(cz+d) = a/c + (bc-ad)/(c(cz+d))$, then because of (1.54), we obtain by (1.63)

$$m(\zeta) = \frac{E_0(\zeta,x)}{D_0(\zeta,x)} - \frac{1}{D_0^2(\zeta,x)(t(\zeta)+w(\zeta))} \quad (\operatorname{Im}\zeta > 0). \tag{1.68}$$

The representation (1.64) is equivalent to the representation

$m(\zeta) = \Sigma_{\alpha=1}^{N} \mu_\alpha m_\alpha(\zeta)$ (m_α corresponds to σ_α). The latter is equivalent to

$$\frac{1}{t(\zeta)+w(\zeta)} = \sum_{\alpha=1}^{N} \frac{\mu_\alpha}{t_\alpha + w(\zeta)} \quad (\operatorname{Im}\zeta > 0). \tag{1.69}$$

Here t_α is the real number which corresponds to the orthogonal σ_α; one of these numbers, say t_{α_0}, may equal ∞. This means that in (1.69), the corresponding term is missing, i.e. we may in fact assume that $\mu_{\alpha_0} = 0$.

We show that if $\sigma \in \Sigma_0$, then the representation (1.65) is valid. Consider at first the case when σ is of the form (1.64); then (1.69) holds, and it follows that $t(\zeta)$ is a function of $w(\zeta)$: $t(\zeta) = t^*(w(\zeta))$, where $t^*(w)$ is a function which satisfies the relation $(t^*(w) + w)^{-1} = \Sigma_{\alpha=1}^{N} \mu_\alpha (t_\alpha + w)^{-1}$. The function $F(w) = -(t^*(w) + w)^{-1} = \Sigma_{\alpha=1}^{N} \mu_\alpha (-t_\alpha - w)^{-1}$ has the form (1.67), where $\tau((-\infty, \infty)) = \Sigma_{\alpha=1}^{N} \mu_\alpha \leq 1$. But then by Lemma 1.7, $t^*(w) = -w - 1/F(w) \in N$, which proves (1.65).

Now suppose that σ is the limit in the weak sense of a sequence of measures $\sigma^{(n)}$ of the form (1.64). Since, for each ζ ($\operatorname{Im}\zeta > 0$), $1/(\lambda - \zeta) \in C(Q)$, then, with the natural notation, $\lim_{n\to\infty} m^{(n)}(\zeta) = m(\zeta)$. It follows from (1.68) that the function $(t(\zeta) + w(\zeta))^{-1}$ for these ζ is a limit of sums of the type (1.69); in other words, on the set of values of the function $w(\zeta)$ (and hence, for all w, $\operatorname{Im} w > 0$) $F(w) = -(t(\zeta) + w)^{-1}$ is equal to the limit of the corresponding sums $\Sigma_{\alpha=1}^{N} \mu_\alpha(-t_\alpha - w)^{-1}$. But this limit must have the form $F(w) = \int_{-\infty}^{\infty} d\tau(\lambda)/(\lambda - w)$ for a nonnegative measure $d\tau(\lambda)$ such that $0 < \tau((-\infty, \infty)) \leq 1$.[1] Hence by Lemma 1.7 we conclude that $t^*(w) = -w - 1/F(w) \in N$, as required.

Conversely, if $t(\zeta)$ has the form (1.65), we must show that $\sigma \in \Sigma_0$. Consider the function $F(w) = -(t^*(w) + w)^{-1}$. Making use of the representation of the type (1.66) for $t^*(w)$ we find that $\lim_{v\to+\infty} vF(iv) = i(\beta + 1)^{-1}$ ($\beta \in [0, \infty)$). Thus, $F(w)$ is represented in the form (1.67) with $\tau((-\infty, \infty)) = (\beta + 1)^{-1} \leq 1$. We will approximate the integral $\int_{-\infty}^{\infty}(-\lambda + w)^{-1} d\tau(\lambda) = -F(w)$ by integral Riemann sums

$$\sum_{\alpha=1}^{N} \mu_\alpha (t_\alpha + w)^{-1} \quad \text{where} \quad \mu_\alpha = \tau(\Delta_\alpha) \geqslant 0; \ \sum_{\alpha=1}^{N} \mu_\alpha = \tau((-\infty, \infty)) \leqslant 1; \ -t_\alpha = \lambda_\alpha \in \Delta_\alpha.$$

If $\Sigma_{\alpha=1}^{N} \mu_\alpha < 1$, then introduce formally another $\mu_{\alpha_0} = 1 - \Sigma_{\alpha=1}^{N} \mu_\alpha > 0$ and set

---

[1] In fact, these sums may be written in the form $\int_{-\infty}^{\infty} (\lambda - w)^{-1} d\tau^{(n)}(\lambda)$, where $d\tau^{(n)}(\lambda)$ is a measure where $0 < \epsilon < \tau^{(n)}((-\infty, \infty)) \leq 1$. The limit of these integrals, as follows easily from Helly's Theorem, must be a similar integral.

$t_{\alpha_0} = \infty$. By changing the notation somewhat if necessary, we may assume that the integral under consideration is approximated by the sums $\Sigma_{\alpha=1}^N \mu_\alpha (t_\alpha + w)^{-1}$; $\mu_\alpha \geq 0$; $\Sigma_{\alpha=1}^N \mu_\alpha = 1$; $t_\alpha \in [-\infty, \infty]$. Let $d\sigma_\alpha(\lambda)$ denote the orthogonal spectral measure, corresponding to t_α in formula (1.63). To the spectral density $\sigma^{(n)}(\Delta) = \Sigma_{\alpha=1}^N \mu_\alpha \sigma_\alpha(\Delta)$ there will correspond a function $t^{(n)}(\zeta)$, connected by the relation $(t^{(n)}(\zeta) + w(\zeta))^{-1} = \Sigma_{\alpha=1}^N \mu_\alpha (t_\alpha + w(\zeta))^{-1}$. Since the last sum approximates the integral $\int_{-\infty}^{\infty} (-\lambda + w(\zeta))^{-1} d\tau(\lambda) = -f(w(\zeta)) = (t^*(w) + w(\zeta))^{-1}$, $t^{(n)}(\zeta)$ approximates the function $t(\zeta)$ for each ζ ($\operatorname{Im} \zeta > 0$). By (1.68) the functions $m^{(n)}(\zeta)$ corresponding to the measures $\sigma^{(n)}$ approximate $m(\zeta)$ for the ζ under consideration. By Theorem 1.15 we can extract a subsequence $\sigma^{(n')}$ from $\sigma^{(n)}$, which converges weakly to some spectral measure ρ. Since $(\lambda - z)^{-1} \in C(Q)$, $\int_{-\infty}^{\infty} (\lambda - \zeta)^{-1} d\rho(\lambda) = \lim_{n' \to \infty} m^{(n')}(\zeta) = m(\zeta)$ ($\operatorname{Im} \zeta > 0$), but this means that $\rho = \sigma$. Thus the combinations $\Sigma_{\alpha=1}^N \mu_\alpha \sigma_\alpha(\Delta)$, corresponding to the indices n', approximate σ in the weak sense, i.e. $\sigma \in \Sigma_0$. The theorem is proved.

Since the functions (1.65) do not represent the whole class N, Σ_0 is a proper subset of Σ. Hence *the set of extreme spectral measures in the case of the indeterminate expression L is always larger than the set of orthogonal measures.* In fact, suppose that these sets coincide; then by the Kreĭn-Milman Theorem [1)] any point of Σ belongs to Σ_0, which is absurd. It can be shown that if $t(\zeta)$ is replaced by a rational function of the class N in (1.63), then the corresponding $d\sigma(\lambda)$ is extreme. This gives us the following interesting result: *each spectral measure is the limit in the weak sense of a sequence of extreme spectral measures (it is not necessary to take convex combinations).* In fact, each function $t \in N$ can be approximated by rational functions $t^{(n)} \in N$ (for example, take Riemann sums of the integral in (1.66)). Then by (1.63), $m(\zeta)$ can be approximated by functions $m^{(n)}(\zeta)$, and the proof is completed in the same way as the proof of the second part of Theorem 1.16.

With this we complete the discussion of extreme points of the set Σ. In conclusion we establish two more theorems of another type.

Theorem 1.17. *Let L be an arbitrary difference expression, $d\sigma(\lambda)$ one of its spectral measures. For each $\mu \in (-\infty, \infty)$ the jump of the function $\sigma(\lambda)$ at this point satisfies the inequality*

---

1) That is: Each compact convex set in the weak topology of the conjugate space to some normed space or even a locally convex linear topological space contains extreme points, and it coincides with the closed convex hull in the weak topology of these points.

$$\sigma(\mu+0)-\sigma(\mu)\leqslant\frac{1}{\sum_{j=0}^{\infty}P_j^2(\mu)} \tag{1.70}$$

(the series here may be divergent). In the determinate case, equality holds in (1.70), *and in the indeterminate case equality holds for the orthogonal spectral measures whose Stieltjes transform is obtained by* (1.59) *with* $x=\mu$ *and* $t=\infty$.

Proof. For any polynomial $P(\lambda)$ we obviously have $\int_{-\infty}^{\infty}P^2(\lambda)\,d\sigma(\lambda)\geq P^2(\mu)(\sigma(\mu+0)-\sigma(\mu))$. Set $P(\lambda)=(\Sigma_{j=0}^{n}P_j^2(\mu))^{-1}\times\Sigma_{j=0}^{n}P_j(\mu)P_j(\lambda)$; $P(\mu)=1$. Since the polynomials $P_j(\lambda)$ are orthonormal we have

$$\sigma(\mu+0)-\sigma(\mu)\leqslant\int_{-\infty}^{\infty}\left\{\frac{\sum_{j=0}^{n}P_j(\mu)P_j(\lambda)}{\sum_{j=0}^{n}P_j^2(\mu)}\right\}^2 d\sigma(\lambda)=\frac{1}{\sum_{j=0}^{n}P_j^2(\mu)}\quad(n=0,1,\ldots).$$

If we take the limit here as $n\to\infty$, we get (1.70).

We establish the second part of the theorem, at first supposing that L is indeterminate. Put $x=\mu$ in (1.59) and take the limit as $t\to\infty$; using (1.51), we obtain

$$m(\zeta)=\int_{-\infty}^{\infty}\frac{d\sigma(\lambda)}{\lambda-\zeta}=\frac{E_0(\zeta,\mu)}{D_0(\zeta,\mu)}=\frac{1+(\zeta-\mu)\sum_{j=0}^{\infty}Q_j(\zeta)P_j(\mu)}{-(\zeta-\mu)\sum_{j=0}^{\infty}P_j(\zeta)P_j(\mu)}\quad(\operatorname{Im}\zeta\neq 0). \tag{1.71}$$

This shows that $m(\zeta)$ has a pole at $\zeta=\mu$; the expansion of m in a neighborhood of μ has the form

$$m(\zeta)=-((\sigma(\mu+0)-\sigma(\mu))(\zeta-\mu)^{-1}+\sum_{n=0}^{\infty}c_n(\zeta-\mu)^n.$$

On comparing this expansion with (1.71), we obtain $\sigma(\mu+0)-\sigma(\mu)=(\Sigma_{j=0}^{\infty}P_j^2(\mu))^{-1}$, which proves the theorem in the nonorthogonal case.

If L is determinate, it is easy to see that we need only consider the case when $\Sigma_{j=0}^{\infty}P_j^2(\mu)<\infty$. First of all we show that now

$$\lim_{\varepsilon\to 0}\{-i\varepsilon R_{\mu+i\varepsilon}\delta_0\}=(\sigma(\mu+0)-\sigma(\mu))(P_0(\mu),P_1(\mu),\ldots) \tag{1.72}$$

in the sense of weak convergence in $l_2([0,\infty))$. Indeed, by (1.37) for j fixed,

$$-i\varepsilon\,(R_{\mu+i\varepsilon}\delta_0)_j=\int_{-\infty}^{\infty}\frac{i\varepsilon P_j(\lambda)}{i\varepsilon+\mu-\lambda}\,d\sigma(\lambda)\underset{\varepsilon\to 0}{\to}(\sigma(\mu+0)-\sigma(\mu))\,P_j(\mu), \tag{1.73}$$

since the sequence of functions $i\epsilon P_j(\lambda)/(i\epsilon+\mu-\lambda)$ of λ converges to 0 for $\lambda\neq\mu$, to $P_j(\lambda)$ for $\lambda=\mu$, and is bounded by the summable function $|P_j(\lambda)|$. It follows from (1.73) that $(-i\epsilon R_{\mu+i\epsilon}\delta_0,\,u)_0$ converges to the required limit for each $u\in l_{2,0}([0,\infty))$. For the proof of (1.72) it remains to observe that the norms of the vectors of the sequence under consideration are uniformly bounded: $\|-i\epsilon R_{\mu+i\epsilon}\delta_0\|_0\le|\epsilon|\,\|R_{\mu+i\epsilon}\|\,\|\delta_0\|_0\le 1$. Thus (1.72) is established.

In a manner similar to the argument used to deduce equation (1.40) above we obtain (here $\mu+i\eta$ and $\mu+i\epsilon$ play the roles of z and ζ respectively):

$$(\varepsilon+\eta)\sum_{j=0}^{\infty}\{-i\eta R_{\mu+i\eta}\delta_0\}_j\,\overline{\{-i\varepsilon R_{\mu+i\varepsilon}\delta_0\}_j}=i\varepsilon\eta\,(m(\mu-i\varepsilon)-m(\mu+i\eta))$$

$$(\varepsilon,\eta\neq 0).$$

Pass to the limit here as $\eta\to 0$, using (1.72) and (1.73) for $j=0$ (i.e. the relation $-i\eta m(\mu+i\eta)\to\sigma(\mu+0)-\sigma(\mu)$) as $\eta\to 0$. After cancellation of ϵ we get

$$(\sigma(\mu+0)-\sigma(\mu))\sum_{j=0}^{\infty}P_j(\mu)\,\overline{\{-i\varepsilon R_{\mu+i\varepsilon}\delta_0\}_j}=\sigma(\mu+0)-\sigma(\mu)\quad(\varepsilon\neq 0).$$

Once again, taking the limit now as $\epsilon\to 0$ and using (1.72), we obtain $(\sigma(\mu+0)-\sigma(\mu))\sum_{j=0}^{\infty}P_j^2(\mu)=1$, as required. The theorem is proved.

We have the following criteria for indeterminateness of L.

Theorem 1.18. *In order that the difference expression L be indeterminate, it is necessary that the series $\sum_{j=0}^{\infty}|P_j(z)|^2$ and $\sum_{j=0}^{\infty}|Q_j(z)|^2$ converge for arbitrary z, and sufficient that one of the following conditions holds:* 1) *one of these series converges for some nonreal z;* 2) *one of these series converges for uncountably many real z;* 3) *both series converge for some real z.*

Proof. The necessity of the conditions has already been established (see Lemma 1.5); the sufficiency of the condition $\sum_{j=0}^{\infty}|P_j(z)|^2<\infty$ $(\operatorname{Im}z\neq 0)$ is also clear. Assume now that for some z $(\operatorname{Im}z\neq 0)$ $\sum_{j=0}^{\infty}|Q_j(z)|^2<\infty$; since we always have $\sum_{j=0}^{\infty}|Q_j(z)+m(z)P_j(z)|^2<\infty$ (see (1.41)), $|m(z)|^2\sum_{j=0}^{\infty}|P_j(z)|^2<\infty$. But $m(z)\neq 0$ (see the remark after Theorem 1.12), and therefore we arrive at the previous requirement: $\sum_{j=0}^{\infty}|P_j(z)|^2<\infty$.

We prove the sufficiency of conditions 2). Assume that $\sum_{j=0}^{\infty}|P_j(x)|^2<\infty$

for an uncountable number of $x \in (-\infty, \infty)$ and at the same time that L is determinate. Then the unique spectral measure $\sigma(\lambda)$ must have jumps at these points equal to $(\sum_{j=0}^{\infty} |P_j(x)|^2)^{-1}$ (see Theorem 1.17), which contradicts the countability of the set of points of discontinuity of a nondecreasing function. Further, assume that $\sum_{j=0}^{\infty} |Q_j(x)|^2 < \infty$ for uncountably many $x \in (-\infty, \infty)$. As has already been noted (see subsection 6), the polynomials $a_0 Q_j(z)$ may be regarded as polynomials $\hat{P}_{j-1}(z)$ of the first kind for the shifted difference expression $\hat{L}$ and therefore by the part of the theorem already proved, $\hat{L}$ is indeterminate. Consequently, for any z ($\operatorname{Im} z \neq 0$) $a_0^2 \sum_{j=1}^{\infty} |Q_j(z)|^2 = \sum_{j=0}^{\infty} |\hat{P}_j(z)|^2 < \infty$; by virtue of 1), L is indeterminate.

We prove the sufficiency of condition 3).[1] The general solution of the inhomogeneous difference equation

$$(Lu)_j - zu_j = f_j \quad (j = 0, 1, \cdots) \tag{1.74}$$

may be obtained by the method of variation of parameters. By elementary calculations and use of (1.54), we find

$$\begin{aligned} u_n = C_1 P_n(z) + C_2 Q_n(z) + \sum_{j=0}^{n-1} (P_j(z) Q_n(z) - P_n(z) Q_j(z)) f_j = C_1 P_n(z) \\ + C_2 Q_n(z) + (V_z f)_n \qquad (n = 0, 1, \ldots); \end{aligned} \tag{1.75}$$

C_1 and C_2 are arbitrary constants (for $n = 0$ the sum in (1.75) is taken to be zero). The operator V_z on the sequences $(f_0, f_1, \cdots)$ is called a Cauchy operator. It is easy to show that if $\sum_{j=0}^{\infty} |P_j(z)|^2$, $\sum_{j=0}^{\infty} |Q_j(z)|^2 < \infty$, then V_z is an operator of Hilbert-Schmidt type in the space $l_2([0, \infty))$. In fact,

$$\begin{aligned} \sum_{n=0}^{\infty} \sum_{j=0}^{n-1} |P_j(z) Q_n(z) - P_n(z) Q_j(z)|^2 \leqslant \sum_{n,j=0}^{\infty} |P_j(z) Q_n(z) - P_n(z) Q_j(z)|^2 \\ \leqslant 4 \sum_{n,j=0}^{\infty} |P_j(z) Q_n(z)|^2 < \infty. \end{aligned}$$

Now let $x \in (-\infty, \infty)$ be fixed such that $\sum_{j=0}^{\infty} P_j^2(x)$, $\sum_{j=0}^{\infty} Q_j^2(x) < \infty$. The sequence $(P_0(\zeta), P_1(\zeta), \cdots)$ satisfies an equation of the form (1.74):

---

[1] Here one might use one of the general operator arguments (see Ahiezer and Glazman [1], Chapter 7, p. 343, Theorem 4; English transl., Vol. II, p. 109. We provide another argument, which is useful in dealing with equations with operator coefficients (see § 2).

$$(LP(\zeta))_j - xP_j(\zeta) = (\zeta - x)P_j(\zeta) \qquad (j = 0, 1, \ldots; \; P_{-1}(\zeta) = 0, \; P_0(\zeta) = 1).$$

Writing out formula (1.75) for this solution gives

$$P_n(\zeta) = P_n(x) + (\zeta - x)(V_x P(\zeta))_n \qquad (n = 0, 1, \ldots).$$

In other words, $P_j(\zeta)$ coincides with the solution of the equation

$$((E - \mu V_x)u)_n = P_n(x) \qquad (n = 0, 1, \ldots; \; \mu = \zeta - x); \qquad (1.76)$$

Conversely, each solution of this equation, i.e. an equation of the type (1.75), coincides with $P_j(\zeta)$. Since $(P_0(x), P_1(x), \cdots) \in l_2([0, \infty))$, and since V_x is bounded in $l_2([0, \infty))$ and in fact of Hilbert-Schmidt type, (1.76) may be regarded as an equation in this space. But it is invertible for all μ except a countable sequence diverging to ∞. Thus, there exists a nonreal ζ for which $P_j(\zeta) = u_j = ((E - \mu V_x)^{-1} P(x))_j \in l_2([0, \infty))$. On the basis of 1), the expression L is indeterminate. The theorem is proved.

10. **The difference equation on the semi-axis as a limit of the difference equation on finite intervals.** We will show that in this way we can obtain the fundamental facts in the theory developed above from the spectral theory on a finite interval. We will consider the difference expression (1.1) on the integral points of a finite interval, explicitly for $j = 0, \cdots, N$. It is presupposed here that the "boundary conditions" $u_{-1} = u_{N+1} = 0$ hold, i.e. for the calculation of $(Lu)_j$ $(j = 0, \cdots, N)$ in the cases $j = 0$ or $j = N$, we set $u_{-1} = u_{N+1} = 0$. In the $(N+1)$-dimensional complex euclidean space C_{N+1} of vectors $u = (u_0, \cdots, u_N)$ we can define an operator by $(\mathrm{L}_N u)_j = (Lu)_j$ $(j = 0, \cdots, N)$; in other words, $\mathrm{L}_N u$ is obtained as the action on u by the truncated Jacobi matrix

$$J_{N+1} = \left\| \begin{matrix} b_0 & a_0 & 0 & 0 & 0 & \cdots & 0 & 0 & 0 \\ a_0 & b_1 & a_1 & 0 & 0 & \cdots & 0 & 0 & 0 \\ 0 & a_1 & b_2 & a_2 & 0 & \cdots & 0 & 0 & 0 \\ \cdot & \cdot & \cdot & \cdot & \cdot & \cdots & \cdot & \cdot & \cdot \\ 0 & 0 & 0 & 0 & 0 & \cdots & 0 & a_{N-1} & b_N \end{matrix} \right\| . \qquad (1.77)$$

Clearly, L_N is Hermitian. We show that the spectrum of L_N coincides with the set of zeros of the polynomial $P_{N+1}(\lambda)$. In fact, the spectrum of L_N (i.e. the spectrum of the matrix J_{N+1}) consists of the roots of the equation $\mathrm{Det}(J_{N+1} - \lambda E) = 0$. Let $\Delta_j(\lambda) = \mathrm{Det}(J_j - \lambda E)$ $(j = 1, 2, \cdots)$. By expanding the determinant $\mathrm{Det}(J_{j+1} - \lambda E)$ by the elements of the last row, it is easy to show that $\Delta_{j+1}(\lambda) = (b_j - \lambda)\Delta_j(\lambda) - a_{j-1}^2 \Delta_{j-1}(\lambda)$ $(j = 1, 2, \cdots)$. On dividing this equation by $a_0, \cdots, a_{j-1}$, we find that the sequence

$d_j = (-1)^j (a_0 \cdots a_{j-1})^{-1} \Delta_j(\lambda)$ $(j = 1, 2, \cdots;\ d_0 = 1,\ d_{-1} = 0)$ satisfies the equation $(Ld)_j = \lambda d_j$ $(j = 0, 1, \cdots)$. Thus $d_j = P_j(\lambda)$ $(j = 0, 1, \cdots)$, and hence $\Delta_j(\lambda) = (-1)^j a_0 \cdots a_{j-1} P_j(\lambda)$ $(j = 1, 2, \cdots)$. The assertion is proved.

Let $\lambda_1^{(N)} < \cdots < \lambda_{N+1}^{(N)}$ be the zeros of the polynomial $P_{N+1}(\lambda)$, i.e. the spectrum of L_N (the zeros of $P_{N+1}(\lambda)$ are all distinct by Lemma 1.4). Let $\phi(\lambda_\nu^{(N)}) = (\phi_0(\lambda_\nu^{(N)}), \cdots, \phi_N(\lambda_\nu^{(N)}))$ be an orthonormal system of eigenvectors corresponding to the eigenvalues $\lambda_\nu^{(N)}$. We will show that

$$\varphi(\lambda_\nu^{(N)}) = \frac{1}{\sqrt{\sum_{j=0}^{N} P_j^2(\lambda_\nu^{(N)})}} (P_0(\lambda_\nu^{(N)}), \ldots, P_N(\lambda_\nu^{(N)})) \quad (\nu = 1, \ldots, N+1). \tag{1.78}$$

Indeed, the vector $\phi(\lambda_\nu^{(N)})$ satisfies the relation $J_{N+1}\phi(\lambda_\nu^{(N)}) = \lambda_\nu^{(N)}\phi(\lambda_\nu^{(N)})$, i.e. the sequence $\phi_0(\lambda_\nu^{(N)}), \cdots, \phi_N(\lambda_\nu^{(N)})$ satisfies $(L\phi(\lambda_\nu^{(N)}))_j = \lambda_\nu^{(N)}\phi_j(\lambda_\nu^{(N)})$ $(j = 0, \cdots, N;\ \phi_{-1}(\lambda_\nu^{(N)}) = \phi_{N+1}(\lambda_\nu^{(N)}) = 0)$. Hence we obtain (1.78) , where the coefficient in (1.78) is the normalization constant.

The relation (1.78) allows us to express the usual Parseval's equation for Hermitian matrices in the following form. Let $u, v \in l_{2,0}([0, \infty))$ be such that their coordinates vanish beginning with the $(N + 1)$st; let $\widetilde{u}(\lambda)$, $\widetilde{v}(\lambda)$ be the Fourier transforms defined by (1.22). Then

$$(u, v)_0 = \sum_{\nu=1}^{N+1} \widetilde{u}(\lambda_\nu^{(N)}) \overline{\widetilde{v}(\lambda_\nu^{(N)})} \cdot \frac{1}{\sum_{j=0}^{N} P_j^2(\lambda_\nu^{(N)})} = \int_{-\infty}^{\infty} \widetilde{u}(\lambda)\widetilde{v}(\lambda)\, d\sigma_N(\lambda), \tag{1.79}$$

where the measure $d\sigma_N(\lambda)$ (the spectral measure of L_N) is concentrated only on the spectrum of L_N, where $\sigma_N(\lambda_\nu^{(N)} + 0) - \sigma_N(\lambda_\nu^{(N)}) = (\Sigma_{j=0}^N P_j^2(\lambda_\nu^{(N)}))^{-1}$.

It is not difficult to show now that for fixed u, v, we can take the limit as $N \to \infty$ in (1.79), the result of which will be Parseval's equation (1.30). First of all, note that *for each* $m = 0, 1, \cdots$ *and any* $N = 1, 2, \cdots$ *we have*

$$\int_{-\infty}^{\infty} |\lambda|^m d\sigma_N(\lambda) \leqslant C_m < \infty.$$

Indeed, $|\lambda|^m \leq 1 + \lambda^{2m}$, so $\int_{-\infty}^{\infty} |\lambda|^m\, d\sigma_N(\lambda) \leq \int_{-\infty}^{\infty} (1 + \lambda^{2m})\, d\sigma_N(\lambda) = 1 + (J_{N+1}^{2m}\delta_0, \delta_0)$. But for N sufficiently large $(J_{N+1}^{2m}\delta_0, \delta_0)_0 = (J^{2m}\delta_0, \delta_0)_0$, and (1.80) follows.

By (1.80) and Helly's first theorem, we can extract a subsequence $\sigma_{N'}^{(m)}$ from the generalized measures $\sigma_N^{(m)}(\Delta) = \int_\Delta \lambda^m \, d\sigma_N(\lambda)$ $(m = 0, 1, \cdots; N = 1, 2, \cdots;$ $\sigma_N^{(0)} = \sigma_N)$ by the diagonalization process, such that for each m, $\sigma_{N'}^{(m)} \to \sigma^{(m)}$ as $N' \to \infty$ in the ordinary sense. Hence in particular $\sigma_{N'}^{(m)}((-\infty, \infty)) \to \sigma^{(m)}((-\infty, \infty))$ as $N' \to \infty$. On the other hand, in view of Helly's second theorem, for each bounded Δ, $\int_\Delta \lambda^m d\sigma_{N'}(\lambda) \to \int_\Delta \lambda^m d\sigma(\lambda) = \sigma^{(m)}(\Delta)$ $(\sigma = \sigma^{(0)})$ as $N' \to \infty$; thus $d\sigma^{(m)}(\lambda) = \lambda^m \, d\sigma(\lambda)$. Therefore

$$\int_{-\infty}^{\infty} \lambda^m d\sigma_{N'}(\lambda) = \sigma_{N'}^{(m)}((-\infty, \infty)) \to \sigma^{(m)}((-\infty, \infty)) = \int_{-\infty}^{\infty} \lambda^m d\sigma(\lambda)$$

$$(m = 0, 1, \ldots).$$

Thus there is a subsequence $d\sigma_{N'}(\lambda)$ of the sequence of spectral measures $d\sigma_N(\lambda)$ of the operators L_N which converges in the ordinary sense to a measure $d\sigma(\lambda)$, where for each polynomial $P(\lambda)$

$$\int_{-\infty}^{\infty} P(\lambda) \, d\sigma_{N'}(\lambda) \to \int_{-\infty}^{\infty} P(\lambda) \, d\sigma(\lambda) \tag{1.81}$$

as $N' \to \infty$. The measure $d\sigma(\lambda)$ is a spectral measure of the expression L considered on the semi-axis $[0, \infty)$.

We clarify the last assertion. If we set $N = N'$ in (1.79), it follows from (1.81) that we can pass to the limit as $N' \to \infty$ in (1.79).

Therefore, Parseval's equation (1.30) holds for any $u, v \in l_2([0, \infty))$. By Theorem 1.9 this means that $d\sigma(\lambda)$ is a spectral measure for L on $[0, \infty)$.

If L is determinate, then as a result of this limit process we obtain the unique spectral measure; moreover, the zeros of the orthogonal polynomials $P_N(\lambda)$ will be concentrated on the spectrum of the problem on the semi-axis. In the indeterminate case such procedure gives a certain spectral measure $d\sigma(\lambda)$; apparently, by taking all possible subsequences the $d\sigma(\lambda)$ will describe all spectral measures corresponding to L. In the determinate case obviously we have the relation

$$\sigma(\Delta) = \lim_{N\to\infty} \sum_{\lambda_\nu^{(N)} \in \Delta} \frac{1}{\sum_{j=0}^{N} P_j^2(\lambda_\nu^{(N)})}, \quad m(z) = \lim_{N\to\infty} \sum_{\nu=1}^{N+1} \frac{1}{(\lambda_\nu^{(N)} - z) \sum_{j=0}^{N} P_j^2(\lambda_\nu^{(N)})}. \tag{1.82}$$

It is clear that many of the other results of subsections 1–9 can be "approximated" by results on a finite interval; however we will stop here.

11. Two examples. We confine ourselves to the simplest examples of difference expressions.

a) The difference analogue of the differential expression u'' is $(\Delta_\ell \Delta_n u)_j = u_{j-1} + u_{j+1} - 2u_j$. The study of $\Delta_\ell \Delta_n$ is, obviously, equivalent to the study of the expression

$$(Lu)_j = \frac{1}{2} u_{j-1} + \frac{1}{2} u_{j+1} \quad (j = 0, 1, \ldots; u_{-1} = 0),$$

$$J = \begin{Vmatrix} 0 & \frac{1}{2} & 0 & 0 & \ldots \\ \frac{1}{2} & 0 & \frac{1}{2} & 0 & \ldots \\ 0 & \frac{1}{2} & 0 & \frac{1}{2} & \ldots \\ \cdot & \cdot & \cdot & \cdot & \cdot \end{Vmatrix}. \tag{1.83}$$

We now turn to the examination of (1.83). First of all, we find $P_j(z)$. These polynomials are a solution of the Cauchy problem

$$\frac{1}{2} u_{j-1} + \frac{1}{2} u_{j+1} = zu_j \quad (j = 0, 1, \ldots; u_{-1} = 0, u_0 = 1).$$

If $z = \cos\theta$, then the solution of the resulting recursion relation will, as before, be unique; on the other hand, the sequence $u_j = \sin(j+1)\theta/\sin\theta$ $(j = -1, 0, 1, \cdots)$ obviously satisfies it. Thus

$$P_j(z) = \frac{\sin((j+1)\arccos z)}{\sin(\arccos z)} \quad (j = -1, 0, 1, \ldots) \tag{1.84}$$

will be the solution of the Cauchy problem: hence it follows that the quotient in (1.84) is a polynomial of degree j in z. Thus, (1.84) gives the required answer; these polynomials are known as Čebyšev polynomials of the second kind. The polynomials $Q_j(z)$ $(j = 1, 2, \cdots)$ form the solution of the Cauchy problem $v_{j-1}/2 + v_{j+1}/2 = zv_j$ $(j = 1, 2, \cdots; v_0 = 0, v_1 = 1/a_0 = 2)$. Comparing this problem with the previous, we obtain, obviously, $Q_j(z) = 2P_{j-1}(z)$ $(j = 0, 1, \cdots)$.

Since the coefficients of L are bounded, the operator L is bounded by Theorem 1.2; moreover, the expression L is determinate. The unique spectral measure is

$$d\sigma(\lambda) = \begin{cases} \frac{2}{\pi}\sqrt{1-\lambda^2}\,d\lambda, & |\lambda| \leqslant 1; \\ 0, & |\lambda| > 1. \end{cases} \tag{1.85}$$

This follows from Theorem 1.9 and the orthogonality relations

$$\frac{2}{\pi}\int_{-1}^{1} P_j(\lambda) P_k(\lambda)\sqrt{1-\lambda^2}\,d\lambda = \frac{2}{\pi}\int_{0}^{\pi} \sin(j+1)\theta \cdot \sin(k+1)\theta\, d\theta = \delta_{jk}$$

$$(j,\ k = 0,\ 1,\ \ldots).$$

Thus, the spectrum of L fills the segment $[-1, 1]$, $\|L\| = 1$. The function $m(z)$ has the form

$$m(z) = -\frac{2}{\pi}\int_{-1}^{1} \frac{\sqrt{1-\lambda^2}}{\lambda - z}\,d\lambda = 2(\sqrt{z^2-1} - z) \qquad (z \overline{\in} [-1,\ 1]). \tag{1.86}$$

b) Consider the expression L corresponding to the Jacobi matrix

$$J = \left\| \begin{matrix} 0 & \frac{1}{\sqrt{2}} & 0 & 0 & 0 & \ldots \\ \frac{1}{\sqrt{2}} & 0 & \frac{1}{2} & 0 & 0 & \ldots \\ 0 & \frac{1}{2} & 0 & \frac{1}{2} & 0 & \ldots \\ \cdot & \cdot & \cdot & \cdot & \cdot & \cdot \end{matrix} \right\|. \tag{1.87}$$

The polynomials $P_j(z)$ form a solution of the Cauchy problem

$$\frac{1}{2}u_{j-1} + \frac{1}{2}u_{j+1} = zu_j \ (j = 2,\ 3,\ \ldots), \ \frac{1}{\sqrt{2}}u_0 + \frac{1}{2}u_2 = zu_1,$$

$$a_{-1}u_{-1} + \frac{1}{\sqrt{2}}u_1 = zu_0 \qquad (u_{-1} = 0,\ u_0 = 1).$$

Set, as before, $z = \cos\theta$. It is not difficult to see that the solution of the resulting recursion relation is the sequence $u_j = \sqrt{2}\cos j\theta$ ($j = 1, 2, \cdots$; $u_{-1} = 0$, $u_0 = 1$). Thus, the polynomials (Čebyšev polynomials of the first kind)

$$P_0(z) = 1,\ P_j(z) = \sqrt{2}\cos(j\arccos z) \qquad (j = 1,\ 2,\ \ldots) \tag{1.88}$$

are the ones sought for. The polynomials $Q_j(z)$ satisfy the relation

$$\frac{1}{2}v_{j-1}+\frac{1}{2}v_{j+1}=zv_j\ (j=2,3,\ldots),\ \frac{1}{\sqrt{2}}v_0+\frac{1}{2}v_2=zv_1$$
$$\left(v_0=0,\ v_1=\frac{1}{a_0}=\sqrt{2}\right),$$

i.e. by a) $Q_j(z)=\sqrt{2}\sin(j\arccos z)/\sin(\arccos z)\ (j=0,1,\cdots)$.

As in the previous example, it is easy to see that L is bounded ($\|L\|=1$), its spectrum fills $[-1,1]$, and

$$d\sigma(\lambda)=\begin{cases}\dfrac{d\lambda}{\pi\sqrt{1-\lambda^2}}, & |\lambda|\leqslant 1;\\ 0, & |\lambda|>1;\end{cases}\qquad m(z)=\frac{1}{\pi}\int_{-1}^{1}\frac{d\lambda}{(\lambda-z)\sqrt{1-\lambda^2}} \tag{1.89}$$
$$=-\frac{1}{\sqrt{z^2-1}}\qquad (z\,\overline{\in}\,[-1,1]).$$

12. **General boundary conditions.** It is possible to form a generalization of the problem introduced in subsection 1. The general linear homogeneous boundary condition in a neighborhood of the origin obviously has the form

$$\alpha u_{-1}+\beta u_0=0\quad (|\alpha|+|\beta|>0). \tag{1.90}$$

The adjoint condition, i.e. the relation between v_{-1} and v_0, so that $(Lu,v)_0=(u,Lv)_0$ for any sequence $(u_{-1},u_0,u_1,\cdots)$ finite at ∞ which satisfies (1.90), can be found easily with the aid of Green's formula (1.4) by the usual argument (see the proof of Theorem 1.1, Chapter II). It has the form $\bar{\alpha}v_{-1}+\bar{\beta}v_0=0$. Thus, the condition (1.90) is selfadjoint if and only if $\operatorname{Im}\alpha=\operatorname{Im}\beta=0$.

All of the theory developed in subsections 1–10 can be carried over to problems of the form

$$(Lu)_j=a_{j-1}u_{j-1}+a_ju_{j+1}+b_ju_j=\lambda u_j;\ \alpha u_{-1}+\beta u_0=0$$
$$(j=0,1,\ldots,\ \operatorname{Im}\alpha=\operatorname{Im}\beta=0;\ \alpha^2+\beta^2>0). \tag{1.91}$$

We will not do this however, and only remark that the roles of the polynomials $P_j(z)$ and $Q_j(z)$ are played by two linearly independent solutions of the equation $(Lu)_j=zu_j\ (j=0,1,\cdots)$, the first of which satisfies the condition $\alpha u_{-1}+\beta u_0=0$, and the second of which is connected with the first by means of (1.35).

§2. SECOND ORDER DIFFERENCE EXPRESSIONS WITH OPERATOR COEFFICIENTS ON THE SEMI-AXIS

The results of §1 are generalized here to the case of a difference expression of the form $(Lu)_j = a_{j-1}u_{j-1} + a_j u_{j+1} + b_j u_j$, where a_j, b_j are operators in some Hilbert space H, and $(u_0, u_1, \cdots)$ is a sequence of vectors in H. Due to a certain awkwardness of the constructions, we will not present the complete theory, but will restrict ourselves just to the basic facts, corresponding, for instance, to subsections 1–6 of §1. In §§3–4 applications of these results to ordinary difference equations on the whole real line and to partial difference equations will be given. It is appropriate now to emphasize that partial difference expressions, and also ordinary difference expressions of even order are special cases of expressions with operator coefficients.

First, we present, in subsections 1–4, an auxiliary construction which generalizes the Hilbert space concept and is also of independent interest. We start by forming a certain module, and then introduce an analogue of the scalar product and topology for it. In this connection recall that an abelian group G under addition is called a module (more precisely, a right module) if for each u in G a product $u \cdot \lambda$ is defined for all λ in a fixed ring R with identity ("a ring of scalars"). This product must possess the usual properties: $(u + v) \cdot \lambda = u \cdot \lambda + v \cdot \lambda$, $u \cdot (\lambda + \mu) = u \cdot \lambda + u \cdot \mu$, $u \cdot (\lambda\mu) = (u \cdot \lambda) \cdot \mu$, $u \cdot e = u$ ($u, v \in G$; $\lambda, \mu \in R$; e is the identity of the ring R).

1. **Definition of a pseudo-Hilbert space.** Let H and $\mathfrak{H}$ be complete Hilbert spaces, which, for simplicity, we assume are separable. The elements of the space H will be denoted by $x, y, \cdots$; $(\cdot, \cdot)_H$ and $\|\cdot\|_H$ are the scalar product and norm in H. For $\mathfrak{H}$ we use the corresponding notation $u, v, \cdots$; $(\cdot, \cdot)_{\mathfrak{H}}$, $\|\cdot\|_{\mathfrak{H}}$. The case when H and $\mathfrak{H}$ coincide is not excluded, but the case of most interest for applications is when H is a certain quotient space of $\mathfrak{H}$. Consider the set $L(H, \mathfrak{H})$ of all continuous linear operators which map all of H into $\mathfrak{H}$; these will be denoted by $U, V, \cdots$. $L(H, \mathfrak{H})$ is a vector space under ordinary addition of operators. The elements of $L(H, \mathfrak{H})$ can be multiplied on the right by continuous linear operators Λ in H (i.e. by elements of $L(H, H)$): $U\Lambda$; this product satisfies the usual requirements of associativity and distributivity. Thus $L(H, \mathfrak{H})$ is a module.

We may introduce a "scalar" product in $L(H, \mathfrak{H})$ by setting $\{U, V\} = U^*V \in L(H, H)$ $(U, V \in L(H, \mathfrak{H}))$, where U^* is the adjoint of U (it acts from $\mathfrak{H}$

to H). Clearly $\{U, U\}$ is a nonnegative operator and

$$(\{U, V\} x, y)_H = (Vx, Uy)_{\mathfrak{H}} \quad (x, y \in H;\ U, V \in L(H, \mathfrak{H})). \tag{2.1}$$

$\{\cdot, \cdot\}$ satisfies analogues of the usual properties of scalar products:

$$\{U, V+W\} = \{U, V\} + \{U, W\},\ \{U, V\Lambda\} = \{U, V\}\Lambda,\ \{U, V\}^* = \{V, U\};$$
$$\{U+V, W\} = \{U, W\} + \{V, W\},\ \{U\Lambda, V\} = \Lambda^*\{U, V\}; \tag{2.2}$$
$$(U, V, W \in L(H, \mathfrak{H});\ \Lambda \in L(H, H)).$$

The set $L(H, \mathfrak{H})$ will be called a pseudo-Hilbert space, its elements pseudo-vectors, operators $\Lambda, \mathrm{M}, \cdots \in L(H, H)$ pseudo-scalars, and $\{\cdot, \cdot\}$ a pseudo-scalar product. The topology on $L(H, \mathfrak{H})$ is to be the strong operator topology: $U^{(n)} \to U$, if for each $x \in H$, $U^{(n)}x \to Ux$ in $\mathfrak{H}$. The basic neighborhoods of a pseudo-vector U are the sets $O(U; x_1, \cdots, x_p; \epsilon)$ of all pseudo-vectors V such that

$$\|Ux_1 - Vx_1\|_{\mathfrak{H}} < \varepsilon, \ \ldots,\ \|Ux_p - Vx_p\|_{\mathfrak{H}} < \varepsilon \ (x_1, \ldots, x_p \in H;$$
$$p = 1, 2, \ldots;\ \varepsilon > 0).$$

It is well known that the topology introduced converts $L(H, \mathfrak{H})$ into a Hausdorff space. It is complete in the sense that if $U^{(n)} \in L(H, \mathfrak{H})$ are such that $U^{(n)}x$ is a fundamental sequence in $\mathfrak{H}$ for each $x \in H$, then $U^{(n)} \to U \in L(H, \mathfrak{H})$. It is useful to observe that $U^{(n)} \to U$ if and only if $\{U^{(n)} - U, U^{(n)} - U\} \to 0$ in the sense of weak convergence of operators in H or, equivalently, $(\{U^{(n)} - U, U^{(n)} - U\}x, x)_H \to 0$ $(x \in H)$.

It is clear from (2.1) that the pseudo-scalar product is continuous in the sense of weak convergence of operators in H as a function of both of its factors (continuity in the sense of strong convergence in $L(H, H)$ does not hold in general). It should be emphasized that the product $U\Lambda$ is, in general, not continuous in $L(H, \mathfrak{H})$ as a function of the two variables $U \in L(H, \mathfrak{H})$ and Λ in the sense of weak convergence in $L(H, H)$. The sum $U + V$ is obviously continuous in both variables simultaneously in the introduced topology.

In concluding this subsection, we show that a pseudo-Hilbert space is in fact a generalization of Hilbert space. Consider the case when $H = C_1$ is ordinary one-dimensional complex space, and $\mathfrak{H}$ is arbitrary. Each operator U from C_1 to $\mathfrak{H}$ is of the form $Ux = xu$ $(x \in C_1)$ where u is some vector in $\mathfrak{H}$ (in fact,

$Ux = xU1 = xu$, $u = U1$); therefore U may be identified with the corresponding $u \in \mathfrak{H}$. Clearly, this is an isomorphism between $L(C_1, \mathfrak{H})$ and $\mathfrak{H}$, where $\{U, V\} = \mathfrak{H}(v, u)$ (the latter follows from (2.1): $\{U, V\}\bar{x}y = (\{U, V\}x, y)_H = (Vx, Uy)_{\mathfrak{H}} = x\bar{y}(v, u)_{\mathfrak{H}}$). Thus, it may be assumed that $L(C_1, \mathfrak{H})$ coincides with $\mathfrak{H}$.

2. Some geometric facts about pseudo-Hilbert space. We show that certain constructions, analogous to constructions in ordinary Hilbert space, are possible in the space $L(H, \mathfrak{H})$. We call a system (finite or not[1]) $E^{(0)}, E^{(1)}, \dots \in L(H, \mathfrak{H})$ pseudo-orthonormal, if

$$\{E^{(j)}, E^{(k)}\} = \delta_{jk}E \quad (j, k = 0, 1, \dots) \tag{2.3}$$

(E is the identity operator in H). The essential difference then between pseudo-Hilbert space and ordinary Hilbert space is that not every sequence of pseudo-vectors can be "orthogonalized" (see below concerning this). We will assume in what follows that $E^{(0)}, E^{(1)}, \dots$ is a given pseudo-orthonormal system.

Theorem 2.1. *If $U \in L(H, \mathfrak{H})$ and if the expansion*

$$U = \sum_{j=0}^{\infty} E^{(j)}U_j \quad (U_j \in L(H, H)), \tag{2.4}$$

converges in $L(H, \mathfrak{H})$, then the series

$$\sum_{j=0}^{\infty} U_j^*U_j = \{U, U\}.^{2)} \tag{2.5}$$

is weakly convergent in $L(H, H)$.

Conversely, if $U_0, U_1, \dots \in L(H, H)$ is a given sequence for which the series in (2.5) converges, then the series (2.4) converges, and moreover, its sum U satisfies the equation (2.5).

---

[1] For the definition below, we assume that the system is finite.

[2] Note that if the series $\Sigma_{j=0}^{\infty} U_j^* U_j$ $(U_j \in L(H, H))$ converges weakly, then, since its summands are nonnegative, it converges strongly. Now suppose that we have a weakly convergent series $\Sigma_{j=0}^{\infty} V_j^* V_j$ $(V_j \in L(H, H))$. It is elementary to prove that the series $\Sigma_{j=0}^{\infty} U_j^* V_j$ converges weakly. More than this, it is not difficult to show that *it converges strongly.* In fact, by the properties (2.2) of a pseudo-scalar product we have

Proof. Suppose that the expansion (2.4) is valid, i.e. $\Sigma_{j=0}^{n} E^{(j)} U_j \to U$ in $L(H, \mathfrak{H})$. Then $\Sigma_{j=0}^{n} U_j^* U_j = \{\Sigma_{j=0}^{n} E^{(j)} U_j, \Sigma_{j=0}^{n} E^{(j)} U_j\} \to \{U, U\}$, in the sense of weak convergence in $L(H, H)$, i.e. (2.5) holds. Conversely, if $U_0, U_1, \cdots \in L(H, H)$ are such that the series (2.5) converges weakly, then for each $x \in H$ $\Sigma_{j=0}^{\infty} \| U_j x \|_H^2 = (\Sigma_{j=0}^{\infty} U_j^* U_j x, x)_H < \infty$. Hence the sequence $\Sigma_{j=0}^{n} E^{(j)} U_j$ is fundamental in $L(H, \mathfrak{H})$:

$$\left(\left\{ \sum_{j=n}^{m} E^{(j)} U_j, \sum_{j=n}^{m} E^{(j)} U_j \right\} x, x \right)_H = \sum_{j=n}^{m} \| U_j x \|_H^2 \underset{n,m\to\infty}{\to} 0 \ (x \in H).$$

Since $L(H, \mathfrak{H})$ is complete, it converges to $U \in L(H, \mathfrak{H})$, and the assertion follows. The theorem is proved.

On taking the scalar product of (2.4) by $E^{(k)}$ on the left we find that the coefficients U_j in the expansion (2.4), i.e. the coordinates of U, are uniquely determined by the formula

$$U_j = \{E^{(j)}, U\} \quad (j = 0, 1, \ldots). \tag{2.6}$$

It is also easy to show that if $V \in L(H, \mathfrak{H})$ has an expansion of the type (2.4), then

$$\{U, V\} = \sum_{j=0}^{\infty} U_j^* V_j, \tag{2.7}$$

where convergence is in the weak sense in $L(H, H)$.

We say that the space $L(H, \mathfrak{H})$ admits a pseudo-orthonormal basis $E^{(0)}$, $E^{(1)}, \cdots$, if this system is pseudo-orthonormal and if (2.4) holds for all $U \in L(H, \mathfrak{H})$. Clearly in this case $L(H, \mathfrak{H})$ can be identified with all possible sequences $(U_0, U_1, \cdots) = U$ such that the series $\Sigma_{j=0}^{\infty} U_j^* U_j$ converges weakly in $L(H, H)$. The operations on U appear as follows: $(U+V)_j = U_j + V_j$, $(U\Lambda)_j = U_j \Lambda$ $(j = 0, 1, \cdots)$; $\{U, V\} = \Sigma_{j=0}^{\infty} U_j^* V_j$.

$$\{U, V\} = \frac{1}{4}[\{U+V, U+V\} - \{U-V, U-V\} + i\{Ui+V, Ui+V\} - i\{Ui-V, Ui-V\}]$$

$$(U, V \in L(H, \mathfrak{H});\ Ui = U\,(iE)). \tag{$*$}$$

The series $\Sigma_{j=0}^{\infty}(U_j \pm V_j)^* (U_j \pm V_j)$, $\Sigma_{j=0}^{\infty}(iU_j \pm V_j)^* (iU_j \pm V_j)$, obviously converges weakly, and hence strongly. But then by $(*)$, $\{U, V\} = \Sigma_{j=0}^{\infty} U_j^* V_j$ converges strongly, as required.

Everywhere in what follows it is convenient for us to talk about weak convergence of series of this form, but one must bear in mind that in fact strong convergence occurs.

Example. *The spaces* $l_2(H; [0, \infty))$ *and* $\mathbf{1}_2(H; [0, \infty))$. These spaces play an essential part in the general theory of pseudo-Hilbert spaces, and in their applications to difference equations. Denote by $l_2(H; [0, \infty))$ the orthogonal sum of an infinite sequence of the spaces H, i.e.

$$l_2(H; [0, \infty)) = H \oplus H \oplus \cdots .$$

In other words, a vector in $l_2(H; [0, \infty))$ is a sequence $u = (u_0, u_1, \cdots)$ of vectors $u_0, u_1, \cdots \in H$ such that $\sum_{j=0}^{\infty} \|u_j\|_H^2 < \infty$. In this connection

$$(u+v)_j = u_j + v_j,\ (\lambda u)_j = \lambda u_j\ (j = 0, 1, \ldots);\ (u, v)_{l_2(H;[0,\infty))} = \sum_{j=0}^{\infty} (u_j, v_j)_H$$
$$(u, v \in l_2(H; [0, \infty)).$$

We define the pseudo-Hilbert space $\mathbf{1}_2(H; [0, \infty))$ to be the space $\mathbf{1}_2(H; [0, \infty)) = L(H, l_2(H; [0, \infty)))$. First note that it has a pseudo-orthonormal basis $E^{(j)} = \Delta^{(j)}$ $(j = 0, 1, \cdots)$; we denote by $\Delta^{(j)}$ the continuous map of H into $l_2(H; [0, \infty))$ given by $\Delta^{(j)} x = (0, \cdots, 0, x, 0, \cdots)$ where x is the jth coordinate. By (2.1), it follows easily that $\{\Delta^{(j)}, \Delta^{(k)}\} = \delta_{jk} E$ $(j, k = 0, 1, \cdots)$. The system $\Delta^{(0)}, \Delta^{(1)}, \cdots$ is in fact a basis for $\mathbf{1}_2(H; [0, \infty))$: for each $U \in \mathbf{1}_2(H; [0, \infty))$ if we define the pseudo-scalars $U_j = \{\Delta^{(j)}, U\}$, then $\sum_{j=0}^{\infty} \Delta^{(j)} U_j = U$. In fact, we need only show that for each $x \in H$ $\sum_{j=0}^{n} \Delta^{(j)} U_j x \to Ux$ as $n \to \infty$ in the sense of convergence in the norm of $l_2(H; [0, \infty))$. Let $Ux = (u_0, u_1, \cdots) \in l_2(H; [0, \infty))$; then $U_j x = u_j$ and because of (2.1) we have $(U_j x, y)_H = (\{\Delta^{(j)}, U\} x, y)_H = (Ux, \Delta^{(j)} y)_{l_2(H;[0,\infty))} = (u_j, y)_H$ for any $y \in H$. Thus, $\sum_{j=0}^{n} \Delta^{(j)} U_j x = (u_0, \cdots, u_n, 0, 0, \cdots)$ and convergence of this sequence to $(u_0, u_1, \cdots) = Ux$ is obvious. This argument also shows that $\mathbf{1}_2(H; [0, \infty))$ can be defined by the "coordinate" method; it is the space of sequences $U = (U_0, U_1, \cdots)$ of bounded operators in H such that the series $\sum_{j=0}^{\infty} U_j^* U_j$ converges weakly in $L(H, H)$. The algebraic operations in $\mathbf{1}_2(H; [0, \infty))$ and the pseudo-scalar product are defined by the equations

$$(U+V)_j = U_j + V_j,\ (U\Lambda)_j = U_j \Lambda\ (j = 0, 1, \ldots);\ \{U, V\} = \sum_{j=0}^{\infty} U_j^* V_j$$
$$(U, V \in \mathbf{1}_2(H; [0, \infty)).$$

Thus, if the space $\mathfrak{H}$ is of the form $H \oplus H \oplus \cdots$, then there exists an infinite pseudo-orthonormal basis for $L(H, \mathfrak{H}) = \mathbf{1}_2(H; [0, \infty))$. The converse result also holds.

Theorem 2.2. *If $L(H, \mathfrak{H})$ contains a pseudo-orthonormal basis $E^{(0)}, E^{(1)}, \cdots$, then for each $u \in \mathfrak{H}$ the sequence*

$$u_j = (E^{(j)})^* u \quad (j = 0, 1, \ldots) \tag{2.8}$$

of vectors in H is such that

$$u = \sum_{j=0}^{\infty} E^{(j)} u_j, \quad \sum_{j=0}^{\infty} (u_j, u_j)_H = (u, u)_{\mathfrak{H}} < \infty, \tag{2.9}$$

where the first series converges strongly in $\mathfrak{H}$.

Conversely, if $u_0, u_1, \cdots \in H$ is a sequence such that the second series in (2.9) converges, then there is a $u \in \mathfrak{H}$ such that $(E^{(j)})^* u = u_j$. In other words, under the hypothesis of the theorem, $\mathfrak{H} = H \oplus H \oplus \cdots = l_2(H; [0, \infty))$[1] *and $L(H, \mathfrak{H}) = \mathbf{l}_2(H; [0, \infty))$.*

Proof. We apply equation (2.4) to the vector $x \in H$: $Ux = \sum_{j=0}^{\infty} E^{(j)} U_j x$. But $U_j = \{E^{(j)}, U\} = (E^{(j)})^* U$, so $U_j x = (E^{(j)})^* Ux$. Thus $U_j x$ is determined by the vector $u = Ux$ and does not depend on its representation in the form Vy $(V \in L(H, \mathfrak{H}), y \in H)$. Hence the expansion (2.9) holds for u with u_j defined by (2.8). The second equation in (2.9) follows immediately from (2.5) and (2.1).

To prove the second part of the theorem it is sufficient to show that if $u_0, u_1, \cdots \in H$ is such that $\sum_{j=0}^{\infty} \|u_j\|_H^2 < \infty$, then for any nonzero $x \in H$ there is a sequence $U_0, U_1, \cdots \in L(H, H)$ for which the series (2.5) converges, such that $u_j = U_j x$. Denote by V_j the unitary operator in H which sends x into $(\|x\|_H / \|u_j\|_H) u_j$; then $U_j = (\|u_j\|_H / \|x\|_H) V_j$ sends x into u_j $(j = 0, 1, \cdots)$. Moreover, for any $y \in H$

$$\sum_{j=0}^{\infty} \| U_j y \|_H^2 = \sum_{j=0}^{\infty} \frac{\| u_j \|_H^2}{\| x \|_H^2} \| V_j y \|_H^2 = \frac{\| y \|_H^2}{\| x \|_H^2} \sum_{j=0}^{\infty} \| u_j \|_H^2 < \infty,$$

i.e. the series (2.5) converges weakly. The theorem is proved.

In a similar way, one can define the space $l_2(H; [0, N]) = H \oplus \cdots \oplus H$ $(N + 1$ times$)$ for $N = 0, 1, \cdots$ and hence construct the space $\mathbf{l}_2(H; [0, N]) = L(H, l_2(H; [0, N]))$. As above, it is easy to see that $\mathbf{l}_2(H; [0, N])$ contains a

[1] More precisely, $\mathfrak{H}$ is isometric to $H \oplus H \oplus \cdots$. For the sake of shortening the formulation we later replace isometry by equality. In this connection, two pseudo-Hilbert spaces $L(H, \mathfrak{H}')$ and $L(H, \mathfrak{H}'')$ are said to be isometric if $\mathfrak{H}'$ and $\mathfrak{H}''$ are isometric; the pseudo-scalar products in these spaces agree on corresponding pseudo-vectors.

pseudo-orthonormal basis consisting of $N+1$ pseudo-vectors. Conversely, if $L(H, \mathfrak{H})$ contains a pseudo-orthonormal basis consisting of $N+1$ pseudo-vectors, then $\mathfrak{H} = l_2(H; [0, N])$ and $L(H, \mathfrak{H}) = \mathbf{l}_2(H; [0, N])$.

From all that has been said, it is easy to perceive that there exists a pseudo-orthonormal basis in $L(H, \mathfrak{H})$ for "almost any H and $\mathfrak{H}$". More precisely, it exists in the following (and only in these) cases:

a) The dimensions $d(\mathfrak{H})$ and $d(H)$ of the spaces $\mathfrak{H}$ and H are finite, and $d(\mathfrak{H}) = kd(H)$ ($k = 1, 2, \cdots$). In this case the basis consists of k pseudo-vectors.

b) The dimensions $d(\mathfrak{H}) = \infty$. A basis always exists in this case if $d(H) < \infty$, and then it necessarily consists of an infinite number of pseudo-vectors. If $d(H) = \infty$, then it may be constructed with any preassigned number $k = 1, 2, \cdots, \infty$ of pseudo-vectors.

For the proof, note that in these cases we always have the representation $\mathfrak{H} = H \oplus H \oplus \cdots$ with the corresponding number k of summands. This shows that $L(H, \mathfrak{H}) = \mathbf{l}_2(H; [0, k-1])$ and therefore there exists a basis of k pseudo-vectors in $L(H, \mathfrak{H})$. By Theorem 2.2 and the analogous fact concerning $\mathbf{l}_2(H; [0, N])$, it follows that a) and b) comprise all possible cases in which a basis exists.

We now consider the question of the existence of orthogonal complements and subspaces. A set $\mathbf{G} \subseteq L(H, \mathfrak{H})$ is called a pseudo-linear manifold, if for any U, $V \in \mathbf{G}$, $U + V \in \mathbf{G}$, $U\Lambda \in \mathbf{G}$ ($\Lambda \in L(H, H)$). A closed pseudo-linear manifold is called a pseudo-linear subspace. The set $\hat{\mathbf{G}}$ of all $V \in L(H, \mathfrak{H})$ for which $\{V, U\} = 0$ ($U \in \mathbf{G}$) obviously also forms a pseudo-linear subspace, namely the pseudo-orthogonal complement of $\mathbf{G}$. If each $U \in L(H, \mathfrak{H})$ admits a representation $U = V + W$, where $V \in \mathbf{G}$ and $W \in \hat{\mathbf{G}}$, then we say that $L(H, \mathfrak{H})$ decomposes into the pseudo-orthogonal sum of $\mathbf{G}$ and $\hat{\mathbf{G}}$: $L(H, \mathfrak{H}) = \mathbf{G} \oplus \hat{\mathbf{G}}$.

Let $x \in H$, $x \neq 0$, and let $G = \mathbf{G}x$. Since $\mathbf{G}$ contains any $U\Lambda$ whenever it contains U, G is independent of x; clearly, G is a linear manifold in $\mathfrak{H}$. We say that $\mathbf{G}$ is maximal, if G is closed, and if for any $U \in L(H, \mathfrak{H})$ such that $Ux \in G$ for $x \in H$, it follows that $U \in \mathbf{G}$. We now prove a simple theorem, of which an important application is given in subsection 9 (Lemma 2.4).

Theorem 2.3. *Let $\mathbf{G}$ be a pseudo-subspace. A necessary and sufficient condition for the decomposition $L(H, \mathfrak{H}) = \mathbf{G} \oplus \hat{\mathbf{G}}$, is that $\mathbf{G}$ be maximal. In this case the decomposition $U = U_{\mathbf{G}} + U_{\hat{\mathbf{G}}}$ ($U \in L(H, \mathfrak{H})$, $U_{\mathbf{G}} \in \mathbf{G}$, $U_{\hat{\mathbf{G}}} \in \hat{\mathbf{G}}$) is unique.*

Proof. Assume that $\mathbf{G}$ is maximal and consider the decomposition $\mathfrak{H} = G \oplus \hat{G}$, where $\hat{G}$ is the orthogonal complement of G in $\mathfrak{H}$. If $U \in L(H, \mathfrak{H})$ and $x \in H$, then $Ux \in \mathfrak{H}$ and therefore we can write $Ux = v_x + w_x$ ($v_x \in G$, $w_x \in \hat{G}$). Clearly, the correspondence $x \longrightarrow v_x$ is linear, and because of the inequality $\|v_x\|_{\mathfrak{H}} \leq \|Ux\|_{\mathfrak{H}} \leq \|U\| \, \|x\|_H$ it is continuous; therefore $v_x = U_{\mathbf{G}}x$, where $U_{\mathbf{G}} \in L(H, \mathfrak{H})$. Since for each $x \in H$, $U_{\mathbf{G}}x = v_x \in G$, because of the maximality of $\mathbf{G}$, $U_{\mathbf{G}} \in \mathbf{G}$. If we set $U_{\hat{\mathbf{G}}} = U - U_{\mathbf{G}}$, we obtain that for any $V \in \mathbf{G}$ $(\{U_{\hat{\mathbf{G}}}, V\}y, x)_H = (Vy, U_{\hat{\mathbf{G}}}x)_{\mathfrak{H}} = (Vy, w_x)_{\mathfrak{H}} = 0$ $(x, y \in H)$, since $w_x \in \hat{G}$, and $Vy \in G$. Thus $U_{\hat{\mathbf{G}}} \perp \mathbf{G}$, i.e. $U_{\hat{\mathbf{G}}} \in \hat{\mathbf{G}}$. The required decomposition is established. Uniqueness follows easily from the uniqueness of the decomposition $\mathfrak{H} = G \oplus \hat{G}$.

We prove the necessity. Suppose that any $U \in L(H, \mathfrak{H})$ can be decomposed as $U = U_{\mathbf{G}} + U_{\hat{\mathbf{G}}}$ $(U_{\mathbf{G}} \in \mathbf{G}, U_{\hat{\mathbf{G}}} \in \hat{\mathbf{G}})$. Then $Ux = U_{\mathbf{G}}x + U_{\hat{\mathbf{G}}}x$ $(x \in H, U_{\mathbf{G}}x \in G, U_{\hat{\mathbf{G}}}x \in \hat{G})$; this equation can be interpreted as a decomposition of Ux with respect to G and $\hat{G}$. Since Ux runs through all of $\mathfrak{H}$ as U and x vary, any vector in $\mathfrak{H}$ can be decomposed with respect to G and $\hat{G}$. This proves that G is closed. Suppose now that $U \in L(H, \mathfrak{H})$ is such that $Ux \in G$ for any $x \in H$. We have the decomposition $U = U_{\mathbf{G}} + U_{\hat{\mathbf{G}}}$. If $U_{\hat{\mathbf{G}}} \neq 0$ there is an $x \in H$ such that $0 \neq U_{\hat{\mathbf{G}}}x \,\overline{\in}\, G$, and therefore $Ux = U_{\mathbf{G}}x + U_{\hat{\mathbf{G}}}x \,\overline{\in}\, G$; this is absurd. Thus $U = U_{\mathbf{G}} \in \mathbf{G}$. The theorem is proved.

In conclusion of this subsection we show that not every system $W^{(0)}, W^{(1)}, \ldots$ can be "pseudo-orthogonalized", i.e. pseudo-orthonormalized. Indeed, for the normalization of $W^{(0)} \in L(H, \mathfrak{H})$ it is necessary and sufficient that $\{W^{(0)}, W^{(0)}\}^{-1}$ exist; in this connection, by normalization we mean the construction of an $E^{(0)} \in L(H, \mathfrak{H})$ such that $\{E^{(0)}, E^{(0)}\} = E$ and $W^{(0)}L(H, H) = E^{(0)}L(H, H)$. Thus if $\{W^{(0)}, W^{(0)}\}^{-1}$ exists we can take $E^{(0)} = W^{(0)}\sqrt{\{W^{(0)}, W^{(0)}\}^{-1}}$. Conversely, if $E^{(0)}$ exists, then there is a $\Lambda \in L(H, H)$ such that $W^{(0)}\Lambda = E^{(0)}$. Therefore $\Lambda^* \{W^{(0)}, W^{(0)}\Lambda\} = E$, and this is possible only if $\{W^{(0)}, W^{(0)}\}^{-1}$ exists.

Assume that $W^{(0)}$ can be normalized, replacing it by $E^{(0)}$. The next step of our process is to choose $\Lambda \in L(H, H)$ such that $W^{(1)} + E^{(0)}\Lambda$ will be pseudo-orthogonal to $E^{(0)}$. It is easy to compute that $\Lambda = -\{E^{(0)}, W^{(1)}\}$. Thus, we must now normalize the pseudo-vector $W^{(1)} - E^{(0)}\{E^{(0)}, W^{(1)}\}$. At the same time $\{W^{(1)} - E^{(0)}\{E^{(0)}, W^{(1)}\}, W^{(1)} - E^{(0)}\{E^{(0)}, W^{(1)}\}\} = \{W^{(1)}, W^{(1)}\} - \{E^{(0)}, W^{(1)}\}^* \{E^{(0)}, W^{(1)}\} = (W^{(1)})^* W^{(1)} - (W^{(1)})^* E^{(0)}(E^{(0)})^* W^{(1)}$ and it is possible that the latter operator is different from zero, but not invertible. In this case, the pseudo-orthogonalization process is broken. In certain cases one can guarantee that such a situation cannot occur and then the process can be continued. See for example subsection 8.

3. **Operator integrals and spaces of the type L_2.** First of all, we present a simple generalization of the concept of the Riemann-Stieltjes integral. The proofs can be obtained by the standard arguments in the theory of integration and so are omitted. We assume that H is a separable Hilbert space.

Consider the operator function $\mathrm{T}(\lambda)$ $(-\infty < \lambda < \infty)$, whose values are bounded operators in H. We will assume that it is of weak bounded variation, i.e. that for any $x, y \in H$ the function $f(\lambda) = (\mathrm{T}(\lambda)x, y)_H$ is of bounded variation. In all that follows, we will assume that $\mathrm{T}(\lambda)$ is normalized: $\lim_{\lambda\to-\infty}\mathrm{T}(\lambda) = 0$, $\lim_{\lambda\to\lambda_0-0}\mathrm{T}(\lambda) = \mathrm{T}(\lambda_0)$ $(\lambda_0 \in (-\infty, \infty))$ in the sense of weak convergence. Let Δ be a finite or infinite interval on the real axis $(-\infty, \infty)$, and let $F(\lambda)$ and $G(\lambda)$ be functions defined on Δ, whose values are bounded operators in H. Form the Riemann-Stieltjes sums $\Sigma_{\alpha=1}^N F(\lambda_\alpha)\mathrm{T}(\Delta_\alpha)G(\lambda_\alpha)$, where $\{\Delta_1, \cdots, \Delta_N\}$ is a finite partition of Δ, $\lambda_\alpha \in \Delta_\alpha$; Δ_α is of the form $[a, b)$, and $\mathrm{T}(\Delta_\alpha) = \mathrm{T}(b) - \mathrm{T}(a)$. If these sums converge weakly to some limit as the partitioning is continued, independently of the method of partitioning and the choice of points $\lambda_\alpha \in \Delta_\alpha$, then we say that the integral

$$\int_\Delta F(\lambda)\,d\mathrm{T}(\lambda)\,G(\lambda) = \lim \sum_{\alpha=1}^{N} F(\lambda_\alpha)\,\mathrm{T}(\Delta_\alpha)\,G(\lambda_\alpha) \tag{2.10}$$

exists. If one of the functions $F(\lambda)$ or $G(\lambda)$ is identically equal to E, we obtain an integral of the form $\int_\Delta d\mathrm{T}(\lambda)G(\lambda)$ or $\int_\Delta F(\lambda)\,d\mathrm{T}(\lambda)$.

It is not difficult to show that if for $\mathrm{T}(\lambda)$ all of the integrals

$$\int_{-\infty}^{\infty} |\lambda|^m\, |d(\mathrm{T}(\lambda)x, y)_H| \quad (x, y \in H;\ m = 0, 1, \ldots) \tag{2.11}$$

converge, then the integral (2.10) exists for any Δ and operator polynomials $F(\lambda)$ and $G(\lambda)$, i.e. operator functions of the form $\lambda^n C_n + \cdots + C_0$, where C_j are bounded operators in H. The usual properties of integrals follow immediately from the definition (2.10) for this integral, as well as the equation

$$\Big(\int_\Delta d\mathrm{T}(\lambda)\,x, y\Big)_H = \int_\Delta d(\mathrm{T}(\lambda)x, y)_H, \quad \int_\Delta F(\lambda)\,d\Big(\int_{-\infty}^{\lambda} d\mathrm{T}(\mu)\,G(\mu)\Big)$$

$$= \int_\Delta F(\lambda)\,d\mathrm{T}(\lambda)\,G(\lambda), \quad \Big[\int_\Delta F(\lambda)\,d\mathrm{T}(\lambda)\,G(\lambda)\Big]^* = \int_\Delta G^*(\lambda)\,d\mathrm{T}^*(\lambda)\,F^*(\lambda). \tag{2.12}$$

Similar to (2.10), we can define integration of vector-functions $f(\lambda)$ and $g(\lambda)$

with values in H:

$$\int_{\Delta} (dT(\lambda) g(\lambda), f(\lambda))_H = \lim \sum_{\alpha=1}^{N} (T(\Delta_\alpha) g(\lambda_\alpha), f(\lambda_\alpha))_H. \tag{2.13}$$

If the integrals in (2.11) exist, then the integral (2.13) exists for any vector polynomial (i.e. any function of the form $\lambda^n c_n + \cdots + c_0$, $c_j \in H$). Note that

$$\Big(\int_{\Delta} F(\lambda)\, dT(\lambda) G(\lambda) x, y\Big)_H = \int_{\Delta} (dT(\lambda) G(\lambda) x, F^*(\lambda) y)_H \quad (x, y \in H). \tag{2.14}$$

The definition and properties of the following integral are also clear:

$$\int_{\Delta} F(\lambda)\, dT(\lambda) g(\lambda) = \lim \sum_{\alpha=1}^{N} F(\lambda_\alpha) T(\Delta_\alpha) g(\lambda_\alpha). \tag{2.15}$$

In what follows, we make use of a natural generalization of the space $L_2((-\infty, \infty), d\sigma(\lambda))$. Consider an operator function $T(\lambda)$ $(-\infty < \lambda < \infty)$ whose values are bounded operators in H, uniformly bounded in λ, such that $(T(\Delta) x, x)_H \geq 0$ $(x \in H)$, i.e. a nonnegative finite operator measure $dT(\lambda)$; $T([a, b)) = T(b) - T(a)$.[1] Clearly, such a $T(\lambda)$ is of weak bounded variation. Denote by $C_{00}(H; (-\infty, \infty))$, the set of all strongly continuous finite vector-functions $f(\lambda)$ $(-\infty < \lambda < \infty)$ whose values lie in a finite-dimensional subspace of H depending on λ. We define a scalar product for $f, g \in C_{00}(H; (-\infty, \infty))$ by the equation

$$(f, g)_{L_2(H;(-\infty,\infty),dT(\lambda))} = \int_{-\infty}^{\infty} (dT(\lambda) f(\lambda), g(\lambda))_H; \tag{2.16}$$

it is easy to see that this integral exists. If we identify with zero those f for which $(f, f)_{L_2(H;(-\infty,\infty),dT(\lambda))} = 0$, and then take the completion, we obtain a complete separable Hilbert space. We denote it by $L_2(H; (-\infty, \infty), dT(\lambda))$.

The nature of the elements of $L_2(H; (-\infty, \infty) dT(\lambda))$ is not of interest to us; we note only that it may be very complicated. In the simplest case, when $T(\lambda) = 0$ $(\lambda \leq 0)$ and $T(\lambda) = K$ $(\lambda > 0)$, where K is a nonnegative bounded operator in H, the scalar product (2.16) degenerates into $(f, g)_{L_2(H;(-\infty,\infty), dT(\lambda))} = (Kf(0), g(0))_H$. As a result, the completion of the latter scalar product may

---

[1] The $dT(\lambda)$ introduced earlier might be called an operator measure of weak bounded variation with "changing signs". When H is finite-dimensional the measures are naturally also called matrix measures.

contain generalized vectors (see p. 65), and therefore the elements of the space $L_2(H; (-\infty, \infty), d\mathrm{T}(\lambda))$ will not, in general, be vector-functions with values in H. Moreover it is not difficult to show that if the vector-function $f(\lambda)$ is strongly continuous on $(-\infty, \infty)$ and $\int_{-\infty}^{\infty}(d\mathrm{T}(\lambda) f(\lambda), f(\lambda))_H < \infty$, then $f \in L_2(H; (-\infty, \infty), d\mathrm{T}(\lambda))$. The scalar product in $L_2(H; (-\infty, \infty), d\mathrm{T}(\lambda))$ of two such vector-functions is equal to the integral $\int_{-\infty}^{\infty}(d\mathrm{T}(\lambda) f(\lambda), g(\lambda))_H$, i.e. formula (2.16) is preserved.

The space $\mathbf{L}_2(H; (-\infty, \infty), d\mathrm{T}(\lambda))$ is defined analogously to $\mathbf{l}_2(H; [0, \infty))$ as $L(H, L_2(H; (-\infty, \infty), d\mathrm{T}(\lambda)))$. We will not go into a detailed description of this space, and note only that because of what has been said above this space contains a pseudo-orthonormal basis; at the same time one cannot, in general, pseudo-orthogonalize a system of pseudo-vectors. We will describe certain elements of the space $\mathbf{L}_2(H; (-\infty, \infty), d\mathrm{T}(\lambda))$. Let $F(\lambda)$ $(-\infty < \lambda < \infty)$ be an operator function with values in $L(H, H)$, which is strongly continuous with respect to the operator norm, such that the integral $\int_{-\infty}^{\infty} F^*(\lambda)\, d\mathrm{T}(\lambda)\, F(\lambda)$ exists. Then by (2.12), for each $x \in H$ $\int_{-\infty}^{\infty}(d\mathrm{T}(\lambda) F(\lambda) x, F(\lambda) x)_H < \infty$, i.e. $F(\lambda) x \in L_2(H; (-\infty, \infty), d\mathrm{T}(\lambda))$; obviously, $\|F(\lambda) x\|^2_{L_2(H; (-\infty, \infty), d\mathrm{T}(\lambda))} \leq \|\int_{-\infty}^{\infty} F^*(\lambda)\, d\mathrm{T}(\lambda)\, F(\lambda)\|\, \|x\|^2_H$. Thus the operator $x \longrightarrow F(\lambda) x$ is a continuous mapping of H into $L_2(H; (-\infty, \infty), d\mathrm{T}(\lambda))$, i.e.

$$F(\lambda) \in L(H, L_2(H; (-\infty, \infty), d\mathrm{T}(\lambda)) = \mathbf{L}_2(H; (-\infty, \infty), d\mathrm{T}(\lambda)).$$

It follows from (2.1), (2.12), and (2.14), that the pseudo-scalar product of two such operator functions can be expressed in the form

$$\{F, G\} = \int_{-\infty}^{\infty} F^*(\lambda)\, d\mathrm{T}(\lambda)\, G(\lambda) \tag{2.17}$$

(the existence of this integral is easily established). It is not difficult to prove that the $F(\lambda)$ under consideration form a dense set in $\mathbf{L}_2(H; (-\infty, \infty), d\mathrm{T}(\lambda))$.

We suggest that the reader carry out the constructions of this subsection for the case where $\mathrm{T}(\lambda)$ $(-\infty < \lambda < \infty)$ is locally of weak bounded variation (i.e. this function is of weak bounded variation on any finite interval $(-N, N)$).

4. Operators in pseudo-Hilbert space. Consider a pseudo-Hilbert space $L(H, \mathfrak{H})$ and an operator $\mathbf{A}$ defined on the whole space. Such an operator is called *pseudo-linear* if $\mathbf{A}(U + V) = \mathbf{A}U + \mathbf{A}V$, $\mathbf{A}(U\Lambda) = (\mathbf{A}U)\Lambda$ $(U, V \in L(H, \mathfrak{H})$; $\Lambda \in L(H, H))$, and *continuous* if it is continuous in the topology of $L(H, \mathfrak{H})$.

Assume that $L(H, \mathfrak{H})$ contains a pseudo-orthonormal basis $E^{(0)}, E^{(1)}, \cdots$. Then every continuous pseudo-linear operator $\mathbf{A}$ on $L(H, \mathfrak{H})$ admits the matrix representation

$$(\mathbf{A}U)_j = \sum_{k=0}^{\infty} A_{jk} U_k, \quad A_{jk} = \{E^{(j)}, \mathbf{A}E^{(k)}\} \in L(H, H) \quad (j, k = 0, 1, \ldots) \tag{2.18}$$

(V_j is the coordinate of V in the basis $E^{(0)}, E^{(1)}, \cdots$ obtained by (2.6); the series in (2.18) converges in the sense of weak convergence in $L(H, H)$). Indeed, by the continuity of $\mathbf{A}$ we have $\mathbf{A}U = \mathbf{A}(\Sigma_{k=0}^{\infty} E^{(k)} U_k) = \Sigma_{k=0}^{\infty} (\mathbf{A}E^{(k)}) U_k$. Hence $(\mathbf{A}U)_j = \{E^{(j)}, \mathbf{A}U\} = \{E^{(j)}, \Sigma_{k=0}^{\infty} (\mathbf{A}E^{(k)}) U_k\} = \Sigma_{k=0}^{\infty} \{E^{(j)}, \mathbf{A}E^{(k)}\} U_k$, as required.

The converse is obvious: the relation (2.18) with an arbitrary matrix $A_{jk} \in L(H, H)$ $(j, k = 0, 1, \cdots)$ defines a continuous pseudo-linear operator in $L(H, \mathfrak{H})$, if only this matrix is such that the relation $U \to \mathbf{A}U$ is defined on all of $L(H, \mathfrak{H})$ and is continuous.

Each continuous linear operator A in $\mathfrak{H}$ induces, in a unique way, a continuous pseudo-linear operator $\mathbf{A}$ in $L(H, \mathfrak{H})$: $(\mathbf{A}U)x = A(Ux)$ $(U \in L(H, \mathfrak{H}),\ x \in H)$ (it is clear that A cannot always be recovered from $\mathbf{A}$). The matrix representation (2.18) implies an analogous representation for A: we will describe the vectors $v \in \mathfrak{H}$ by means of coordinates $v_0, v_1, \cdots \in H$ in the basis $E^{(j)}$ (see (2.8)). Then the expansion

$$(Au)_j = \sum_{k=0}^{\infty} A_{jk} u_k, \quad A_{jk} = \{E^{(j)}, \mathbf{A}E^{(k)}\} \in L(H, H) \qquad (u \in \mathfrak{H};\ j, k = 0, 1, \ldots) \tag{2.19}$$

is valid (the series converges strongly in H). In fact, the equations

$$U_j x = (Ux)_j, \quad (\mathbf{A}U)_j x = (A(Ux))_j \quad (x \in H; U \in L(H, \mathfrak{H});\ j = 0, 1, \ldots) \tag{2.20}$$

hold; the first of these follows from (2.8) and was actually established in the proof of Theorem 2.2, and the second follows from the first: $(\mathbf{A}U)_j x = ((\mathbf{A}U)x)_j = (A(Ux))_j$. On considering (2.20) and applying equation (2.18) to $x \in H$, we obtain (2.19), written with $u = Ux$. But for $x \neq 0$ the vectors Ux obviously run through all of $\mathfrak{H}$; this shows that (2.19) holds for any $u \in \mathfrak{H}$. The assertion is proved.

If the operator A is selfadjoint in $\mathfrak{H}$, then $\mathbf{A}$ satisfies the relations

$$\{\mathbf{A}U, V\} = \{U, \mathbf{A}V\} \quad (U, V \in L(H, \mathfrak{H})), \quad A_{jk} = A_{kj}^{*} \quad (j, k = 0, 1, \ldots). \tag{2.21}$$

In fact, because of (2.1),

$$(\{\mathbf{A}U, V\}\,x, y)_H = (Vx, (\mathbf{A}U)\,y)_{\mathfrak{H}} = (Vx, A\,(Uy))_{\mathfrak{H}} = (A\,(Vx), Uy)_{\mathfrak{H}}$$
$$= ((\mathbf{A}V)\,x, Uy)_{\mathfrak{H}} = (\{U, \mathbf{A}V\}\,x, y)_H,$$

for any $x, y \in H$, from which the first of equations (2.21) follows. The second is obtained from the first by setting $U = E^{(j)}$, $V = E^{(k)}$.

Up to this point only continuous operators in $L(H, \mathfrak{H})$ have been considered. We now say a few words about discontinuous operators. Let $\mathfrak{D}(\mathbf{A})$ be a pseudo-linear manifold in $L(H, \mathfrak{H})$; an operator $\mathbf{A}$ defined on $\mathfrak{D}(\mathbf{A})$ is naturally called pseudo-linear if $\mathbf{A}(U + V) = \mathbf{A}U + \mathbf{A}V$, $\mathbf{A}(U\Lambda) = (\mathbf{A}U)\,\Lambda\,(U, V \in L(H, \mathfrak{H});$ $\Lambda \in L(H, H))$.

A linear operator A in $\mathfrak{H}$ with domain $\mathfrak{D}(A)$ induces a pseudo-linear operator in $L(H, \mathfrak{H})$: $\mathfrak{D}(\mathbf{A})$ is the set of all $U \in L(H, \mathfrak{H})$ such that $Ux \in \mathfrak{D}(A)$ for any $x \in H$, and we set $(\mathbf{A}U)\,x = A(Ux)$ $(U \in \mathfrak{D}(\mathbf{A}),\ x \in H)$.

We give a useful example. Define the operator A on $L_2(H; (-\infty, \infty), d\mathrm{T}(\lambda))$ of multiplication by λ in the following way: define it first by $f(\lambda) \to \lambda f(\lambda)$ on the set $C_{00}(H; (-\infty, \infty))$ of vector-functions described on p. 556, and then take the closure. The resulting operator is obviously Hermitian; furthermore, it is selfadjoint. It suffices to show that $(A - zE)\,C_{00}(H; (-\infty, \infty))$ is dense in $L_2(H; (-\infty, \infty), d\mathrm{T}(\lambda))$ if $\operatorname{Im} z \neq 0$. If $f \in C_{00}(H; (-\infty, \infty))$, then $g(\lambda) = f(\lambda)/(\lambda - z) \in C_{00}(H; (-\infty, \infty))$, where $(A - zE)\,g = f$. In other words, $C_{00}(H; (-\infty, \infty)) \subseteq (A - zE)\,C_{00}(H; (-\infty, \infty))$, and the result follows since the smaller set is dense in $L_2(H; (-\infty, \infty), dT(\lambda))$.

Let $\mathbf{A}$ be the operator in $\mathbf{L}_2(H; (-\infty, \infty), d\mathrm{T}(\lambda))$ induced by A; it is natural to call it the pseudo-linear operator of multiplication by λ in $\mathbf{L}_2(H; (-\infty, \infty), d\mathrm{T}(\lambda))$. It is easy to see that finite functions $U(\lambda)$ which are continuous with respect to the operator norm in H belong to $\mathfrak{D}(\mathbf{A})$ and $(\mathbf{A}U)(\lambda) = \lambda U(\lambda)$.

5. Difference expressions and operators. Consider the difference expression

$$(Lu)_j = A_{j-1}u_{j-1} + A_j u_{j+1} + B_j u_j \quad (j = 0, 1, \ldots), \tag{2.22}$$

where $u_j \in H$, and A_j, B_j are bounded selfadjoint operators in H, and assume also that A_j has a bounded inverse.[1] We can construct by (2.22) a difference expression L, which acts on sequences of bounded operators in H:

---

[1] Actually, one might consider even more general difference expressions of the form $(Lu)_j = A_{j-1}^* u_{j-1} + A_j u_{j+1} + B_j u_j$ $(j = 0, 1, \cdots)$, where A_j and B_j are bounded operators in H, where A_j^{-1} exists, and B_j is selfadjoint.

$$(LU)_j = A_{j-1}U_j + A_jU_{j+1} + B_jU_j \quad (j = 0, 1, \ldots). \tag{2.23}$$

In (2.22) and (2.23) we always assume, for the computation of $(Lu)_0$ and $(LU)_0$, that $u_{-1} = 0$ and $U_{-1} = 0$ respectively.

It is easy to see that the following versions of Green's formula hold (cf. (1.4)):

$$\sum_{j=k}^{l} [(u_j, (Lv)_j)_H - ((Lu)_j, v_j)_H] = ((A_l u_l, v_{l+1})_H - (A_l u_{l+1}, v_l)_H) - ((A_{k-1}u_{k-1}, v_k)_H - (A_{k-1}u_k, v_{k-1})_H), \tag{2.24}$$

$$\sum_{i=k}^{l} [(LU)_i^* V_i - U_i^* (LV)_i] = (U_{l+1}^* A_l V_l - U_l^* A_l V_{l+1}) - (U_k^* A_{k-1} V_{k-1} - U_{k-1}^* A_{k-1} V_k). \tag{2.25}$$

We construct the operator L in $l_2(H; [0, \infty)) = H_0$ corresponding to L. For this, let $(\mathrm{L}'u)_j = (Lu)_j$ for finite sequences u (the set of which is denoted by $l_{2,0}(H; [0, \infty)))$; in view of (2.24) this operator is Hermitian; we define L as the closure of L$'$. The operator L is Hermitian, but in general not selfadjoint. Like the assertions of §1.1, it is easy to show that *the domain of the adjoint operator* L^* *consists of all those* $v \in l_2(H; [0, \infty))$ *for which* $Lv \in l_2(H; [0, \infty))$, *and moreover* $(\mathrm{L}^* v)_j = (Lv)_j$ $(j = 0, 1, \cdots)$. We go into the problems of selfadjointness of the operator L somewhat later, but now we pass directly io the construction of an eigenfunction expansion. As usual, we will use the notation $(\cdot, \cdot)_0 = (\cdot, \cdot)_{H_0}$, $\|\cdot\|_0 = \|\cdot\|_{H_0}$.

6. Polynomials of the first kind and the eigenfunction expansion. In analogy with §1 we introduce operator polynomials of the first kind. Denote by $P_j(z)$ $(j = 0, 1, \cdots)$ the solution of the Cauchy problem $(LU)_j = zU_j$ $(j = 0, 1, \cdots;$ $U_{-1} = 0,\ U_0 = E)$. Defining $U_1, U_2, \cdots$ in succession, we obtain

$$P_0(z) = E,\ P_1(z) = A_0^{-1}(zE - B_0),\ \ P_2(z) = A_1^{-1}[(zE - B_1)P_1(z) - A_0], \ldots. \tag{2.26}$$

Thus, $P_j(z)$ has the form of an operator polynomial of degree j. The leading coefficient C_j of $P_j(z)$, i.e. the coefficient of z^j, as is easily seen from (2.26), has the form

$$C_j = A_{j-1}^{-1} \ldots A_0^{-1} \qquad (j = 1, 2, \ldots). \tag{2.27}$$

Consider the finite sequences in $\mathbf{1}_2(H; [0, \infty))$, the set of which is denoted $\mathbf{1}_{2,0}(H; [0, \infty))$. In analogy with (1.22), we introduce the Fourier transform of a pseudo-vector $U \in \mathbf{1}_{2,0}(H; [0, \infty))$ by setting

$$\widetilde{U}(z) = \sum_{j=0}^{\infty} P_j^*(\bar{z}) U_j; \tag{2.28}$$

$\widetilde{U}(z)$ is an operator polynomial in z.

Let E_λ be, in general, a generalized resolution of the identity corresponding to the operator L introduced in subsection 5; let $\mathbf{E}_\lambda$ be the induced operator in $1_2(H; [0, \infty))$, according to subsection 4. Construct the operator spectral measure $d\Sigma(\lambda)$ with respect to E_λ by setting

$$\Sigma(\lambda) = \{\Delta^{(0)}, \mathbf{E}_\lambda \Delta^{(0)}\} = \{\mathbf{E}_\lambda \Delta^{(0)}, \Delta^{(0)}\} \qquad (-\infty < \lambda < \infty), \tag{2.29}$$

where the basis $\Delta^{(j)}$ has the form: $\Delta^{(j)} = (0, \cdots, 0, E, 0, \cdots)$ (E is in the jth position).

We will examine the properties of $\Sigma(\lambda)$ (and even more general functions), which ensure the possibility of constructing operator integrals.

Lemma 2.1. *For fixed $j, k = 0, 1, \cdots$ the operator function*

$$\{\Delta^{(j)}, \mathbf{E}_\lambda \Delta^{(k)}\} \qquad (-\infty < \lambda < \infty) \tag{2.30}$$

is of weak bounded variation, and all the integrals (2.11) *converge for this function. For $j = k$ this function is nonnegative.*

Proof. Since $E(\Delta)$ is nonnegative for any $j, k = 0, 1, \cdots$ and $x, y \in H$ we have

$$|(\{\Delta^{(j)}, \mathbf{E}(\Delta)\Delta^{(k)}\}x, y)_H|^2 = |((\mathbf{E}(\Delta)\Delta^{(k)})x, \Delta^{(j)}y)_0|^2$$
$$= |(E(\Delta)(\Delta^{(k)}x), \Delta^{(j)}y)_0|^2 \leqslant (E(\Delta)(\Delta^{(k)}x), \Delta^{(k)}x)_0 (E(\Delta)(\Delta^{(j)}y), \Delta^{(j)}y)_0$$
$$= (\{\Delta^{(k)}, \mathbf{E}(\Delta)\Delta^{(k)}\}x, x)_H (\{\Delta^{(j)}, \mathbf{E}(\Delta)\Delta^{(j)}\}y, y)_H. \tag{2.31}$$

Therefore if $\{\Delta_1, \cdots, \Delta_N\}$ is a partition of the real axis $(-\infty, \infty)$ by intervals we have

$$\sum_{\alpha=1}^{N} |(\{\Delta^{(j)}, \mathbf{E}(\Delta_\alpha)\Delta^{(k)}\}x, y)_H| \leqslant \sum_{\alpha=1}^{N} (\{\Delta^{(k)}, \mathbf{E}(\Delta_\alpha)\Delta^{(k)}\}x, x)_H^{\frac{1}{2}}$$
$$\times (\{\Delta^{(j)}, \mathbf{E}(\Delta_\alpha)\Delta^{(j)}\}y, y)_H^{\frac{1}{2}} \leqslant \left(\sum_{\alpha=1}^{N} (\{\Delta^{(k)}, \mathbf{E}(\Delta_\alpha)\Delta^{(k)}\}x, x)_H\right)^{\frac{1}{2}}$$
$$\times \left(\sum_{\alpha=1}^{N} (\{\Delta^{(j)}, \mathbf{E}(\Delta_\alpha)\Delta^{(j)}\}y, y)_H\right)^{\frac{1}{2}} = \|\Delta^{(k)}x\|_0 \|\Delta^{(j)}y\|_0$$
$$\leqslant \|x\|_H \|y\|_H \quad (x, y \in H). \tag{2.32}$$

This shows that the function (2.30) is of weak bounded variation. This function is nonnegative for $j = k$: for any $x \in H$ we have $(\{\Delta^{(j)}, \mathbf{E}(\Delta)\Delta^{(j)}\}x, x)_H = ((\mathbf{E}(\Delta)\Delta^{(j)})x, \Delta^{(j)}x)_0 = (\mathbf{E}(\Delta)(\Delta^{(j)}x), \Delta^{(j)}x)_0 \geq 0$.

In the proof of convergence of the integrals (2.11) we make use of the following general remark: if a generalized measure $\omega(\Delta)$ on the real axis satisfies the inequality $|\omega(\Delta)|^2 \leq \rho_1(\Delta)\rho_2(\Delta)$, for any Δ, where the ρ_j are ordinary measures, then for any continuous function $f(\lambda)$

$$\int_{-\infty}^{\infty} |f(\lambda)||d\omega(\lambda)| \leqslant \left(\int_{-\infty}^{\infty} |f(\lambda)|\, d\varrho_1(\lambda)\right)^{\frac{1}{2}} \left(\int_{-\infty}^{\infty} |f(\lambda)|\, d\varrho_2(\lambda)\right)^{\frac{1}{2}} \tag{2.33}$$

(for the proof of (2.33) one must approximate the integrals by sums and apply the Cauchy-Bunjakovskiĭ inequality). Now by (2.31), the problem is reduced to the convergence of the integrals $\int_{-\infty}^{\infty} |\lambda|^m\, d(\{\Delta^{(k)}, \mathbf{E}_\lambda \Delta^{(k)}\}x, x)_H$ $(x \in H)$. Clearly it is sufficient to consider m even. In this case we have

$$\int_{-\infty}^{\infty} |\lambda|^m d(\{\Delta^{(k)}, \mathbf{E}_\lambda \Delta^{(k)}\}x, x)_H = \int_{-\infty}^{\infty} \lambda^m d(E_\lambda(\Delta^{(k)}x), \Delta^{(k)}x)_0$$

$$= (\mathbf{L}^m(\Delta^{(k)}x), \Delta^{(k)}x)_0 < \infty,$$

since $\Delta^{(k)}x$ is a finite vector and therefore belongs to the domain of any power of L. Thus, the integrals (2.11) converge. The lemma is proved.

Note that in particular the inequality

$$\|\{\Delta^{(j)}, \mathbf{E}_\lambda \Delta^{(k)}\|\leqslant 1 \qquad (-\infty < \lambda < \infty;\ j, k = 0, 1, \ldots). \tag{2.34}$$

is established (cf. the derivation of (2.32)).

We now prove the central theorem of the spectral theory of expressions (2.22), the generalization of Theorem 1.6.

Theorem 2.4. *Let E_λ be a resolution of the identity (ordinary or generalized), which corresponds to the operator* L *of subsection* 5, *and* $\mathbf{E}_\lambda$ *the corresponding operator in* $\mathbf{1}_2(H; [0, \infty))$. *Construct the operator spectral measure* $d\Sigma(\lambda)$ *by formula* (2.29). *The polynomials* $P_j^*(\lambda)$ *form a pseudo-orthonormal system in the space* $\mathbf{L}_2(H; (-\infty, \infty), d\Sigma(\lambda))$, *i.e.*

$$\int_{-\infty}^{\infty} P_j(\lambda)\, d\Sigma(\lambda)\, P_k^*(\lambda) = \delta_{jk} E \qquad (j, k = 0, 1, \ldots). \tag{2.35}$$

Parseval's equation for finite pseudo-vectors $U, V \in \mathbf{1}_{2,0}(H; [0, \infty))$ *appears in the form*

$$\{U, \mathbf{E}(\Delta) V\} = \int_{\Delta} \widetilde{U}^{*}(\lambda)\, d\Sigma(\lambda)\, \widetilde{V}(\lambda), \tag{2.36}$$

where the Fourier transforms are defined by formula (2.28).

A proof of the theorem can be obtained in any one of the three ways indicated in §1.3. The simplest proof is obtained by the second method; we present it now. Like Lemma 1.2, the following lemma is not difficult to establish.

Lemma 2.2. *Suppose that* $F(\lambda) = (F_0(\lambda), F_1(\lambda), \cdots)$ $(-\infty < \lambda < \infty)$ *is a sequence of operator functions of weak bounded variation such that*

$$\int_{-\infty}^{\infty} |\lambda|^m |d(F_j(\lambda) x, y)_H| < \infty \quad (x, y \in H;\ m = 0, 1, \ldots),$$

$$(LF(\lambda))_j = \int_{-\infty}^{\lambda} \mu\, dF_j(\mu) \tag{2.37}$$

$$(j = 0, 1, \ldots;\ F_{-1}(\lambda) = 0).$$

Then the representation

$$F_j(\lambda) = \int_{-\infty}^{\lambda} P_j(\mu)\, dF_0(\mu) \qquad (j = 0, 1, \ldots). \tag{2.38}$$

holds.

Proof of the theorem. For fixed k, consider the sequence $F_j(\lambda) = \{\Delta^{(j)}, \mathbf{E}_\lambda \Delta^{(k)}\}$ $(j = 0, 1, \cdots;\ -\infty < \lambda < \infty)$. By Lemma 2.1 these functions satisfy the first of the conditions (2.37). They also satisfy the second: for $x, y \in H$ we have

$$((LF(\lambda))_j x, y)_H = (A_{j-1}\{\Delta^{(j-1)}, \mathbf{E}_\lambda \Delta^{(k)}\} x, y)_H + (A_j \{\Delta^{(j+1)}, \mathbf{E}_\lambda \Delta^{(k)}\} x, y)_H$$

$$+ (B_j \{\Delta^{(j)}, \mathbf{E}_\lambda \Delta^{(k)}\} x, y)_H = (\{\Delta^{(j-1)}, \mathbf{E}_\lambda \Delta^{(k)}\} x, A^*_{j-1} y)_H$$

$$+ \ldots = ((\mathbf{E}_\lambda \Delta^{(k)}) x, \Delta^{(j-1)} A^*_{j-1} y)_0 + \ldots = (E_\lambda (\Delta^{(k)} x), \Delta^{(j-1)} A^*_{j-1} y)_0$$

$$+ \ldots = ((E_\lambda (\Delta^{(k)} x))_{j-1}, A^*_{j-1} y)_H + \ldots = (A_{j-1} (E_\lambda (\Delta^{(k)} x))_{j-1}, y)_H$$

$$+ \ldots = ((L [E_\lambda (\Delta^{(k)} x)])_j, y)_H = ((\mathrm{L} E_\lambda (\Delta^{(k)} x))_j, y)_H$$

$$= \left(\left(\int_{-\infty}^{\lambda} \mu\, dE_\mu (\Delta^{(k)} x) \right)_j, y \right)_H = \int_{-\infty}^{\lambda} \mu\, d((E_\mu (\Delta^{(k)} x))_j, y)_H =$$

$$= \int_{-\infty}^{\lambda} \mu d\, ((\mathbf{E}_\mu \Delta^{(k)})\, x, \Delta^{(j)} y)_0 = \int_{-\infty}^{\lambda} \mu d\, (\{\Delta^{(j)}, \mathbf{E}_\mu \Delta^{(k)}\}\, x, y)_H$$

$$= \left(\left(\int_{-\infty}^{\lambda} \mu dF_j(\mu) \right) x, y \right)_H ,$$

from which the required relation follows.

By applying Lemma 2.2 we obtain

$$\{\Delta^{(j)}, \mathbf{E}_\lambda \Delta^{(k)}\} = \int_{-\infty}^{\lambda} P_j(\mu)\, d\, \{\Delta^{(0)}, \mathbf{E}_\mu \Delta^{(k)}\} \qquad (j, k = 0, 1, \ldots). \tag{2.39}$$

This gives us

$$\{\Delta^{(j)}, \mathbf{E}_\lambda \Delta^{(k)}\} = \{\mathbf{E}_\lambda \Delta^{(k)}, \Delta^{(j)}\}^* = \{\Delta^{(k)}, \mathbf{E}_\lambda \Delta^{(j)}\}^*$$

$$= \left(\int_{-\infty}^{\lambda} P_k(\mu)\, d\, \{\Delta^{(0)}, \mathbf{E}_\mu \Delta^{(j)}\} \right)^* = \int_{-\infty}^{\lambda} d\, \{\Delta^{(0)}, \mathbf{E}_\mu \Delta^{(j)}\}^*\, P_k^*(\mu)$$

$$= \int_{-\infty}^{\lambda} d\, \{\Delta^{(j)}, \mathbf{E}_\mu \Delta^{(0)}\}\, P_k^*(\mu)$$

$$(j, k = 0, 1, \ldots).$$

Using these equations, we can continue from (2.39):

$$\{\Delta^{(j)}, \mathbf{E}_\lambda \Delta^{(k)}\} = \int_{-\infty}^{\lambda} P_j(\mu)\, d_\mu \left(\int_{-\infty}^{\mu} d\, \{\Delta^{(0)}, \mathbf{E}_\nu \Delta^{(0)}\}\, P_k^*(\nu) \right)$$

$$= \int_{-\infty}^{\lambda} P_j(\mu)\, d\, \{\Delta^{(0)}, \mathbf{E}_\mu \Delta^{(0)}\}\, P_k^*(\mu);$$

$$\{\Delta^{(j)}, \mathbf{E}(\Delta)\, \Delta^{(k)}\} = \int_{\Delta} P_j(\lambda)\, d\, \{\Delta^{(0)}, \mathbf{E}_\lambda \Delta^{(0)}\}\, P_k^*(\lambda) \qquad (j, k = 0, 1, \ldots). \tag{2.40}$$

On setting $\Delta = (-\infty, \infty)$ here, we arrive at (2.35). Furthermore, with the help of the expansion (2.18) $(E^{(j)} = \Delta^{(j)})$ we find that for $U, V \in \mathbf{l}_{2,0}(H; [0, \infty))$,

$$\{U, \mathbf{E}(\Delta) V\} = \sum_{j=0}^{\infty} U_j^* (\mathbf{E}(\Delta) V)_j = \sum_{j,k=0}^{\infty} U_j^* \int_{\Delta} P_j(\lambda)\, d\Sigma(\lambda)\, P_k^*(\lambda)\, V_k$$

$$= \int_{\Delta} \widetilde{U}^*(\lambda)\, d\Sigma(\lambda)\, \widetilde{V}(\lambda).$$

The relation (2.36) and with it the theorem are proved.

The theory of eigenfunction expansions of finite vectors in $l_2(H; [0, \infty))$ for the expression (2.22) follows from the results obtained. If $u \in l_{2,0}(H; [0, \infty))$, we will call the vector function

$$\widetilde{u}(z) = \sum_{j=0}^{\infty} P_j^*(\bar{z})\, u_j \tag{2.41}$$

its Fourier transform. Obviously, for $U \in \mathbf{1}_{2,0}(H; [0, \infty))$ and $x \in H$ we have $\widetilde{(Ux)}(z) = (\widetilde{U}(z))x$. From (2.36) we obtain

$$((E(\Delta)(Vx), Uy)_0 = ((\mathbf{E}(\Delta)V)x, Uy)_0 = (\{U, \mathbf{E}(\Delta)V\}x, y)_H$$

$$= \left(\left(\int_\Delta \widetilde{U}^*(\lambda)\, d\Sigma(\lambda)\, \widetilde{V}(\lambda)\right)x, y\right)_H = \int_\Delta (d\Sigma(\lambda)\widetilde{V}(\lambda)x, \widetilde{U}(\lambda)y)_H$$

$$= \int_\Delta (d\Sigma(\lambda)\widetilde{(Vx)}(\lambda), \widetilde{(Uy)}(\lambda))_H. \tag{2.42}$$

But if $x \neq 0$ is fixed, and if U runs through all of $\mathbf{1}_2(H; [0, \infty))$, then Ux runs through all of $l_2(H; [0, \infty))$. Clearly, as U varies throughout $\mathbf{1}_{2,0}(H; [0, \infty))$, Ux runs through all of $l_{2,0}(H; [0, \infty))$. Thus from (2.42) we obtain Parseval's equation in the form

$$(E(\Delta)u, v)_0 = \int_\Delta (d\Sigma(\lambda)\, \widetilde{u}(\lambda), \widetilde{v}(\lambda))_H \qquad (u, v \in l_{2,0}(H; [0, \infty))) \tag{2.43}$$

7. **Study of Fourier transforms.** We will carry over the basic contents of §1.4 to the case under consideration. First we show that *the Fourier transforms of the finite pseudo-vectors, i.e.* $\widetilde{\mathbf{1}_{2,0}(H; [0, \infty))}$, *describe the set of all operator polynomials* (*and even more precisely*: *the polynomials of degree* n *are obtained from pseudo-vectors of the form* U; $U = (U_0, \cdots, U_n, 0, 0, \cdots)$). In fact, every polynomial of degree zero, $R_0(z) = C_0$, can be considered as the Fourier transform of the pseudo-vector $U = (C_0, 0, 0, \cdots)$. Assume now that the assertion is proved for polynomials $R_j(z)$ of degree $j \leq n-1$; we establish it for a polynomial $R_n(z)$ of degree n. We have $R_n(z) = z^n C_n + R_{n-1}(z)$. Since the leading coefficient of $P_n(z)$ is $A_{n-1}^{-1} \cdots A_0^{-1}$ (see (2.27)), then, by setting $U_n = A_{n-1}^* \cdots A_0^* C_n$, we obtain $P_n^*(\bar{z})U_n = z^n C_n + Q_{n-1}(z)$. Let $(U_0, \cdots, U_{n-1}, 0, 0, \cdots)$ be such that $\widetilde{(U_0, \cdots, U_{n-1}, 0, 0, \cdots)} = R_{n-1}(z) - Q_{n-1}(z)$. Then

$$\widetilde{(U_0, \ldots, U_{n-1}, U_n, 0, 0, \ldots)} = \widetilde{(U_0, \ldots, U_{n-1}, 0, 0, \ldots)} + P_n^*(\bar{z})U_n$$
$$= R_{n-1}(z) + z^n C_n = R_n(z).$$

The assertion is proved.

In other words: *every operator polynomial* $P(z)$ *of degree* n *admits a unique decomposition with respect to the polynomials* $P_j(z)$:

$$P(z) = \sum_{j=0}^{n} P_j^*(\bar{z})U_j, \qquad U_j = \int_{-\infty}^{\infty} P_j(\lambda)\, d\Sigma(\lambda) P(\lambda)$$
$$(j = 0, \ldots, n) \tag{2.44}$$

(uniqueness and the expression for U_j follow from (2.35)).

Since for $x \neq 0$ $(\mathbf{l}_{2,0}(H; [0, \infty)))x = l_{2,0}(H; [0, \infty))$ and $\widetilde{(Ux)}(z) = (\widetilde{U}(z))x$, then the abovementioned facts show that *the Fourier transforms of the finite vectors in* $l_2(H; [0, \infty))$, *i.e.* $\widetilde{l_{2,0}(H; [0, \infty))}$, *describe the set of all vector polynomials. Any such polynomial* $\mathrm{p}(z)$ *of degree* n *is uniquely representable in the form*

$$p(z) = \sum_{j=0}^{n} P_j^*(\bar{z})u_j, \qquad u_j = \int_{-\infty}^{\infty} P_j(\lambda)\, d\Sigma(\lambda)\, p(\lambda) \qquad (j = 0, \ldots, n). \tag{2.45}$$

A point is called a point of growth of the operator function $\mathrm{T}(\lambda)$ of weak bounded variation if it is a point of growth of the scalar function $(\mathrm{T}(\lambda)x, y)_H$ $(x, y \in H)$ for some x and y. In the same way as in §1.4 it is proven that *the set of points of growth corresponding to the operator spectral measure* $d\Sigma(\lambda)$ *is infinite.* It is not difficult to show that *if for some operator polynomial* $P(\lambda)$ $\int_{-\infty}^{\infty} P^*(\lambda)\, d\Sigma(\lambda) P(\lambda) = 0$, *then* $P(\lambda) \equiv 0$. In fact, the expansion (2.44) shows that $P(z) = \widetilde{U}(z)$ where $U = (U_0, \cdots, U_n, 0, 0, \cdots)$. It follows from Parseval's equation (2.36) (for $V = U$ and $\Delta = (-\infty, \infty)$) that $\{U, U\} = 0$, i.e. $U_0 = \cdots = U_n = 0$. Since the representation (2.44) implies this equation for each z, it follows that $P(z) \equiv 0$. In a similar way, it is easy to prove with the help of (2.43) and (2.45) that *if for some vector polynomial* $\mathrm{p}(\lambda)$, $\int_{-\infty}^{\infty} (d\Sigma(\lambda)\,\mathrm{p}(\lambda), \mathrm{p}(\lambda))_H = 0$, *then* $\mathrm{p}(\lambda) \equiv 0$.

It follows from what has been said that the mapping $U \to \widetilde{U}(\lambda)$ is a one-to-one correspondence between the finite sequences $U \in \mathbf{l}_{2,0}(H; [0, \infty))$ and the operator polynomials $U(\lambda)$, understood as elements of the space $\mathbf{L}_2(H; (-\infty, \infty), d\Sigma(\lambda))$. This correspondence preserves the pseudo-scalar product (see (2.36): $\Delta = (-\infty, \infty)$):

$$\{U, V\}_{\mathbf{l}_2(H;[0,\infty))} = \int_{-\infty}^{\infty} \tilde{U}^*(\lambda)\, d\Sigma(\lambda)\, \tilde{V}(\lambda) = \{\tilde{U}(\lambda), \tilde{V}(\lambda)\}_{\mathbf{L}_2(H;(-\infty,\infty),d\Sigma(\lambda))} \tag{2.46}$$

$$(U, V \in \mathbf{l}_{2,0}(H; [0, \infty))).$$

The last equation, as in the scalar case, allows us to extend the mapping $U \to \tilde{U}(\lambda)$ to all of $\mathbf{l}_2(H; [0, \infty))$. In fact, let $U = (U_0, U_1, \cdots) \in \mathbf{l}_2(H; [0, \infty))$; then $U^{(n)} = (U_0, \cdots, U_n, 0, 0, \cdots) \in \mathbf{l}_{2,0}(H; [0, \infty))$ converges to U as $n \to \infty$ in the topology of $\mathbf{l}_2(H; [0, \infty))$. It follows from (2.46) that for each $x \in H$, $(\widetilde{U^{(n)}}(\lambda))\, x$ is fundamental in $L_2(H; (-\infty, \infty), d\Sigma(\lambda))$, i.e. $\widetilde{U^{(n)}}(\lambda)$ is fundamental in $\mathbf{L}_2(H; (-\infty, \infty), d\Sigma(\lambda)) = L(H, L_2(H; (-\infty, \infty), d\Sigma(\lambda)))$. Since the latter space is complete, $\widetilde{U^{(n)}}(\lambda)$ converges to some $\tilde{U}(\lambda)$, which is regarded as the Fourier transform of U. Thus, after extension, the mapping $U \to \tilde{U}(\lambda)$ transforms all of $\mathbf{l}_2(H; [0, \infty))$ onto $\widetilde{\mathbf{l}_2(H; [0, \infty))}$, the closure in $\mathbf{L}_2(H; (-\infty, \infty), d\Sigma(\lambda))$ of the set $\widetilde{\mathbf{l}_{2,0}(H; [0, \infty))}$ of all operator polynomials.

The remaining results of §1.4 may be carried over to the operator case. We note only the following generalization of Theorem 1.9.

Theorem 2.5. *Let $d\Sigma(\lambda)$ be a nonnegative operator measure on the real axis $(-\infty, \infty)$ for which the integrals (2.11) exist. If Parseval's equation (2.46) holds for any finite sequences U, V and their Fourier transforms $\tilde{U}(\lambda)$, $\tilde{V}(\lambda)$ (defined by (2.28)) (or, equivalently, if the pseudo-orthogonality relations (2.35) hold), then $d\Sigma(\lambda)$ is an operator spectral measure of the difference expression L under consideration.*

Proof. Note that (2.46) implies Parseval's equation in the form

$$(u, v)_0 = \int_{-\infty}^{\infty} (d\Sigma(\lambda)\, \tilde{u}(\lambda), \tilde{v}(\lambda))_H \qquad (u, v \in l_{2,0}(H; [0, \infty))), \tag{2.47}$$

where $\tilde{u}(\lambda)$ and $\tilde{v}(\lambda)$ are obtained by (2.41) (see the arguments at the end of subsection 6). Thus, the mapping $u \to \tilde{u}(\lambda)$ is a one-to-one correspondence between $l_{2,0}(H; [0, \infty))$ and the set of vector polynomials $\widetilde{l_{2,0}(H; [0, \infty))}$ regarded as elements of $L_2(H; (-\infty, \infty), d\Sigma(\lambda))$. Extending this mapping by isometry, we obtain a mapping from all of $l_2(H; [0, \infty))$ onto $\widetilde{l_2(H; [0, \infty))}$, the closure in

$L_2(H, (-\infty, \infty), d\Sigma(\lambda))$ of the set of such polynomials. In fact, the proof proceeds in just the same way as for Theorem 1.9.

8. The inverse problem of spectral analysis. We will show how the difference expression (2.22) can be recovered from its operator spectral measure. Let $d\Sigma(\lambda)$ be a nonnegative operator measure on the real axis $(-\infty, \infty)$, for which the integrals (2.11)[1] exist, such that $\int_{-\infty}^{\infty} d\Sigma(\lambda) = E$. For any operator polynomial $P(\lambda)$ the integral

$$\{P, P\} = \{P, P\}_{\mathbf{L}_2(H;(-\infty,\infty),d\Sigma(\lambda))} = \int_{-\infty}^{\infty} P^*(\lambda)\, d\Sigma(\lambda)\, P(\lambda), \tag{2.48}$$

is obviously a bounded nonnegative operator. We will also require of $d\Sigma(\lambda)$ that the operator (2.48) be invertible for any polynomial $P(\lambda)$ whose leading coefficient is E. We will now carry out the process of pseudo-orthogonalization of the operator polynomials $E, \lambda E, \lambda^2 E, \cdots$, considered as elements of $\mathbf{L}_2(H; (-\infty, \infty), d\Sigma(\lambda))$.

Let $P_0(\lambda) = E$. Consider the polynomial $S_1(\lambda) = \lambda E + X_1 P_0(\lambda)$ and determine the unknown operator X_1 from the equation $\{S_1^*(\lambda), P_0^*(\lambda)\} = 0$; after this let $N_1 = \{S_1^*(\lambda), S_1^*(\lambda)\}$ and set $P_1(\lambda) = N_1^{-1/2} S_1(\lambda)$. Consider the polynomial $S_2(\lambda) = \lambda^2 N_1^{-1/2} + Y_2 P_1(\lambda) + X_2 P_0(\lambda)$ and determine X_2 and Y_2 from the equations $\{S_2^*(\lambda), P_0^*(\lambda)\} = 0$ and $\{S_2^*(\lambda), P_1^*(\lambda)\} = 0$. Set $N_2 = \{S_2^*(\lambda), S_2^*(\lambda)\}$, and set $P_2(\lambda) = N_2^{-1/2} S_2(\lambda)$. Then, consider $S_3(\lambda) = \lambda^3 N_2^{-1/2} N_1^{-1/2} + Z_3 P_2(\lambda) + Y_3 P_1(\lambda) + X_3 P_0(\lambda)$ and determine X_3, Y_3 and Z_3 according to the conditions $\{S_3^*(\lambda), P_0^*(\lambda)\} = 0$, $\{S_3^*(\lambda), P_1^*(\lambda)\} = 0$ and $\{S_3^*(\lambda), P_2^*(\lambda)\} = 0$. If we make the normalization and continue the process, we will obtain a sequence of operator polynomials $P_0(\lambda), P_1(\lambda), \cdots$ (P_j has degree j) such that $P_j^*(\lambda)$ is pseudo-orthonormalized: $\{P_j^*(\lambda), P_k^*(\lambda)\} = \delta_{jk} E$ $(j, k = 0, 1, \cdots)$.

Note now that because of the relations (2.35), formulas (1.33), expressing the coefficients of L in terms of polynomials of the first kind, are easily generalized to the operator case. Namely,

---

[1] The existence of the integrals (2.11) is equivalent to existence of the integrals $\int_{-\infty}^{\infty} |\lambda|^m\, d(\Sigma(\lambda)x, x)_H$, $(x \in H;\ m = 0, 1, \cdots)$. This follows from $|(\Sigma(\Delta)x, y)_H|^2 \le (\Sigma(\Delta)x, x)_H (\Sigma(\Delta)y, y)_H$ $(x, y \in H)$, which follows in turn from the fact that $\Sigma(\Delta) \ge 0$.

$$A_j = \int_{-\infty}^{\infty} \lambda P_j(\lambda)\, d\Sigma(\lambda)\, P_{j+1}^*(\lambda). \qquad B_j = \int_{-\infty}^{\infty} \lambda P_j(\lambda)\, d\Sigma(\lambda)\, P_j^*(\lambda)$$
$$(j = 0, 1, \ldots). \tag{2.49}$$

We will recover the coefficients of the expression (2.22) by means of formulas (2.49): substitute the given $d\Sigma(\lambda)$ in these formulas along with the $P_j(\lambda)$ constructed. We obtain bounded operators A_j and B_j which we accept as the coefficients of L. The operators B_j are obviously selfadjoint. The operators A_j are positive and invertible; for the proof we use the equation (cf. (2.49)) $N_{j+1}^{-1/2} A_j = \int_{-\infty}^{\infty} \lambda N_{j+1}^{-1/2} P_j(\lambda)\, d\Sigma(\lambda)\, P_{j+1}^*(\lambda)$; the polynomial $\lambda N_{j+1}^{-1/2} P_j(\lambda)$ of degree $j+1$ has the same leading coefficient as $P_{j+1}(\lambda)$, and it can therefore be represented in the form $P_{j+1}(\lambda) + C_j P_j(\lambda) + \cdots + C_0 P_0(\lambda)$, where C_j are certain operator coefficients. Using (2.35), we conclude that $N_{j+1}^{-1/2} A_j = \int_{-\infty}^{\infty} (P_{j+1}(\lambda) + \cdots)\, d\Sigma(\lambda) P_{j+1}^*(\lambda) = E$; thus $A_j = N_{j+1}^{-1/2}$ as required. So A_j and B_j can in fact serve as coefficients of L.

The polynomials constructed are polynomials of the first kind for the expression L. In fact, it is easy to see that

$$\int_{-\infty}^{\infty} [A_{j-1}P_{j-1}(\lambda) + A_j P_{j+1}(\lambda) + B_j P_j(\lambda) - \lambda P_j(\lambda)]\, d\Sigma(\lambda) P_k^*(\lambda) = 0 \quad (k = 0, 1, \ldots)$$

(it is necessary to assume that $P_{-1}(\lambda) = 0$). Hence $\int_{-\infty}^{\infty} [\cdots]\, d\Sigma(\lambda) [\cdots]^* = 0$. But the polynomial in the square brackets has an invertible leading coefficient, and so the last relation means that $[\cdots] = 0$, and this is what was required.

Thus, the polynomials $P_j(\lambda)$, which satisfy the pseudo-orthogonality relations (2.35), are polynomials of the first kind for the constructed difference expression L. By Theorem 2.3, $d\Sigma(\lambda)$ is an operator spectral measure for L; the inverse problem is now solved. We will not formulate the obtained generalization of Theorem 1.11, and note only that the coefficients A_j turn out to be positive. At the same time it was assumed in addition that the operator (2.48) is invertible (this is a stronger requirement than the property of $d\Sigma(\lambda)$ in the proof of Lemma 2.1).

9. **Calculation of the deficiency numbers of the operator L.** Unlike the scalar case, the deficiency numbers of the operator L under consideration may vary from 0 to ∞; in addition, they are not necessarily equal; in this connection, their determination is considerable complicated. In this and the succeeding subsections we prove rather general theorems concerning the calculation of the deficiency

numbers. The first of these generalizes the first part of Theorem 1.1.

Theorem 2.6. *The strong limit*

$$\Gamma(z) = \lim_{n\to\infty}\left[\sum_{j=0}^{n} P_j^*(z) P_j(z)\right]^{-1}, \tag{2.50}$$

exists for any complex z *and represents a bounded nonnegative operator in* H *with norm at most* 1. *The dimension of the orthogonal complement in* H *of the subspace of zeros of the operator* $\Gamma(\bar z)$ (*i.e. the subspace of* $x \in H$ *such that* $\Gamma(\bar z)x = 0$) *is the same for all points* z *in a connected component of the field of regularity of the operator* L *and it agrees with the corresponding deficiency number.*

First of all we establish a general lemma.

Lemma 2.3. *Let* A *and* B *be positive, bounded operators in some Hilbert space* H, *each of which has a bounded inverse, If* $(Ax, x) \le (Bx, x)$ $(x \in H)$, *then* $(A^{-1}x, x) \ge (B^{-1}x, x)$ $(x \in H)$.

Proof. Set $C = \sqrt{B^{-1}}A\sqrt{B^{-1}}$. For each $y = \sqrt{B}x$ we have

$$(Cy, y) = (\sqrt{B^{-1}}A\sqrt{B^{-1}}y, y) = (A\sqrt{B^{-1}}y, \sqrt{B^{-1}}y) = (Ax, x) \leqslant (Bx, x) = (y, y). \tag{2.51}$$

Since C is nonnegative the Cauchy-Bunjakovskiĭ inequality for the scalar product $(x, y) = (Cx, y)$, and (2.51), give us

$$(y, y)^2 = (CC^{-1}y, y)^2 \leqslant (CC^{-1}y, C^{-1}y)(Cy, y) = (y, C^{-1}y)(Cy, y) \leqslant (y, C^{-1}y)(y, y),$$

whence $(y, y) \le (y, C^{-1}y)$. Setting $y = \sqrt{B}x$ here we find that $(\sqrt{B}x, \sqrt{B}x) \le (\sqrt{B}x, \sqrt{B}A^{-1}\sqrt{B}\sqrt{B}x)$, i.e. $(Bx, x) \le (Bx, A^{-1}Bx)$ $(x \in H)$. Since B has an inverse operator, $Bx = z$ runs through all of H, so from the last inequality we obtain $(z, B^{-1}z) \le (z, A^{-1}z)$ $(z \in H)$. The lemma is proved.

Proof of the theorem. We will prove it in steps.

1. Because of Lemma (2.3), it is easy to prove existence of the limit (2.50): let $B_n(z) = \Sigma_{j=0}^n P_j^*(z)P_j(z) = E + \Sigma_{j=1}^n P_j^*(z)P_j(z)$, each of these operators being positive. In addition,

$$(x, x)_H = (B_0(z)x, x)_H \leqslant (B_1(z)x, x)_H \leqslant (B_2(z)x, x)_H \leqslant \dots \quad (x \in H).$$

By the proof of the lemma

$$(x, x)_H = (B_0^{-1}(z)x, x)_H \geqslant (B_1^{-1}(z)x, x)_H \geqslant (B_2^{-1}(z)x, x)_H \geqslant \dots \quad (x \in H),$$

i.e. $B_0^{-1}(z)$, $B_1^{-1}(z), \cdots$ forms a decreasing sequence of positive operators, and therefore the strong limit $\lim_{n\to\infty} B_n^{-1}(z)$, i.e. the limit (2.50), exists.

2.[1] We show now that for any $v \in \mathbf{l}_{2,0}(H; [0, \infty))$ such that $\widetilde{V}(\bar{z}) = E$, the relation

$$\{V, V\} \geq \Gamma(z) \tag{2.52}$$

holds.

Consider the special case when a bounded operator V_0^{-1} exists in H. Then the operator $\Sigma_{j=0}^n V_j^* V_j = V_0^* V_0 + \Sigma_{j=1}^n V_j^* V_j$ has a bounded inverse. Let $y = [\Sigma_{j=0}^n V_j^* V_j]^{-1} x$ $(x \in H)$. Then

$$\left(\left[\sum_{j=0}^n V_j^* V_j\right]^{-1} x, x\right)_H^2 = \left(\widetilde{V}(\bar{z})\left[\sum_{j=0}^n V_j^* V_j\right]^{-1} x, x\right)_H^2 = \left(\left[\sum_{j=0}^n P_j^*(z) V_j\right] y, x\right)_H^2$$

$$= \left[\sum_{j=0}^n (V_j y, P_j(z) x)_H\right]^2 \leqslant \left[\sum_{j=0}^n (V_j^* V_j y, y)_H\right]\left[\sum_{j=0}^n (P_j^*(z) P_j(z) x, x)_H\right]$$

$$= \left(\left[\sum_{j=0}^n V_j^* V_j\right]^{-1} x, x\right)_H \left(\left[\sum_{j=0}^n P_j^*(z) P_j(z)\right] x, x\right)_H.$$

On cancelling a nonnegative factor from this inequality, we obtain

$$\left(\left[\sum_{j=0}^n V_j^* V_j\right]^{-1} x, x\right)_H \leqslant \left(\left[\sum_{j=0}^n P_j^*(z) P_j(z)\right] x, x\right)_H \quad (x \in H).$$

Hence it follows from Lemma 2.3 that

$$\left(\left[\sum_{j=0}^n V_j^* V_j\right] x, x\right)_H \geqslant \left(\left[\sum_{j=0}^n P_j^*(z) P_j(z)\right]^{-1} x, x\right)_H \quad (x \in H).$$

On passing to the limit as $n \longrightarrow \infty$, we obtain $(\{V, V\} x, x)_H \geq (\Gamma(z) x, x)_H$ $(x \in H)$, i.e. (2.52).

Now consider the general case: V_0^{-1} may not exist. Select any orthonormal basis $e_1, e_2, \cdots$ in H, and for any bounded operator C in H, denote by $\|c_{jk}\|_0^\infty$ the matrix representing C in this basis. Denote by $\|{}^{(N)}c_{jk}\|_0^\infty$ a "square section" of the matrix $\|c_{jk}\|_0^\infty$ (i.e. ${}^{(N)}c_{jk} = c_{jk}$ for $j, k \leq N$ and ${}^{(N)}c_{jk} = 0$ for the

---

[1] It follows from Lemma 2.4 and Theorem 2.7 that the deficiency subspace, corresponding to z, coincides with the set of sequences $P_j(\bar{z})x$ $(j = 0, 1, \cdots)$, where $x \in H$ is such that $(P_0(\bar{z})x, P_1(\bar{z}, x, \cdots) \in l_2(H; [0, \infty))$. On the basis of this, the proof of the theorem can be completed more simply than below. We retain this presentation however, since a series of relations (for instance (2.54), (2.58)) are useful in themselves.

remaining j, k); denote by $^{(N)}C$ the bounded operator corresponding to this section.

If we let $\widetilde{U}(\lambda) = {}^{(N)}\widetilde{V}(\lambda)$, then by what was said at the beginning of subsection 7 $\widetilde{U}(\lambda)$ is in fact the Fourier transform of some finite pseudo-vector $U = (U_0, U_1, \cdots)$, the components of which are recovered by the formula $U_j = \int_{-\infty}^{\infty} P_j(\lambda)\, d\Sigma(\lambda)\, \widetilde{U}(\lambda)$ $(j = 0, 1, \cdots)$. In particular, $U_0 = \int_{-\infty}^{\infty} d\Sigma(\lambda)\, \widetilde{U}(\lambda)$; hence all but a finite number of the columns of the matrix of this operator in the basis e_j consists of zeros, i.e. the operator U_0 is finite-dimensional. If we set $\widetilde{W}(\lambda) = (\widetilde{U}(\lambda) - \epsilon E)({}^{(N)}E - \epsilon E)^{-1}$, as above $\widetilde{W}(\lambda)$ is the Fourier transform of some $W = (W_0, W_1, \cdots) \in 1_{2,0}(H; [0, \infty))$. We have

$$W_j = \int_{-\infty}^{\infty} P_j(\lambda)\, d\Sigma(\lambda)\, W(\lambda) = \begin{cases} (U_0 - \varepsilon E)\, ({}^{(N)}E - \varepsilon E)^{-1} & (j = 0), \\ U_j\, ({}^{(N)}E - \varepsilon E)^{-1} & (j \geqslant 1). \end{cases}$$

The operator W_0^{-1} exists if and only if ϵ is not an eigenvalue of the finite-dimensional operator U_0. In any case, this will occur for an infinite sequence of $\epsilon \to 0$. In addition, since $\widetilde{U}(\overline{z}) = {}^{(N)}\widetilde{V}(\overline{z}) = {}^{(N)}E$, then $\widetilde{W}(\overline{z}) = (\widetilde{U}(\overline{z}) - \epsilon E)({}^{(N)}E - \epsilon E)^{-1} = E$. Thus the part of the assertion already proved can be applied to W and so

$$(\{W, W\}\, x, x)_H \geqslant (\Gamma(z)\, x, x)_H \qquad (x \in H). \tag{2.53}$$

Now let $x \in H$ be a finite vector with respect to the chosen basis e_j. Choose a number N so large that $x_j = 0$ for $j > N$. Then $({}^{(N)}E - \epsilon E)^{-1} x = 1/(1 - \epsilon) x$ and therefore

$$\begin{aligned} (\{W, W\}\, x, x)_H &= (Wx, Wx)_{l_2(H;[0,\infty))} = \| W_0 x \|_H^2 + \sum_{j=1}^{\infty} \| W_j x \|_H^2 \\ &= \| (U_0 - \varepsilon E)\, ({}^{(N)}E - \varepsilon E)^{-1} x \|_H^2 + \sum_{j=1}^{\infty} \| U_j\, ({}^{(N)}E - \varepsilon E)^{-1} x \|_H^2 \\ &= \frac{1}{(1-\varepsilon)^2} \left(\| (U_0 - \varepsilon E)\, x \|_H^2 + \sum_{j=1}^{\infty} \| U_j x \|_H^2 \right) = \frac{1}{(1-\varepsilon)^2} \sum_{j=0}^{\infty} \| U_j x \|_H^2 \\ &\quad - \frac{2\varepsilon}{(1-\varepsilon)^2} \operatorname{Re} (U_0 x, x)_H + \frac{\varepsilon^2}{(1-\varepsilon)^2} \| x \|_H^2 = \frac{1}{(1-\varepsilon)^2} (\{U, U\}\, x, x)_H + o(\varepsilon). \end{aligned}$$

Thus, passing to the limit as $\epsilon \to 0$ in (2.53), we obtain $(\{U, U\} x, x)_H \geq (\Gamma(z)\, x, x)_H$. But

$$(\{U,U\}\, x, x)_H = \int_{-\infty}^{\infty} (d\Sigma(\lambda)\widetilde{U}(\lambda)\, x, \widetilde{U}(\lambda)\, x)_H = \int_{-\infty}^{\infty} (d\Sigma(\lambda)^{(N)}\widetilde{V}(\lambda)\, x, {}^{(N)}\widetilde{V}(\lambda) x)_H$$

$$= \int_{-\infty}^{\infty} (d\Sigma(\lambda)\widetilde{V}(\lambda)\, x, \widetilde{V}(\lambda)\, x)_H = (\{V, V\}\, x, x)_H;$$

therefore $(\{V, V\}x, x)_H \geq (\Gamma(z)x, x)_H$ for any finite x, and hence for any $x \in H$. The inequality (2.52) is completely established.

3. We establish the relation

$$(\Gamma(z)\, x, x)_H = \inf_{V \in 1_{2,0}(H;\, [0,\infty)),\ \widetilde{V}(\bar{z}) = E} (\{V, V\}\, x, x)_H \qquad (x \in H). \tag{2.54}$$

It follows from (2.52) that

$$(\Gamma(z)\, x, x)_H \leqslant \inf_{V \in 1_{2,0}(H;\, [0,\infty)),\ \widetilde{V}(\bar{z}) = E} (\{V, V\}\, x, x) \qquad (x \in H).$$

Therefore for the proof of (2.54) it is sufficient to show that there exists a sequence $V^{(n)} \in 1_{2,0}(H;\ [0, \infty))$, $\widetilde{V}^{(n)}(\bar{z}) = E$, such that $(\{V^{(n)}, V^{(n)}\}x, x)_H \to (\Gamma(z)x, x)_H$ as $n \to \infty$ $(x \in H)$.

Let $F_j = P_j(z)[\Sigma_{k=0}^{n} P_k^*(z) P_k(z)]^{-1}$ $(j = 0, \cdots, n)$. Then $\Sigma_{j=0}^{n} F_j^* F_j = [\Sigma_{j=0}^{n} P_j^*(z) P_j(z)]^{-1}$ and therefore

$$\left(\left[\sum_{j=0}^{n} P_j^*(z)\, P_j(z)\right]^{-1} x, x\right)_H = \sum_{j=0}^{n} \| F_j x \|_H^2 \qquad (x \in H). \tag{2.55}$$

If we let $V^{(n)} = (F_0, \cdots, F_n, 0, 0, \cdots) \in 1_{2,0}(H;\ [0, \infty))$, obviously $\widetilde{V}^{(n)}(\bar{z}) = \Sigma_{j=0}^{n} P_j^*(z) F_j = E$. In addition, by (2.55)

$$(\{V^{(n)}, V^{(n)}\}\, x, x)_H = (V^{(n)}x, V^{(n)}x)_{l_2(H;[0,\infty))} = \sum_{j=0}^{n} \| F_j x \|_H^2$$

$$= \left(\left[\sum_{j=0}^{n} P_j^*(z)\, P_j(z)\right]^{-1} x, x\right)_H \underset{n\to\infty}{\longrightarrow} (\Gamma(z)\, x, x)_H \qquad (x \in H).$$

The required sequence $V^{(n)}$ is constructed and (2.54) is established.

4. Consider H as a subset of the space $L_2(H;\ (-\infty, \infty),\ d\Sigma(\lambda))$ (as the set of constant functions). The scalar product in $L_2(H;\ (-\infty, \infty),\ d\Sigma(\lambda))$ induces a scalar product in H, which coincides with the original. In fact since

$\int_{-\infty}^{\infty} d\Sigma(\lambda) = E$, then $\int_{-\infty}^{\infty} (d\Sigma(\lambda)x, y)_H = (\int_{-\infty}^{\infty} d\Sigma(\lambda)x, y)_H = (x, y)_H$. Therefore, since H is complete, H is closed in $L_2(H; (-\infty, \infty), d\Sigma(\lambda))$.

We show that *the deficiency number of the operator* L *at a point* z *is equal to the dimension of the orthogonal complement in* H *of the subspace of all vectors of* H *which are at zero distance (in* $L_2(H; (-\infty, \infty), d\Sigma(\lambda))$ *from the set* $\widetilde{(\mathrm{L} - zE)l_{2,0}(H; [0, \infty))} \subseteq L_2(H; (-\infty, \infty), d\Sigma(\lambda))$.

In fact, the desired deficiency number is equal to the dimension of the orthogonal complement of $(\mathrm{L} - zE)l_{2,0}(H; [0, \infty))$ in $l_2(H; [0, \infty))$. On taking the Fourier transform, we conclude that it is equal to the dimension of the orthogonal complement of $\widetilde{(\mathrm{L} - zE)l_{2,0}(H; [0, \infty))}$ in $\widetilde{l_2(H; [0, \infty))} \subseteq L_2(H; (-\infty, \infty), d\Sigma(\lambda))$. Since $\widetilde{l_{2,0}(H; [0, \infty))}$ consists of all the vector polynomials (see proof of Theorem 2.5), $\widetilde{(\mathrm{L} - zE)l_{2,0}(H; [0, \infty))}$ consists of all the vector polynomials which vanish at the point z. Therefore $\widetilde{(\mathrm{L} - zE)l_{2,0}(H; [0, \infty))} + H = \widetilde{l_{2,0}(H; [0, \infty))}$ (H is regarded as the set of constant vector-functions). Denote closure in $L_2(H; (-\infty, \infty), d\Sigma(\lambda))$ by a bar, and take into account that $\overline{\widetilde{l_{2,0}(H; [0, \infty))}} = \widetilde{l_2(H; [0, \infty))}$, $\overline{H} = H$, $\overline{\widetilde{(\mathrm{L} - zE)l_{2,0}(H; [0, \infty))}} \subseteq \widetilde{l_2(H; [0, \infty))}$. Obviously

$$\widetilde{l_{2,0}(H; [0, \infty))} \subseteq \overline{\widetilde{(\mathrm{L} - zE)l_{2,0}(H; [0, \infty))} + H}. \tag{2.56}$$

Let G be the orthogonal complement of $H \cap \overline{\widetilde{(\mathrm{L} - zE)l_{2,0}(H; [0, \infty))}}$ in H, i.e. of the set of vectors in H which are at zero distance from $\widetilde{(\mathrm{L} - zE)l_{2,0}(H; [0, \infty))}$. Then (2.56) can be rewritten in the form

$$\widetilde{l_{2,0}(H; [0, \infty))} \subseteq \overline{\widetilde{(\mathrm{L} - zE)l_{2,0}(H; [0, \infty))}} \dotplus G, \tag{2.57}$$

where the $\dotplus$ means direct sum.

We will use the following simple fact, the proof of which we leave to the reader. Let $\mathfrak{H}$ be a separable Hilbert space. $\mathfrak{H}_1$ and $\mathfrak{H}_2$ subspaces such that $\mathfrak{H}_1 \cap \mathfrak{H}_2 = 0$. Assume that $\mathfrak{H}' \subseteq \mathfrak{H}_1 \dotplus \mathfrak{H}_2$ for some set $\mathfrak{H}'$ which is dense in $\mathfrak{H}$. Then the dimension of the orthogonal complement of $\mathfrak{H}_1$ in $\mathfrak{H}$ agrees with the

$\overline{\text{dimension of } \mathfrak{H}_2}$. Now set $\mathfrak{H} = \overline{l_2(H; [0, \infty))}$, $\mathfrak{H}' = \overline{l_{2,0}(H; [0, \infty))}$, $\mathfrak{H}_1 = \overline{(L - zE)\, l_{2,0}(H; [0, \infty))}$, $\mathfrak{H}_2 = G$. In view of (2.57), the dimension of the orthogonal complement of $\overline{(L - zE)\, l_{2,0}(H; [0, \infty))}$ in $\overline{l_2(H; [0, \infty))}$ – the deficiency number – is equal to the dimension of G. The assertion is proved.

5. We will show that the distance of a vector $x \in H$ to the linear manifold $\overline{(L - zE)\, l_{2,0}(H; [0, \infty))}$ is determined by the formula

$$\rho^2(x, \overline{(L - zE)\, l_{2,0}(H; [0, \infty))}) = (\Gamma(\bar{z})\, x, x)_H. \tag{2.58}$$

In fact, $\overline{(x, 0, 0, \cdots)} = x$, so since the Fourier transform is an isometry, $\rho(x, \overline{(L - zE)\, l_{2,0}(H; [0, \infty))}) = \rho((x, 0, 0, \cdots), (L - zE)\, l_{2,0}(H; [0, \infty))) = \rho((x, 0, 0, \cdots), (L - zE)\, l_{2,0}(H; [0, \infty)))$. Since we may confine ourselves to the case $x \neq 0$, $(L - zE)\, l_{2,0}(H; [0, \infty)) = [(L - zE)\, \mathrm{l}_{2,0}(H; [0, \infty))]\, x$; in addition, $(x, 0, 0, \cdots) = \Delta^{(0)} x$ $(\Delta^{(0)} = (E, 0, 0, \cdots))$. Thus,

$$\varrho^2 (x, \overline{(L - zE)\, l_{2,0} (H; [0, \infty))}) = \varrho^2 (\Delta^{(0)} x, [(L - zE)\, \mathrm{l}_{2,0} (H; [0, \infty))]\, x)$$

$$= \inf \| (\Delta^{(0)} - U)\, x \|^2_{l_2(H; [0, \infty))} = \inf (\{\Delta^{(0)} - U, \Delta^{(0)} - U\}\, x, x)_H,$$

where U runs through the set of pseudo-vectors of the form $(L - zE)\, \mathrm{l}_{2,0}(H; [0, \infty))$, i.e. the set of finite pseudo-vectors whose Fourier transform coincides with the class of operator polynomials which vanish at the point z. Since $\widetilde{\Delta}^{(0)} = E$, $V = \Delta^{(0)} - U$ runs through the set of finite pseudo-vectors whose Fourier transform at the point z equals E. Therefore we can write

$$\varrho^2 (x, \overline{(L - zE)\, l_{2,0} (H; [0, \infty))}) = \inf (\{V, V\}\, x, x)_H \quad (x \in H)$$
$$V \in \mathrm{l}_{2,0} (H; [0, \infty)),\ \widetilde{V}(z) = E.$$

Hence (2.58) follows from (2.54).

6. Now it is easy to complete the proof of the theorem: by step 4, the desired deficiency number equals the dimension of the orthogonal complement of the subspace of all $x \in H$ for which $\rho(x, \overline{(L - zE)\, l_{2,0}(H; [0, \infty))}) = 0$, or by (2.58), for which $(\Gamma(\bar{z})\, x, x)_H = 0$. The theorem is proved.

We turn to a generalization of the second part of Theorem 1.1. First we carry out a general construction. Consider Hilbert spaces H and $\mathfrak{H}$ and the pseudo-Hilbert space $L(H, \mathfrak{H})$. Let A be a closed Hermitian operator acting in $\mathfrak{H}$, construct the operator $\mathbf{A}$ which acts in $L(H, \mathfrak{H})$ (see subsection 4), and consider the pseudo-linear manifold $(\mathbf{A} - z\mathbf{E})\mathfrak{D}(\mathbf{A})$ and its pseudo-orthogonal complement $\widehat{(\mathbf{A} - z\mathbf{E})\mathfrak{D}(\mathbf{A})}$, i.e. the set of all $U \in L(H, \mathfrak{H})$ such that $\{U, V\} = 0$ for any $V \in (\mathbf{A} - z\mathbf{E})\mathfrak{D}(\mathbf{A})$.

Lemma 2.4. *For each nonreal* z, *we have the decomposition*

$$L(H, \mathfrak{H}) = (\mathbf{A} - z\mathbf{E})\mathfrak{D}(\mathbf{A}) \oplus \widehat{(\mathbf{A} - z\mathbf{E})\mathfrak{D}(\mathbf{A})} \tag{2.59}$$

into a pseudo-orthogonal sum of pseudo-subspaces. For each nonzero $x \in H$, $[(\mathbf{A} - z\mathbf{E})\mathfrak{D}(\mathbf{A})]x = (A - zE)\mathfrak{D}(A)$; $[\widehat{(\mathbf{A} - z\mathbf{E})\mathfrak{D}(\mathbf{A})}]x$ *coincides with the orthogonal complement of* $(A - zE)\mathfrak{D}(A)$ *in* $\mathfrak{H}$, *i.e. with the corresponding deficiency subspace of the operator* A.

Proof. Since $\mathfrak{D}(\mathbf{A})x = \mathfrak{D}(A)$, then $[(\mathbf{A} - z\mathbf{E})\mathfrak{D}(\mathbf{A})]x = (A - zE)\mathfrak{D}(A)$ and therefore, since A is a closed operator, the set $[(\mathbf{A} - z\mathbf{E})\mathfrak{D}(\mathbf{A})]x$ is closed in $\mathfrak{H}$. If $U \in L(H, \mathfrak{H})$ and $Ux \in (A - zE)\mathfrak{D}(A)$ for all $x \in H$, we will show that $U \in (\mathbf{A} - z\mathbf{E})\mathfrak{D}(\mathbf{A})$. In fact, for any $x \in H$ there is a $v_x \in \mathfrak{D}(A) \subseteq \mathfrak{H}$ such that $Ux = (A - zE)v_x$. Since z is not real, v_x is uniquely determined by x and $\|U\|\,\|x\|_H \geq \|Ux\|_{\mathfrak{H}} = \|(A - zE)v_x\|_{\mathfrak{H}} \geq k\,\|v_x\|_{\mathfrak{H}}$; hence $\|v_x\|_{\mathfrak{H}} \leq C\,\|x\|_H$. The correspondence $x \longrightarrow v_x$ is clearly additive and homogeneous; thus there exists an operator $V \in L(H, \mathfrak{H})$ such that $Vx = v_x \in \mathfrak{D}(A)$; by the definition of $\mathfrak{D}(\mathbf{A})$, $V \in \mathfrak{D}(\mathbf{A})$. Thus $Ux = (A - zE)v_x = (A - zE)Vx = [(\mathbf{A} - z\mathbf{E})V]x$ $(x \in H)$, i.e. $U = (\mathbf{A} - z\mathbf{E})V$, as required. It follows obviously from what was proved above that $(\mathbf{A} - z\mathbf{E})\mathfrak{D}(\mathbf{A})$ is a maximal pseudo-subspace (see the proof of Theorem 2.3).

On the basis of Theorem 2.3 we conclude that the representation (2.59) holds. It is also clear that $[\widehat{(\mathbf{A} - z\mathbf{E})\mathfrak{D}(\mathbf{A})}]x$ is the orthogonal complement of $(A - zE)\mathfrak{D}(A)$ in $\mathfrak{H}$. The lemma is proved.

It follows from the lemma that *the deficiency subspace of the operator* A *is completely described, if the pseudo-subspace* $\widehat{(\mathbf{A} - z\mathbf{E})\mathfrak{D}(\mathbf{A})}$ *is described.* We will now describe this pseudo-subspace for the case $A = \mathbf{L}$. Below, $\mathbf{L}$ denotes the corresponding operator in $\mathbf{l}_2(H; [0, \infty)) = L(H, l_2(H; [0, \infty)))$ (not to be confused with the expression L).

Theorem 2.7. *The pseudo-subspace* $\widehat{(\mathbf{L} - z\mathbf{E})\mathfrak{D}(\mathbf{L})}$ *coincides with the set of pseudo-vectors* $U \in \mathbf{l}_2(H; [0, \infty))$, *whose coordinates are connected by the relation*

$$U_j = P_j(\bar{z})U_0 \quad (j = 1, 2, \cdots). \tag{2.60}$$

Proof. If $U \in \widehat{(\mathrm{L} - z\mathrm{E})\mathfrak{D}(\mathrm{L})}$, then for any $x \in H$ $Ux \in \widehat{(\mathrm{L} - zE)\mathfrak{D}(\mathrm{L})}$ and therefore $\mathrm{L}^*(Ux) = \bar{z}Ux$, i.e. $L[Ux] = \bar{z}Ux$, where $U_{-1}x = 0$. In other words, $(LU)_j = A_{j-1}U_{j-1} + A_jU_{j+1} + B_jU_j = \bar{z}U_j$ $(j = 0, 1, \cdots; U_{-1} = 0)$. But $A_{j-1}P_{j-1}(\bar{z}) + A_jP_{j+1}(\bar{z}) + B_jP_j(\bar{z}) = \bar{z}P_j(\bar{z})$ $(j = 0, 1, \cdots; P_{-1}(\bar{z}) = 0, P_0(\bar{z}) = E)$; therefore, on multiplication of the last relation on the right by U_0, we observe that $P_j(\bar{z})U_0$ satisfies the same difference equation and Cauchy conditions as U_j. Hence (2.60) follows.

Conversely, suppose that U_0 is such that $U = (U_0, U_1, \cdots)$, obtained by (2.60), belongs to $1_2(H; [0, \infty))$. We will show that $U \in \widehat{(\mathrm{L} - z\mathrm{E})\mathfrak{D}(\mathrm{L})}$. Clearly, $(LU)_j = \bar{z}U_j$ $(j = 0, 1, \cdots; U_{-1} = 0)$, so for any $x \in H$ $(L(Ux))_j = \bar{z}(Ux)_j$ $(j = 0, 1, \cdots; U_{-1}x = 0)$, i.e. $Ux \in \widehat{(\mathrm{L} - zE)\mathfrak{D}(L)}$. But $\widehat{(\mathrm{L} - z\mathrm{E})\mathfrak{D}(\mathrm{L})}$ is a maximal pseudo-subspace (this follows from the decomposition (2.59) and from the necessity of Theorem 2.3), so the inclusion $Ux \in \widehat{(\mathrm{L} - zE)\mathfrak{D}(\mathrm{L})}$ $(x \in H)$ implies the inclusion $U \in \widehat{(\mathrm{L} - z\mathrm{E})\mathfrak{D}(\mathrm{L})}$, as required. The theorem is proved.

10. Polynomials of the second kind. Resolvents. As in the scalar case, the solution of the equation $(LU)_j = zU_j$, which is linearly independent of the solution $(P_0(z), P_1(z), \cdots)$, plays an important part. Namely, consider the equation $(LU)_j = zU_j$ $(j = 1, 2, \cdots)$ with initial data $U_0 = 0$, $U_1 = A_0^{-1}$. Let $(Q_1(z) = A_0^{-1}, Q_2(z), \cdots)$ be a solution of this problem; $Q_j(z)$ is an operator polynomial of degree $j - 1$, a polynomial of the second kind. As in the scalar case (cf. §1.6) it is easy to establish the formula

$$Q_j(z) = \int_{-\infty}^{\infty} \frac{P_j(\lambda) - P_j(z)}{\lambda - z} d\Sigma(\lambda) \qquad (j = 0, 1, \ldots). \tag{2.61}$$

Let A be some selfadjoint extension (possibly extending outside of $l_2(H; [0, \infty))$ of the operator L, $E(\Delta)$ and R_z – the corresponding generalized resolution of the identity and resolvent, $\mathrm{E}(\Delta)$ and R_z – their corresponding operators in $1_2(H; [0, \infty))$. By the general considerations of subsection 4 the last operators can be expressed by matrices in the basis $\Delta^{(0)} = (E, 0, 0, \cdots)$, $\Delta^{(1)} = (0, E, 0, \cdots), \cdots$; the elements of these matrices have the form

$$E(\Delta)_{jk} = \{\Delta^{(j)}, \mathbf{E}(\Delta)\Delta^{(k)}\} = \int_\Delta P_j(\lambda)\, d\Sigma(\lambda)\, P_k^*(\lambda),$$

$$R_{z;jk} = \{\Delta^{(j)}, \mathbf{R}_z\Delta^{(k)}\} = \int_{-\infty}^{\infty} \frac{1}{\lambda - z} P_j(\lambda)\, d\Sigma(\lambda)\, P_k^*(\lambda) \tag{2.62}$$

$$(j, k = 0, 1, \ldots);$$

the first equation follows from (2.40), and the second follows from the first and the representation $R_z = \int_{-\infty}^{\infty} (\lambda - z)^{-1} dE_\lambda$. As in the scalar case, the operator spectral measure $d\Sigma(\lambda)$ is recovered from the operator function

$$M(z) = R_{z;00} = \int_{-\infty}^{\infty} \frac{1}{\lambda - z}\, d\Sigma(\lambda) \qquad (\operatorname{Im} z \neq 0); \tag{2.63}$$

it suffices to pass from (2.63) to $\int_{-\infty}^{\infty} (\lambda - z)^{-1} d(\Sigma(\lambda)x, y)_H = (M(z)x, y)_H$ $(x, y \in H)$ and use the inversion formula for Stieltjes transforms. In the case where the extension does not go outside of $l_2(H; [0, \infty))$, the function $M(z)$ satisfies a relation of the type (1.40). We give it as an illustration. If z and ζ are not real, then by (2.62) we obtain

$$\{\mathbf{R}_\zeta\Delta^{(0)}, \mathbf{R}_z\Delta^{(0)}\} = \sum_{j=0}^{\infty} (\mathbf{R}_\zeta\Delta^{(0)})_j^* (\mathbf{R}_z\Delta^{(0)})_j;$$

$$(\mathbf{R}_z\Delta^{(0)})_j = R_{z;j0} = \int_{-\infty}^{\infty} \frac{P_j(\lambda)}{\lambda - z}\, d\Sigma(\lambda) = \int_{-\infty}^{\infty} \frac{P_j(\lambda) - P_j(z)}{\lambda - z}\, d\Sigma(\lambda)$$

$$+ P_j(z) \int_{-\infty}^{\infty} \frac{1}{\lambda - z}\, d\Sigma(\lambda) = Q_j(z) + P_j(z)M(z) \qquad (j = 0, 1, \ldots).$$

Therefore $\{\mathbf{R}_\zeta\Delta^{(0)}, \mathbf{R}_z\Delta^{(0)}\} = \sum_{j=0}^{\infty}[Q_j(\zeta) + P_j(\zeta)M(\zeta)]^*[Q_j(z) + P_j(z)M(z)]$. On the other hand, with the help of the identity $\mathbf{R}_\mu - \mathbf{R}_\lambda = (\mu - \lambda)\mathbf{R}_\mu\mathbf{R}_\lambda$, which follows from the ordinary Hilbert identity, and the equation $R_z^* = R_{\bar z}$, we obtain

$$\{\mathbf{R}_\zeta\Delta^{(0)}, \mathbf{R}_z\Delta^{(0)}\} = \{\mathbf{R}_{\bar z}\mathbf{R}_\zeta\Delta^{(0)}, \Delta^{(0)}\} = \left\{\frac{\mathbf{R}_{\bar z} - \mathbf{R}_\zeta}{\bar z - \zeta}\Delta^{(0)}, \Delta^{(0)}\right\}$$

$$= \frac{M(\bar\zeta) - M(z)}{\bar\zeta - z}.$$

Thus

$$\frac{M(\bar{\zeta})-M(z)}{\bar{\zeta}-z}=\sum_{j=0}^{\infty}[Q_j(\zeta)+P_j(\zeta)M(\zeta)]^*[Q_j(z)+P_j(z)M(z)] \quad (\zeta \neq z). \tag{2.64}$$

It is easy now to prove a generalization of the assertion given in the last part of §1.6.

Theorem 2.8. *There exists at least one operator function* $F(z)$ *such that the pseudo-vector with coordinates* $Q_j(z)+P_j(z)F(z)$ $(j=0,1,\cdots)$ *belongs to* $\mathbf{1}_2(H;[0,\infty))$ *for each nonreal* z. *If the operator* L *is selfadjoint, then there is only one such function and it coincides with* $M(z)$.

Proof. It follows from formula (2.64) with $\zeta = z$ that $F(z)=M(z)$ satisfies the conditions of the theorem. Suppose now that L is selfadjoint and that $F_1(z)$ and $F_2(z)$ are two functions such that $Q_j(z)+P_j(z)F_1(z)$, $Q_j(z)+P_j(z)F_2(z)\in \mathbf{1}_2(H;[0,\infty))$. Then the difference of these pseudo-vectors belongs to $\mathbf{1}_2(H;[0,\infty))$. i.e. $P_j(z)(F_1(z)-F_2(z))\in \mathbf{1}_2(H;[0,\infty))$. Therefore it is necessary that $F_1(z)=F_2(z)$, since in the contrary case the deficiency subspace of L would, by Theorem 2.7, be nonzero, which contradicts the assumption that L is selfadjoint. The theorem is proved.

11. **Conditions for selfadjointness of the operator L. Further results.** The majority of the remaining results of §1 carry over in some form to the operator case. Sometimes this can be done very simply, but sometimes it is necessary to make auxiliary constructions. Thus, it is simple to generalize Theorem 1.3 concerning the selfadjointness of L.

Theorem 2.9. *If the series* $\sum_{j=0}^{\infty} 1/\|A_j\|$ *diverges, then* L *is selfadjoint.*

Proof. If $\operatorname{Im} z\neq 0$, then by Green's formula (2.25) we obtain

$$(\bar{z}-z)\sum_{j=0}^{n}P_j^*(z)P_j(z)=\sum_{j=0}^{n}((LP(z))_j^*P_j(z)-P_j^*(z)(LP(z))_j)$$
$$=P_{n+1}^*(z)A_nP_n(z)-P_n^*(z)A_nP_{n+1}(z).$$

Hence for $n=0,1,\cdots$

$$(\bar{z}-z)\sum_{j=0}^{n}\|P_j(z)x\|_H^2=(\bar{z}-z)\left(\sum_{j=0}^{n}P_j^*(z)P_j(z)x,\, x\right)_H$$
$$=(A_nP_n(z)x,\, P_{n+1}(z)x)_H-(A_nP_{n+1}(z)x,\, P_n(z)x)_H;$$

$$|\bar{z}-z|\,\|x\|_H^2 \leqslant |\bar{z}-z|\sum_{j=0}^{n}\|P_j(z)x\|_H^2$$

$$\leqslant 2\|A_n\|\,\|P_n(z)x\|_H\,\|P_{n+1}(z)x\|_H \qquad (x\in H).$$

Thus, $\|A_n\|^{-1} \le 2\|P_n(z)x\|_H \|P_{n+1}(z)x\|_H / |\bar{z}-z|\, \|x\|_H^2$ $(x \neq 0)$, whence

$$\infty = \sum_{n=0}^{\infty}\frac{1}{\|A_n\|} < C\sum_{n=0}^{\infty}\|P_n(z)x\|_H\,\|P_{n+1}(z)x\|_H$$

$$\leqslant C\sqrt{\sum_{n=0}^{\infty}\|P_n(z)x\|_H^2}\sqrt{\sum_{n=0}^{\infty}\|P_{n+1}(z)x\|_H^2} < C\sum_{n=0}^{\infty}\|P_n(z)x\|_H^2,$$

i.e. $\sum_{n=0}^{\infty}\|P_n(z)x\|_H^2 = \infty$ for each nonzero $x \in H$. This shows that there is no $U \in \mathbf{l}_2(H; [0, \infty))$, different from zero, which satisfies (2.60) (with z replaced by $\bar{z}$). By Theorem 2.7, the deficiency numbers of the operator $\mathbf{L}$ equal zero. The theorem is proved.

It is even easier to establish that if the norms of the operators A_j and B_j are uniformly bounded, then $\mathbf{L}$ is bounded and even selfadjoint.

The results of §1 concerning the description of all spectral measures in the indeterminate case can also be generalized to the operator case, but the situation here is more complicated, since the deficiency numbers may now vary from 0 to ∞. The most symmetric case of maximal deficiency numbers is characterized by the condition that in each finite region G of the complex plane the inequality $\|\sum_{j=0}^{\infty}P_j^*(z)P_j(z)\|_H \le C_G$ $(z \in G)$ holds (it is possible to put sufficient conditions on $\mathbf{L}$ of the type of Theorem 1.5 so that this so-called absolutely indeterminate case will occur). In this case the operator $\Gamma(z)$ is invertible; moreover $\Gamma^{-1}(z) = \{P(z), P(z)\}$. The operator $M(z)$ for fixed z and variable extensions traces out an operator circle of the type (1.49); the function $M(z)$ is described by formulas similar to (1.50) and (1.59). We will not go into these considerations.

§3. SECOND ORDER DIFFERENCE OPERATORS ON THE WHOLE AXIS

The spectral theory of such operators is in many instances similar to the theory on the semi-axis; the difference is that now the spectrum may, in general, have multiplicity two (i.e. $N_\lambda \le 2$). This multiplicity of the spectrum, for instance, leads, instead of to a spectral measure, to a two-dimensional matrix measure.

It is shown below (subsection 2) how the study of this problem is reduced to the results of the previous section. We remark that a similar reduction can be carried out for the equation with operator coefficients on the whole real line.

1. **The difference operator and a proof of Parseval's equation.** We will consider operators which act in the space $l_2((-\infty, \infty)) = H_0$ of sequences $u = (\cdots, u_{-1}, u_0, u_1, \cdots)$ such that $\sum_{j=-\infty}^{\infty}|u_j|^2 < \infty$. Define the operator L′ on finite sequences by setting

$$(\mathrm{L}'u)_j = (Lu)_j = a_{j-1}u_{j-1} + a_j u_{j+1} + b_j u_j \qquad (u \in l_{2,0}((-\infty, \infty))),$$

where $a_j > 0$, $\operatorname{Im} b_j = 0$ for all j. This operator is Hermitian; denote the closure of L′ by L. In the same way as in §1.1, it is easy to establish that $\mathfrak{D}(\mathrm{L}^*)$ consists of all $v \in l_2(-\infty, \infty))$ such that $Lv \in l_2((-\infty, \infty))$; in this connection $\mathrm{L}^* v = Lv$.

In what follows, we make use of the following fundamental system of solutions of the equation $Lu = zu$:

$$\begin{gathered}(LP_{-1,\cdot}(z))_j = zP_{-1;j}(z) \qquad (P_{-1;-1}(z) = 1,\ P_{-1;0}(z) = 0),\\ (LP_{0;\cdot}(z))_j = zP_{0;j}(z) \quad (P_{0;-1}(z) = 0,\ P_{0;0}(z) = 1);\\ u_j = u_{-1}P_{-1;j}(z) + u_0 P_{0;j}(z) \qquad (j = \ldots, -1, 0, 1, \ldots).\end{gathered} \tag{3.1}$$

By the Fourier transform of the sequence $u \in l_{2,0}((-\infty, \infty))$ we mean the two-dimensional vector-function $\widetilde{u}(z) = (\widetilde{u}_{-1}(z), \widetilde{u}_0(z))$, where

$$\widetilde{u}_\alpha(z) = \sum_{j=-\infty}^{\infty} u_j P_{\alpha;j}(z) \qquad (\alpha = -1, 0). \tag{3.2}$$

Parseval's equation for the operator L can be proved by any of the three methods presented in §1.3. The first method is especially descriptive; we outline it now.

The relation (1.16) and (1.17) obviously remain; one need only take the summation from $-\infty$ to $+\infty$. At the same time, equation (1.18) is substantially changed. Indeed, if we repeat the earlier arguments we see that each vector $\phi \in \Re(P(\lambda))$ satisfies the equation $((L - \lambda E)\phi)_j = 0$ $(j = \cdots, -1, 0, 1, \cdots)$; however it satisfies no boundary conditions. Therefore by (3.1) $\phi_j = \sum_{\alpha=-1,0}\phi_\alpha P_{\alpha;j}(\lambda)$. Hence for any k $\Phi_{jk}(\lambda) = \sum_{\alpha=-1,0}\Phi_{\alpha k}(\lambda)P_{\alpha;j}(\lambda)$ and, furthermore, $\Phi_{\alpha k}(\lambda) = \overline{\Phi_{k\alpha}(\lambda)} = \overline{\sum_{\beta=-1,0}\Phi_{\beta\alpha}(\lambda)P_{\beta;k}(\lambda)} = \sum_{\beta=-1,0}\Phi_{\alpha\beta}(\lambda)P_{\beta;k}(\lambda)$ for all k. On performing the substitution, we obtain

$$\Phi_{jk}(\lambda) = \sum_{\alpha,\beta=-1,0} \Phi_{\alpha\beta}(\lambda) P_{\alpha;j}(\lambda) P_{\beta;k}(\lambda) \, (j,k = \ldots, -1, 0, 1, \ldots). \tag{3.3}$$

It follows from (1.16) and (3.3) that

$$(E(\Delta)\delta_k, \delta_j)_0 = E(\Delta)_{jk} = \int_\Delta \Phi_{jk}(\lambda)\, d\varrho(\lambda) = \sum_{\alpha\,\beta=-1,0} \int_\Delta P_{\alpha;j}(\lambda) P_{\beta;k}(\lambda) d\sigma_{\alpha\beta}(\lambda)$$

$$(j,k = \ldots, -1, 0, 1, \ldots); \tag{3.4}$$

$$d\sigma_{\alpha\beta}(\lambda) = \Phi_{\alpha\beta}(\lambda)\, d\varrho(\lambda) \quad (\alpha,\beta = -1,0; \; -\infty < \lambda < \infty)$$

(here $\delta_k = (\cdots, \delta_{-1k}, \delta_{0k}, \delta_{1k}, \cdots)$ for all k). Taking into account the initial values for $P_{\alpha;j}(\lambda)$ (see (3.1)), we obtain, from (3.4),

$$\sigma_{\alpha\beta}(\Delta) = E(\Delta)_{\alpha\beta} = (E(\Delta)\delta_\beta, \delta_\alpha)_0 \quad (\alpha,\beta = -1,0). \tag{3.5}$$

Since $E(\Delta) \geq 0$, the matrix $\|\sigma_{\alpha\beta}(\Delta)\|_{-1}^{0}$ is positive definite. Equation (3.4) for $\Delta = (-\infty, \infty)$ implies the following orthogonality relation of the polynomials $P_{\alpha;j}(\lambda)$:

$$\sum_{\alpha,\beta=-1,0} \int_{-\infty}^{\infty} P_{\alpha;j}(\lambda) P_{\beta;k}(\lambda)\, d\sigma_{\alpha\beta}(\lambda) = \delta_{jk} \quad (j,k = \ldots, -1, 0, 1, \ldots). \tag{3.6}$$

Using (3.4) and the notation (3.2), we obtain Parseval's equations

$$(E(\Delta)u, v)_0 = \sum_{\alpha,\beta=-1,0} \int_\Delta \tilde{u}_\alpha(\lambda) \overline{\tilde{v}_\beta(\lambda)}\, d\sigma_{\alpha\beta}(\lambda) \; (u, v \in l_{2,0}((-\infty, \infty))) \tag{3.7}$$

from the formula $(E(\Delta)u, v)_0 = \int_\Delta d(E_\lambda u, v)_0$. Thus the following theorem holds.

Theorem 3.1. *Let* $E(\Delta)$ *be a resolution of the identity (ordinary or generalized) corresponding to the operator* L. *Construct the matrix spectral measure according to formula* (3.5), *the so-called spectral matrix. Then the orthogonality relations* (3.6) *hold; the eigenfunction expansion is expressed by* (3.7) *and* (3.2).

2. **Reduction to an equation with operator coefficients ("duplication").** As we continue to carry over results of §1 directly to the operator L, difficulties arise in a series of cases, since the form of the possible formulations are not entirely clear. We now show how to reduce the problems under consideration to the construction of §2 and by the same token obtain the complete spectral theory for L. In particular, we obtain another proof of Theorem 3.1 – as a special case of Theorem 2.4. The spaces $l_2((-\infty, \infty))$ and $l_2(C_2; [0, \infty))$ are isometric; the isometry is established by the relation

$$l_2((-\infty, \infty)) \ni u = (\ldots, u_{-1}, u_0, u_1, \ldots) \longleftrightarrow \hat{u}$$

$$= (\hat{u}_0, \hat{u}_1, \ldots) \in l_2(C_2; [0, \infty)), \tag{3.8}$$

$$\hat{u}_j = (u_{-j-1}, u_j) \quad (j = 0, 1, \ldots).$$

It is not difficult to compute that the image of the expression L under this isometry is the expression $\hat{L}$ with operator coefficients of the form

$$(\hat{L}\hat{u})_j = A_{j-1}\hat{u}_{j-1} + A_j\hat{u}_{j+1} + B_j\hat{u}_j \quad (j = 0, 1, \ldots);$$

$$A_j = \begin{Vmatrix} a_{-j-2} & 0 \\ 0 & a_j \end{Vmatrix} \quad (j = 0, 1, \ldots), \tag{3.9}$$

$$B_j = \begin{Vmatrix} b_{-j-1} & 0 \\ 0 & b_j \end{Vmatrix} \quad (j = 1, 2, \ldots), \quad B_0 = \begin{Vmatrix} b_{-1} & a_{-1} \\ a_{-1} & b_0 \end{Vmatrix}.$$

For the computation of $(\hat{L}\hat{u})_0$, it is necessary in all that follows to set $\hat{u}_{-1} = 0$, and therefore the value of A_{-1} plays no part. Obviously the coefficients of $\hat{L}$ satisfy the requirements of §2.5.

Define the operator $\hat{\mathrm{L}}$ associated with $\hat{L}$; since $l_{2,0}((-\infty, \infty))$ and $l_{2,0}(C_2; [0, \infty))$ are transformed into each other by the isomorphism (3.8), L and $\hat{\mathrm{L}}$ are isomorphic and therefore the results corresponding to $\hat{\mathrm{L}}$ can be rephrased for L. Denote by $\hat{P}_j(z)$ and $\hat{Q}_j(z)$ the polynomials of the first and second kinds respectively for $\hat{L}$, i.e. the solutions of the problems $(\hat{L}\hat{P}(z))_j = z\hat{P}_j(z)$ $(j = 0, 1, \cdots; \hat{P}_{-1}(z) = 0, \hat{P}_0(z) = E)$ and $(\hat{L}\hat{Q}(z))_j = z\hat{Q}_j(z)$ $(j = 1, 2, \cdots;$ $\hat{Q}_0(z) = 0, \hat{Q}_1(z) = A_0^{-1})$. Writing the latter equations as elements of a matrix and taking into account (3.1), we easily obtain the following connection with $P_{\alpha;j}(z)$:

$$\hat{P}_j(z) = \begin{Vmatrix} P_{-1;-j-1}(z) & P_{0;-j-1}(z) \\ P_{-1;j}(z) & P_{0;j}(z) \end{Vmatrix},$$

$$\hat{Q}_j(z) = -\frac{1}{a_{-1}} \begin{Vmatrix} P_{0;-j-1}(z) & 0 \\ 0 & P_{-1;j}(z) \end{Vmatrix} \quad (j = 0, 1, \ldots). \tag{3.10}$$

Theorem 2.4 is valid for the operator $\hat{\mathrm{L}}$, and therefore Parseval's equation holds in the form (2.43). We show that it coincides with (3.7). On computing the Fourier transform (2.41) of the vector $\hat{u}$, which corresponds to the vector $u = (\cdots, u_{-1}, u_0, u_1, \cdots)$ via (3.8), we obtain

$$\widetilde{\hat{u}}(z) = \sum_{j=0}^{\infty} P_j^*(\bar{z})\hat{u}_j = \sum_{j=0}^{\infty} \begin{Vmatrix} P_{-1;-j-1}(z) & P_{-1;j}(z) \\ P_{0;-j-1}(z) & P_{0;j}(z) \end{Vmatrix} (u_{-j-1}, u_j) \tag{3.11}$$
$$= (\widetilde{u}_{-1}(z), \widetilde{u}_0(z)),$$

where $\widetilde{u}_\alpha(z)$ is defined by (3.2). Let

$$\Sigma(\lambda) = \begin{Vmatrix} \sigma_{-1,-1}(\lambda) & \sigma_{-1,0}(\lambda) \\ \sigma_{0,-1}(\lambda) & \sigma_{0,0}(\lambda) \end{Vmatrix} \tag{3.12}$$

be the spectral matrix from (2.43); for $u, v \in l_{2,0}((-\infty, \infty))$ we find by means of (2.43) and (3.11) that

$$(E(\Delta)u, v)_{l_2((-\infty,\infty))} = (E(\Delta)\hat{u}, \hat{v})_{l_2(C_2;[0,\infty))} = \int_\Delta (d\Sigma(\lambda)\widetilde{\hat{u}}(\lambda), \widetilde{\hat{v}}(\lambda))_{C_2}$$

$$= \int_\Delta \sum_{\alpha,\beta=-1,0} \widetilde{u}_\beta(\lambda)\overline{\widetilde{v}_\alpha(\lambda)}\, d\sigma_{\alpha\beta}(\lambda) = \sum_{\alpha,\beta=-1,0} \int_\Delta \widetilde{u}_\alpha(\lambda)\overline{\widetilde{v}_\beta(\lambda)}\, d\sigma_{\alpha\beta}(\lambda).$$

Thus we pass from Parseval's equation in the form (2.43) to the equation in the form (3.7).

The relations (3.8)–(3.11) make it possible to rephrase easily the results of §2 for the operator L under investigation. We clarify this for only a few of the facts, just as in §2 the list of theorems we mentioned was incomplete in comparuson with §1.

Thus, if we note that $\|A_j\| = \max(a_{-j-2}, a_j)$, $j = 0, 1, \cdots$ (cf. (3.9)), it follows from Theorem 2.9 that *the operator* L *is selfadjoint if* $\sum_{j=0}^{\infty} 1/\max(a_{-j-2}, a_j) = \infty$ (we will not be concerned with refinement of this condition). Since the coefficients of the expression L are real, the deficiency numbers of the operator L are equal. Since the deficiency subspaces consist of those solutions of the equation $(Lu)_j = zu_j$ ($j = 0, 1, \cdots$; $\operatorname{Im} z \neq 0$), which belong to $l_2((-\infty, \infty))$, they are at most two-dimensional. Thus, a deficiency number of the operator L may have the values 0, 1, or 2. A rule for its computation in terms of the polynomials $P_{\alpha;j}(z)$ ($\alpha = -1, 0$; $j = \cdots, -1, 0, 1, \cdots$) follows from Theorem 2.6 with $P_j(z)$ replaced by $\hat{P}_j(z)$ from (3.10). It is also clear how such a rule is formulated from the representation (3.1) of the general solution of the equation $Lu = zu$.

Suppose that L is selfadjoint. Then the Stieltjes transform $M(z)$ of its spectral matrix $d\Sigma(\lambda)$ may in some cases be found by means of Theorem 2.8. Namely, suppose that we started with a matrix function $M(z)$ of nonreal z (its values are second degree matrices), such that $\hat{Q}_j(z) + \hat{P}_j(z)M(z) \in \mathbf{l}_2(C_2; [0, \infty))$ for any nonreal z. Then $M(z)$ is the unknown Stieltjes transform. We illustrate this method on the simplest example of an expression with constant coefficients (of course it might also be simply studied with the help of the Fourier transform $(\cdots, u_{-1}, u_0, u_1, \cdots) \to \tilde{u}(\xi) = \sum_{j=-\infty}^{\infty} u_j e^{-ij\xi}$ $(\xi \in [0, 2\pi))$; cf. Chapter VI, §3.2).

Consider the difference expression

$$(Lu)_j = \frac{1}{2} u_{j-1} + \frac{1}{2} u_{j+1} \quad (j = \ldots, -1, 0, 1, \ldots). \tag{3.13}$$

Obviously, the corresponding operator L is bounded and selfadjoint. It is not difficult to compute that the solutions $P_{\alpha;j}(z)$ have the form

$$P_{-1;j}(z) = \begin{cases} -U_{j-1}(z) & (j \geqslant 1), \\ 0 & (j = 0), \\ U_{|j|-1}(z) & (j \leqslant -1), \end{cases} \quad P_{0;j}(z) = \begin{cases} U_j(z) & (j \geqslant 0), \\ 0 & (j = -1), \\ -U_{|j|-2}(z) & (j \leqslant -2), \end{cases}$$

where $U_j(z)$ are the Čebyšev polynomials of the second kind, i.e. $U_j(z) = \sin((j+1)\arccos z)/\sin(\arccos z)$ $(j = -1, 0, \cdots)$. Thus, we obtain the following formulas for the matrix polynomials $\hat{P}_j(z)$ and $\hat{Q}_j(z)$ (cf. (3.10)):

$$\hat{P}_j(z) = \begin{Vmatrix} U_j(z) & -U_{j-1}(z) \\ -U_{j-1}(z) & U_j(z) \end{Vmatrix}, \quad \hat{Q}_j(z) = 2 \begin{Vmatrix} U_{j-1}(z) & 0 \\ 0 & U_{j-1}(z) \end{Vmatrix} \tag{3.14}$$

$$(j = 0, 1, \ldots).$$

Now recall example a) in §1.11, namely the expression (3.13) on the semi-axis. For this problem the polynomials of the first and second kind are $P_j^+(z) = U_j(z)$ $(j = -1, 0, 1, \cdots)$ and $Q_j^+(z) = 2U_{j-1}(z)$ $(j = 0, 1, \cdots)$; the spectral measure $d\sigma(\lambda)$ and its Stieltjes transform have the form (1.85) and (1.86). On rewriting (3.14) in terms of $P_j^+(z)$ and $Q_j^+(z)$, we obtain

$$\hat{P}_j(z) = \begin{Vmatrix} P_j^+(z) & -\frac{1}{2} Q_j^+(z) \\ -\frac{1}{2} Q_j^+(z) & P_j^+(z) \end{Vmatrix}, \quad \hat{Q}_j(z) = \begin{Vmatrix} Q_j^+(z) & 0 \\ 0 & Q_j^+(z) \end{Vmatrix} \tag{3.15}$$

$$(j = 0, 1, \ldots).$$

Let the matrix function $M(z) = \|M_{jk}\|_{-1}^{0}$ be such that $\hat{Q}_j(z) + \hat{P}_j(z)M(z) \in \mathbf{l}_2(C_2; [0, \infty))$, i.e. such that for each $\alpha, \beta = -1, 0$ the element $(\hat{Q}_j(z) + \hat{P}_j(z)M(z))_{\alpha\beta} \in l_2([0, \infty))$ $(\operatorname{Im} z \neq 0)$. If we take (3.15) into account, we can rewrite this condition. We obtain

$$
\begin{gathered}
Q_j^+(z)\left(1-\frac{1}{2}M_{0,-1}(z)\right)+P_j^+(z)M_{-1,-1}(z)\in l_2([0,\infty)),\\
Q_j^+(z)\left(-\frac{1}{2}M_{0,0}(z)\right)+P_j^+(z)M_{-1,0}(z)\in l_2([0,\infty)),\\
Q_j^+(z)\left(-\frac{1}{2}M_{-1,-1}(z)\right)+P_j^+(z)M_{0,-1}(z)\in l_2([0,\infty)),\\
Q_j^+(z)\left(1-\frac{1}{2}M_{-1,0}(z)\right)+P_j^+(z)M_{0,0}(z)\in l_2([0,\infty)).
\end{gathered}
\tag{3.16}
$$

But, as is known (see the end of §1.6), the function $m(z)$ is uniquely determined by the condition $Q_j^+(z)+m(z)P_j^+(z)\in l_2([0,\infty))$, so from (3.16) it follows that

$$
\frac{M_{-1,-1}(z)}{1-\frac{1}{2}M_{0,-1}(z)}=m(z),\quad \frac{M_{-1,0}(z)}{-\frac{1}{2}M_{0,0}(z)}=m(z),
$$

$$
\frac{M_{0,-1}(z)}{-\frac{1}{2}M_{-1,-1}(z)}=m(z),\quad \frac{M_{0,0}(z)}{1-\frac{1}{2}M_{-1,0}(z)}=m(z).
$$

Solving for $M_{\alpha\beta}(z)$ and using formula (1.86), we find that

$$
M(z)=\left\|\begin{matrix}-\frac{1}{\sqrt{z^2-1}} & 1-\frac{z}{\sqrt{z^2-1}}\\ 1-\frac{z}{\sqrt{z^2-1}} & -\frac{1}{\sqrt{z^2-1}}\end{matrix}\right\|. \tag{3.17}
$$

If we apply the Stieltjes inversion formula to (3.17), we obtain the following expression for the spectral matrix of the problem under consideration:

$$
\begin{gathered}
d\Sigma(\lambda)=\frac{1}{\pi}\left\|\begin{matrix}\frac{1}{\sqrt{1-\lambda^2}} & \frac{\lambda}{\sqrt{1-\lambda^2}}\\ \frac{\lambda}{\sqrt{1-\lambda^2}} & \frac{1}{\sqrt{1-\lambda^2}}\end{matrix}\right\| d\lambda \quad \text{for} \quad |\lambda|\leqslant 1\\
d\Sigma(\lambda)=0 \quad \text{for} \quad |\lambda|>1.
\end{gathered}
\tag{3.18}
$$

3. **The inverse problem of spectral analysis.** Because of the general results of §2.7, the spectral matrix (3.12) is such that

$$\int_{-\infty}^{\infty} |\lambda|^m \, d\sigma_{\alpha\alpha}(\lambda) < \infty \quad (\alpha = -1, 0; \quad m = 0, 1, \ldots)^{1)},$$

$$\int_{-\infty}^{\infty} d\sigma_{\alpha\beta}(\lambda) = \delta_{\alpha\beta} \quad (\alpha, \beta = -1, 0);$$

$\Sigma(\lambda)$ has an infinite number of points of growth. Conversely, suppose that $d\Sigma(\lambda)$ is a nonnegative operator (matrix) measure of the form (3.12) which satisfies the stated requirements. Then $d\Sigma(\lambda)$ is a spectral matrix of some difference expression of the form (2.22) on the semi-axis, of which A_j and B_j are matrices of second order. This follows from the results of §2.8 if it is noted that when H is finite-dimensional, the condition that $\Sigma(\lambda)$ have an infinite number of points of growth implies that the integral (2.48) has an inverse. We will clarify the last fact. Let $P(\lambda)$ be taken from (2.48), and let $x \in H$ be such that $\{P, P\}x = 0$. We have

$$0 = (\{P, P\} x, x)_H = \int_{-\infty}^{\infty} (P^*(\lambda) \, d\Sigma(\lambda) P(\lambda) x, x)_H$$

$$= \int_{-\infty}^{\infty} (d\Sigma(\lambda) P(\lambda) x, P(\lambda) x)_H.$$

Since $\Sigma(\lambda)$ is assumed to have an infinite number of points of increase, it follows from the last equation that $P(\lambda)x = 0$, i.e. $x = 0$. Since H is finite-dimensional, this means that $\{P, P\}^{-1}$ exists.

If in addition it is known that the second order matrices A_j and B_j, constructed with respect to $d\Sigma(\lambda)$ by (2.49), are such that A_j for $j = 0, 1, \cdots$ and B_j for $j = 1, 2, \cdots$ are diagonal, the elements on the diagonals of the matrices A_j are positive, and B_0 has the form $\|c_{\alpha\beta}\|_{-1}^{0}$ where $c_{0,-1} = c_{-1,0} > 0$, then it is not difficult to see that the constructed expression (2.22) is equivalent to the difference expression of the form being investigated on the whole axis. The procedure of constructing such an expression is described in §2.8.

---

1) The existence of the integrals (2.11) for our case follows from the existence of these integrals; see the footnote on p. 568.

§4. PARTIAL DIFFERENCE OPERATORS OF THE SECOND ORDER IN A HALF-PLANE

We turn to the construction of a spectral theory of partial difference equations. We consider the simplest and most typical case of a second order expression in a half-plane. A detailed examination of such an expression in the whole plane can be made by means of the method of duplication, §3.2, for ordinary differences.

1. The difference operator and a proof of Parseval's equation. Consider a difference expression of the form

$$(Lu)_{jk} = a_{j-1,k}u_{j-1,k} + a_{jk}u_{j+1,k} + b_{j,k-1}u_{j,k-1} + b_{jk}u_{j,k+1} + c_{jk}u_{jk}, \tag{4.1}$$

where (j, k) is an integral point of a half-plane, i.e. $j, k = \cdots, -1, 0, 1, \cdots$. Its coefficients a_{jk}, b_{jk}, c_{jk} are assumed to be real. A version of Green's formula, which we now formulate, holds for L. We will call a set G of integral points in a half-plane an integral finite region if after connecting these points by line segments of length 1 it is converted into a system of squares which form a connected finite region in the plane. A point of G, not all four adjoining points of which belong to G, is called a boundary point; the set of boundary points is denoted by Γ. The points of G which are not boundary points are called interior points, the set of which is denoted by G'. It is not difficult to prove the following version of Green's formula:

$$\sum_{(j,k)\in G'} [(Lu)_{jk}\bar{v}_{jk} - u_{jk}\overline{(Lv)_{jk}}] = \sum_{(j,k)\in\Gamma} [(\Re u)_{jk}\bar{v}_{jk} - u_{jk}\overline{(\Re v)_{jk}}]. \tag{4.2}$$

Here $(\Re u)_{jk}$ is a boundary expression which has the following form: at each point (j, k) of the boundary it is equal to the sum of two or three differences of u, multiplied by certain constants, omitting $c_{jk}u_{jk}$. The differences are taken among the points of G adjoining (j, k), and the point (j, k); in this connection, if the subtraction is carried out along the axis Oj (Ok) and if the point with the smaller coordinate is subtracted from the point with the larger coordinate, then the difference is multiplied by $a(b)$, taken at the point (j, k), and at the point from which it is subtracted, in the contrary case.

It follows from (4.2) that the expression (4.1) is formally selfadjoint, i.e. $\sum_{j,k=-\infty}^{\infty} (Lu)_{jk}\bar{v}_{jk} = \sum_{j,k=-\infty}^{\infty} u_{jk}\overline{(Lv)}_{jk}$, if only one of u and v is finite.

Let Π denote the set of all integral points in the right half-plane, i.e. points (j, k) where $j = 0, 1, \cdots$; $k = \cdots, -1, 0, 1, \cdots$. In what follows, we consider the expression (4.1) on sequences u_{jk}, defined for $(j, k) \in \Pi$. For the evaluation of

$(Lu)_{0k}$, we assume as in §1 that $u_{-1,k} = 0$ for all k. This condition plays the role of the zero boundary condition. Note that, as in §1.12, one might consider even more general conditions, namely conditions of the form $\alpha_k u_{-1,k} + \gamma_k (\Re u)_{-1,k} = 0$ $(k = \cdots, -1, 0, 1, \cdots)$, where α_k and γ_k are two fixed sequences of real numbers: $\alpha_k^2 + \gamma_k^2 > 0$.

We now define an operator associated with the expression (4.1) in the Hilbert space $l_2(\Pi) = H_0$, which consists of all sequences $u_{jk}((j, k) \in \Pi)$ such that $\Sigma_{(j,k)\in\Pi} |u_{jk}|^2 < \infty$; $(u, v)_{l_2(\Pi)} = (u, v)_0 = \Sigma_{(j,k)\in\Pi} u_{jk}\bar{v}_{jk}$. To this end, we consider the linear manifold $l_{2,0}(\Pi)$ of sequences u_{jk} which are finite at ∞, i.e. such that $u_{jk} = 0$ if the distance of the point (j, k) from $(0, 0)$ is sufficiently large. Set $(\mathrm{L}'u)_{jk} = (Lu)_{jk}$ $(u \in l_{2,0}(\Pi);\ (j, k) \in \Pi)$. Because of Green's formula (4.2), it is easy to see that L' is Hermitian; let L be its closure. The operator L is Hermitian but in general not selfadjoint. The adjoint L^* of this operator, as is easily proved by means of Green's formula (cf. §1.1), has the form $\mathrm{L}^* u = Lu$, where $\mathfrak{D}(\mathrm{L}^*)$ consists of all $u \in l_2(\Pi)$ such that $Lu \in l_2(\Pi)$. We now turn to the construction of an eigenfunction expansion of a selfadjoint extension of the operator L. *In all that follows we assume that* $a_{jk} > 0$ $(j = -1, 0, 1, \cdots;$ $k = \cdots, -1, 0, 1, \cdots)$.

This condition allows us to introduce polynomials of the first kind for the expression (4.1) – the analogue of the polynomials $P_j(z)$. Namely, consider the equation

$$(Lu)_{jk} = a_{j-1,k}u_{j-1,k} + a_{jk}u_{j+1,k} + b_{j,k-1}u_{j,k-1} + b_{jk}u_{j,k+1} + c_{jk}u_{jk} = zu_{jk} \quad ((j, k) \in \Pi). \tag{4.3}$$

for complex z. Let $P_{\alpha;(j,k)}(z)$ $(\alpha = \cdots, -1, 0, 1, \cdots)$ be the solution of this equation which satisfies the initial conditions $u_{-1,k} = 0$, $u_{0k} = \delta_{k\alpha}$ $(k = \cdots, -1, 0, 1, \cdots)$. Since $a_{jk} \neq 0$, the solution is uniquely determined by the recursion relation (4.3). It is clear that $P_{\alpha;(j,k)}(z)$ is equal to 0 outside of the angle $A\alpha B$ (see Figure 13), and inside this angle each $P_{\alpha;(j,k)}(z)$ will be a polynomial in z with real coefficients; the corresponding degrees of these polynomials is shown in Figure 13.

Let $u_{jk}((j, k) \in \Pi)$ be an arbitrary solution of equation (4.3) which satisfies, naturally, the condition $u_{-1,k} = 0$ for all k. Obviously, this solution can be expressed by means of $P_{\alpha;(j,k)}(z)$ and u_{0k}:

$$u_{jk} = \sum_{\alpha=-\infty}^{\infty} u_{0\alpha}P_{\alpha;(j,k)}(z) \quad ((j, k) \in \Pi). \tag{4.4}$$

Note that for fixed (j, k), $P_{\alpha;(j,k)}(z)$ vanishes for all α outside the interval $[k - j, k + j]$ (see Figure 13); hence for each (j, k) the sum in (4.4) is finite.

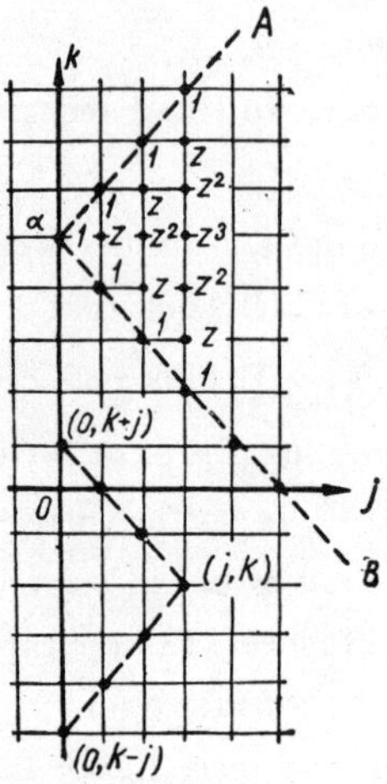

Figure 13.

Let $E(\Delta)$ be, generally speaking, a generalized resolution of the identity corresponding to L. The operator L acts in the space $l_2(\Pi)$, which (after re-enumerating the points of Π) coincides with $l_2([0, \infty))$. Therefore, the results of Chapter V, §4.4 can be applied to L: the representation

$$E(\Delta) = \int_\Delta P(\lambda)\, d\varrho(\lambda), \tag{4.5}$$

holds, where $P(\lambda)$ is a generalized projection operator which maps the weighted space $l_2(\Pi, p_{jk})$ into the weighted space $l_2(\Pi, 1/p_{jk})$. Here the sequence $p_{jk} \geq 1$ $((j, k) \in \Pi)$ is such that $\sum_{(j,k)\in\Pi} 1/p_{jk} < \infty$. The operator $P(\lambda)$ is represented by means of a positive definite kernel $\Phi((j, k), (l, m); \lambda)$ $((j, k), (l, m) \in \Pi)$. The kernel $\Phi((j, k), (l, m); \lambda)$ satisfies the equation $Lu = \lambda u$ and the condition $u_{-1,k} = 0$ for all k in each of the variables (j, k) and (l, m). This follows as in the proof of Lemma 1.1 above. Therefore, the representation (4.4) can be applied to $\Phi((j, k), (l, m); \lambda)$ in each of the variables, and as a result we obtain

$$\Phi((j, k), (l, m); \lambda) = \sum_{\alpha,\beta=-\infty}^{\infty} \Phi((0, \alpha), (0, \beta); \lambda) P_{\alpha;(j,k)}(\lambda) P_{\beta;(l,m)}(\lambda) \tag{4.6}$$

(the sum here is finite).

Let $\delta_{(j,k)}$ be as usual the δ-sequence concentrated at $(j, k) \in \Pi$ ($\delta_{(j,k)}$ equals 1 at (j, k) and zero at the remaining points of Π). Thus $\Phi((j, k), (l, m); \lambda) = (P(\lambda)\delta_{(l,m)}, \delta_{(j,k)})_0$ and it follows from (4.5) and (4.6) that

$$(E(\Delta)\delta_{(l,m)}, \delta_{(j,k)})_0 = \sum_{\alpha,\beta=-\infty}^{\infty} \int_\Delta P_{\alpha;(j,k)}(\lambda) P_{\beta;(j,k)}(\lambda)\, d\sigma_{\alpha\beta}(\lambda) \tag{4.7}$$

$$((j, k), (l, m) \in \Pi),$$

where

$$d\sigma_{\alpha\beta}(\lambda) = \Phi((0, \alpha), (0, \beta); \lambda)\, d\varrho(\lambda) \quad (\alpha, \beta = \ldots, -1, 0, 1, \ldots). \tag{4.8}$$

The matrix $d\Sigma(\lambda) = \|d\sigma_{\alpha\beta}(\lambda)\|_{-\infty}^{\infty}$ is called a spectral matrix. On setting $(j, k) = (0, \alpha)$ and $(l, m) = (0, \beta)$ in (4.7) we obtain

$$\sigma_{\alpha\beta}(\Delta) = (E(\Delta)\,\delta_{(0,\beta)},\ \delta_{(0,\alpha)})_0 \quad (\alpha, \beta = \dots, -1, 0, 1, \dots); \tag{4.9}$$

thus the spectral matrix is a "boundary value" of the kernel operator $E(\Delta)$, i.e. a spectral function.

Equation (4.7) for $\Delta = (-\infty, \infty)$ reduces to the following orthogonality relations for the polynomials $P_{\alpha;(j,k)}(\lambda)$:

$$\sum_{\alpha,\beta=-\infty}^{\infty} \int_{-\infty}^{\infty} P_{\alpha;(j,k)}(\lambda)\, P_{\beta;(l,m)}(\lambda)\, d\sigma_{\alpha\beta}(\lambda) = \delta_{(j,k),\,(l,m)} \qquad ((j, k),\ (l, m) \in \Pi). \tag{4.10}$$

We introduce the Fourier transform $\tilde{u}(\lambda) = (\dots, \tilde{u}_{-1}(\lambda), \tilde{u}_0(\lambda), \tilde{u}_1(\lambda), \dots)$ of finite sequences by setting

$$\tilde{u}_\alpha(\lambda) = \sum_{(j,k)\in\Pi} u_{jk} P_{\alpha;(j,k)}(\lambda) \quad (\alpha = \dots, -1, 0, 1, \dots;\ u \in l_{2,0}(\Pi)). \tag{4.11}$$

Clearly, $\tilde{u}_\alpha(\lambda)$ is a finite sequence in α. Using (4.7) we can rewrite Parseval's equation in the form

$$(E(\Delta)\,u, v)_0 = \sum_{\alpha,\beta=-\infty}^{\infty} \int_{\Delta} \tilde{u}_\alpha(\lambda)\, \overline{\tilde{v}_\beta(\lambda)}\, d\sigma_{\alpha\beta}(\lambda) \quad (u, v \in l_{2,0}(\Pi)). \tag{4.12}$$

We can now formulate the following theorem.

Theorem 4.1. *Let* $E(\Delta)$ *be a resolution of the identity (ordinary or generalized) corresponding to the operator* L. *Construct the spectral matrix* $d\Sigma(\lambda) = \|d\sigma_{\alpha\beta}(\lambda)\|_{-\infty}^{\infty}$ *by formula* (4.9). *Then the orthogonality relation* (4.10) *holds; the eigenfunction expansion is expressed by* (4.12) *and* (4.11).[1)]

---

1) In the case where the expression (4.1) acts on the whole plane (j, k) $(j, k = \cdots, -1, 0, 1, \cdots)$, the previous arguments can be modified in the following way. It is necessary, as in § 3.1, to introduce two systems of linearly independent solutions of equation (4.3) $P_{-1,\alpha;(j,k)}(z)$ and $P_{0,\alpha;(j,k)}(z)$ $(\alpha, j, k = \cdots, -1, 0, 1, \cdots)$, which satisfy the conditions

$$P_{-1,\alpha;(-1,k)}(z) = \delta_{\alpha k}, \quad P_{-1,\alpha;(0,k)}(z) = 0;$$

$$P_{0,\alpha;(-1,k)}(z) = 0, \quad P_{0,\alpha;(0,k)}(z) = \delta_{\alpha k} \quad (\alpha, k = \dots, -1, 0, 1, \dots).$$

Then for any solution of equation (4.3) we obtain, instead of (4.4), the representation

It is easy to see that the integral (4.12) may be interpreted as an operator integral of the type considered in §2.3. In fact, denote by Q the orthogonal projection of the space $l_2(\Pi)$ onto its subspace consisting of sequences which vanish off the axis Ok. Then obviously $\Sigma(\Delta)$ is the matrix operator $QE(\Delta)Q$. This family of operators is a nonnegative operator measure and the integral in (4.12) may be interpreted as an integral with respect to this measure. Introduce the Hilbert space $L_2(l_2((-\infty, \infty)); (-\infty, \infty), d\Sigma(\Delta))$, which we will call $L_2(\infty; d\Sigma(\lambda))$ for short. Then Parseval's equation may be rewritten in the form

$$(E(\Delta)u, v)_0 = \int_{\Delta} (d\Sigma(\lambda)\tilde{u}(\lambda), \tilde{v}(\lambda))_{l_2((-\infty,\infty))} \quad (u, v \in l_{2,0}(\Pi)). \tag{4.13}$$

2. **Study of Fourier transforms.** The Fourier transform $\tilde{u}(\lambda)$ of a sequence $u \in l_{2,0}(\Pi)$ can be regarded as an element of the space $L_2(\infty; d\Sigma(\lambda))$. We now study the set $\widetilde{l_{2,0}(\Pi)}$ of all such $\tilde{u}(\lambda)$ in more detail. To this end, we consider a certain orthogonalization process, which we will also need for the analysis of the inverse problem.

Let $\Sigma(\Delta)$ be a nonnegative operator measure whose values are bounded operators in the space $l_2((-\infty, \infty))$. If we express $\Sigma(\Delta)$ in the basis δ_k $(k = \cdots, -1, 0, 1, \cdots)$, we obtain the matrix $\|\sigma_{\alpha\beta}(\Delta)\|_{-\infty}^{\infty}$; it will also be denoted $\Sigma(\Delta)$. Assume that

$$\int_{-\infty}^{\infty} |\lambda|^m d\sigma_{\alpha\alpha}(\lambda) < \infty \, (m = 0, 1, \ldots; \ \alpha = \ldots, -1, 0, 1, \ldots). \tag{4.14}$$

Hence for each finite sequence $\xi(\lambda) = (\cdots, \xi_{-1}(\lambda), \xi_0(\lambda), \xi_1(\lambda), \cdots)$, where $\xi_\alpha(\lambda)$ is a polynomial, the integral $\int_{-\infty}^{\infty} (d\Sigma(\lambda)\xi(\lambda), \xi(\lambda))_{l_2((-\infty,\infty))} < \infty$. This shows that $\xi(\lambda) \in L_2(\infty; d\Sigma(\lambda))$.

$$u_{jk} = \sum_{\alpha=-\infty}^{\infty} (u_{-1,\alpha} P_{-1,\alpha;(j,k)}(z) + u_{0,\alpha} P_{0,\alpha;(j,k)}(z)) \quad (j,k = \ldots, -1, 0, 1, \ldots).$$

If, as in (4.6), this representation is used, then we obtain, instead of the spectral matrix $\|d\sigma_{\alpha\beta}(\lambda)\|_{-\infty}^{\infty}$ a spectral matrix of the form

$$\left\| \begin{matrix} d\sigma_{-1,-1;\alpha\beta}(\lambda) & d\sigma_{-1,0;\alpha\beta}(\lambda) \\ d\sigma_{0,-1;\alpha\beta}(\lambda) & d\sigma_{0,0;\alpha\beta}(\lambda) \end{matrix} \right\|_{\alpha,\beta=-\infty}^{\infty}$$

Formulas (4.10), (4.11), and (4.12) are to be changed into the proper form, similar to the way in which the formulas of § 3 were changed in comparison with § 1. A detailed study of expansions arising from this, analogous to those obtained in the case of the half-plane in subsections 3 and 4 below, can be made by means of the method of duplication (§3.2).

We will assume that for each $(j, k) \in \Pi$ the system

$$\begin{matrix} \delta_{k+j} \\ \delta_{k+j-1} & \lambda\delta_{k+j-1} \\ \delta_{k+j-2} & \lambda\delta_{k+j-2} & \lambda^2\delta_{k+j-2} \\ \cdot & \cdot & \cdot \\ \cdot & \cdot & & \dots \lambda^j\delta_k \\ \cdot & & \cdot \\ \delta_{k-j+2} & \lambda\delta_{k-j+2} & \lambda^2\delta_{k-j+2} \\ \delta_{k-j+1} & \lambda\delta_{k-j+1} \\ \delta_{k-j} \end{matrix} \tag{4.15}$$

of $(j+1)^2$ vectors in $L_2(\infty; d\Sigma(\lambda))$ are linearly independent in this space. Let $D_{jk} \in L_2(\infty; d\Sigma(\lambda))$ be the vector of unit length which is a linear combination of the vectors (4.15) with real coefficients, which is orthogonal to all of these vectors with the exception of $\lambda^j \delta_k$, and is such that the coefficient of the latter vector in the expansion of D_{jk} is positive. D_{jk} is uniquely determined by these conditions. Note that the following orthogonality relation holds for the vectors D_{jk}: $(D_{lm}, D_{jk})_{L_2(\infty; d\Sigma(\lambda))} = 0$, if the points $(l, m) \neq (j, k)$ lie inside or on the boundary of the triangle $(0, k+j)$, (j, k), $(0, k-j)$ (see Figure 13).

Lemma 4.1. *If $d\Sigma(\lambda)$ is a spectral matrix of some difference expression (4.1), then the relations (4.14) hold and the vectors (4.15) are linearly independent for any $(j, k) \in \Pi$. In addition, $D_{jk} = P_{\cdot;(j,k)}(\cdot)$ in $L_2(\infty; d\Sigma(\lambda))$ and the real linear span of the vectors $P_{\cdot;(l,m)}(\cdot)$, where (l, m) varies inside and on the boundary of the triangle $(0, k+j)$, (j, k), $(0, k-j)$ coincides with the real linear span of the vectors (4.15).*

Proof. Since for $u \in l_{2,0}(\Pi)$ $\widetilde{(L^m u)}(\lambda) = \lambda^m \tilde{u}(\lambda)$ $(m = 0, 1, \cdots)$ (this follows at least from (4.2)), by means of (4.12) we obtain for even m:

$$\infty > (L^m\delta_{(0,\alpha_0)}, \delta_{(0,\alpha_0)})_0 = \sum_{\alpha,\beta=-\infty}^{\infty} \int_{-\infty}^{\infty} \widetilde{(L^m\delta_{(0,\alpha_0)})}(\lambda) \widetilde{(\delta_{(0,\alpha_0)})}(\lambda) d\sigma_{\alpha\beta}(\lambda)$$

$$= \sum_{\alpha,\beta=-\infty}^{\infty} \int_{-\infty}^{\infty} \lambda^m \delta_{\alpha\alpha_0}\delta_{\beta\alpha_0} d\sigma_{\alpha\beta}(\lambda) = \int_{-\infty}^{\infty} \lambda^m d\sigma_{\alpha_0\alpha_0}(\lambda).$$

Hence inequality (4.14) follows.

We now show that the system of vectors (4.15) is linearly independent. Indeed, it is easily seen by Figure 13 that the vector $P_{\cdot;(j,k)}(\cdot)$ is a linear combination of the vectors of this system, with real coefficients. Hence it follows that the real linear span of the $(j+1)^2$ vectors (4.15) contains the orthonormal (by virtue of (4.10)) system of vectors

$$\begin{array}{llll} P_{\cdot;(0,k+j)}(\cdot), & & & \\ P_{\cdot;(0,k+j-1)}(\cdot) & P_{\cdot;(1,k+j-1)}(\cdot), & & \\ P_{\cdot;(0,k+j-2)}(\cdot) & P_{\cdot;(1,k+j-2)}(\cdot) & P_{\cdot;(2,k+j-2)}(\cdot), & \\ \vdots & \vdots & \vdots & \ldots P_{\cdot;(j,k)}(\cdot), \\ P_{\cdot;(0,k-j+2)}(\cdot) & P_{\cdot;(1,k-j+2)}(\cdot) & P_{\cdot;(2,k-j+2)}(\cdot), & \\ P_{\cdot;(0,k-j+1)}(\cdot) & P_{\cdot;(1,k-j+1)}(\cdot), & & \\ P_{\cdot;(0,k-j)}(\cdot); & & & \end{array} \quad (4.16)$$

the number of which is also $(j+1)^2$. This means, of course, that the system (4.15) is linearly independent.

Finally, the real linear span of the vectors (4.15), with the exception of $\lambda^j\delta_k$, coincides with the real linear span of the vectors (4.16), with the exception of $P_{\cdot;(j,k)}(\cdot)$, since the latter system of vectors is obtained from the former by taking linear combinations with real coefficients, and the dimension of each of these spaces is $(j+1)^2-1$. Therefore, since $P_{\cdot;(j,k)}(\cdot)$ is orthogonal to $P_{\cdot;(l,m)}(\cdot)$ $((j,k)\neq(l,m))$, it follows that $P_{\cdot;(j,k)}(\cdot)$ is orthogonal to the vectors (4.15), with the exception of $\lambda^j\delta_k$. Moreover, $P_{\cdot;(l,k)}(\cdot)$ has unit length and the coefficient of $\lambda^j\delta_k$ in its expansion is positive (the latter follows from the construction of the polynomials $P_{\alpha;(j,k)}(\lambda)$ as solutions of equation (4.3) and the positivity of the coefficients a_{lm}). Therefore, we conclude, in view of the uniqueness of the vectors D_{jk}, that $P_{\cdot;(j,k)}(\cdot)=D_{jk}$ $((j,k)\in\Pi)$ in $L_2(\infty;\, d\Sigma(\lambda))$. The lemma is proved.

The lemma gives us

Theorem 4.2. *The set* $\widetilde{l_{2,0}(\Pi)}$ *of Fourier transforms of sequences in* $l_{2,0}(\Pi)$ *consists of all finite sequences of the form* $\xi(\lambda)=(\ldots,\xi_{-1}(\lambda),\xi_0(\lambda),\xi_1(\lambda),\ldots)$, *where* $\xi_\alpha(\lambda)$ *is a polynomial in* λ $(\alpha=\ldots,-1,0,1,\ldots)$. *If* $\xi_\alpha(\lambda)\in\widetilde{l_{2,0}(\Pi)}$ *is such that* $(\xi(\lambda),\xi(\lambda))_{L_2(\infty;d\Sigma(\lambda))}=0$, *then* $\xi_\alpha(\lambda)\equiv 0$ *for all* α.

Proof. To prove the first assertion it suffices to show that each $\lambda^j\delta_k\in\widetilde{l_{2,0}(\Pi)}$ $(j=0,1,\ldots;\ k=\ldots,-1,0,1,\ldots)$. This follows from the fact that $\lambda^j\delta_k$ is a linear combination of the corresponding set of vectors $P_{\cdot;(l,m)}(\cdot)$, each of which is the Fourier transform of the sequence $\delta_{(l,m)} \in l_{2,0}(\Pi)$. The second assertion follows from the fact that the vector $\xi(\lambda) \in \widetilde{l_{2,0}(\Pi)}$ is a linear combination of the linearly independent vectors (4.15), if j is sufficiently large. Therefore if $(\xi(\lambda), \xi(\lambda))_{L_2(\infty; d\Sigma(\lambda))} = 0$, then all the coefficients of this combination are zero. This means of course that $\xi_\alpha(\lambda) \equiv 0$ for all α. The theorem is proved.

This theorem shows that the transform $u \to \tilde{u}(\lambda)$ is a one-to-one correspondence between the finite sequences and the finite sequences of polynomials. Parseval's equation (4.13) (for $\Delta = (-\infty, \infty)$) asserts that this is an isometry between $l_{2,0}(\Pi) \subset l_2(\Pi)$ and $\widetilde{l_{2,0}(\Pi)} \subset L_2(\infty;\, d\Sigma(\lambda))$. This isometry can be extended by continuity to the full space $l_2(\Pi)$; its image $\widetilde{l_2(\Pi)}$ is the closure of the manifold $\widetilde{l_{2,0}(\Pi)}$ in $L_2(\infty;\, d\Sigma(\lambda))$. The operator L is transformed by this isometry into the operator $\tilde{\mathrm{L}}$ of multiplication by λ (i.e. the operator $\tilde{u}(\lambda) \to \lambda\tilde{u}(\lambda)$), defined at first on $\widetilde{l_{2,0}(\Pi)}$, and then by closure on all of $\mathfrak{D}(\tilde{\mathrm{L}})$.

Analogues of Theorems 1.7 and 1.9 (or 2.5) hold in our case; it is not difficult to discover the proper modifications of the earlier proofs. In particular, the analogue of Theorem 1.9 shows that *if $d\Sigma(\lambda)$ is a nonnegative operator measure such that Parseval's equation* (4.13) *holds for $\Delta = (-\infty, \infty)$ (or instead the orthogonality relations* (4.10) *hold), then $d\Sigma(\lambda)$ is a spectral matrix, constructed with respect to some resolution of the identity $E(\Delta)$ of the operator* L.

In conclusion we note that the condition of linear independence of each system of vectors (4.15) ($(j, k) \in \Pi$) in some space $L_2(\infty;\, d\Sigma(\lambda))$ (condition (4.14) is assumed to hold) implies that $\Sigma(\lambda)$ has an infinite number of points of growth. Indeed, assume the contrary. Then the number of points of growth of fixed $\sigma_{\alpha_0\alpha_0}(\lambda)$ is finite. Construct a polynomial $R(\lambda) = C_n\lambda^n + \cdots + C_0 \neq 0$ such that

$$I = \int_{-\infty}^{\infty} |R(\lambda)|^2\, d\sigma_{\alpha_0\alpha_0}(\lambda) = 0.$$

For $\xi(\lambda) = C_n\lambda^n\delta_{\alpha_0} + \cdots + C_0\delta_{\alpha_0}$ we have

$$(\xi(\lambda),\ \xi(\lambda))_{L_2(\infty;\, d\Sigma(\lambda))} = I = 0,$$

i.e. the system (4.15) is linearly dependent, which is absurd.

The converse assertion is false; an appropriate simple example will be given in subsection 5.

3. Reduction to an equation with operator coefficients. So far we have carried over only the elementary facts of §1 to the partial difference expression (4.1). Now we present a method by which the remaining results can be obtained. It consists of the reduction of the problem to the analysis of an expression with operator coefficients of the type (2.22).

The spaces $l_2(\Pi)$ and $l_2(l_2((-\infty,\infty)); [0,\infty))$ are isometric. The isometry is established by the relation

$$l_2(\Pi) \ni u = u_{jk} \longleftrightarrow \hat{u} = (\hat{u}_0, \hat{u}_1, \ldots) \in l_2(l_2((-\infty, \infty)); [0, \infty)).$$

$$\hat{u}_j = (\ldots, u_{j,-1}, u_{j,0}, u_{j,1}, \ldots) \quad (j=0, 1, \ldots). \tag{4.17}$$

In this connection, the corresponding image of the expression L is the expression $\hat{L}$ with operator coefficients of the form

$$(\hat{L}\hat{u})_j = A_{j-1}\hat{u}_{j-1} + \hat{A}_j\hat{u}_{j+1} + \hat{B}_j\hat{u}_j;$$

$$\hat{A}_j = \begin{Vmatrix} \ddots & & & & \\ & a_{j,-1} & & 0 & \\ & & a_{j,0} & & \\ & 0 & & a_{j,1} & \\ & & & & \ddots \end{Vmatrix}, \tag{4.18}$$

$$\hat{B}_j = \begin{Vmatrix} \ddots & \ddots & \ddots & & & & \\ b_{j,-3} & c_{j,-2} & b_{j,-2} & & & & \\ & b_{j,-2} & c_{j,-1} & b_{j,-1} & & 0 & \\ & & b_{j,-1} & c_{j,0} & b_{j,0} & & \\ & 0 & & b_{j,0} & c_{j,1} & b_{j,1} & \\ & & & & b_{j,1} & c_{j,2} & b_{j,2} \\ & & & & \ddots & \ddots & \ddots \end{Vmatrix}$$

$$(j = 0, 1, \ldots).$$

In this subsection and the next one we will require that

$$\sup_k a_{jk},\ \sup_k |b_{jk}|,\ \sup_k |c_{jk}| < \infty, \qquad \inf_k a_{jk} > 0 \qquad (j=0,\ 1, \ldots). \tag{4.19}$$

Conditions (4.19) ensure boundedness of the operators $\hat{A}_j$, $\hat{B}_j$, and $\hat{A}_j^{-1}$, which are necessary for §2 (in connection with the proof of boundedness of $\hat{B}_j$ see Theorem 1.2). We remark that one might not impose the restrictions (4.19), and develop a theory of expressions with unbounded operator coefficients of the special form (4.18), similar to the theory of §2. However, we will not deal with these questions.

Construct an operator $\hat{\mathrm{L}}'$ in the space $l_2(l_2((-\infty, \infty)); [0, \infty))$, corresponding to the expression (4.18) by setting $(\hat{\mathrm{L}}'\hat{u})_j = (\hat{L}\hat{u})_j$, where $\hat{u} \in \mathfrak{D}(\hat{\mathrm{L}}') = l_{2,0}(l_2((-\infty, \infty)); [0, \infty))$. The operator $\hat{\mathrm{L}}'$ is not the image of the operator L' constructed in subsection 1 (i.e. $\hat{\mathrm{L}}' \neq \widehat{\mathrm{L}'}$), since $\widehat{l_{2,0}(\Pi)}$ is a smaller set than $l_{2,0}(l_2((-\infty, \infty)); [0, \infty))$. However, it is not difficult to see that the closure of $\widehat{\mathrm{L}'}$ coincides with $\hat{\mathrm{L}}'$. This is a consequence of the boundedness of the operators $\hat{A}_j$ and $\hat{B}_j$ for each j, which allows us to write the relation: in $l_2(l_2((-\infty, \infty)); [0, \infty))$ $\lim_{N\to\infty} \hat{L}\hat{u}^{(N)} = \hat{L}\hat{u}$, where $\hat{u} \in l_{2,0}(l_2((-\infty, \infty)); [0, \infty))$ and $\hat{u}_j^{(N)}$ differs from $\hat{u}_j$ in that the coordinates of the latter vector with index k, $|k| > N$ are replaced by zeros. It is clear from what has been said that the image of the operator $\tilde{\mathrm{L}}$ constructed in subsection 1 is the operator $\hat{\mathrm{L}}$ – the closure of $\hat{\mathrm{L}}'$. Thus, the studies of the operators L and $\hat{\mathrm{L}}$ are equivalent.

We find now polynomials $\hat{P}_j(z)$ of the first kind for the expression (4.18). If we take into account that they satisfy the equation $(\hat{L}\hat{U})_j = z\hat{U}_j$ $(j = 0, 1, \cdots;$ $U_{-1} = 0,\ U_0 = E)$ and write this equation as elements of a matrix, we easily obtain

$$\hat{P}_j(z) = \| P_{\beta;(j,\alpha)}(z) \|_{\alpha,\beta=-\infty}^{\infty} \quad (j = 0,\ 1, \ldots). \tag{4.20}$$

Note that the elements of the last matrix with index $\beta; (j, \alpha)$ vanish if $|\alpha - \beta| > j$. The operators $\hat{P}_j(z)$ are of course bounded in the space $l_2((-\infty, \infty))$.

It is clear that the eigenfunction expansion for the operator $\hat{\mathrm{L}}$ given by Theorem 2.4 coincides with the similar expansion for the operator L given in subsection 1. If the operator spectral measure $d\Sigma(\lambda)$ of Theorem 2.4 is expressed as a matrix with respect to the basis δ_α of the space $l_2((-\infty, \infty))$, then we obtain the spectral matrix of Theorem 4.1. We will not go into these considerations in detail, and note only that the Fourier transforms calculated for $u \in l_{2,0}(\Pi)$ by (4.11) and by (2.41) actually coincide. Indeed, taking into account the fact that the coefficients of the polynomials in z, which appear as the elements of the matrix (4.20), are real, we obtain

$$\tilde{\hat{u}}_\alpha(z) = \left(\sum_{j=0}^{\infty} \hat{P}_j^*(\bar{z})\hat{u}_j\right)_\alpha = \sum_{j=0}^{\infty}\sum_{\beta=-\infty}^{\infty} P_{\alpha;(j,\beta)}(z)\, u_{j\beta} = \tilde{u}_\alpha(z)$$
$$(\alpha = \ldots, -1, 0, 1, \ldots).$$

The results of §2.7 reduce, as is easily seen, to Theorem 4.2 and the subsequent facts in subsection 2. Thus the contents of subsections 6 and 7 of §2 include (under the additional restrictions (4.19)) the basic material of subsections 1 and 2 of this section.

4. Further theory of partial difference operators. We now take a look at applications of the later material in §2 to the expression (4.1), written in the form (4.18).

We concern ourselves now with the calculation of the deficiency number of the operator L; these numbers are equal since the coefficients of the expression L are real.

For fixed nonreal z, *consider all* $x \in l_2((-\infty, \infty))$ *for which* $\phi_{jk} = \Sigma_{\alpha=-\infty}^{\infty} x_\alpha P_{\alpha;(j,k)}(\bar{z})$ *belongs to* $l_2(\Pi)$; *such* $\phi = (\phi_{jk})$ *run through the appropriate deficiency subspace of the operator* L.

In fact, the vectors $\phi \in l_2(\Pi)$ belong to the deficiency subspace if and only if they satisfy the equation $L^*\phi = \bar{z}\phi$. If we take into account the form of L^* and formula (4.4), we arrive at the assertion, which in fact agrees with Theorem 2.7. The following theorem follows from Theorem 2.6.

Theorem 4.3. *Assume that the restrictions* (4.19) *hold. Then the strong limit* (2.50) *exists for the operator polynomials* $P_j(z)$ *introduced by means of* (4.20), *and defines a nonnegative operator* $\Gamma(z)$ *in the space* $l_2((-\infty, \infty))$ *which is bounded by* 1. *The dimension of the orthogonal complement of the null space of the operator* $\Gamma(z)$ *is the same for all nonreal* z *and it coincides with the deficiency number of the operator* L.

The next theorem follows from Theorem 2.9.

Theorem 4.4. *Assume that the conditions* (4.19) *hold. If*

$$\sum_{j=0}^{\infty} \frac{1}{\sup_k a_{jk}} = \infty,$$

then the operator L *is selfadjoint.*[1)]

---

1) This result can be strengthened. Namely, conditions (4.19) can be replaced by the conditions: $\sup_k |b_{jk}|$, $\sup_k |a_{j-1,k} + a_{jk} + c_{jk}| < \infty$, $\inf_k a_{jk} > 0$ $(j = 0, 1, \cdots)$.

It is easy to rephrase the other facts in subsections 10 and 11 of §2 for this case. It is essential to observe that results of the type of Theorems 1.12, 1.14, 1.17, and 1.18 can be obtained for the partial difference expression (4.1), although we cannot go into these questions since those theorems were not stated for general equations with operator coefficients.

5. **The inverse problem of spectral analysis for partial difference expressions.** First we set forth the solution of this problem, independent of the appropriate considerations for equations with operator coefficients (§2.8), and then compare these results. As in the previous cases (§§1.5, 2.8, and 3.3) L will be reconstructed from the spectral matrix.

We introduce formulas analogous to formulas (1.33), which express the coefficients of the expression (4.1) in terms of $P_{\alpha;(j,k)}(\lambda)$. We have

$$a_{j-1,k}P_{\alpha;(j-1,k)}(\lambda)+a_{jk}P_{\alpha;(j+1,k)}(\lambda)+b_{j,k-1}P_{\alpha;(j,k-1)}(\lambda)$$
$$+b_{jk}P_{\alpha;(j,k+1)}(\lambda)+c_{jk}P_{\alpha;(j,k)}(\lambda)=\lambda P_{\alpha;(j,k)}(\lambda)$$
$$((j,k)\in\Pi;\ \alpha=\ldots,-1,\ 0,\ 1,\ldots;\ -\infty<\lambda<\infty).$$

On taking the scalar product of the left and right sides of this equation with $P_{\cdot;(j+1,k)}(\cdot)$, $P_{\cdot;(j,k+1)}(\cdot)$ and $P_{\cdot;(j,k)}(\cdot)$ and using the relations (4.10) we obtain the required formulas

$$a_{jk}=\sum_{\alpha,\beta=-\infty}^{\infty}\int_{-\infty}^{\infty}\lambda P_{\alpha;(j,k)}(\lambda)P_{\beta;(j+1,k)}(\lambda)\,d\sigma_{\alpha\beta}(\lambda),$$

$$b_{jk}=\sum_{\alpha,\beta=-\infty}^{\infty}\int_{-\infty}^{\infty}\lambda P_{\alpha;(j,k)}(\lambda)P_{\beta;(j,k+1)}(\lambda)\,d\sigma_{\alpha\beta}(\lambda), \tag{4.21}$$

$$c_{jk}=\sum_{\alpha,\beta=-\infty}^{\infty}\int_{-\infty}^{\infty}\lambda P_{\alpha;(j,k)}(\lambda)P_{\beta;(j,k)}(\lambda)\,d\sigma_{\alpha\beta}(\lambda)$$

$$((j,k)\in\Pi).$$

The following uniqueness theorem holds.

Theorem 4.5. *If two difference expressions of the form* (4.1) *correspond to the same spectral measure, then the coefficients of these expressions coincide.*

Proof. Let $d\Sigma(\lambda)$ be a spectral matrix of an expression (4.1), and let $P_{\alpha;(j,k)}(\lambda)$ be its corresponding polynomials of the first kind. The formulas (4.21) can be rewritten as

$$\begin{aligned} a_{jk} &= (\lambda P_{.;(j,k)}(\lambda), P_{.;(j+1,k)}(\lambda))_{L_2(\infty;d\Sigma(\lambda))}, \\ b_{jk} &= (\lambda P_{.;(j,k)}(\lambda), P_{.;(j,k+1)}(\lambda))_{L_2(\infty;d\Sigma(\lambda))}, \\ c_{jk} &= (\lambda P_{.;(j,k)}(\lambda), P_{.;(j,k)}(\lambda))_{L_2(\infty;d\Sigma(\lambda))} \qquad ((j,k) \in \Pi). \end{aligned} \tag{4.22}$$

Consider the vectors $D_{jk} \in L_2(\infty;\, d\Sigma(\lambda))$, obtained by means of the orthogonalization process described in subsection 2. By Lemma 4.1, $D_{jk} = P_{.;(j,k)}(\cdot)$ in $L_2(\infty;\, d\Sigma(\lambda))$, and hence $\lambda P_{.;(j,k)}(\lambda) = \lambda D_{jk}$ $((j,k) \in \Pi)$. Therefore equations (4.22) assume the form

$$a_{jk} = (\lambda D_{jk}, D_{j+1,k})_{L_2(\infty;d\Sigma(\lambda))},\; b_{jk} = (\lambda D_{jk}, D_{j,k+1})_{L_2(\infty;d\Sigma(\lambda))},$$
$$c_{jk} = (\lambda D_{jk}, D_{jk})_{L_2(\infty;\, d\Sigma(\lambda))}\; ((j,k) \in \Pi). \tag{4.23}$$

Formulas (4.23) show that the coefficients of the expression (4.1) are uniquely determined by $d\Sigma(\lambda)$. The theorem is proved.

The following theorem is fundamental.

Theorem 4.6. *Let $d\Sigma(\lambda) = \|d\sigma_{\alpha\beta}\|_{-\infty}^{\infty}$ be a nonnegative operator measure whose values are bounded operators in $l_2((-\infty, \infty))$. For $\|d\sigma_{\alpha\beta}\|_{-\infty}^{\infty}$ to be a spectral matrix of some difference expression (4.1) with boundary condition $u_{-1,k} = 0$ $(k = \cdots, -1, 0, 1, \cdots)$, it is necessary and sufficient that:* 1) *the inequalities (4.14) hold, where*

$$\int_{-\infty}^{\infty} d\sigma_{\alpha\alpha}(\lambda) = 1 \qquad (\alpha = \ldots, -1,\ 0,\ 1, \ldots); \tag{4.24}$$

2) *each system of vectors (4.15) is linearly independent in $L_2(\infty;\, d\Sigma(\lambda))$;* 3) *the vectors D_{jk}, constructed with respect to $\|d\sigma_{\alpha\beta}\|_{-\infty}^{\infty}$, satisfy the orthogonality relations*

$$(D_{jk}, D_{lm})_{L_2(\infty;d\Sigma(\lambda))} = \delta_{(j,k)(l,m)} \qquad ((j,k),(l,m) \in \Pi).$$

If these conditions hold then the coefficients of the difference expression are constructed by formula (4.23).

Proof. If $d\Sigma(\lambda)$ is a spectral matrix of some expression (4.1), then, by setting $(j,k) = (l,m) = (0, \alpha_0)$, in (4.10), we arrive at (4.24). The remaining parts of conditions 1) and 2) follow from Lemma 4.1. Condition 3) follows from the equation $D_{jk} = P_{.;(j,k)}(\cdot)$ and the orthogonality relations (4.10).

We come now to the proof of the sufficiency. Define the numbers a_{jk}, b_{jk}, and c_{jk} $((j,k) \in \Pi)$ by formula (4.23).

We show that $a_{jk} > 0$. In fact, $D_{jk} = A\lambda^j\delta_k + S(A > 0)$ in $L_2(\infty; d\Sigma(\lambda))$ where S is a linear combination of the vectors (4.15) (excluding $\lambda^j\delta_k$) with real coefficients. Therefore $\lambda D_{jk} = A\lambda^{j+1}\delta_k + S'$, where S' is a linear combination of the vectors (4.15) with j replaced by $j+1$ (excluding $\lambda^{j+1}\delta_k$) with real coefficients. In addition, put $D_{j+1,k} = B\lambda^{j+1}\delta_k + S''$ $(B > 0)$, where S'' is a linear combination of the same form as S'. But S' and S'' are orthogonal to $D_{j+1,k}$; hence

$$\begin{aligned} a_{jk} &= (\lambda D_{jk}, D_{j+1,k})_{L_2(\infty;d\Sigma(\lambda))} = (A\lambda^{j+1}\delta_k, D_{j+1,k})_{L_2(\infty;d\Sigma(\lambda))} \\ &= \frac{A}{B}(B\lambda^{j+1}\delta_k, D_{j+1,k})_{L_2(\infty;d\Sigma(\lambda))} = \frac{A}{B}(D_{j+1,k}, D_{j+1,k})_{L_2(\infty;d\Sigma(\lambda))} \\ &= \frac{A}{B} > 0 \qquad ((j,k) \in \Pi). \end{aligned}$$

The numbers b_{jk} and c_{jk} are real. This follows from the orthogonality relation for D_{jk} and the fact that λD_{jk} can be expanded as a linear combination of a certain number of the vectors D_{lm} with real coefficients. Thus, a_{jk}, b_{jk}, and c_{jk} can be taken as coefficients of a difference expression of the form (4.1).

We assume that $D_{-1,k} = 0$ for all k and set

$$\xi = a_{j-1,k}D_{j-1,k} + a_{jk}D_{j+1,k} + b_{j,k-1}D_{j,k-1} + b_{jk}D_{j,k+1} + c_{jk}D_{jk}.$$

We show that

$$(\xi, D_{lm})_{L_2(\infty;d\Sigma(\lambda))} = (\lambda D_{jk}, D_{lm})_{L_2(\infty;d\Sigma(\lambda))}((j,k),(l,m) \in \Pi). \tag{4.25}$$

Indeed, if (l, m) is adjacent to or coincident with (j, k), for instance $l = j+1$, $m = k$, then by virtue of the orthogonality relations for D_{rs}, $(\xi, D_{j+1,k})_{L_2(\infty;d\Sigma(\lambda))} = a_{jk} = (\lambda D_{jk}, D_{j+1,k})_{L_2(\infty;d\Sigma(\lambda))}$. If (l, m) is not adjacent to (j, k), then by orthogonality, $(\xi, D_{lm})_{L_2(\infty;d\Sigma(\lambda))} = 0$. But in this case also $(\lambda D_{jk}, D_{lm})_{L_2(\infty;d\Sigma(\lambda))} = 0$. In fact, λD_{jk} is a linear combination of D_{rs}, where (r,s) varies in the interior and on the boundary of the triangle $(0, k+j+1)$, $(j+1, k)$, $(0, k-j-1)$; hence if (l, m) lies outside of this triangle, $(\lambda D_{jk}, D_{lm})_{L_2(\infty;d\Sigma(\lambda))} = 0$. Suppose now that (l, m) lies inside this triangle and is not adjacent to or coincident with (j, k). It is obvious that $(\lambda D_{jk}, D_{lm})_{L_2(\infty;d\Sigma(\lambda))} = (D_{jk}, \lambda D_{lm})_{L_2(\infty;d\Sigma(\lambda))}$. But λD_{lm} can be expanded in terms of those D_{rs} for which (r, s) lies interior to or on the boundary of the triangle $(0, m+l+1)$, $(l+1, m)$ $(0, m-l-1)$, and (j, k) does not lie in this triangle. Therefore by orthogonality $0 = (D_{jk}, \lambda D_{lm})_{L_2(\infty;d\Sigma(\lambda))} = (\lambda D_{jk}, D_{lm})_{L_2(\infty;d\Sigma(\lambda))}$. Thus (4.25) is proved.

Since ξ and λD_{jk} are linear combinations of the vectors (4.15), with real coefficients, and hence likewise of the vectors D_{lm}, by the arbitrariness of (l, m) in (4.25) we have $\xi = \lambda D_{jk}$. Thus

$$a_{j-1,k}D_{j-1,k} + a_{jk}D_{j+1,k} + b_{j,k-1}D_{j,k-1} + b_{jk}D_{j,k+1} + c_{jk}D_{jk} = \lambda D_{jk} \quad (4.26)$$
$$((j, k) \in \Pi).$$

in $L_2(\infty; d\Sigma(\lambda))$.

Thus the sequence composed of the vectors $D_{jk} \in L_2(\infty; d\Sigma(\lambda))$ $((j, k) \in \Pi)$ is a solution of equation (4.26) which satisfies the initial conditions $D_{-1,k} = 0$, $D_{0k} = \delta_k$ for all k. On the other hand, the orthogonal polynomials $P_{\cdot;(j,k)}(\cdot)$ of the first kind, corresponding to the difference expression constructed in the process of the proof, also satisfy (4.26) and the initial conditions $P_{\cdot;(-1,k)}(\cdot) = 0$, $P_{\cdot;(0,k)}(\cdot) = \delta_k$ for all k. A solution of equation (4.26) of the form $S_{jk} \in L_2(\infty; d\Sigma(\lambda))$ $((j, k) \in \Pi)$, which satisfies certain initial conditions for $j = -1, 0$, is unique since $a_{jk} \neq 0$; hence $D_{jk} = P_{\cdot;(j,k)}(\cdot)$ $((j, k) \in \Pi)$ in $L_2(\infty; d\Sigma(\lambda))$. Thus it follows from 3) that $P_{\cdot;(j,k)}(\cdot)$ satisfies the orthogonality relations. Therefore the orthogonal polynomials of the first kind, corresponding to the difference expression constructed, satisfy the orthogonality relations in the space $L_2(\infty; d\Sigma(\lambda))$. This shows (see the end of subsection 2) that $d\Sigma(\lambda)$ is a spectral matrix of the expression constructed. The theorem is proved.

In addition to this theorem, it should be shown that the vectors (4.15) are not linearly independent for all $d\Sigma(\lambda)$ which satisfy conditions (4.14) and (4.24); and further, even if they are linearly independent, the orthogonality relations $(D_{jk}, D_{lm})_{L_2(\infty; d\Sigma(\lambda))} = \delta_{(j,k),(l,m)}$ $((j, k), (l, m) \in \Pi)$ do not necessarily hold.

In fact, let $d\sigma(\lambda)$ be a nonnegative measure such that

$$\int_{-\infty}^{\infty} |\lambda|^m d\varrho(\lambda) < \infty, \qquad \int_{-\infty}^{\infty} d\varrho(\lambda) = 1 \qquad (m = 0, 1, \ldots).$$

Define a nonnegative operator measure by setting $\sigma_{\alpha\beta}(\Delta) = \rho(\Delta)$ $(\alpha, \beta = \cdots, -1, 0, 1, \cdots)$. It obviously satisfies conditions (4.14) and (4.24), but at the same time the vectors (4.15) are linearly dependent: for $m \neq n$

$$(\delta_m - \delta_n, \delta_m - \delta_n)_{L_2(\infty; d\Sigma(\lambda))} = (\delta_m, \delta_m)_{L_2(\infty; d\Sigma(\lambda))} - 2(\delta_m, \delta_n)_{L_2(\infty; d\Sigma(\lambda))}$$

$$+ (\delta_n, \delta_n)_{L_2(\infty; d\Sigma(\lambda))} = \int_{-\infty}^{\infty} d\sigma_{mm}(\lambda) - 2\int_{-\infty}^{\infty} d\sigma_{mn}(\lambda) + \int_{-\infty}^{\infty} d\sigma_{nn}(\lambda) = 0.$$

We can assume above that $\rho(\lambda)$ has an infinite number of points of increase, and then the same is true of $\Sigma(\lambda)$. Thus, the existence of an infinite number of points of growth of $\Sigma(\lambda)$ still does not imply linear independence of the vectors (4.15).

We show next, as a preliminary to construction of the second example, that *if* $d\Sigma(\lambda) = \|d\sigma_{\alpha\beta}(\lambda)\|_{-\infty}^{\infty}$ *is such that* $\|d\sigma_{\alpha\beta}(\lambda)\|_{-\infty}^{\infty}$ *is a Jacobi matrix (i.e.* $d\sigma_{\alpha\beta}(\lambda) = 0$ *for* $|\alpha - \beta| > 1$*), where each of the functions* $\sigma_{\alpha,\alpha+1}(\lambda) = \sigma_{\alpha+1,\alpha}(\lambda)$ $(\alpha = \cdots, -1, 0, 1, \cdots)$ *has an infinite number of points of growth, then the system of vectors* (4.15) *is linearly independent in* $L_2(\infty; d\Sigma(\lambda))$.

Indeed, suppose that there exist real numbers $C_\mu^{(\nu)}$ such that

$$C_{k-j}^{(0)}\delta_{k-j} + \ldots + C_{k+j}^{(0)}\delta_{k+j} + C_{k-j+1}^{(1)}\delta_{k-j+1} + \ldots + C_{k+j-1}^{(1)}\delta_{k+j-1} + \ldots$$
$$+ C_k^{(j)}\lambda^j\delta_k = 0. \tag{4.27}$$

in $L_2(\infty; d\Sigma(\lambda))$. Take the scalar product of (4.27) with $\lambda^l\delta_{k-j-1}$ $(l = 0, 1, \cdots)$. Since

$$(P(\lambda)\delta_r, Q(\lambda)\delta_s)_{L_2(\infty; d\Sigma(\lambda))} = \sum_{\alpha,\beta=-\infty}^{\infty} \int_{-\infty}^{\infty} P(\lambda)\overline{Q(\lambda)}\,\delta_{\alpha r}\delta_{\beta s}\,d\sigma_{\alpha\beta}(\lambda)$$
$$= \int_{-\infty}^{\infty} P(\lambda)\overline{Q(\lambda)}\,d\sigma_{rs}(\lambda) = 0 \tag{4.28}$$

for $|r - s| > 1$, where $P(\lambda)$ and $Q(\lambda)$ are arbitrary polynomials, then after multiplication we obtain

$$\int_{-\infty}^{\infty} C_{k-j}^{(0)}\lambda^l d\sigma_{k-j,k-j-1}(\lambda) = 0 \qquad (l = 0, 1, \ldots),$$

i.e. $C_{k-j}^{(0)} = 0$. Taking this equality into account, we multiply (4.27) by $\lambda^l\delta_{k-j}$ $(l = 0, 1, \cdots)$. By (4.28) we obtain

$$\int_{-\infty}^{\infty} (C_{k-j+1}^{(0)} + C_{k-j+1}^{(1)}\lambda)\lambda^l d\sigma_{k-j+1,k-j}(\lambda) = 0 \qquad (l = 0, 1, \ldots),$$

and thus at points of growth $\sigma_{k-j+1,k-j}(\lambda)\, C^{(0)}_{k-j+1} + C^{(1)}_{k-j+1}\lambda = 0$, i.e. $C^{(0)}_{k-j+1} = 0$, $C^{(1)}_{k-j+1} = 0$. Continuing this process, we find that all $C^{(\nu)}_{\mu} = 0$. The assertion is proved.

Obviously, one can prove in a similar way that the vectors (4.15) are linearly independent if $\|d\sigma_{\alpha\beta}(\lambda)\|_{-\infty}^{\infty}$ is such that $d\sigma_{\alpha\beta} = 0$ for $|\alpha - \beta| > N$ (N fixed), where the elements $\sigma_{\alpha\beta}$ in the extreme diagonal have an infinite number of points of growth. In particular, this will occur for a diagonal matrix $\|d\sigma_{\alpha\beta}(\lambda)\|_{-\infty}^{\infty}$ whose diagonal elements satisfy the stated condition.

Consider now, for construction of the second example, the function $\rho(\lambda)$ defined above with the additional requirement of existence of an infinite number of points of increase, and set $\sigma_{\alpha\alpha}(\lambda) = \rho(\lambda)$, $\sigma_{\alpha,\alpha+1}(\lambda) = \sigma_{\alpha+1,\alpha}(\lambda) = \epsilon\rho(\lambda)$, $\sigma_{\alpha\beta}(\lambda) = 0$ for $|\alpha - \beta| > 1$. Here $\epsilon > 0$ is so small that $\Sigma(\Delta) \geq 0$. Thus the defined $d\Sigma(\lambda)$ satisfies conditions (4.14), and (4.15), and, in view of what was said above, the vectors (4.15) are linearly independent in $L_2(\infty;\, d\Sigma(\lambda))$. Moreover,

$$(D_{0k}, D_{0,k+1})_{L_2(\infty;d\Sigma(\lambda))} = (\delta_k, \delta_{k+1})_{L_2(\infty;d\Sigma(\lambda))}$$
$$= \int_{-\infty}^{\infty} d\sigma_{k,k+1}(\lambda) = \varepsilon \int_{-\infty}^{\infty} d\varrho(\lambda) \neq 0,$$

i.e. D_{lm} do not form an orthogonal system.

The inverse problem under consideration can also be approached from the point of view of expressions with operator coefficients. In connection with this, let $d\Sigma(\lambda) = \|d\sigma_{\alpha\beta}\|_{-\infty}^{\infty}$ be a nonnegative operator measure whose values are bounded operators in $l_2((-\infty, \infty))$. Assume that the conditions (4.14) and $\int_{-\infty}^{\infty} d\Sigma(\lambda) = E$ hold; these are already required in Theorem 4.6. Assume in addition that the operator (2.48) is invertible. Then by the discussion in §2.8 a difference expression of the form $(\hat{L}\hat{u})_j = \hat{A}_{j-1}\hat{u}_{j-1} + \hat{A}_j\hat{u}_{j+1} + \hat{B}_j\hat{u}_j$ $(j = 0, 1, \cdots)$ can be constructed with respect to $d\Sigma(\lambda)$, where $\hat{A}_j$ and $\hat{B}_j$ are certain bounded self-adjoint operators in $l_2((-\infty, \infty))$, with $\hat{A}_j$ invertible. Later the problem will arise of choosing $d\Sigma(\lambda)$ so that the coefficients constructed acquire the form stated in (4.18); conditions 2) and 3) of Theorem 4.6 distinguish these $d\Sigma(\lambda)$. It is clear that the complexity of the formulation of conditions 2) and 3) is connected with the essence of the matter.

In conclusion we emphasize that the process of constructing the coefficients of L with respect to $d\Sigma(\lambda)$ (if it is known that $d\Sigma(\lambda)$ is a spectral matrix for some expression of the type (4.1)) is sufficiently simple and realizable.

6. **Separation of variables. An example.** We limit ourselves to just one example of the eigenfunction expansion of an expression of the form (4.1). As a preliminary we set forth general considerations concerning separation of variables for partial difference equations in a half-plane.

Consider the difference equation on the semi-axis

$$(L'u)_j = a'_{j-1}u_{j-1} + a'_j u_{j+1} + b'_j u_j \qquad (j = 0, 1, \ldots; u_{-1} = 0) \tag{4.29}$$

of the form studied in §1. Let $P'_j(z)$ and $d\sigma'(\lambda)$ be the corresponding polynomial of the first kind and spectral density. Further, consider the expression on the whole axis

$$(L''u)_k = a''_{k-1}u_{k-1} + a''_k u_{k+1} + b''_k u_k \qquad (k = \ldots, -1, 0, 1, \ldots), \tag{4.30}$$

of the type studied in §3; $P''_{\alpha;k}(z)$ is the corresponding solution of the form (3.1), and $\|d\sigma''_{\alpha\beta}(\lambda)\|_{-1}^{0}$ is its spectral matrix. Construct from (4.29) and (4.30) the partial difference expression

$$(Lu)_{jk} = ((L'_j + L''_k)\,u)_{jk}$$

$$= a'_{j-1}u_{j-1,k} + a'_j u_{j+1,k} + a''_{k-1}u_{j,k-1} + a''_k u_{j,k+1} + (b'_j + b''_k)\,u_{jk}$$

$$((j, k) \in \Pi;\ u_{-1,k} = 0,\ k = \ldots, -1, 0, 1, \ldots). \tag{4.31}$$

Let L′, L″, and L be the Hermitian operators constructed from the expressions (4.29), (4.30), and (4.31) respectively. It is clear that L admits the separation of variables $\mathrm{L} = \mathrm{L}' \otimes E'' + E' \otimes \mathrm{L}''$, where $u \otimes v$ is ordinary multiplication: $u_j \otimes v_k = u_j v_k$. Let $E'_\lambda (E''_\lambda)$ be an ordinary resolution of the identity corresponding to L′ (L″). By formula (4.2), Chapter 6, the family of operators E_λ in $l_2(\Pi)$, defined by the relation

$$(E_\lambda (f' \otimes f''), g' \otimes g'')_{l_2(\Pi)} = \int_{-\infty}^{\infty} (E'_{\lambda-\mu} f', g')_{l_2([0,\infty))} d_\mu (E''_\mu f'', g'')_{l_2((-\infty,\infty))}$$

$$(f', g' \in l_2([0, \infty));\ f'', g'' \in l_2((-\infty, \infty))), \tag{4.32}$$

is an ordinary resolution of the identity corresponding to L.

From (4.32) we obtain immediately the formula for the spectral matrix of the expression L, corresponding to E_λ. In fact, if we set $f' = g' = \delta_0$, $f'' = \delta_\beta$, $g'' = \delta_\alpha$ and observe that $\delta_0 \otimes \delta_\gamma = \delta_{(0,\gamma)}$, we obtain

$$\sigma_{\alpha\beta}(\lambda) = (E_\lambda \delta_{(0,\beta)}, \delta_{(0,\alpha)})_{l_2(\Pi)} = \int_{-\infty}^{\infty} (E'_{\lambda-\mu}\delta_0, \delta_0)_{l_2([0,\infty))}\, d_\mu (E''_\mu \delta_\beta,$$

$$\delta_\alpha)_{l_2((-\infty,\infty))} = \int_{-\infty}^{\infty} \sigma'(\lambda-\mu) \sum_{\nu,\tau=-1,0} P''_{\nu;\beta}(\mu)\, P''_{\tau;\alpha}(\mu)\, d\sigma''_{\nu\tau}(\mu).$$

Thus

$$\sigma_{\alpha\beta}(\lambda) = \sum_{\nu,\tau=-1,0} \int_{-\infty}^{\infty} \sigma'(\lambda-\mu)\, P''_{\nu;\alpha}(\mu)\, P''_{\tau;\beta}(\mu)\, d\sigma''_{\nu\tau}(\mu)$$

$$(\alpha, \beta = \ldots, -1,\ 0,\ 1, \ldots; -\infty < \lambda < \infty). \tag{4.33}$$

We find the polynomials $P_{\alpha;(j,k)}(z)$ of the first kind for L, using the eigenfunction expansion of the problem (4.30). Denote by $\tilde{u}_{j,\nu}(\mu)$ $(\nu = -1, 0)$ the Fourier transform (3.2), with respect to these eigenfunctions, of the sequence u_{jk} finite with respect to k $(j = 0, 1, \cdots$ fixed). Going over to the Fourier transform in (4.31), we obtain

$$a'_{j-1}\tilde{u}_{j-1,\nu}(\mu) + a'_j\tilde{u}_{j+1,\nu}(\mu) + b'_j\tilde{u}_{j,\nu}(\mu) = (z-\mu)\tilde{u}_{j,\nu}(\mu)$$

$$(\nu = -1,\ 0;\ j = 0,\ 1, \ldots). \tag{4.34}$$

The initial conditions $u_{-1,k} = 0$, $u_{0k} = \delta_{kk_0}$ $(k = \cdots, -1, 0, 1, \cdots)$ become $\tilde{u}_{-1,\nu}(\mu) = 0$ and $\tilde{u}_{0\nu}(\mu) = P''_{\nu;k_0}(\mu)$ $(\nu = -1, 0)$. Then

$$\tilde{u}_{j,\nu}(\mu) = P''_{\nu;k_0}(\mu)\, P'_j(z-\mu) \qquad (j = 0,\ 1, \ldots;\ \nu = -1,\ 0). \tag{4.35}$$

serves as a solution to equation (4.34) for these initial conditions.

If in equation (3.7) we set $\Delta = (-\infty, \infty)$, and then $v = \delta_k$, we obtain the following general formula for the reconstruction of u_j in terms of $\tilde{u}_\alpha(\lambda)$ $(\alpha = \cdots, -1, 0, 1, \cdots; -\infty < \lambda < \infty)$:

$$u_k = \sum_{\nu,\tau=-1,0} \int_{-\infty}^{\infty} \tilde{u}_\nu(\mu)\, P_{\tau;k}(\mu)\, d\sigma_{\nu\tau}(\mu) \quad (k = 0,\ 1, \ldots).$$

Using this and (4.35), we find that

$$u_{jk} = \sum_{\nu,\tau=-1,0} \int_{-\infty}^{\infty} P''_{\nu;k_0}(\mu)\, P'_j(z-\mu)\, P''_{\tau;k}(\mu)\, d\sigma_{\nu\tau}(\mu).$$

But $u_{jk} = P_{k_0;(j,k)}(z)$; thus

$$P_{\alpha;(j,k)}(z)=\sum_{\nu,\tau=-1,0}\int_{-\infty}^{\infty}P'_j(z-\mu)\,P''_{\nu;\alpha}(\mu)\,P''_{\tau;k}(\mu)\,d\sigma_{\nu\tau}(\mu)$$

$$((j,k)\in\Pi;\ \alpha=\ldots,-1,\ 0,\ 1,\ldots). \tag{4.36}$$

The required formula for the polynomials of the first kind is established.

We now turn to an example. Consider the expression

$$(Lu)_{jk}=\frac{1}{2}u_{j-1,k}+\frac{1}{2}u_{j+1,k}+\frac{1}{2}u_{j,k-1}+\frac{1}{2}u_{j,k+1} \tag{4.37}$$

in the half-plane Π with boundary condition $u_{-1,k}=0$ for all k. It obviously admits a separation of variables, where $(L'u)_j=(L''u)_j=u_{j-1}/2+u_{j+1}/2$. By formulas (4.36) and (4.33) and by the results of §§1.11 and 2.3 it follows that ($\kappa_{(-1,1)}(t)$ is the characteristic function of the interval $(-1,1)$):

$$P_{\alpha;(j,k)}(z)=\frac{\operatorname{sign}\alpha\cdot\operatorname{sign}k}{\pi}\int_0^{\pi}[\sin|\alpha+1|t\cdot\sin|k+1|t$$

$$+\sin|\alpha|t\cdot\sin|k|t-\cos t\cdot(\sin|\alpha+1|t\cdot\sin|k|t$$

$$+\sin|\alpha|t\cdot\sin|k+1|t)]\frac{\sin((j+1)\arccos(z-\cos t))}{\sin^2 t\cdot\sqrt{1-(z-\cos t)^2}}\,dt$$

$$((j,k)\in\Pi;\ \alpha=\ldots,-1,\ 0,\ 1,\ldots); \tag{4.38}$$

$$d\sigma_{\alpha\beta}(\lambda)=\frac{2\operatorname{sign}\alpha\cdot\operatorname{sign}k}{\pi^2}\int_0^{\pi}[\sin|\alpha+1|t\cdot\sin|\beta+1|t$$

$$+\sin|\alpha|t\cdot\sin|\beta|t-\cos t\cdot(\sin|\alpha+1|t\cdot\sin|\beta|t$$

$$+\sin|\alpha|t\cdot\sin|\beta+1|t)]\frac{\varkappa_{(-1,1)}(\lambda-\cos t)\sqrt{1-(\lambda-\cos t)^2}}{\sin^2 t}\,dt\,d\lambda$$

$$(\alpha,\ \beta=\ldots,-1,\ 0,\ 1,\ldots). \tag{4.39}$$

The operator L, constructed by (4.37), is obviously bounded and selfadjoint. Therefore the spectral matrix associated with L is unique and has the form (4.39).

CHAPTER VIII

REPRESENTATION OF A POSITIVE DEFINITE KERNEL IN TERMS OF ELEMENTARY KERNELS

By a well-known theorem of Bochner every continuous positive definite (p. d.) function $k(x)$, i. e. every function for which the kernel $K(x, y) = k(y - x)$ $(x, y \in E_q;\ q \geq 1)$ is positive definite, admits an integral representation

$$k(x) = \int_{E_q} e^{i\lambda x} d\sigma(\lambda) \quad (\lambda = (\lambda_1, \ldots, \lambda_q),\ \lambda x = \lambda_1 x_1 + \ldots + \lambda_q x_q),[1] \qquad (*)$$

where $d\sigma(\lambda)$ is a nonnegative finite measure in E_q. A generalization of this theorem in which the role of elementary positive definite functions $e^{i\lambda x}$ is played by the solutions of differential equations, is of interest. In order to formulate the problem more precisely, we write the representation $(*)$ for the kernel $K(x, y)$ in a different form:

$$K(x, y) = \int_{E_q} \Omega_\lambda(x, y)\, d\sigma(\lambda). \qquad (**)$$

Here $\Omega_\lambda(x, y) = e^{i\lambda(y-x)}$ are "elementary" p. d. kernels. The kernel $K(x, y)$ has the property that in the sense of the generalized functions of L. Schwartz

$$L_{x_j}^{(j)} K = \overline{L_{y_j}^{(j)} K} \qquad (j = 1, \ldots, q), \qquad (***)$$

where $L_{x_j}^{(j)} = i\,\partial/\partial x_j$. The p. d. kernels $\Omega_\lambda(x, y)$ are elementary in the sense that they are eigenelements for the system

$$L_{x_j}^{(j)} \Omega_\lambda = \lambda_j \Omega_\lambda,\ \overline{L_{y_j}^{(j)} \Omega_\lambda} = \lambda_j \Omega_\lambda \quad (j = 1, \ldots, q). \qquad (****)$$

The problem that arises, in general terms, consists in carrying over the representation $(**)$ to the case of arbitrary differential expressions $L^{(j)}$ involving both ordinary and partial derivatives, and also to the case of difference expressions. It will be solved by the method of Chapter V, and it will be convenient

[1] In this chapter it will be convenient to denote the scalar product in E_n by $xy\ (x, y \in E_n)$.

for us to carry out the argument in the first two sections abstractly, with abstract p. d. kernels. In what follows the cases $q = 1$ and $q > 1$ will be essentially different. While for $q = 1$ one can study the question completely, in the second the discussion is incomplete. All the spaces figuring in what follows are taken to be separable.

§1. GENERAL OUTLINE

1. **The concept of an elementary p. d. kernel and *-commutativity.** Suppose that we have a chain $H_- \supseteq H_0 \supseteq H_+$ of spaces with involution $\alpha \to \bar{\alpha}$. We form the chain $H_- \otimes H_- \supseteq H_0 \otimes H_0 \supseteq H_+ \otimes H_+$. Each element $K \in H_- \otimes H_-$ we have called a generalized kernel. If $(K, u \otimes \bar{u})_0 \geq 0$ $(u \in H_+)$, then K was called p. d.

Suppose that some operator A operates in H_0, and that A has a complete region of definition $\mathfrak{D}(A)$. We shall suppose that A admits an extension of equipment and that $Д$ is the space connected with this extension. The family of p. d. kernels $\Omega_\lambda \in H_- \otimes H_-$ (λ is a real number) is called a family of elementary p. d. kernels (relative to A), if for all λ $\|\Omega_\lambda\|_{H_- \otimes H_-} \leq C < \infty$ and

$$(\Omega_\lambda, ((A^* - \lambda E) v) \otimes \bar{u})_0 = 0, \qquad (\Omega_\lambda, v \otimes \overline{(A^* - \lambda E) u})_0 = 0 \tag{1.1}$$

$$(u, v \in Д)$$

(since Ω_λ is Hermitian each of the equations (1.1) implies the other).

Equations (1.1), roughly speaking, denote relations (****) with $q = 1$ and $L = A$. We shall write such relationships more precisely. To this end we need to carry out a transition similar to that which was accomplished in Chapter V in passing from (2.7) to (2.10).

Suppose that H is any Hilbert space with involution $f \to \bar{f}$. We shall consider in H an operator S with an everywhere dense domain of definition $\mathfrak{D}(S)$, and put

$$\bar{S}f = \overline{S\bar{f}} \qquad (f \in \mathfrak{D}(\bar{S}) = \overline{\mathfrak{D}(S)}). \tag{1.2}$$

It is not hard to see that $\mathfrak{D}(\bar{S}^*) = \mathfrak{D}(\overline{S^*}) = \overline{\mathfrak{D}(S^*)}$, $\bar{S}^* = \overline{S^*}$. If $\bar{S} = S$, the operator S is said to be real relative to the involution $f \to \bar{f}$.

We shall suppose that the $Д$ considered above is invariant relative to involution: $\bar{Д} = Д$. Then $Д$ works for the extension of equipment with respect to both A and $\bar{A}$: it will be a linear set in H_+, lying in $\mathfrak{D}(A^*) \cap \mathfrak{D}(\bar{A}^*)$ and going under the operators A^* and $\overline{A}^*$ into a portion of H_+. One may topologize $Д = Д_+$ in the manner discussed on page 333. We construct the extensions $\tilde{A} \supseteq A$, $\tilde{\overline{A}} \supseteq \overline{A}$. These will be operators operating continuously from H_- into $Д' = Д_-$. The role of the chain (2.8) of Chapter V is played by the chain

$$Д_- \supset H_- \supset H_0 \supset H_+ \supset Д_+. \tag{1.3}$$

If we understand the identity operator E as an imbedding operator for H_- into $Д_-$, then equations (1.1) may be rewritten in the following equivalent form:

$$(\tilde{A} \otimes E)\, \Omega_\lambda = \lambda \Omega_\lambda, \qquad (E \otimes \tilde{\overline{A}})\, \Omega_\lambda = \lambda \Omega_\lambda. \tag{1.4}$$

Let us for example verify the second of the relations (1.4). We have

$$\begin{aligned}
(((E \otimes \tilde{\overline{A}}) - \lambda E)\, \Omega_\lambda, v \otimes \overline{u})_0 &= ((E \otimes (\tilde{\overline{A}} - \lambda E))\, \Omega_\lambda, v \otimes \overline{u})_0 \\
= ((E \otimes (\overline{A}^{*+} - \lambda E))\, \Omega_\lambda, v \otimes \overline{u})_0 &= ((E \otimes (\overline{A}^* - \lambda E))^+ \Omega_\lambda, v \otimes \overline{u})_0 \\
= (\Omega_\lambda, (E \otimes (\overline{A}^* - \lambda E))\, (v \otimes \overline{u}))_0 &= (\Omega_\lambda, v \otimes ((\overline{A}^* - \lambda E)\, \overline{u}))_0 \\
&= (\Omega_\lambda, v \otimes \overline{(A^* - \lambda E)\, u})_0 \quad (u, v \in Д),
\end{aligned}$$

as was asserted.

Now we describe abstractly a relation of type (***). Suppose that $K \in H_- \otimes H_-$ is some kernel, and A the operator described above. We agree to say that the kernel K and the operator A *-commute if

$$(K, (A^* v) \otimes \overline{u})_0 = (K, v \otimes \overline{(A^* u)})_0 \quad (u, v \in Д). \tag{1.5}$$

Just as in (1.4) relation (1.5) is equivalent to the equation

$$(\tilde{A} \otimes E)\, K = (E \otimes \tilde{\overline{A}})\, K. \tag{1.6}$$

Indeed, for any u, $v \in Д$

$$\begin{aligned}
((\tilde{A} \otimes E)\, K, v \otimes \overline{u})_0 &= ((A^{*+} \otimes E)\, K, v \otimes \overline{u})_0 = ((A^* \otimes E)^+ K, v \otimes \overline{u})_0 \\
&= (K, (A^* \otimes E)\, (v \otimes \overline{u}))_0 = (K, (A^* v) \otimes \overline{u})_0, \\
((E \otimes \tilde{\overline{A}})\, K, v \otimes \overline{u})_0 &= ((E \otimes \overline{A}^{*+})\, K, v \otimes \overline{u})_0 = ((E \otimes \overline{A}^*)^+ K, v \otimes \overline{u})_0 \\
&= (K, (E \otimes \overline{A}^*)\, (v \otimes \overline{u}))_0 = (K, v \otimes (\overline{A}^* \overline{u}))_0 = (K, v \otimes \overline{(A^* u)})_0,
\end{aligned}$$

from which the required equivalence follows.

On the other hand, the condition of $*$-equivalence of K and A may be described in the following equivalent way. We introduce into H_+ a scalar product, writing

$$\langle u, v \rangle = (K, v \otimes \bar{u})_0 \quad (u, v \in H_+). \tag{1.7}$$

Generally speaking, the fact that $\langle u, u \rangle = 0$ for $u \in H_+$ does not imply that $u = 0$. *For simplicity of exposition we shall first suppose that there is no degeneracy, i. e. that* $\langle u, u \rangle = 0$ *for* $u \in H_+$ *implies* $u = 0$. At the end of this section we will show what alterations in the proofs of the theorems presented below are needed in the case of degeneracy. Their formulations will not change.

Thus H_+ completed with the scalar product (1.7) yields a Hilbert space H_K. Since

$$\langle u, u \rangle = (K, u \otimes \bar{u})_0 \leqslant \| K \|_- \| u \otimes \bar{u} \|_+ = \| K \|_- \| u \|_+^2 \quad (u \in H_+), \tag{1.8}$$

the metric $\langle \cdot , \cdot \rangle$ is weaker than the metric $(\cdot , \cdot)_+$, i. e. as a result of the completion we obtain a space $H_K \supseteq H_+$.

Suppose that A satisfies (1. 5)–(1.6). Then the restriction of A^* to Д may be considered as an operator in H_K, where, from (1. 5), we have

$$\langle A^* u, v \rangle = (K, v \otimes \overline{(A^* u)})_0 = (K, (A^* v) \otimes \bar{u})_0 = \langle u, A^* v \rangle \quad (u, v \in Д).$$

This relation shows that the restriction of A^* to Д is Hermitian in H_K. The converse is also clear: the Hermiticity of the restriction of A^* to Д in the sense of H_K implies (1. 5)–(1.6). Thus, *$*$-commutativity of K and A and Hermiticity of the restriction of A^* to Д in H_K are equivalent requirements.*

If $H_+ = H_0$, then $(K, v \otimes \bar{u})_0 = B_K(u, v)$ is a continuous bilinear form in H_0 and therefore admits a representation $(K, v \otimes \bar{u})_0 = (Su, v)_0 \, (u, v \in H_0)$ with a continuous nonnegative operator S. Suppose that the operator A is also bounded. Then the $*$-commutativity of K and A is indeed equivalent to a relation of the type of commutativity (although nonsymmetric):

$$SA^* = AS. \tag{1.9}$$

2. Representation theorem. The case $q = 1$. We shall now show that $*$-commutativity of K with A is a necessary and sufficient condition for the representation of K in the form of a linear combination of elementary kernels Ω_λ. It is true that generally speaking the Ω_λ will be more generalized than K.

Theorem 1. 1. *Consider a chain of the type* (1. 10) *of Chapter* I, *made out of separable spaces with involution:*

$$H_{--} \supseteq H_{-} \supseteq H_0 \supseteq H_{+} \supseteq H_{++}, \tag{1.10}$$

where it is assumed that the imbedding $H_{++} \to H_{+}$ *is quasinuclear. Suppose that an operator* A *with complete domain of definition* $\mathfrak{D}(A)$ *operates in* H_0, *while the chain* $H_{--} \supseteq H_0 \supseteq H_{++}$ *(which means also the chain* $H_{-} \supseteq H_0 \supseteq H_{+}$*) admits an extension of its equipment, i. e. it suffices to require the existence of a linear set* $Д \subseteq \mathfrak{D}(A^*)$ *invariant relative to involution, dense in* H_{++}, *and such that* $A^* Д \subseteq H_{++}$.

Suppose that $K \in H_{-} \otimes H_{-}$ *is* p. d. *For it to have a representation*

$$K = \int_{-\infty}^{\infty} \Omega_\lambda d\rho(\lambda), \tag{1.11}$$

where the Ω_λ *form a family of elementary* p. d. *kernels of* $H_{--} \otimes H_{--}$ *"more generalized than* K*",* $d\rho(\lambda)$ *is a nonnegative finite measure, and the integral converges in the norm of the space* $H_{--} \otimes H_{--}$, *it is necessary and sufficient that* K *and* A **-commute, i. e. that the restriction of* A^* *to* $Д$ *be a Hermitian operator in* H_K. *In the representation* (1. 11) *the expression* $\Omega_\lambda d\rho(\lambda)$ *is defined in a unique way if and only if the closure of the restriction of* A^* *in* H_K *is maximal.*

Before proving the theorem we note that in its formulation there appeared an arbitrarily long chain of spaces, because K, generally speaking, is a generalized kernel, and therefore for its definition the chain $H_{-} \supseteq H_0 \supseteq H_{+}$ is already necessary. The spaces H_{++} and $Д$ appeared thanks to the use of the expansion theorem.

Proof. We shall establish the sufficiency as a consequence of Theorem 2. 3 of Chapter V. Indeed, we shall consider an expansion into generalized eigenvectors of the Hermitian operator A^* operating in the space H_K. We have $H_K \supseteq H_{+} \supseteq H_{++}$, while H_{++} is dense in H_K and the imbedding $H_{++} \to H_K$ is quasinuclear as a composition of the quasinuclear imbedding $H_{++} \to H_{+}$ and the continuous imbedding $H_{+} \to H_K$. We shall consider H_K as a null space and H_{++} as a positive space. We let $H_{--,K}$ be the corresponding negative space. Because of the quasinuclearity of the imbedding $H_{++} \to H_K$ the chain

$$H_{--,K} \supseteq H_K \supseteq H_{++} \tag{1.12}$$

may be used for the construction of the decomposition. From (2. 14), Chapter V, for the generalized resolution of the identity $E(\Delta)$ of the restriction onto $Д$ of the operator A^* we have the equation

$$\langle E(\Delta)u, v\rangle = \int_{\Delta} \langle P(\lambda)u, v\rangle \, d\varrho(\lambda) \quad (u, v \in H_{++}), \tag{1.13}$$

where the operators $P(\lambda)$ operating from H_{++} to $H_{--, K}$ are generalized projection operators onto the generalized eigensubspaces of the restriction A^*.

We shall show that

$$\langle P(\lambda)u, v\rangle = (\Omega_\lambda, v \otimes \bar{u})_0 \quad (u, v \in H_{++}), \tag{1.14}$$

where Ω_λ is a certain family of elementary p. d. kernels. Indeed, suppose that $\mathbf{I}_1$ is the operator $\mathbf{I}$ constructed relative to the chain (1. 12). Then $\langle P(\lambda)u, v\rangle = (\mathbf{I}_1 P(\lambda)u, v)_{++}$. Since the operator $P(\lambda)$ is a Hilbert-Schmidt operator from H_{++} to $H_{--, K}$, then $\mathbf{I}_1 P(\lambda)$ is a Hilbert-Schmidt operator in H_{++}. From Lemma 2. 1, Chapter I, we may write $(\mathbf{I}_1 P(\lambda)u, v)_{++} = (S_\lambda, v \otimes \bar{u})_{H_{++} \otimes H_{++}}$ $(u, v \in H_{++})$, where $S_\lambda \in H_{++} \otimes H_{++}$. Suppose that $\mathbf{I}_2$ is the operator $\mathbf{I}$ constructed relative to the chain $H_{--} \otimes H_{--} \supseteq H_0 \otimes H_0 \supseteq H_{++} \otimes H_{++}$. Putting $\Omega_\lambda = \mathbf{I}_2^{-1} S_\lambda$, we arrive at (1. 14). Since $|P(\lambda)| \le 1$, $(P(\lambda)u, u)_0 \ge 0$ $(u \in H_{++})$, then clearly $\|\Omega_\lambda\|_{H_{--} \otimes H_{--}} \le C$ and Ω_λ is a p. d. kernel. Finally, $\phi = P(\lambda)u$ for any $u \in Д$ will be a generalized eigenvector of the restriction A^*. Thus, from (2. 7) of Chapter V,

$$(\Omega_\lambda, ((A^* - \lambda E)v) \otimes \bar{u})_0 = \langle P(\lambda)u, (A^* - \lambda E)v\rangle = 0 \quad (u, v \in Д).$$

We put $\Delta = (-\infty, \infty)$ in (1. 13). Using (1. 14), we find

$$(K, v \otimes \bar{u})_0 = \langle u, v\rangle = \int_{-\infty}^{\infty} (\Omega_\lambda, v \otimes \bar{u})_0 d\varrho(\lambda) \quad (u, v \in H_{++}).$$

Therefore the representation (1. 11) follows. The convergence of the integral in it follows from the estimate $\|\Omega_\lambda\|_{H_{--} \otimes H_{--}} \le C$ and the finiteness of the measure $d\rho(\lambda)$.

Conversely, suppose that the representation (1. 11) holds for K with some family of elementary p. d. kernels Ω_λ. Taking (1. 1) into account, we find for $u, v \in Д$

$$(K, (A^*v) \otimes \bar{u})_0 = \int_{-\infty}^{\infty} (\Omega_\lambda, (A^*v) \otimes \bar{u})_0 d\varrho(\lambda) = \int_{-\infty}^{\infty} \lambda (\Omega_\lambda, v \otimes \bar{u})_0 d\varrho(\lambda),$$

$$(K, v \otimes \overline{(A^*u)})_0 = \int_{-\infty}^{\infty} (\Omega_\lambda, v \otimes \overline{(A^*u)})_0 d\varrho(\lambda) = \int_{-\infty}^{\infty} \lambda (\Omega_\lambda, v \otimes \bar{u})_0 \, d\varrho(\lambda),$$

from which (1. 5) follows. Thus $*$-commutativity of K and A is a necessary and sufficient condition for the validity of the representation (1. 1).

It remains to investigate the uniqueness of this representation. First we establish a lemma.

Lemma 1. 1. *Suppose for the p. d. kernel K the representation* (1. 11) *holds for some family of p. d. kernels Ω_λ. Then in the space H_K there exists a generalized resolution of the identity $E(\Delta)$ for the operator A^* restricted to Д, such that for any Borel Δ*

$$\langle E(\Delta)u,\ v\rangle = \int_\Delta (\Omega_\lambda,\ v\otimes\bar{u})_0 d\varrho(\lambda) \quad (u,\ v\in H_{++}). \tag{1.15}$$

Proof. Fix Δ and consider the bilinear form $B_\Delta(u, v) = (\int_\Delta \Omega_\lambda d\rho(\lambda), v\otimes\bar{u})_0 = \int_\Delta(\Omega_\lambda, v\otimes\bar{u})_0 d\rho(\lambda)$ $(u, v\in H_{++})$. It is evidently nonnegative and therefore $|B_\Delta(u, v)|^2 \le B_\Delta(u, u)B_\Delta(v, v)$. But

$$B_\Delta(u,\ u) = \int_\Delta (\Omega_\lambda,\ u\otimes\bar{u})_0 d\varrho(\lambda) \leqslant \int_{-\infty}^{\infty} (\Omega_\lambda,\ u\otimes\bar{u})_0 d\varrho(\lambda)$$

$$= (K,\ u\otimes\bar{u})_0 = \langle u,\ u\rangle \quad (u\in H_{++}),$$

so that $|B_\Delta(u, v)|^2 \le \langle u, u\rangle\ \langle v, v\rangle$ $(u, v\in H_{++})$. Thus $B_\Delta(u, v)$ is uniformly continuous in H_K on the linear set H_{++} dense in that set. Hence

$$B_\Delta(u,\ v) = \int_\Delta (\Omega_\lambda,\ v\otimes\bar{u})_0 d\varrho(\lambda) = \langle E(\Delta)u,\ v\rangle \quad (u,\ v\in H_{++}). \tag{1.16}$$

The family of operators $E_\lambda = E((-\infty, \lambda))$ $(-\infty<\lambda<\infty)$ evidently satisfies the requirements imposed on the generalized resolution of the identity: for $\lambda''>\lambda'$ $E_{\lambda''} - E_{\lambda'} \ge 0$, $E_{-\infty} = 0$, $E_{+\infty} = E$. We shall show that E_λ is the generalized resolution of the identity for the restriction of A^* to Д, i. e. that the representation

$$\langle A^*u,\ v\rangle = \int_{-\infty}^{\infty} \lambda d\,\langle E_\lambda u,\ v\rangle,\quad \langle A^*u,\ A^*u\rangle = \int_{-\infty}^{\infty} \lambda^2 d\,\langle E_\lambda u,\ u\rangle \tag{1.17}$$

$$(u\in Д,\ v\in H_K)$$

holds.

For $u, v\in$ Д we have $\langle A^*u, v\rangle = (K, v\otimes\overline{(A^*u)})_0$. Hence from (1. 11), (1. 1) and (1. 16) it follows that

$$\langle A^*u, v\rangle = \int_{-\infty}^{\infty} (\Omega_\lambda, v \otimes \overline{(A^*u)})_0 d\varrho(\lambda) = \int_{-\infty}^{\infty} \lambda(\Omega_\lambda, v \otimes \bar{u})_0 d\varrho(\lambda)$$

$$= \int_{-\infty}^{\infty} \lambda d_\lambda \left\{ \int_{-\infty}^{\lambda} (\Omega_\mu, v \otimes \bar{u})_0 d\varrho(\mu) \right\} = \int_{-\infty}^{\infty} \lambda d_\lambda \langle E_\lambda u, v\rangle \quad (u, v \in Д).$$

Thus we have obtained the first of the equations (1. 17), though only for $v \in Д$. Since $Д$ is dense in H_K, we may pass to the limit and obtain it completely. The second equation (1. 17) is proved analogously. One need only replace above v by A^*u ($u \in Д$) and make use of the relation $(\Omega_\lambda, (A^*u) \otimes \overline{(A^*u)})_0 = \lambda(\Omega_\lambda, (A^*u) \otimes \bar{u})_0 = \lambda^2(\Omega_\lambda, u \otimes \bar{u})_0$ (see (1. 1)).

Thus $E(\Delta)$ is a generalized resolution of the identity for the restriction A^*, and (1. 16) holds. The lemma is proved.

This lemma shows that each representation of the kernel K in the form (1.11) may be obtained by means of some generalized resolution of the identity $E(\Delta)$ of the operator A^* restricted to $Д$. From (1. 15), the uniqueness of the differentials $\Omega_\lambda d\rho(\lambda)$ is equivalent to the uniqueness of the generalized decomposition $E(\Delta)$ of the restriction of A^*, and, as is known, this uniqueness holds if and only if the closure of the operator in question is maximal. The theorem is completely proved.

3. **Construction of integral representations of a p. d. kernel in the case $q>1$.** In the case $q = 1$ we have used essentially the circumstance that every Hermitian operator, in particular the restriction of A^* to $Д$, admits a selfadjoint extension, generally speaking going out into a wider space, i. e. such that there exists a generalized resolution of the identity for it. In the case $q > 1$, in order to make it possible to apply Theorem 2. 6 of Chapter V, we need in addition to require the existence of commuting selfadjoint extensions of the corresponding operators, since such extensions do not always exist (recall that two selfadjoint, possibly unbounded, operators, are said to commute if their resolutions $E_\lambda^{(1)}$ and $E_\lambda^{(2)}$ of the identity commute for any $\lambda_1, \lambda_2 \in (-\infty, \infty)$. In the case of bounded operators this definition is obviously equivalent to the usual definition of commutativity). With similar remarks the considerations of the preceding subsections carry over to the case $q > 1$. Here we only note such a carryover. From the point of view of applications this remark is essential, since the possibility of the construction of commuting selfadjoint extensions has only been proved for special cases (see §2).

Suppose that in the equipped space $H_0(H_- \supseteq H_0 \supseteq H_+)$ there operates a system of operators $A_1, \cdots, A_q$ with complete regions of definition $\mathfrak{D}(A_1), \cdots, \mathfrak{D}(A_q)$. Suppose that each of the operators A_j admits an extension of equipment to a topological space Д common for all of them. The family of p. d. kernels $\Omega_\lambda \in H_- \otimes H_-$ $(\lambda = (\lambda_1, \cdots, \lambda_q) \in E_q)$ is said to be a family of elementary p. d. kernels relative to the system $A_1, \cdots, A_q$ if, for all λ, $\|\Omega_\lambda\|_{H_- \otimes H_-} \leq C < \infty$ and

$$(\Omega_\lambda, ((A_j^* - \lambda_j E) v) \otimes \bar{u})_0 = 0, \; (\Omega_\lambda, v \otimes \overline{((A_j^* - \lambda_j E) u)})_0 = 0 \tag{1.18}$$
$$(u, v \in Д; \; j = 1, \ldots, q).$$

Equations (1. 18) may be written in a form similar to (1. 4). To this end we suppose that we may choose an invariant, relative to involution, set $Д \subseteq \mathfrak{D}(A_j^*)$ $(j = 1, \cdots, q)$, dense in H_+ and such that $A_j^* Д \subseteq H_+$ $(j = 1, \cdots, q)$. We topologize $Д = Д_+$ by means of an appropriately chosen scalar product. Now we may construct the chain (1. 3) and the extensions $\widetilde{A}_j \supseteq A_j$, $\widetilde{\bar{A}}_j \supseteq \bar{A}_j$ $(j = 1, \cdots, q)$, operating from H_- to $Д_-$. Equation (1. 18) is rewritten in the form

$$(\widetilde{A}_j \otimes E)\, \Omega_\lambda = \lambda_j \Omega_\lambda, \quad (E \otimes \widetilde{\bar{A}}_j)\, \Omega_\lambda = \lambda_j \Omega_\lambda \tag{1.19}$$
$$(j = 1, \ldots, q).$$

As with $q = 1$, the first of the equations (1. 18), (1. 19) implies the second, and conversely.

As earlier, we shall use the concept of $*$-commutativity of the kernel K with each of the operators A_j. $*$-commutativity of K with A_j is equivalent to Hermiticity of the restriction of the operator A_j^* to Д in the scalar product (1. 7).

Theorem 1. 2. *Suppose that we have a separable space H_0 equipped as in Theorem 1. 1 and in it a system of operators $A_1, \cdots, A_q$, each of which satisfies the requirements of that theorem with a common Д.*

Suppose that $K \in H_- \otimes H_-$ is p. d.. For it to have a representation

$$K = \int_{E_q} \Omega_\lambda \, d\rho(\lambda), \tag{1.20}$$

where Ω_λ is some family of elementary p. d. kernels of $H_{--} \otimes H_{--}$, $d\rho(\lambda)$ is a nonnegative finite measure, and the integral converges in the norm of the space $H_{--} \otimes H_{--}$, it is necessary and sufficient that the two following requirements be satisfied: a) *the kernel K $*$-commutes with each A_j, i. e. the restriction of A_j^* to Д is Hermitian in H_K,* b) *the q Hermitian operators obtained by* *restricting the* A_j^* *to* Д *admit extension to* H_K *or else, by going out to a wider Hilbert space, to a system of commuting selfadjoint operators. In the representation* (1. 20) *the expression* $\Omega_\lambda d\rho(\lambda)$ *is defined uniquely if and only if for the restrictions of* $A_1^*, \cdots, A_q^*$ *to* Д *there exists only one q-dimensional generalized resolution of unity.*

The proof of this theorem is carried out on the plan of the preceding proof and we shall only note it here. Suppose that conditions a) and b) are satisfied. We consider in the space H_K Hermitian operators equal to the restrictions of the A_j^* to Д. We shall construct expansions with respect to common eigenvectors of these operators, applying Theorem 2. 6 of Chapter V, and taking H_{++} as the positive space. Using considerations similar to those presented on page 614, we obtain the representation (1. 20) from a Parseval equation of type (1. 13).

Conversely, suppose that we have a representation (1. 20). Again just as in the earlier proof it is easy to show that the restrictions of the A_j^* to Д are Hermitian operators in H_K. We shall show that they admit commuting selfadjoint restrictions. To this end we note that as in Lemma 1. 1, from the representation (1. 20) there follows the existence of an operator measure $E(\Delta)$ on the Borel sets of E_q, whose values are bounded nonnegative operators in H_K, while $E(E_q) = E$ and

$$\langle A_j^* u, v\rangle = \int_{E_q} \lambda_j d\langle E_\lambda u, v\rangle, \quad \langle A_j^* u, A_j^* u\rangle = \int_{E_q} \lambda_j^2 d\langle E_\lambda u, u\rangle$$

$$(u \in Д,\ v \in H_K;\ \ j = 1, \ldots, q). \tag{1. 21}$$

As is well known, H_K may be extended to some Hilbert space $\widetilde{H}_K$ in such a way that $E(\Delta)$ will be equal to $P\widetilde{E}(\Delta)$, where $\widetilde{E}(\Delta)$ is some q-dimensional resolution of the identity in $\widetilde{H}_K$ and P is the orthogonal projection operator from $\widetilde{H}_K$ onto H_K. In other words, $E(\Delta)$ is a q-dimensional generalized resolution of the identity. The operators B_j in $\widetilde{H}_K$ defined by the equations $B_j u = \int_{E_q} \lambda_j d\widetilde{E}_\lambda u$ on the vectors $u \in \widetilde{H}_K$ for which $\int_{E_q} \lambda_j^2 d\langle \widetilde{E}_\lambda u, u\rangle_{\widetilde{H}_K} < \infty$ $(j = 1, \cdots, q)$, will be selfadjoint commuting. By (1. 21), each $B_j \supseteq A_j^*$. Hence requirement b) is established.

The conclusion of the theorem on the uniqueness of $\Omega_\lambda d\rho(\lambda)$ follows directly from the analog of Lemma 1. 1, which, as was already indicated, holds. The theorem is proved.

4. Case of degeneracy of the form $\langle \cdot, \cdot \rangle$. We shall show how the preceding arguments change when it does not follow from the equation $\langle u, u\rangle = 0$ that $u = 0$.

We need certain general constructions, connected with the concept of negative norm. Suppose that

$$H_{--} \supseteq H_{-} \supseteq H_0 \supseteq H_{+} \supseteq H_{++}$$

is a chain of the type (1. 10), Chapter I. The notations for scalar products and norms of the spaces are the usual, the case $H_+ = H_0$ not being excluded. We suppose that on some of the H_+ there has been introduced a quasiscalar product $\langle u, v\rangle$ $(u, v \in H_+)$ which is a bilinear nonnegative and generally speaking degenerate form, with $\langle u, u\rangle \le (u, u)_+$ $(u \in H_+)$. We identify to zero all those $u \in H_+$ for which $\langle u, u\rangle = 0$. The space of such u will be denoted by Θ. In other words, we consider the factor-space H_+/Θ, consisting of the classes $u + \Theta$ of vectors of H_+. After completion we obtain a Hilbert space, for which we retain the notation H_K. Suppose that $u \to Fu$ is the operator of transition from a vector $u \in H_+$ to its class $Fu \in H_+/\Theta$, $u \to Ou$ the imbedding operator for H_{++} into H_+, and $R = FO$. All of these operators are continuous; we denote by $H_{++,K}$ the orthogonal complement in H_{++} to the subspace of all the $u \in H_{++}$ such that $Ru = 0$, i.e. to the subspace $\Theta \cap H_{++}$. Let P_K be the orthogonal projector in H_{++} onto $H_{++,K}$. It is clear that $H_{++,K}$ may be regarded as imbedded in H_K. For this we need to identify $u \in H_{++,K}$ with the class $u + \Theta$; R will play the role of the imbedding operator. For such an inclusion $\langle u, u\rangle \le (u, u)_{H_{++,K}} = (u, u)_{++}$ $(u \in H_{++,K})$ and $H_{++,K}$ will be dense in H_K. This makes it possible to consider $H_K \supseteq H_{++,K}$ as the null and positive spaces and to construct the corresponding space $H_{--,K}$. We obtain the chain

$$H_{--,K} \supseteq H_K \supseteq H_{++,K} \qquad (1.22)$$

(cf. §3.7, Chapter I).

If the imbedding $H_{++} \to H_+$ were quasinuclear then the imbedding $H_{++,K} \to H_K$ would also be quasinuclear. This follows from the fact that the imbedding operator R is equal to FO, and therefore if O is Hilbert-Schmidt R is also.

Suppose that $Д \subseteq H_{++}$ is some set which is linear and dense in H_{++}, S a linear operator with $\mathfrak{D}(S) = Д$, $\mathfrak{R}(S) \subseteq H_{++}$, while $\langle Su, v\rangle = \langle u, Sv\rangle$ $(u, v \in Д)$ (Hermiticity in $\langle\cdot,\cdot\rangle$). *Then S carries class into class and this operator may be considered as a Hermitian operator in H_K.* More precisely, we need to show that if $u, v \in Д$ are such that $u - v \in \Theta$, then $Su - Sv \in \Theta$. In other words, if $w \in \Theta \cap Д$, then $Sw \in \Theta$. Suppose that $w \in Д$ is such that $\langle w, w\rangle = 0$. Then for any $u \in Д$ $\langle Sw, u\rangle = \langle w, Su\rangle = 0$; this follows from the Cauchy-Bunjakovskiĭ inequality $|\langle u, v\rangle|^2 \leq \langle u, u\rangle \times \langle v, v\rangle$ $(u, v \in H_+)$). Thanks to the denseness of $Д$ in H_{++} one may, by vectors $u_n \in Д$, $(n = 1, 2, \cdots)$ approximate Sw in the metric H_{++} and therefore in the sense of $\langle \cdot, \cdot \rangle$. Thus $\langle Sw, Sw\rangle = \lim_{n\to\infty} \langle Sw, u_n\rangle = 0$, i. e. $Sw \in \Theta$. The assertion is proved.

The result just proved shows that S induces a Hermitian operator $\check{S}$ in H_K, for which $\mathfrak{D}(\check{S}) = P_K Д$, $\mathfrak{R}(\check{S}) \subseteq P_K H_{++} = H_{++, K}$. Indeed, for $u \in P_K Д$ we put $\check{S}u = FSu'$, where u' is any vector of $Д$ such that $u - u' \in \Theta$. The definition of $\check{S}$ is correct, i. e. it does not depend on the way of choosing u', since if u'' is a second vector of the same form as u', then $Su' - Su'' \in \Theta$ and $FSu' = FSu''$. It is clear that $\check{S}$ is Hermitian: for $u, v \in P_K Д$ we have

$$\langle \check{S}u, v \rangle = \langle FSu', Fv' \rangle = \langle Su', v' \rangle = \langle u', Sv' \rangle = \langle u, \check{S}v \rangle$$

Moreover, $\mathfrak{D}(\check{S}) = P_K Д$ is dense in $P_K H_{++, K}$, and therefore in H_K.

Suppose that $E(\Delta)$ is a resolution (generalized) of the identity, corresponding to $\check{S}$. We shall construct an expansion in terms of its generalized eigenvectors, making use of the chain (1. 22) (the imbedding $H_{++} \to H_+$ is supposed quasi-nuclear). Then relations (2. 14) and (2. 7) of Chapter V may be rewritten in the form

$$\langle E(\Delta) P_K u, P_K v \rangle = \int_\Delta \langle P(\lambda) P_K u, P_K v \rangle \, d\varrho(\lambda) \qquad (u, v \in H_{++}), \tag{1.23}$$

$$\langle \varphi, (\check{S} - \lambda E) P_K u \rangle = 0 \qquad (\varphi \in \mathfrak{R}(P(\lambda)) \subseteq H_{--,K};\ u \in Д).$$

We turn to the study of p. d. kernels. We shall show how to carry out the proof of Theorem 1. 1 when (1. 7) is degenerate. We consider the same chain (1. 10) as before, with the imbedding $H_{++} \to H_+$ quasinuclear, and the form (1. 7). Without loss of generality in the estimate (1. 8) we may suppose that $\|K\|_+ \leq 1$. Thus all the constructions just made are now applicable. We shall take as S the restriction of the operator A^* to $Д$ (see page 612). For the corresponding $E(\Delta)$ we write down formulas (1. 23). For the derivation of the analog of relation (1. 14) we consider an operator $\mathbf{I}_1$: the operator $\mathbf{I}$ constructed relative to the chain (1. 22). We have

$$\langle P(\lambda) P_K u, P_K v \rangle = (\mathbf{I}_1 P(\lambda) P_K u, P_K v)_{++} = (P_K \mathbf{I}_1 P(\lambda) P_K u, v)_{++} \qquad (u, v \in H_{++}). \tag{1.24}$$

Since $P(\lambda)$ is the Hilbert-Schmidt operator from $H_{++, K}$ to $H_{--, K}$, it follows that $P_K I_1 P(\lambda) P_K$ will be a Hilbert-Schmidt operator in H_{++} and therefore, from Lemma 2. 1, Chapter I, one may extend (1. 24): there exists an $S_\lambda \in H_{++} \otimes H_{++}$ such that $(P_K I_1 P(\lambda) P_K u, v)_{++} = (S_\lambda, v \otimes \bar{u})_{H_{++} \otimes H_{++}}$ $(u, v \in H_{++})$. Repeating the argument of page 614, we find a p. d. kernel $\Omega_\lambda \in H_{--} \otimes H_{--}$, $\|\Omega_\lambda\|_{H_{--} \otimes H_{--}} \leq C$, such that

$$\langle P(\lambda) P_K u, P_K v \rangle = (\Omega_\lambda, v \otimes \bar{u})_0 \qquad (u, v \in H_{++}). \tag{1. 25}$$

We shall show that Ω_λ satisfies the first of relations (1. 1). Since for $u \in H_{++}$ $P(\lambda) P_K u \in \Re(P(\lambda))$, then, from the second equation (1. 23) and relation (1. 25), we have

$$\begin{aligned} 0 &= \langle P(\lambda) P_K u, (\check{S} - \lambda E) P_K v \rangle = \langle P(\lambda) P_K u, F A^* v - \lambda P_K v \rangle \\ &= \langle P(\lambda) P_K u, P_K A^* v - \lambda P_K v \rangle = \langle P(\lambda) P_K u, P_K (A^* - \lambda E) v \rangle \\ &= (\Omega_\lambda, ((A^* - \lambda E) v) \otimes \bar{u})_0 \qquad (u, v \in Д), \end{aligned}$$

as required. Thus Ω_λ is indeed a family of elementary p. d. kernels.

Putting in the second formula (1. 23) $\Delta = (-\infty, \infty)$ and using (1. 25), we find that

$$\langle P_K u, P_K v \rangle = \int_{-\infty}^{\infty} (\Omega_\lambda, v \otimes \bar{u})_0 \, d\varrho(\lambda) \qquad (u, v \in H_{++}). \tag{1. 26}$$

But on the vectors $u - P_K u$, $v - P_K v$ the form $\langle \cdot, \cdot \rangle$ degenerates, so that $\langle P_K u, P_K v \rangle = \langle u, v \rangle = (K, v \otimes \bar{u})_0$. Substituting this expression in (1. 26), we arrive at the representation (1. 11).

That the $*$-commutativity of K and A follows from (1. 11) is proved in exactly the same way as before.

The last part of Theorem 1. 1, relating to the uniqueness of the representation (1. 11), may also easily be proved using the constructions just presented in the case of degeneracy of $\langle \cdot, \cdot \rangle$. We observe only that from the estimate $|B_\Delta(u, v)|^2 \leq \langle u, u \rangle \langle v, v \rangle$ $(u, v \in H_{++})$, proved as before, it follows that the bilinear form is defined and continuous on the class of vectors, i. e. on the elements of $H_{++, K} \subseteq H_K$. Therefore it admits as before the representation (1. 16).

The results of subsection 3 carry over to the degenerate case exactly as the results of subsection 2.

§2. EXISTENCE OF SELFADJOINT COMMUTING EXTENSIONS, AND THE QUESTION OF UNIQUENESS

We obtain some theorems relative to the existence of selfadjoint commuting extensions for the restrictions to Δ of the operators A_j^*. The results will be of two types: 1) when the required extensions are obtained by passage to a closure; 2) when one makes wider extensions. In analogy with the expressions $L^{(j)}$ in (***) and (****) we are going to consider operators A_j, operating relative to "various variables"; only in this case have we succeeded in establishing some facts on the extensions.

1. **Form of operators; elementary theorems on the existence of selfadjoint commuting extensions.** Consider a chain of spaces with involution

$$H_- \supset H_0 \supset H_+. \tag{2.1}$$

Suppose that $K \in H_- \otimes H_-$ is a generalized p. d. kernel. As before, we define for $u, v \in H_+$ a scalar product $\langle u, v\rangle = (K, v \otimes \bar{u})_0$, after identifying if there is a degeneracy, and completion, we obtain a Hilbert space H_K.

The spaces of the chain (2.1) will have for us a special form, generalizing the interpretation of the space of functions $f(x_1, \cdots, x_q)$ as a tensor product of functions $f(x_j)$ relative to each of the variables. Indeed, suppose there are q chains of spaces

$$H_-^{(j)} \supset H_0^{(j)} \supset H_+^{(j)} \quad (j = 1, \ldots, q), \tag{2.2}$$

to each of which is connected its involution $u_j \to \bar{u}_j^j$. We obtain $H_0 = H_0^{(1)} \otimes \cdots \otimes H_0^{(q)}$, $H_+ = H_+^{(1)} \otimes \cdots \otimes H_+^{(q)}$, as is known (see Chapter I, §2.2). Tensor-multiplying the involution operators for the various chains (2.2), we obtain some involution $- = -_1 \otimes \cdots \otimes -_q$ for the spaces (2.1). It is in fact this involution which we shall associate to the chain (2.1).[1]

Suppose that B_j is some operator in the space $H_+^{(j)}$ with a dense region of definition $\mathfrak{D}(B_j)$. We construct operators C_j $(j = 1, \cdots, q)$ in the space H_+:

$$C_j = E \otimes \ldots \otimes E \otimes B_j \otimes E \otimes \ldots \otimes E$$
$$(\mathfrak{D}(C_j) = H_+^{(1)} \otimes \ldots \otimes H_+^{(j-1)} \otimes \mathfrak{D}(B_j) \otimes H_+^{(j+1)} \otimes \ldots \otimes H_+^{(q)}) \tag{2.3}$$

(in the first product B_j stands at the jth place). We shall require that the equation

1) The tensor product of involution operators is defined as in Chapter I, §2.1.

$$\langle C_j u, v\rangle = \langle u, C_j v\rangle \quad (u, v \in \mathfrak{D}(C_j);\ \ j = 1, \ldots, q) \tag{2.4}$$

be satisfied.

Therefore it easily follows (see §1.4) that if $\langle u, u\rangle = 0$, then $\langle C_j u, C_j u\rangle = 0$ as well, so that the operator C_j may be understood as an operator in H_K. Because of (2.4) all the C_j are Hermitian operators in H_K. It is clear that these operators, in a definite sense, commute: $C_j C_k u = C_k C_j u$ for $u \in H_+^{(1)} \otimes \cdots \otimes H_+^{(j-1)} \otimes \mathfrak{D}(B_j) \otimes H_+^{(j+1)} \otimes \cdots \otimes H_+^{(k-1)} \otimes \mathfrak{D}(B_k) \otimes H_+^{(k+1)} \otimes \cdots \otimes H_+^{(q)}$ (for definiteness we suppose $j < k$).

In this section we shall take up the commutativity of the selfadjoint extensions of the operators C_j. These results apply directly in §§4–5 to the problem arising in §1.3, if as a C_j we take the restriction of the operator A_j^* to $Д \subseteq H_{++} \subseteq H_+$. Since $A_j^* Д \subseteq H_{++} \subseteq H_+$, this restriction may be considered as an operator in H_+ (clearly the operators A_j must have a definite structure guaranteeing that the A_j^* operate coordinatewise.

First of all we establish a general fact.

Lemma 2.1. *Suppose that in the Hilbert space H there operate two, generally speaking, unbounded selfadjoint operators S_1 and S_2. For S_1 and S_2 to commute it is necessary and sufficient that their resolvents $R_{z_1}^{(1)}$ and $R_{z_2}^{(2)}$ commute for some fixed z_1 and z_2.*

Proof. The necessity is obvious. If $E^{(1)}(\Delta_1)$ and $E^{(2)}(\Delta_2)$ are resolutions of the identity corresponding to S_1 and S_2 respectively, then from their commutativity for arbitrary Δ_1 and Δ_2 follows the commutativity of the resolvent $R_\zeta^{(j)} = \int_{-\infty}^{\infty} 1/(\lambda - \zeta)\, dE_\lambda^{(j)}$ $(j = 1, 2)$. We shall establish the sufficiency. First of all we note that if z and ζ are regular points of some operator S and R_λ their resolvent, then the operator $(E - (\zeta - z)R_z)^{-1}$ exists and is equal to $E - (z - \zeta)R_\zeta$. This follows from the identity

$$(E - (\zeta - z) R_z)(E - (z - \zeta) R_\zeta) = E - (z - \zeta) R_\zeta - (\zeta - z) R_z$$
$$+ (\zeta - z)(z - \zeta) R_z R_\zeta = E - (\zeta - z)[R_z - R_\zeta - (z - \zeta) R_z R_\zeta] = E.$$

Now suppose that S_1 and S_2 are selfadjoint and such that $R_{z_1}^{(1)}$ and $R_{z_2}^{(2)}$ commute. From the Hilbert identity $R_z^{(1)} - R_{z_1}^{(1)} = (z - z_1) R_z^{(1)} R_{z_1}^{(1)}$ and from the fact just established it follows that $R_z^{(1)}(E - (z - z_1)R_{z_1}^{(1)}) = R_{z_1}^{(1)}$, $R_z^{(1)} = (E - (z - z_1)R_{z_1}^{(1)})^{-1} R_{z_1}^{(1)}$. Hence $R_z^{(1)}$ and $R_{z_2}^{(2)}$ commute. Analogously we conclude that $R_\zeta^{(2)}$ and $R_z^{(1)}$ commute for arbitrary nonreal ζ and z.

From a well-known formula, for arbitrary intervals Δ_1 and Δ_2 we have

$$\begin{aligned} E^{(1)}(\Delta_1) &= \lim_{\varepsilon\to+0} \frac{1}{2\pi i} \int\limits_{\Delta_1+i\varepsilon} (R_z^{(1)} - R_{\bar z}^{(1)})\, dz, \\ E^{(2)}(\Delta_2) &= \lim_{\delta\to+0} \frac{1}{2\pi i} \int\limits_{\Delta_2+i\delta} (R_\zeta^{(2)} - R_{\bar\zeta}^{(2)})\, d\zeta \end{aligned} \tag{2.5}$$

the limits being understood in the weak sense. From what has already been proved the integrals in (2. 5) commute. But then their weak limits $E^{(1)}(\Delta_1)$ and $E^{(2)}(\Delta_2)$ commute as well. The lemma is proved.

Theorem 2. 1. *Suppose for each* $j = 1, \cdots, q$ *the set* $(B_j - zE)\mathfrak{D}(B_j)$ *is dense in* $H_+^{(j)}$ *for at least one value of* z *from the upper halfplane and at least one from the lower. Then the closures of the operators* C_1 *are selfadjoint in* H_K *and commute.*

Proof. In order to simplify the notation we shall carry out the proof for $q = 2$. Suppose that $(B_j - zE)\mathfrak{D}(B_j)$ is dense in $H_+^{(j)}$ for $z = z_j$, ζ_j ($\operatorname{Im} z_j > 0$, $\operatorname{Im}\zeta_j < 0$, $j = 1, 2$). We have

$$\begin{aligned} (C_1 - z_1E)\mathfrak{D}(C_1) &= (B_1 \otimes E - z_1E)(\mathfrak{D}(B_1) \otimes H_+^{(2)}) \\ &= ((B_1 - z_1E)\otimes E)(\mathfrak{D}(B_1)\otimes H_+^{(2)}) = ((B_1 - z_1E)\mathfrak{D}(B_1)) \otimes H_+^{(2)}. \end{aligned}$$

Since $(B_1 - z_1E)\mathfrak{D}(B_1)$ is dense in $H_+^{(1)}$, the last product is dense in $H_+^{(1)} \otimes H_+^{(2)} = H_+$ and thus also in H_K. In a similar way $((B_1 - \zeta_1E)\mathfrak{D}(B_1))\otimes H_+^{(2)}$ is also dense in H_K, so that the closure of C_1 is selfadjoint. An analogous picture holds also for C_2.

We shall verify the commutativity of the closures of C_1 and C_2. Because of Lemma 2. 1 it suffices to verify the commutativity of their resolvents $R_{z_1}^{(1)}$ and $R_{z_2}^{(2)}$. It suffices to establish this on the set $((B_1 - z_1E)\mathfrak{D}(B_1)) \otimes ((B_2 - z_2E)\mathfrak{D}(B_2))$, which is dense in $H_+^{(1)} \otimes H_+^{(2)} = H_+$ and therefore in H_K. Commutativity on this set follows from commutativity on elements of the form $w = ((B_1 - z_1E)u_1) \otimes ((B_2 - z_2E)u_2)$ ($u_1 \in \mathfrak{D}(B_1)$, $u_2 \in \mathfrak{D}(B_2)$). Since $w \in \mathfrak{R}(E \otimes B_2 - z_2E)$, it follows that $R_{z_2}^{(2)} w = (E \otimes B_2 - z_2E)^{-1} w$ and we obtain

$$R^{(1)}_{z_1}R^{(2)}_{z_2}(((B_1-z_1E)u_1)\otimes((B_2-z_2E)u_2)) = R^{(1)}_{z_1}(E\otimes B_2-z_2E)^{-1}(((B_1-z_1E)u_1)\otimes((B_2-z_2E)u_2)) = R^{(1)}_{z_1}(E\otimes(B_2-z_2E)^{-1})(((B_1-z_1E)u_1)\otimes\otimes((B_2-z_2E)u_2)) = R^{(1)}_{z_1}(((B_1-z_1E)u_1)\otimes u_2) = (B_1\otimes E-z_1E)^{-1}(((B_1-z_1E)u_1)\otimes u_2) = ((B_1-z_1E)^{-1}\otimes E)(((B_1-z_1E)u_1)\otimes u_2) = u_1\otimes u_2.$$

We arrive at the same answer if we calculate $R^{(2)}_{z_2}R^{(1)}_{z_1}(((B_1-z_1E)u_1)\otimes((B_2-z_2E)u_2))$, i.e. when the commutativity of $R^{(1)}_{z_1}$ and $R^{(2)}_{z_2}$ on the elements in question is established. The theorem is proved.

Remark. From this theorem it follows that for the commutativity of the resolvents $R^{(1)}_{z_1}$ and $R^{(2)}_{z_2}$ of the operators obtained by the closure of C_1 and C_2, it is sufficient that the set $((B_1-z_1E)\mathfrak{D}(B_1))\otimes((B_2-z_2E)\mathfrak{D}(B_2))$ should be dense in H_K.

We shall present a more refined theorem of the same type. First we introduce some concepts. We fix vectors $w_2\in H^{(2)}_+, \cdots, w_q\in H^{(q)}_+$ and consider for the vectors $u_1, v_1\in H^{(1)}_+$ the scalar (more precisely, quasiscalar) product

$$\langle u_1, v_1\rangle_{w_2,\dots,w_q} = \langle u_1\otimes w_2\otimes\dots\otimes w_q, v_1\otimes w_2\otimes\dots\otimes w_q\rangle \tag{2.6}$$

where the product on the right is in H_K. The completion of $H^{(1)}_+$ with this scalar product, after identification, will be denoted by $H^{(1)}_{K;w_2,\dots,w_q}$. Evidently $H^{(1)}_{K;w_2,\dots,w_q}$ is isometric with the subspace of H_K obtained by the closure of the linear set $H^{(1)}_+\otimes w_2\otimes\cdots\otimes w_q$.

If the operator B_1 is such that the corresponding C_1 (see (2.3)) is Hermitian in H_K, then

$$\langle B_1u_1, v_1\rangle_{w_2,\dots,w_q} = \langle u_1, B_1v_1\rangle_{w_2,\dots,w_q} \quad (u_1, v_1\in\mathfrak{D}(B_1)).$$

This relation is similar to (2.4), and it follows from it that the operator B_1 may be considered as operating in $H^{(1)}_{K;w_2,\dots,w_q}$ and that it is there Hermitian. It is clear that this operator is isometric to the part of C_1 operating in the closure of $H^{(1)}_+\otimes w_2\otimes\cdots\otimes w_q$ (evidently this last subspace is invariant relative to C_1).

Fixing the elements w of the other subspaces $H^{(j)}_+$, we may in an analogous way construct spaces $H^{(2)}_{K;w_1,w_3,\dots,w_q}, \dots, H^{(q)}_{K;w_1,w_2,\dots,w_{q-1}}$ and state for them assertions analogous to those presented for $H^{(1)}_{K;\, w_2, \cdots, w_q}$.

Theorem 2. 2. *Suppose that for each* $j = 1, \cdots, q$ *the closure of the operator* B_j *in any space* $H^{(j)}_{K;\, w_1, \cdots, w_{j-1}, w_{j+1}, \cdots, w_q}$ $(w_l \in H^{(l)}_+,\ l \neq j)$ *is selfadjoint. Then the closures of the operators* C_j *are selfadjoint in* H_K *and commute.*

Proof. We first carry out the proof for $q = 2$. Suppose that $j = 1$. Taking the isometric image of $H^{(1)}_{K;\, w_2}$, we find that by the hypothesis of the theorem the restriction of C_1 to $\mathfrak{D}(B_1) \otimes w_2$, after closure, is selfadjoint in the closure of $H^{(1)}_+ \otimes w_2$. In other words, for nonreal z, $((B_1 - zE)\mathfrak{D}(B_1)) \otimes w_2$ is dense in $H^{(1)}_+ \otimes w_2$. Since $w_2 \in H^{(2)}_+$ is arbitrary, $(C_1 - zE)\mathfrak{D}(C_1) = ((B_1 - zE)\mathfrak{D}(B_1)) \otimes H^{(2)}_+$ is dense in the sense of the metric of H_K in $H^{(1)}_+ \otimes H^{(2)}_+ = H_+$. Thus the closure of C_1 is selfadjoint. Analogously we show that the closure of C_2 is selfadjoint.

To establish the commutativity of C_1 and C_2 we first observe that from the preceding proof it is clear that also *the closures of certain restrictions of* C_1 *will be selfadjoint in* H_K. *Indeed this is so for every restriction to a set* $\mathfrak{D}(B_1) \otimes G_2$, *where* G_2 *is a linear set of* $H^{(1)}_+$ *such that* $H^{(1)}_+ \otimes G_2$ *is dense in* H_K. The analogous situation holds also for C_2: one may consider the restriction of C_2 to $G_1 \otimes \mathfrak{D}(B_2)$, where $G_1 \otimes H^{(2)}_+$ is dense in H_K.

From the remark to Theorem 2. 1 and Lemma 2. 1, for the proof of the commutativity of the closures of C_1 and C_2 it suffices to establish the denseness in H_K of the set $((B_1 - z_1E)\mathfrak{D}(B_1)) \otimes ((B_2 - z_2E)\mathfrak{D}(B_2))$ for arbitrary nonreal z_1 and z_2. Consider the restriction of C_1 to the set $\mathfrak{D}(B_1) \otimes G_2$, where $G_2 = ((B_2 - z_2E)\mathfrak{D}(B_2))$. The choice of such a G_2 is possible, since $H^{(1)}_+ \otimes G_2 = H^{(1)}_+ \otimes ((B_2 - z_2E)\mathfrak{D}(B_2)) = (C_2 - z_2E)\mathfrak{D}(C_2)$ is dense in H_K because the closure of C_2 is selfadjoint. The closure of the restriction of C_1 in question is selfadjoint in H_K, so that $(C_1 - z_1E)(\mathfrak{D}(B_1) \otimes G_2) = ((B_1 - z_1E)\mathfrak{D}(B_1)) \otimes G_2 = ((B_1 - z_1E)\mathfrak{D}(B_1)) \otimes ((B_2 - z_2E)\mathfrak{D}(B_2))$ is dense in H_K, which was required. The theorem is proved.

2. Connection with the problem of uniqueness in the Cauchy problem for differential equations. We now establish a deeper criterion for the closures of the operators C_j to be selfadjoint and commute. To this end we shall develop the method of §1. 7, Chapter VI. It is convenient for us now to repeat the definition of a weak solution in Chapter VI, §1. 7 (for $r = 1$).

Suppose that in a Hilbert space H there operates an operator S with an everywhere dense region of definition $\mathfrak{D}(S)$. Consider the differential equation

$$\frac{du}{dt} - S^*u = 0 \quad (0 \leqslant t < \infty). \tag{2.7}$$

By a weak solution of this equation we understand a vector-function $u(t)$ $(0 \leq t < \infty)$ with values in H, weakly differentiable with respect to t and satisfying the equation

$$\frac{d}{dt}(u(t), f)_H - (u(t), Sf)_H = \left(\frac{du(t)}{dt}, f\right)_H - (u(t), Sf)_H = 0 \tag{2.8}$$

$$(f \in \mathfrak{D}(S),\ 0 \leqslant t < \infty).$$

We shall say that for the equation (2.7) we have uniqueness of the weak solutions of the Cauchy problem, if each weak solution $u(t)$ equal to zero for $t = 0$ annihilates also for every $t > 0$.

Theorem 2.3. *Suppose that for each $j = 1, \cdots, q$ for both equations*

$$\frac{du}{dt} \pm (iB_j)^*u = 0 \quad (0 \leqslant t < \infty), \tag{2.9}$$

considered in the spaces $H_+^{(j)}$, we have uniqueness of the weak solutions of the Cauchy problem. Then the closures of the operators C_j are selfadjoint in H_K and commute. Here we are supposing in addition that each C_j has in H_K equal defect numbers.

As before, the proof will be carried out for $q = 2$. We first establish the following general fact.

Lemma 2.2. *Suppose that G_2 is some linear set of $H_+^{(2)}$. We denote by F_{G_2} the restriction of the operator C_1 to $\mathfrak{D}(B_1) \otimes G_2 = \mathfrak{D}(F_{G_2})$. This operator is Hermitian with a dense region of definition in a Hilbert space $\mathfrak{H}_{G_2} \subseteq H_K$ which is the closure in H_K of the linear set $H_+^{(1)} \otimes G_2$. If the operator B_1 is such that for both equations (2.9) for $j = 1$ one has uniqueness of the weak solutions of the Cauchy problem, then the closure of F_{G_2} is maximal in $\mathfrak{H}_{G_2}$ (the lemma is valid without any hypotheses as to the equality of the defect numbers of the operator C_1).*

Proof of the lemma. Since F_{G_2} is Hermitian in $\mathfrak{H}_{G_2}$, there exists a self-adjoint extension $\widetilde{F}_{G_2}$ of that operator, generally speaking going out into a wider space $\widetilde{\mathfrak{H}}_{G_2} \supseteq \mathfrak{H}_{G_2}$. Suppose that $\widetilde{E}_\lambda$ is its resolution of the identity, $E_\lambda = P\widetilde{E}_\lambda P$ a generalized resolution of the identity of the operator F_{G_2} (P is the projection operator from $\widetilde{\mathfrak{H}}_{G_2}$ to $\mathfrak{H}_{G_2}$). We construct a vector-function $v(t)$ with values in $\mathfrak{H}_{G_2} \subseteq H_L$:

$$v(t) = \int_{-\infty}^{\infty} e^{i\lambda t}\, dE_\lambda v(0) \qquad (0 \leqslant t < \infty), \tag{2.10}$$

where $v(0)$ is an arbitrary vector of $\mathfrak{D}(F_{G_2})$. Since $\int_{-\infty}^{\infty} \lambda^2 d\langle E_\lambda v(0), v(0)\rangle < \infty$, then $v(t)$ is strongly differentiable in t and $dv(t)/dt = i\int_{-\infty}^{\infty} \lambda e^{i\lambda t} dE_\lambda v(0)$.

Since H_+ is dense in H_K and $\|u\|_{H_K} \leq C\|u\|_+$ $(u \in H_+)$, then H_K may be taken as the null space and H_+ as the positive space. Consider the corresponding operator I, defined by $\langle f, u\rangle = (If, u)_+$ $(f \in H_K,\ u \in H_+)$. It continuously carries all of H_K into a dense part of H_+ and has in general an unbounded inverse. We define a vector-function with values in H_+ by the equation $u(t) = Iv(t)$ $(0 \leq t < \infty)$; since $v(t)$ is strongly differentiable, $u(t)$ is also. We shall show that $u(t)$ satisfies the following relation for any $w \in \mathfrak{D}(F_{G_2})$:

$$\left(\frac{du(t)}{dt}, w\right)_+ - (u(t), iF_{G_2}w)_+ = \frac{d}{dt}(u(t), w)_+ - (u(t), iF_{G_2}w)_+ = 0$$
$$(0 \leqslant t < \infty) \tag{2.11}$$

(we do not refer to the weak solution of the corresponding differential equation in H_+, since density of $\mathfrak{D}(F_{G_2})$ in H_+ is not assumed). We have

$$\frac{d}{dt}(u(t), w)_+ - (u(t), iF_{G_2}w)_+ = \frac{d}{dt}(Iv(t), w)_+ - (Iv(t), iF_{G_2}w)_+$$
$$= \frac{d}{dt}\langle v(t), w\rangle - \langle v(t), iF_{G_2}w\rangle = i\int_{-\infty}^{\infty} \lambda e^{i\lambda t}\, d\langle E_\lambda v(0), w\rangle$$
$$- i\int_{-\infty}^{\infty} e^{i\lambda t}\, d\langle E_\lambda v(0), F_{G_2}w\rangle. \tag{2.12}$$

But

$$\langle E_\lambda v(0), F_{G_2} w\rangle = \langle P\widetilde{E}_\lambda P v(0), F_{G_2} w\rangle = \langle \widetilde{E}_\lambda v(0), F_{G_2} w\rangle_{\widetilde{\mathfrak{H}}_{G_2}}$$

$$= \langle \widetilde{E}_\lambda v(0), \widetilde{F}_{G_2} w\rangle_{\widetilde{\mathfrak{H}}_{G_2}} = \int_{-\infty}^{\lambda} \mu d\langle \widetilde{E}_\mu v(0), w\rangle_{\widetilde{\mathfrak{H}}_{G_2}}$$

$$= \int_{-\infty}^{\lambda} \mu d\langle E_\mu v(0), w\rangle.$$

Substituting in (2. 12), we find that the integrals converge. Thus (2. 11) is proved.

Since in (2. 11) $w \in \mathfrak{D}(F_{G_2}) = \mathfrak{D}(B_1) \otimes G_2$ is arbitrary, (2.11) is equivalent to the same equation, in which $w = w_1 \otimes w_2$, where $w_1 \in \mathfrak{D}(B_1)$ and $w_2 \in G_2$. In other words, (2. 11) is equivalent to

$$\left(\frac{du(t)}{dt}, w_1 \otimes w_2\right)_+ - (u(t), (iB_1 w_1) \otimes w_2)_+ = 0$$

$$(0 \leqslant t < \infty, \; w_1 \in \mathfrak{D}(B_1), \; w_2 \in G_2). \tag{2. 13}$$

For the sequel we need the following construction. Suppose that $w_2 \in H_+^{(2)}$ is fixed. Consider the expression $B(f, u_1) = (f, u_1 \otimes w_2)_+$, where $f \in H_+$, $u_1 \in H_+^{(1)}$. This is a bilinear functional. It is continuous:

$$|B(f, u_1)| = |(f, u_1 \otimes w_2)_+| \leqslant \|f\|_+ \|u_1 \otimes w_2\|_+$$

$$= \|f\|_+ \|u_1\|_{H_+^{(1)}} \|w_2\|_{H_+^{(2)}} = C\|f\|_+ \|u_1\|_{H_+^{(1)}} \quad (f \in H_+, \; u_1 \in H_+^{(1)}),$$

so that it admits a representation in terms of an operator in the scalar product of the spaces H_+ or $H_+^{(1)}$. A representation in terms of $(\cdot\,,\cdot)_+$ figured in the definition of $B(f, u_1)$. Representation in terms of $(\cdot\,,\cdot)_{H_+^{(1)}}$ yields

$$(f, u_1 \otimes w_2)_+ = B(f, u_1) = (Q_{w_2} f, u_1)_{H_+^{(1)}} \quad (f \in H_+, \; u_1 \in H_+^{(1)}), \tag{2. 14}$$

where Q_{w_2} is a linear operator, operating continuously from H_+ to $H_+^{(1)}$.

Let us carry out the proof of the lemma. Construct a vector-function with values in the space $H_+^{(1)}$: $q_{w_2}(t) = Q_{w_2} u(t)$ $(0 \leq t < \infty, \; w_2 \in G_2 \subseteq H_+^{(2)})$. Since $u(t)$ is strongly differentiable, then $q_{w_2}(t)$ is also, while $(d/dt)q_{w_2}(t) = Q_{w_2} du(t)/dt$. Now, using (2. 14), we may rewrite (2. 13) as

$$0 = \left(\frac{du(t)}{dt}, w_1 \otimes w_2\right)_+ - (u(t), (iB_1 w_1) \otimes w_2)_+$$

$$= \left(Q_{w_2}\frac{du(t)}{dt}, w_1\right)_{H_+^{(1)}} - (Q_{w_2} u(t), iB_1 w_1)_{H_+^{(1)}}$$

$$= \frac{d}{dt}(q_{w_2}(t), w_1)_{H_+^{(1)}} - (q_{w_2}(t), iB_1 w_1)_{H_+^{(1)}}$$

$$(0 \leqslant t < \infty,\ w_1 \in \mathfrak{D}(B_1)).$$

In other words, $q_{w_2}(t)$ is a weak solution of equation (2. 9) for $j = 1$ and with the minus sign. The initial conditions are

$$q_{w_2}(0) = Q_{w_2} u(0) = Q_{w_2} Iv(0). \tag{2.15}$$

Suppose that the closure of F_{G_2} is not maximal in $\mathfrak{H}_{G_2}$. Then there exist two distinct resolutions of the identity, E'_λ and E''_λ, generated by this operator. Carrying out the preceding construction with the initial data $v(0)$ for each of these resolutions, we find two solutions $q'_{w_2}(t)$ and $q''_{w_2}(t)$ of equation (2. 9) ($j = 1$, minus sign), having, from (2. 15), the same initial conditions. Because of the hypothesized uniqueness of the weak solutions, $q'_{w_2}(t) = q''_{w_2}(t)$ $(0 \leq t < \infty)$. Suppose that $v'(t)$ and $v''(t)$ denote functions constructed with respect to E'_λ and E''_λ, and let $u'(t)$ and $u''(t)$ have analogous meanings. For arbitrary $w_1 \in \mathfrak{D}(B_1)$, $w_2 \in G_2$ we obtain

$$\langle v'(t) - v''(t), w_1 \otimes w_2\rangle = (I(v'(t) - v''(t)), w_1 \otimes w_2)_+$$

$$= (u'(t) - u''(t), w_1 \otimes w_2)_+ = (Q_{w_2}(u'(t) - u''(t)), w_1)_{H_+^{(1)}}$$

$$= (q'_{w_2}(t) - q''_{w_2}(t), w_1)_{H_+^{(1)}} = 0 \quad (0 \leqslant t < \infty).$$

This last equation holds also for linear combinations of vectors $w_1 \otimes w_2$, and these combinations describe the set $\mathfrak{D}(B_1) \otimes G_2$, dense in $\mathfrak{H}_2$. So, $v'(t) - v''(t) = 0$ $(0 \leq t < \infty)$. Taking (2. 10) into account, we find for arbitrary $u \in \mathfrak{H}_G$

$$\int_{-\infty}^{\infty} e^{i\lambda t}\, d\langle (E'_\lambda - E''_\lambda) v(0), u\rangle = \langle v'(t) - v''(t), u\rangle = 0 \quad (0 \leqslant t < \infty). \tag{2.16}$$

Now consider the equation $du/dt + (iB_1)^* u = 0$ for $t \geq 0$ and make the change of variables $t = -\tau$ in it. As a result we obtain the equation $du/d\tau - (iB_1)^* u = 0$ for $\tau \leq 0$, for which uniqueness of the weak solutions of the Cauchy problem holds in view of the hypothesized uniqueness for the original equation. Repeating for this equation all the preceding, we arrive at equation (2.16), in which $-\infty < t \leq 0$.

The function $\omega(\lambda) = \langle (E'_\lambda - E''_\lambda) v(0), u\rangle$ has bounded variation on the real axis. (2.16) means that its Fourier-Stieltjes transform annihilates for all real t. By the theorem on uniqueness for the Fourier-Stieltjes transform $\omega(\lambda) = 0$ $(-\infty < \lambda < \infty)$, i.e. $\langle (E'_\lambda - E''_\lambda) v(0) u\rangle = 0$, where $v(0) \in \mathfrak{D}(F_{G_2})$, $u \in \mathfrak{H}_{G_2}$. Since $\mathfrak{D}(F_{G_2})$ is dense in $\mathfrak{H}_{G_2}$, then $E'_\lambda = E''_\lambda$, which contradicts the assumption. The lemma is proved.

Lemma 2.2 implies:

Lemma 2.3. *Suppose that the hypotheses of the preceding lemma are satisfied, while in addition it is known that:* 1) *the set* G_2 *is such that* $H_+^{(1)} \otimes G_2$ *is dense in* H_K (*i.e.* $\mathfrak{H}_{G_2} = H_K$); 2) *the operator* C_1 *has in* H_K *equal defect numbers. Then the closure of* F_{G_2} *is selfadjoint in* H_K.

Proof. From Lemma 2.2 the closure of F_{G_2} is maximal in H_K. Therefore for the proof it suffices to verify that F_{G_2} has equal defect numbers. But F_{G_2} is a restriction of the operator C_1, whose defect numbers are by hypothesis equal. Since C_1 admits selfadjoint extensions in H_K, then F_{G_2} admits them, i.e. its defect numbers are equal. The lemma is proved.

Proof of the theorem. For $G_2 = H_+^{(1)}$ the operator F_{G_2} coincides with C_1. Applying Lemma 2.3, we conclude that the closure of $C_1 = F_{G_2}$ in H_K is selfadjoint. Analogously we establish the selfadjointness of the closure of C_2.

To prove the commutativity of the closures of C_1 and C_2, because of Lemma 2.1 and the remark to Theorem 2.1 it suffices to show that the sets

$$((B_1 - z_1E)\,\mathfrak{D}(B_1)) \otimes ((B_2 - z_2E)\,\mathfrak{D}(B_2)) \tag{2.17}$$

for nonreal z_1 and z_2 are dense in H_K. Consider the restriction F_{G_2} of the operator C_1 to $\mathfrak{D}(F_{G_2}) = \mathfrak{D}(B_1) \otimes G_2$, where $G_2 = (B_2 - z_2E)\mathfrak{D}(B_2)$. The set G_2 satisfies the requirements of Lemma 2.3, since $H_+^{(1)} \otimes G_2 = H_+^{(1)} \otimes ((B_2 - z_2E)\mathfrak{D}(B_2)) = (C_2 - z_2E)\mathfrak{D}(C_2)$ is dense in H_K because of the selfadjointness of the closure of C_2. Therefore by Lemma 2.3 the closure of F_{G_2} is selfadjoint, i.e. $(F_{G_2} - z_1E)\mathfrak{D}(F_{G_2}) = (B_1 \otimes E - z_1E)(\mathfrak{D}(B_1) \otimes ((B_2 - z_2E)\mathfrak{D}(B_2))) = ((B_1 - z_1E)\mathfrak{D}(B_1)) \otimes ((B_2 - z_2E)\mathfrak{D}(B_2))$ is dense in H_K. Thus, the density of the sets (2. 17) is established and the theorem proved.

Now we present a scheme of proof of the uniqueness of the solutions of the Cauchy problem, showing that the solvability of the Cauchy problem for sufficiently arbitrary initial conditions implies the uniqueness of the adjoint problem. See pages 391–394.

First of all we note that for uniqueness of the weak solutions of the Cauchy problem for equation (2. 7) on the entire interval $[0, \infty)$ it is sufficient that this should hold locally, i. e. that there exists a $T > 0$ such that if (2. 8) holds for $t \in [0, T]$ and $u(0) = 0$, then $u(t) = 0$ for $t \in [0, T]$. Indeed, because the operator A in (2. 8) does not depend on t, the weak solutions of equation (2. 7) may be shifted arbitrarily: if $u(t)$ satisfies (2. 8) for $t \in [a, b]$, then $v(t) = u(t - s)$ satisfies (2. 8) for $t \in [s, T + s]$. Therefore if one has uniqueness on the interval $[0, T]$, then one has it on any interval $[s, T + s]$ as well. In other words, if $u(t)$ satisfies (2. 8) for $t \in [s, T + s]$ and $u(s) = 0$, then $u(t) = 0$ for $t \in [s, T + s]$. In particular, this holds on the intervals $[0, T]$, $[T, 2T]$, $[2T, 3T]$, $\cdots$ and hence on the whole semiaxis $[0, \infty)$.

Theorem 2. 4. *For the uniqueness of the weak solution of the Cauchy problem for equation* (2. 7) *on the interval* $[0, \infty)$ *it suffices that the following situation holds. There exist two linear topological spaces* Φ *and* Ψ *such that* $\Phi \subseteq \Psi \subseteq \dot{\mathfrak{D}}(S)$, *convergence in* Φ *implies convergence in* Ψ, *which in turn implies convergence in* H; Φ *is dense in* H; *for some* $T > 0$ *there exists an operator function* $Q(t_0, t)$, *where* $0 \leq t_0$, $t \leq T$, *whose values are continuous operators operating from* Φ *to* Ψ *such that for any* $\phi \in \Phi$ $\phi(t) = Q(t_0, t)\phi$ *is a weak solution* (*in the sense of* H) *of the equation*

$$\frac{d\varphi(t)}{dt} + S(\varphi(t)) = 0 \tag{2. 18}$$

on the entire interval $[0, T]$, *turning into* ϕ *when* $t = t_0$.

The proof follows directly from Lemma 1. 4 of Chapter VI (for $r = 1$), after a slight rephrasing.

In the case $q = 1$ Theorems 2. 1 and 2. 3 yield sufficient conditions for the selfadjointness of an operator in H_K. These conditions may obviously be formulated in the form of the following theorem.

Theorem 2. 5. *Consider the spaces and operators introduced in* §2. 1, *for* $q = 1$. *In order that the closure of the operator* $B = C$ *should be selfadjoint in*

H_K, *it is sufficient that one of the following conditions be satisfied:*

1) *the set* $(B - zE)\mathfrak{D}(B)$ *is dense in* H_+ *for at least one value* z *of the upper halfplane and one in the lower halfplane;*

2) *for both equations*

$$\frac{du}{dt} \pm (iB)^* u = 0 \qquad (0 \leqslant t < \infty), \tag{2.19}$$

considered in the space H_+, *the weak solutions of the Cauchy problem are unique and the defect numbers in the space* H_K *are equal (without the last condition the closure of* B *is only maximal).*

We note that *for the validity of the results of this and the preceding subsection the presence of the involutions* j *and* $- = -_1 \otimes \cdots \otimes -_q$ *is inessential;* one could simply give some scalar product $\langle \cdot , \cdot \rangle$ in H_+. The construction with the involution was useful for us only in connection with the fact that the latter scalar product was constructed with respect to the kernel.

3. **Further commutative selfadjoint extensions of systems of operators.** In Theorems 2.1–2.3 we constructed commutative selfadjoint extensions of the operators $C_1, \cdots, C_q$ by means of closure procedures. Now we shall obtain some results on extension for operators which are not selfadjoint after closure. From the point of view of integral representations of p. d. kernels, these results lead to nonunique representations. For simplicity we take $q = 2$.

We shall suppose that in the spaces $H_+^{(1)}$ and $H_+^{(2)}$ there are given antilinear transformations $u_1 \to \overset{\circ_1}{u}_1$, $u_2 \to \overset{\circ_2}{u}_2$, $\circ_1^2 = \circ_2^2 = E$, such that the tensor product $\circ = \circ_1 \otimes \circ_2$ is, after closure relative to continuity, an involution in H_K.

Theorem 2.6. *Suppose that the operators* C_1 *and* C_2 *are real relative to the involution* $\circ$ *and that the closure of the restriction of* C_1 *to the set* $\mathfrak{D}(B_1) \otimes w_2$ *for any* $w_2 \in H_+^{(2)}$ *is selfadjoint in the space* $H_{K;w_2}^{(1)}$, *the completion of* $H_+^{(1)}$ *with the scalar product* $\langle u_1, v_1 \rangle_{w_2} = \langle u_1 \otimes w_2, v_1 \otimes w_2 \rangle$ *(hence it follows from Theorem* 2.2 *that the closure of* C_1 *in* H_K *is selfadjoint). Then there exists a selfadjoint extension of the operator* C_2 *commuting with the closure of* C_1.

Proof. Consider for fixed nonreal z_1, z_2 the Cayley transforms $U_{z_j}^{(j)} = (C_j - \bar{z}_j E)(C_j - z_j E)^{-1}$ $(j = 1, 2)$. The operators $U_{z_j}^{(j)}$ realize isometric mappings of the following pairs of sets:

$$U_{z_1}^{(1)}: (C_1 - z_1E)\mathfrak{D}(C_1) = ((B_1 - z_1E)\mathfrak{D}(B_1)) \otimes H_+^{(2)} \to$$
$$\to (C_1 - \bar{z}_1E)\mathfrak{D}(C_1) = ((B_1 - \bar{z}_1E)\mathfrak{D}(B_1)) \otimes H_+^{(2)},$$
$$U_{z_2}^{(2)}: (C_2 - z_2E)\mathfrak{D}(C_2) = H_+^{(1)} \otimes ((B_2 - z_2E)\mathfrak{D}(B_2)) \to$$
$$\to (C_2 - \bar{z}_2E)\mathfrak{D}(C_2) = H_+^{(1)} \otimes ((B_2 - \bar{z}_2E)\mathfrak{D}(B_2)).$$

The sets of the first pair, because of the selfadjointness of the closure of C_1, are dense in H_K and therefore $U_{z_1}^{(1)}$ extends by continuity to a unitary operator, which we denote as before by $U_{z_1}^{(1)}$. The sets of the second pair are not dense in H_K. Suppose that N_{z_2} and $N_{\bar{z}_2}$ are orthogonal complements to the first and second of them (i. e. the defect subspaces of C_2). We shall show that the operator $U_{z_2}^{(2)}$ may be extended to a unitary operator in H_K commuting with $U_{z_1}^{(1)}$.

We shall in the course of the proof of this and the following theorems denote the closure of the set M in H_K by $[M]$. We verify that the subspaces

$$\mathfrak{R}_{z_2} = [H_+^{(1)} \otimes ((B_2 - z_2E)\mathfrak{D}(B_2))], \quad \mathfrak{R}_{\bar{z}_2} = [H_+^{(1)} \otimes ((B_2 - \bar{z}_2E)\mathfrak{D}(B_2)] \quad (2.20)$$

are invariant relative to $U_{z_1}^{(1)}$ and that $U_{z_1}^{(1)}$ is a unitary operator in them. We carry through the proof for the first of these subspaces. From the conditions of the theorem (see the proof of Theorem 2. 2) it follows that for any linear set $G_2 \subseteq H_+^{(2)}$ the closure of the restriction of C_1 to $\mathfrak{D}(B_1) \otimes G_2$ is selfadjoint in $[H_+^{(1)} \otimes G_2]$, i. e. that $(C_1 - \zeta E)(\mathfrak{D}(B_1) \otimes G_2) = ((B_1 - \zeta E)\mathfrak{D}(B_1)) \otimes G_2$ $(\operatorname{Im}\zeta \neq 0)$ is dense in $[H_+^{(1)} \otimes G_2]$. Putting $G_2 = (B_2 - z_2E)\mathfrak{D}(B_2)$ and $\zeta = z_1, \bar{z}_1$, we find that the sets $((B_1 - z_1E)\mathfrak{D}(B_1)) \otimes ((B_2 - z_2E)\mathfrak{D}(B_2))$ and $((B_1 - \bar{z}_1E)\mathfrak{D}(B_1)) \otimes ((B_2 - z_2E)\mathfrak{D}(B_2))$ are dense in $\mathfrak{R}_{z_2}$. At the same time, for arbitrary $u_1 \in \mathfrak{D}(B_1)$ and $u_2 \in \mathfrak{D}(B_2)$ we find that

$$U_{z_1}^{(1)}(((B_1 - z_1E)u_1) \otimes ((B_2 - z_2E)u_2)) = (B_1 \otimes E - \bar{z}_1E)$$
$$\times (B_1 \otimes E - z_1E)^{-1}(((B_1 - z_1E)u_1) \otimes ((B_2 - z_2E)u_2))$$
$$= ((B_1 \otimes E - \bar{z}_1E)u_1) \otimes ((B_2 - z_2E)u_2)$$
$$= ((B_1 - \bar{z}_1E)u_1) \otimes ((B_2 - z_2E)u_2),$$

i. e. that $U_{z_1}^{(1)}$ carries a dense set in $\mathfrak{R}_{z_2}$ into the same set. In other words, $U_{z_1}^{(1)}$ (after closure) is unitary in the first of the subspaces (2. 20).

Since N_{z_2} and $N_{\bar{z}_2}$ are orthogonal complements to the subspaces (2. 20), and $U^{(1)}_{z_1}$ is unitary in all of H_K and in these subspaces, then N_{z_2} and $N_{\bar{z}_2}$ are invariant for it and it is unitary in them. Since $C_1 = (\bar{z}_1 E - z_1 U^{(1)}_{z_1})\cdot(E - U^{(1)}_{z_1})^{-1}$, the subspaces are invariant also relative to C_1, which means also relative to its resolution of the identity $E(\Delta)$.

Hence the operator $U^{(1)}_{z_1}$ is unitary in each of the subspaces (2.20), and $U^{(2)}_{z_2}$ carries the first of these into the second. Thus on the subspace $\mathfrak{R}_{z_2}$ both products $U^{(1)}_{z_1} U^{(2)}_{z_2}$ and $U^{(2)}_{z_2} U^{(1)}_{z_1}$ have meaning. We shall prove that these products are here equal. Since the set $((B_1 - z_1 E)\mathfrak{D}(B_1)) \otimes ((B_2 - z_2 E)\mathfrak{D}(B_2))$ is dense in the subspace in question, then it suffices to verify commutativity on the vectors $((B_1 - z_1E)u_1) \otimes ((B_2 - z_2 E)u_2)$ $(u_1 \in \mathfrak{D}(B_1),\ u_2 \in \mathfrak{D}(B_2))$. We have

$$U^{(1)}_{z_1} U^{(2)}_{z_2}(((B_1 - z_1E)\, u_1) \otimes ((B_2 - z_2E)\, u_2))$$
$$= U^{(1)}_{z_1} (E \otimes B_2 - \bar{z}_2 E)(E \otimes B_2 - z_2 E)^{-1}(((B_1 - z_1 E)\, u_1) \otimes ((B_2 - z_2 E)\, u_2))$$
$$= U^{(1)}_{z_1}(((B_1 - z_1 E)\, u_1) \otimes ((B_2 - \bar{z}_2 E)\, u_2))$$
$$= (B_1 \otimes E - \bar{z}_1 E)(B_1 \otimes E - z_1 E)^{-1}(((B_1 - z_1 E)\, u_1) \otimes ((B_2 - \bar{z}_2 E)\, u_2))$$
$$= ((B_1 - \bar{z}_1 E)\, u_1) \otimes ((B_2 - \bar{z}_2 E)\, u_2).$$

In exactly the same way we show that $U^{(2)}_{z_2} U^{(1)}_{z_1}(((B_1 - z_1E)u_1) \otimes ((B_2 - z_2E)u_2)) = ((B_1 - \bar{z}_1 E)u_1) \otimes ((B_2 - \bar{z}_2 E)u_2)$, from which the required commutativity follows.

We shall denote by X some isometric operator carrying all of N_{z_2} into all of $N_{\bar{z}_2}$. We have

$$U^{(1)}_{z_1} (U^{(2)}_{z_2} \oplus X)(\mathfrak{R}_{z_2} \oplus N_{z_2}) = U^{(1)}_{z_1} U^{(2)}_{z_2} \mathfrak{R}_{z_2} \oplus U^{(1)}_{z_1} X N_{z_2},$$
$$(U^{(2)}_{z_2} \oplus X) U^{(1)}_{z_1} (\mathfrak{R}_{z_2} \oplus N_{z_2}) = (U^{(2)}_{z_2} \oplus X)(U^{(1)}_{z_1} \mathfrak{R}_{z_2} \oplus U^{(1)}_{z_1} N_{z_2})$$
$$= U^{(2)}_{z_2} U^{(1)}_{z_1} \mathfrak{R}_{z_2} \oplus X U^{(1)}_{z_1} N_{z_2}.$$

Since on $\mathfrak{R}_{z_2}$ $U^{(1)}_{z_1}$ and $U^{(2)}_{z_2}$ commute, *then* $U^{(1)}_{z_1}$ *and* $U^{(2)}_{z_2} \oplus X$, *the extension of* $U^{(2)}_{z_2}$ *to all of* H_K, *will commute if and only if* X *is chosen so that*

$$U^{(1)}_{z_1} X f = X U^{(1)}_{z_1} f \qquad (f \in N_{z_2}). \tag{2.21}$$

But $U^{(1)}_{z_1} = \int_{-\infty}^{\infty}((\lambda - \bar{z}_1)/(\lambda - z_1))dE_\lambda$, so that this last commutativity follows from the equation

$$E(\Delta) X f = X E(\Delta) f \qquad (f \in N_{z_2}), \tag{2.22}$$

Here Δ is any Borel set (this equation has meaning since N_{z_2} and $N_{\bar{z}_2}$ are invariant relative to $E(\Delta)$). Now we choose X in such a way that (2. 22) is satisfied.

The operator C_2 is real relative to the involution $\circ$, so that C_2^* is real as well. Accordingly, if $C_2^*\phi = z\phi$, then $C_2^*(\phi^\circ) = \bar{z}\phi^\circ$, i.e. $(N_{z_2})^\circ = N_{\bar{z}_2}$. Further, C_1 is also real relative to $\circ$ so that any $E(\Delta)$ is also real. Fix $f_1 \in N_{z_2}$, and consider the linear span of the vectors $E(\Delta)f_1$ for arbitrary Borel sets Δ, denoting this by $N_{z_2}^{(1)}$. Clearly $f_1 \subseteq N_{z_2}^{(1)} \subseteq N_{z_2}$. If $N_{z_2}^{(1)}$ does not exhaust all of N_{z_2}, we consider a vector $f_2 \in N_{z_2}$, $f_2 \perp N_{z_1}^{(1)}$, and construct $N_{z_2}^{(2)}$ as the closure of the linear span of the vectors $E(\Delta)f_2$. Obviously $N_{z_2}^{(2)} \perp N_{z_2}^{(1)}$. If $N_{z_2}^{(1)} \oplus N_{z_2}^{(2)}$ does not exhaust N_{z_2}, we consider a vector $f_3 \in N_{z_2}$, $f_3 \perp N_{z_2}^{(1)} \oplus N_{z_2}^{(2)}$ and construct $N_{z_2}^{(3)}$ and so forth. Obviously $N_{z_2}^{(1)} \oplus N_{z_2}^{(2)} \oplus \cdots$ $\cdots = N_{z_2}$. Taking $\circ$ over this equation we obtain $(N_{z_2}^{(1)})^\circ \oplus (N_{z_2}^{(2)})^\circ \oplus \cdots =$ $(N_{z_2})^\circ = N_{\bar{z}_2}$.

Since $N_{z_2}^{(j)}$ and $(N_{z_2}^{(j)})^\circ$ are invariant relative to any $E(\Delta)$, then for the construction of the operator X it suffices to construct an operator which carries all of $N_{z_2}^{(j)}$ isometrically into all of $(N_{z_2}^{(j)})^\circ$ and satisfies (2. 22) for $f \in N_{z_2}^{(j)}$, $(j = 1, 2, \cdots)$. It suffices to define it on vectors of the form $f = \Sigma_{k=1}^n c_k E(\Delta_k) f_j$: we put $X(\Sigma_{k=1}^n c_k E(\Delta_k) f_j) = \Sigma_{k=1}^n c_k E(\Delta_k) f_j^\circ = (\Sigma_{k=1}^n \bar{c}_k E(\Delta_k) f_j)^\circ \in (N_{z_2}^{(j)})^\circ$. We have

$$\left\langle X\left(\sum_{k=1}^n c_k E(\Delta_k) f_j\right),\ X\left(\sum_{l=1}^n d_l E(\Delta_l) f_j\right)\right\rangle$$

$$= \left\langle \left(\sum_{k=1}^n \bar{c}_k E(\Delta_k) f_j\right)^\circ,\ \left(\sum_{l=1}^n \bar{d}_l E(\Delta_l) f_j\right)^\circ\right\rangle$$

$$= \overline{\left\langle \sum_{k=1}^n \bar{c}_k E(\Delta_k) f_j,\ \sum_{l=1}^n \bar{d}_l E(\Delta_l) f_j \right\rangle} = \sum_{k,l=1}^n c_k \bar{d}_l\ \overline{\langle E(\Delta_k) f_j, E(\Delta_l) f_j \rangle}$$

$$= \sum_{k,l=1}^n c_k \bar{d}_l\ \overline{\langle E(\Delta_k \cap \Delta_l) f_j, f_j \rangle} = \sum_{k,l=1}^n c_k \bar{d}_l \langle E(\Delta_k) f_j, E(\Delta_l) f_j \rangle$$

$$= \left\langle \sum_{k=1}^n c_k E(\Delta_k) f_j,\ \sum_{l=1}^n d_l E(\Delta_l) f_j \right\rangle$$

This equation on the one hand shows that X is correctly defined: if $\Sigma_{k=1}^n c_k E(\Delta_k) f_j = 0$, then $(\Sigma_{k=1}^n \bar{c}_k E(\Delta_k) f_j)^\circ = 0$. On the other hand, it implies the isometricity of X. Further, it is clear that X carries all of $N_{z_2}^{(j)}$ into all of $(N_{z_2}^{(j)})^\circ$. Finally,

$$E(\Delta)X\left(\sum_{k=1}^n c_k E(\Delta_k) f_j\right) = E(\Delta)\sum_{k=1}^n c_k E(\Delta_k) f_j^\circ = \sum_{k=1}^n c_k E(\Delta \cap \Delta_k) f_j^\circ,$$

$$X\left(E(\Delta)\sum_{k=1}^n c_k E(\Delta_k) f_j\right) = X\left(\sum_{k=1}^n c_k E(\Delta \cap \Delta_k) f_j\right)$$

$$= \sum_{k=1}^n c_k E(\Delta \cap \Delta_k) f_j^\circ,$$

i. e. (2. 22) is satisfied on $f = \Sigma_{k=1}^n c_k E(\Delta_k) f_j$ and thus on all of $N_{z_2}^{(j)}$ as well. The required vector X, and thus the extension of $U_{z_2}^{(2)}$ to a unitary operator commuting with $U_{z_1}^{(1)}$, has thus been constructed.

To the extension of the operator $U_{z_2}^{(2)}$ corresponds the selfadjoint extension of the operator C_2. The commutativity of this extension with the closure of C_1 follows from

Lemma 2. 4. *Suppose that in a Hilbert space H there operate two selfadjoint operators S_1 and S_2. For S_1 and S_2 to commute it is necessary and sufficient that their Cayley transforms $U_{z_1}^{(1)}$ and $U_{z_2}^{(2)}$ commute for fixed nonreal z_1, z_2.*

Indeed, the resolvent of an operator is expressed in terms of its Cayley transform by the formula $R_z = (1/(z-\bar{z}))(U_z - E)$. Therefore the commutativity of the Cayley transforms $U_{z_1}^{(1)}$ and $U_{z_2}^{(2)}$ is equivalent to the commutativity of the resolvents $R_{z_1}^{(1)}$ and $R_{z_2}^{(2)}$. From here we use Lemma 2. 1. The lemma is proved.

Note that the requirement of the presence of an involution $\circ$ and the reality of C_1, C_2 were used only in the construction of the operator X satisfying (2. 21). If under other hypotheses the operator X may be chosen in some way or other then these requirements become superfluous. The following theorem in a certain sense is one of the realizations of this remark.

Theorem 2. 7. *Suppose that the operator C_1 is such that the closure of its restriction to the set $\mathfrak{D}(B_1) \otimes w_2$ for any $w_2 \in H_+^{(2)}$ is selfadjoint in the space $H_{K;\, w_2}^{(1)}$. Suppose that the operator C_2 has a real point of regular type.*

Then there exists a selfadjoint extension of the operator C_2, *commuting with the closure of* C_1.

Proof. Consider the Cayley transform $U^{(1)}_{z_1}$ of C_1 for a fixed nonreal z_1. This operator, after closure, turns into a unitary operator in H_K. Suppose that λ_2 is a real point of regular type of C_2 and that the operator $R^{(2)}_{\lambda_2} = (C_2 - \lambda_2 E)^{-1}$ is a bounded Hermitian operator operating from the set $H^{(1)}_+ \otimes ((B_2 - \lambda_2 E)\mathfrak{D}(B_2))$, not dense in H_K, to the dense set $H^{(1)}_+ \otimes \mathfrak{D}(B_2)$. If we succeed in extending this operator to some bounded selfadjoint operator $\widetilde{R}^{(2)}_{\lambda_2}$ defined on all of H_K and commuting with $U^{(1)}_{z_1}$, then this gives rise to an extension $\widetilde{C}_2$ of C_2 to a selfadjoint one, whose resolvent at the point λ_2 will be equal to $\widetilde{R}^{(2)}_{\lambda_2}$. Indeed, we need to put $\widetilde{C}_2 = (\widetilde{R}^{(2)}_{\lambda_2})^{-1} + \lambda_2 E$. We explain that $(\widetilde{R}^{(2)}_{\lambda_2})^{-1}$ exists as an unbounded operator, since from $\widetilde{R}^{(2)}_{\lambda_2} f = 0$ it follows that $f = 0$; if $g \in H^{(1)}_+ \otimes ((B_2 - \lambda_2 E)\mathfrak{D}(B_2))$, then $0 = \langle \widetilde{R}^{(2)}_{\lambda_2} f, g\rangle = \langle f, \widetilde{R}^{(2)}_{\lambda_2} g\rangle = \langle f, R^{(2)}_{\lambda_2} g\rangle$, where $R^{(2)}_{\lambda_2} g$ runs through the set $H^{(1)}_K \otimes \mathfrak{D}(B_2)$, which is dense in H_K; because of its density $f = 0$. The extension $\widetilde{C}_2$ will commute with C_1, since the commutativity of $U^{(1)}_{z_1}$ and $\widetilde{R}^{(2)}_{\lambda_2}$ implies the commutativity of $R^{(1)}_{z_1} = (1/(z_1 - \bar{z}_1))(U^{(1)}_{z_1} - E)$ and $\widetilde{R}^{(2)}_{\lambda_2}$.

For what follows we note that the subspaces $\mathfrak{R}_{\lambda_2} = [H^{(1)}_+ \otimes ((B_2 - \lambda_2 E)\mathfrak{D}(B_2))]$ and $N_{\lambda_2} = H_K \ominus R_{\lambda_2}$ are invariant subspaces for the operator $U^{(1)}_{z_1}$ and that it is unitary in them. The proof of this is exactly the same as that of the corresponding assertion in the proof of the previous theorem.

Now we shall establish the following general lemmas.

Lemma 2.5. *Suppose that in the Hilbert space* $G = G_1 \oplus G_2$ *constructed relative to the Hilbert spaces* G_1 *and* G_2, *there operates a continuous Hermitian operator* S *with a nondense region of definition* G_1. *Then there exists a selfadjoint continuous extension* T *of this operator to the entire space* H. *All such extensions may be described by the formulas*

$$Tf = T_X f = Sf_1 + Qf_2 + Xf_2 \qquad (f = f_1 + f_2;\ f_1 \in G_1,\ f_2 \in G_2). \quad (2.23)$$

Here Q *is a fixed operator operating from* G_2 *to* G_1 *and adjoint to the operator* $P_2 S$ *operating from* G_1 *to* G_2, P_2 *being the orthogonal projection operator onto* G_2; *and* X *is any continuous selfadjoint operator operating in the space* G_2.

Proof. Suppose that the required extension T exists. Let us find its form.

Since

$$Tf = Sf_1 + P_1TP_2f_2 + P_2TP_2f_2 \tag{2.24}$$

(P_1 is the orthogonal projector onto G_1), then since T and S are Hermitian we obtain

$$0 = (Tf, g)_H - (f, Tg)_H = (Sf_1 + P_1Tf_2 + P_2Tf_2, g_1 + g_2)_H$$
$$- (f_1 + f_2, Sg_1 + P_1Tg_2 + P_2Tg_2)_H = (P_2Sf_1, g_2)_H - (f_1, P_1TP_2g_2)_H$$
$$+ (P_1TP_2f_2, g_1)_H - (f_2, P_2Sg_1)_H + (P_2TP_2f_2, g_2)_H - (f_2, P_2TP_2g_2)_H. \tag{2.25}$$

Now putting first $f_2 = 0$, and then $f_1 = g_1 = 0$, we find $P_1TP_2 = (P_2S)^*$, $P_2TP_2 = (P_2TP_2)^*$. Comparing (2.23) and (2.24), we find that $Q = P_1TP_2 = (P_2S)^*$; the operator $X = P_2TP_2 = (P_2TP_2)^*$ is selfadjoint in G_2. Thus if the required extension exists it has the form (2.23). Conversely formula (2.23) obviously defines some continuous extension of S onto all of H; regarding the equation (2.25) in the opposite direction, we verify that this extension is Hermitian. The lemma is proved.

Lemma 2.6. *Suppose that the hypotheses of Lemma 2.5 are fulfilled, and moreover that there operates in the space H a unitary operator U for which G_1 and G_2 are invariant and which commutes with S: $SUf_1 = USf_1$ $(f_1 \in G_1)$. All the selfadjoint extensions to H of the operator S which commute with U may be described by the earlier formula (2.23), in which one simply takes as X any continuous operator selfadjoint in G_2 and commuting with the portion of U in G_2.*

Proof. Suppose that X commutes with U in G_2. We shall show that T_X commutes with U. From (2.23) and the commutativity of S with U it follows that we need only verify the equation $QUf_2 = UQf_2$ $(f_2 \in G_2)$. Noting that $Q = (P_2S)^*$, for arbitrary $f_2 \in G_2$, $f_1 \in G_1$ we obtain $(Qf_2, f_1)_H = (f_2, P_2Sf_1)_H = (f_2, Sf_1)_H$. Hence $(QUf_2, f_1)_H = (Uf_2, Sf_1)_H = (f_2, U^{-1}Sf_1)_H = (f_2, SU^{-1}f_1)_H = (Qf_2, U^{-1}f_1)_H = (UQf_2, f_1)_H$ $(f_1 \in G_1, f_2 \in G_2)$, i.e. $QUf_2 = UQf_2$ $(f_2 \in G_2)$ as required.

Conversely, if T_X commutes with U, then in particular $QUf_2 + XUf_2 = T_XUf_2 = UT_Xf_2 = UQf_2 + UXf_2$ $(f_2 \in G_2)$. Taking account of the invariance of G_1 and G_2 relative to U, we conclude from the last equation that $XUf_2 = UXf_2$. Thus X commutes with U in G_2. The lemma is proved.

We shall complete the proof of the theorem. We apply Lemma 2.6, putting

$H = H_K$, $G_1 = \Re_{\lambda_2}$, $G_2 = N_{\lambda_2}$, $U = U_{z_1}^{(1)}$ and S equal to the closure of the operator $R_{\lambda_2}^{(2)} = (C_2 - \lambda_2 E)^{-1}$. In order to apply it we need to verify the commutativity of $U_{z_1}^{(1)}$ and $U_{z_2}^{(2)}$ in Theorem 2.6. If we now put $X = E$ in (2.23), then the required commutativity of X with $U_{z_1}^{(1)}$ in N_λ will be satisfied and we obtain an extension of $R_{\lambda_2}^{(2)}$, commuting with $U_{z_1}^{(1)}$. This completes the proof of the theorem.

From the proofs of Theorems 2.6 and 2.7 it is easy to see that all the selfadjoint extensions of C_2 in H_K which commute with the closure of C_1 (we shall refer to them as admissible) may be described. The following theorem holds.

Theorem 2.8. *Suppose that the closure of the restriction of the operator C_1 to the set $\mathfrak{D}(B_1) \otimes w_2$ for any $w_2 \in H_+^{(2)}$ is selfadjoint in the space $H_{K;w_2}^{(1)}$, and that the operator C_2 is any operator of type (2.3). Denote by $U_z^{(1)}$ and $U_\zeta^{(2)}$ the Cayley transforms for C_1 and C_2 respectively in the space H_K. $U_z^{(1)}$ after closure is a unitary operator in H_+, for which any defect subspace N_ζ of C_2 is invariant. Fix nonreal z_1 and z_2. The Cayley transforms $\widetilde{U}_{z_2}^{(2)}$ of the admissible extensions of C_2 have the form $\widetilde{U}_{z_2}^{(2)} = U_{z_2}^{(2)} \oplus X$, where X is any operator isometrically mapping all of N_{z_2} onto all of $N_{\bar{z}_2}$ and commuting with $U_{z_1}^{(1)}$:*

$$U_{z_1}^{(1)} X f = X U_{z_1}^{(1)} f \quad (f \in N_{z_2}). \tag{2.26}$$

Suppose that the conditions of the first part of the theorem are satisfied and that in addition C_2 has a real point λ_2 of regular type. Put $R_{\lambda_2}^{(2)} = (C_2 - \lambda_2 E)^{-1}$. The closure G_1 of the region of definition of this operator and the orthogonal complement G_2 to it are invariant subspaces for $U_z^{(1)}$. Fix a nonreal z_1. The resolvent $\widetilde{R}_{\lambda_2}^{(2)}$ of the admissible extensions of C_2 has the form

$$\widetilde{R}_{\lambda_2}^{(2)} f = R_{\lambda_2}^{(2)} f_1 + R f_2 + X f_2 \quad (f = f_1 + f_2 \in H_K;\ f_1 \in G_1, f_2 \in G_2). \tag{2.27}$$

Here R is a fixed operator operating from G_2 to G_1 and adjoint to the operator $P_2 R_{\lambda_2}^{(2)}$ from G_1 to G_2 (P_2 is the orthogonal projector onto G_2), and X is any selfadjoint operator in G_2 commuting with $U_{z_1}^{(1)}$.

Theorem 2.6 essentially reduces to the fact that in the presence of the involution $\circ$ and with real C_1 and C_2 one may construct an X satisfying (2.26), and Theorem 2.7 to the fact that X may always be constructed from (2.7), putting $X = E$.

Some further remarks. The selfadjointness of the closure of the restriction of C_1 to $\mathfrak{D}(B_1) \otimes w_2$ in the space $H^{(1)}_{K;\, w_2}$, necessary for the application of Theorems 2. 6, may be verified by means of Lemma 2. 2. From the proof of these theorems it is clear that instead of that requirement we may require somewhat less: the closure of the restriction of C_1 to $\mathfrak{D}(B_1) \otimes ((B_2 - z_2 E)\mathfrak{D}(B_2))$ or to $\mathfrak{D}(B_1) \otimes ((B_2 - \lambda_2 E)\mathfrak{D}(B_2))$ is selfadjoint in the space $[H^{(1)}_+ \otimes ((B_2 - z_2 E)\mathfrak{D}(B_2))]$ or $[H^{(1)}_+ \otimes ((B_2 - \lambda_2 E)\mathfrak{D}(B_2))]$. As to the necessity of the involution $^- = {}^-_1 \otimes {}^-_2$, one may make the same remark as at the end of subsection 2.

§3. CONTINUOUS POSITIVE DEFINITE KERNELS, *-COMMUTING WITH ONE DIFFERENTIAL OPERATOR

Now we consider applications of the results of the preceding two sections. For simplicity we shall investigate the case of continuous p. d. kernels. The case of discontinuous and generalized kernels may be studied analogously. In this section we suppose that $q = 1$ and that A is a differential operator.

1. **General differential expression.** Suppose that $G \subseteq E_n$ is some region of n-dimensional space with boundary Γ, $K(x, y) \in C(G \times G)$ a kernel. We recall that this kernel is said to be p. d. if for any points $x_1, \cdots, x_N \in G$ and arbitrary complex numbers $\xi_1, \cdots, \xi_N$

$$\sum_{j,k=1}^{N} K(x_j, x_k)\, \xi_k \bar{\xi}_j \geqslant 0. \tag{3. 1}$$

It is easy to verify that condition (3. 1) is equivalent to the requirement

$$B_K(u, u) \geqslant 0 \ (u \in C_0^\infty(G)); \ B_K(u, v) = \langle u, v \rangle$$
$$= \iint_{GG} K(x, y)\, u(y)\, \overline{v(x)}\, dxdy \qquad (u, v \in C_0^\infty(G)). \tag{3. 2}$$

From (3. 1) it follows that $K(x, x) \geq 0$ and $|K(x, y)|^2 \leq K(x, x)K(y, y)$ $\quad (x, y \in G)$.

Select a function $p(x) \in C^\infty(G)$, $p(x) \geq 1$ $(x \in G)$ which as $x \to \Gamma$ and ∞ increases so rapidly that

$$\int_G \frac{K(x, x)}{p(x)}\, dx < \infty. \tag{3. 3}$$

Then $K \in L_2(G \times G;\, p^{-1}(x)p^{-1}(y)\, dx\, dy)$. In all of what follows we shall suppose $H_0 = L_2(G)$. Now we have proved that if we put $H_+ = L_2(G, pdx)$, where $p(x)$ is selected from condition (3.3), then $K \in H_- \otimes H_-$. The space H_K now coincides with the completion of $L_2(G, pdx)$ (or $C_0^\infty(G)$) relative to the scalar product (3.2) (possibly after preparatory identification).

We suppose that in G the expression

$$Lu = \sum_{|\alpha| \leq r} a_\alpha(x) D^\alpha u$$

is defined, where $a_\alpha \in C^{|\alpha|}(G)$. Let Λ be the minimal operator in $L_2(G)$ corresponding to it (i.e. the closure of the operator $u \to Lu$, $u \in C_0^\infty(G)$). As the operator A of §1 we take Λ. We take as an involution in $L_2(G)$ the usual passage to the complex conjugate. The operator Λ of course admits an extension of its equipment; as $Д$ we may take $C_0^\infty(G)$, topologized in a suitable way. The operator Λ^* adjoint to Λ in $L_2(G)$ coincides with $Л^+$, the maximal operator constructed relative to L^+, its restriction to $Д = C_0^\infty(G)$ (i.e. $C = B$; see §2.1) with the action here of Λ^+, i.e. with the relationship $u \to L^+u$ $(u \in C_0^\infty(G))$. Because of what was said in §1.1, *-commutativity of K and A is equivalent to the equation

$$\langle L^+ u, v \rangle = \langle u, L^+ v \rangle \quad (u, v \in C_0^\infty(G)), \quad \text{i.e. } L_x K = \overline{L}_y K \tag{3.4}$$

(the second equation is satisfied within $G \times G$; if $K \in W_{2,\mathrm{loc}}^r(G \times G)$, then it must be understood in the sense of the generalized functions of L. Schwartz; the corresponding identity evidently coincides with the first of the equations (3.4)).

We construct the space H_{++} so that the imbedding $H_{++} \to H_+$ is quasinuclear. Using the remark at the end of Chapter V, §3, we choose $(u, v)_{++} = (u\sqrt{p}, v\sqrt{p})_{\mathfrak{H}}$, where $\mathfrak{H} \subset L_2(G)$ is such that the imbedding $\mathfrak{H} \to L_2(G)$ is quasinuclear. We may put $\mathfrak{H} = W_2^{(l,q)}(G)$. Here $l > n/2$, and the integral (3.17) of Chapter I converges for $q(x)$. As a result we find that as H_{++} we may adopt the space $W_2^{(l,q)}(G)$, where $l > n/2$, and $s(x) = \sqrt{p(x)}\, q(x)$, i.e. $s \in C^\infty(G)$, $s(x) \geq 1$ $(x \in G)$ and

$$\int_G \frac{p(x) A^2(x)}{s^2(x)} dx < \infty \tag{3.5}$$

(the function $A(x)$ was introduced in Chapter I, §3.3). Evidently $Д \subset H_{++}$. Thus,

$$Д' \supseteq H_{--} \supseteq H_- \supseteq H_0 \supseteq H_+ \supseteq H_{++} \supseteq Д.$$

The definition of the family of elementary p. d. kernels figuring in Theorem 1.1 is now as follows. Suppose that the coefficients $a_\alpha \in C^{|\alpha|+l}(G)$. The p. d. kernels $\Omega_\lambda \in W_2^{-(l,s)}(G) \otimes W_2^{-(l,s)}(G)$ ($\|\Omega_\lambda\|_{W_2^{-(l,s)}(G)\otimes W_2^{-(l,s)}(G)} \leq C < \infty$) form a family of elementary p. d. kernels, if within $G \times G$

$$L_x \Omega_\lambda = \lambda\Omega_\lambda, \qquad \bar{L}_y \Omega_\lambda = \lambda\Omega_\lambda,$$

i. e.

$$(\Omega_\lambda, ((L^+ - \lambda E)\, v)(x)\, \overline{u(y)})_0 = 0, \quad (\Omega_\lambda, v(x)\, \overline{((L^+ - \lambda E)\, u)(y)})_0 = 0$$
$$(u, v \in C_0^\infty(G)). \tag{3.6}$$

We formulate Theorem 1.1 for the special case in question.

Theorem 3.1. *Suppose that $K(x, y) \in C(G \times G)$ is a p. d. kernel, that $p, s \in C^\infty(G)$ ($p(x), s(x) \geq 1$, $x \in G$) are chosen from the condition that the integrals* (3.3) *and* (3.5) *converge, and that the coefficients L $a_\alpha(x) \in C^{|\alpha|+l}(G)$ $(l > n/2)$. In order that the representation*

$$K = \int_{-\infty}^{\infty} \Omega_\lambda \, d\rho(\lambda), \tag{3.7}$$

should hold, where $\Omega_\lambda W_2^{-(l,s)}(G) \otimes W_2^{-(l,s)}(G)$ is some family of elementary p. d. kernels, $d\rho(\lambda)$ is a nonnegative finite measure, and the integral (3.7) *converges in the norm of the space $W_2^{-(l,s)}(G) \otimes W_2^{-(l,s)}(G)$, it is necessary and sufficient that relations* (3.4) *should hold. In* (3.7) *$\Omega_\lambda d\rho(\lambda)$ is defined uniquely if and only if the closure in H_K of the operator $u \to L^+ u$ $(u \in C_0^\infty(G))$ is maximal.*

2. **Case of elliptic expressions.** We suppose that L is elliptic with sufficiently smooth coefficients. Then Theorem 3.1 may be substantially improved. Thus, suppose that $a_\alpha \in C^{|\alpha|+r+l+1}$. From equations (3.6), using Theorem 4.4 of Chapter III, we conclude that Ω_λ in each region which is bounded and strictly interior relative to $G \times G$ lies in $W_2^{r+l+1} \otimes W_2^{r+l+1}$, and moreover is summable in it. Applying Theorem 4.2 of Chapter III, we find that the derivatives $(D_x^\alpha D_y^\beta \Omega_\lambda)(x, y)$, for $|\alpha|, |\beta| \leq r + l + 1$ exist and are continuous relative to the point $(x, y) \in (G \times G)$.

Lemma 3.1. *For any $x, y \in G$,*

$$\int_{-\infty}^{\infty} |\Omega_\lambda(x, y)| \, d\rho(\lambda) \leqslant \sqrt{K(x, x)\, K(y, y)}. \tag{3.8}$$

Proof. From (3.7), for $u, v \in C_0^\infty(G)$ we have

$$\iint\limits_{GG} K(x, y) u(y) \overline{v(x)}\, dxdy = \int\limits_{-\infty}^{\infty} \iint\limits_{GG} \Omega_\lambda(x, y) u(y) \overline{v(x)}\, dxdyd\varrho(\lambda). \quad (3.9)$$

Suppose that $\kappa_\nu(x) \geq 0$ is a singular sequence of functions of $C_0^\infty(G)$, converging to δ_{x_0}. Put $u = v = \kappa_\nu$ in (3.9). Since for $\nu \to \infty$

$$0 \leqslant \iint\limits_{GG} \Omega_\lambda(x, y) \varkappa_\nu(y) \varkappa_\nu(x)\, dxdy \to \Omega_\lambda(x_0, x_0),$$

then, from Fatou's lemma, equation (3.9), and the continuity of the kernel $K(x, y)$ we obtain

$$\int\limits_{-\infty}^{\infty} \Omega_\lambda(x_0, x_0)\, d\varrho(\lambda) \leqslant \lim_{\nu\to\infty} \int\limits_{-\infty}^{\infty} \iint\limits_{GG} \Omega_\lambda(x, y) \varkappa_\nu(y) \varkappa_\nu(x)\, dxdyd\varrho(\lambda)$$

$$= \lim_{\nu\to\infty} \iint\limits_{GG} K(x, y) \varkappa_\nu(y) \varkappa_\nu(x)\, dxdy = K(x_0, x_0).$$

Applying this inequality to the p. d. kernel $\Omega_\lambda(x, y)$, we obtain for $x_0, y_0 \in G$

$$\left(\int\limits_{-\infty}^{\infty} |\Omega_\lambda(x_0, y_0)|\, d\varrho(\lambda)\right)^2 \leqslant \left(\int\limits_{-\infty}^{\infty} \sqrt{\Omega_\lambda(x_0, x_0)}\, \sqrt{\Omega_\lambda(y_0, y_0)}\, d\varrho(\lambda)\right)^2$$

$$\leqslant \int\limits_{-\infty}^{\infty} \Omega_\lambda(x_0, x_0)\, d\varrho(\lambda) \cdot \int\limits_{-\infty}^{\infty} \Omega_\lambda(y_0, y_0)\, d\varrho(\lambda) \leqslant K(x_0, x_0) K(y_0, y_0), \quad (3.10)$$

i. e. (3.8). The lemma is proved.

It follows from the lemma that in the elliptic case the integral (3.7) converges absolutely for any $x, y \in G$. The function $\Omega_\lambda(x, y)$ of the point (x, y, λ) is summable relative to the measure $dx\, dy\, d\rho(\lambda)$ in the region $G' \times G' \times (-\infty, \infty)$, where $G' \subseteq G$ is any bounded subregion lying strictly within G.

Theorem 3.1 may now be so formulated that the space $H_{--} \otimes H_{--} = W_2^{-(l, s)}(G) \otimes W_2^{-(l, s)}(G)$ does not figure in it.

Theorem 3.2. *Suppose that L is an elliptic expression whose coefficients are $a_\alpha(x) \in C^{|\alpha|+r+l+1}(G)$ $(l > n/2)$. The family of p. d. kernels $\Omega_\lambda(x, y)$ $(x, y \in G)$ will be called a family of elementary p. d. kernels, if the derivatives $(D_x^\alpha D_y^\beta \Omega_\lambda)(x, y)$ $(|\alpha|, |\beta| \leq r + l + 1)$ exist and are continuous relative to $(x, y) \in (G \times G)$ and if the first two equations in (3.6) hold.*

In order that the p. d. kernel $K(x, y) \in C(G \times G)$ be representable in the *form of an absolutely convergent integral*

$$K(x, y) = \int_{-\infty}^{\infty} \Omega_\lambda(x, y)\, d\rho(\lambda) \qquad (x, y \in G), \tag{3.11}$$

where $d\rho(\lambda)$ *is a nonnegative finite measure and* $\Omega_\lambda(x, y)$ *is some family of elementary p. d. kernels, it is necessary and sufficient that relation* (3.4) *be satisfied.* $\Omega_\lambda d\rho(\lambda)$ *in* (3.11) *is uniquely defined if and only if the closure in* H_K *of the operator* $u \to L^+(u)$ $(u \in C_0^\infty(G))$ *is maximal.*

Proof. Suppose that K is such that (3.4) holds. From Theorem 3.1 and Lemma 3.1 representation (3.7) holds, in which the integral converges absolutely, i.e. (3.11) is valid. Conversely, suppose the representation (3.11) holds. Putting in it $y = x$, we find that $K(x, x) = \int_{-\infty}^{\infty} \Omega_\lambda(x, x) d\rho(\lambda)$ $(x \in G)$. Hence analogously to (3.10) we conclude that $\Omega_\lambda(x, y)$ is summable over the set $(x, y, \lambda) \in G' \times G' \times (-\infty, \infty)$ (G' lies inside G and is bounded) relative to the measure $dx\,dy\,d\rho(\lambda)$. Because of this the following calculation is legitimate, proving (3.4):

$$\langle L^+ u, v \rangle = \iint_{GG} \left\{ \int_{-\infty}^{\infty} \Omega_\lambda(x, y)\, d\rho(\lambda) \right\} (L^+ u)(y) \overline{v(x)}\, dx dy$$

$$= \int_{-\infty}^{\infty} \left\{ \iint_{GG} \Omega_\lambda(x, y) (L^+ u)(y) \overline{v(x)}\, dx dy \right\} d\rho(\lambda)$$

$$= \int_{-\infty}^{\infty} \left\{ \iint_{GG} (\bar{L}_y \Omega_\lambda)(x, y)\, u(y) \overline{v(x)}\, dx dy \right\} d\rho(\lambda)$$

$$= \int_{-\infty}^{\infty} \left\{ \iint_{GG} (L_x \Omega_\lambda)(x, y)\, u(y) \overline{v(x)}\, dx dy \right\} d\rho(\lambda)$$

$$= \int_{-\infty}^{\infty} \left\{ \iint_{GG} \Omega_\lambda(x, y)\, u(y) \overline{(L^+ v)(x)}\, dx dy \right\} d\rho(\lambda) = \langle u, L^+ v \rangle$$

$$(u, v \in C_0^\infty(G)).$$

We now prove the last assertion of the theorem. It is established just as on page 616, given only that the following analog of Lemma 1.1 has been established. Suppose that we have the representation (3.11); $\Delta \subseteq (-\infty, \infty)$ is a Borel set. The bilinear forms $B_\Delta(u, v) = \int_\Delta \{\int_G \int_G \Omega_\lambda(x, y) \times u(y) \overline{v(x)}\, dx\, dy\} d\rho(\lambda)$ $(u, v \in C_0^\infty(G))$ are continuous in H_K and define operators $E(\Delta)$, forming generalized resolutions of the identity for the restriction of the operator Λ^* to $\mathcal{D} = C_0^\infty(G)$. The proof of this fact is exactly as that of Lemma 1. 1, it being necessary only to replace in the derivation of (1. 16) the H_{++} by $C_0^\infty(G)$ and to have in mind that $\Omega_\lambda(x, y)$ is summable relative to $dx\,dy\,d\rho(\lambda)$ over the set $(x, y, \lambda) \in G' \times G' \times (-\infty, \infty)$. The theorem is proved.

We shall study for the representations of subsection 1 the generalized resolvent R_z of a Hermitian operator $u \to L^+u$ $(u \in C_0^\infty(G))$ operating in H_K. For this we need the following supplement to Theorem 2. 2 of Chapter I.

Theorem 3. 3. *Suppose that the conditions of Theorem 2. 2 of Chapter I are satisfied, and that moreover we have the chain* $\mathfrak{H}_- \supseteq \mathfrak{H}_0 \supseteq \mathfrak{H}_+ = H_+$. *Then representation* (2. 18) *of Chapter* I *may be written also in the form*

$$B(u, v) = (\Psi, v \otimes \bar{u})_{\mathfrak{H}_0} \quad (u, v \in H_+), \tag{3.12}$$

where $\Psi \in \mathfrak{H}_- \otimes \mathfrak{H}_-$.

The proof follows immediately from (2. 18) of Chapter I and the following general fact, which we need to apply to the chains $H_- \otimes H_- \supseteq H_0 \otimes H_0 \supseteq H_+ \otimes H_+$ and $\mathfrak{H}_- \otimes \mathfrak{H}_- \supseteq \mathfrak{H}_0 \otimes \mathfrak{H}_0 \supseteq H_+ \otimes H_+$.

Lemma 3. 2. *Suppose that we have two chains with a common positive space:* $H_-^{(1)} \supseteq H_0^{(1)} \supseteq H_+^{(1)}$ *and* $H_-^{(2)} \supseteq H_0^{(2)} \supseteq H_+^{(2)} = H_+^{(1)}$. *Then to every* $\alpha \in H_-^{(1)}$ *there corresponds a* $\beta \in H_-^{(2)}$ *such that*

$$(\alpha, u)_{H_0^{(1)}} = (\beta, u)_{H_0^{(2)}} \quad (u \in H_+^{(1)}).[1] \tag{3.13}$$

Indeed, suppose that I_1 and I_2 are operators I, constructed relative to the first and second chains respectively. Then $(\alpha, u)_{H_0^{(1)}} = (\mathrm{I}_1\alpha, u)_{H_+^{(1)}} = (\mathrm{I}_1\alpha, u)_{H_+^{(2)}} = (\mathrm{I}_2^{-1}\mathrm{I}_1\alpha, u)_{H_0^{(2)}}$ $(u \in H_+^{(1)})$. Putting $\beta = \mathrm{I}_2^{-1}\mathrm{I}_1\alpha$, we obtain (3. 13). The lemma, and therefore the theorem, is proved.

Suppose that K is such that the form $\langle \cdot, \cdot \rangle$ is nondegenerate. We may apply Theorem 3. 3 to the case of the chains $H_- \supseteq H_0 \supseteq H_+$ and $\mathfrak{H}_- \supseteq \mathfrak{H}_0 \supseteq H_+$ of the type $H_{--,K} \supseteq H_K \supseteq H_{++} = W_2^{(l,s)}(G)$ and $W_2^{-(l,s)}(G) = H_{--} \supseteq H_0 = L_2(G) \supseteq H_{++} = W_2^{(l,s)}(G)$, and of the form $B(u, v) = \langle R_z u, v \rangle$ $(u, v \in W_2^{(l,s)}(G))$. As a result we obtain the representation

$$\langle R_z u, v \rangle = (\mathrm{R}_z, v(x)\overline{u(y)})_0 \quad (u, v \in C_0^\infty(G)) \tag{3.14}$$

---

[1] This fact essentially already figured in the proof of Theorem 1. 1.

with generalized kernel $\mathrm{R}_z \in W_2^{-(l,s)}(G) \otimes W_2^{-(l,s)}(G)$. We shall show that R_z within $G \times G$ is a generalized solution of the equations

$$L_x \mathrm{R}_z - z\mathrm{R}_z = K, \quad L_y^{+} \mathrm{R}_z - z\mathrm{R}_z = K. \tag{3.15}$$

Indeed, in (3.14) u may of course be replaced by $(L - zE)u$ $(u \in C_0^\infty(G))$, and we obtain

$$(\mathrm{R}_z, v(x)\overline{((L - zE)u)(x)})_0 = \langle R_z(L - zE)u, v\rangle = \langle u, v\rangle$$
$$= \int_G\int_G K(x,y)u(y)\overline{v(x)}\,dxdy = (K, v(x)\overline{u(y)})_0 \quad (u, v \in C_0^\infty(G)),$$

i.e. the second of equations (3.15). The first is proved analogously.

The proofs of relations (3.14) and (3.15) in the case of degeneracy of $\langle\cdot,\cdot\rangle$ may be left to the reader. We note only that now instead of Theorem 3.3 we need to apply the following generalization of it: suppose that the conditions of Theorem 2.2 of Chapter I are satisfied, and that we have the chain $\mathfrak{H}_- \supseteq \mathfrak{H}_0 \supseteq \mathfrak{H}_+ \supseteq H_+$ where H_+ is a subspace of $\mathfrak{H}_+$. Then representation (3.12) is valid with $\Psi \in \mathfrak{H}_- \otimes \mathfrak{H}_-$. For the proof of this fact we need to construct the chain $\mathfrak{H}'_- \supseteq \mathfrak{H}'_0 \supseteq \mathfrak{H}'_+ = H_+$, where $\mathfrak{H}'_0$ is the closure of $\mathfrak{H}'_+ = H_+$ in the metric of $\mathfrak{H}_0$. It is not hard to show that $\mathfrak{H}_-$ is isometric to the subspace of $\mathfrak{H}_-$ consisting of all $\alpha \in \mathfrak{H}_-$ which are annihilated on the orthogonal complement in $\mathfrak{H}_+$ to $\mathfrak{H}'_+$. Therefore we may apply Theorem 3.3 to the chains $H_+ \supseteq H_0 \supseteq H_-$ and $\mathfrak{H}'_- \supseteq \mathfrak{H}'_0 \supseteq \mathfrak{H}'_+ = H_+$, obtain a representation of type (3.12), and then pass to the representation with $\Psi \in \mathfrak{H}_- \otimes \mathfrak{H}_-$.

We turn again to elliptic L.

Theorem 3.4. *Suppose that the conditions of Theorem* 3.2 *are satisfied,* R_z *is a generalized resolvent of the Hermitian operator* $u \to L^+u$ $(u \in C_0^\infty(G))$, *operating in* H_K. *Then the generalized kernel* R_z *of the resolvent* R_z *is in reality sufficiently smooth: the derivatives* $D_x^\alpha D_y^\beta \mathrm{R}_z$ *exist and are continuous relative to* $(x, y) \in G \times G$, *where* $|\alpha| \le q'$, $|\beta| \le r + q'' - 1$ *or* $|\alpha| \le r + q' - 1$, $|\beta| \le q''$, *given only that the derivatives* $D_x^\alpha D_y^\beta K$ $(|\alpha| \le q' \le l + 1,\ |\beta| \le q'' \le l + 1)$ (*therefore for* $q', q'' \ge 1$ *equation* (3.15) *is satisfied in the usual sense*). *Representation* (3.14) *may be written in the form*

$$\langle R_z u, v\rangle = \int_G\int_G R(x, y; z)\,u(y)\overline{v(x)}\,dxdy \quad (u, v \in C_0(G)));\ \mathrm{R}_z = R(\cdot, \cdot; z). \tag{3.16}$$

Moreover,

$$R(x, y; z) = \overline{R(y, x; \bar{z})}, \quad R(x, y; z) = \int_{-\infty}^{\infty} \frac{\Omega_\lambda(x, y)}{\lambda - z}\, d\varrho(\lambda),$$

$$\int_\Delta \Omega_\lambda(x, y)\, d\varrho(\lambda) = \lim_{\varepsilon \to +0} \frac{1}{\pi} \int_{\Delta + i\varepsilon} \operatorname{Im} R(x, y; z)\, dz \quad (x, y \in G). \tag{3.17}$$

Proof. We apply to the generalized kernel R_z, satisfying (3.15), Theorem 4.4 of Chapter III. We find that R_z in every bounded strictly interior subregion of $G \times G$ lies in

$$(W_2^{q'} \otimes W_2^{r+q''-1}) \cup (W_2^{r+q'-1} \otimes W_2^{q''})$$

and moreover is summable in it. Therefore we may apply also Theorem 4.2 of Chapter III, in view of which the derivatives $D_x^\alpha D_y^\beta R_z$ indicated in the formulation of the theorem exist and are continuous relative to $(x, y) \in G \times G$. The portion of the theorem dealing with the smoothness of R_z is thus established.

The first of equations (3.17) follows from (3.16) and the fact that $R_z^* = R_{\bar{z}}$, and the third from the second. Let us establish the second. It follows from (3.8) that the integral in this equation converges and the following transformations are legitimate:

$$\int_G \int_G R(x, y; z)\, u(y) \overline{v(x)}\, dx dy = \langle R_z u, v \rangle = \int_{-\infty}^{\infty} \frac{1}{\lambda - z}\, d \langle E_\lambda u, v \rangle,$$

$$= \int_{-\infty}^{\infty} \frac{1}{\lambda - z} \left\{ \int_G \int_G \Omega_\lambda(x, y)\, u(y) \overline{v(x)}\, dx dy \right\} d\varrho(\lambda)$$

$$= \int_G \int_G \left\{ \int_{-\infty}^{\infty} \frac{\Omega_\lambda(x, y)}{\lambda - z}\, d\varrho(\lambda) \right\} u(y) \overline{v(x)}\, dx dy \quad (u, v \in C_0^\infty(G)).$$

Therefore the second of equations (3.17) holds. The theorem is proved.

We can arrive at representations of the resolvent (3.14) and (3.16) also in other situations. Indeed, in subsection 7 it will be shown that the spaces H_K contain δ_ξ, i.e. the δ-function concentrated at the point $\xi \in G$. If in (3.14) as u and v one chooses δ-sequences u_ν, v_ν pulling into δ_η and δ_ξ respectively (i.e. sequences of functions of $C_0^\infty(G)$ which approximate δ_η and δ_ξ respectively in H_K), then we find that the limit $\lim_{\nu\to\infty} (R_z, v_\nu(x) \overline{u_\nu(y)})_0 =$

$\lim_{\nu\to\infty}\langle R_z u_\nu, v_\nu\rangle = \langle R_z \delta_\eta, \delta_\xi\rangle$ exists. This shows that *the kernel* R_z *in the case of a general expression* L *is the ordinary one* (it is true that we will then be unable to prove sufficient smoothness in the elliptic case). A formula of the second type in (3.17) is also preserved for this kernel, but for it of course the integral will converge only in the sense of the space $W_2^{-(l,s)}(G)\otimes W_2^{-(l,s)}(G)$, and not absolutely. We shall not consider this approach further in the general case. Some details are contained in subsection 9 (formula (3.68)) and in §6.

We note also that formulas of type (3.14), (3.16) and (3.17) (the second) may be obtained also for arbitrary bounded functions of the operator $u \to L^+u$ ($u \in C_0^\infty(G)$).

In what follows we shall consider basically ordinary differential expressions L. §6 is devoted to examples for the case of partial derivatives.

3. The case of ordinary differential expressions. Suppose that G is one-dimensional, $G \subseteq E_1$, and that L is an ordinary differential expression. Theorem 3.1 is valid for all $n = 1, 2, \cdots$, and therefore it holds in our case. However, because of the fact that all the solutions of an ordinary equation are smooth, here we have also the situation described in subsection 2. More precisely, we suppose that the coefficients of L $a_\alpha \in C^{\alpha+l}(G)$, where $l \geq 1$. Applying Theorem 5.1, Chapter VI, we find that the derivatives $(D_x^\alpha D_y^\beta \Omega_\lambda)(x, y)$ for $\alpha, \beta \leq r + l$ exist and are continuous relative to $(x, y) \in G \times G$. This makes it possible to repeat all the considerations of pages 643–646, in particular to prove Lemma 3.1, and to formulate the following theorem.

Theorem 3.5. *Suppose that* L *is an ordinary differential expression whose coefficients* $a_\alpha(x) \in C^{\alpha+l}(G)$ $(l \geq 1)$. *Then all the assertions of Theorem* 3.2 *are valid for it with* $r + l + 1$ *replaced by* $r + l$.

In our earlier considerations concerning the resolvent R_z we also did not exclude the case $n = 1$. Therefore the generalized kernel R_z exists also for an ordinary L. Moreover, again applying Theorem 5.1 of Chapter VI, we prove, just as before, the analog of Theorem 3.4.

Theorem 3.6. *Suppose that* L *is an ordinary expression, whose coefficients* $a_\alpha(x) \in C^{\alpha+l}(G)$ $(l \geq 1)$. *Suppose that the* p. d. *kernel* $K(x, y)$ *is such that the derivatives* $D_x^\alpha D_y^\beta K$ *exist and are continuous relative to* $(x, y) \in G \times G$ *for* $\alpha \leq q' = 0, 1, \cdots$ *and* $\beta \leq q'' = 0, 1, \cdots$. *Then the kernel* R_z *of the resolvent is sufficiently smooth: the derivatives* $D_x^\alpha D_y^\beta K$ *exist and are continuous relative to* $(x, y) \in G \times G$, *where* $\alpha \leq r + \min(l, q')$, $\beta \leq r + \min(l, q'')$. *Equations*

(3.15) *are satisfied in the ordinary sense and relations* (3.17) *are true.*

For an ordinary expression L the representation (3.11) may be substantially improved, if one carries through a transformation of the type presented at the beginning of Chapter VI, §5.2. Indeed, suppose that $\chi_0(x;\lambda), \cdots, \chi_{r-1}(x;\lambda)$ is a fundamental system of solutions of the equation $Lu - \lambda u = 0$ $(x \in G)$ satisfying the conditions

$$\frac{d^k}{dx^k}\chi_j(x;\lambda)\bigg|_{x=a} = \delta_{jk} \qquad (j, k = 0, \ldots, r-1), \tag{3.18}$$

where a is some point of G (we are supposing that G is a finite or infinite interval).[1] Each solution u of the equation $Lu - \lambda u = 0$ may be expressed in terms of the $\chi_j(x;\lambda)$ according to the formula $u(x) = \sum_{j=0}^{r-1}(d^ju/dx^j)(a)\chi_j(x;\lambda)$ $(x \in G)$. Taking account of relations (3.6) and applying this formula twice to $\Omega_\lambda(x, y)$, we obtain

$$\Omega_\lambda(x, y) = \sum_{j=0}^{r-1}\left(\frac{\partial^j\Omega_\lambda}{\partial x^j}\right)(a, y)\,\chi_j(x;\lambda)$$

$$= \sum_{j,k=0}^{r-1}\left(\frac{\partial^{j+k}\Omega_\lambda}{\partial x^j\,\partial y^k}\right)(a, a)\,\chi_j(x;\lambda)\,\overline{\chi_k(y;\lambda)} \qquad (x, y \in G). \tag{3.19}$$

Substituting (3.19) into (3.11) and putting $d\sigma_{jk}(\lambda) = (\partial^{j+k}\Omega_\lambda/\partial x^j\,\partial x^k)(a, a)d\rho(\lambda)$, we find that

$$K(x, y) = \int_{-\infty}^{\infty}\sum_{i,k=0}^{r-1}\chi_j(x;\lambda)\,\overline{\chi_k(y;\lambda)}\,d\sigma_{jk}(\lambda) \qquad (x, y \in G). \tag{3.20}$$

Theorem 3.7. *Suppose that G is a finite or infinite interval on the axis $(-\infty, \infty)$. Let $K(x, y) \in C(G \times G)$ be a p. d. kernel, L an ordinary differential expression of order r, whose coefficients $a_\alpha(x) \in C^{\alpha+l}(G)$ $(l \geq 1)$ and $\chi_j(x;\lambda)$, $j = 0, \cdots, r-1$, be a fundamental system of solutions of the equation $Lu = \lambda u$ $(x \in G)$, satisfying the initial conditions* (3.18). *In order that the representation* (3.20) *be valid with some nonnegative matrix measure $\|d\sigma_{jk}(\lambda)\|_0^{r-1}$, it is necessary and sufficient that condition* (3.4) *be satisfied (the integral in* (3.20) *for each $x, y \in G$ converges in the sense of the space $L_2(C_r; (-\infty, \infty), \|d\sigma_{jk}(\lambda)\|_0^{r-1})$, see pages 556–557; C_r is r-dimensional complex space). The measure $\|d\sigma_{jk}(\lambda)\|_0^{r-1}$ is defined in terms of the kernel $K(x, y)$ in a unique way if and only if the closure in H_K of the operator $u \to L^+u$ $(u \in C_0^\infty(G))$ is maximal.*

[1] The fundamental system may also be chosen in any other way.

Proof. Suppose that condition (3.4) is satisfied. From Theorem 3.5 we have the representation (3.11), which means, as we just showed, that (3.20) holds as well with $d\Sigma(\lambda) = \|d\sigma_{jk}(\lambda)\|_0^{r-1}$ as constructed above. As follows from Lemma 5.1, Chapter VI, $\Sigma(\Delta)$ is a nonnegative matrix measure. It is clear as well that the convergence of the integral (3.11) implies the convergence of (3.20) in the sense of $L_2(C_r; (-\infty, \infty), d\Sigma(\lambda))$. Conversely, suppose that the representation (3.20) is valid. Put

$$\varrho(\Delta) = \sum_{j=0}^{r-1} \int_\Delta f(\lambda)\, d\sigma_{jj}(\lambda),$$

where $f(\lambda) \in C((-\infty, \infty))$ is positive and decreases so rapidly for $|\lambda| \to \infty$ that $\rho((-\infty, \infty)) < \infty$. If $\rho(\Delta) = 0$, then $\sigma_{ij}(\Delta) = 0$ $(j = 0, \cdots, r-1)$ and therefore, from the inequality $\sigma_{jk}^2(\Delta) \le \sigma_{jj}(\Delta)\sigma_{kk}(\Delta)$, we have $\Sigma(\Delta) = 0$. Therefore the matrix $\|d\sigma_{jk}(\lambda)/d\rho(\lambda)\|_0^{r-1}$ exists and is nonnegative definite, so that the kernel

$$\Omega_\lambda(x, y) = \sum_{j,k=0}^{r-1} \frac{d\sigma_{jk}(\lambda)}{d\varrho(\lambda)} \chi_j(x; \lambda)\overline{\chi_k(y; \lambda)} \quad (x, y \in G)$$

is p.d.. It is clear that the family $\Omega_\lambda(x, y)$ is a family of elementary p.d. kernels in the sense of the definition of Theorem 3.2. The representation (3.20) may now be rewritten in the form (3.11) with an absolutely converging integral. From Theorem 3.5, the kernel $K(x, y)$ satisfies (3.4), as was required.

Finally, the last assertion of the theorem follows from the fact that the expression $\Omega_\lambda(x, y)\,d\rho(\lambda)$ and the matrix $d\Sigma(\lambda)$ for fixed $\chi_j(x; \lambda)$ uniquely determine one another. The theorem is proved.

In conclusion of this subsection we observe that sufficiently strong degeneration of the form $\langle \cdot, \cdot \rangle$ implies uniqueness of the representation (3.20).

Theorem 3.8. *Suppose that the conditions of Theorem 3.7 are fulfilled. Assume that there exist r finite (relative to $(-\infty, \infty)$) linearly independent functions of bounded variation $\omega^{(0)}(x), \cdots, \omega^{(r-1)}(x)$ $(x \in G)$ such that*

$$\int_G \int_G K(x, y)\, d\omega^{(\alpha)}(y)\, d\overline{\omega^{(\alpha)}(x)} = 0 \quad (\alpha = 0, \ldots, r-1). \tag{3.21}$$

Then the closure in H_K of the operator $u \to L^+u$ $(u \in C_0^\infty(G))$ is selfadjoint, the representation (3.20) is unique and the matrix $\|\sigma_{jk}(\lambda)\|_0^{r-1}$ has at most countably many growth points (i.e. the integral (3.20) degenerates in sum).

Proof. We shall transform formula (3.20) somewhat. To this end we put $\sigma(\Delta) = \sum_{j=0}^{r-1} \sigma_{jj}(\Delta)$. Clearly all the measures $\sigma_{jk}(\Delta)$ are absolutely continuous relative to $\sigma(\Delta)$ and therefore $\Sigma'(\lambda) = \|d\sigma_{jk}(\lambda)/d\sigma(\lambda)\|_0^{r-1}$ exists and is a nonnegative matrix. Now (3. 20) takes the form

$$K(x, y) = \int_{-\infty}^{\infty} [\Sigma'(\lambda)\chi(x; \lambda), \chi(y; \lambda)]\, d\sigma(\lambda) \quad (x, y \in G), \tag{3.22}$$

where $\chi(x; \lambda)$ is the vector $(\chi_0(x; \lambda), \cdots, \chi_{r-1}(x; \lambda)) \in C_r$, and $[\cdot, \cdot]$ is the scalar product in the space C_r. Integrating (3. 22) with respect to $d\omega^{(\alpha)}(y)\, \overline{d\omega^{(\alpha)}(x)}$ and using (3. 21), we obtain

$$\int_{-\infty}^{\infty} [\Sigma'(\lambda)\widetilde{\omega}^{(\alpha)}(\lambda), \widetilde{\omega}^{(\alpha)}(\lambda)]\, d\sigma(\lambda) = 0 \quad (\alpha = 0, \ldots, r-1). \tag{3.23}$$

Here $\widetilde{\omega}^{(\alpha)}(\lambda)$ is the vector with coordinates $\widetilde{\omega}_j^{(\alpha)}(\lambda) = \int_G \chi_j(x; \lambda)\, \overline{d\omega^{(\alpha)}(x)}$ $(j = 0, \cdots, r-1)$.

As is well known from the theory of ordinary differential equations, the solution $\chi_j(x; \lambda)$ for fixed x is an entire function of the complex parameter λ. But then every integral $\widetilde{\omega}_j^{(\alpha)}$ will be the same kind of function of λ, which therefore is also the determinant $F(\lambda) = \operatorname{Det} \|\widetilde{\omega}_k^{(j)}(\lambda)\|_0^{r-1}$.

Suppose that $\mathfrak{N}$ is a countable set on $(-\infty, \infty)$, consisting of all the zeros of the function $F(\lambda)$. We shall show that $\Sigma'(\lambda) = 0$ σ-almost everywhere for $\lambda \in (-\infty, \infty)\backslash\mathfrak{N}$. Write $\tau(\lambda) = \max_{j=0,\cdots,r-1}\{\tau_j(\lambda)\}$, where $\tau_0(\lambda), \cdots, \tau_{r-1}(\lambda)$ are the eigenvalues of the matrix $\Sigma'(\lambda)$. We need to show that $\tau(\lambda) = 0$ for the indicated λ's. Suppose the contrary. Then there exists an $\epsilon_0 > 0$ and a set $\Delta \subseteq (-\infty, \infty)\backslash\mathfrak{N}$ such that $\tau(\lambda) \geq \epsilon_0$ $(\lambda \in \Delta)$ and $\sigma(\Delta) > 0$. Suppose that the point $\lambda_0 \in \Delta$ is such that for any $\delta > 0$ $\sigma((\lambda_0 - \delta, \lambda_0 + \delta) \cap \Delta) > 0$. Since $F(\lambda_0) \neq 0$, then the vectors $\widetilde{\omega}^{(\alpha)}(\lambda)$ $(\alpha = 0, \cdots, r-1)$ in some δ_0-neighborhood of the point λ_0 are linearly independent, and we may decompose in terms of them any vector of C_r. In particular, we decompose with respect to them the vector ϕ_λ, with $|\phi_\lambda| = 1$, which is an eigenvector for the matrix $\Sigma'(\lambda)$ and which corresponds to an eigenvalue $\tau_j(\lambda) = \tau_{j(\lambda)}(\lambda)$ for which $\tau(\lambda) = \tau_j(\lambda)$; here $\lambda \in (\lambda_0 - \delta_0, \lambda_0 + \delta_0) \cap \Delta$. Thus for the indicated λ $\phi_\lambda = \Sigma_{\alpha=0}^{r-1} c_\alpha(\lambda)\widetilde{\omega}^{(\alpha)}(\lambda)$ and therefore $[\Sigma'(\lambda)\phi_\lambda, \phi_\lambda] = \Sigma_{\alpha,\beta=0}^{r-1} c_\alpha(\lambda)\overline{c_\beta(\lambda)}\, [\Sigma'(\lambda)\widetilde{\omega}^{(\alpha)}(\lambda), \widetilde{\omega}^{(\beta)}(\lambda)]$. We have from (3. 23):

$$0 < \varepsilon_0\sigma((\lambda_0 - \delta_0, \lambda_0 + \delta_0) \cap \Delta) \leqslant \int_{(\lambda_0-\delta_0,\, \lambda_0+\delta_0)\cap\Delta} [\Sigma'(\lambda)\varphi_\lambda, \varphi_\lambda]\, d\sigma(\lambda)$$

$$= \sum_{\alpha,\beta=0}^{r-1} \int_{(\lambda_0-\delta_0,\, \lambda_0+\delta_0)\cap\Delta} c_\alpha(\lambda)\overline{c_\beta(\lambda)}\, [\Sigma'(\lambda)\widetilde{\omega}^{(\alpha)}(\lambda), \widetilde{\omega}^{(\beta)}(\lambda)]\, d\sigma(\lambda) \leqslant$$

$$\leqslant C \max_{\alpha,\beta} \int_{-\infty}^{\infty} |[\Sigma'(\lambda)\widetilde{\omega}^{(\alpha)}(\lambda), \widetilde{\omega}^{(\beta)}(\lambda)]|\, d\sigma(\lambda)$$

$$\leqslant C \max_{\alpha,\beta} \int_{-\infty}^{\infty} [\Sigma'(\lambda)\widetilde{\omega}^{(\alpha)}(\lambda), \widetilde{\omega}^{(\alpha)}(\lambda)]^{\frac{1}{2}} [\Sigma'(\lambda)\widetilde{\omega}^{(\beta)}(\lambda), \widetilde{\omega}^{(\beta)}(\lambda)]^{\frac{1}{2}} d\sigma(\lambda)$$

$$\leqslant C \max_{\alpha} \int_{-\infty}^{\infty} [\Sigma'(\lambda)\widetilde{\omega}^{(\alpha)}(\lambda), \widetilde{\omega}^{(\alpha)}(\lambda)]\, d\sigma(\lambda) = 0,$$

which is absurd. Above we have used the obvious estimate $|c_\alpha(\lambda)| \leq C_1 |\phi_\lambda| = C_1$. Thus $\Sigma'(\lambda) = 0$ σ-almost everywhere for $\lambda \in (-\infty, \infty) \setminus \mathfrak{N}$.

Thus the integral in the representation (3.22), and thus also in (3.20), is replaced by a sum extended over the $\lambda \in \mathfrak{N}$. In other words, the matrix function $\Sigma(\lambda)$ has at maximum a countable number of growth points, while independently of the form of $\Sigma(\lambda)$ its points of growth are situated on a fixed no more than countable set $\mathfrak{N}$. Now this may be interpreted in the following way: all selfadjoint extensions (in H_K or extending beyond it) of the operator $u \to L^+ u$ $(u \in C_0^\infty(G))$ have the property that their spectra lie on $\mathfrak{N}$. But it is well known that if the closure of a Hermitian operator is not selfadjoint, then one may always extend it to selfadjointness in such a way that any real point of regular type becomes an eigenvalue of the extended operator. We have arrived at an absurdity, since evidently any point of $(-\infty, \infty) \setminus \mathfrak{N}$ is a point of regular type of the original operator. The theorem is proved.

4. Selfadjointness of operators in H_K corresponding to ordinary differential expressions with constant coefficients on the entire axis. In this and in the following subsection, using the results of §2.2, we obtain certain facts on the selfadjointness of the closure in H_K of the operator $u \to L^+ u$ $(u \in C_0^\infty(E_n))$. We shall present them in a form suitable for utilization in the following section in the study of commutative extensions. For simplicity we shall first consider the case of the ordinary expression L: $n = 1$.

We need the theory of spaces of type S. We recall the necessary definitions and facts (Gel'fand and Šilov [2], Chapter 4). We fix $\alpha, \beta \geq 0$ and $A, B > 0$ and introduce the space $S_{\alpha, A}^{\beta, B}$ in the following way. Consider functions $\phi \in C^\infty(E_1)$ satisfying the inequalities

$$|x^k (D^q \varphi)(x)| \leqslant C_{\varphi, a, b} (A + a)^k (B + b)^q k^{k\alpha} q^{q\beta}$$
$$(x \in E_1; \quad k, q = 0, 1, \ldots; \quad a, b > 0), \tag{3.24}$$

the constant $C_{\phi, a, b}$ depending on the choice of ϕ, a, and b. It is clear that the smaller the constants α, β, A and B the stricter the estimate (3.24), and the narrower the stock of functions satisfying it. The collection of functions ϕ satisfying (3.24) forms a linear set, which will be denoted by $S_{\alpha, A}^{\beta, B}$. Into this set we introduce a countable system of norms, putting

$$\|\varphi\|_{a, b} = \sup_{x, k, q} \frac{|x^k (D^q \varphi)(x)|}{(A+a)^k (B+b)^q k^{k\alpha} q^{q\beta}} \left(a, b = 1, \frac{1}{2}, \frac{1}{3}, \ldots\right). \quad (3.25)$$

We topologize $S_{\alpha, A}^{\beta, B}$ as a countably-normed space with the norms (3.25), i.e. as neighborhoods of zero we shall understand finite intersections of collections $\phi \in S_{\alpha, A}^{\beta, B}$ satisfying inequalities of the form $\|\phi\|_{a, b} < \epsilon$. One can show that $S_{\alpha, A}^{\beta, B}$ will be a complete countably-normed space, while convergence $\phi_n \to 0$ in its topology is equivalent to having the sequence $\phi_n(x)$ bounded in $S_{\alpha, A}^{\beta, B}$ (i.e. $\|\phi_n\|_{a, b} \le C_{a, b}$ $(n = 1, 2, \cdots)$ for all a, b) and converging to zero uniformly on each bounded interval along with any of its derivatives. It is easy to see that if $A'' > A' > 0$ and $B'' > B' > 0$, then $S_{\alpha, A'}^{\beta, B'} \subseteq S_{\alpha, A''}^{\beta, B''}$, the imbedding being topological, i.e. convergence in the left space implying convergence in the right.

Functions of the space $S_{\alpha, A}^{\beta, B}$ have a definite order of decrease to ∞ and definite analyticity properties. In general one may show that if for $\phi \in C^\infty(E_1)$ the estimates

$$|x^k (D^q \varphi)(x)| \leqslant C_\varphi A^k B^q k^{k\alpha} q^{q\beta} \quad (x \in E_1;\ \ k, q = 0, 1, \ldots) \qquad (3.26)$$

are satisfied for fixed α, $\beta \ge 0$ and A, $B > 0$, then the following conclusions are valid. If $\alpha = 0$, then ϕ is finite. If $\alpha > 0$, then ϕ satisfies the estimate

$$|(D^q \varphi)(x)| \leqslant C_{1, \varphi} B^q q^{q\beta} e^{-K_{\alpha, A} |x|^{\frac{1}{\alpha}}} \quad (x \in E_1;\ \ q = 0, 1, \ldots), \qquad (3.27)$$

where

$$K_{\alpha, A} = \frac{\alpha}{e A^{\frac{1}{\alpha}}}, \qquad (3.28)$$

and $C_{1, \phi}$ is some new constant (in particular we may put $C_{1, \phi} = C_\phi e^{\alpha e/2}$). Above $\beta \ge 0$ and $B \ge 0$ were arbitrary.

If $\beta \le 1$ in (3.26), then ϕ extends to an analytic function in some strip around the real axis, while if $\beta < 1$ this function is simply entire. In the case

$\alpha > 0$ and $\beta < 1$ the extended function $\phi(z) = \phi(x+iy)$ satisfies the estimate

$$|\varphi(x+iy)| \leqslant C_{2,\varphi} e^{-K_{\alpha, A}|x|^{\frac{1}{\alpha}} + Q_{\beta, B}|y|^{\frac{1}{1-\beta}}} \qquad (-\infty < x,\ y < \infty), \tag{3.29}$$

where $C_{2,\phi}$ is some constant. $K_{\alpha, A}$ is calculated from (3.28), and $Q_{\beta, B}$ is any number larger than

$$\frac{1-\beta}{e} (Be)^{\frac{1}{1-\beta}}. \tag{3.30}$$

For us the question as to which differential operators of infinite order are defined in the spaces $S_{\alpha, A}^{\beta, B}$ and where they operate continuously will be important. We adopt the following definition. Suppose that $\Pi(s) = \sum_{q=0}^{\infty} c_q s^q$ is some entire function of the complex variable s. We assign to it the differential expression of infinite order $\Pi(D) = \sum_{q=0}^{\infty} c_q D^q$. Suppose that we have two linear topological spaces Φ and Ψ, consisting of certain infinitely differentiable functions on E_1. We shall say that the operator $\Pi(D)$ is defined in Φ and that it operates continuously into Ψ, if for each $\phi \in \Phi$ the series $(\Pi(D)\phi)(x) = \sum_{q=0}^{\infty} c_q (D^q \phi)(x)$ converges in the sense of convergence in Ψ and that the relation $\phi \to \Pi(D)$ is continuous from Φ into Ψ.

The following assertion is valid: if $\Pi(s)$ is an entire function of order of growth $\leq 1/\beta$ $(\beta > 0)$ and of type $\leq \beta/B^{1/\beta} e^2$,[1] then the operator $\Pi(D)$ is defined on $S_{\alpha, A}^{\beta, B}$ and operates continuously into $S_{\alpha, A}^{\beta, Be^{\beta}}$. Here the only restriction imposed on the parameters $\alpha, \beta \geq 0$, $A, B > 0$ is that $\beta > 0$.

Now we turn to the latter question, touching on the properties of spaces of type S. The inequalities (3.24) may be so restrictive that there are no functions other than $\phi(x) \equiv 0$ which satisfy them. Thus, there arises a natural question as to the nontriviality of the spaces $S_{\alpha, A}^{\beta, B}$, i.e. on the presence in them of at least one function distinct from 0. It turns out that these spaces are nontrivial in the following cases:

a) $S_{\alpha, A}^{\beta, B}$ with arbitrary $\alpha, \beta \geq 0$, $\alpha + \beta > 1$ and $A, B > 0$;

b) $S_{\alpha, A}^{\beta, B}$ with arbitrary $\alpha, \beta > 0$, $\alpha + \beta = 1$ and A, B such that $AB > \gamma_{\alpha, \beta}$, where $\gamma_{\alpha, \beta}$ is some positive number calculated in a definite way from

---

[1] We recall that the entire function $f(s)$ is said to be an entire function of order $M \in (0, \infty)$ and of type $N \in [0, \infty)$, if for any $\epsilon > 0$ the estimate $|f(s)| \leq C_\epsilon e^{(N+\epsilon)|s|^M}$ is valid for all s, while M and N are the minimal numbers for which this inequality is valid.

α and β.

With the nontrivial spaces there is closely connected the concept of a sufficient supply of functions in them. We shall say that some topological space Φ of infinitely differentiable functions on E_1 is sufficiently rich in functions if for a function $f(x)$ $(x \in E_1)$ which is locally summable relative to Lebesgue measure, it follows from the equation $\int_{-\infty}^{\infty} f(x)\phi(x)\,dx = 0$ for all $\phi \in \Phi$ that $f(x) = 0$ almost everywhere. We can show that nontrivial $S_{\alpha, A}^{\beta, B}$ with $\alpha, \beta > 0$ are sufficiently rich in functions.

We turn to the investigation of selfadjointness, imposing definite restrictions on the growth of the kernel K to ∞. Thus, suppose that the p. d. kernel $K(x, y) \in C(E_1 \times E_1)$ satisfies (3.4) with some ordinary expression L of order r whose coefficients are constant. We suppose that the estimate

$$|K(x, y)| \leqslant Ce^{N(|x|^M + |y|^M)} \quad (x, y \in E_1) \tag{3.31}$$

holds, where $M > 1$ and $N > 0$ are fixed. It follows from (3.31) that as $p(x)$ (see (3.3)) one may choose for example

$$p(x) = e^{\sigma N|x|^M} \quad (\sigma > 2). \tag{3.32}$$

Thus the form of the space $H_+ = L_2(E_1;\ pdx)$ is defined.

In what follows in the investigation of the selfadjointness in H_K of the operator $u \to L^+u$ $(u \in C_0^\infty(G))$, i. e. the restriction of $A^* = \Lambda^* = Л^+$ to $Д$, we may apply Theorems 2.4–2.5 with the spaces Φ and Ψ of type $S_{\alpha, A}^{\beta, B}$ not consisting of finite functions. Thus we have first to extend the operator in question somewhat and then take that extended operator as $C = B$ in the theory of §2.

Lemma 3.3. *Denote by Θ the collection of functions of $C^\infty(E_1)$ which satisfy the estimates*

$$|(D^q u)(x)| \leqslant C_{u,q} e^{-\varrho N|x|^M} \quad (x \in E_1;\ q = 0, 1, \ldots), \tag{3.33}$$

where $\rho > \sigma/2$. Clearly Θ, $L^+[\Theta] \subset L_2(E_1, pdx) = H_+ \subseteq H_K$. Define an operator B in H_K by putting $Bu = L^+u$ $(u \in \mathfrak{D}(B) = \Theta)$. Then B is contained in the closure in H_K of the operator $u \to L^+u$ $(u \in C_0^\infty(E_1))$. [1)]

In fact, suppose that $u \in \Theta$; since $u, Du, \cdots, D^r u \in L_2(E_1, pdx)$, we may construct a sequence $u_n \in C_0^\infty(E_1)$ such that $u_n \to u, \cdots, D^r u_n \to D^r u$ in $L_2(E_1, pdx)$.

---

1) The set Θ was chosen only for simplification of the exposition. We could have defined the operator B by the equation $Bu = L^+u$ on $\mathfrak{D}(B) = \Psi$.

Thus in $H_+ = L_2(E_1, pdx)$ and hence also in H_K we have $u_n \to u$ and $L^+u_n \to L^+u$. The lemma is proved.

Lemma 3.4. *Suppose that* $\Pi(s)$ *is an entire function of order* $\mu \in [1, \infty)$ *and of type* $\nu \in (0, \infty)$. *Suppose that* $M \geq 1$ *for* $\mu > 1$ *is such that* $1/M + 1/\mu = 1$, *and that* M *is arbitrary for* $\mu = 1$. *For* $\mu > 1$ ν *is sufficiently small, and for* $\mu = 1$ *also arbitrary. Then there exist two spaces* Φ *and* Ψ *of type* $S_{\alpha, A}^{\beta, B}$ *such that* 1) $\Phi \subset \Psi \subset \Theta$, 2) *convergence in* Φ *implies convergence in* Ψ, *and the latter implies convergence in* $L_2(E_1, pdx)$, 3) Φ *is dense in* $L_2(E_1, pdx)$, 4) *the operator* $\Pi(D)$ *is defined in* Φ *and carries it continuously into* Ψ.

Proof. Suppose that first $\mu > 1$. We consider the space $S_{\alpha, A}^{\beta, B}$, in which α and A are for the time being arbitrary, and $\beta > 0$, $1/\beta \geq \mu$ and $\beta/B^{1/\beta}e^2 \geq \nu$, i.e. $0 < \beta \leq 1/\mu$ and $0 < B \leq \beta^\beta/\nu^\beta e^{2\beta}$. According to what was said earlier, the operator $\Pi(D)$ carries $\Phi = S_{\alpha, A}^{\beta, B}$ continuously into $\Psi = S_{\alpha, A}^{\beta, Be^\beta} \supset S_{\alpha, A}^{\beta, B} = \Phi$ (the inclusion follows from the inequality $e^\beta > 1$). In particular, we put $\beta = 1/\mu$. Then the admissible limits for B are given by the inequality

$$0 < B \leqslant \frac{1}{\nu^{\frac{1}{\mu}} \mu^{\frac{1}{\mu}} e^{\frac{2}{\mu}}}. \tag{3.34}$$

Put $\alpha = 1 - \beta = 1 - 1/\mu = 1/M > 0$. Then $\Phi = S_{1/M, A}^{1/\mu, B} \subset S_{1/M, A}^{1/\mu, Be^{1/\mu}} = \Psi$ with the so-far unselected $A, B > 0$. From (3.27) and (3.24) the functions $\phi \in \Psi$ satisfy the estimate

$$|(D^q\varphi)(x)| \leqslant C_{\varphi,q}\, e^{-\frac{1}{eM(A+a)^M}|x|^M} \quad (x \in E_1;\ q = 0, 1, \ldots), \tag{3.35}$$

where $a > 0$ is some fixed number. Comparing (3.35) and (3.33), we conclude that for $A > 0$ sufficiently small we may choose a so small that $1/eM(A+a)^M > \rho N$. We fix such an A. In this case

$$\Phi \subset \Psi \subset \Theta \subset L_2(E_1, pdx). \tag{3.36}$$

It is easy to understand that convergence in Ψ implies convergence in $L_2(E_1, pdx)$. Indeed, if $\phi_n \to 0$ in Ψ, then $\phi_n(x) \to 0$ on every bounded interval of the axis E_1 and $\|\phi_n\|_{a,b} \leq C_{a,b} < \infty$ $(n = 1, 2, \cdots; a, b = 1, 1/2, \cdots)$. This last inequality means that for all n

$$|x^k (D^q \varphi_n)(x)| \leqslant C_{a,b} (A+a)^k (Be^{\frac{1}{\mu}} + b)^q k^{\frac{k}{M}} q^{\frac{q}{\mu}}$$

$$\left(x \in E_1;\ k,\ q = 0, 1, \ldots;\ a,\ b = 1,\ \frac{1}{2}, \ldots \right),$$

so that, from (3. 27), the ϕ_n satisfy an estimate of type (3. 35) uniformly in n, with a sufficiently small and fixed. Taking account of the choice of A, we obtain in particular $|\phi_n(x)| \leq Ce^{-\rho N|x|^M}$ $(x \in E_1;\ n = 1, 2, \cdots)$. This makes it possible to pass to the limit under the integral sign and to prove the assertion:

$$\| \varphi_n \|^2_{L_2(E_1,\ pdx)} = \int_{-\infty}^{\infty} |\varphi_n(x)|^2 e^{\sigma N|x|^M} dx \underset{n \to \infty}{\to} 0.$$

So far we have not been concerned with the nontriviality of the spaces Φ and Ψ. Now we shall remove the gap. Since $\Phi = S^{1/\mu,\ B}_{1/M,\ A}$ and $1/M + 1/\mu = 1$, it follows that Φ (and thus Ψ) is nontrivial for $AB > \gamma_{\alpha,\ \beta} = \gamma_{1/M,\ 1/\mu}$ (see above). We take B so large that this inequality is satisfied, and then choose ν so small that (3. 34) is satisfied. Therefore Φ is nontrivial, and, from what was said above, it is sufficiently rich in functions $(\alpha = 1/M,\ \beta = 1/\mu > 0)$. Thus it follows that Φ is dense in $H_+ = L_2(E_1,\ pdx)$; if not there would be a $f \in L_2(E_1, pdx)$, $f \neq 0$, such that $\int_{-\infty}^{\infty} \phi(x) \overline{f(x)} p(x)\, dx = 0$ $(\phi \in \Phi)$, and this is absurd. Thus the lemma is proved for $\mu > 1$.

Now consider the case $\mu = 1$. As before we choose $\Phi = S^{\beta,\ B}_{\alpha,\ A}$ and $\Psi = S^{\beta,\ Be^{\beta}}_{\alpha,\ A} \supset \Phi$, where $\beta = 1/\mu = 1$ and B must satisfy the estimate (3. 34). Also we put $\alpha = 1/2M > 0$. For functions $\phi \in \Psi$ we will have estimate (3. 35), in which M is replaced by $2M$. Therefore these functions decrease towards ∞ faster than functions of Θ for which (3. 33) was assumed, and relation (3. 36) is preserved. As before, we verify that convergence in Ψ implies convergence in $L_2(E_1,\ pdx)$. Here $\alpha + \beta = 1/2M + 1 > 1$, so that Φ is nontrivial, sufficiently rich in functions, and therefore dense in $L_2(E_1,\ pdx)$. Thus the case $\mu = 1$ has also been examined. The lemma is proved.

As follows from the proof of the lemma, the spaces Φ and Ψ were constructed thus: 1) in the case $\mu > 1$ we put $\Phi = S^{1/\mu,\ B}_{1/M,\ A}$, $\Psi = S^{1/\mu,\ Be^{1/\mu}}_{1/M,\ A}$, where $A > 0$ was chosen so small that $1/eMA^M > \rho N$, and $B > 0$ so large that $AB > \gamma_{1/M,\ 1/\mu}$. After this $\nu > 0$ was taken so small that $B \leq (\nu^{1/\mu} \mu^{1/\mu} e^{2/\mu})^{-1}$; 2) in the case $\mu = 1$ we put $\Phi = S^{1,\ B}_{1/2M,\ A}$, $\Psi = S^{1,\ Be}_{1/2M,\ A}$, where $A > 0$ is arbitrary and $B > 0$ satisfies the inequality $B \leq (\nu e^2)^{-1}$.

Suppose that $\overline{L}(s) = \Sigma_{\alpha=0}^{r} \overline{a}_\alpha s^\alpha$ is a polynomial in the complex variable s corresponding to the expression L^+. The function $\Pi(s;\ t_0,\ t) = e^{i(t_0-t)\overline{L}(s)}$ $(0 \leq t_0 < t \leq T < \infty)$ for fixed t_0, t will be an entire function of order r and of some type less than or equal to $\nu(T) < \infty$; $\nu(T) \to 0$ as $T \to 0$. To this function Lemma 3.4 may be applied. In the case $r > 1$ we must take $T > 0$ sufficiently small, and in the case $r = 1$ we may take $T \in (0, \infty)$ arbitrary. It is clear that the Φ and Ψ of this lemma may be chosen in common for all t_0, $t \in [0,\ T]$. Then the operator $Q(t_0,\ t) = \Pi(D;\ t_0, t)$ for arbitrary t_0, $t \in [0,\ T]$ continuously maps all of Φ into Ψ, while $\phi(t) = Q(t_0,\ t)\phi$ $\quad(\phi \in \Phi)$ is equal to ϕ for $t = t_0$.

Lemma 3.5. *The operator $Q(t_0,\ t)$ just constructed has the property that the vector function $\phi(t) = Q(t_0,\ t)\phi$ $\quad(\phi \in \Phi,\quad t \in [0,\ T];\ t_0 \in [0,\ T]$ fixed$)$ with values in $L_2(E_1,\ pdx)$ is strongly differentiable and satisfies the equation*

$$\frac{d\varphi(t)}{dt} + iB\varphi(t) = 0 \qquad (t \in [0,\ T]) . \tag{3.37}$$

Proof. For $t \in [0,\ T]$, $\phi(t) \in \Psi \subset \Theta$ and the equation (3.37) essentially has the form $d\phi(t)/dt + iL^+[\phi(t)] = 0$. Convergence in Ψ implies convergence in $L_2(E_1,\ pdx)$, so that to prove the lemma it suffices to verify that $\phi(t)$ is differentiable in the topology of Ψ and that the derivative satisfies the last equation. But this was proved in the theory of generalized functions (I. M. Gel'fand, G. E. Šilov [3], Chapter 2, §3, Russian pages 54–56). The lemma is proved.

Theorem 3.9. *Suppose that L is an ordinary differentiable expression of order r with constant coefficients. Let $K(x,\ y) \in C(E_1 \times E_1)$ be a p. d. kernel satisfying* (3.4). *Thus the representation* (3.20) *holds with a fixed fundamental system of solutions $\chi_j(x;\ \lambda)$ of the equation $Lu = \lambda u$. Suppose that $r > 1$. In order that the matrix $\|d\sigma_{jk}(\lambda)\|_0^{r-1}$ in the representation* (3.20) *be determined uniquely by $K(x,\ y)$, it is sufficient that the estimate $|K(x,\ y)| \leq Ce^{N(|x|^{r'} + |y|^{r'})}$ $(C > 0,\ x,\ y \in E_1)$ be satisfied for some $N > 0$, where $1/r + 1/r' = 1$.*

If $r = 1$ $d\sigma_{00}(\lambda)$ is always uniquely defined.

It is clear that under the conditions of the theorem the closure of the operator $u \to L^+u$ $\quad(u \in C_0^\infty(E_1))$ will be selfadjoint, given only that it has equal defect numbers. For example, if it is real relative to some involution in H_K

(this will always be the case for real $K(x, y)$ and coefficients L).

Here we shall prove the theorem only for the case $r > 1$. For $r = 1$ we shall establish a weaker result: $d\sigma_{00}(\lambda)$ is defined uniquely if for some $M \geq 1$

$$|K(x, y)| \leqslant Ce^{|x|^M+|y|^M} \qquad (C > 0;\ x,\ y \in E_1). \tag{3.38}$$

This result is needed only as a model for the argument in the analogous part of Theorem 3.10, in which it is no longer possible to establish uniqueness without restrictions on the growth of the kernel K. For convenience, the proof of the assertion of the theorem for $r = 1$ is left to subsection 10, below.

Thus, suppose that the conditions of the theorem are satisfied for $r > 1$ and the restriction (3.38) when $r = 1$. From Theorem 3.7, we need to show that the closure in H_K of the operator $u \to L^+u$ $(u \in C_0^\infty(G))$ is maximal. From Lemma 3.3 we may restrict ourselves to the proof of maximality of the closure of the operator B $(Bu = L^+u,\ \ u \in \Theta)$. Making use of Theorem 2.5, 2), we reduce the question to the establishment of uniqueness for the weak solutions of the Cauchy problem in $H_+ = L_2(E_1, pdx)$ with a $p(x)$ of the form (3.32) for both equations $du/dt \pm (iB)^* u = 0$ $(0 \leq t < \infty)$. But this, from Theorem 2.4, follows from Lemmas 3.4 and 3.5, the latter lemma being applicable also to the expression $-L^+$. The theorem is proved, as modified.

In conclusion we note that application of Theorem 2.5, 1) yields a considerably weaker result. The uniqueness of the representation (3.20) under the hypotheses of Theorem 3.9 is guaranteed only in the case when its conditions are replaced by the estimate $|K(x, y)| \leq Ce^{N(|x|+|y|)}$ $(C, N > 0;\ x, y \in E_1)$; the order r is arbitrary.[1)] We shall explain what has been said. Because of the estimate on K we may put $p(x) = e^{\sigma N|x|}$ $(\sigma > 2)$, $H_+ = L_2(E_1, pdx)$, $Bu = L^+u(u \in \mathfrak{D}(B) = C_0^\infty(E_1))$. Suppose that $0 \neq h \in L_2(E_1, pdx)$ is orthogonal in H_+ to $(B - zE)\mathfrak{D}(B)$, i.e. $\int_{-\infty}^{\infty} (L^+ - zE)u \cdot \bar{h}pdx = 0$ $(u \in C_0^\infty(E_1))$. Because of what has been said in Chapter VI, §5.1, $hp \in C^\infty(E_1)$ and $(L - \bar{z}E)\,[hp] = 0$. Therefore $h(x)p(x) = \sum_{j=1}^r c_j e^{\mu_j x}$, where μ_j are the roots of the equation $L(\mu) - \bar{z} = 0$ (z may always be so changed that the roots are distinct). Taking account of the form of p, we find $|h(x)|^2 p(x) = |\sum_{j=1}^r c_j e^{\mu_j x}|^2 e^{-\sigma N|x|}$. It is clear that we may always choose z from the upper and lower halfplanes so that $|\mu_j| > \sigma N/2$ $(j = 1, \cdots, r)$. Then $\int_{-\infty}^{\infty} |h|^2 pdx = \infty$, which is absurd. The

---

1) It is true that the analogous application of Theorem 2.1 in the case $q \geq 1$ does not assume the equality of the defect numbers of the operators (cf. Theorem 4.3).

assertion is proved.

5. **The case of expressions in partial derivatives with constant coefficients in all of E_n.** We may apply to this case considerations analogous to those presented in subsection 4, and establish the analog of Theorem 3.9. We shall make use of the spaces $S_{\alpha, A}^{\beta, B}$ with vector indices $\alpha = (\alpha_1, \cdots, \alpha_n)$, $\beta = (\beta_1, \cdots, \beta_n)$, $A = (A_1, \cdots, A_n)$ and $B = (B_1, \cdots, B_n)$, where $\alpha_j, \beta_j \geq 0$ and $A_j, B_j > 0$, $j = 1, \cdots, n$. Such a space $S_{\alpha, A}^{\beta, B}$ is defined as a collection of functions $\phi \in C^\infty(E_n)$ satisfying inequalities (3.24), in which k, q, a and b are replaced by vector indices of the indicated type, while, as usual, expressions of the form x^k, $x^{k\alpha}$ denote respectively $x_1^{k_1} \cdots x_n^{k_n}$ and $k_1^{k_1 \alpha_1} \cdots k_n^{k_n \alpha_n}$. In these inequalities $x = (x_1, \cdots, x_n) \in E_n$; $k_j, q_j = 0, 1, \cdots$; $a_j, b_j > 0$ $(j = 1, \cdots, n)$. The space $S_{\alpha, A}^{\beta, B}$ is countably normalized relative to the system of norms (3.25), in which $a_j, b_j = 1, 1/2, 1/3, \cdots$ $(j = 1, \cdots, n)$. In a similar way one paraphrases the remaining definitions and results presented on pages 653–656. Here the exponentials in estimates of type (3.27) are replaced by products of the corresponding exponentials computed coordinate-by-coordinate. Thus for example in (3.27) $\exp(-K_{\alpha, A}|x|^{1/\alpha})$ is replaced by $\exp(-K_{\alpha_1, A_1}|x_1|^{1/\alpha_1} - \cdots - K_{\alpha_n, A_n}|x_n|^{1/\alpha_n})$.

Repeating the arguments, one may show that the following theorem is valid.

Theorem 3.10. *Suppose that L is an expression of order r with constant coefficients, $K(x, y) \in C(E_n \times E_n)$ a p.d. kernel satisfying (3.4), so that one has a representation (3.7) (or (3.11) in the case of an elliptic L). In order that $\Omega_\lambda d\rho(\lambda)$ be defined uniquely relative to $K(x, y)$, it is sufficient that the following estimate hold: for some $N > 0$*

$$|K(x, y)| \leqslant Ce^{N(|x_1|^{r'} + \ldots + |x_n|^{r'} + |y_1|^{r'} + \ldots + |y_n|^{r'})} \qquad (C > 0;\ x, y \in E_n),$$

where $1/r + 1/r' = 1$ for $r > 1$, and r' arbitrary and positive in the case $r = 1$.

6. **Ordinary p.d. functions.** Suppose that $G = (-l, l)$, where $0 < l \leq \infty$. As is known, the function $k(t) \in C((-2l, 2l))$ is called p.d. if the kernel $K(x, y) = k(y - x)$, $(x, y \in G)$ is p.d., i.e. for arbitrary points $x_1, \cdots, x_N \in G$ and arbitrary complex numbers $\xi_1, \cdots, \xi_N$

$$\sum_{j, k=1}^{N} k(x_k - x_j)\xi_k \bar{\xi}_j \geqslant 0.$$

Since for a p.d. kernel $K(x, y) = \overline{K(y, x)}$, $|K(x, y)|^2 \leq K(x, x)K(y, y)$

$(x, y \in G)$, we have $k(y-x) = \overline{k(x-y)}$, $|k(y-x)|^2 \le k^2(0)$. Setting $y - x = t$ we obtain

$$k(t) = \overline{k(-t)}, \quad |k(t)| \leqslant k(0) \qquad (t \in (-2l, 2l)). \tag{3.39}$$

Directly from the definition we may obtain also a series of other properties of p. d. functions. We shall not dwell on these, since such results follow also from the integral representation which we now obtain. This representation easily follows from Theorem 3.7.

Theorem 3.11. *The function* $k(x) \in C((-2l, 2l))$ $(0 < l \le \infty)$ *is p. d. if and only if it is representable in the form*

$$k(t) = \int_{-\infty}^{\infty} e^{i\lambda t} d\sigma(\lambda) \qquad (t \in (-2l, 2l)), \tag{3.40}$$

where $d\sigma(\lambda)$ *is a nonnegative finite measure. In the case* $l = \infty$ *this measure is uniquely defined relative to* k; *if* $l < \infty$ *uniqueness in general does not hold.*

Proof. The fact that a function of type (3.40) is p. d. is verified directly. Let us establish the representation (3.40). Put $L = i(d/dx) = L^+$. If $k(t)$ is sufficiently smooth, (3.4) is satisfied:

$$\begin{aligned} L_x[K(x, y)] &= i\frac{d}{dx}k(y-x) = -i\frac{d}{dy}k(y-x) \\ &= \overline{L}_y[K(x, y)] \qquad (x, y \in G). \end{aligned} \tag{3.41}$$

In the general case for $u, v \in C_0^\infty(G)$ we have

$$\begin{aligned} \langle L^+u, v \rangle &= i\int_{-\infty}^{\infty}\int_{-\infty}^{\infty} k(y-x)u'(x)\overline{v(y)}\,dxdy \\ &= i\int_{-\infty}^{\infty}\left(\int_{-\infty}^{\infty} k(x)u'(y-x)\,dx\right)\overline{v(y)}\,dy \\ &= i\int_{-\infty}^{\infty} k(x)\left(\int_{-\infty}^{\infty} u'(y-x)\,\overline{v(y)}\,dy\right)dx \\ &= i\int_{-\infty}^{\infty} k(x)\left(\int_{-\infty}^{\infty} u(y-x)\overline{v'(y)}\,dy\right)dx = \langle u, L^+v \rangle, \end{aligned} \tag{3.42}$$

i.e. (3.4) is also satisfied. Thus, the kernel K $*$-commutes with $i(d/dx)$. Evidently in our case $\chi_0(x; \lambda) = e^{-i\lambda x}$, if we consider $a = 0$. Therefore (3.20) yields the representation

$$k(y-x) = K(x, y) = \int_{-\infty}^{\infty} e^{i\lambda(y-x)}\, d\sigma_{00}(\lambda) \quad (x, y \in G),$$

which after replacement of $y - x$ by t goes into (3.40).

The uniqueness of the measure $d\sigma(\lambda)$ for $l = \infty$ follows from condition (3.38) and the boundedness of $K(x, y)$ (see (3.39)). In what follows we shall show that generally speaking if $l < \infty$ then $d\sigma(\lambda)$ is defined nonuniquely. The theorem is proved.

This theorem in essense also gives an answer to a nontrivial question: suppose that $k(t) \in C((-2l, 2l))$ is p. d., while $l < \infty$. Can it be extended to a p. d. function on the entire axis? Indeed, such a function on $(-2l, 2l)$ coincides with the integral $\int_{-\infty}^{\infty} e^{i\lambda t}\, d\sigma(\lambda)$, which is defined and p. d. for all $t \in (-\infty, \infty)$, i. e. the required extension is constructed. In subsections 8 and 9 we shall study this question in detail.

7. **The spaces H_K as negative spaces.** First we shall establish some facts relative to the spaces H_K, constructed relative to general p. d. kernels $K(x, y)$. Suppose that G is a bounded region of the space E_n, $K(x, y) \in C(G \times G)$ is a p. d. kernel which in addition is regarded as bounded in $G \times G$. We introduce a scalar product on the functions $f, g \in L_2(G)$, putting

$$\langle f, g \rangle = \int_G \int_G K(x, y) f(y) \overline{g(x)}\, dx dy. \tag{3.43}$$

Obviously $\langle f, f \rangle \le C \|f\|^2_{L_2(G)}$ $(C > 0,\ f \in L_2(G))$. *We shall suppose that the form* $\langle \cdot , \cdot \rangle$ *is nondegenerate* (i.e. $\langle f, f \rangle \ne 0$ for $f \in L_2(G)$, $f \ne 0$). We denote the completion of $L_2(G)$ (or $C_0^\infty(G)$) by H_K. From Theorem 3.7 of Chapter I, H_K may be considered as a negative space, constructed relative to the null space $H_0 = L_2(G)$ and some positive space $H_{+, K}$. Thus

$$H_K \supseteq H_0 = L_2(G) \supseteq H_{+, K}. \tag{3.44}$$

The space $H_{+, K}$ is constructed (see Chapter I, §3.6) as the closure of $\Re(K)$ relative to the metric $(u, v)_{+, K} = (K^{-1} u, v)_0$, where $K = \hat{I}$ is the operator in $L_2(G)$ defined by the equation $(Kf, g)_0 = \langle f, g \rangle$ $(f, g \in L_2(G))$. Comparing this relation with (3.43) we find that

$$(Kf)(x) = \int_G K(x, y) f(y)\, dy \qquad (f \in L_2(G)). \tag{3.45}$$

From (3.45) and the continuity of the kernel $K(x, y)$ it follows that $\Re(K) \subseteq C(G)$.

Lemma 3.6. *Suppose that $\xi \in G$. There is in the space H_K a vector δ_ξ (δ-function concentrated at the point ξ) such that for each $u \in \Re(K) \subseteq H_{+,K}$*

$$(\delta_\xi, u)_0 = \overline{u(\xi)}; \quad \langle \delta_\xi, \delta_\eta \rangle = K(\eta, \xi) \quad (\xi, \eta \in G). \tag{3.46}$$

Proof. Denote by $\kappa_{\xi,\epsilon}(x)$ $(x \in G)$ the characteristic function of the ball with center at the point ξ and of radius $\epsilon > 0$, divided by its volume. Clearly as $\epsilon, \delta \to 0$ $\langle \kappa_{\xi,\epsilon}, \kappa_{\eta,\delta} \rangle \to K(\eta, \xi)$, and thus as $\epsilon_n \to 0$ $\langle \kappa_{\xi,\epsilon_n} - \kappa_{\xi,\epsilon_m}, \kappa_{\xi,\epsilon_n} - \kappa_{\xi,\epsilon_m} \rangle \to 0$ as $n, m \to \infty$, i.e. the sequence $\kappa_{\xi,\epsilon_n}(x)$ is fundamental in H_K, and in view of the completeness of the latter it converges to some one of its elements, which we denote by δ_ξ. The second equation in (3.46) is evident. The first follows from the relation $(\kappa_{\xi,\epsilon}, u)_0 = \int_G \kappa_{\xi,\epsilon}(x)\overline{u(x)}\,dx$ and the continuity of the function $u \in \Re(K) \subseteq C(G)$. The lemma is proved.

It follows directly from the second equation in (3.46) that $\langle \delta_{\xi_n} - \delta_\xi, \delta_{\xi_n} - \delta_\xi \rangle \to 0$ as $\xi_n \to \xi$, i.e. *δ_ξ is a continuous vector-function of ξ with values in H_K*. It follows from (3.46) that $\langle \delta_\xi, \delta_\xi \rangle$ is bounded for $\xi \in G$ and therefore for each closed region F lying strictly inside G we have for $u \in \Re(K)$: $|u(\xi)| = |(\delta_\xi, u)_0| \le \sqrt{\langle \delta_\xi, \delta_\xi \rangle}\, \|u\|_{+,K} \le C\|u\|_{+,K}$ $(\xi \in F)$. In other words, for $u \in \Re(K)$

$$\|u\|_{C(F)} \leqslant C\|u\|_{+,K} \qquad (C > 0). \tag{3.47}$$

Since $H_{+,K}$ is the completion of $\Re(K)$ with respect to the norm $\|\cdot\|_{+,K}$, then (3.47) shows that *each element of $H_{+,K}$ is a continuous function $u(x)$ $(x \in G)$ satisfying the estimate* (3.47) *for every closed $F \subset G$*. Therefore it follows that the first equation of (3.46) is valid for any $u \in H_{+,K}$.

We shall show further that *the linear envelope of the vectors δ_ξ, where ξ runs through a dense set in G, is complete in the space H_K*. Indeed, suppose that $\alpha \in H_K$ is such that $\langle \alpha, \delta_\xi \rangle = 0$ for every ξ in consideration. Using the operator **I**, constructed relative to the chain (3.44), we obtain

$$0 = \langle \alpha, \delta_\xi \rangle = (\mathbf{I}\alpha, \delta_\xi)_0 = (\mathbf{I}\alpha)(\xi) \in H_{+,K} \subseteq C(G).$$

Since the points ξ are dense in G it follows that $(\mathbf{I}\alpha)(x) = 0$ $(x \in G)$, i.e. $\mathbf{I}\alpha = 0$ and $\alpha = 0$. The assertion is proved.

We denote by $V_0(G)$ the collection of all complex-valued measures of bounded variation defined on Borel subsets of G and concentrated strictly inside G.

Each such measure generates in the usual way a linear continuous functional in the space $C(F)$. From (3. 47), this functional will be a continuous functional also over $H_{+,K}$, i.e. we may suppose that $V_0(G) \subseteq H_K$. It is not hard to see that

$$(\omega, u)_0 = \int_G \overline{u(x)}\, d\omega(x), \qquad \langle \omega, \theta \rangle = \int_G \int_G K(x, y)\, d\omega(y)\, d\overline{\theta(x)}$$

$$(\omega, \theta \in V_0(G); \quad u \in H_{+,K}). \tag{3. 48}$$

We shall dwell on a useful criterion for a function u in $C(G)$ to belong to the space $H_{+,K}$. First of all we note that, from Theorem 1. 1 of Chapter I, the space $H_{+,K}$ coincides with $\mathfrak{D}(D)$, where $D = \sqrt{\hat{I}^{-1}}$, i.e. $H_{+,K} = \Re(\sqrt{\hat{I}})$. Taking into account that $\hat{I} = K$, we find that

$$H_{+,K} = \Re(\sqrt{K}). \tag{3. 49}$$

Lemma 3. 7. *Denote by* $w_1(x)$, $w_2(x)$, $\cdots$, *a complete collection of orthonormalized eigenfunctions from* $L_2(G)$ *of the kernel* $K(x, y)$, *corresponding to the eigenvalues* $\rho_1, \rho_2, \cdots$ $(\rho_j > 0,\ j = 1, 2, \cdots)$. *A function* $u \in L_2(G)$ *enters into* $H_{+,K}$ *if and only if*

$$\| u \|^2_{+,K} = \sum_{j=1}^{\infty} \frac{|(u, w_j)_0|^2}{\rho_j} < \infty. \tag{3. 50}$$

Indeed, from (3. 49), $u \in L_2(G)$ if and only if $u = \sqrt{K f}$, where $f \in L_2(G)$. Here, according to (1. 13) of Chapter I, $\| u \|^2_{+,K} = \| Du \|^2_0 = \| f \|^2_0$. But $f = \sqrt{K^{-1}} u$; $(f, w_j)_0 = (u, w_j)_0 / \sqrt{\rho_j}$, and the lemma follows.

We shall now indicate those additional facts which will hold when the kernel $K(x, y)$ is continuous up to the boundary, i.e. $K(x, y) \in C((G \cup \Gamma) \times (G \cup \Gamma))$. In this case δ_ξ is defined for all $\xi \in C(G \cup \Gamma)$, while (3. 46) is valid for $\xi, \eta \in G \cup \Gamma$ and δ_ξ is a continuous vector-function with values in H_K of $\xi \in G \cup \Gamma$. In inequality (3. 47) we may also put $F = G \cup \Gamma$. $H_{+,K} \subseteq C(G \cup \Gamma)$. Finally, we denote by $V(G \cup \Gamma)$ the collection of all complex-valued measures defined on Borel subsets of $G \cup \Gamma$. Then $V(G \cup \Gamma) \subseteq H_K$, while relation (3. 48) holds.

Thus we have shown that in the case of a bounded G and a bounded and nondegenerate K there are δ-functions in the space H_K. We leave it to the reader to clear up the situation in the case of general G and K.

8. The problem of prolonging a p. d. function from a finite interval to the

entire axis. Operator approach.[1] We note first of all that between the questions presented below and the results of §1, Chapter VII, according to the theory of Jacobian matrices there is a deep analogy, which will be further emphasized in §5. Thus, we consider a p. d. function $k(t) \in C((-2l, 2l))$ for $0 < l < \infty$. The question of its extension is closely connected with the study of the spectral properties of the operator generated by $L = i(d/dx)$ in the corresponding space H_K. Since for $k(t)$ we have the representation (3.40), then $k(t) \in C([-2l, 2l])$. Therefore the kernel $K(x, y) = k(y-x) \in C([-l, l] \times [-l, l])$ and in the space H_K constructed above (we also denote it by H_k) we may put $p(x) \equiv 1$. Thus we may use the general results just established relative to spaces of the chain (3.44), including what was said at the end of subsection 7, given only that we assume that the form $\langle \cdot, \cdot \rangle$ is nondegenerate. *Throughout what follows we shall suppose that the form* (3.43) *is nondegenerate, when it is constructed relative to* $K(x, y) = k(y-x)$ $(x, y \in (-l, l))$. If this form is degenerate, then from Theorem 3.8 the representation (3.40) is unique, i.e. there is a unique extension of $k(t)$ to the entire axis. Here the integral in (3.40) goes into a sum.

The presence in the space H_k of δ-functions approximates the theory of decompositions relative to eigenfunctions of operators in H_k to the similar theory in the space $l_2(-\infty, \infty)$. We note further, that *because of the first of relations* (3.39), *the mapping* $u(x) \to u^\circ(x) = \overline{u(-x)}$ $(u \in L_2((-l, l)))$, *after closure by continuity, generates an involution in* H_k.

According to the general schema we consider in H_k the operator $Cu = L^+u = i(du/dx)$ $(u \in \mathfrak{D}(C) = C_0^\infty((-l, l)))$, is equal to the restriction to $C_0^\infty((-l, l))$ of the corresponding operator A^*. This operator is Hermitian in H_k, the measure $d\sigma(\lambda)$ in the representation (3.40) is the spectral measure of one of its selfadjoint extensions (in H_k or extending beyond it). Conversely, each measure $d\sigma(\lambda)$ of (3.40) is generated in that way. *The operator* C *is real relative to the involution* $\circ$ $(i\,\overline{(u(-x))}' = i\overline{u'}(-x))$ *and therefore has equal defect numbers. Thus the measure* $d\sigma(\lambda)$ *in the representation* (3.40) *will be unique if and only if the closure of* C *is selfadjoint in* H_k.

Analogous to the case of Jacobian matrices the problem of extension of a p. d. function $k(t) \in C((-2l, 2l))$ to the entire axis will be called determinate or not according to whether or not its extension is unique. As we have

---

[1] In the exposition of the results of subsections 8 and 9 on the prolongation of p. d. functions, the author has made use of an unpublished manuscript of M. G. Kreĭn.

already said, this is equivalent to the uniqueness or nonuniqueness of the measure $d\sigma(\lambda)$ in the representation (3.40). Thus we have just obtained a necessary and sufficient criterion for the determinateness of the problem of extension.

Substituting in (3.43) the expression for k from (3.43), we obtain

$$\langle f, g \rangle = \int_{-\infty}^{\infty} \tilde{f}(\lambda)\overline{\tilde{g}(\lambda)}\, d\sigma(\lambda), \quad \tilde{f}(\lambda) = \int_{-l}^{l} e^{i\lambda x} f(x)\, dx \quad (f, g \in L_2((-l, l))). \tag{3.51}$$

It is clear that this is Parseval's equation, constructed relative to the selfadjoint extension of the operator C corresponding to $d\sigma(\lambda)$.

If $E(\Delta)$ is the corresponding (generalized) resolution of the identity, then

$$\langle E(\Delta) f, g \rangle = \int_{\Delta} \tilde{f}(\lambda)\overline{\tilde{g}(\lambda)}\, d\sigma(\lambda).$$

Suppose that $f \in L_2((-l, l))$ is such that $\int_{-\infty}^{\infty} |\tilde{f}(\lambda)|^2 d\sigma(\lambda) = 0$. Then, from (3.51), $\langle f, f \rangle = 0$, which means that because of the hypothesis on the nondegeneracy of $\langle \cdot, \cdot \rangle$, $f = 0$ in $L_2((-l, l))$ as well. Thus, $\tilde{f}(\lambda) \equiv 0$. This useful remark is analogous to what was said in Chapter VII, §1.4 relative to polynomials.

Passing to the limit in (3.51), we obtain Parseval's equation for arbitrary $f, g \in H_k$. Here $\tilde{f}(\lambda) \in L_2((-\infty, \infty), d\sigma(\lambda))$ may be understood as a limit in $L_2((-\infty, \infty))$ of functions $\tilde{f}_n(\lambda)$, where $f_n \in L_2((-l, l))$ approximates f in H_k. In particular, $\tilde{\delta}_\xi(\lambda) = e^{i\lambda\xi}$ $(\xi \in [-l, l])$ (this follows for example from the approximation of the element δ_ξ by the functions $\kappa_{\xi,\epsilon}(x)$). It is easy also to show that for $\omega \in V([-l, l])$ $\tilde{\omega}(\lambda) = \int_{-l}^{l} e^{i\lambda x}\, d\omega(x)$. So, Parseval's equation in its general form may be written as

$$\langle E(\Delta)\alpha, \beta \rangle = \int_{\Delta} \tilde{\alpha}(\lambda)\overline{\tilde{\beta}(\lambda)}\, d\sigma(\lambda) \quad (\alpha, \beta \in H_k). \tag{3.52}$$

Comparing what was said above with what was said in Chapter VII (loc. cit.), it is easy to discern an analogy with the case of a Jacobian matrix in $l_2([0, \infty])$. Here the role of the polynomials is played by the functions $\tilde{u}(\lambda) = \int_{-l}^{l} e^{i\lambda x} u(x)\, dx$, where $\tilde{u} \in \tilde{C}_0^\infty((-l, l))$ are the Fourier transforms of the vectors $u \in C_0^\infty((-l, l)) \subset H_k$. The family $\tilde{C}_0^\infty((-l, l))$ of "polynomials" may be described in an intrinsic manner (see Gel'fand and Šilov [1], Chapter 2, §1, Russian page 195). Indeed $\tilde{u}(\lambda) \in \tilde{C}_0^\infty((-l, l))$ if and only if $\tilde{u}(\lambda)$ is an entire function of the complex variable λ, admitting for all λ the estimate

$$|\lambda^k \tilde{u}(\lambda)| \leq C_{\tilde{u},k} e^{l_{\tilde{u}} |\operatorname{Im} \lambda|} \qquad (C_{\tilde{u},k} > 0; \quad k = 0, 1, \ldots) \tag{3.53}$$

($l_{\tilde{u}} \in (0, l)$ such that $u(x) = 0$ for $|x| \geq l_{\tilde{u}}$).

The passage $u \to \tilde{u}(\lambda)$ $(u \in C_0^\infty((-l, l)))$ is an isometry between a dense portion of the space H_k and the linear set $\widetilde{C_0^\infty((-l, l))} \subset L_2((-\infty, \infty), d\sigma(\lambda))$. Extending it by continuity, we obtain an isometry between H_k and $\tilde{H}_k$, the closure in $L_2((-\infty, \infty), d\sigma(\lambda))$ of all the "polynomials" $\widetilde{C_0^\infty((-l, l))}$. Evidently $\widetilde{C_0^\infty((-l, l))} \subset \widetilde{L_2((-l, l))} \subset \widetilde{V([-l, l])} \subset \tilde{H}_k$. Under the isometry $u \to \tilde{u}(\lambda)$ the operator C goes into the operator of multiplication by λ, defined on $\widetilde{C_0^\infty((-l, l))}$.

In what follows we shall make use of an analog of formula (1.20), Chapter VII. For its deduction we put $\alpha = \beta = \delta_0$ in (3.52). Since $\tilde{\delta}_0(\lambda) \equiv 1$, then

$$\sigma(\Delta) = \langle E(\Delta)\delta_0, \delta_0 \rangle. \tag{3.54}$$

Repeating the proof of Theorem 1.7 of Chapter VII, in which we need only to replace $l_2([0, \infty))$, $l_{2,0}([0, \infty))$ and $\widetilde{l_{2,0}([0, \infty))}$ by H_k, $C_0^\infty((-l, l))$ and $\widetilde{C_0^\infty((-l, l))}$ respectively, we arrive at the following result.

Theorem 3.12. *A collection of functions of* $C_0^\infty((-l, l))$ *will be dense in* $L_2((-\infty, \infty), d\sigma(\lambda))$, *if and only if* $d\sigma(\lambda)$ *is generated by the ordinary resolution of the identity. Such spectral measures* $d\sigma(\lambda)$ *will be called, as before, orthogonal.*

We note that a result of the type of Theorem 1.9 of Chapter VII has already been established by us. The analog of Theorem 1.10 in the case at hand appears as follows: for denseness in $L_1((-\infty, \infty), d\sigma(\lambda))$ of a collection of functions of $C_0^\infty((-2l, 2l))$, it is necessary and sufficient that $d\sigma(\lambda)$ should be extreme. Questions of the type of the inverse problem (§1.5, Chapter VII) do not here arise in the preceding form.

We turn to the investigation of the selfadjointness of the closure of the operator C, i.e. to the investigation of the determinateness or nondeterminateness of the extension problem. We first indicate examples of p.d. functions $k(t) \in C((-2l, 2l))$, for which the problem of extension is nondeterminate.

1. Let $k(t) \in C((-\infty, \infty))$ be some even nonnegative convex (below) function tending to zero as $|t|$ approaches infinity. Such a function is p.d. Indeed,

as is known, the integral $s(\lambda) = (2/\pi)\int_0^\infty k(t)\cos\lambda t\,dt$ for $\lambda \neq 0$ converges, while $s(\lambda) \geq 0$, $\int_{-\infty}^{\infty} s(\lambda)d\lambda < \infty$, and we have the representation

$$k(t) = \int_{-\infty}^{\infty} e^{i\lambda t} s(\lambda)\,d\lambda = \int_{-\infty}^{\infty} e^{i\lambda t} d\left(\int_{-\infty}^{\lambda} s(\mu)\,d\mu\right) \quad (t \in (-\infty, \infty)).$$

From this it follows that $k(t)$ is p. d.

If $k(t) \in C((-2l, 2l))$ $(0 < l < \infty)$ is an even positive convex (below) function, then it may be extended to the entire axis with the preservation of these properties in such a way that $\lim_{|t|\to\infty} k(t) = 0$. According to what has been proved the extended function is p. d., which implies that the original one was as well. Since there is an infinite collection of possible extensions, then for the original function the problem of extension is nondeterminate.

2. If $k_1(t), k_2(t) \in C((-2l, 2l))$ are p. d., then $k_1(t)k_2(t)$ is also p. d. This follows immediately from the definition of a p. d. function and the fact that if the matrices $\|a_{jk}\|_1^N$, $\|b_{jk}\|_1^N$ are nonnegative definite, then $\|a_{jk}b_{jk}\|_1^N$ is as well. The p. d. function $f(t) = k(t)\sum_{j=1}^m c_j e^{i\lambda_j t}$ $(c_j > 0)$, where $k(t)$ has the form indicated in 1, is nonuniquely extensible from $(-2l, 2l)$ to a p. d. function on the entire axis, since $k(t)$ is. Moreover, in distinction from example 1, $f(t)$ is nonmonotone for $t < 0$ and $t > 0$.

3. A function of type (3.40), for any $l < \infty$, is nonuniquely extensible to a p. d. function on the entire axis, if

$$\int_{-\infty}^{\infty} \frac{\log \sigma'(\lambda)}{1+\lambda^2}\,d\lambda > -\infty. \tag{3.55}$$

Indeed, suppose that (3.55) is satisfied, and $k(t)$ is uniquely extensible. From Theorem 3.12 there is now in $L_2((-\infty, \infty), d\sigma(\lambda))$ a dense collection of functions $\widetilde{C_0^\infty((-l, l))} \subseteq \widetilde{H}_K \subseteq L_2((-\infty, \infty), d\sigma(\lambda))$. Thus also $\widetilde{H}_K$ is dense in $L_2((-\infty, \infty), d\sigma(\lambda))$. But the linear combinations of the δ_ξ with $\xi \in [-l, l]$ are dense in H_K and therefore the combinations $\widetilde{\delta}(\lambda) = e^{i\lambda\xi}$ are dense in $\widetilde{H}_K$, and thus in $L_2((-\infty, \infty), d\sigma(\lambda))$ as well. Hence it clearly follows that the linear combinations $e^{i\lambda\eta}$, with $\eta \in [0, 2l]$, are dense in $L_2((-\infty, \infty), d\sigma(\lambda))$. This in turn is impossible along with the condition (3.55) (see the theorem cited in the proof of Theorem 1.8, Chapter VII). The assertion is proved.

4. We shall prove that smoothness of a p. d. function has no effect on its unique extensibility; there exist p. d. functions $k(t) \in C^\infty([-2l, 2l])$ which are

not uniquely extensible. Indeed, suppose that $l < l_1 < \infty$ and $k_1(t) \in C((-2l_1, 2l_1))$ is p. d. and nonuniquely extensible. We denote by $k_1(t)$, $k_2(t)$ two of its distinct extensions. Consider $\chi(t) \in C_0^\infty((-\infty, \infty))$, annihilating outside $(-\epsilon, \epsilon)$ $(\epsilon > 0)$. Then the convolution $k_j * \chi$ lies in $C^\infty((-\infty, \infty))$, as well as the convolution $k_j * \chi * \chi^\circ$ $(j = 2, 3)$. Moreover this last convolution, as is easily verified, will be p. d.. For ϵ sufficiently small $(k_2 * \chi * \chi^\circ)(t) = (k_3 * \chi * \chi^\circ)(t)$ for $t \in [-2l, 2l]$, since $k_2(t) = k_3(t) = k_1(t)$ for $t \in (-2l_1, 2l_1)$. But in $(-\infty, \infty)$ $k_2 \not\equiv k_3$, so that with an appropriate choice of χ also $k_2 * \chi * \chi^\circ \not\equiv k_3 * \chi * \chi^\circ$. Thus, we have found a p. d. function $k_2 * \chi * \chi^\circ \in C^\infty([-2l, 2l])$ having two distinct extensions into a p. d. function on the entire axis $(-\infty, \infty)$.

We note that the example which we have just constructed may also be easily found on the basis of Example 3. Indeed, the function $k(t) = \int_{-\infty}^{\infty} e^{i\lambda t} e^{-|\lambda|^{1/2}} d\lambda \in C^\infty((-\infty, \infty))$ is p. d. as well, and moreover since now $\sigma'(\lambda) = e^{-|\lambda|^{1/2}}$, then the integral (3. 55) converges.

We shall not dwell any further on examples. We note only that Examples 1–3 bore the following character: the p. d. function $k(t)$ was given on $(-2l, 2l)$ $(0 < l < \infty)$, and it could be nonuniquely extended to any interval $(-2m, 2m)$, where $0 < m < l$. It turns out that one may adduce also examples of p. d. functions given on $(-2l, 2l)$ $(0 < l < \infty)$, which from any interval $(-2m, 2m)$ with $0 < m < l$ extend nonuniquely, and extend from $(-2l, 2l)$ uniquely. There exist examples of p. d. functions which can be extended nonuniquely from $(-2l, 2l)$, and from any interval $(-2m, 2m)$, where $m > l$, uniquely.

We shall present a sufficient criterion for determinateness of the problem of extension. In doing this we use a result from the theory of moments, which will be presented in §5. First of all we verify a lemma.

Lemma 3. 8. *Consider the p. d. function* $k(t) \in C((-2l, 2l))$ $(0 < l \leq \infty)$, *and let* (3. 40) *be its integral representation. If for some* $m = 0, 1, \cdots$

$$\int_{-\infty}^{\infty} \lambda^{2m} d\sigma(\lambda) < \infty, \tag{3. 56}$$

then $k(t) \in C^{2m}([-2l, 2l])$. *On the other hand, if the derivative* $(d^{2m}k/dt^{2m})(0)$ *exists, then the integral* (3. 56) *converges.*

Proof. Suppose that (3. 56) is satisfied. Then we may differentiate the integral in (3. 40) and $k \in C^{2m}([-2l, 2l])$. Conversely, suppose that the derivative $(d^{2m}k/dt^{2m})(0)$ exists. We have $(\Delta_h^{2m}k)(0) \to_{h\to 0} (d^{2m}k/dt^{2m})(0)$, where

$(\Delta_h f)(t) = [f(t+h) - f(t-h)]/2h$. Moreover $(\Delta_h e^{i\lambda\cdot})(t) = (i/h)\sin \lambda h \cdot e^{i\lambda t}$, $(\Delta_h^{2m} e^{i\lambda\cdot})(t) = ((i/h)\sin\lambda h)^{2m} \cdot e^{i\lambda t}$. Therefore, subtracting from both sides of equation (3. 40) the difference Δ_h^{2m} for $t = 0$, we find that

$$(-1)^m (\Delta_h^{2m} k)(0) = \int_{-\infty}^{\infty} \left(\frac{\sin \lambda h}{h}\right)^{2m} d\sigma(\lambda) \geqslant \int_{-N}^{N} \left(\frac{\sin \lambda h}{\lambda h}\right)^{2m} \lambda^{2m} d\sigma(\lambda)\ (N > 0).$$

Now passing to the limit as $h \to 0$ and taking account of the existence of the limit on the left side, we find that (3. 56) holds. The lemma is proved.

Theorem 3. 13. *Suppose that $k(t) \in C((-2l, 2l))$ $(0 < l < \infty)$ is p. d. and such that all the derivatives $k^{(m)}(0)$, $m = 1, 2, \cdots$, exist. If*

$$\sum_{m=0}^{\infty} \frac{1}{\sqrt[2m]{(-1)^m k^{(2m)}(0)}} = \infty, \tag{3. 57}$$

then the problem of extension is determinate.

Proof. It follows from Lemma 3. 8 that $k(t) \in C^\infty([-2l, 2l])$. If $d\sigma(\lambda)$ is some measure yielding the representation (3. 40) for $k(t)$ for $t \in [-2l, 2l]$, then the integral (3. 56) converges for any $m = 0, 1, \cdots$. Thus the representation (3. 40) may be differentiated under the integral sign. Putting $t = 0$, we find that

$$(-i)^m k^{(m)}(0) = \int_{-\infty}^{\infty} \lambda^m d\sigma(\lambda) \quad (m = 0, 1, \ldots).$$

We have found that the numbers $s_m = (-1)^m k^m(0)$, $m = 0, 1, \cdots$ form a moment sequence. For determinateness of the problem of moments, i. e. for the unique definition of $d\sigma(\lambda)$ from s_m, it suffices that the criterion $\Sigma_{m=0}^\infty (s_{2m})^{-1/2m} = \infty$ holds (see §5. 4). It follows from (3. 57) that in our case the last condition is satisfied. Thus $d\sigma(\lambda)$ is uniquely determined by $k(t)$ $(t \in (-2l, 2l))$, i. e. the problem of extension is determinate. The theorem is proved.

We wish to emphasize that Lemma 3. 8 implies the infinite differentiability of $k(t)$, for which the $k^{(m)}(0)$ $(m = 1, 2, \cdots)$ exist, and of its extension. For an $f(z)$ analytic in the neighborhood of 0 the estimate $|f^{(m)}|(0) \leq CR^m m!$ $(m = 0, 1, \cdots)$ holds. Then condition (3. 57) is satisfied and such an $f(t)$ extends uniquely. Besides, this result is a consequence of a more simple fact: if the p. d. function $k(t) \in C(-\infty, \infty)$ is analytic in the neighborhood of 0, then it is analytic everywhere. The proof of this fact uses arguments close to those in the proof of Lemma 4. 2 of Chapter V. Indeed, we need to construct from the kernel $K(x, y) = k(y - x)$ the space $\mathfrak{H}_K$ and to prove that e_x depends analytically on x.

In what follows we shall need the form of the adjoint operator C^* to an operator C. *Suppose that* $\mathbf{I}$ *is constructed relative to the chain* $H_k \supseteq H_0 \supseteq H_{+,k}$. *Then*

$$C^*\alpha = i\mathbf{I}^{-1}(\mathbf{I}\alpha)'; \tag{3.58}$$

$\mathfrak{D}(C)$ *consists of those and only those* $\alpha \in H_k$ *for which* $\mathbf{I}\alpha \in ([-l, l])$, *while* $(\mathbf{I}\alpha)' \in H_{+,k}$. In fact, suppose that $\alpha \in H_k$ is such that $\langle iu', \alpha\rangle = \langle u, \beta\rangle$ $(u \in C_0^\infty(-l, l))$ for some $\beta = C^*\alpha$. Then $(iu', \mathbf{I}\alpha)_0 = (u, \mathbf{I}\beta)_0$ for those same u, while $\mathbf{I}\beta \in H_{+,K} \subseteq C([-l, l])$. Therefore, thanks to what was said in Chapter VI, §5. 1, $\mathbf{I}\alpha \in C^1([-l, l])$ and $i(\mathbf{I}\alpha)' = \mathbf{I}\beta$, i.e. $C^*\alpha = \beta = i\mathbf{I}^{-1}(\mathbf{I}\alpha)'$.

On one side the inclusion is established; by inverting the argument, we prove it also on the other side. Relation (3. 58) is proved.

It follows from (3. 58) that the operator C^* differs essentially from the analogous operator L^* in the case of difference equations; in distinction from L^* it generally speaking is not defined on the δ-functions δ_ξ $(\xi \in [-l, l])$, since $(\mathbf{I}\delta_\xi)(y) = k(y - \xi)$ in the general case is not differentiable. This distinction will somewhat disturb the analogy between the following constructions of subsection 9 and the exposition of §1, Chapter VII. On the other hand we note that the latter exposition could have been somewhat modified in the direction of the proofs presented in the following subsection.

As usual, we denote by $\overline{C}$ the closure of the operator C in H_K. Consider the subspace $\mathfrak{R}(\overline{C} - zE)$ $(\operatorname{Im} z \neq 0)$ of the space H_K and the orthogonal complement N_z to it, the defect subspace. It follows from (3. 58) that *the defect index of the operator* C *has the form* $(0, 0)$ *or* $(1, 1)$; *in the latter case the defect subspace* N_z *consists of scalar multiples of the vector* $\mathbf{I}^{-1}e^{-i\bar{z}x} \in H_k$. In fact, the defect numbers of C are equal because of their reality relative to the involution $\circ$. Suppose now that the operator $\overline{C}$ is nonselfadjoint. Then N_z coincides with the subspace of solutions of the equation $C^*\phi = \bar{z}\phi$. From (3. 58), this last equation means that on $[-l, l]$ $i(\mathbf{I}\phi)' = \bar{z}\mathbf{I}\phi$, i.e. $\mathbf{I}\phi = ae^{-i\bar{z}x}$ $(x \in [-l, l])$, where a is a scalar. Thus $\phi = a\mathbf{I}^{-1}e^{-i\bar{z}x}$, as required.

Thus the selfadjointness of $\overline{C}$ is a delicate fact, resting on the structure of $k(t)$. If this function is such that for $\operatorname{Im} z \neq 0$ $e^{-izx}\overline{\in} H_{+,k}$, then $\overline{C}$ is selfadjoint, and in the contrary case not. Thus, and from Lemma 3.7, we immediately obtain

Theorem 3.14. *Suppose that $k(t) \in C((-2l, 2l))$ $(0 < l < \infty)$ is a p. d. function. Consider a complete collection of orthonormalized eigenfunctions $w_1(x)$, $w_2(x), \cdots \in L_2((-l, l))$ of the kernel $K(x, y) = k(y-x)$ $(x, y \in (-l, l))$, corresponding to positive eigenvalues:*

$$\int_{-l}^{l} k(y-x)\, w_j(y)\, dy = \varrho_j w_j(x) \quad (x \in (-l, l),\ \varrho_j > 0,\ j = 1, 2, \ldots).$$

In order that the problem of extending $k(t)$ should be determinate, it is sufficient that for some nonreal z, and necessary that for any nonreal z, the following condition be satisfied:

$$\sum_{j=1}^{\infty} \frac{1}{\varrho_j} \left| \int_{-l}^{l} e^{-izx}\, \overline{w_j(x)}\, dx \right|^2 = \infty. \tag{3.59}$$

We note that while in equation (3.57) there appear only values of $k(t)$ near zero, in condition (3.59) there figure values of $k(t)$ on the entire interval $(-2l, 2l)$. In the first case the extension of $k(t)$ from any interval $(-l, l)$ is unique, and in the second case only from the interval in question.

In concluding this subsection we make some observations. First of all *we shall show that $C^1([-l, l]) \subset \mathfrak{D}(C^*)$ and*

$$C^* v = i\left[\frac{dv}{dx} + v(-l)\,\delta_{-l} - v(l)\,\delta_l\right] \quad (v \in C^1([-l, l])). \tag{3.60}$$

Indeed, suppose that $u \in C_0^{\infty}((-l, l))$. Extending it to zero on the entire axis, we obtain

$$\langle Cu, v\rangle$$

$$= \int_{-l}^{l}\int_{-l}^{l} k(y-x)\, iu'(y)\, \overline{v(x)}\, dx dy$$

$$= i \int_{-l}^{l} \left(\int_{-\infty}^{\infty} k(y-x)\, u'(y)\, dy \right) \overline{v(x)}\, dx$$

$$= i \int_{-l}^{l} \frac{d}{dx} \left(\int_{-\infty}^{\infty} k(t)\, u(t+x)\, dt \right) \overline{v(x)}\, dx =$$

$$= i \int_{-\infty}^{\infty} k(t)\, u(t+l)\, dt\, \overline{v(l)}$$

$$- i \int_{-\infty}^{\infty} k(t)\, u(t-l)\, dt\, \overline{v(-l)}$$

$$- i \int_{-l}^{l} \left(\int_{-\infty}^{\infty} k(t)\, u(t+x)\, dt \right) \overline{v'(x)}\, dx$$

$$= i \int_{-l}^{l} k(y-l)\, u(y) \overline{v(l)}\, dy - i \int_{-l}^{l} k(y+l)\, u(y)\, \overline{v(-l)}\, dy + \langle u, iv' \rangle$$

$$= \langle u, i\, [v' + v(-l)\, \delta_{-l} - v(l)\, \delta_l]\ \rangle ,$$

which proves (3.60).

We assume that the p. d. *function* $k(t) \in C^2([-2l, 2l])$. *Then* $C^1([-l, l]) \subset \mathfrak{D}(\overline{C})$ *and*

$$\overline{C}u = i\left[\frac{du}{dx} + u(-l)\, \delta_{-l} - u(l)\, \delta_l\right] \quad (u \in C^1([-l, l])). \tag{3.61}$$

Indeed,, suppose that the sequence $u_n \in C_0^\infty((-l, l))$ is such that in $L_2((-l, l))$ (and therefore also in H_k) it converges to $u \in C^1([-l, l])$. Then Cu_n is fundamental in H_k. Integrating by parts, we obtain

$$\langle Cu_n - Cu_m, Cu_n - Cu_m \rangle = \int_{-l}^{l} \int_{-l}^{l} k(y-x)\, (u_n(y)$$

$$- u_m(y))' \overline{(u_n(x) - u_m(x))'}\, dx dy$$

$$= - \int_{-l}^{l} \int_{-l}^{l} k''(y-x)\, (u_n(y) - u_m(y))\, \overline{(u_n(x) - u_m(x))}\, dx dy \underset{n,m\to\infty}{\longrightarrow} 0.$$

Because of the completeness of H_k there is an $\alpha \in H_k$ such that $Cu_n \to \alpha$ in H_k. Hence for $u \in C^1([-l, l])$ we have found a sequence $u_n \in C_0^\infty((-l, l))$ such that in H_k $u_n \to u$ and $Cu_n \to \alpha$. This shows that $u \in \mathfrak{D}(\overline{C})$. Since C is Hermitian, $C \subseteq C^*$; thus also $\overline{C} \subseteq C^*$. But on $C([-l, l])$ the operator C^* operates according to (3.60), so that for $\overline{C}u = C^* u$ equation (3.61) holds. The assertion is proved.

It follows from (3.60) and (3.61) that if $k(t) \in C^2([-2l, 2l])$, then the operators $\overline{C}$ and C^* coincide on $C^1([-l, l])$. However it does not follow from this that $\overline{C} = C^*$, since in distinction from ordinary differential operators in the space $L_2(G)$, generally speaking, C^* does not coincide with its closure from functions on $C^1([-l, l])$.

For any $\alpha \in \mathfrak{D}(C^*)$, from what was proved earlier $\mathbf{I}\alpha \in C^1([-l, l]) \subset \mathfrak{D}(C^*)$, i.e. $\mathbf{I}\mathfrak{D}(C^*) \subset \mathfrak{D}(C^*)$.

From (3.58) and (3.60) follows the following commutativity relation for the operators C^* and $\mathbf{I}$:

$$C^* \mathbf{I}\alpha - \mathbf{I}C^*\alpha = i\,[(\mathbf{I}\alpha)(-l)\,\delta_{-l} - (\mathbf{I}\alpha)(l)\,\delta_l] \quad (\alpha \in \mathfrak{D}(C^*)). \tag{3.62}$$

Indeed,

$$C^*\mathbf{I}\alpha - \mathbf{I}C^*\alpha = i\,[(\mathbf{I}\alpha)' + (\mathbf{I}\alpha)(-l)\delta_{-l} - (\mathbf{I}\alpha)(l)\delta_l] - i\,\mathbf{I}\mathbf{I}^{-1}(\mathbf{I}\alpha)' = i\,[(\mathbf{I}\alpha)(-l)\delta_{-l} - (\mathbf{I}\alpha)(l)\delta_l].$$

9. **Description of all extensions.** We turn to the description of all extensions of a p.d. function $k(t)$ $(t \in (-2l, 2l))$ to a p.d. function on the entire axis in the case of their nonuniqueness. As we have already said, we obtain a theory analogous to the theory of the nondeterminate case for Jacobian matrices.

First of all we present a construction similar to that given on pages 524–526. We fix a nonreal z and decompose the vector $\delta_0 \in H_k$ relative to $\mathfrak{R}(\overline{C} - zE)$ and N_z:

$$\delta_0 = e_z + i_z \qquad (e_z \in \mathfrak{R}(\overline{C} - zE),\ i_z \in N_z).$$

We shall show that *the operator $\overline{C}$ is selfadjoint if and only if $i_z = 0$.* Indeed, if $\overline{C}$ is selfadjoint then $\mathfrak{R}(\overline{C} - zE) = H_k$ and $i_z = 0$. If $\overline{C}$ is nonselfadjoint, then $N_z = \{a\mathbf{I}^{-1}e^{-i\bar{z}x}\}$. We have $\langle \delta_0, \mathbf{I}^{-1}e^{-i\bar{z}x}\rangle = (\delta_0, e^{-i\bar{z}x})_0 = 1$, i.e. the component of δ_0 in N_z differs from zero. In other words, $i_z \neq 0$. The assertion is proved.

Suppose that ψ is a normed vector $\mathbf{I}^{-1}e^{-i\bar{z}x}$, i.e. $\psi = \mathbf{I}^{-1}e^{-i\bar{z}x} \times \langle \mathbf{I}^{-1}e^{-i\bar{z}x}, \mathbf{I}^{-1}e^{-i\bar{z}x}\rangle^{-1/2}$. Since $i_z = \langle \delta_0, \psi\rangle\psi$, we have $\langle i_z, i_z\rangle = |\langle \delta_0, \psi\rangle|^2$ and we obtain the following formula for the square of the distance in H_k of the vector δ_0 to $\sigma(\overline{C} - zE)$:

$$\rho^2(\delta_0, \mathfrak{R}(\overline{C} - zE)) = \langle i_z, i_z\rangle = \langle \mathbf{I}^{-1}e^{-i\bar{z}x}, \mathbf{I}^{-1}e^{-i\bar{z}x}\rangle^{-1}.$$

This formula remains valid also for selfadjoint $\overline{C}$: now $\mathbf{I}^{-1}e^{-i\bar{z}x} \overline{\in} H_k$, i.e. $\langle \mathbf{I}^{-1}e^{-i\bar{z}x}, \mathbf{I}^{-1}e^{-i\bar{z}x}\rangle = \infty$, while moreover $i_z = 0$.

We introduce an analogue of polynomials of the first kind. In distinction from the difference case their construction is nonunique.[1] Moreover, they are not "polynomials" in our sense: they do not belong to $C_0^\infty((-l, l))$. Suppose that $x_0 = 0, x_1, x_2, \cdots$ is a countable sequence of points everywhere dense on $[-l, l]$. We include among their number the point 0, though this was not essential. Consider the sequence of δ-functions $\delta_{x_0} = \delta_0, \delta_{x_1}, \delta_{x_2}, \cdots \in H_k$, and carry out their orthogonalization: $p_0 = \delta_0, p_1, p_2, \cdots \in H_k$ is the resulting orthonormalized system. Since the linear envelope of the vectors δ_{x_j} is dense in H_k (see page 664), then $p_0, p_1, \cdots$ form an orthonormalized basis in H_k. We have $\tilde{\delta}_{x_j}(\lambda) = e^{i\lambda x_j}$, so that each $\tilde{p}_j(\lambda) = P_j(\lambda)$ is a linear combination of a finite number of exponentials $e^{i\lambda x_k}$. The system of "functions of the first kind" $P_0(\lambda) \equiv 1, P_1(\lambda), \cdots$, forms an orthonormalized basis in $\tilde{H}_k$. We emphasize that the construction of the $P_j(\lambda)$ does not depend on the choice of $d\sigma(\lambda)$, i.e. on the form of the selfadjoint extension of the operator C.

We shall consider the nondeterminate case of extension, i.e. $\overline{C}$ is supposed nonselfadjoint. We have $\left\langle \mathrm{I}^{-1} e^{-i\bar{z}x}, \delta_{x_j} \right\rangle = (e^{-i\bar{z}x}, \delta_{x_j})_0 = e^{i\bar{z}x_j}$, so that

$$\langle \mathrm{I}^{-1} e^{-i\bar{z}x}, p_j \rangle = P_j(-\bar{z}) \ (j = 0, 1, \ldots ; \ \mathrm{Im}\, z \neq 0). \tag{3.63}$$

Therefore we have the important equation

$$\langle \mathrm{I}^{-1} e^{izx}, \mathrm{I}^{-1} e^{izx} \rangle = \sum_{j=0}^{\infty} | P_j(z) |^2, \ \varrho^2(\delta_0, \mathfrak{R}(\overline{C} - zE)) = \langle i_z, i_z \rangle$$
$$= \frac{1}{\sum_{j=0}^{\infty} | P_j(-\bar{z}) |^2} \quad (\mathrm{Im}\, z \neq 0). \tag{3.64}$$

The series above are in fact infinite and not finite sums, since the latter is possible only when the process of orthogonalization leads to a system $\{p_j\}$ for which beginning with some index k $p_k = p_{k+1} = \cdots = 0$. But then, from Theorem 3.8, the problem of extension is determinate, which contradicts our hypothesis. It follows from (3.64) that in the nondeterminate case for any nonreal z the series

$$\sum_{j=0}^{\infty} | P_j(z) |^2 \tag{3.65}$$

---

[1] The functions $P_j(\lambda)$ and $Q_j(\lambda)$ considered below may be called analogs of polynomials of the first and second kind only very conditionally-only on the basis of the closeness of the constructions of this subsection and of Chapter VII, §§1.6–1.8. True analogs of these polynomials arise in the continual "orthogonalization" δ_x (see "Literature notes").

converges. Conversely, if for some nonreal z the series (3.65) converges, then the extension problem is indeterminate.

We turn to the construction of analogs of polynomials of the second kind. Suppose that z and ζ are arbitrary complex numbers, and that $\xi \in [-l, l]$. There exists a vector $\gamma_{\xi, z} \in L_2((-l, l)) \subseteq H_k$ such that

$$\tilde{\gamma}_{\xi,z}(\zeta) = \frac{e^{i\zeta\xi} - e^{iz\xi}}{\zeta - z} = \tilde{\gamma}_{\xi,\zeta}(z). \tag{3.66}$$

If ζ and z coincide we take the limit in (3.66). Here $\gamma_{\xi, z}$ is a continuous vector-function with values in $L_2((-l, l))$ of the point (ξ, z) and holomorphic (entire), as a function of the point z for each fixed ξ. Indeed, put $\gamma_{\xi, z}(x) = i\kappa_{(0, \xi)}(x)e^{iz(\xi - x)} \in L_2((-l, l))$ ($\kappa_{(a, b)}(x)$ is the characteristic function of the interval (a, b)). Evidently $\gamma_{\xi, z}$ possesses the required properties of continuity in (ξ, z) and holomorphicity in z. (3.66) is also satisfied: for $\zeta \neq z$

$$\tilde{\gamma}_{\xi,z}(\zeta) = \int_{-l}^{l} \gamma_{\xi,z}(x)\, e^{i\zeta x}\, dx = i\int_{0}^{\xi} e^{iz(\xi - x)}\, e^{i\zeta x}\, dx = \frac{e^{i\zeta\xi} - e^{iz\xi}}{\zeta - z}.$$

Since $p_j = \sum_{k=0}^{j} c_k \delta_{x_k}$ it follows that $q_{j, z} = \sum_{k=0}^{j} c_k \gamma_{x_k, z} \in H_k$ $(j = 0, 1, \ldots)$ has, from (3.66), the property that $\tilde{q}_{j, z}(\lambda) = (P_j(\lambda) - P_j(z))\,(\lambda - z)^{-1}$; $q_{j, z}$ is a holomorphic vector-function of z with values in H_k. Consider the holomorphic function $Q_j(z) = \langle q_{j, z}, \delta_0\rangle$. Using Parseval's equation (3.52) (with $\Delta = (-\infty, \infty)$) we obtain for any z

$$Q_j(z) = \langle q_{j\, z}, \delta_0 \rangle = \int_{-\infty}^{\infty} \frac{P_j(\lambda) - P_j(z)}{\lambda - z}\, d\sigma(\lambda) \quad (j = 0, 1, \ldots;\ Q_0(z) = 0). \tag{3.67}$$

As earlier, as z approaches the real axis we have to take the limit of the integrand. The "functions of the second kind" $Q_j(z)$ will play the role of the polynomials $Q_j(z)$ in our problem. We note that the definition in terms of $\langle \cdot, \cdot \rangle$ shows that their form does not depend on the choice of the measure $d\sigma(\lambda)$, i.e. on the extension of C.

Each of the functions $Q_j(z)$ is bounded on the real axis and therefore lies in $L_2((-\infty, \infty), d\sigma(\lambda))$. For the proof of boundedness we note that $(P_j(\lambda) - P_j(z))\,(\lambda - z)^{-1} = (dP_j/d\lambda)(\theta_{\lambda, z})$, where $\theta_{\lambda, z}$ is some point of the segment joining λ and z. But $P_j(\lambda) = \sum_{k=0}^{j} c_k e^{i\lambda x_k}$, so that $(dP_j/d\lambda)(\theta_{\lambda, z}) = i\sum_{k=0}^{j} c_k x_k e^{i\theta_{\lambda, z} x_k}$, which proved the uniform boundedness relative to λ and

z of the quotient $(P_j(\lambda) - P_j(z))\,(\lambda - z)^{-1}$. The assertion follows from this and from (3.67).

Now the results of §1.6, Chapter VII carry over to our case. First of all we establish some equations connected generally speaking with the generalized resolvent R_z of the operator C. Thus, its kernel $R(x, y; z)$ has a representation analogous to the representation (1.37) of Chapter VII:

$$R(x, y; z) = \langle R_z\delta_y, \delta_x \rangle = \int_{-\infty}^{\infty} \frac{e^{i\lambda(y-x)}}{\lambda - z}\, d\sigma(\lambda) \quad (x, y \in [-l, l]). \tag{3.68}$$

Indeed, suppose that $x, y \in (-l, l)$. We need to use the representation (3.16), taking as u and v in it singular sequences of continuous functions, converging in the sense of H_k to δ_x and δ_y respectively (cf. page 648). After passing to the limit we obtain $R(x, y; z) = \langle R_z\delta_y, \delta_x\rangle$ $(x, y \in (-l, l))$. The kernel R at the endpoints $-l, l$ is defined simply as the corresponding limit of $\langle R_z\delta_y, \delta_x\rangle$ (it exists because δ_ξ is a continuous vector-function with values in H_k: $\xi \in [-l, l]$). The second equation in (3.68) follows either from (3.17) or from (3.52).

However the representation (3.68) is not very useful for our purposes, since the δ_x are not orthonormalized in H_k. Therefore we proceed as follows. We write R_z in terms of an orthonormalized basis in H_k of the form $p_0 = \delta_0, p_1, \cdots$, and then for the matrices of this operator we obtain the formula, analogous to (1.37):

$$R_{z;jk} = \langle R_z p_k, p_j \rangle = \int_{-\infty}^{\infty} \frac{\overline{P_j(\lambda)}\, P_k(\lambda)}{\lambda - z}\, d\sigma(\lambda) \quad (j, k = 0, 1, \ldots). \tag{3.69}$$

The measure $d\sigma(\lambda)$ is uniquely restored by holomorphy outside the spectrum of the corresponding extension of the operator C of the function

$$m(z) = R_{z;00} = R(0, 0; z) = \int_{-\infty}^{\infty} \frac{d\sigma(\lambda)}{\lambda - z}. \tag{3.70}$$

We introduce for functions of the form $F(z) = \sum_{k=0}^{n} c_k e^{izx_k}$ $(x_k \in [-l, l])$ the operation

$$F(z) \to \bar{F}(z) = \overline{F(\bar{z})} = \sum_{k=0}^{n} \bar{c}_k\, e^{-izx_k}.$$

Repeating the calculations of page 522 for arbitrary regular z and ζ, we obtain

$$(R_z p_0)_j = \bar{Q}_j(z) + m(z)\bar{P}_j(z) \quad (j = 0, 1, \ldots). \tag{3.71}$$

$$\frac{\overline{m(\zeta)} - m(z)}{\bar{\zeta} - z} = \sum_{j=0}^{\infty} (\bar{Q}_j(z) + m(z)\bar{P}_j(z))\,\overline{(\bar{Q}_j(\zeta) + m(\zeta)\bar{P}_j(\zeta))} \quad (\bar{\zeta} \neq z),$$

$$\frac{\overline{m(z)} - m(z)}{\bar{z} - z} = \sum_{j=0}^{\infty} |\bar{Q}_j(z) + m(z)\bar{P}_j(z)|^2 \quad (\operatorname{Im} z \neq 0).$$

In these two equations we assume that R_z is an ordinary resolvent. If it is generalized, then only the first and third relations remain, while in the third the equal sign may be replaced by $\geq$.

We need some information on trigonometric polynomials.[1] We fix $A > 0$ and consider on the interval $[-A, A)$ a trigonometric polynomial of the nth order with real coefficients, i. e. a function of the form

$$P(z) = a_0 + \sum_{j=1}^{n} \left(a_j \cos\frac{j z\pi}{A} + b_j \sin\frac{j z\pi}{A}\right) \quad (\operatorname{Im} a_j = \operatorname{Im} b_j = 0).$$

$P(z)$ has on $[-A, A)$ not more than $2n$ roots. It follows from its continuity that the number of zeros on $[-A, A)$, at which a change of sign takes place, is necessarily even. We denote these zeros by $\alpha_1, \ldots, \alpha_{2p}$, $0 \leq p \leq n$. The following representation holds:

$$P(z) = \pm \prod_{k=1}^{2p} \sin\frac{(z - \alpha_k)\pi}{2A} \left|\sum_{\nu=0}^{n-p} c_\nu e^{i\frac{\nu z\pi}{A}}\right|^2, \tag{3.72}$$

where the c_ν are complex coefficients.[1]

We shall establish one fact, analogous to Lemma 1.4 of Chapter VII. Consider the complex linear envelope of the functions

$$1, \cos\frac{z\pi}{A}, \sin\frac{z\pi}{A}, \ldots, \cos\frac{jz\pi}{A}, \sin\frac{jz\pi}{A}, \ldots, \tag{3.73}$$

---

[1] See for example G. Pólya and G. Szegö [1], section VI, problems 11, 40, Formula (3.72) follows from the representation $g(\theta) = e^{-in\theta} G(e^{i\theta})$ of problem 11, if one extracts from the polynomial $G(z)$ the factors corresponding to the real zeros $g(\theta)$ of type α_j (they yield a product of sines), and to the remaining portion apply the result of problem 40.

i. e. the collection of all complex polynomials with a fixed A. We suppose that we have introduced onto these polynomials a nondegenerate scalar product of the form $(P, Q) = \int_{-\infty}^{\infty} P(\lambda)\overline{Q(\lambda)}\,d\sigma(\lambda)$, where $d\sigma(\lambda)$ is a nonnegative finite measure. We carry out an orthogonalization of the sequence (3.73), using real linear combinations. Suppose that $P_0(z), P_1'(z), P_1''(z), \cdots, P_j'(z), P_j''(z), \cdots$ is the resulting orthogonal system. We assert that $P_n'(z)P_n''(z)$ *has exactly* $2n$ *real roots on* $[-A, A)$, *and that these roots are simple.* Consider, for example, the polynomial $P_n'(z)$. Suppose the contrary. Then in the representation (3.72) for $P_n'(z)$ we will have $p < n$. Put

$$R(z)=\prod_{k=1}^{2p}\sin\frac{(z-\alpha_k)\pi}{2A}\times\sum_{\nu=0}^{n-p}c_\nu e^{i\frac{\nu z\pi}{A}}.$$

Replacing the sine by Euler's formula, we find that $R(z)$ is a linear combination of functions $1, e^{iz\pi/A}, \cdots, e^{inz\pi/A}$, i. e. a trigonometric polynomial with complex coefficients. By hypothesis $(R, R) > 0$. At the same time

$$(R, R)=\left(P_n'(z), \prod_{k=1}^{2p}\sin\frac{(z-\alpha_k)\pi}{2A}\right)=0,$$

since as a product of sines it is a linear combination with real coefficients of the first $1 + 2p$ functions of (3.73), i. e. of the polynomials $P_0(z), \cdots, P_p'(z), P_p''(z)$. The assertion is proved.

From this it follows that *for the polynomials* $P_0(z), P_1'(z), P_1''(z), \cdots$ *estimates of the following form are valid*:

$$|P(x+iy')| \leqslant |P(x+iy'')| \qquad (|y'| \leqslant |y''|). \tag{3.74}$$

In fact, for these polynomials, in the representation (3.72) there appeared only a product of sines. Noting that $|\sin(x + iy - \alpha_k)\pi/2A|$ is a monotonically increasing function of $|y|$, we arrive at (3.74).

Now we turn to the problem of extension of a p. d. function. The role of Lemma 1.5, Chapter VII, is played by the following lemma.

Lemma 3.9. *In the nondeterminate case the series* $\sum_{j=0}^{\infty}|P_j(z)|^2$ *and* $\sum_{j=0}^{\infty}|Q_j(z)|^2$ *converge for any* z, *while their sums are uniformly bounded in each bounded portion of the complex plane.*

Proof. This will be accomplished in steps.

1. Suppose that G is a bounded region of the complex plane, situated at a positive distance from the real axis. We first show that for $z \in G\setminus\mathfrak{N}$, where $\mathfrak{N}$

is some maximal finite set of points, the series $\Sigma_{j=0}^{\infty} |P_j(z)|^2$, $\Sigma_{j=0}^{\infty} |Q_j(z)|^2$ converge uniformly. The proof will follow the proof of Lemma 1.5 of Chapter VII. Consider some function $m(z)$ of the form (3.70). Suppose that $z \in G'$ (G' is the set of points complexly conjugate to G). For such z the last series in (3.71), i.e. $\Sigma_{j=0}^{\infty} |\overline{Q}_j(z) + m(z)\overline{P}_j(z)|^2$, will converge to a continuous function and therefore by Dini's theorem will converge uniformly. Suppose that $m_1(z)$ is another function of the form (3.70). From the uniform convergence of the second series $\Sigma_{j=0}^{\infty} |\overline{Q}_j(z) + m_1(z)\overline{P}_j(z)|^2$ in G', we may compute that $|m(z) - m_1(z)| \Sigma_{j=0}^{\infty} |\overline{P}_j(z)|^2$ also converges uniformly for $z \in G'$, i.e. $\Sigma_{j=0}^{\infty} |\overline{P}_j(z)|^2$ for $z \in G' \backslash \mathfrak{N}'$, which means $\Sigma_{j=0}^{\infty} |P_j(z)|^2 = \Sigma_{j=0}^{\infty} |\overline{P}_j(\overline{z})|^2$ for $z \in G \backslash \mathfrak{N}$. Comparing the series $\Sigma_{j=0}^{\infty} |\overline{P}_j(z)|^2$ and $\Sigma_{j=0}^{\infty} |\overline{Q}_j(z) + m(z)\overline{P}_j(z)|^2$ for $z \in G' \backslash \mathfrak{N}'$, we conclude that the series $\Sigma_{j=0}^{\infty} |\overline{Q}_j(z)|^2$ converges uniformly for $z \in G' \backslash \mathfrak{N}'$ and therefore also the series $\Sigma_{j=0}^{\infty} |Q_j(z)|^2$ for $z \in G \backslash \mathfrak{N}$. The assertion is proved.

2. Now we shall prove the uniform convergence of the series (3.65) in any bounded region of the complex plane for a special choice of the points $x_0 = 0$, $x_1, x_2, \cdots \in [-l, l]$, defining the functions $P_j(z)$. Indeed, for these points we may choose a sequence, everywhere dense in $[-l, l]$:

$$0; -\frac{1}{2}l, \frac{1}{2}l; -\frac{3}{4}l, -\frac{1}{4}l, \frac{1}{4}l, \frac{3}{4}l;$$

$$-\frac{7}{8}l, -\frac{5}{8}l, -\frac{3}{8}l, -\frac{1}{8}l, \frac{1}{8}l, \frac{3}{8}l, \frac{5}{8}l, \frac{7}{8}l; \dots \tag{3.75}$$

(we successively divide each interval into two equal parts). The orthogonalization of the vectors $\delta_{x_0}, \delta_{x_1}, \cdots$, in H_k, i.e. the orthogonalization of the functions $e^{i\lambda x_0}$, $e^{i\lambda x_1}, \cdots$, in $L_2((-\infty, \infty), d\sigma(\lambda))$, will be carried out as follows. We normalize $e^{i\lambda x_0} = 1$, and then instead of $e^{i\lambda(-l/2)}$ and $e^{i\lambda(l/2)}$ consider $\cos\lambda((1/2)t)$ and $\sin\lambda((1/2)t)$ and carry out the orthonormalization of 1, $\cos\lambda((1/2)t)$, and $\sin\lambda((1/2)t)$, using real linear combinations. Analogously we proceed further, replacing functions of the form $e^{-i\lambda s}$ and $e^{i\lambda s}$ by $\cos\lambda s$ and $\sin\lambda s$. As a result of such an orthogonalization the sequence $P_0(z)$, $P_1(z), \cdots$, will appear as $P_0(z)$, $P_1'(z)$, $P_1''(z)$, $P_2'(z)$, $\cdots$. But then for the functions of the first kind $P_0(z)$, $P_1(z), \cdots$, we will have estimates (3.74), which obviously make it possible to deduce from step 1 the required convergence of (3.65).

3. We shall establish the portion of the lemma relating to (3.65). Now we

denote by G any bounded region of the complex plane. Suppose that $P_0(z)$, $P_1(z), \cdots$, are functions of the first kind, constructed relative to any sequence $x_0 = 0$, $x_1, \cdots$, and $\hat{P}_0(z)$, $\hat{P}_1(z), \cdots$, the functions constructed in step 2. From (3.64), for $\operatorname{Im} z \neq 0$ we have $\Sigma_{j=0}^{\infty} |P_j(z)|^2 = \langle i_z, i_z \rangle^{-1} = \Sigma_{j=0}^{\infty} |\hat{P}_j(z)|^2$. But from step 2 the latter series converges uniformly in any bounded portion of the plane, so that the sum is continuous and $\Sigma_{j=0}^{\infty} |\hat{P}_j(z)|^2 \leq C_G (z \in G)$. For $z \in G \setminus (-\infty, \infty)$ we have $\Sigma_{j=0}^{N} |P_j(z)|^2 \leq \Sigma_{j=0}^{\infty} |\hat{P}_j(z)|^2 \leq C_G$. Now passing to the limit for z approaching the axis $(-\infty, \infty)$, we obtain $\Sigma_{j=0}^{N} |P_j(z)|^2 \leq C_G$ $(z \in G)$, i.e. $\Sigma_{j=0}^{\infty} |P_j(z)|^2 \leq C_G$ $(z \in G)$, as required.

4. Now we prove the portion of the lemma relating to the series $\Sigma_{j=0}^{\infty} |Q_j(z)|^2$. Here we do not use the preceding arguments at all, since for the functions $Q_j(z)$, even in the case of points of the form (3.75) there is no estimate of type (3.74), and we must proceed differently. Suppose that G and G' are as in step 3. From (3.70) there follows the estimate $|m(z)| \leq C_1 / |\operatorname{Im} z|$ $(\operatorname{Im} z \neq 0)$. Using this, we find from the last equation in (3.71) and from step 3 that

$$\sum_{j=0}^{\infty} |\overline{Q}_j(z) + m(z)\overline{P}_j(z)|^2 < \frac{C_1}{|\operatorname{Im} z|^2} \quad (\operatorname{Im} z \neq 0),$$

$$\sum_{j=0}^{\infty} |m(z)\overline{P}_j(z)|^2 < \frac{C_1^2 C_{\widetilde{G}'}}{|\operatorname{Im} z|^2} \quad (z \in \widetilde{G}',\ \operatorname{Im} z \neq 0),$$

where $\widetilde{G}'$ denotes the region consisting of the union of disks of radius 1 with centers at the points of G'. From the two estimates just obtained it follows that

$$\sum_{j=0}^{\infty} |\overline{Q}_j(z)|^2 < \frac{C_2}{|\operatorname{Im} z|^2} \quad (z \in \widetilde{G}',\ \operatorname{Im} z \neq 0). \tag{3.76}$$

We shall use the function $\log^+ t = \log t$ for $t \geq 1$ and equal to zero for $0 \leq t \leq 1$. It is easy to see that $\log^+(ab) \leq \log^+ a + \log^+ b$. From (3.76) it follows that $\log^+(\Sigma_{j=0}^{\infty} |\overline{Q}_j(z)|^2) \leq \log^+ C_2 + 2\log^+ (1/|\operatorname{Im} z|)$ $(z \in \widetilde{G}',\ \operatorname{Im} z \neq 0)$. Fix an integer N. Now we obtain $(z = x + iy)$:

$$\iint_{\widetilde{G}'} \overset{+}{\log}\left(\sum_{j=0}^{N} |\overline{Q}_j(z)|^2\right) dxdy < \iint_{\widetilde{G}'} \left(\overset{+}{\log} C_2 + 2\overset{+}{\log}\frac{1}{|y|}\right) dxdy = C_3 < \infty. \tag{3.77}$$

We shall show that the function $\log^+(\Sigma_{j=0}^N |\overline{Q}_j(z)|^2)$ is subharmonic.[1] In fact, $\log|\overline{Q}_j(z)|^2 = 2\log|\overline{Q}_j(z)|$ is subharmonic, since $\overline{Q}_j(z) = \overline{Q_j(\overline{z})}$ is an entire function. In other words, $|\overline{Q}_j(z)|^2$ is a logarithmic subharmonic function. It is known that a finite sum of logarithmic subharmonic functions is a logarithmic subharmonic function, i. e. $\log(\Sigma_{j=0}^N |\overline{Q}_j(z)|^2)$ is subharmonic. But then the upper envelope of this function and 0, i. e. $\log^+(\Sigma_{j=0}^N |\overline{Q}_j(z)|^2)$, is also subharmonic.

As is known, for a subharmonic function $f(z)$ the theorem of the mean is valid: $f(\zeta) \le (1/\pi r^2)\int_{|\zeta - z| \le r} f(z)\,dz$, given only that $r > 0$ is not so large that the disk $|\zeta - z| \le r$ extends beyond the region of definition of $f(z)$. Applying this theorem for $r = 1$ and $\zeta \in G'$ to the function $f(z) = \log^+(\Sigma_{j=0}^N |\overline{Q}_j(z)|^2)$ and using inequality (3.77), we obtain

$$\overset{+}{\log}\left(\sum_{j=0}^{N} |\overline{Q}_j(\zeta)|^2\right) \leqslant \frac{1}{\pi} \int\limits_{|\zeta - z| \leqslant 1} \overset{+}{\log}\left(\sum_{j=0}^{N} |\overline{Q}_j(z)|^2\right) dz$$

$$\leqslant \frac{1}{\pi} \iint\limits_{\widetilde{G'}} \overset{+}{\log}\left(\sum_{j=0}^{N} |\overline{Q}_j(z)|^2\right) dxdy \leqslant C_3.$$

Therefore $\Sigma_{j=0}^N |\overline{Q}_j(\zeta)|^2 \le e^{C_3}$, and thus $\Sigma_{j=0}^\infty |\overline{Q}_j(\zeta)|^2 \le e^{C_3}$ $(\zeta \in G')$, i. e. $\Sigma_{j=0}^\infty |Q_j(\zeta)|^2 \le e^{C_3}$ $(\zeta \in G)$. Step 4, and with it the lemma, is proved.

In distinction from Lemma 1. 5, Chapter VII, we have not established uniform convergence for $|z| \le C < \infty$ of the series of Lemma 3. 9 (although it holds). Restricting consideration to the series (3. 65), we shall prove this convergence. Similarly to the derivation of (3. 63) and (3. 64) we easily verify that in any case, determinate or not, we have the equation

$$\sum_{j=0}^{\infty} |P_j(z)|^2 = \langle \mathrm{I}^{-1} e^{izx}, \mathrm{I}^{-1} e^{izx} \rangle \tag{3.78}$$

for arbitrary complex z (∞ may appear on both sides of (3. 78)). Taking first as the functions $P_j(z)$ in (3. 78) specially constructed $\hat{P}_j(z)$, we show that $\langle \mathrm{I}^{-1} e^{izx}, \mathrm{I}^{-1} e^{izx} \rangle = \Sigma_{j=0}^\infty |\hat{P}_j(z)|^2$ continuously for any z. It follows from (3. 78) that also $\Sigma_{j=0}^\infty |P_j(z)|^2$ is continuous. Our assertion now follows from Dini's theorem.

---

1) For the facts used below on subharmonic functions, see for example I. I. Privalov [1], Chapter 3.

Thus we have established analogs of the basic facts used to prove Theorem 1.12, Chapter VII. Almost without changing the argument, we arrive at the proof of the following result.

Theorem 3.15. *Suppose that the extension problem for a p. d. function is nondeterminate. Fix a nonreal* z *and consider the point* $m(z) = \int_{-\infty}^{\infty}(\lambda-z)^{-1}d\sigma(\lambda)$, *where* $d\sigma(\lambda)$ *is an orthogonal (i. e. corresponding to an extension into* H_k) *spectral density. Running through all possible such densities, one finds that the point* $m(z)$ *describes a circumference* K_z *(analogous to the Weyl-Hamburger circumference), whose center and radius are computed from the formulas*

$$O(z) = -\frac{1}{\sum_{i=0}^{\infty} |\bar{P}_i(z)|^2}\left(\frac{1}{z-\bar{z}} + \sum_{i=0}^{\infty} P_i(\bar{z})\bar{Q}_i(z)\right)$$

and

$$R(z) = \frac{1}{|z-\bar{z}|\sum_{i=0}^{\infty}|\bar{P}_i(z)|^2}. \tag{3.79}$$

If the extension problem is determinate, then this circumference degenerates to a point.

The points w *of the circumference* K_z *stand in a* 1-1 *relationship with the orthogonal spectral measures* $d\sigma(\lambda)$, *and therefore, from* (3.52), *with the resolutions of the identity themselves. Indeed, to each* $d\sigma(\lambda)$ *there corresponds the point* $w^{\sigma} = m(z) = \int_{-\infty}^{\infty}(\lambda - z)^{-1}\,d\sigma(\lambda)$. *Conversely, to each* $w \in K_z$ *there corresponds a* $d\sigma(\lambda)$ *whose Stieltjes transform is computed according to the formula*

$$m(\zeta) = \frac{E_0(\zeta, z)\,w + E_1(\zeta, z)}{D_0(\zeta, z)\,w + D_1(\zeta, z)}, \tag{3.80}$$

where $E_0(\zeta, z)$, $E_1(\zeta, z)$, $D_0(\zeta, z)$ *and* $D_1(\zeta, z)$ *are entire functions in each variable with the other fixed, expressed by the series*

$$E_0(\zeta, z) = 1 + (\zeta - z)\sum_{i=0}^{\infty}\bar{Q}_i(\zeta)\bar{P}_i(z), \quad E_1(\zeta, z) = (\zeta - z)\sum_{i=0}^{\infty}\bar{Q}_i(\zeta)\bar{Q}_i(z),$$

$$D_0(\zeta, z) = -(\zeta - z)\sum_{i=0}^{\infty}\bar{P}_i(\zeta)\bar{P}_i(z), \quad D_1(\zeta, z) = 1 - (\zeta - z)\sum_{i=0}^{\infty}\bar{P}_i(\zeta)\bar{Q}_i(z).$$

The coefficients in (3.79) *and* (3.80) *do not depend on the choice of the points* $x_0 = 0, x_1, \cdots$ *according to which the sequence* $P_0(z), P_1(z), \cdots$ *was constructed, nor on the form of the orthogonalization procedure.*

We note only some particulars of the proof. In Lemma 3.9 we did not establish uniform convergence of the series. Hence in the proof of analyticity of the coefficients in formula (3.80) we proceed as follows. Consider for example $E_0(\zeta, z)$ as a function of ζ. Suppose that G_1 and G_2 are two bounded regions of the complex plane such that, from Lemma 3.9, there exist constants C_{G_1} and C_{G_2} such that $\sum_{j=0}^{\infty} |\overline{Q}_j(\zeta)|^2 \leq C_{G_1}$, $\sum_{j=0}^{\infty} |\overline{P}_j(z)|^2 \leq C_{G_2}$ $(\zeta \in G_1,\ z \in G_2)$. By the Cauchy-Bunjakovskiĭ inequality it follows that $|\sum_{j=0}^{N} \overline{Q}_j(\zeta) \overline{P}_j(z)| \leq \sum_{j=0}^{\infty} |\overline{Q}_j(\zeta) \overline{P}_j(z)| \leq \sqrt{C_{G_1} C_{G_2}}$ $(\zeta \in G_1,\ z \in G_2)$. We fix a z. The sequence $f_N(\zeta) = \sum_{j=0}^{N} \overline{Q}_j(\zeta) \overline{P}_j(z)$ of holomorphic functions is uniformly bounded in G_1. Therefore their limit, the series $\sum_{j=0}^{\infty} \overline{Q}_j(\zeta) \overline{P}_j(z)$, and thus $E_0(\zeta, z)$ as well, are holomorphic in ζ.

Let us explain the independence of the coefficients in (3.79) and (3.80). The circumference K_z is defined independently of $x_0, x_1, \cdots$, and of the form of the procedure of orthogonalization, as a circle along which the point $m(z)$ varies, where the corresponding $d\sigma(\lambda)$ is orthogonal. Therefore its radius and center, and therefore the sums $\sum_{j=0}^{\infty} |\overline{P}_j(z)|^2$, $\sum_{j=0}^{\infty} P_j\overline{(z)}\, \overline{Q}_j(z)$ as well (see (3.79)), do not depend on the indicated factors. Formula (3.80) accomplishes the conversion from $K_z \ni w$ to $K_\zeta \ni m(\zeta)$; the independence from $x_0, x_1, \cdots$ and from the form of the orthogonalization procedure for the coefficients of this formula follows from the independence of K_z and K_ζ. The theorem may be considered proved.

The independence of the coefficients in (3.79) and (3.80) from the choice of the points $x_0, x_1, \cdots$, and from the orthogonalization procedure also follows partly from relations (3.63) and (3.64). These give analytic representations for certain of these coefficients which do not depend on the construction of $P_j(z)$. Similar analytic representations may also be obtained for the remaining coefficients.

It follows from (3.80) that the function $m(\zeta)$ corresponding to the selfadjoint extension of the operator C into the space H_k (i.e. to orthogonal $d\sigma(\lambda)$) is meromorphic. Therefore, as in the case of a Jacobian matrix, the spectrum of such an extension is discrete and does not have limit points at a finite distance.

The further results of §1.7, Chapter VII also carry over to the case at hand.

Difficulty occurs only in the proof of the identity (1.54). We note that *an analog to Theorem* 1.13 *of Chapter* VII *is valid verbatim in the same form as that theorem.* The proof likewise is a verbatim repetition. Facts analogous to those formulated in §1.8, Chapter VII also may be obtained for the extension problem. We note only that if $m(z)$ is constructed relative to a nonorthogonal $d\sigma(\lambda)$, then for a fixed z the points $m(z)$ fill out the interior of the circumference K_z.

Of the results of §1.9, Chapter VII, we shall consider only an analog of Theorem 1.17.

Theorem 3.16. *Consider the problem of extension of a p. d. function. Suppose that $d\sigma(\lambda)$ is some spectral measure, $\mu \in (-\infty, \infty)$. In any case (determinate or not) the jump of the function $\sigma(\lambda)$ at the point μ satisfies the estimate*

$$\sigma(\mu+0)-\sigma(\mu) \leqslant \frac{1}{\sum_{j=0}^{\infty} |P_j(-\mu)|^2} = \frac{1}{\langle \mathrm{I}^{-1} e^{-i\mu x}, \mathrm{I}^{-1} e^{-i\mu x} \rangle} \tag{3.81}$$

(*the series here may diverge, i. e. possibly* $\langle \mathrm{I}^{-1} e^{-i\mu x}, \mathrm{I}^{-1} e^{-i\mu x} \rangle$ *equals* ∞). *The estimate* (3.81) *is exact. In the determinate case* (3.81) *turns into an equality, and in the indeterminate case equality is present for an orthogonal spectral measure whose Stieltjes transform is given by formula* (1.59) *of Chapter* VII (*written for the extension problem*), *where we put* $x=\mu$ *and* $t=\infty$.

The proof runs just as in the proof of Theorem 1.17, Chapter VII. The only difference is that it is natural to prove the equation $\sigma(\mu+0)-\sigma(\mu) = \langle \mathrm{I}^{-1} e^{-i\mu x}, \mathrm{I}^{-1} e^{-i\mu x} \rangle^{-1}$ in the determinate case using representation (3.68) rather than (3.69).

10. **Exponentially convex functions.** We obtain an integral representation of this class of functions as a second example for the general Theorem 3.7. Suppose that $G=(-l,l)$ $(-\infty \leq l' < l'' \leq \infty)$. The function $k(t) \in C((2l', 2l''))$ is said to be exponentially convex if $K(x,y)=k(x+y)$ $(x, y \in G)$ is p. d. .

Theorem 3.17. *The functional $k(t) \in C((2l', 2l''))$ is exponentially convex if and only if it is representable in the form*

$$k(t)=\int_{-\infty}^{\infty} e^{\lambda t}\, d\sigma(\lambda) \quad (t \in (2l', 2l'')), \tag{3.82}$$

where $d\sigma(\lambda)$ is a nonnegative measure. The measure $d\sigma(\lambda)$ is always defined uniquely by k.

Proof. The exponential convexity of the function (3.82) is verified directly. We shall establish the representation (3.82). Put $L = d/dx = -L^+$. If $k(t)$ is sufficiently smooth, then

$$L_x [K(x, y)] = \frac{d}{dx} k(x+y) = \frac{d}{dy} k(x+y) = \bar{L}_y [K(x, y)] \quad (x, y \in G),$$

i.e. (3.4) is satisfied. In the case of a nonsmooth k we confirm the validity of this relation in a manner similar to the verification of (3.42). In the case at hand $r = 1$, $\chi_0(x; \lambda) = e^{\lambda x}$. Therefore representation (3.20) takes the form

$$k(x+y) = K(x, y) = \int_{-\infty}^{\infty} e^{\lambda(x+y)} d\sigma_{00}(\lambda) \qquad (x, y \in G),$$

which after replacement of $x + y$ by t yields (3.82).

Suppose that $d\sigma(\lambda)$ is such that the integral (3.82) exists. Then also the integral $F(s) = \int_{-\infty}^{\infty} e^{\lambda(t+i\tau)} d\sigma(\lambda)$ $(s = t + i\tau)$ exists for $s \in (2l', 2l'') \times (-\infty, \infty)$, and is analytic in this strip. Accordingly, it is defined uniquely relative to $F((t, 0)) = k(t)$ $(t \in (2l', 2l''))$, and in particular the function $f(\tau) = F((t_0, \tau)) = \int_{-\infty}^{\infty} e^{i\lambda\tau} e^{\lambda t_0} d\sigma(\lambda)$ $(-\infty < \tau < \infty$, $t_0 \in (2l', 2l'')$ fixed$)$ uniquely as well. But $f(\tau)$ is p.d., and the latter representation is the representation (3.40) for it. Therefore $e^{\lambda t_0} d\sigma(\lambda)$, i.e. $d\sigma(\lambda)$, is defined relative to $f(\tau)$ and therefore relative to k, uniquely. The theorem is proved.

Now we carry out the omitted proof of the last fact of Theorem 3.9. We need to show that if $r = 1$ and L is an ordinary differential expression with constant coefficients and $G = (-\infty, \infty)$, then $d\sigma_{00}(\lambda)$ in the representation (3.20) is uniquely defined relative to $K(x, y)$. Suppose that $Lu = (1/b)du/dx + a_0 u$. Then $\chi_0(x; \lambda) = e^{b(\lambda - a_0)x}$ (we take $a = 0$) and representation (3.20) goes into the representation

$$K(x, y) = \int_{-\infty}^{\infty} e^{b(\lambda - a_0)x} \overline{e^{b(\lambda - a_0)y}} d\sigma_{00}(\lambda)$$

$$= e^{-ba_0 x - \bar{b}\bar{a}_0 y} \int_{-\infty}^{\infty} e^{\lambda(bx + \bar{b}y)} d\sigma_{00}(\lambda) \qquad (x, y \in (-\infty, \infty)). \qquad (3.83)$$

Put $b = \alpha + i\beta$. We may suppose that $\alpha\beta \neq 0$, since in the contrary case the question as to the uniqueness of representation (3.83) reduces to the corresponding question in Theorem 3.11 for $l = \infty$ or in Theorem 3.17 for $l' = -\infty$, $l'' = +\infty$ and is solved positively. If $\alpha\beta \neq 0$, then for any complex s the equation $bx + \bar{b}y = s$ relative to $x, y \in (-\infty, \infty)$ is always solvable. It then follows from (3.83) that the integral $F(s) = \int_{-\infty}^{\infty} e^{\lambda s}\, d\sigma_{00}(\lambda)$ exists for any s and that its value is uniquely determined relative to $K(x, y)$. But $F((0, \tau)) = \int_{-\infty}^{\infty} e^{i\lambda\tau} d\sigma_{00}(\lambda)$ $(\tau \in (-\infty, \infty))$, so that in view of Theorem 3.11 $d\sigma_{00}(\lambda)$ is defined in terms of $F((0, \tau))$, and therefore in terms of K, uniquely. The assertion is proved.

11. **The expression d^2/dx^2.** We consider two examples connected with representation (3.20) and relating to d^2/dx^2.

1) Suppose that $G = (-l, l)$, where $0 < l \leq \infty$. We shall consider an even function $k(t) \in C((-2l, 2l))$, for which the kernel $K(x, y) = \frac{1}{2}[k(x+y) + k(x-y)]$ $(x, y \in G)$ is p.d. . In this case we may put $L = d^2/dx^2 = L^+$. As in subsection 6 it is easy to verify that inside $G \times G$ the relation $L_x[K(x, y)] = \bar{L}_y[K(x, y)]$ holds, so that, from (3.20), we have the representation

$$\frac{1}{2}[k(x+y) + k(x-y)] = K(x, y)$$

$$= \int_{-\infty}^{\infty} \cos\sqrt{\lambda}x \cdot \cos\sqrt{\lambda}y\, d\sigma_{00}(\lambda) + \int_{-\infty}^{\infty} \cos\sqrt{\lambda}x \frac{\sin\sqrt{\lambda}y}{\sqrt{\lambda}}\, d\sigma_{01}(\lambda)$$

$$+ \int_{-\infty}^{\infty} \frac{\sin\sqrt{\lambda}x}{\sqrt{\lambda}} \cos\sqrt{\lambda}y\, d\sigma_{10}(\lambda)$$

$$+ \int_{-\infty}^{\infty} \frac{\sin\sqrt{\lambda}x \cdot \sin\sqrt{\lambda}y}{\lambda}\, d\sigma_{11}(\lambda) \qquad (x, y \in (-l, l)) \tag{3.84}$$

(we should note that we have taken $a = 0$ and therefore $\chi_0(x; \lambda) = \cos\sqrt{\lambda}x$, $\chi_1(x; \lambda) = \sin\sqrt{\lambda}x/\sqrt{\lambda}$). It is easy to see that because of the evenness of $k(t)$ (3.84) may be rewritten so that only the first integral remains in it. Indeed, we have $K(x, y) = K(-x, y) = K(x, -y) = K(-x, -y)$, so that

$$K(x, y) = \frac{1}{4}[K(x, y) + K(-x, y) + K(x, -y) + K(-x, -y)].$$

Substituting representation (3.84) into this equation, we find that

$$\frac{1}{2}[k(x+y)+k(x-y)] = K(x, y)$$

$$= \int_{-\infty}^{\infty} \cos\sqrt{\lambda}x\cdot\cos\sqrt{\lambda}y\,d\sigma_{00}(\lambda) \quad (x, y\in(-l, l)). \tag{3.85}$$

Comparing (3.84) and (3.85), we find that the sum of the last three integrals in (3.84) is equal to zero for any $x, y \in (-l, l)$.

Putting $y = x$ in (3.85), we find that $\frac{1}{2}[k(2x)+k(0)] = \int_{-\infty}^{\infty}\cos^2\sqrt{\lambda}x\,d\sigma_{00}(\lambda)$. But

$$k(0) = \int_{-\infty}^{\infty} d\sigma_{00}(\lambda),$$

so that

$$k(2x) = \int_{-\infty}^{\infty} (2\cos^2\sqrt{\lambda}x - 1)\,d\sigma_{00}(\lambda)$$

$$= \int_{-\infty}^{\infty} \cos\sqrt{\lambda}2x\,d\sigma_{00}(\lambda) \qquad (x\in(-l, l)). \tag{3.86}$$

Theorem 3.18. *In order that the even function* $k(t) \in C((-2l, 2l))$ $(0<l\leq\infty)$ *have the property that the kernel* $K(x, y) = \frac{1}{2}[k(x+y)+k(x-y)]$ $(x, y \in (-l, l))$ *is* p. d., *it is necessary and sufficient that the representation*

$$k(t) = \int_{-\infty}^{\infty} \cos\sqrt{\lambda}t\,d\sigma(\lambda) \qquad (t\in(-2l, 2l)) \tag{3.87}$$

hold, where $d\sigma(\lambda)$ *is a nonnegative finite measure. If* $l=\infty$ *and* $k(t)$ *is such that for some* $N>0$

$$|k(t)| \leqslant Ce^{Nt^2} \qquad (C>0;\ t\in(-\infty, \infty)), \tag{3.88}$$

then the measure $d\sigma(\lambda)$ *is uniquely defined by* k.

Proof. Representation (3.87) follows from (3.86). Conversely, if $k(t)$ has the form (3.87), then in view of the equation

$$\frac{1}{2}[\cos\sqrt{\lambda}(x+y)+\cos\sqrt{\lambda}(x-y)] = \cos\sqrt{\lambda}x\cdot\cos\sqrt{\lambda}y$$

the fact that the kernel $K(x, y) = \frac{1}{2}[k(x+y) + k(x-y)]$ is p. d. is immediately verified. Further from (3.88) it follows that

$$|K(x, y)| \leqslant \frac{C}{2}[e^{N(x+y)^2} + e^{N(x-y)^2}] \leqslant Ce^{2N(x^2+y^2)} \qquad (x, y \in (-\infty, \infty))$$

and therefore the last assertion of the theorem follows from Theorem 3.9.

Corollary. *Consider the functions* $f(t)$ $(t \in (-\infty, \infty))$, *represented by the absolutely convergent integrals*

$$f(t) = \int_{-\infty}^{\infty} \cos\sqrt{\lambda}t d\omega(\lambda) \qquad (t \in (-\infty, \infty)), \tag{3.89}$$

where the complex-valued measure $d\omega(\lambda)$ *is such that for some* $N > 0$

$$\int_{-\infty}^{0} e^{\sqrt{\lambda}\, t} |d\omega(\lambda)| \underset{t\to+\infty}{=} O(e^{Nt^2}). \tag{3.90}$$

Then from $f(t) = 0$ $(t \in (-\infty, \infty))$ *it follows that* $d\omega(\lambda) = 0$.

Indeed, it suffices to consider the case of a real $d\omega(\lambda)$. Suppose $f(t) \equiv 0$, $\omega(\Delta) = \omega_+(\Delta) - \omega_-(\Delta)$ is a decomposition of the corresponding measure $\omega(\Delta)$ into positive and negative parts, $k_\pm(t) = \int_{-\infty}^{\infty} \cos\sqrt{\lambda}t d\omega_\pm(\lambda)$. We have $k_+(t) = k_-(t)$ $(t \in (-\infty, \infty))$, while by (3.90) the estimate (3.88) is valid for the functions k_+ and k_-. From Theorem 3.18, $\omega_+(\Delta) = \omega_-(\Delta)$, i.e. $\omega(\Delta) = 0$, as required.

Thus, from uniqueness in Theorem 3.18 we have obtained uniqueness in the transformation (3.89). The converse is also clear; from the latter uniqueness follows uniqueness in Theorem 3.18.

2) Suppose that $G = (-l, l)$, where $0 < l \leq \infty$. We shall consider the even function $k(t) \in C((-2l, 2l))$, $k(0) = 0$, for which the kernel $K(x, y) = \frac{1}{2}[k(x+y) - k(x-y)]$ $(x, y \in G)$ is p.d. As in example 1) we may take $L = d^2/dx^2$. Then for our kernel K we obtain representation (3.84). However now $K(x, y) = -K(-x, y) = -K(x, -y) = K(-x, -y)$ and therefore we must use the equation $K(x, y) = \frac{1}{4}[K(x, y) - K(-x, y) - K(x, -y) + K(-x, -y)]$, which leads not to representation (3.85), but to the representation

$$\frac{1}{2}[k(x+y) - k(x-y)] = K(x, y)$$

$$= \int_{-\infty}^{\infty} \frac{\sin\sqrt{\lambda}x \cdot \sin\sqrt{\lambda}y}{\lambda} d\sigma_{11}(\lambda) \, (x, y \in (-l, l)). \tag{3.91}$$

Theorem 3.19. *In order that the even function* $k(t) \in C((-2l, 2l))$ $(0<l\leq\infty)$, $k(0)=0$, *should have the property that the kernel* $K(x, y) = \frac{1}{2}[k(x+y)-k(x-y)]$ $(x, y \in (-l, l))$ *is p. d., it is necessary and sufficient that the following representation hold:*

$$k(t) = \int_{-\infty}^{\infty} \frac{2\sin^2 \sqrt{\lambda}\, \frac{t}{2}}{\lambda}\, d\sigma(\lambda) \qquad (t \in (-2l, 2l)), \tag{3.92}$$

where $d\sigma(\lambda)$ *is a nonnegative measure. If* $l=\infty$ *the condition of uniqueness of the measure* $d\sigma(\lambda)$ *is the same as in Theorem* 3.18.

The theorem follows from (3.91), if we put there $x=y=t/2$, and from remarks similar to those made in the proof of Theorem 3.18.

Theorems 3.18 and 3.19 contain a statement on the possibility of extending the function $k(t)$ $(t \in (-2l, 2l))$, for which the corresponding kernel $K(x,y)$ is p. d., to the entire axis with this property preserved. Here we could have developed a theory of extensions analogous to that presented in subsections 8 and 9 for the usual p. d. functions. We shall not dwell on these questions.

The technique of forming a kernel $*$-commuting with the expression d^2/dx^2 from the function $k(t)$ may be generalized also to the case of the expressions

$$L = \frac{d^r}{dx^r}, \tag{3.93}$$

given only that the functions $k(t)$ in question are analytic. Indeed, denote by $\epsilon_1, \cdots, \epsilon_r$ the rth roots of unity. Suppose that $k(s)$ is an entire function of the complex variable s such that the kernel $K(x, y) = \sum_{\alpha, \beta=1}^{r} c_{\alpha\beta} k(\epsilon_\alpha x + \epsilon_\beta y)$ is p. d. ($c_{\alpha\beta}$ are certain coefficients; $x, y \in (-\infty, \infty)$). Then for the expression (3.93) we have

$$L_x[K(x, y)] = \sum_{\alpha,\beta=1}^{r} c_{\alpha\beta}\varepsilon_\alpha^r k^{(r)}(\varepsilon_\alpha x + \varepsilon_\beta y)$$

$$= \sum_{\alpha,\beta=1}^{r} c_{\alpha\beta} k^{(r)}(\varepsilon_\alpha x + \varepsilon_\beta y) = \overline{L}_y[K(x, y)],$$

and therefore the kernel K may be decomposed in terms of the eigenfunctions of the expression (3.93). From this decomposition certain representations for the original function $k(s)$ will follow. We shall restrict ourselves to only one general remark.

12. **The Sturm-Liouville expression.** We shall show that by specializing the general representation (3.20) one may extend example 1) of the preceding subsection to such expressions. Thus we may consider

$$Lu = -\frac{d^2u}{dx^2} + q(x)u \qquad (x \in G = (-l, l);\ 0 < l \leqslant \infty), \tag{3.94}$$

where $q(x) \in C((-l, l))$ is some complex-valued even coefficient. If $K(x, y) \in C(G \times G)$ is a p. d. kernel satisfying inside $G \times G$ the relation

$$L_x[K(x, y)] = \bar{L}_y[K(x, y)], \tag{3.95}$$

then on the basis of Theorem 3.7 we may write down the representation (3.20) for it, with $r = 2$. From the evenness of $q(x)$ it easily follows that $\chi_0(x; \lambda)$ is even and $\chi_1(x; \lambda)$ odd. Here χ_0 and χ_1 are solutions of the equation $Lu - \lambda u$, satisfying conditions (3.18) for $a = 0$. Therefore if we require in addition that $K(x, y)$ is even in each of its variables with the others fixed, then, similarly to example 1) the sum of the three integrals in (3.20) will be equal to zero and we will obtain, after introducing the notation $d\sigma(\lambda) = d\sigma_{00}(\lambda)$,

$$K(x, y) = \int_{-\infty}^{\infty} \chi_0(x; \lambda)\overline{\chi_0(y; \lambda)}d\sigma(\lambda) \qquad (x, y \in (-l, l)). \tag{3.96}$$

In the case at hand we may also formulate in an appropriate way the concept of a p. d. function of one variable. To this end we introduce the so-called generalized translation operators T_y, connected with (3.94). We extend $q(x)$ evenly to a function of $C((-2l, 2l))$. Suppose that $u(x) \in C^2((-2l, 2l))$ and is even. We denote by $U(x, y)$ the solution of the hyperbolic equation (3.95), satisfying the initial conditions $U(x, 0) = u(x)$, $(\partial/\partial y)U(x, 0) = 0$ $(x \in (-2l, 2l))$. This solution clearly is defined in the open square Q with vertices at the points $(-2l, 0)$, $(0, 2l)$, $(2l, 0)$, $(0, -2l)$ and lies in $C^2(Q)$. If we integrate equation (3.95) by the method of Riemann, then for $U(x, y)$ we obtain the formula

$$U(x, y) = \frac{1}{2}[u(x + y) + u(x - y)] + \int_{x-y}^{x+y} w(x, y, s)u(s)\,ds \qquad ((x, y) \in Q), \tag{3.97}$$

where $w(x, y, s)$ is some function expressed in terms of a Riemann function. From the evenness of $q(x)$ and $u(x)$ and the uniqueness of the solution of the

Cauchy problem for equation (3.95) it easily follows that $U(x, y)$ is even in each variable with the other fixed.

Now suppose that $u(x) \in C((-2l, 2l))$. Define in Q a kernel $U(x, y)$ using formula (3.97). This kernel will not be sufficiently smooth. However, in the sense of the distributions of L. Schwartz it satisfies equation (3.95) inside $G \times G$. Moreover it preserves evenness in each of its variables. We introduce the operator T_y by putting

$$(T_y u)(x) = U(x, y) \qquad ((x, y) \in Q). \tag{3.98}$$

Thus for each $y \in (-2l, 2l)$ $(T_y u)(x)$ is defined for $x \in (-2l + |y|, 2l - |y|)$. In particular $(T_y u)(x)$ is defined for $(x, y) \in G \times G$.

A function $k(t) \in C((-2l, 2l))$ is said to be p.d. relative to the family of operators (3.98) if the kernel $K(x, y) = (T_y k)(x)$ $(x, y \in G)$ is p.d. From what has been said it is clear that representation (3.96) holds for this kernel. Putting $y = 0$ in it, we get

$$k(x) = \int_{-\infty}^{\infty} \chi_0(x; \lambda)\, d\sigma(\lambda) \qquad (x \in (-l, l)). \tag{3.99}$$

If $l = \infty$, then representation (3.99) holds on the entire region of definition of the function k. In this case it is easy to show that also every function of the form (3.99) with a nonnegative finite measure $d\sigma(\lambda)$ will be p.d. in our sense. Here we need to use the fact that $(T_y \chi_0(\cdot; \lambda))(x) = \chi_0(x; \lambda)\chi_0(y; \lambda)$.

We shall not go into uniqueness questions for the representation (3.99). In conclusion we note that it is frequently convenient to define generalized translation operators on functions given on $[0, 2l)$. In this case we extend such functions to be even on $(-2l, 2l)$ and then apply the definitions given above.

§4. THE CASE OF $q > 1$ DIFFERENTIAL OPERATORS

We shall in what follows extend the results of §3 to the case of q operators. We shall consider only the case when the operators operate relative to distinct variables, and we shall use the general facts of §2.

1. **General differential expressions.** Suppose that n-dimensional space E_n is decomposed into an orthogonal sum $E_n = E^{(1)}_{n_1} \oplus \cdots \oplus E^{(q)}_{n_q}$ of q spaces $E^{(j)}_{n_j}$ of dimension n_j: $n = n_1 + \cdots + n_q$. The point $x \in E_n$ will be represented in the form $x = (x^{(1)}, \ldots, x^{(q)}) = (x^{(1)}_1, \ldots, x^{(1)}_{n_1}; \ldots; x^{(q)}_1, \ldots, x^{(q)}_{n_q})$, where

$x^{(j)}$ runs through $E^{(j)}_{n_j}$. As G we shall consider regions of the form $G = G^{(1)} \times \cdots \times G^{(q)}$, where $G^{(j)} \subseteq E^{(j)}_{n_j}$ $(j = 1, \cdots, q)$.

Consider a p. d. kernel $K(x, y) \in C(G \times G)$ and choose for it a function $p(x)$ $(x \in G)$ satisfying (3. 3). We will construct this function in the form $p(x) = p^{(1)}(x^{(1)}) \cdots p^{(q)}(x^{(q)})$, where $p^{(j)}(x^{(j)}) \in C^{\infty}(G^{(j)})$, $p^{(j)}(x^{(j)}) \geq 1$ $(x^{(j)} \in G^{(j)};\ j = 1, \cdots, q)$ (the possibility of such a choice of p follows from Lemma 4. 1, which will be presented at the end of this subsection). Consider the chain

$$H_{-}^{(j)} = L_2\left(G^{(j)}, \frac{1}{p^{(j)}(x^{(j)})}\, dx^{(j)}\right) \supseteq H_0^{(j)} = L_2(G^{(j)}, dx^{(j)})$$

$$\supseteq H_{+}^{(j)} = L_2(G^{(j)}, p^{(j)}(x^{(j)})\, dx^{(j)})$$

$$(j = 1, \ldots, q),$$

which will play the role of the chain (2. 2). Then $H_0 = H_0^{(1)} \otimes \cdots \otimes H_0^{(q)} = L_2(G, dx)$, $H_+ = H_+^{(1)} \otimes \cdots \otimes H_+^{(q)} = L_2(G, p(x)dx)$, $H_- = H_-^{(1)} \otimes \cdots \otimes H_-^{(q)} = L_2(G, p^{-1}(x)\,dx)$. Thus $K(x, y) \subseteq H_- \otimes H_- = L_2(G \times G, p^{-1}(x)p^{-1}(y)\,dx\,dy)$. The role of the involution $u \to \bar{u}$ in these spaces is played by inversion in the complex line.

Suppose given q differential expressions

$$L^{(1)}u = \sum_{|\alpha| \leqslant r_1} a_\alpha^{(1)}(x^{(1)}) D_{(1)}^\alpha u, \ldots, L^{(q)}u = \sum_{|\alpha| \leqslant r_q} a_\alpha^{(q)}(x^{(q)}) D_{(q)}^\alpha u, \tag{4. 1}$$

where $a_\alpha^{(j)}(x^{(j)}) \in C^{|\alpha|}(G^{(j)})$, $D_{(j)}$ denotes differentiation with respect to the jth group of corrdinates, $\Lambda^{(j)}$ the minimal operator in $H_0 = L_2(G)$ corresponding to $L^{(j)}$. Put $A_j = \Lambda^{(j)}$. Each of the operators A_j admits an extension of equipment with $\mathcal{D} = C_0^\infty(G)$, appropriately topologized. The restriction of A_j^* to $\mathcal{D}$ coincides with the relation $u \to L^{(j)^+}u$ $(u \in C_0^\infty(G))$. The condition of *-commutativity of K and A_j is written in terms of equations of type (3. 4), in which L is replaced by $L^{(j)}$ $(j = 1, \cdots, q)$.

As the operators B_j defined in §2. 1, we may apply the operators $u \to L^{(j)^+}u$ $(u \in C_0^\infty(G^{(j)}))$, operating in the space $H_+^{(j)} = L_2(G^{(j)}, p^{(j)}(x^{(j)})dx^{(j)})$. The role of the operators C_j will be played by operators in H_+ of the form $u \to L^{(j)^+}u$, where $u \in \mathfrak{D}(C_j) = H_+^{(1)} \otimes \cdots \otimes H_+^{(j-1)} \otimes C_0^\infty(G^{(j)}) \otimes H_+^{(j+1)} \otimes \cdots \otimes H_+^{(q)}$. Recall that we often consider the C_j as operating in H_K. It is not hard to see that *the closure in* H_K *of the operator* $u \to L^{(j)^+}u$ $(u \in C_0^\infty(G))$

contains the operator C_j, *so that the extension of their closures into* H_K *are equivalent problems.* This circumstance will be used frequently in what follows, without particular emphasis on it. It is clear that the condition of *-commutativity of K and A_j and the Hermiticity of C_j in H_K are equivalent requirements.

The space H_{++}, necessary for the construction of decompositions relative to eigenfunctions, is constructed just as in §3.1: $H_{++} = W_2^{-(l,s)}(G)$, where $l > n/2$ and $s(x)$ satisfies (3.5). The space H_K is as before the completion, after identification if necessary, of H_+ relative to the scalar product $\langle \cdot , \cdot \rangle$ of type (3.2). Finally, the family Ω_λ (where $\lambda = (\lambda_1, \cdots, \lambda_q) \in E_q$) of elementary p. d. kernels from Theorem 1.2 now is defined as a family of p. d. kernels $\Omega_\lambda \in W_2^{-(l,s)}(G) \otimes W_2^{-(l,s)}(G)$, $\|\Omega_\lambda\|_{W_2^{-(l,s)}(G) \otimes W_2^{-(l,s)}(G)} \leq C$, satisfying relations (3.6) for each $L = L^{(j)}$ with λ replaced by λ_j $(j = 1, \cdots, q)$. Analogously to Theorem 3.1, Theorem 1.2, for the special case of operators in question, appears as follows:

Theorem 4.1. *Suppose that* $K(x, y) \in C(G \times G)$ *is a p. d. kernel, and that the functions* $p(x)$, $s(x)$ *are selected above, the coefficients of the expression* $L^{(j)}$ *(see (4.1))* $a_\alpha^{(j)}(x^{(j)}) \in C^{|\alpha|+l}(G^{(j)})$, *where* $l > n/2$ $(j = 1, \cdots, q)$. *In order that the representation*

$$K = \int_{E_q} \Omega_\lambda d\rho(\lambda) \tag{4.2}$$

should hold, where $\Omega_\lambda \in W_2^{-(l,s)}(G) \otimes W_2^{-(l,s)}(G)$ *is some family of elementary p. d. kernels,* $d\rho(\lambda)$ *is a nonnegative finite measure, and the integral* (4.2) *converges in the norm of the space* $W_2^{-(l,s)}(G) \otimes W_2^{-(l,s)}(G)$, *it is necessary and sufficient that the following two requirements be satisfied:* a) *relations* (3.4) *are satisfied with* L *replaced by* $L^{(j)}$ $(j = 1, \cdots, q)$; b) *the* q *Hermitian operators in* H_K $u \to L^{(j)+}u$ $(u \in C_0^\infty(G))$ *admit extension into* H_K *or going into a larger Hilbert space to a system of commuting selfadjoint operators. In representation* (4.2) *the expression* $\Omega_\lambda d\rho_\lambda$ *is defined uniquely if and only if for the operators* $u \to L^{(j)+}u$ $(u \in C_0^\infty(G))$ *there exists only one* q*-dimensional resolution of the identity.*

In conclusion we prove a lemma, thanks to which it was possible to select a function $p(x)$ in the form $p^{(1)}(x^{(1)}) \cdots p^{(q)}(x^{(q)})$.

Lemma 4.1. *Suppose that the nonnegative function* $M(x) \in C(G)$. *Then there* *exist functions* $p^{(j)}(x^{(j)}) \in C^\infty(G^{(j)})$, $p^{(j)}(x^{(j)}) \geq 1$ $(x^{(j)} \in G^{(j)};\ j = 1, \cdots, q)$ *such that*

$$\int_G \frac{M(x)}{p^{(1)}(x^{(1)}) \ldots p^{(q)}(x^{(q)})}\, dx < \infty. \tag{4.3}$$

Proof. To shorten the calculations we consider the case $q = 2$. First we prove that if $\| m_{jk} \|_1^\infty$ is any matrix consisting of nonnegative elements, then we can always find two sequences $(\rho_1, \rho_2, \cdots)$ and $(\sigma_1, \sigma_2, \cdots)$ such that

$$\sum_{j,k=1}^{\infty} m_{jk} \varrho_j \sigma_k < \infty; \quad \varrho_j, \sigma_j > 0 \qquad (j = 1, 2, \ldots). \tag{4.4}$$

For consider the sequences $(m_{j1}, m_{j2}, \cdots)$ $(j = 1, 2, \cdots)$, and construct a majorizing sequence $(\mu_1, \mu_2, \cdots)$ by putting $\mu_j = \max\{m_{1j}, \cdots, m_{jj}\}$ $(j = 1, 2, \cdots)$. Evidently, for each sequence $(m_{j1}, m_{j2}, \cdots)$, beginning with sufficiently large indices k (indeed, for $k \geq j$) we will have $m_{jk} \leq \mu_k$. We choose a sequence $(\sigma_1, \sigma_2, \cdots)$, $\sigma_k > 0$ $(k = 1, 2, \cdots)$ such that $\sum_{k=1}^\infty \mu_k \sigma_k < \infty$. Then for each $j = 1, 2, \cdots$ $s_j = \sum_{k=1}^\infty m_{jk}\sigma_k \leq C_j \sum_{k=1}^\infty \mu_k \sigma_k < \infty$. Now we select $(\rho_1, \rho_2, \cdots)$, $\rho_j > 0$ $(j = 1, 2, \cdots)$ so that $\sum_{j=1}^\infty s_j \rho_j < \infty$. Thus relation (4.4) is satisfied.

We turn to the proof of the lemma. Suppose that $G = G^{(1)} \times G^{(2)}$. We represent $G^{(1)}$ in the form of a union of closures of certain regions, having as common points only points of their boundaries and situated strictly inside $G^{(1)}$: $G^{(1)} = \bigcup_{j=1}^\infty G_j^{(1)}$. Suppose that $G^{(2)} = \bigcup_{k=1}^\infty G_k^{(2)}$ is an analytic representation for the region $G^{(2)}$. Then

$$\int_G \frac{M(x)}{p^{(1)}(x^{(1)})\, p^{(2)}(x^{(2)})}\, dx = \sum_{j,k=1}^{\infty} \int_{G_j^{(1)}} \int_{G_k^{(2)}} \frac{M(x^{(1)}, x^{(2)})}{p^{(1)}(x^{(1)})\, p^{(2)}(x^{(2)})}\, dx^{(1)} dx^{(2)}$$

$$\leqslant \sum_{j,k=1}^{\infty} m_{jk} \int_{G_j^{(1)}} \frac{dx^{(1)}}{p^{(1)}(x^{(1)})} \cdot \int_{G_k^{(2)}} \frac{dx^{(2)}}{p^{(2)}(x^{(2)})};$$

$$m_{jk} = \max_{x^{(1)} \in G_j^{(1)},\, x^{(2)} \in G_k^{(2)}} M(x^{(1)}, x^{(2)}) \qquad (j, k = 1, 2, \ldots). \tag{4.5}$$

According to what has been proved we choose sequences ρ_j and σ_k such that (4.4) is satisfied with the matrix $\|m_{jk}\|_1^\infty$ of (4.5). Now we choose a function $p^{(1)}(x^{(1)}) \in C^\infty(G^{(1)})$ such that $p^{(1)}(x^{(1)}) \geq 1$ $(x^{(1)} \in G^{(1)})$ and $\int_{G_j^{(1)}} (1/p^{(1)}(x^{(1)}))\, dx^1 \leq \rho_j$ $(j = 1, 2, \cdots)$, and we select $p^{(2)}(x^{(2)})$ analogously relative to σ_k. Then the series on the right side of (4.5) is majorized above by the converging series $\sum_{j,k=1}^\infty m_{jk}\rho_j\sigma_k$, i.e. the integral on the left side of (4.5) converges. The lemma is proved.

The application of this lemma to our case is obvious: we need to put $M(x) = K(x, x)$.

2. **Ordinary differential expressions.** If in the schema of subsection 1 the expression $L^{(j)}$ is elliptic or is an ordinary expression, then the kernel Ω_λ will be smooth in the jth "coordinates" x and y. We dwell only on the simplest case, when $q = n$, $n_1 = \cdots = n_q = 1$, and all the expressions $L^{(1)}, \cdots, L^{(n)}$ are ordinary. The case of partial differential expressions is left for the reader to consider. Using Theorem 5.1 of Chapter VI, and considerations of the type presented in §3.2, it is not difficult to prove the following theorem.

Theorem 4.2. *Suppose that* $G = G^{(1)} \times \cdots \times G^{(n)}$, *where the* $G^{(j)}$ *are one-dimensional finite or infinite intervals. Consider* n *ordinary expressions*

$$L^{(1)}u = \sum_{0 \leqslant \alpha \leqslant r_1} a_\alpha^{(1)}(x_1) D_1^\alpha u, \ldots, L^{(n)}u = \sum_{0 \leqslant \alpha \leqslant r_n} a_\alpha^{(n)}(x_n) D_n^\alpha u, \qquad (4.6)$$

where $a_\alpha^{(j)}(x_j) \in C^{\alpha + l_j}(G^{(j)})$, $l_j \geq 1$ $(j = 1, \cdots, n)$. *The family* $\Omega_\lambda(x, y)$ $(x, y \in G;\ \lambda = (\lambda_1, \cdots, \lambda_n))$ *of p.d. kernels will be said to be a family of elementary p.d. kernels if the derivatives* $(D_{x_1}^{\alpha_1} \cdots D_{x_n}^{\alpha_n} D_{y_1}^{\beta_1} \cdots D_{y_n}^{\beta_n} \Omega_\lambda)(x, y)$ *exist and are continuous relative to* $(x, y) \in G \times G$, *for* $\alpha_j, \beta_j \leq r_j + l_j$ $(j = 1, \cdots, n)$ *and if*

$$L_{x_j}^{(j)}\Omega_\lambda = \lambda_j \Omega_\lambda, \quad \overline{L_{y_j}^{(j)}} \Omega_\lambda = \lambda_j \Omega_\lambda \quad (x, y \in G;\ j = 1, \ldots, n). \qquad (4.7)$$

In order that the p.d. kernel $K(x, y) \in C(G \times G)$ *be representable in the form of an absolutely convergent integral*

$$K(x, y) = \int_{E_n} \Omega_\lambda(x, y)\, d\rho(\lambda) \qquad (x, y \in G), \qquad (4.8)$$

where $\rho(\Delta)$ *is a nonnegative finite measure and* $\Omega_\lambda(x, y)$ *is some family of elementary p.d. kernels, it is necessary and sufficient that the requirements formulated at the end of Theorem* 4.1 *be satisfied for* $q = n$. *The uniqueness criterion formulated in that theorem gives uniqueness in the representation* (4.5).

For the generalized resolvent $R_z^{(j0)}$ of the Hermitian operator $u \to L^{(j0)^+} u$ ($u \in C_0^\infty(G)$) operating in H_K, results of the type of Theorem 3.4 are valid. For their derivation it is now convenient to proceed as follows. We consider a system of commuting selfadjoint extensions of the operators $u \to L^{(j)^+} u$ ($u \in C_0^\infty(G)$), giving the representation (4.8), and we shall study the resolvent $R_z^{(j0)}$ of just such an extension. It is easy to see that the ordinary kernel

$$R^{(j_0)}(x, y; z) = \int_{E_n} \frac{\Omega_\lambda(x, y)}{\lambda_{j_0} - z} d\varrho(\lambda) \qquad (x, y \in G) \tag{4.9}$$

(the integral converges absolutely in view of the convergence of the integral (4.8); see also estimate (3.8), whose analog is valid in the case at hand) is the kernel of the resolvent $R_z^{(j0)}$, i.e. equation (3.16) holds with R_z and $R_z(x, y; z)$ replaced by $R_z^{(j0)}$ and $R^{(j0)}(x, y; z)$ respectively. This equation is established in the same way as the second of the equations (3.17).

From representation (4.9) and the commutativity of the kernel $\Omega_\lambda(x, y)$ relative to $(x, y) \in G \times G$ it follows that $R^{(j0)}(\cdot, \cdot; z) \in C(G \times G)$. Moreover, similarly to (3.15), in the generalized sense inside $G \times G$

$$L_{x_{j_0}}^{(j_0)} [R^{(j_0)}(x, y; z)] - zR^{(j_0)}(x, y; z) = K(x, y),$$

$$L_{y_{j_0}}^{(j_0)\oplus} [R^{(j_0)}(x, y; z)] - zR^{(j_0)}(x, y; z) = K(x, y).$$

These equations make it possible to apply Theorem 5.1 of Chapter VI, and the remark to it, and to establish sufficient smoothness of the kernel $R^{(j0)}(x, y; z)$.

Now we turn to the derivation of representations of type (3.20). We fix in each interval $G^{(j)}$ some point a_j and denote by $\chi_0^{(j)}(x_j; z), \cdots, \chi_{r_j-1}^{(j)}(x_j; z)$ a fundamental system of solutions of the equation $L^{(j)} u - zu = 0$ ($x_j \in G^{(j)}$), satisfying the conditions

$$\left.\frac{d^k}{dx_j^k} \chi_m(x_j; z)\right|_{x_j = a_j} = \delta_{mk} \qquad (m, k = 0, \ldots, r_j - 1;\ j = 1, \ldots, n). \tag{4.10}$$

Put

$$X_\alpha(x; \lambda) = \chi_{\alpha_1}^{(1)}(x_1; \lambda_1) \ldots \chi_{\alpha_n}^{(n)}(x_n; \lambda_n)$$
$$(x = (x_1, \ldots, x_n) \in G,\ \lambda \in (\lambda_1, \ldots, \lambda_n) \in E_n), \tag{4.11}$$

where the vector index $\alpha = (\alpha_1, \cdots, \alpha_n)$ varies over the integer-valued parallelepiped A with coordinates $\alpha_i = 0, \cdots, r_i - 1$ ($i = 1, \cdots, n$).

Taking into account that the kernels $\Omega_\lambda(x, y)$ satisfy equations (4.7), and expressing them in terms of the fundamental system of solutions introduced above, we obtain, analogously to (3.19),

$$\Omega_\lambda(x, y) = \sum_{\alpha,\beta\in A} \left(\frac{\partial^{\alpha_1+\dots+\alpha_n+\beta_1+\dots+\beta_n}\Omega_\lambda}{\partial x_1^{\alpha_1}\dots\partial x_n^{\alpha_n}\partial y_1^{\beta_1}\dots\partial y_n^{\beta_n}} \right)(a, a)\, X_\alpha(x; \lambda)\, \overline{X_\beta(y; \lambda)} \quad (4.12)$$
$$(a = (a_1, \dots, a_n)).$$

Substituting (4.12) into (4.8) and introducing the notation

$$d\sigma_{\alpha\beta}(\lambda) = \left(\frac{\partial^{\alpha_1+\dots+\alpha_n+\beta_1+\dots+\beta_n}\Omega_\lambda}{\partial x_1^{\alpha_1}\dots\partial x_n^{\alpha_n}\partial y_1^{\beta_1}\dots\partial y_n^{\beta_n}} \right)(a, a)\, d\varrho(\lambda), \quad (4.13)$$

we arrive at a representation of the kernel $K(x, y)$ generalizing (3.20):

$$K(x, y) = \int_{E_n} \sum_{\alpha,\beta\in A} X_\alpha(x; \lambda)\, \overline{X_\beta(y; \lambda)}\, d\sigma_{\alpha\beta}(\lambda) \qquad (x, y \in G). \quad (4.14)$$

The matrix $\|d\sigma_{\alpha\beta}(\lambda)\|_{\alpha,\,\beta\in A}$ with vector notation for the row and column indices is p.d. in the usual sense, i.e. $\sum_{\alpha,\,\beta\in A} \sigma_{\alpha\beta}(\Delta)\xi_\alpha\bar{\xi}_\beta \geq 0$ for arbitrary ξ_α ($\alpha \in A$). We verify this in the same way as in the proof of Lemma 5.1, Chapter VI.

Thus if one introduces the fundamental system of solutions (4.10) *and constructs the products* (4.11), *then the representation* (4.8) *may be rewritten in the form* (4.14) *with some nonnegative matrix measure* $\|d\sigma_{\alpha\beta}(\lambda)\|_{\alpha,\beta\in A}$. *It is clear also that every such representation* (4.14) *may be rewritten in the form* (4.8). The integral (4.14) converges in the sense of the space $L_2(C_l; (-\infty, \infty), \|d\sigma_{\alpha\beta}(\lambda)\|_{\alpha,\beta\in A})$, where C_l is a complex space of dimension l equal to the order of the matrix $\|d\sigma_{\alpha\beta}(\lambda)\|_{\alpha,\,\beta\in A}$.

So far all the representations of this section, namely formulas (4.2), (4.8) and (4.14), have had a special character, since it was not clear in which cases there existed commutative selfadjoint representations. Here, by means of Theorem 2.3 and the techniques developed in §3.4, we shall find some additional conditions under which these representations hold for the case of ordinary differential equations with constant coefficients.

Theorem 4.3. *Suppose that the* p.d. *kernel* $K(x, y) \in C(E_n \times E_n)$ *satisfies, in the sense of generalized functions, the relations*

$$L_{x_j}^{(j)}K = \overline{L_{y_j}^{(j)}}K \qquad (j = 1, \dots, n). \quad (4.15)$$

Here $L^{(j)}$ *is an ordinary differential expression in the variable* x_j *of order* r_j *with constant coefficients. Suppose we have the estimate*

$$|K(x_1, \ldots, x_n; y_1, \ldots, y_n)| \leqslant Ce^{N(|x_1|^{r'_1}+\ldots+|x_n|^{r'_n}+|y_1|^{r'_1}+\ldots+|y_n|^{r'_n})} \quad (C > 0; \quad x, y \in E_n), \tag{4.16}$$

where $1/r_j + 1/r'_j = 1$ *for* $r_j > 1$, *and in the case* $r_j = 1$ r'_j *is any positive number. Then for the kernel K we have the representation* (4.14), *and the measure* $\|d\sigma_{\alpha\beta}(\lambda)\|_{\alpha,\,\beta\in A}$ *in it is uniquely defined. Here it is supposed in addition that each of the operators* $u \to L^{(j)^+}u$ $(u \in C_0^\infty(G);\ j = 1, \cdots, n)$ *in* H_K *has distinct defect numbers* (*for example,* $K(x, y)$ *and the coefficients of the expressions* $L^{(1)}, \cdots, L^{(n)}$ *are real*).

Proof. Thanks to the estimate (4.16), we may put, similarly to (3.32), $p(x) = e^{\sigma N(|x_1|^{r'_1} + \cdots + |x_n|^{r'_n})}$, $\sigma > 2$ $(x \in E_n)$, so that $p^{(j)}(x_j) = e^{\sigma N|x_j|^{r'_j}}$ $(j = 1, \cdots, n)$. The operators B_j have the form $u \to L^{(j)^+}u$ $(u \in C_0^\infty((-\infty, \infty)))$ and operate in the space $H_+^{(j)} = L_2((-\infty, \infty), p^{(j)}(x_j)\,dx_j)$. We shall show that the closures in H_K of the operators $u \to L^{(j)^+}u$ $(u \in C_0^\infty(G))$ (or, what is the same thing, the closures of the operators C_j constructed from (2.3)), are self-adjoint and commute.

Analogously to the case $n = 1$ we note that the region of definition of the operator B_j (and thus C_j as well) may be somewhat extended (see Lemma 3.3). Indeed, denote by Θ_j the family of functions $u \in C^\infty((-\infty, \infty))$ satisfying the estimates

$$|(D^q u)(x_j)| \leqslant C_{u,q} e^{-\varrho N|x_j|^{r'_j}} \qquad (x_j \in (-\infty, \infty);\ q = 0, 1, \ldots),$$

where $\rho > \sigma/2$. Instead of the operator B_j we consider a wider operator in $H_+^{(j)}$, operating according to the law $u \to L^{(j)^+}u$, $u \in \Theta_j \supset C_0^\infty((-\infty, \infty))$. We extend C_1 similarly. As in Lemma 3.3, one proves in an elementary manner that this extension of the operator C_j lies in the closure in H_K of the preceding operator C_j. Therefore we may now suppose that $B_j u = L^{(j)^+}u$, $u \in \Theta_j$.

From Theorem 2.3 it suffices to prove that for the $2n$ equations $du/dt \pm i(B_j)^* u = 0$ $(0 \leq t < \infty)$, the jth of which is considered in the space $H_+^{(j)}$, there is uniqueness for the weak solutions of the Cauchy problem. This same uniqueness, as was proved earlier, results from Theorem 2.4 and Lemmas 3.4 and 3.5. The theorem is proved.

Remark. Theorem 4.3 remains valid if inequality (4.16) is replaced by the following. Suppose that the expressions $L^{(1)}, \cdots, L^{(m)}$ are of order >1 and the rest of order 1 $(m \le n)$. Then it suffices to require that

$$|K(x_1, \ldots, x_n; y_1, \ldots, y_n)| \leqslant C(x_{m+1}, \ldots, x_n; y_{m+1}, \ldots, y_n)\, e^{N(|x_1|^{r'_1}+\ldots+|x_m|^{r'_m}+|y_1|^{r'_1}+\ldots+|y_m|^{r'_m})} \quad (x, y \in E_n), \tag{4.17}$$

where $C(\cdot\,;\,\cdot)$ is any continuous function. The assumption that the defect numbers have to be equal must be strengthened, replacing it for example by the requirement that the coefficients of $L^{(1)}, \cdots, L^{(n)}$ be real and that $K(x_1, \cdots, x_n; y_1, \cdots, y_n)$ should be symmetric relative to each pair of variables x_i, y_j.

Indeed, we may take $p(x) = e^{\sigma N(|x_1|^{r'_1}+\cdots+|x_m|^{r'_m})} p^{(m+1)}(x_{m+1}), \cdots, p^{(n)}(x_n)$ $(x \in E_n)$, where $\sigma > 2$, and the $p^{(j)}$ for $j \ge m+1$ are selected according to Lemma 4.1 relative to $M(x) = C(x_{m+1}, \cdots, x_n; x_{m+1}, \cdots, x_n)$. After the choice of $p(x)$ the forms of the spaces $H_+^{(j)}$ are determined. Now we note that the scalar product (2.6) $\langle u_1, v_1\rangle_{w_2, \cdots, w_n} = \langle u_1 \otimes w_2 \otimes \cdots \otimes w_n, v_1 \otimes w_2 \otimes \cdots \otimes w_n\rangle$, where $w_j \in H_+^{(j)}$ $(j > 1)$ are fixed, and $u_1, v_1 \in H_+^{(1)}$, is the scalar product generated because of the symmetry properties of $K(x, y)$ by the real kernel

$$K_{w_2,\ldots,w_n}(x_1, y_1) = \iint\limits_{E_{n-1}\times E_{n-1}} K(x_1, \ldots, x_n; y_1, \ldots, y_n)\, w_2(y_2)\overline{w_2(x_2)} \ldots w_n(y_n)\overline{w_n(x_n)}\, dx_2 \ldots dx_n dy_2 \ldots dy_n. \tag{4.18}$$

For this kernel, from (4.17) we have the estimate

$$|K_{w_2,\ldots,w_n}(x_1, y_1)| \leqslant C_1 e^{N(|x_1|^{r'_1}+|y_1|^{r'_1})} \qquad (C_1 > 0;\ x_1, y_1 \in (-\infty, \infty)).$$

Therefore, from Theorem 3.9, the closure of the operator $u \to L^{(1)^+}u$ $(u \in C_0^\infty((-\infty, \infty))$ is maximal in the space $H^{(1)}_{K;\, w_2, \cdots, w_n}$ and therefore, in view of the equality of its defect numbers, is selfadjoint as well (their equality follows from the realness of the kernel (4.18) and of the coefficients $L^{(1)^+}$). An analogous situation holds on the replacement of the index 1 by $2, \cdots, n$ (for indices beginning with $m+1$ we must use the last assertion of Theorem 3.9). Thus, the hypotheses of Theorem 2.2 are satisfied. This proves the assertion.

3. **Examples.** The results of subsection 2 and the corresponding facts of §3 make it possible to construct a number of examples of representations.

1. *Ordinary p. d. functions of several variables.* A function $k(t) \in C(E_n)$ is

said to be a p. d. function if the kernel $K(x, y) = k(y - x)$ $(x, y \in E_n)$ is p. d. As in the one-dimensional case, it is always bounded.

Theorem 4.4. *A function $k(t) \in C(E_n)$ is p. d. if and only if it has a representation*

$$k(t) = \int_{E_n} e^{i\lambda t} d\sigma(\lambda) \qquad (\lambda t = \lambda_1 t_1 + \dots + \lambda_n t_n; \quad t \in E_n), \qquad (4.19)$$

where $d\sigma(\lambda)$ is a nonnegative finite measure. This measure is determined uniquely by k.

This theorem follows from Theorem 4.3; we need to put $L^{(1)} = i(\partial/\partial x_1), \dots$ $\dots, L^{(n)} = i(\partial/\partial x_n)$, observe the equality of the defect numbers of the corresponding operators (see page 666), write down for the kernel $K(x, y)$ the representation (4.14), taking $a = 0$ in the construction of X_a, and replace $y - x$ by t.

In a direct derivation of Theorem 4.4 we may use Theorem 3.11 and Theorem 2.1, or Theorem 2.2 (cf. the proof of Theorem 4.5).

In the above it was essential that the p. d. function $k(t)$ was given for all of E_n. The situation when $k(t)$ is given in a portion of E_n is not trivial and will be considered in subsection 4.

2. *Exponentially convex functions of several variables.* Suppose that $G = G^{(1)} \times \dots \times G^{(n)} = (l'_1, l''_1) \times \dots \times (l'_n, l''_n)$, where $-\infty \leq l'_j < l''_j \leq \infty$ $(j = 1, \dots$ $\dots, n)$. The function $k(t) \in C(2G)$ $(2G = (2l'_1, 2l''_1) \times \dots \times (2l'_n, 2l''_n))$ is said to be exponentially convex if the kernel $K(x, y) = k(x + y)$ $(x, y \in G)$ is p. d. . Clearly $k(t)$ is necessarily real.

Theorem 4.5. *The function $k(t) \in C(2G)$ is exponentially convex if and only if it admits the representation*

$$k(t) = \int_{E_n} e^{\lambda t} d\sigma(\lambda) \qquad (t \in 2G), \qquad (4.20)$$

where $d\sigma(\lambda)$ is a nonnegative measure. This measure is uniquely determined by k.

In the case $G = E_n$ this theorem follows simply from the remark to Theorem 4.3. In the general case it has been possible to prove it only thanks to the uniqueness in the representation (3.82) of the measure, independent of the form of (l', l'').

Proof. We shall construct, as indicated in subsection 1, a function $p(x)\in G$ and spaces H_+ and $H_+^{(1)}, \cdots, H_+^{(n)}$. Put $L^{(1)} = \partial/\partial x_1, \cdots, L^{(n)} = \partial/\partial x_n$. Then the kernel $K(x, y) = k(x+y)$ will satisfy relations (4.15). The existence of commuting selfadjoint extensions of the operators $u \to L^{(j)^+}u$ $(u \in C_0^\infty(G))$ or of the corresponding operators C_j is proved using Theorem 2.2. Indeed, the scalar product (2.6) is now generated by a kernel of type (4.18), while $K_{w_2,\cdots,w_n}(x_1, y_1) = k_{w_2,\cdots,w_n}(x_1+y_1)$, where the function $k_{w_2,\cdots,w_n}$ is obtained from the function k by integrations. Theorem 3.17 is applicable to the exponentially convex function $k_{w_2,\cdots,w_n}(t_1)$ $(t_1 \in (2l_1', 2l_1''))$. From the uniqueness in that theorem it follows that the closure of the operator $u \to L^{(1)^+}u$ $(u \in C_0^\infty((l_1', l_1'')))$, operating in the space $H^{(1)}_{K;\, w_2,\cdots,w_n}$, is selfadjoint (we note that this operator has equal defect numbers because of the reality of $k_{w_2,\cdots,w_n}(x_1+y_1)$ and $L^{(1)}$). Analogously we consider the case when the index 1 is replaced by $2, \cdots, n$. Thus the conditions of Theorem 2.2 are satisfied and the required extensions exist. This makes it possible to write the representation (4.14) for the kernel $K(x, y)$, from which formula (4.20) follows. The theorem is proved.

In the following examples we take $n = 2$ for simplicity.

3. We consider a function $k(t) = k(t_1, t_2) \in C(E_2)$, even in each variable and such that $K(x, y) = \frac{1}{2}[k(x+y) + k(x-y)]$ is p.d.. Moreover we assume that for some $N > 0$

$$|k(t)| \leqslant Ce^{N(t_1^2+t_2^2)} \qquad (C>0;\, t_1, t_2 \in (-\infty, \infty)). \tag{4.21}$$

Then such a function is representable in the form

$$k(t) = \int\int_{-\infty}^{\infty} \cos\sqrt{\lambda_1}t_1 \cdot \cos\sqrt{\lambda_2}t_2\, d\sigma(\lambda_1, \lambda_2) \qquad (t \in E_2), \tag{4.22}$$

where $d\sigma(\lambda_1, \lambda_2)$ is a finite nonnegative measure which is uniquely defined. Conversely, every function (4.22) has the property that the kernel $K(x, y) = \frac{1}{2}[k(x+y) + k(x-y)]$ $(x, y \in E_2)$ is p.d..

This assertion follows from Theorem 4.3, applied to the kernel $K(x, y)$ and to the expressions $L^{(1)} = \partial^2/\partial x_1^2$, $L^{(2)} = \partial^2/\partial x_2^2$. Here we need additional arguments of the same type as in the proof of Theorem 3.18. We must observe that the restrictions on $k(t)$ imply that it is real.

4. Example 3 remains valid if one replaces the kernel $K(x, y)$ in it by the kernel $K(x, y) = \frac{1}{2}[k(x+y) - k(x-y)]$ and assumes in addition that $k(0, t_2) = k(t_1, 0) = 0$ $(t_1, t_2 \in (-\infty, \infty))$. The representation (4.22) goes into

$$k(t) = \int_{-\infty}^{\infty}\!\!\int \frac{2\sin^2\sqrt{\lambda_1}\,\frac{t_1}{2}}{\lambda_1}\cdot\frac{2\sin^2\sqrt{\lambda_2}\,\frac{t_2}{2}}{\lambda_2}\,d\sigma(\lambda_1, \lambda_2) \qquad (t \in E_2).$$

5. Example 3 remains valid if one replaces in it the kernel $K(x, y)$ by the kernel $K(x, y) = \frac{1}{2}[k(x_1 + y_1, y_2 - x_2) + k(x_1 - y_1, y_2 - x_2)]$, while concerning the function $k(t)$ one requires only evenness relative to the first variable, and the estimate (4.21) is replaced by the following:

$$|k(t)| \leqslant C(t_2)e^{Nt_1^2} \qquad (C(t_2) > 0;\ t_1 \in (-\infty, \infty)).$$

With some modification of the arguments presented at the end of subsection 2, we obtain the representation

$$k(t) = \int_{-\infty}^{\infty}\!\!\int \cos\sqrt{\lambda_1}t_1\cdot e^{i\lambda_2 t_2}d\sigma(\lambda_1, \lambda_2) \qquad (t \in E_2).$$

It is clear that we may write down a number of further examples, combining one-dimensional cases as in 5. Here, if we are going to use the expressions $i\,\partial/\partial x_2$ or $\partial^2/\partial x_2^2$, then the variable t_2 must vary along the entire axis $(-\infty, \infty)$, and if we are going to use $\partial/\partial x_2$, then t_2 must vary in a finite interval (cf. the proof of Theorem 4.5). The common property of all of these examples, as in the examples 1–5, will be the uniqueness of the measure $d\sigma(\lambda)$.

4. **Extension of p. d. functions of two variables.** Suppose that $G = G^{(1)} \times G^{(2)} = (-l_1, l_1) \times (-l_2, l_2)$, where $0 < l_1, l_2 < \infty$; $2G = (-2l_1, 2l_1) \times (-2l_2, 2l_2)$. The function $k(t) \in C(2G)$ is said to be p. d. if the kernel $K(x, y) = k(x - y)$ is p. d. $(x, y \in G)$. In distinction from the case of one variable the resulting integral representation (4.19) for such a function, i. e. its extension into a p. d. function on the entire E_2 plane, is not always possible (there are counterexamples). The complication of the situation is connected with the circumstance that the extension of a p. d. function of one variable from the interval $(-l, l)$ to the entire axis is generally speaking nonunique. Below we shall nevertheless obtain some results touching on the possibility of extension. We note that the consideration of the case of two, and not of n, variables, is done here only for ease of exposition.

From (3.39), $K(x, y)$ is defined for $x, y \in G$, so that as the function $p(x)$ of (3.3) we may choose $p(x) = 1$. Thus $H_+ = H_0 = L_2(G)$, $H_+^{(j)} = L_2((-l_j, l_j))$. Clearly $L^{(j)} = i\,\partial/\partial x_j = L^{(j)+}$ satisfy relations (4.15) within G ($j = 1, 2$). We are required to elucidate the existence of commuting selfadjoint extensions of Hermitian operators $u \to i\,\partial/\partial x_j$ ($u \in C_0^\infty(G)$) ($j = 1, 2$) operating in H_K, or, what is the same thing, of the Hermitian operators

$$C_1 u = i\frac{\partial u}{\partial x_1} (u \in C_0^\infty((-l_1, l_1)) \otimes L_2((-l_2, l_2)))$$

and

$$C_2 u = i\frac{\partial u}{\partial x_2} \quad (u \in L_2((-l_1, l_1)) \otimes C_0^\infty((-l_2, l_2))).$$

Using Theorem 2.6 it is easy to prove the following theorem.

Theorem 4.6. *Suppose that the p.d. function $k(t) = k(t_1, t_2) \in C(2G)$ has the property that the p.d. function of one variable $k(t_1, 0)$ can be uniquely extended from the interval $(-2l_1, 2l_1)$ to the entire axis. Then the function $k(t)$ may also be extended (generally speaking nonuniquely) from the rectangle $2G$ as a p.d. function on the entire plane E_2. Thus, for $t \in 2G$ the function $k(t)$ admits a representation (4.19) (with $n = 2$), the measure being generally speaking determined nonuniquely.*

Proof. The role of the transformation $\circ_j$ is played by the transition $u(x_j) \to \overline{u(-x_j)}$ ($j = 1, 2$). Then $\circ = \circ_1 \otimes \circ_2$ has the form $u^\circ(x) = \overline{u(-x)}$ ($x \in G$), and after closure by continuity becomes an involution in H_K (for the latter we need to take account of the equation $k(t) = \overline{k(-t)}$ ($t \in 2G$), see (3.39)). Clearly the operators C_1 and C_2 are real relative to $\circ$.

We shall show that the closure of the restriction of C_1 to the set $C_0^\infty((-l_1, l_1)) \otimes w_2 = \mathfrak{D}(B_1) \otimes w_2$ for any $w_2 \in H_+^{(2)}$ is selfadjoint in $H_{K;\,w_2}^{(1)}$, i.e. in the completion of $H_+^{(1)}$ relative to the scalar product

$$\langle u_1, v_1\rangle_{w_2} = \langle u_1 \otimes w_2, v_1 \otimes w_2\rangle = \int_{-l_1}^{l_1}\int_{-l_2}^{l_2}\int_{-l_1}^{l_1}\int_{-l_2}^{l_2} k(y_1 - x_1, y_2 - x_2)$$
$$\times u_1(y_1) w_2(y_2) \overline{v_1(x_1)}\, \overline{w_2(x_2)}\, dx_1 dx_2 dy_1 dy_2.$$

The function $f(t_2) = \int_{-l_1}^{l_1}\int_{-l_1}^{l_1} k(y_1 - x_1, t_2) u_1(y_1) \overline{u_1(x_1)}\, dx_1 dy_1 \in C((-2l_2, 2l_2))$ is obviously p.d., so that $|f(t_2)| \le f(0)$ $(t_2 \in (-2l_2, 2l_2))$. Therefore

$$\langle u_1, u_1\rangle_{w_2} = \int_{-l_2}^{l_2}\int_{-l_2}^{l_2} f(y_2 - x_2)\, w_2(y_2)\,\overline{w_2(x_2)}\, dx_2 dy_2 \leqslant C_{w_2} f(0)$$
$$= C_{w_2}\int_{-l_1}^{l_1}\int_{-l_1}^{l_1} k(y_1 - x_1, 0)\, u_1(y_1)\,\overline{u_1(x_1)}\, dx_1 dy_1 \quad (u_1 \in H_+^{(1)} = L_2((-l_1, l_1))). \tag{4.23}$$

Thus the scalar product $\langle \cdot, \cdot \rangle_{w_2}$ is majorized by the scalar product constructed in $L_2((-l_1, l_1))$ relative to the p.d. function $k(t_1, 0)$. Therefore if the set of functions $i\,\partial u/\partial x_1 - zu$ ($\operatorname{Im} z \neq 0$, $u \in C_0^\infty((-l_1, l_1))$) is dense in the space $H_{k(y_1 - x_1, 0)}$, then it is all the more dense in $H^{(1)}_{K; w_2}$. But the first denseness is present, since by hypothesis the function $k(t_1, 0)$ extends uniquely and the corresponding operator is selfadjoint. Accordingly the second density is also present, i.e. the closure of the restriction of C_1 in question is selfadjoint.

The conditions of Theorem 2.6 are satisfied, so that there exist selfadjoint commuting extensions of the operators C_1 and C_2. Now we apply Theorem 4.2. The theorem is proved.

We now make some remarks. Changing the argument somewhat, we see that *the p.d. function* $k(t) = k(t_1, t_2)$, *defined in the strip* $(-\infty, \infty) \times (-2l_2, 2l_2)$, *is always extendable to* E_2 *(in general nonuniquely). If the p.d. function* $k(t) = k(t_1, t_2) \in C((-2l_1, 2l_1) \times (-2l_2, 2l_2))$ $(0 < l_1, l_2 < \infty)$ *has the property that the p.d. functions of one variable* $k(t_1, 0)$ *and* $k(0, t_2)$ *are extendable to the entire axis uniquely, then* $k(t)$ *also extends to* E_2 *uniquely.* This follows from Theorem 2.2, using the arguments applied in the proof of Theorem 4.6.

Here we shall note the description of the extensions of a p.d. function $k(t)$ appearing in Theorem 4.6 which correspond to selfadjoint extensions in H_K. First we carry over to the case of p.d. functions of two variables some of the results of subsections 8 and 9 of the preceding section. Thus we shall consider an arbitrary p.d. function $k(t) \in C(2G) = C((-2l_1, 2l_1) \times (-2l_2, 2l_2))$ $(0 < l_1, l_2 < \infty)$.

We shall show that *necessarily* $k(t) \in C([-2l_1, 2l_1] \times [-2l_2, 2l_2])$, *i.e.* $k(t)$ *is uniformly continuous on* $2G$. Indeed, we use the construction applied in the proof of Lemma 4.2, Chapter V. Put $K(x, y) = k(y - x)$ $(x, y \in G)$. We need to verify that this kernel is uniformly continuous relative to this kernel, for $(x, y) \in (G \times G)$. As follows from the above-mentioned proof, for this it suffices to verify the uniform continuity of the vector function $e_x (x \in G)$ with values in the space $\mathfrak{H}_K$. On the basis of (4.19), Chapter V, we obtain

$$\|e_x - e_y\|_K^2 = (e_x - e_y,\ e_x - e_y)_K = K(x,\ x) - 2\operatorname{Re} K(x,\ y) + K(y,\ y) = 2[k(0) - \operatorname{Re} k(y - x)].$$

This equation shows that the uniform continuity of e_x in G follows from the continuity of $k(t)$ at 0. The assertion is proved.

From what has been proved it follows that for the kernel $K(x, y)$ $(x, y \in G)$ all the results of §3.7 are valid, including what was said at the end of that subsection (we suppose in addition that the form constructed relative to the kernel K is nondegenerate). The chain (3.44) will also be denoted $H_k \supseteq H_0 = L_2(G) \supseteq H_{+,k}$. In the space H_k the Hermitian operators C_1 and C_2 introduced above also operate. If they admit selfadjoint commuting extensions S_1 and S_2, in or out of H_k, then for $k(t)$, with $t \in 2G$, representation (4.19) is valid $(n = 2)$. Substituting this representation into (3.43) we obtain, analogously to (3.51), Parseval's equation

$$\langle E(\Delta) f, g \rangle = \int_\Delta \tilde{f}(\lambda) \overline{\tilde{g}(\lambda)}\, d\sigma(\lambda), \quad \tilde{f}(\lambda) = \int_G e^{i\lambda x} f(x)\, dx \ (f, g \in L_2(G)), \tag{4.24}$$

where $E(\Delta)$ is a two-dimensional (generalized) partition of unity, corresponding to these extensions. Similarly to the one-dimensional case, one may pass to the limit in (4.24) and obtain the equation

$$\langle E(\Delta) \alpha, \beta \rangle = \int_\Delta \tilde{\alpha}(\lambda) \overline{\tilde{\beta}(\lambda)}\, d\sigma(\lambda) \quad (\alpha, \beta \in H_k), \tag{4.25}$$

where by $\tilde{\alpha}(\lambda)$ we understand the limit in $L_2(E_2, d\sigma(\lambda))$ of the functions $\tilde{f}_n(\lambda)$ for $f_n \in L_2(G)$, approximating α in H_k. It is clear that for $\xi \in [-2l_1, 2l_1] \times [-2l_2, 2l_2]$ $\tilde{\delta}_\xi(\lambda) = e^{i\lambda\xi}$. The form of (3.54) is also preserved: $\sigma(\Delta) = \langle E(\Delta)\delta_0, \delta_0 \rangle$.

For the kernels $R^{(1)}(x, y; z)$ and $R^{(2)}(x, y; z)$ of the resolvents $R^{(1)}$ and $R^{(2)}$ of the operators S_1 and S_2, representations of the type (3.68) are valid. They follow directly from (4.9) and the form of $\Omega_\lambda(x, y)$ (or from (4.25)) and are as follows:

$$R^{(j)}(x, y; z) = \langle R_z^{(j)} \delta_y, \delta_x \rangle = \int_{E_2} \frac{e^{i\lambda(y-x)}}{\lambda_j - z}\, d\sigma(\lambda)$$
$$(x, y \in [-l_1, l_1] \times [-l_2, l_2]; \quad j = 1, 2). \tag{4.26}$$

Analogous representations hold also for kernels of more general operators

$F(S_1, S_2) = \int_{E_2} F(\lambda_1, \lambda_2)dE_\lambda$, where $F(\lambda_1, \lambda_2)$ is a bounded Borel-measurable function. In this case, the term $1/(\lambda_j - z)$ in (4.26) must be replaced by $F(\lambda_1, \lambda_2)$.

Similarly to the one-dimensional case, for the operators C_1 and C_2 one proves, without the assumption of the existence of commutative selfadjoint extensions, the following: suppose that $\mathbf{I}$ is constructed relative to the chain $H_k \supseteq H_0 \supseteq H_{+,k}$. Then

$$C_1^* \alpha = i\mathbf{I}^{-1}\left(\frac{\partial}{\partial x_1}(\mathbf{I}\alpha)\right), \quad C_2^* \alpha = i\mathbf{I}^{-1}\left(\frac{\partial}{\partial x_2}(\mathbf{I}\alpha)\right). \tag{4.27}$$

$\mathfrak{D}(C_1^*)$ $(\mathfrak{D}(C_2^*))$ consists of those and only those $\alpha \in H_k$ for which $\mathbf{I}\alpha$ is continuously differentiable relative to $x_1(x_2)$, while $\partial/\partial x_1(\mathbf{I}\alpha) \in H_{+,k}$ $(\partial/\partial x_2(\mathbf{I}\alpha) \in H_{+,k})$.

Denote by N_z $(\operatorname{Im} z \neq 0)$ the defect subspace of the operator C_2. N_z coincides with the subspace of solutions of the equation $C_2^*\phi = \bar{z}\phi$. In view of (4.27) this means that $[-l_1, l_1] \times [-l_2, l_2]$ $i((\partial/\partial x_2)\mathbf{I}\phi) = \bar{z}\mathbf{I}\phi$, i.e. $(\mathbf{I}\phi)(x_1, x_2) = a(x_1)e^{-i\bar{z}x_2}$ $(x \in [-l_1, l_1] \times [-l_2, l_2])$. The function $a(x_1)$ is some continuous function on $[-l_2, l_2]$, having the property that $a(x_1)e^{-i\bar{z}x_2} \in H_{+,k}$. Thus, N_z *consists of vectors of the form*

$$\varphi = \mathbf{I}^{-1}(a(x_1)e^{-i\bar{z}x_2}) \in H_k, \tag{4.28}$$

where $a(x_1) \in C([-l_1, l_1])$ *is such that* $a(x_1)e^{-i\bar{z}x_2} \in H_{+,k}$. In the same way one may describe also the defect subspaces of the operator C_1; however we shall consider later the case when the closure $\bar{C}_1$ is selfadjoint in H_k.

We shall supplement somewhat the abstract constructions of §2. What we will do is to detail the form of the operator X in relation (2.26).

Lemma 4.2. *Under the assumptions of Theorem 2.6 the set* $\mathfrak{D}(\bar{C}_1) \cap N_{z_2}$ *is dense in the space* N_{z_2}. *The restriction* Γ_{z_2} *of the operator* $\bar{C}_1$ *to this set is selfadjoint in* N_{z_2}.

Proof. Consider the subspaces $N_{z_2}^{(j)}$ selected on page 636. They are pairwise orthogonal, $N_{z_2}^{(1)} \oplus N_{z_2}^{(2)} \oplus \cdots = N_{z_2}$, and $N_{z_2}^{(j)}$ consists of the closure of the linear envelope of the vectors $E(\Delta)f_j$ for any Borel set Δ. Each such closure coincides with the family of vectors of the type $\int_{-\infty}^{\infty} F(\lambda)dE_\lambda f_j$, where $F(\lambda)$ is such that $\int_{-\infty}^{\infty} |F(\lambda)|^2 d\langle E_\lambda f_j, f_j\rangle < \infty$. Therefore any $f \in N_{z_2}$ is representable in the form

$$f=\sum_{j=1}^{\infty}\int_{-\infty}^{\infty}F_j(\lambda)\,dE_\lambda f_j,\quad \langle f,f\rangle=\sum_{j=1}^{\infty}\int_{-\infty}^{\infty}|F_j(\lambda)|^2\,d\langle E_\lambda f_j,f_j\rangle<\infty. \tag{4.29}$$

The sequence of functions $F_1(\lambda)$, $F_2(\lambda)$, $\cdots$ is generally speaking not uniquely determined relative to f. The scalar product $\langle f, g\rangle$ $(f, g \in N_{z_2})$ is written in terms of an equation similar to the second equation in (4.29). It is clear that $f \in N_{z_2}$ lies in $\mathfrak{D}(\overline{C}_1)$ if and only if $\sum_{j=1}^{\infty}\int_{-\infty}^{\infty}|\lambda F_j(\lambda)|^2\,d\langle E_\lambda f_j, f_j\rangle<\infty$, while $\overline{C}_1 f=\sum_{j=1}^{\infty}\int_{-\infty}^{\infty}\lambda f_j(\lambda)dE_\lambda f_j$. The assertion of the lemma follows easily from the resulting decomposition of the space N_{z_2}.

Denote by X_0 the operator X constructed in the proof of Theorem 2.6. In the terms of the decomposition (4.29) we have

$$X_0\left(\sum_{j=1}^{\infty}\int_{-\infty}^{\infty}F_j(\lambda)\,dE_\lambda f_j\right)=\sum_{j=1}^{\infty}\int_{-\infty}^{\infty}F_j(\lambda)\,dE_\lambda \mathring{f}_j. \tag{4.30}$$

The operator X_0 carries isometrically all of N_{z_2} into all of $N_{\bar{z}_2}$, and satisfies relation (2.26): $U_{z_1}^{(1)}X_0 f=X_0U_{z_1}^{(1)}f$ $(f\in N_{z_2})$.

Suppose that Y is a unitary operator in the space N_{z_2} commuting with the selfadjoint operator Γ_{z_2}. Since the part of $U_{z_1}^{(1)}$ operating in N_{z_2} may be considered as a function Γ_{z_2}, then Y will commute also with N_{z_2}. Therefore $X=X_0Y$ satisfies (2.26). Conversely, if X satisfies (2.26), then $X_0^{-1}X$ will be a unitary operator in the space N_{z_2}, commuting with $U_{z_2}^{(1)}$, i.e. with Γ_{z_2}. Thus we have found that *in the formula* (2.26) X *has the form*

$$X=X_0Y, \tag{4.31}$$

where X_0 *is determined by equation* (4.30), *and* Y *is any unitary operator in* N_{z_2}, *commuting with* Γ_{z_2}.

We turn again to the consideration of the p.d. function $k(t)$ of Theorem 4.6. For simplicity we take $z_2=i$. From (4.28) $\phi=\mathbf{I}^{-1}(a(x_1)e^{-x_2})$, $\psi=\mathbf{I}^{-1}(b(x_1)e^{-x_2})\in N_i$, given only that $a, b\in C([-l_1, l_1])$ are such that $a(x_1)e^{-x_2}$, $b(x_1)e^{-x_2}\in H_{+,k}$; in addition $\langle\phi,\psi\rangle=(a(x_1)e^{-x_2}, b(x_1)e^{-x_2})_{+,k}$. Taking account of the form of the operator $\overline{C}_1=C_1^*$ (see (4.27)), we may make the following assertion. *Introduce on the functions* $a(x_1)\in C([-l_1, l_1])$, *for which* $(a(x_1)e^{-x_2}, a(x_1)e^{-x_2})_{+,k}<\infty$, *the scalar product*

$$[a, b] = (a(x_1)\, e^{-x_2},\ b(x_1)\, e^{-x_2})_{+,k}.$$

As a result we obtain a complete Hilbert space $\mathfrak{H}$ *isometric to* N_i. *The role of the operator* Y *of* (4.31) *is played by any unitary operator in* $\mathfrak{H}$ *commuting with the selfadjoint operator* $a(x_1) \to ia'(x_1)$ *in this space, defined for all* $a \in \mathfrak{H} \cap C^1([-l_1, l_1])$, *for which* $a' \in \mathfrak{H}$.

The structure of the space $\mathfrak{H}$ and of that selfadjoint operator in it, which in the end depends on the form of $k(t)$, defines a set of operators Y and thus a set of extensions of $k(t)$ from $(-2l_1, 2l_1) \times (-2l_2, 2l_2)$ to E_2, described by extensions into H_k. The fact that the situation here can be quite diverse is shown by the following simple example.

First of all we note that if $k_j(t_j) \in C((-2l_j, 2l_j))$ $(0 < l_j \leq \infty;\ j = 1, 2)$ are p.d. functions, then also $k(t) = k(t_1, t_2) = k(t_1)k(t_2)$ is a p.d. function. This follows from the fact that if the matrices $\|a_{jk}\|_1^n$ and $\|b_{jk}\|_1^n$ are nonnegative definite, then $\|a_{jk}b_{jk}\|_1^n$ is as well. Consider the following p.d. function on $(-\infty, \infty) \times (-2l_2, 2l_2)$:

$$k(t) = \sum_{\alpha=1}^{N} e^{i\lambda_1^{(\alpha)} t_1}\, k_2(t_2), \tag{4.32}$$

where $\lambda_1^{(\alpha)}$ is a fixed point of the axis $(-\infty, \infty)$ and $k_2(t_2) \in C((-2l_2, 2l_2))$ is p.d. and extends to the entire axis nonuniquely. Suppose that $k_2^{(\alpha)}(t_2)$ $(\alpha = 1, \cdots, N)$ are various such prolongations. Then

$$\sum_{\alpha=1}^{N} e^{i\lambda_1^{(\alpha)} t_1}\, k_2^{(\alpha)}(t_2)$$

will be extensions of (4.32) to E_2. Since $k_2^{(\alpha)}$ describe the extensions of k_2 independently, the "collection" of prolongations of k depends on N.

One can obtain analytic formulas making it possible to write extensions for an operator Y, i.e. the corresponding measure $d\sigma(\lambda_1, \lambda_2)$ may be obtained by use of Theorem 2.8. According to this theorem and (4.31), an admissible extension of the operator C_2 has a Cayley transform of the form $\widetilde{U}_i^{(2)} = U_i \oplus X_0 Y$. If we then use a representation of type (4.26), we may express $d\sigma(\lambda_1, \lambda_2)$ in the same way as in §1.7, Chapter VII and §3.9 of Chapter VIII. We shall however not dwell on this, but shall mention a somewhat different idea, more symmetric and natural, for obtaining "analysis" in the theory of extension of p.d. functions of two variables. In what follows it will be convenient to consider functions given in a strip.

Consider a p. d. operator function $K(t)$, $t \in (-2l, 2l)$, $(0 < l \leq \infty)$. Its values will be continuous linear operators operating in some separable Hilbert space H. They are continuous in the norms of the operators relative to t. The fact that it is p. d. means that for any $x_1, \cdots, x_N \in (-l, l)$ and vectors $\xi_1, \cdots, \xi_N \in H$ $\Sigma_{j,k=1}^N (K(x_k - x_j)\xi_k, \xi_j)_H \geq 0$. Using a construction analogous to that presented in §2, Chapter VII, we may carry over a number of results of the theory of subsections 6, 8, and 9 of §3 to the case of p. d. operator functions. Representation (3.40) will take the form

$$K(t) = \int_{-\infty}^{\infty} e^{i\lambda t}\, d\Sigma(\lambda) \qquad (t \in (-2l, 2l)), \tag{4.33}$$

where $d\Sigma(\lambda)$ is a nonnegative finite operator measure. In the case $l < \infty$ all the $d\Sigma(\lambda)$ (i. e. all the extensions of $K(t)$ to a p. d. function on $(-\infty, \infty)$) may be described by a theorem of the type of Theorem 3.15 (see also what was said at the end of §2, Chapter VII). In this theorem the role of the point w, chosen on the circumference K_2, will be played by some operator $\mathbb{W}$ situated on the operator analog of the Weyl-Hamburger circumference.

We turn now from the operator case of the function $K(t)$ to the case of a p. d. function of two variables $k(t_1, t_2)((t_1, t_2) \in (-\infty, \infty) \times (-l_2, l_2))$. This passage is analogous to the passage in §4, Chapter VII from operator equations to partial difference equations. Indeed, let us choose as H the completion of $C_0^\infty((-\infty, \infty))$ (possibly after identification) relative to the scalar product

$$(f, g)_H = \int_{-\infty}^{\infty}\int_{-\infty}^{\infty} k(y_1 - x_1, 0) f(y_1) \overline{g(x_1)}\, dx_1\, dy_1 \qquad f, g \in C_0^\infty((-\infty, \infty))$$

and then define the function $K(t_2)$ by the relation

$$(K(t_2) f, g)_H = \int_{-\infty}^{\infty}\int_{-\infty}^{\infty} k(y_1 - x_1, t_2) f(y_1) \overline{g(x_1)}\, dx_1 dy_1 (f, g \in C_0^\infty((-\infty, \infty))). \tag{4.34}$$

It is clear that the positive definiteness of the function $k(t_1, t_2)$ implies the positive definiteness of the operator function $K(t_2)$ $(t_2 \in (-2l_2, 2l_2))$. Therefore, from (4.33), $K(t_2) = \int_{-\infty}^{\infty} e^{i\lambda_2 t_2} d\Sigma(\lambda_2)$ $(t \in (-2l_2, 2l_2))$ with some $d\Sigma(\lambda_2)$. This representation is more general than (4.19). Indeed, the latter, using (4.34), may be written in the form $(f \in C_0^\infty(-\infty, \infty))$:

$$(K(t_2) f)(x_1) = \int_{-\infty}^{\infty} k(y_1 - x_1, t_2) f(y_1)\, dy_1 =$$

$$= \int_{-\infty}^{\infty} \left(\int_{E_2} e^{i(\lambda_1(y_1-x_1)+\lambda_2 t_2)} \, d\sigma(\lambda_1, \lambda_2) \right) f(y_1)\, dy_1 = \int_{-\infty}^{\infty} e^{i\lambda_2 t_2} \, (d\Sigma(\lambda_2) f)(x_1);$$

$$(\Sigma(\Delta) f)(x_1) = \int_{-\infty}^{\infty} \left(\int_{(-\infty,\infty)\times\Delta} e^{i\lambda_1(y_1-x_1)} \, d\sigma(\lambda_1, \lambda_2) \right) f(y_1)\, dy_1. \qquad (4.35)$$

It is easy to see that the operator $\Sigma(\Delta)$ will be nonnegative in H.

Thus the special p. d. operator function $K(t_2)$ generated according to (4.34) by the p. d. function $k(t_1, t_2)$, admits in some cases, for instance in the case of Theorem 4.6, the representation (4.35), more special than (4.33). In order to obtain all representations (4.35) we need in formulas of the type of Theorem 3.15 to choose special operators W with operator circumferences of Weyl-Hamburger type. Indeed: these W must commute with a selfadjoint operator isomorphic to the operator $a \to ia'$ in the space $\mathfrak{H}$ described above and equal to the closure in H of the operator $f \to if'$ $(f \in C_0^\infty((-\infty, \infty)))$. Now we include the case of extensions which go out of H_K, but require the maximality of the defect numbers of the operator C_2.

§5. POSITIVE DEFINITE KERNELS *-COMMUTING WITH DIFFERENCE OPERATORS

In this section, using the general constructions of §§1–2, we present the difference analog of the questions considered in §§3–4. In particular, we shall consider the theory of the problem of moments and its generalizations. As we have already said, this section is closely connected with Chapter VII.

1. One ordinary difference expression. Consider the case of an expression operating on the entire axis, i. e. operating on the sequence $u = (\cdots, u_{-1}, u_0, u_1, \cdots) = (u_j)$. Such an expression of order r may be conveniently written in the form

$$(Lu)_j = \sum_{\alpha=-r^-}^{r^+} a_{j\alpha} u_{j+\alpha} = \sum_{\alpha=-r^-}^{r^+} a_{j\alpha} (T^\alpha u)_j \quad ((Tu)_j = u_{j+1};$$

$$j = \ldots, -1, 0, 1, \ldots), \qquad (5.1)$$

where $r = r^- + r^+$ is a fixed decomposition of r into nonnegative integers, and $a_{j\alpha}$ are complex coefficients, while $a_{j,-r^-}, a_{j,r^+} \neq 0$ $(j = \cdots, -1, 0, 1, \cdots)$. The adjoint expression L^+ is defined from the equation $\sum_{j=-\infty}^{\infty} (Lu)_j \bar{v}_j = \sum_{l=-\infty}^{\infty} u_j \overline{(L^+ v)_j}$, where at least one of the sequences u, v, is finite. Clearly

$$(T^+u)_j = u_{j-1}, \quad (L^+u)_j = \sum_{\alpha=-r^-}^{r^+} (T^{+\alpha} a_{.\alpha} u_.)_j \quad (j = \ldots, -1, 0, 1, \ldots). \tag{5.2}$$

We shall denote the expression $\Sigma_{\alpha=-r^-}^{r^+} \bar{a}_{j\alpha} T^\alpha$ by $\bar{L}$.

Consider the kernel (more correctly, infinite matrix) $K = \|K_{jk}\|_{-\infty}^{\infty}$; K_{jk} $(j, k = \cdots; -1, 0, 1, \cdots)$ are complex numbers. This kernel is said to be p. d. if for any finite sequence $(\cdots, \xi_{-1}, \xi_0, \xi_1, \cdots)$ of complex numbers

$$\sum_{j,k=-\infty}^{\infty} K_{jk} \xi_k \bar{\xi}_j \geqslant 0. \tag{5.3}$$

It is obvious from (5.3) that $K_{jj} \geq 0$, $|K_{jk}|^2 \leq K_{jj} K_{kk}$ $(j, k = \cdots, -1, 0, 1, \cdots)$. We select a sequence (p_j), $p_j \geq 1$ $(j = \cdots, -1, 0, 1, \cdots)$ such that

$$\sum_{j=-\infty}^{\infty} \frac{K_{jj}}{p_j} < \infty. \tag{5.4}$$

Then $K \in l_2((-\infty, \infty), p_j^{-1}) \otimes l_2((-\infty, \infty), p_j^{-1})$. We shall take $H_0 = l_2((-\infty, \infty), 1) = l_2((-\infty, \infty))$, $H_+ = l_2((-\infty, \infty), p_j)$. Thus, $K \in H_- \otimes H_-$. The space H_K coincides with the completion of $l_2((-\infty, \infty), p_j) = H_+$ (or $l_{2,0}((-\infty, \infty))$), possibly after identification relative to the scalar product

$$\langle u, v \rangle = \sum_{j,k=-\infty}^{\infty} K_{jk} u_k \bar{v}_j. \tag{5.5}$$

As the operator A of §1, operating in $l_2((-\infty, \infty)) = H_0$, we take the closure Λ in this space of the mapping $u \to Lu$, $u \in l_{2,0}((-\infty, \infty))$. The involution will be reflection in the complex line. The operator Λ admits an extension of equipment. As $\mathcal{D}$ one may choose $l_{2,0}((-\infty, \infty))$, topologized in an appropriate way. The operator Λ^* adjoint to Λ in $l_2((-\infty, \infty))$, as is easily seen (see Chapter VII, §1. 1), coincides with the operator $u \to L^+u$, defined on all those $u \in l_2((-\infty, \infty))$ for which $L^+u \in l_2((-\infty, \infty))$, and the operator $C = B$ with its restriction to $l_{2,0}((-\infty, \infty))$. The condition of *-commutativity of K and A takes the form

$$L_j K = \bar{L}_k K. \tag{5.6}$$

The space H_{++} will bear a character which is simple in comparison with page 642. Indeed, as we did there we may put $(u, v)_{++} = (u\sqrt{p_j}, v\sqrt{p_j})_{\mathfrak{H}}$, where $\mathfrak{H} \subset l_2((-\infty, \infty))$ is such that the imbedding $\mathfrak{H} \to l_2((-\infty, \infty))$ is quasilinear. We take $\mathfrak{H} = l_2((-\infty, \infty), q_j)$, where $q_j \geq 1$ and $\sum_{j=-\infty}^{\infty} q_j^{-1} < \infty$. Thus $H_{++} = l_2((-\infty, \infty), s_j)$, $s_j \geq 1$, while

$$\sum_{j=-\infty}^{\infty} \frac{p_j}{s_j} < \infty.$$

The family $\Omega_\lambda = \|\Omega_{\lambda;\, jk}\|_{-\infty}^{\infty}$ of p.d. kernels figuring in Theorem 1.1 will be represented by p.d. kernels such that

$$L_j\Omega_\lambda = \lambda\Omega_\lambda, \qquad \overline{L}_k\Omega_\lambda = \lambda\Omega_\lambda, \qquad \sum_{j,k=-\infty}^{\infty} \frac{|\Omega_{\lambda;jk}|^2}{s_j s_k} \leqslant C < \infty. \tag{5.7}$$

As in the case of ordinary differential equations, the kernels Ω_λ may be decomposed relative to a fundamental system of solutions on $(-\infty, \infty)$ of the difference equation $Lu - \lambda u = 0$. A fundamental system $\chi_{0;\, j}(\lambda), \cdots, \chi_{r-1;\, j}(\lambda)$ ($j = \cdots, -1, 0, 1, \cdots$) may be selected for example according to the Cauchy conditions, imposed at the r points $a - r^-, \cdots, a + r^+ - 1$, where a is a fixed integer:

$$\chi_{k;j}(\lambda) = \delta_{j,k+a-r^-} \qquad (j = a - r^-, \ldots, a + r^+ - 1;\ k = 0, \ldots, r-1). \tag{5.8}$$

From Theorem 1.1, with the aid of arguments similar to those presented in §3, we obtain the following theorem.

Theorem 5.1. *Consider the p.d. kernel* $K = \|K_{jk}\|_{-\infty}^{\infty}$, *the difference expression* (5.1), *and the fundamental system* $\chi_{0;\, j}(\lambda), \cdots, \chi_{r-1;\, j}(\lambda)$ *of solutions of the equation* $Lu - \lambda u = 0$, *selected according to conditions* (5.8). *The representation*

$$K_{jk} = \int_{-\infty}^{\infty} \sum_{\alpha,\beta=0}^{r-1} \chi_{\alpha;j}(\lambda)\overline{\chi_{\beta;k}(\lambda)}\, d\sigma_{\alpha\beta}(\lambda) \qquad (j, k = \ldots, -1, 0, 1, \ldots) \tag{5.9}$$

will hold with some nonnegative matrix measures $\|d\sigma_{\alpha\beta}(\lambda)\|_0^{r-1}$, *if and only if condition* (5.6) *is satisfied. The integral in* (5.9) *converges for each fixed* j, k *in the sense of the space* $L_2(C_r; (-\infty, \infty), \|d\sigma_{\alpha\beta}(\lambda)\|_0^{r-1})$. *The measure*

$\|d\sigma_{\alpha\beta}(\lambda)\|_0^{r-1}$ *is defined uniquely if and only if the closure in* H_K *of the operator* $u \to L^+u$, $u \in l_{2,0}((-\infty, \infty))$ *is maximal.*

Thus we have considered the case of the expression (5. 1) on the entire axis. The case of the semiaxis is also of interest. Without loss of generality we may suppose that this semiaxis is $[0, \infty)$, i. e. L operates on the sequences $u = (u_0, u_1, \cdots) = (u_j)$. The coefficients L may be supposed determined for all $j = \cdots, -1, 0, 1, \cdots$; however in the calculation of $(Lu)_j$ for $j = 0, \cdots, r^- - 1$ we put $u_{-r^-} = \cdots = u_{-1} = 0$. This condition plays the role of a boundary condition at zero (see Chapter VII, §1. 1). Its character depends on the representation of r in the form $r^- + r^+$.

In order that the equation $\sum_{j=0}^\infty (Lu)_j \bar{v}_j = \sum_{j=0}^\infty u_j \overline{(L^+v)_j}$ should hold, where at least one of the sequences is finite at ∞, we need to put $u_{-r^+} = \cdots = u_{-1} = 0$ in calculating $(L^+u)_j$ according to formula (5. 2) $(j = 0, \cdots, r^+ - 1)$. This convention will be adopted in what follows.

After what has been said, Theorem 5. 1 easily carries over to the case of the semiaxis. In its proof we must replace spaces on $(-\infty, \infty)$ by analogous spaces on $[0, \infty)$, and understand finiteness as finiteness towards $+\infty$. The functions $\chi_{\alpha;j}(\lambda)$ figuring in (5. 9) change. Indeed, by $\chi_{\alpha;j}(\lambda)$ we need to understand a system of linearly independent solutions of the equation $(Lu)_j - \lambda u_j = 0$ $(j = 0, 1, \cdots)$, satisfying the "boundary" conditions for L at zero (i. e. we need to take into account the stated rule for calculating $(Lu)_j$ for $j = 0, \cdots, r^- - 1$). Since there are r^- such conditions, then there will be r^+ of the indicated solutions. In particular, as these solutions one may take $\chi_{r^-;j}(\lambda), \cdots$ $\cdots, \chi_{r^-+r^+-1;j}(\lambda)$, satisfying at the points $0, \cdots, r^+ - 1$ the conditions

$$\chi_{k;j}(\lambda) = \delta_{j,k-r^-} \quad (j = 0, \ldots, r^+ - 1;\ k = r^-, \ldots, r-1;\ a = 0). \tag{5. 10}$$

Thus we may make the following assertion.

Theorem 5.2. *Consider expressions* (5. 1) *and* (5. 2) *on the semiaxis* $[0, \infty)$, *taking the indicated rules for the computation of* $(Lu)_j$ *and* $(L^+u)_j$ *for* j *close to zero. Suppose that* $K = \|K_{jk}\|_0^\infty$ *is a* p. d. *kernel. Theorem* 5. 1 *holds for it, given only that the system of* r *solutions* $\chi_{0;j}(\lambda), \cdots, \chi_{r-1;j}(\lambda)$ *is replaced by the system of* r^+ *solutions* $\chi_{r^-;j}(\lambda), \cdots, \chi_{r-1;j}(\lambda)$ *of the equation* $(Lu)_j - \lambda u_j = 0$ $(j = 0, 1, \cdots)$ *and the matrix* $\|d\sigma_{\alpha\beta}(\lambda)\|$ *of order* r *by a matrix of order*

r^+. *We need to replace the operator figuring at the end of the theorem by the closure of the operator* $u \to L^+u$, $u \in l_{2,0}([0,\infty))$, *considered in the space* H_K, *the completion (possibly after identification) of* $l_{2,0}([0,\infty))$ *relative to the scalar product* (5.5), *where* $-\infty$ *is replaced by* 0.

Theorem 3.8 on degenerate forms carries over to the representation (5.9) after the natural modifications.

In conclusion we note that for the difference cases in question one could of course have representations of type (3.16)–(3.17) for the (generalized) resolvent R_z of the Hermitian operator $u \to L^+u$ ($u \in l_{2,0}((-\infty,\infty))$ or $u \in l_{2,0}([0,\infty))$) or for the bounded functions of that operator. These formulas for R_z in the case of the axis are

$$\langle R_z u, v\rangle = \sum_{j,k=-\infty}^{\infty} R_{z;jk}\, u_k \bar{v}_j \qquad (u, v \in l_{2,0}((-\infty,\infty))),$$

$$R_{z;jk} = \langle R_z\delta_k, \delta_j\rangle = \overline{R_{\bar z;kj}} = \int_{-\infty}^{\infty} \frac{\Omega_{\lambda;jk}}{\lambda - z}\, d\varrho(\lambda) \tag{5.11}$$

$$\int_\Delta \Omega_{\lambda;jk}\, d\varrho(\lambda) = \lim_{\varepsilon\to+0} \frac{1}{\pi} \int_{\Delta+i\varepsilon} \operatorname{Im} R_{z;jk}\, dz \qquad (j, k = \ldots, -1, 0, 1, \ldots)$$

(here $\Omega_{\lambda;jk}\, d\rho(\lambda)$ is the integrand in (5.9)).

2. Selfadjoint operators in H_K corresponding to ordinary difference expressions with constant coefficients. Here we obtain for difference expressions results of the type of §3.4. We shall use the general schema of §2.2, although the role of the spaces $S^{\beta,B}_{\alpha,A}$ will be played by certain normed spaces.

We denote by $K_{p,\rho}$ (p, ρ fixed and positive) the Banach space of sequences $\phi = (\ldots, \phi_{-1}, \phi_0, \phi_1, \ldots)$ with norm

$$\|\varphi\|_{p,\varrho} = \sum_{j=-\infty}^{\infty} |\varphi_j|\, p^{|j|}\, |j|^{\frac{|j|}{\varrho}} < \infty, \tag{5.12}$$

i.e. $K_{p,\rho} = l_1((-\infty,\infty), p^{|j|}|j|^{|j|/\rho})$. We shall suppose that the coefficients of (5.1) are constant, i.e. $a_{j\alpha} = a_\alpha$ does not depend on j. We define on the sequences $\phi \in K_{p,\rho}$, corresponding to the function $e^{\zeta s}$ of the variable s (ζ a fixed complex number), an operator $e^{\zeta L}$, putting

$$(e^{\zeta L}\varphi)_j = \sum_{q=0}^{\infty} \frac{\zeta^q}{q!}(L^q\varphi)_j \qquad (j = , \ldots , -1, 0, 1, \ldots). \quad (5.13)$$

In our case it is convenient to change somewhat the method of introducing operators of type $\Pi(D)$ (cf. §3. 4). The following lemma is fundamental.

Lemma 5. 1. *If* $\rho = \max(r^-, r^+)$, $0 < p' < p$ *and* $|\zeta| \le T_{p, p', \rho}$, *where* $T_{p, p', \rho}$ *is sufficiently small, then the operator* $e^{\zeta L}$ *operates continuously from the space* $K_{p, \rho}$ *to the space* $K_{p', \rho}$.

Proof. We need to prove that for every $\phi \in K_{p, \rho}$ the series (5. 13) converges for any j, the resulting sequence lies in $K_{p', \rho}$ and

$$\left\| \sum_{q=0}^{\infty} \frac{\zeta^q}{q!}(L^q\varphi)_{.} \right\|_{p',\varrho} \leqslant C\,\|\varphi\|_{p,\varrho} \qquad (C > 0). \quad (5.14)$$

To this end we make a number of estimates. For the expression T^α we have, with $\mu = p'/p$,

$$\|T^\alpha\varphi\|_{p',\varrho} = \sum_{j=-\infty}^{\infty} |\varphi_{j+\alpha}|\, p'^{|j|}\, |j|^{\frac{|j|}{\varrho}}$$

$$= \sum_{j=-\infty}^{\infty} |\varphi_{j+\alpha}|\, p^{|j+\alpha|}\, |j+\alpha|^{\frac{|j+\alpha|}{\varrho}} \cdot \frac{p'^{|j|}\, |j|^{\frac{|j|}{\varrho}}}{p^{|j+\alpha|}\, |j+\alpha|^{\frac{|j+\alpha|}{\varrho}}}$$

$$\leqslant \sup_j \left[\mu^{|j|} p^{|j|-|j+\alpha|} \left| \frac{j}{j+\alpha} \right|^{\frac{|j+\alpha|}{\varrho}} |j|^{\frac{|j|}{\varrho} - \frac{|j+\alpha|}{\varrho}} \right] \|\varphi\|_{p,\varrho}$$

$$\leqslant p^{|\alpha|} e^{\frac{|\alpha|}{\varrho}} \sup_j [\mu^{|j|}\, |j|^{\frac{|\alpha|}{\varrho}}]\, \|\varphi\|_{p,\varrho}. \quad (5.15)$$

We have made use of the estimates $|a| - |b| \le |a - b|$ and $|a/b|^{|b|} \le e^{|a-b|}$ for real a, b.

We have the inequality

$$\mu^t t^\sigma \leqslant \left(-\frac{\sigma}{e \log \mu}\right)^\sigma \qquad (0 < t,\ \sigma;\ 0 < \mu < 1). \quad (5.16)$$

Indeed, let us find the largest value of the function $f(t) = \mu^t t^\sigma$ on $[0, \infty)$. Since

$f(0) = f(\infty) = 0$, the maximum is achieved at some point $t_{\max}$. Because of the monotonicity of $\log x$, $t_{\max}$ for $f(t)$ and $g(t) = \log f(t) = t \log \mu + \sigma \log t$ coincide. But $g'(t) = \log \mu + \sigma/t$, so that $t_{\max} = -\sigma/\log \mu$. Substituting this value in $f(t)$, we obtain (5. 16).

Extending (5. 15) with the aid of (5. 16), we get

$$\| T^{\alpha} \varphi \|_{p',\varrho} \leqslant p^{|\alpha|} \left(-\frac{|\alpha|}{\varrho \log \mu} \right)^{\frac{|\alpha|}{\varrho}} \| \varphi \|_{p,\varrho}. \tag{5.17}$$

Using this we find an estimate for $\|L^q \phi\|_{p',\rho}$. The expression for L^q will have order qr. Suppose it has the form $L^q = \Sigma^{qr^+}_{\alpha=-qr^-} a^{(q)}_{\alpha} T^{\alpha}$ $(a^{(1)}_{j\alpha} = a_{j\alpha})$. We write $A_q = \max_{\alpha}\{|a^{(q)}_{\alpha}|\}$. From the relation $L^q = L \cdot L^{q-1}$ it easily follows that $A_q \leq (2r+1) A_1 A_{q-1}$ $(q = 2, 3, \cdots)$, so that $A_q \leq (2r+1)^{q-1} A_1^q \leq (2r+1)^q A_1^q$ $(q = 1, 2, \cdots)$. Thus

$$\|L^q\varphi\|_{p',\varrho} \leqslant \sum_{\alpha=-qr^-}^{qr^+} |a_{\alpha}^{(q)}| \, \| T^{\alpha}\varphi\|_{p',\varrho} \leqslant A_q \sum_{\alpha=-qr^-}^{qr^+} p^{|\alpha|} \left(-\frac{|\alpha|}{\varrho \log \mu} \right)^{\frac{|\alpha|}{\varrho}} \|\varphi\|_{p,\varrho}$$

$$\leqslant (2r+1)^q A_1^q (2q\varrho+1)\, p^{q\varrho} \left(-\frac{q}{\log \mu} \right)^q \| \varphi \|_{p,\varrho}$$

$$= (2q\varrho+1) \left[-\frac{(2r+1) A_1 p^{\varrho}}{\log \mu} \right]^q q^q \| \varphi \|_{p,\varrho}$$

$$= C_1^q (2q\varrho+1) q^q \| \varphi \|_{p,\varrho} \qquad (q = 1, 2, \ldots), \tag{5.18}$$

where C_1 does not depend on q. Clearly the same estimate is valid also for $q = 0$.

Using (5. 18) we get

$$\left\| \sum_{q=0}^{\infty} \frac{\zeta^q}{q!} L^q \varphi \right\|_{p',\varrho} \leqslant \sum_{q=}^{\infty} \frac{|\zeta|^q}{q!} \| L^q \varphi \|_{p',\varrho}$$

$$\leqslant \left[\sum_{q=0}^{\infty} \frac{T^q_{p,p',\varrho}}{q!} C_1^q (2q\varrho+1) q^q \right] \| \varphi \|_{p,\varrho}.$$

For sufficiently small $T_{p,p',\rho}$ the series in square brackets converges. Thus, inequality (5. 14), and along with it the lemma, are proved.

The following theorem, analogous to Theorem 3. 9, holds.

Theorem 5. 3. *Suppose that L is an ordinary difference expression on the*

$(-\infty, \infty)$ *axis of order* r *(see (5.1)) whose coefficients are constant, i.e.* $a_{j\alpha} = a_\alpha$. *Let* $K = \|K_{jk}\|_{-\infty}^{\infty}$ *be a p. d. kernel satisfying (5.6). From Theorem 5.1, a representation (5.9) holds for K. In order that the matrix measure* $\| d\sigma_{\alpha\beta}(\lambda)\|_0^{r-1}$ *should be uniquely defined in (5.9), it is sufficient that the estimate*

$$|K_{jk}| \leqslant CN^{|j|+|k|} |j|^{\frac{|j|}{\rho}} |k|^{\frac{|k|}{\rho}} \qquad (j, k = \ldots, -1, 0, 1, \ldots) \quad (5.19)$$

hold, where $\rho = \max(r^-, r^+)$ *and* $C, N > 0$ *are certain constants.*

If the defect numbers are equal the closure of the operator $u \to L^+u$ $(u \in l_{2,0}((-\infty, \infty)))$ will be selfadjoint in H_K.

Proof. It follows from (5.19) that the sequence

$$p_j = N^{\sigma|j|} |j|^{\frac{2|j|}{\rho}} \qquad (j = \ldots, -1, 0, 1, \ldots),$$

where $\sigma > 2$ is fixed, satisfies (5.4) and therefore may be adopted for the construction of subsection 1 ($p_j \geq 1$, since without loss of generality we may take $N \geq 1$). The choice of p_j determines the space $H_+ = l_2((-\infty, \infty), p_j)$.

We need to prove the maximality of the closure in H_K of the operator $u \to L^+u$ $(u \in l_{2,0}((-\infty, \infty)))$. We shall use Theorems 2.5 and 2.4, putting $\Phi = K_{p,\rho} \subset K_{p',\rho} = \Psi$ $(0 < p' < p)$, with p' chosen so large that $N^\sigma \leq p'^{3/2}$. The last inequality guarantees the imbedding $\Psi = K_{p',\rho} \subset l_2((-\infty, \infty); p_j)$. Indeed, if $\phi \in K_{p',\rho}$, then a series of type (5.12) converges, so that

$$|\varphi_j| \leqslant \|\varphi\|_{p',\rho} p'^{-|j|} |j|^{-\frac{|j|}{\rho}} \qquad (j = \ldots, -1, 0, 1, \ldots).$$

Therefore

$$|\varphi_j|^2 N^{\sigma|j|} |j|^{\frac{2|j|}{\rho}} \leqslant \|\varphi\|^2_{p',\rho} p'^{-2|j|} N^{\sigma|j|} \leqslant \|\varphi\|^2_{p',\rho} p'^{-\frac{|j|}{2}}$$

and the series $\sum_{j=-\infty}^{\infty} |\phi_j|^2 N^{\sigma|j|} |j|^{2|j|/\rho} = \|\phi\|^2_{l_2((-\infty,\infty),p_j)}$ converges, while its sum $\leq C_1 \|\phi\|^2_{p',\rho}$.

As in the case of differential expressions, we extend the operator $u \to L^+u$ $(u \in l_{2,0}((-\infty, \infty)))$. Put $Bu = L^+u$, where $u \in \mathfrak{D}(B) = \Psi$. (Because of the simplicity of the situation it is not appropriate here to bring in the analog of Θ.) It follows from (5.18) that $L^+[\Psi] \subseteq l_2((-\infty, \infty), p_j)$. Similarly to Lemma 3.3 it is not hard to show that the operator lies in the closure in H_K of the operator $u \to L^+u$ $(u \in l_{2,0}((-\infty, \infty)))$. Therefore it is enough to establish the maximality of the closure of B.

Thus, fixing the indicated p and p', we obtain a chain $\Phi = K_{p,\rho} \subset \Psi = K_{p',\rho} = \mathfrak{D}(B) \subset l_2((-\infty, \infty), p_j)$. Choose $T_{p,p',\rho} = T > 0$ according to Lemma 5.1. Then for any $t_0, t \in [0, T]$ the operator $Q(t_0, t) = e^{i(t_0 - t)L^+}$ is defined, operating continuously from all of Φ into Ψ. It is not hard to show in the usual manner that for any $\phi \in \Phi$ the function $\phi(t) = Q(t_0, t)\phi$ is a strong solution of the equation $d\phi(t)/dt + iL^+[\phi(t)] = 0$ $(0 \le t \le T)$ in the space Ψ, reducing to ϕ for $t = t_0$. Since convergence in Ψ implies convergence in $H_+ = l_2((-\infty, \infty), p_j)$, then this solution will be strong in H_+ as well. Thus the requirements of Theorem 2.4 are satisfied and the weak solution of the equation $du/dt + (iB)^*u = 0$ $(0 \le t < \infty)$ in the space H_+ is unique. Analogously we verify the uniqueness of the weak solutions of $du/dt - (iB)^*u = 0$ $(0 \le t < \infty)$. From Theorem 2.5, 2), the closure in H_K of the operator B is maximal, as was to be proved.

We turn to the consideration of the case of the semiaxis. Now in comparison with the whole axis there will be some differences, on the basis of the following lemma.

Lemma 5.2. *In the space* $\hat{K}_{p,\rho} = l_1([0, \infty), p^{|j|}|j|^{|j|/\rho})$ $(p, \rho > 0$ *arbitrary*) *the operator* $\phi \to T\phi$ *is bounded with norm* $\le 1/p$.

The proof follows from the estimate

$$\| T\varphi \|_{\hat{K}_{p,\varrho}} = \sum_{j=0}^{\infty} |\varphi_{j+1}| p^j j^{\frac{j}{\varrho}} = \sum_{k=1}^{\infty} |\varphi_k| p^{k-1} (k-1)^{\frac{k-1}{\varrho}}$$

$$\leqslant \frac{1}{p} \sum_{k=1}^{\infty} |\varphi_k| p^k k^{\frac{k}{\varrho}} \leqslant \frac{1}{p} \| \varphi \|_{\hat{K}_{p,\varrho}} \qquad (\varphi \in \hat{K}_{p,\varrho}).$$

We shall establish the analog of Lemma 5.1. First of all we note that it is sufficient to prove inequality (5.14) (in the norms $\hat{K}$) for the case of nonnegative coefficients in L, a nonnegative number ζ and nonnegative coordinates of ϕ. It is easy to pass to such a situation by using the estimate just obtained in terms of the modulus. Suppose that $u = (\dots, u_{-1}, u_0, u_1, \dots)$, $v = (v_0, v_1, \dots)$. Put $\hat{u} = (u_0, u_1, \dots)$, $\tilde{v} = (\dots, 0, 0, v_0, v_1, \dots)$; $L_+ = \Sigma_{\alpha=1}^{r^+} a_\alpha T^\alpha$, $L_- = \Sigma_{\alpha=-r^-}^{0} a_\alpha T^\alpha$. Applying the expressions L, L_+, and L_- as expressions on the entire axis, we obtain $e^{\zeta L}\tilde{\phi} = e^{\zeta L_+ + \zeta L_-}\tilde{\phi} = e^{\zeta L_+}e^{\zeta L_-}\tilde{\phi}$. Hence using Lemmas 5.2 and 5.1 we find that

$$\| e^{\zeta L} \varphi \|_{\hat{K}_{p',\varrho}} \leqslant \| \widehat{e^{\zeta L} \tilde{\varphi}} \|_{\hat{K}_{p',\varrho}} = \| \widehat{e^{\zeta L_+} e^{\zeta L_-} \tilde{\varphi}} \|_{\hat{K}_{p',\varrho}} \leqslant C_1 \| \widehat{e^{\zeta L_-} \tilde{\varphi}} \|_{\hat{K}_{p',\varrho}}$$

$$\leqslant C_1 \| e^{\zeta L_-} \tilde{\varphi} \|_{K_{p',\varrho}} \leqslant C_2 \| \tilde{\varphi} \|_{K_{p,\varrho}} = C_2 \| \varphi \|_{\hat{K}_{p,\varrho}}$$

Thus for the case of the semiaxis Lemma 5.1 is valid, with the spaces K replaced by the spaces $\hat{K}$ and $\rho = r^-$.

Now we may repeat the proof of Theorem 5.3, taking account of the above-stated variant of Lemma 5.1. Since it is applied to the expression L^+, then we arrive at the following theorem.

Theorem 5.4. *For the p. d. kernel $K = \|K_{jk}\|_0^\infty$ Theorem 5.3 holds on the semiaxis $[0, \infty)$. Here we naturally need to take $j, k = 0, 1, \cdots$ in estimate (5.19). The number ρ is equal to r^+.*

3. **The case $q = n > 1$ of ordinary difference expressions.** For these we carry out a discussion similar to that in §4. The situation when there are m complete axes $(\cdots, -1, 0, 1, \cdots)$ $(0 \le m \le n)$ and $n - m$ semiaxes, as which we may adopt $[0, 1, \cdots)$, is of interest. Therefore we denote by G the set of integer points $j = (j_1, \cdots, j_n)$ of the space E_n, where $j_1, \cdots, j_m$ vary over $(\cdots, -1, 0, 1, \cdots)$, and $j_{m+1}, \cdots, j_n$ over $[0, 1, \cdots)$. We will also write $G = G^{(1)} \times \cdots \times G^{(n)}$, where $G^{(1)}, \cdots, G^{(m)}$ are axes and $G^{(m+1)}, \cdots, G^{(n)}$ are semiaxes.

The complex kernel $K = K_{jk}$ $(j, k \in G)$ is said to be p. d. if a condition analogous to (5.3) is valid for it. For any finite sequence of complex numbers ξ

$$\sum_{j,k \in G} K_{jk} \xi_j \bar{\xi}_k \geqslant 0. \tag{5.20}$$

Clearly $K_{jj} \ge 0$, $|K_{jk}|^2 \le K_{jj} K_{kk}$ $(j, k \in G)$.

Select a sequence of $p_j \ge 1$ $(j \in G)$ such that $\Sigma_{j \in G} (K_{jj}/p_j) < \infty$. From what was said on pages 695–696, it may be sought in the form $p_j = p_{j_1}^{(1)} \cdots p_{j_n}^{(n)}$, where $p_{j_\nu}^{(\nu)} \ge 1$ $(\nu = 1, \cdots, n)$, and therefore

$$l_2(G; p_j) = l_2(G^{(1)}, p_{j_1}^{(1)}) \otimes \cdots \otimes l_2(G^{(n)}, p_{j_n}^{(n)}),$$

$$l_2\left(G, \frac{1}{p_j}\right) = l_2\left(G^{(1)}, \frac{1}{p_{j_1}^{(1)}}\right) \otimes \cdots \otimes l_2\left(G^{(n)}, \frac{1}{p_{j_n}^{(n)}}\right); \tag{5.21}$$

$$l_2(G) = l_2(G^{(1)}) \otimes \cdots \otimes l_2(G^{(n)}).^{1)}$$

---

1) Recall that $l_2(G, m_j)$ denotes the "multi-dimensional" l_2 with weight m_j: $l_2(G) = l_2(G, 1)$.

We have $K \in l_2(G, p_j^{-1}) \otimes l_2(G, p_j^{-1})$. We shall suppose that $H_0 = l_2(G)$, $H_+ = l_2(G; p_j)$. Then $H_- = l_2(G, p_j^{-1})$. Relations (5.21) show that we may put

$$H_0^{(\nu)} = l_2(G^{(\nu)}), \qquad H_+^{(\nu)} = l_2(G^{(\nu)}, p_{i_\nu}^{(\nu)}), \qquad H_-^{(\nu)} = l_2\left(G^{(\nu)}, \frac{1}{p_{i_\nu}^{(\nu)}}\right)$$

$$(\nu = 1, \ldots, n).$$

The space H_K coincides with the completion of $l_2(G, p_j)$ or $l_{2,0}(G)$ (possibly after identification) relative to the scalar product

$$\langle u, v\rangle = \sum_{j,k\in G} K_{jk} u_k \bar{v}_j. \tag{5.22}$$

Consider n difference expressions of the form (5.1):

$$L^{(\nu)} = \sum_{\alpha=-r_\nu^-}^{r_\nu^+} a_{j_\nu \alpha}^{(\nu)} T_\nu^\alpha \qquad (r_\nu = r_\nu^- + r_\nu^+;\quad r_\nu^-, r_\nu^+ \geqslant 0;\ \nu = 1, \ldots, n), \tag{5.23}$$

where T_ν is a translation among the νth axis:

$$(T_\nu u)_j = u_{j_1, \ldots, j_{\nu-1},\, j_{\nu+1}, j_{\nu+1}, \ldots, j_n}.$$

The coefficients $L^{(\nu)}$, similarly to the case of differential operators, depend only on j_ν. In the case of a semiaxis (i. e. when $\nu > m$) we shall require that our convention be satisfied relative to the action of $L^{(\nu)}$ near to zero; $L^{(\nu)+}$ and $\overline{L^{(\nu)}}$ have their earlier meanings.

We shall carry out, in analogy with §4, the following constructions. Define in $H_0 = l_2(G)$ n operators $A_1, \cdots, A_n$, taking $A_\nu = \Lambda_\nu$ equal to the closure in this space of the mapping $u \to L^{(\nu)}u$, $u \in l_{2,0}(G) = \mathbb{D}$. The condition of *-commutativity of the kernel K and A_ν may be written in the form

$$L_{j_\nu}^{(\nu)} K = \overline{L_{k_\nu}^{(\nu)}} K \qquad (\nu = 1, \ldots, n). \tag{5.24}$$

For the operators B_ν we shall use the mappings $u \to L^{(\nu)+}u$, $u \in l_{2,0}(G^{(\nu)})$ $(\nu = 1, \cdots, n)$ defined in the spaces $H_+^{(\nu)} = l_2(G^{(\nu)}, p_{j_\nu}^{(\nu)})$. The role of the operators C_ν will be played by operators in $H_+ = l_2(G, p_j)$ of the form $u \in \mathfrak{D}(C_\nu) = H_+^{(1)} \otimes \cdots \otimes H_+^{(\nu-1)} \otimes l_{2,0}(G^{(\nu)}) \otimes H_+^{(\nu+1)} \otimes \cdots \otimes H_+^{(n)}$. As in the differential case, the closure of C_ν in H_K and the closure of its restriction to $l_{2,0}(G)$ coincide.

After what has been said there is no difficulty in proving on the basis of Theorem 1. 2 the difference analog of representation (4. 14). We shall restrict ourselves to formulating it.

Suppose that $\nu = 1, \cdots, m$. We fix a point $a_\nu \in G^{(\nu)} = (\cdots, -1, 0, 1, \cdots)$ and consider a fundamental system of solutions on the $G^{(\nu)}$ axis of the equation $L^{(\nu)}u - \lambda_\nu u = 0$, satisfying conditions (5. 8) with $a = a_\nu$. We denote it by

$$\chi^{(\nu)}_{0;\, j_\nu}(\lambda_\nu), \ldots, \chi^{(\nu)}_{r_\nu - 1;\, j_\nu}(\lambda_\nu) \qquad (\nu = 1, \ldots, m;\ 0 \leqslant m \leqslant n). \tag{5. 25}$$

For $\nu = m + 1, \cdots, n$ we consider a fundamental system of solutions on the semiaxis $G^{(\nu)} = [0, \infty)$ of the same equation, satisfying conditions (5. 10):

$$\chi^{(\nu)}_{\overline{r_\nu};\, j_\nu}(\lambda), \ldots, \chi^{(\nu)}_{r_\nu - 1;\, j_\nu}(\lambda) \qquad (\nu = m+1, \ldots, n). \tag{5. 26}$$

From the solutions (5. 25) and (5. 26) we form products of type (4. 11):

$$\begin{gathered} X_\alpha(j;\ \lambda) = \chi^{(1)}_{\alpha_1;\, j_1}(\lambda_1) \cdots \chi^{(n)}_{\alpha_n;\, j_n}(\lambda_n) \\ (j = (j_1, \ldots, j_n) \in G,\ \lambda = (\lambda_1, \ldots, \lambda_n) \in E_n), \end{gathered} \tag{5. 27}$$

where the vector index $\alpha = (\alpha_1, \cdots, \alpha_n)$ varies over the integer-valued parallelepiped A of points with coordinates

$$\alpha_1 = 0, \ldots, r_1 - 1; \ldots; \alpha_m = 0, \ldots, r_m - 1;$$

$$\alpha_{m+1} = \overline{r_{m+1}}, \ldots, r_{m+1} - 1; \ldots; \alpha_n = \overline{r_n}, \ldots, r_n - 1.$$

Theorem 5. 5. *Consider the p. d. kernel* $K = K_{jk}$ $(j, k \in G)$ *and the* n *difference expressions* (5. 23), *and construct the products* (5. 27). *In order that the representation*

$$K_{jk} = \int_{E_n} \sum_{\alpha, \beta \in A} X_\alpha(j; \lambda) \overline{X_\beta(k; \lambda)}\, d\sigma_{\alpha\beta}(\lambda) \qquad (j, k \in G) \tag{5. 28}$$

should hold with a nonnegative matrix measure $\|d\sigma_{\alpha\beta}(\lambda)\|_{\alpha, \beta \in A}$, *it is necessary and sufficient that the two following requirements be satisfied:* a) *equation* (5. 24) *holds;* b) *the* n *Hermitian operators* $H_K u \to L^{(j)+}u$ $(u \in l_{2,0}(G))$ *admit extensions into* H_K *or into a wider space to a system of commuting self-adjoint operators. The natural criterion for uniqueness of representation* (5. 28) *also holds.*

It is clear that the integral in (5. 28) converges for each j, k in the sense of $L_2(C_l;\ (-\infty, \infty),\ \|d\sigma_{\alpha\beta}(\lambda)\|_{\alpha,\ \beta\in A})$.

Similarly to what was done in §4. 2 for differential operators, we may join the technique of subsection 2 with Theorem 2. 3 and prove the following analog of Theorem 4. 3.

Theorem 5. 6. *Suppose that the p. d. kernels* $K = K_{jk} = K_{j_1, \dots, j_n,\ k_1, \dots, k_n}$ $(j,\ k \in G)$ *satisfy relations* (5. 24) *with difference expressions* (5. 23) *having constant coefficients* (*i. e.* $a^{(\nu)}_{j_\nu\alpha} = a^{(\nu)}_{\alpha}$). *In order that representation* (5. 28) *should hold* (*in which the measure* $\|d\sigma_{\alpha\beta}(\lambda)\|_{\alpha,\ \beta\in A}$ *is defined uniquely*), *it is sufficient that the following estimate hold:*

$$|K_{j_1,\dots,j_n,\ k_1,\dots,k_n}| \leqslant CN^{|j_1|+\dots+|j_n|+|k_1|+\dots+|k_n|}$$

$$\times\ |j_1|^{\frac{|j_1|}{\varrho_1}}\ |j_n|^{\frac{|j_n|}{\varrho_n}}\ |k_1|^{\frac{|k_1|}{\varrho_1}} \dots |k_n|^{\frac{|k_n|}{\varrho_n}} \qquad (j,k \in G), \tag{5.29}$$

where $\rho_\nu = \max(r^-_\nu,\ r^+_\nu)$ *for* $\nu \le m$ *and* $\rho_\nu = r^+_\nu$ *for* $\nu \ge m+1$. *Here we suppose in addition that the defect numbers are equal for each operator in* H_K *of the form* $u \to L^{(\nu)+}u,\ \ u \in l_{2,0}(G)$.

We turn to examples of integral representations of p. d. kernels, connected with ordinary difference expressions.

4. **The classical problem of moments.** This is the following problem: suppose given a sequence of real numbers $s_0, s_1, \dots$. The question is: under what conditions do they admit the representation

$$s_j = \int_{-\infty}^{\infty} \lambda^j d\sigma(\lambda) \qquad (j = 0, 1, \dots), \tag{5.30}$$

where $d\sigma(\lambda)$ is some nonnegative measure (the finiteness of this measure follows from the convergence of the integral for $j = 0$).

From Theorem 5. 2 we obtain the following theorem.

Theorem 5. 7. *The representation* (5. 30) *holds if and only if the kernels*

$$K_{jk} = s_{j+k} \qquad (j, k = 0, 1, \dots) \tag{5.31}$$

are p. d.

Proof. If s_j has the form (5. 30), then that (5. 31) is p. d. is established directly. Conversely, suppose that the s_j are such that $K_{jk} = s_{j+k}$ are p. d.

$(j, k = 0, 1, \cdots)$. Consider the difference expression $(Lu)_j = (Tu)_j = u_{j+1}$ $(r = r^+ = 1, r^- = 0)$ on the semiaxis $[0, \infty)$. Since $L_j K = s_{j+1+k} = L_k K$ and $\bar{L} = L$, then the condition (5.6) for *-commutativity is satisfied and we have the representation (5.9). Calculating $\chi_{0;j}(\lambda)$, we obtain $u_{j+1} - \lambda u_j = 0$ $(j = 0, 1, \cdots)$, $u_0 = 1$, so that $\chi_{0;j}(\lambda) = \lambda^j$. Thus

$$s_{j+k} = K_{jk} = \int_{-\infty}^{\infty} \lambda^{j+k} d\sigma_{00}(\lambda) \qquad (j, k = 0, 1, \ldots),$$

which is equivalent to (5.30). The theorem is proved.

A sequence s_j $(j = 0, 1, \cdots)$ admitting a representation (5.30) is called a moment sequence. The measure $d\sigma(\lambda)$ in (5.30) is generally speaking nonuniquely defined; the closure of the operator $u \to T^+u$ $(u \in l_{2,0}([0, \infty))$ is not always maximal in H_K. The problem of moments is said to be determinant or not according as to whether $d\sigma(\lambda)$ is or is not uniquely defined. It follows from Theorem 5.4, that *the problem of moments is determinate if the following estimate holds*:

$$|s_j| \leqslant CN^j j^j \qquad (C, N > 0; \quad j = 0, 1, \ldots). \tag{5.32}$$

Indeed, for the kernel (5.31) we obtain $|K_{jk}| \le \sqrt{K_{jj} K_{kk}} = \sqrt{s_{2j} s_{2k}} \le C(2N)^{j+k} j^j k^k$ $(j, k = 0, 1, \cdots)$, which guarantees (5.19).

We note that for any moment sequence we have equality of the defect numbers for the operator $Cu = T^+u$ $(u \in l_{2,0}([0, \infty)))$. This follows from its being real relative to the involution in H_K introduced as the closure of the operator $u_j \to \bar{u}_j$ $(u \in l_2([0, \infty)))$. Therefore the question of determinateness is equivalent to the requirement of selfadjointness in H_K of the closure of C.

We shall establish more delicate criteria for the determinateness of the problem of moments. To this end we recall some facts of the theory of quasianalytic functions (see, for example, S. Mandelbrojt [1], Chapter 1).

Suppose that $[a, b]$ is a finite segment of the real axis, $(m_0, m_1, \cdots)$ a fixed sequence of positive integers. The class $C(m_n)$ is defined to be the linear family of all functions $f(t) \in C^\infty([a, b])$, for each of which the following estimates hold:

$$|(D^n f)(t)| \leqslant K_f^n m_n \qquad (t \in [a, b]; \ n = 0, 1, \ldots), \tag{5.33}$$

where $K_f > 0$ is a constant depending on f.

As is well known, the class of analytic functions $f(t)$ on $[a, b]$ is characterized by estimates (5.33) in which $m_n = n!$. For this class $C(n!)$ the following fact is obvious. If $f \in C(n!)$ is such that at a fixed point $t_0 \in [a, b]$ $(D^n f)(t_0) = 0$ for all $n = 0, 1, \cdots$, then $f(t) = 0$ for $t \in [a, b]$. In order to generalize this situation we introduce the following definition. The class $C(m_n)$ is said to be quasianalytic if from the fact that at some fixed point $t_0 \in [a, b]$ the equations $(D^n f)(t_0) = 0$, $n = 0, 1, \cdots$, hold, it follows that $f(t) = 0$ for all $t \in [a, b]$.

The class $C(m_n)$ will be quasianalytic if

$$\sum_{n=0}^{\infty} \frac{1}{\sqrt[n]{m_n}} = \infty. \tag{5.34}$$

A necessary and sufficient condition for quasianalyticity of $C(m_n)$ (Carleman) is expressed as follows: construct for $r \in [1, \infty)$ the function $T(r) = \sup_{n=0,1,\cdots} r^n/m_n$. Then the following condition must hold:

$$\int_1^{\infty} \frac{\log T(r)}{r^2} dr = +\infty. \tag{5.35}$$

From this condition (and also directly) it is clear that quasianalyticity of the class $C(m_n)$ does not depend on the choice of the segment $[a, b]$. Evidently for any $d > 0$ the two classes $C(m_n)$ and $C(d^n m_n)$ are simultaneously quasi-analytic or not. One may say the same thing about the classes $C(m_n)$ and $C(m_n + d)$. We consider an application to the problem of moments. We shall present an approach using the Cauchy problem. This may be carried over to general expressions (5.1) and weaken the restriction (5.19) just as we have here weakened the condition (5.29).

Lemma 5.3. *Consider in Hilbert space* $H = l_2([0, \infty), m_j)$ *the weak solutions of equation* (2.7), *where* $Su = \bar{\zeta} T^+ u$, $u \in l_{2,0}([0, \infty))$; $\zeta \neq 0$ *a fixed complex number. The uniqueness of such solutions of the Cauchy problem holds if and only if the class* $C(\sqrt{m_n})$ *is quasianalytic.*

Proof. The weakly differentiable vector-function $u(t) = (u_0(t), u_1(t), \cdots)$ $(t \in [0, \infty))$ with values in the space $l_2([0, \infty), m_j) = H$ will be a weak solution of our equation, if equation (2.8) is satisfied with $f = \delta_k \in \mathfrak{D}(S)$, where $k = 0, 1, \cdots$ is arbitrary. But $(S\delta_k)_j = \bar{\zeta}\delta_{k,j-1} = \bar{\zeta}(\delta_{k+1})_j$, so that this equation may be rewritten in the form $m_k (du_k(t)/dt - \zeta m_{k+1} u_{k+1}(t) = 0$ $(t \in [0, \infty)$;

$k = 0, 1, \cdots$). Putting $v_j(t) = m_j u_j(t)$, we obtain

$$\frac{dv_k(t)}{dt} - \zeta v_{k+1}(t) = 0 \qquad (t \in [0, \infty);\ k = 0, 1, \ldots). \tag{5.36}$$

The values of the vector-function $v(t) = (v_0(t), v_1(t), \cdots)$ will belong to the space $l_2([0, \infty), m_j^{-1})$ if for each $t \in [0, \infty)$

$$\sum_{j=0}^{\infty} \frac{|v_j(t)|^2}{m_j} = c(t) < \infty. \tag{5.37}$$

Moreover, since $u(t)$ is weakly differentiable, then it is also weakly continuous on $[0, \infty)$ and therefore is bounded for $t \in [0, T]$, where $T > 0$ is arbitrary. Accordingly $c(t) = \|u(t)\|^2 \le C_T$ for $t \in [0, T]$.

Recurrently defining $v_k(t)$ from (5.36), we find that $v_k(t) = (1/\zeta)^k (D_k v_0)(t)$ ($k = 0, 1, \cdots$). Condition (5.37) may be rewritten in the form

$$\sum_{j=0}^{\infty} \frac{1}{|\zeta|^{2j} m_j} |(D^j v_0)(t)|^2 \leqslant C_T < \infty \qquad (t \in [0, T], T > 0). \tag{5.38}$$

Thus the uniqueness in question in the Cauchy problem is equivalent to the following: there exists a function $v_0(t) \in C^\infty([0, \infty))$, satisfying (5.38). In these cases one can conclude from the equations $(D^j v_0)(0)$ ($j = 0, 1, \cdots$) that $v_0(t) \equiv 0$.

Suppose that the class $C(\sqrt{m_n})$ is quasianalytic. Since (5.38) implies the inequalities $|(D^j v_0)(t)| \le \sqrt{C_T} |\zeta|^j \sqrt{m_j}$ ($t \in [0, T]$; $j = 0, 1, \cdots$), then $v_0 \in C(\sqrt{m_n})$. Therefore from the equations $(D^j v_0)(0) = 0$ ($j = 0, 1, \cdots$) it follows that $v_0(t) = 0$ ($t \in [0, T]$), i.e. uniqueness holds.

Conversely, suppose that we have uniqueness in the Cauchy problem. Consider some function $f(t) \in C^\infty([0, T])$ of the class $C(\sqrt{m_n})$ with $(D^n f)(0) = 0$ ($n = 0, 1, \cdots$). The function $v_0(t) = f(\epsilon t)$ ($\epsilon > 0$, $t \in [0, T/\epsilon]$) will also lie in $C(\sqrt{m_n})$ and $(D^n v_0)(0) = 0$ ($n = 0, 1, \cdots$). At the same time, by the choice of a sufficiently small ϵ one may arrange things so that inequalities (5.33) take for it the form $|(D^j v_0)(t)| \le C^j \sqrt{m_j}$ ($t \in [0, T/\epsilon]$; $j = 0, 1, \cdots$), where $C < |\zeta|$. This guarantees the convergence of the series (5.38) and therefore by hypothesis $v_0(t) = 0$ ($t \in [0, T/\epsilon]$), i.e. $f(t) = 0$ in $[0, T]$. Thus the class $C(\sqrt{m_n})$ is quasianalytic. The lemma is proved.

Theorem 5.8. *Suppose that* s_j $(j = 0, 1, \cdots)$ *is a moment sequence. If the class* $C(\sqrt{s_{2n}})$ *is quasianalytic, then the problem of moments is determinate.*

Proof. Put $K_{jk} = s_{j+k}$, $p_j = d^j(\sqrt{s_{2j}} + 1)^2$ $(j, k = 0, 1, \cdots; d > 1)$. For the p.d. kernel K_{jk} and this series of $p_j \geq 1$, the series (5.4) converges, so that in the schema of subsection 1 we may take $H_+ = l_2([0, \infty), d^j(\sqrt{s_{2j}} + 1)^2)$. We apply Theorem 2.5, 2). The question then reduces to the proof of the uniqueness of the weak solutions of the Cauchy problem in the space H_+ for the equations

$$\frac{du}{dt} \pm (iB)^* u = 0 \quad (0 \leqslant t < \infty),$$

where $Bu = T^+ u$, $u \in l_{2,0}([0, \infty))$. From Lemma 5.3 such uniqueness will hold if the class $C(\sqrt{p_n}) = C(d^{n/2}(\sqrt{s_{2n}} + 1))$ is quasianalytic, or, what is the same thing, the class $C(\sqrt{s_{2n}})$ is quasianalytic. The theorem is proved.

One may show that the conditions of the theorem are close to necessary. From the tests (5.34) and (5.35) for quasianalyticity follows the corollary:

Corollary (Carleman's criterion). *The problem of moments is determinate if*

$$\sum_{j=0}^{\infty} \frac{1}{\sqrt[2j]{s_{2j}}} = \infty \tag{5.39}$$

or, more precisely, if (5.35) *holds, where we have put*

$$T(r) = \sup_{j=0,1,\ldots} \frac{r^j}{\sqrt{s_{2j}}} \quad (r \in [1, \infty)).^{1)} \tag{5.49}$$

Because of the simplicity of the expression L for the case of the problem of moments it is easy to write down the conditions under which the measure $d\sigma(\lambda)$ is concentrated on the semiaxis $[0, \infty)$. This is the so-called Stieltjes moment problem. The same remark holds when $[0, \infty)$ is replaced by a given segment $[a, b]$ (the so-called finite problem of moments).

---

1) Theorem 3.13 on p.d. functions was deduced from the criterion (5.39). On the other hand, it may be deduced directly from criterion (5.34) for quasianalyticity (we need to observe that $|k^{(2n)}(t)| \leq (-1)^n k^{(2n)}(0) = m_{2n}$). Further, this theorem implies criterion (5.39). One must construct in terms of (5.30) a p.d. function (3.40) and take into account that in (3.40) the measure is uniquely determined, since condition (3.57) is satisfied. As we have said, the discussions in this subsection are more general, and carry over to arbitrary expressions (5.1).

Indeed, if $d\sigma(\lambda)$ is concentrated on $[0, \infty)$, then the extension of the operator $Bu = T^+u$ $(u \in l_{2,0}([0, \infty)))$ corresponding to it is nonnegative, so that B itself is nonnegative. Conversely, if this operator is nonnegative, then it admits nonnegative selfadjoint extensions, to which $d\sigma(\lambda)$ corresponds, concentrated on $[0, \infty)$. The condition of nonnegativity has the form: for $u \in l_{2,0}([0, \infty))$

$$0 \leqslant \langle T^+u, u\rangle = \sum_{j,k=0}^{\infty} s_{j+k} u_{k-1} \bar{u}_j = \sum_{j,k=0}^{\infty} s_{j+k+1} u_k \bar{u}_j \ (u_{-1} = 0).$$

Thus, in order that there exist a representation (5.30) with measure $d\sigma(\lambda)$ for the moment sequence s_j, this measure being concentrated on $[0, \infty)$, the condition

$$\sum_{j,k=0}^{\infty} s_{j+k+1} \xi_k \bar{\xi}_j \geqslant 0 \qquad (\xi \in l_{2,0}([0, \infty))) \tag{5.41}$$

is necessary and sufficient.

Analogously, for the finiteness of the problem of moments, it is necessary and sufficient that $a\langle u, u\rangle \leq \langle Bu, u\rangle \leq b\langle u, u\rangle$ $(u \in l_{2,0}([0, \infty)))$, i.e. for the moment sequence s_j the condition

$$a \sum_{j,k=0}^{\infty} s_{j+k} \xi_k \bar{\xi}_j \leqslant \sum_{j,k=0}^{\infty} s_{j+k+1} \xi_k \bar{\xi}_j \leqslant b \sum_{j,k=0}^{\infty} s_{j+k} \xi_k \bar{\xi}_j \qquad (\xi \in l_{2.0}([0, \infty))). \tag{5.42}$$

Thus clearly the problem of moments is determinate in this case.

We shall dwell on the degenerate problem of moments. The moment sequence will be called degenerate if there exists a vector $(\xi_0, \cdots, \xi_N) \neq 0$ such that

$$\sum_{j,k=0}^{N} s_{j+k} \xi_k \bar{\xi}_j = 0. \tag{5.43}$$

It is easy to see that *in this case the problem of moments will be determinate and the measure* $d\sigma(\lambda)$ *concentrated at a finite set of points. The number of these points is equal to the minimal number* N *for which condition* (5.43) *is satisfied. Conversely, if* $d\sigma(\lambda)$ *is concentrated at a finite number of points, then* (5.43) *is degenerate.*

In fact, as we have already said, one can carry Theorem 3.8 over to the difference case. Since now $r = 1$, then for its validity it is sufficient that the form $\langle \cdot, \cdot \rangle$ be degenerate on one vector, i.e. (5.43). The analogy to the solution $\chi_0(x; \lambda)$ figuring in the proof of this theorem for $r = 1$ will be λ^j, a polynomial relative to λ. From the discussion in the original proof it is clear that in this case $d\sigma(\lambda)$ is concentrated on a finite set of points $\{\lambda_1, \cdots, \lambda_m\} \subset (-\infty, \infty)$. Writing $\sigma(\{\lambda_\alpha\}) = \sigma_\alpha$ and substituting the representation (5.30) into (5.34), we obtain $\Sigma_{\alpha=1}^m |\Sigma_{j=0}^N \xi_j \lambda_\alpha^j|^2 \sigma_j = 0$, i.e. the polynomial $\tilde{\xi}(\lambda) = \Sigma_{j=0}^N \xi_j \lambda^j$ is annihilated at the points $\lambda_1, \cdots, \lambda_m$. Therefore the remaining assertions being proved follow easily.

5. **Connection with the theory of Jacobian matrices.** In view of the general theory the space H_K, the completion of $H_+ = l_2([0, \infty), p_j)$ or $l_{2,0}([0, \infty))$ relative to the scalar product $\langle u, v\rangle = \Sigma_{j,k=0}^\infty s_{j+k} u_k \bar{v}_j$, is connected with the problem of moments considered in subsection 4. Here it may be necessary first to identify. We have just seen that in the case of identification, i.e. of degeneracy in the product (5.43), the situation will be simple, and therefore we suppose below that there is no degeneracy. Without loss of generality we may take $s_0 = 1$.

We carry out in H_K an orthogonalization of the δ-sequence $\delta_0, \delta_1, \cdots$, analogous to the one carried out in §3.9. We obtain a sequence of vectors $p_0 = \delta_0, p_1, \cdots \in l_{2,0}([0, \infty))$, which form an orthonormalized basis in H_K. The orthonormalization procedure is unique if we seek each vector $p_n \perp \{\delta_0, \cdots, \delta_{n-1}\}$ in the form $p_n = c_n \delta_n + \cdots + c_0 \delta_0$, where all of the c_j are real and $c_n > 0$. We shall in fact do this. Since nondegeneracy is assumed, the basis $p_0, p_1, \cdots$ is infinite. We could have written out the usual formulas for passing from the basis $\delta_0, \delta_1, \cdots$ to the basis $p_0, p_1, \cdots$, but they were not needed. We shall just denote by F an operator in H_K carrying $\delta_0, \delta_1, \cdots$ into $p_0, p_1, \cdots$: $F\delta_k = p_k$ $(k = 0, 1, \cdots)$. F^{-1} operates on $l_{2,0}([0, \infty)) \subset H_K$, but in general is not bounded.

Sometimes it is convenient to use another interpretation of the space H_K for the case of the problem of moments. To each $u \in l_{2,0}([0, \infty))$ we associate a polynomial $\tilde{u}(\lambda) = \Sigma_{j=0}^\infty u_j \lambda^j$. We shall conceive of H_K as the space of all polynomials $\tilde{u}(\lambda)$ for which the following nondegenerate scalar product is defined:

$$\langle \tilde{u}(\lambda), \tilde{v}(\lambda)\rangle = \langle u, v\rangle = \sum_{j,k=0}^{\infty} s_{j+k} u_k \bar{v}_j \qquad (u, v \in l_{2,0}([0, \infty))). \tag{5.44}$$

If for a sequence s_j we have already obtained a representation (5.30) with some $d\sigma(\lambda)$, then the scalar product (5.44) may obviously be written in the form

$$\langle \tilde{u}(\lambda), \tilde{v}(\lambda)\rangle = \int_{-\infty}^{\infty} \tilde{u}(\lambda)\overline{\tilde{v}(\lambda)}\, d\sigma(\lambda). \tag{5.45}$$

We introduce the polynomials $P_j(\lambda) = \widetilde{p}_j(\lambda)$ $(j = 0, 1, \cdots;\ P_0(\lambda) = \widetilde{\delta}_0(\lambda) \equiv 1)$. They are orthonormal in the scalar product (5.44)–(5.45) and form a basis in H_K.

It is clear from what has been said that H_K may also be interpreted as a space $l_{2,0}([0, \infty))$, if one makes use of the basis $p_0, p_1, \cdots$ (or $P_0(\lambda)$, $P_1(\lambda), \cdots$). In every case for $u \in l_{2,0}([0, \infty))$ one may write $u = \Sigma_{k=0}^{\infty} u_k \delta_k = \Sigma_{j=0}^{\infty} \hat{u}_j p_j$, so that $\hat{u}_j = \Sigma_{k=0}^{\infty} u_k \langle \delta_k, p_j \rangle = \Sigma_{k=0}^{\infty} \mathrm{F}_{jk} u_k$, where $\|\mathrm{F}_{jk}\|_0^{\infty} = \|\langle \delta_k, F\delta_j \rangle\|_0^{\infty} = \mathrm{F}$. u_j is calculated in terms of $\hat{u}_k$ using the formal inverse of the matrix F^{-1}. Since both δ_k and p_k lie in $l_{2,0}([0, \infty))$, the matrices F and F^{-1} carry finite sequences into finite ones.

Write the operator $Bu = T^+ u$ $(u \in l_{2,0}([0, \infty)))$ in the basis $p_0, p_1, \cdots$. Clearly it has the form $\hat{u}_j \to (\mathrm{F}T^+\mathrm{F}^{-1}\hat{u})_j$ $((\hat{u}_0, \hat{u}_1, \cdots) \in l_{2,0}([0, \infty)))$. We calculate the elements of the matrix $\mathrm{F}T^+\mathrm{F}^{-1}$. This is easily done indirectly, using the following argument. Since $T^+\delta_k = \delta_{k+1}$, then $\widetilde{(T^+\delta_k)}(\lambda) = \widetilde{\delta}_{k+1}(\lambda) = \lambda \widetilde{\delta}_k(\lambda)$. Thus, in interpreting H_K as a space of polynomials with the scalar product (5.45), the operator B appears as the operator of multiplication by λ. But we know that such an operator may also be considered as the action of a Jacobian matrix (see §1.5 of Chapter VII; we note that because of the nondegeneracy $\sigma(\lambda)$ has an infinite number of growth points). The elements of this matrix are calculated using formula (1.33) of Chapter VII, where the polynomials $P_j(\lambda)$ coincide with those just introduced. Clearly the action of a Jacobian matrix may be interpreted also as an operator B in some H_K. We sum up what has been said in the following theorem.

Theorem 5.9. *Suppose given a nondegenerate moment sequence* s_j $(j = 0, 1, \cdots)$. *Construct the space* H_K, $K_{jk} = s_{j+k}$ $(j, k = 0, 1, \cdots)$. *We turn in this space from the basis* $\delta_0, \delta_1, \cdots$ *to the orthonormalized basis* $p_0, p_1, \cdots$ *described above. The operator* $Bu = T^+u$ $(u \in l_{2,0}([0, \infty)))$ *may be written in the basis* $p_0, p_1, \cdots$ *as the action of a Jacobian matrix, whose elements are found from the formulas*

$$a_j = \langle T^+ p_j, p_{j+1} \rangle = \langle \lambda P_j(\lambda), P_{j+1}(\lambda) \rangle,$$

$$b_j = \langle T^+ p_j, p_j \rangle = \langle \lambda P_j(\lambda), P_j(\lambda) \rangle \qquad (j = 0, 1, \ldots).$$

Conversely, suppose given some Jacobian matrix (1.5) *of Chapter* VII. *We construct relative to it a system of polynomials of the first kind* $P_0(\lambda), P_1(\lambda), \cdots$.

Let $d\sigma(\lambda)$ *be one of its spectral measures. Let*

$$\lambda^n = c_n^{(n)} P_n(\lambda) + \ldots + c_0^{(n)} P_0(\lambda) \qquad (n = 0, 1, \ldots).$$

Then $s_n = c_0^{(n)} = \int_{-\infty}^{\infty} \lambda^n \cdot 1\, d\sigma(\lambda)$ $(n = 0, 1, \cdots)$ *is a nondegenerate moment sequence. If we construct a Jacobian matrix for it according to the first part of the theorem, we get the original matrix.*

Since the theory of the problem of moments reduces to the spectral theory of the operator B, and since we have constructed in §1 of Chapter VII the spectral theory of just this operator, only written in a different basis, then all the results we have obtained apply directly to the problem of moments. In particular, Theorems 1.12–1.14 of Chapter VII give a description of all solutions $d\sigma(\lambda)$ of the problem of moments, i.e. all spectral densities in the terminology of Chapter VII.

In concluding this subsection we note that the Carleman criterion for determinateness of the problem of moments is a consequence of the criterion (1.8) of Chapter VII for the selfadjointness of a difference operator. In fact, from the construction of polynomials of the first kind $P_j(\lambda)$ it is clear that $P_j(\lambda) = (1/a_0 \cdots a_{j-1})\lambda^j + \cdots$, so that, taking into account their orthogonality relative to any spectral measure $d\sigma(\lambda)$, and formulas (1.33) of Chapter VII, we get

$$a_j = \int_{-\infty}^{\infty} \lambda P_j(\lambda) P_{j+1}(\lambda)\, d\sigma(\lambda) = \int_{-\infty}^{\infty} \left(\frac{\lambda^{j+1}}{a_0 \ldots a_{j-1}} + \lambda(\ldots) \right) P_{j+1}(\lambda) d\sigma(\lambda)$$

$$= \frac{1}{a_0 \ldots a_{j-1}} \int_{-\infty}^{\infty} \lambda^{j+1} P_{j+1}(\lambda)\, d\sigma(\lambda) \leqslant \frac{1}{a_0 \ldots a_{j-1}}$$

$$\times \left(\int_{-\infty}^{\infty} \lambda^{2(j+1)} d\sigma(\lambda) \right)^{\frac{1}{2}} \left(\int_{-\infty}^{\infty} P_{j+1}^2(\lambda)\, d\sigma(\lambda) \right)^{\frac{1}{2}} = \frac{1}{a_0 \ldots a_{j-1}} \sqrt{s_{2(j+1)}},$$

i.e. $a_0 \cdots a_j \leq \sqrt{s_{2(j+1)}}$ $(j = 0, 1, \cdots)$. Suppose that condition (5.39) is satisfied. Then in view of the resulting inequality we have

$$\sum_{j=0}^{\infty} \frac{1}{\sqrt[j]{a_0 \ldots a_j}} = \infty. \tag{5.46}$$

If now we use the general inequality

$$\sum_{n=1}^{\infty}\sqrt[n]{u_1\cdots u_n}\leqslant e\sum_{n=1}^{\infty}u_n \qquad (u_n>0;\ n=1,\ 2,\ldots)$$

(see for example N. I. Ahiezer [2], Chapter 2, Russian pages 110–111), we conclude from (5. 46) that the series $\Sigma_{j=0}^{\infty} 1/a_j$ diverges. From Theorem 1. 3, Chapter VII, the difference operator D is selfadjoint, i. e. the problem of moments is determinate.

6. **Other examples of representations.** We shall present three further examples relating to the general Theorems 5. 1–5. 3. It would be easy to give further examples, as in subsections 11 and 12 of §3.

1) Suppose that c_j $(j=\cdots,-1,0,1,\cdots)$ is a sequence such that the kernel $K_{jk}=c_{j+k}$ $(j, k=\cdots,-1,0,1,\cdots)$ is p. d. As in subsection 4, we put $L=T$. The condition of *-commutativity (5. 6) will be satisfied and therefore (5. 9) holds. Here $r=0$ and $\chi_{0;j}(\lambda)=\lambda^j$ $(j=\cdots,-1,0,1,\cdots)$. Thus we get

$$c_j=\int_{-\infty}^{\infty}\lambda^j d\sigma(\lambda) \qquad (j=\ldots,-1,\ 0,\ 1,\ldots). \tag{5. 47}$$

It is clear that our sequence c_j, considered for $j=0,1,\cdots$, is a moment sequence. This in particular yields sufficient conditions for the uniqueness of $d\sigma(\lambda)$ in (5. 47). However the converse is not true; not every moment sequence s_j $(j=0,1,\cdots)$ can be prolonged to $j=-1,-2,\cdots$ with preservation of the positive definiteness of the kernel $K_{jk}=s_{j+k}$. As is clear from (5. 30), for this it is necessary and sufficient that the measure $d\sigma(\lambda)$ close to $\lambda=0$ should be such that all the integerals $\int_{-\epsilon}^{\epsilon}|\lambda|^j d\sigma(\lambda)$ $(\epsilon>0;\ j=-1,-2,\cdots)$ exist.

2) Consider an even sequence c_j $(c_{-j}=c_j,\ j=\cdots,-1,0,1,\cdots)$ such that the kernel $K_{jk}=\frac{1}{2}[c_{j+k}+c_{j-k}]$ $(j, k=\cdots,-1,0,1,\cdots)$ is p. d. This case is similar to example 1) of §3. 11. Now we take $(Lu)_j=u_{j-1}+u_{j+1}=(T^+u)_j+(Tu)_j$ $(L^+=L=\overline{L})$. We have

$$(L_jK)_{jk}=\frac{1}{2}[c_{j-1+k}+c_{j-1-k}]+\frac{1}{2}[c_{j+1+k}+c_{j+1-k}]=(L_kK)_{jk}$$

$$(j,\ k=\ldots,-1,\ 0,\ 1,\ldots),$$

so that representation (5. 9) holds with the indicated L. Just as in §3. 11, we eliminate the odd solutions of the equation $(Lu)_j = \lambda u_j$ $(j = \cdots, -1, 0, 1, \cdots)$. It is not hard to see that the even solutions will have the form $\chi_{0;j}(\lambda) = P_j(\lambda)$ $(j = \cdots, -1, 0, 1, \cdots)$, where $P_j(\lambda) = \cos(j \arccos \lambda/2)$ are the Čebyšev polynomials of the first kind (cf. (1.88), Chapter VII). Thus for the even sequence c_j the positive definiteness of the kernel $K_{jk} = \frac{1}{2}[c_{j+k} + c_{j-k}]$ $(j, k = \cdots, -1, 0, 1, \cdots)$ is equivalent to the representation

$$c_j = \int_{-\infty}^{\infty} P_j(\lambda)\, d\sigma(\lambda) \qquad (j = \ldots, -1, 0, 1, \ldots) \tag{5.48}$$

with some finite nonnegative measure $d\sigma(\lambda)$. Theorem 5.3 gives criteria for uniqueness of the determination of the measure $d\sigma(\lambda)$ relative to c_j. It is sufficient that $|c_j| \le CN^{|j|}\,|j|^{|j|}$ $(C, N > 0;\ j = \cdots, -1, 0, 1, \cdots)$.

3) There is one important representation which is not formally included in the theory of this chapter.[1)] Indeed, the sequence c_j $(j = \cdots, -1, 0, 1, \cdots)$ is said to be p. d. if the kernel $K_{jk} = c_{j-k}$ $(j, k = \cdots, -1, 0, 1, \cdots)$ is p. d.. Such a sequence admits a representation (theorem of Herglotz)

$$c_j = \int_0^{2\pi} e^{i\lambda j}\, d\sigma(\lambda) \qquad (j = \ldots, -1, 0, 1, \ldots), \tag{5.49}$$

where $d\sigma(\lambda)$ is some nonnegative finite measure. If we construct a space H_K relative to the kernel K_{jk}, then the operator $Bu = T^+u$ $(u \in l_{2,0}((-\infty, \infty)))$ will not be Hermitian in it, but rather isometric, and it will become unitary after closure. If now we employ the spectral theorem for unitary operators, then, analogously to the Hermitian case, we obtain a representation (5.49). The measure in this representation, thanks to the boundedness of the operator in question, is defined uniquely relative to c_j.

We turn to examples connected with $q > 1$ difference expressions.

7. **The multidimensional problem of moments.** We shall consider a set G of integer-valued points $j = (j_1, \cdots, j_n)$, where $j_1, \cdots, j_n = 0, 1, \cdots$ (i. e. $G = G^{(1)} \times \cdots \times G^{(n)}$), with the $G^{(\nu)}$ being semiaxes). One asks under what conditions can the sequence s_j $(j \in G)$ be represented in the form

$$s_j = s_{j_1,\ldots,j_n} = \int_{E_n} \lambda_1^{j_1} \cdots \lambda_n^{j_n}\, d\sigma(\lambda) \qquad (j = (j_1, \ldots, j_n) \in G), \tag{5.50}$$

---

1) It is not hard to generalize the schema of this chapter to the case of operators admitting normal extensions. Then example 3) would have been included in the theory thus constructed.

where $d\sigma(\lambda)$ is some nonnegative measure (finite in view of equation (5.50) for $j=(0,\cdots,0)$). If (5.50) holds, then the kernel $K_{jk}=s_{j+k}$ $(j, k \in G)$ is evidently p.d.. For $n=1$ it is, as we know (subsection 4), sufficient that this kernel be p.d. in order that the representation (5.50) should hold. If $n>1$ positive definiteness is already insufficient. For the corresponding example, resulting from the construction of Hilbert of a positive polynomial of two variables which is not the sum of squares of moduli of such polynomials (see for example I. M. Gel'fand and N. Ja. Vilenkin [1], Chapter 2, §7).

Now we shall cite some conditions which along with the positive definiteness of the kernel $K_{jk}=s_{j+k}$ are sufficient for the validity of (5.50). First we note that the positive definiteness of this kernel implies the reality of the sequence s_j $(j \in G)$, and since the sequence s_j will be connected with expressions with real coefficients, this will imply the equality of the defect numbers of the corresponding operators of type $u \to L^{(\nu)+}u$, $u \in l_{2,0}(G)$.

Theorem 5.10. *Suppose that the sequence* s_j *is such that the kernel* $K_{jk}=s_{j+k}$ $(j, k \in G)$ *is* p.d., *and one has the estimate*

$$|s_j| \leqslant CN^{j_1+\cdots+j_n} j_1^{j_1}\cdots j_n^{j_n} \qquad (j=(j_1,\cdots,j_n)\in G) \tag{5.51}$$

with some $C, N>0$. *Then the representation* (5.50) *holds and the measure* $d\sigma(\lambda)$ *in it is uniquely defined.*

This theorem follows from Theorem 5.6. Indeed, it follows from (5.51) that

$$\begin{aligned} |K_{jk}| &\leqslant \sqrt{K_{jj}K_{kk}}=\sqrt{s_{2j}s_{2k}} \\ &\leqslant C(2N)^{j_1+\cdots+j_n+k_1+\cdots+k_n} j_1^{j_1}\cdots j_n^{j_n}k_1^{k_1}\cdots k_n^{k_n} \qquad (j, k \in G). \end{aligned} \tag{5.52}$$

In Theorem 5.6 we need to put $L^{(\nu)}=T_\nu$ and then $\rho_\nu = r_\nu^+ = 1$ $(\nu=1,\cdots,n)$, and estimate (5.52) guarantees the validity of (5.29). Writing out representation (5.28) for our case, we obtain (5.50).

Remark. In Theorem 5.10 inequality (5.51) may be replaced by the weaker estimate

$$\sqrt{s_{2j}} \leqslant Cm_{j_1}^{(1)}\cdots m_{j_n}^{(n)} \qquad (C>0:\ j\in G), \tag{5.53}$$

where the sequence of positive numbers $m_{j_1}^{(1)},\cdots,m_{j_n}^{(n)}$ is such that each of the classes $C(m_{j_1}^{(1)}),\cdots,C(m_{j_n}^{(n)})$ is quasianalytic.

Indeed, we shall carry out the construction of subsection 3 for $K_{jk}=s_{j+k}$

$(j, k \in G)$, putting $p_j = d_1^{j_1}(m_{j_1}^{(1)}+1)^2 \cdots d_n^{j_n}(m_{j_n}^{(n)}+1)^2$ $(j \in G)$, where $d_1, \cdots, d_n > 1$. This choice of p_j is possible because of estimate (5.53), which guarantees the convergence of the series $\sum_{j \in G} K_{jj}/p_j$. Thus now $H_+^{(\nu)} = l_2([0, \infty), d_\nu^j(m_j^{(\nu)}+1)^2)$ $(\nu = 1, \cdots, n)$. Our assertion follows from the general Theorem 2.3 and Lemma 5.3 (cf. the proof of Theorem 5.8).

Now we shall obtain a somewhat more delicate theorem which does not involve the "multiplicative" estimates (5.51) or (5.53). Its proof is based on Theorem 2.2. First we note that without significant change the proof of Theorem 2.2 may be used to strengthen the formulation of this theorem.

Suppose that for each $\nu = 1, \cdots, q$ $\Re(B_\nu) \subseteq \mathfrak{D}(B_\nu)$ *and that the closure of the operator* B_ν *in any space* $H^{(\nu)}_{K;w_1,\cdots,w_{\nu-1},w_{\nu+1},\cdots,w_q}$ $(w_l \in \mathfrak{D}(B_l),\ l \neq \nu)$ *is unique. Then the closures of the operators* C_ν *are selfadjoint in* H_K *and commute.*

Lemma 5.4. *Suppose that* s_j *is such that the kernel* $K_{jk} = s_{j+k}$ $(j, k \in G)$ *is positive definite. For any* $(N_1, \cdots, N_n) \in G$ *the following estimate holds:*

$$s_{2j} = s_{2j_1,\ldots,2j_n} \leqslant \sum_{l_1=0,2N_1;\ldots;l_n=0,2N_n} s_{l_1,\ldots,l_n} \qquad (5.54)$$
$$(0 \leqslant j_1 \leqslant N_1, \ldots, 0 \leqslant j_n \leqslant N_n).$$

Proof. Suppose that c_l $(l = 0, 1, \cdots)$ is a one-dimensional moment sequence. From Theorem 5.7 it admits a representation $c_l = \int_{-\infty}^{\infty} \lambda^l d\rho(\lambda)$ $(l = 0, 1, \cdots)$. If $l \leq N$, then $\lambda^{2l} \leq 1 + \lambda^{2N}$ $(-\infty < \lambda < \infty)$ and from this representation we obtain the inequality

$$c_{2l} \leqslant c_0 + c_{2N} \qquad (0 \leqslant l \leqslant N). \qquad (5.55)$$

For fixed $j_1, \cdots, j_{\nu-1}, j_{\nu+1}, \cdots, j_n$ the sequence $c_{j_\nu} = s_{2j_1,\cdots,2j_{\nu-1},j_\nu,2j_{\nu+1},\cdots,2j_n}$ $(j_\nu = 0, 1, \cdots)$ is a one-dimensional moment sequence $(\nu = 1, \cdots, n)$. Applying successively (5.55), we get

$$s_{2j_1,\ldots,2j_n} \leqslant s_{0,2j_2,\ldots,2j_n} + s_{2N_1,2j_2,\ldots,2j_n} \leqslant s_{0,0,2j_3,\ldots,2j_n}$$
$$+ s_{0,2N_2,2j_3,\ldots,2j_n} + s_{2N_1,0,2j_3,\ldots,2j_n} + s_{2N_1,2N_2,2j_3,\ldots,2j_n} \leq \cdots$$
$$\cdots \leqslant \sum_{l_1=0,2N_1;\ldots;l_n=0,2N_n} s_{l_1,\ldots,l_n} \qquad (0 \leqslant j_1 \leqslant N_1, \ldots, 0 \leqslant j_n \leqslant N_n).$$

The lemma is proved.

Now we shall prove the following theorem.

Theorem 5.11. *Suppose that the sequence* s_j $(j \in G)$ *is such that the kernel* $K_{jk} = s_{j+k}$ $(j, k \in G)$ *is p.d.. If each one-dimensional moment sequence of the form*

$$c_{j_\nu} = \sum_{\substack{l_1=0,2N;\ldots;l_{\nu-1}=0,2N;\\ l_{\nu+1}=0,2N;\ldots;l_n=0,2N}} s_{l_1,\ldots,l_{\nu-1},j_\nu,l_{\nu+1},\ldots,l_n}, \quad j_\nu = 0, 1, \ldots \tag{5.56}$$

$(N = 0, 1, \cdots;\ \nu = 1, \cdots, n$ *fixed*) *is determinate, then representation* (5.50) *is valid and the measure* $d\sigma(\lambda)$ *in it is determined uniquely.*

Proof. Given the kernel $K_{jk} = s_{j+k}$ $(j, k \in G)$ we shall construct spaces H_0, H_+ and so forth as indicated in subsection 3. Here we need to take $L^{(\nu)} = T_\nu$. The role of the operators B_ν will be played by the mappings $u \to T_\nu^+ u$ $(u \in l_{2,0}([0, \infty)))$ $(\nu = 1, \cdots, n)$. Clearly $\mathfrak{R}(B_\nu) \subseteq \mathfrak{D}(B_\nu)$. If we show that the closure of the operator B_ν in any space $H^{(\nu)}_{K; w_1, \cdots, w_{\nu-1}, w_{\nu+1}, \cdots, w_n}$ $(w_l \in l_{2,0}([0, \infty)) = \mathfrak{D}(B_l),\ (l \neq \nu))$ is selfadjoint, then the condition of the above-formulated variant of Theorem 2.2 will be satisfied. Because of this theorem one may apply Theorem 5.5 to obtain representation (5.50) with a uniquely defined $d\sigma(\lambda)$. Thus it remains for us to establish the selfadjointness of the indicated closures of the operators B_ν. For definiteness we shall take $\nu = 1$.

The scalar product in the space $H^{(1)}_{K; w_2, \cdots, w_n}$ $(w_2, \cdots, w_n \in l_{2,0}([0, \infty)))$ has the form

$$\langle u, v\rangle_{w_2,\ldots,w_n} = \sum_{j_1,\ldots,j_n,k_1,\ldots,k_n=0}^{\infty} s_{j_1+k_1,j_2+k_2,\ldots,j_n+k_n} \times u_{k_1}\bar{v}_{j_1} w_{2;k_2}\bar{w}_{2;j_2}\cdots w_{n;k_n}\bar{w}_{n;j_n} \tag{5.57}$$

$$(u, v \in H^{(1)}_+).$$

The sequence $S_{j_2,\cdots,j_n} = \sum_{j_1,k_1=0}^{\infty} s_{j_1+k_1,j_2,\cdots,j_n} u_{k_1}\bar{u}_{j_1}$ $(u \in l_{2,0}([0, \infty)))$ is evidently such that the kernel $K_{j_2,\cdots,j_n;\, k_2,\cdots,k_n} = S_{j_2+k_2,\cdots,j_n+k_n}$ $(j_2, \cdots, j_n, k_2, \cdots, k_n = 0, 1, \cdots)$ is p.d., so that $|S_{j_2+k_2,\cdots,j_n+k_n}| \leq \sqrt{S_{2j_2,\cdots,2j_n} S_{2k_2,\cdots,2k_n}}$. Taking account of this inequality, we obtain from

(5. 57):

$$\langle u, u\rangle_{w_2,\ldots,w_n} = \sum_{j_2,\ldots,j_n,k_2,\ldots,k_n=0}^{\infty} S_{j_2+k_2,\ldots,j_n+k_n}$$

$$\times w_{2;k_2}\bar{w}_{2;j_2}\cdots w_{n;k_n}\bar{w}_{n;j_n}$$

$$\leqslant \left(\sum_{j_2,\ldots,j_n=0}^{\infty} \sqrt{S_{2j_2,\ldots,2j_n}}\,|w_{2;j_2}|\cdots|w_{n;j_n}|\right)^2 \tag{5. 58}$$

Suppose that $N > 0$ is so large that all the $w_{2;\,l}, \cdots, w_{n;\,l}$ are annihilated for $l > N$. Then, from (5. 58) and with the aid of Lemma 5. 4 applied to $S_{2j_2,\cdots,2j_n}$, we find

$$\langle u, u\rangle_{w_2,\ldots,w_n} \leqslant C \sum_{j_2,\ldots,j_n=0}^{\infty} S_{2j_2,\ldots,2j_n} \leqslant C \sum_{l_2=0,2N;\ldots;l_n=0,2N} S_{l_2,\ldots,l_n}$$

$$= C\sum_{j_1,k_1=0}^{\infty}\left(\sum_{l_2=0,2N;\ldots;l_n=0,2N} s_{j_1+k_1,l_2,\ldots,l_n}\right) u_{k_1}\bar{u}_{j_1} = \langle u, u\rangle_C \tag{5. 59}$$

$$(u \in l_{2,0}([0, \infty))),$$

where $\langle\cdot, \cdot\rangle$ is the scalar product constructed relative to the one-dimensional moment sequence of type (5. 56) for $\nu = 1$. By hypothesis this moment sequence is determinate, so that the closure of the operator $u \to T_1^+ u$ $(u \in l_{2,0}([0, \infty)))$ in the corresponding H_C will be selfadjoint. Thanks to inequality (5. 59) the same will hold for the required closure of this operator. The theorem is proved.

Naturally Theorem 2. 6 is applicable to the multidimensional problem of moments. As in dealing with Theorem 2. 2, we remark in preparation that *in the formulation of Theorem 2. 6 we may regard w_2 not as arbitrary in $H_+^{(2)}$ but rather as varying in $\mathfrak{D}(B_2)$, given only that one assumes the imbedding $\mathfrak{R}(B_2) \subseteq \mathfrak{D}(B_2)$.* In such a form Theorem 2. 6 makes it possible to establish the following result.

Theorem 5. 12. *Suppose that the sequence $s_j = s_{j_1,j_2}(j_1, j_2 = 0, 1, \cdots)$ is such that the kernel $K_{jk} = s_{j+k}$ is p. d. . If each one-dimensional moment sequence of the form*

$$c_{j_1} = s_{j_1,0} + s_{j_1,2N},\ j_1 = 0, 1, \ldots\ (N = 0, 1, \ldots\ \textit{fixed}) \tag{5. 60}$$

is determinate, then representation (5. 50) holds (for $n = 2$) with, generally *speaking, a nonuniquely defined measure* $d\sigma(\lambda)$.

Proof. We shall carry out the same construction as in the derivation of Theorem 5.11. As there we may assert that the closure of the operator $u \to T_1^+ u$ ($u \in l_{2,0}([0, \infty))$) in any space $H_{K;w_2}^{(1)}$ ($w_2 \in l_{2,0}([0, \infty))$) is selfadjoint. Moreover the operators $C_1 u = T_1^+ u$, $C_2 u = T_2^+ u$ ($u \in l_{2,0}(G)$) are real relative to the involution $\circ$, defined as reflection in the complex line. This makes it possible to apply the modified Theorem 2.6 stated above, and Theorem 5.5, and to complete the proof.

In conclusion we note that just as was noted in §4.4 we could have described all possible $d\sigma(\lambda)$ participating in the representation (5.50) for the sequence s_j considered here. We shall not dwell on these questions.

8. Further examples. From the one-dimensional examples of subsections 4 and 6, we may construct a number of multidimensional examples similar to those of §4.3 for the continuous case. For example, we could consider the sequence $c_j = c_{j_1, j_2}$ ($j_1, j_2 = \cdots, -1, 0, 1, \cdots$), even in each variable and such that the kernel $K_{jk} = \frac{1}{2}[c_{j+k} + c_{j-k}]$ is p.d., or a sequence $c_j = c_{j_1, j_2}$ ($j_1 = \cdots, -1, 0, 1, \cdots$; $j_2 = 0, 1, \cdots$), even in the first variable and such that the kernel $K_{jk} = \frac{1}{2}[c_{j_1+k_1, j_2+k_2} + c_{j_1-k_1, j_2+k_2}]$ is p.d.. The representation of these and similar sequences is easily obtained by a further development of the schema. We shall not present the results here.

§6. RESULTS CONNECTED WITH PARTIAL DIFFERENTIAL OPERATORS

As we know, the general representation (3.7) of a p.d. kernel in terms of the family of elementary p.d. kernels Ω_λ in the case of ordinary differential equations is significantly eased since $\Omega_\lambda(x, y)$ may be expressed in terms of a fixed fundamental system of solutions $\chi_j(\cdot\,; \lambda)$ of the equation $Lu - \lambda u = 0$ and formula (3.20) obtained. Here we shall show that in certain cases, for partial differential equations as well, and always for partial difference equations, one may sharpen the representation (3.7). We shall present the simplest examples and will not deal with their generalizations.

1. The case of an elliptic expression in a bounded region and a regular kernel. Suppose that $G \subset E_n$ is a bounded region with a sufficiently smooth boundary Γ. Consider in G a formally selfadjoint elliptic expression L of order r with sufficiently smooth real coefficients $a_\alpha(x)$, on Γ formally selfadjoint boundary conditions (bd), which are also supposed real (i. e. $u(x) \in W_2^r(\text{bd})$ implies $\overline{u(x)} \in W_2^r(\text{bd})$). We suppose that L, Γ, and (bd) are such that the operator $\Lambda'(\text{bd}) = Lu$, $u \in \mathfrak{D}(\Lambda'(\text{bd})) = W_2^r(\text{bd})$, in the space $L_2(G)$, is selfadjoint.[1] We denote by $\Phi_0(x, y; \lambda)$ and $d\rho_0$ the spectral function and measure of this operator.

Now we consider the p. d. kernel $K(x, y) \in C(G \times G)$, real and $*$-commuting with L, and regular in the sense that $K \in L_2(G \times G, dxdy)$ and relation (3. 4) is satisfied not only for $u, v \in C_0^\infty(G)$ but also for $u, v \in W_2^r(\text{bd})$ (if K is sufficiently smooth, then this is equivalent to having $L_x K = L_y K$ and $K(x, y)$ satisfying the conditions (bd) in each variable). We shall suppose that $a_\alpha(x) \in C^{|\alpha| + r + l + 1}(G)$ $(l > n/2)$, so that representation (3. 11) holds.

Theorem 6. 1. *Under the given hypotheses* $\Omega_\lambda(x, y)\, d\rho(\lambda)$ *is defined uniquely by the formula*

$$\Omega_\lambda(x, y)\, d\varrho(\lambda) = \int_G K(x, \xi)\, \Phi_0(\xi, y; \lambda)\, d\xi d\varrho(\lambda) \qquad (x, y \in G). \tag{6. 1}$$

Proof. First of all we note that since $K \in L_2(G \times G, dx\, dy)$, therefore $L_2(G) \subseteq H_K$ and $\langle f, f \rangle \leq C \|f\|^2_{L_2(G)}$ $(f \in L_2(G))$. The mapping $f(x) \to \overline{f(x)}$ guarantees an involution in H_K. We define in H_K an operator S, putting $Su = L^+ u = Lu$, $u \in \mathfrak{D}(S) = W_2^r(\text{bd})$. Since (3. 4) holds for $u, v \in W_2^r(\text{bd})$, S is Hermitian. It is clearly real relative to the involution and therefore has equal defect numbers. Suppose that A is a selfadjoint extension of it into H_K. A serves as a selfadjoint extension also for the operator $u \to L^+ u$ $(u \in C_0^\infty(G))$; thus A generates the representation (3. 11).

Suppose that R_z^0 is the resolvent in $L_2(G)$ of the operator $\Lambda'(\text{bd})$ and $R_0(x, y; z)$ its kernel. For $f \in L_2(G)$, $R_z^0(f) \in \mathfrak{D}(\Lambda'(\text{bd})) = \mathfrak{D}(S)$. Therefore in H_K

$$(A - zE) R_z^0 f = (S - zE) R_z^0 f = (L - zE) R_z^0 f = (\Lambda'(\text{bd}) - zE) R_z^0 f = f. \tag{6. 2}$$

If R_z is the resolvent of the operator A, then $(A - zE) R_z f = f$ $(f \in L_2(G))$. Comparing this relation with (6. 2), we conclude that $(A - zE)(R_z f - R_z^0 f) = 0$ $(f \in L_2(G))$. Because A is selfadjoint we obtain the equation in the sense of H_K:

---

[1] For example, suppose that the hypotheses of Theorem 1. 3 of Chapter VI are satisfied.

$$R_z f = R_z^0 f \qquad (f \in L_2(G)). \tag{6.3}$$

We denote by $R(x, y; z)$ the kernel of the resolvent R_z. From (6.3) and (3.16) we get

$$\iint_{GG} R(x, y; z)\, u(y)\, \overline{v(x)}\, dx dy = \langle R_z u, v \rangle = \langle R_z^0 u, v \rangle$$

$$= \iint_{GG} K(x, \xi) \left(\int_G R_0(\xi, y; z)\, u(y)\, dy \right) \overline{v(x)}\, dx d\xi$$

$$= \iint_{GG} \left(\int_G K(x, \xi)\, R_0(\xi, y; z)\, d\xi \right) u(y)\, \overline{v(x)}\, dx dy \qquad (u, v \in C_0(G)).$$

Hence

$$R(x, y; z) = \int_G K(x, \xi)\, R_0(\xi, y; z)\, d\xi \qquad (x, y \in G). \tag{6.4}$$

Using the last equation in (3.17), and the similar relation for the operator $\Lambda'(\mathrm{bd})$, it is not difficult to deduce formula (6.1). The theorem is proved.

Substituting the expression just found for $\Omega_\lambda\, d\rho(\lambda)$ into (3.11), *we obtain a representation for* $K(x, y)$ *in the form of an absolutely convergent integral*:

$$K(x, y) = \int_{-\infty}^{\infty} \left\{ \int_G K(x, \xi)\, \Phi_0(\xi, y; \lambda)\, d\xi \right\} d\varrho(\lambda) \qquad (x, y \in G). \tag{6.5}$$

For any function $f \in L_2(G)$, in the sense of mean square convergence, one has the equation $f(y) = \int_{-\infty}^{\infty} \{\int_G f(\xi)\Phi_0(\xi, y; \lambda) d\xi\} d\rho(\lambda)$, following from Parseval's equation for the operator $\Lambda'(\mathrm{bd})$. Since $K(x, \cdot) \in L_2(G)$, for almost all x, then, writing this equation for $f(\cdot) = K(x, \cdot)$, we obtain (6.5). However the integrals in this representation will not converge absolutely. The meaning of the theorem being proved consists in that under the hypotheses of positive definiteness and regularity of the kernel $K(x, y)$ these integrals converge absolutely. This fact is an immediate generalization of the theorem of Bochner for Fourier series on the fact that the Fourier series of a continuous function with nonnegative coefficients converges absolutely.

2. **Two-dimensional Laplace expressions.** Now for the p. d. kernel $K(x, y) \in C(E_2 \times E_2)$, $*$-commuting with the expression $\Delta = D_1^2 + D_2^2$, let us specialize representation (3.11) in the direction of transforming it into a form similar to (3.20). First we deduce a formula for the solutions of the equation $\Delta u = \lambda u$.

Suppose that $u(x_1, x_2)$ satisfies the equation

$$\Delta u = D_1^2 u + D_2^2 u = \lambda u \tag{6.6}$$

on the entire plane E_2, with λ a real coefficient. Since each solution of an elliptic equation with analytic coefficients is analytic, then there exists a function $u(z_1, z_2)$, entire in each of the complex variables $z_1 = x_1 + iy_1$ and $z_2 = x_2 + iy_2$, coinciding for $z_1 = x_1$ and $z_2 = x_2$ with $u(x_1, x_2)$, and satisfying the equation $\partial^2 u/\partial z_1^2 + \partial^2 u/\partial z_2^2 = \lambda u$. We write $v(x_1, x_2) = u(x_1, ix_2)$. We have

$$D_1^2 v - D_2^2 v = \lambda v \qquad ((x_1, x_2) \in E_2). \tag{6.7}$$

Solving this by Riemann's method, we obtain the following representation of v in terms of the initial data (see for example A. N. Tihonov and A. A. Samarskiĭ, [1], Chapter 2, §5):

$$v(x_1, x_2) = \frac{1}{2}[v(x_1 - x_2, 0) + v(x_1 + x_2, 0)]$$

$$-\frac{1}{2}\sqrt{-\lambda}\, x_2 \int_{x_1-x_2}^{x_1+x_2} \frac{J_1(\sqrt{-\lambda}\sqrt{(x_1-\xi)^2 - x_2^2})}{\sqrt{(x_1-\xi)^2 - x_2^2}}\, v(\xi, 0)\, d\xi$$

$$+\frac{1}{2}\int_{x_1-x_2}^{x_1+x_2} J_0(\sqrt{-\lambda}\sqrt{(x_1-\xi)^2 - x_2^2})\,(D_2 v)(\xi, 0)\, d\xi \qquad ((x_1, x_2) \in E_2). \tag{6.8}$$

Here J_0 and J_1 are Bessel functions:

$$J_0(s) = 1 - \left(\frac{s}{2}\right)^2 + \frac{1}{(2!)^2}\left(\frac{s}{2}\right)^4 - \frac{1}{(3!)^2}\left(\frac{s}{2}\right)^6 + \cdots,$$

$$J_1(s) = \frac{s}{2} - \frac{1}{2!}\left(\frac{s}{2}\right)^3 + \frac{1}{2!\,3!}\left(\frac{s}{2}\right)^5 - \cdots. \tag{6.9}$$

The function $v(z_1, z_2)$ has a meaning for complex z_1, z_2 and will be entire in each of the variables. In particular, both $v(z_1, 0)$ and $(D_2 v)(z_1, 0)$ will be entire. It follows from the decomposition (6.9) that the kernels $((x_1 - \xi)^2 - x_2^2)^{-1/2} J_1(\sqrt{-\lambda}\sqrt{(x_1-\xi)^2 - x_2^2})$ and $J_0(\sqrt{-\lambda}\sqrt{(x_1-\xi)^2 - x_2^2})$ also will be entire in x_2. Therefore each term on the right side of (6.8) may be extended relative to x_2 into the complex z_2 plane, and formula (6.8) remains valid if in it one replaces x_2 by z_2. Now putting $z_2 = -ix_2$ and noting that $v(x_1, -ix_2) = u(x_1, x_2)$, we obtain the required representation of any solution in E_2 of equation (6.6):

$$u(x_1, x_2) = \frac{1}{2}[u(x_1 + ix_2, 0) + u(x_1 - ix_2, 0)]$$

$$-\frac{1}{2}\sqrt{\lambda}\, x_2 \int_{x_1+ix_2}^{x_1-ix_2} \frac{J_1(\sqrt{-\lambda}\sqrt{(x_1-\xi)^2 + x_2^2})}{\sqrt{(x_1-\xi)^2 + x_2^2}} u(\xi, 0)\, d\xi$$

$$+\frac{1}{2}\int_{x_1+ix_2}^{x_1-ix_2} J_0(\sqrt{-\lambda}\sqrt{(x_1-\xi)^2 + x_2^2})\,(D_2 u)(\xi, 0)\, d\xi \qquad ((x_1, x_2) \in E_2). \quad (6.10)$$

It is clear that here the integration is carried out over any rectifiable arc in the complex plane joining the points $x_1 + ix_2$ and $x_1 - ix_2$.

We shall write formula (6. 10) in a short form. We denote by Z the linear topological space of all entire functions $\phi(\xi)$ of one complex variable ξ. By convergence in Z is understood convergence uniform on every bounded set. The equations

$$(\chi_\xi^{(0)}(x; \lambda), \varphi(\xi)) = \frac{1}{2}[\varphi(x_1 + ix_2) + \varphi(x_1 - ix_2)]$$

$$-\frac{1}{2}\sqrt{\lambda}\, x_2 \int_{x_1+ix_2}^{x_1-ix_2} \frac{J_1(\sqrt{-\lambda}\sqrt{(x_1-\xi)^2 + x_2^2})}{\sqrt{(x_1-\xi)^2 + x_2^2}} \varphi(\xi)\, d\xi,$$

$$(\chi_\xi^{(1)}(x; \lambda), \varphi(\xi)) = \frac{1}{2}\int_{x_1+ix_2}^{x_1-ix_2} J_0(\sqrt{-\lambda}\sqrt{(x_1-\xi)^2 + x_2^2})\,\varphi(\xi)\, d\xi$$

$$(x = (x_1, x_2) \in E_2, \varphi \in Z) \qquad (6.11)$$

define linear continuous functionals $\chi^{(0)}(x; \lambda)$ and $\chi^{(1)}(x; \lambda)$ over Z. In the notation of (6. 11) formula (6. 10) takes the form

$$u(x) = u(x_1, x_2) = (\chi_\xi^{(0)}(x; \lambda), u(\xi, 0)) + (\chi_\xi^{(1)}(x; \lambda), (D_2 u)(\xi, 0))$$

$$(x = (x_1, x_2) \in E_2). \qquad (6.12)$$

Therefore in a definite sense the functions $\chi_\xi^{(0)}(x; \lambda)$, $\chi_\xi^{(1)}(x; \lambda)$, depending on the parameter ξ, the first being generalized in ξ, form a fundamental system of solutions of (6. 6). We shall express the elementary kernels in terms of them.

For this we introduce a space $Z \otimes Z$ consisting of functions $\phi(\xi, \eta)$ of the two complex variables ξ and η, entire in each variable. Convergence in $Z \otimes Z$ is convergence on every set bounded in the space of $(\xi, \eta) \in C_2$. Thus for example

$$(\chi_\xi^{(0)}(x;\lambda)\otimes\chi_\eta^{(1)}(y;\lambda),\varphi(\xi,\eta))\cdot$$

$$=\frac{1}{4}\int_{y_1+iy_2}^{y_1-iy_2}[\varphi(x_1+ix_2,\eta)+\varphi(x_1-ix_2,\eta)]\,J_0(\sqrt{-\lambda}\sqrt{(y_1-\eta)^2+y_2^2})\,d\eta$$

$$-\frac{1}{4}\sqrt{\lambda}x_2\int_{x+ix_2}^{x_1-ix_2}\int_{y_1+iy_2}^{y_1-iy_2}\frac{J_1(\sqrt{-\lambda}\sqrt{(x_1-\xi)^2+x_2^2})}{\sqrt{(x_1-\xi)^2+x_2^2}}$$

$$\times J_0(\sqrt{-\lambda}\sqrt{(y_1-\eta)^2+y_2^2})\,\varphi(\xi,\eta)\,d\xi d\eta\qquad(x=(x_1,x_2),\ y=(y_1,y_2)\in E_2).$$

Suppose that $\Omega_\lambda(x, y)$ is a family of elementary p. d. kernels of the representation (3. 11), written for our kernel $K(x, y)$. Relative to x and y $\Omega_\lambda(x,y)$ satisfies (6. 6), so that this function is entire relative to each of the variables x_1, x_2, y_1, y_2. It is easy to conclude that for any complex ξ $\Omega_\lambda((\xi, 0), y)$ and $\partial\Omega_\lambda/\partial x_2((\xi, 0), y)$ satisfy (6. 6) relative to y, so that one may first apply the representation (6. 12) to $\Omega_\lambda(x, y)$ relative to x and then analogous representations relative to y. The result is

$$\Omega_\lambda(x,y)=\sum_{\alpha,\beta=0}^{1}(\chi_\xi^{(\alpha)}(x;\lambda)\otimes\chi_\eta^{(\beta)}(y;\lambda),\Omega_\lambda^{(\alpha,\beta)}((\xi,0),(\eta,0)))$$

$$(x,y\in E_n),\tag{6. 13}$$

where we have written

$$\Omega_\lambda^{(0,0)}((\xi,0),(\eta,0))=\Omega_\lambda((\xi,0),(\eta,0)),\ \ \Omega_\lambda^{(1,0)}((\xi,0),(\eta,0))=\frac{\partial\Omega_\lambda}{\partial x_2}((\xi,0),(\eta,0))$$

$$\Omega_\lambda^{(0,1)}((\xi,0),(\eta,0))=\frac{\partial\Omega_\lambda}{\partial y_2}((\xi,0)(\eta,0)),\ \Omega_\lambda^{(1,1)}((\xi,0),(\eta,0))$$

$$=\frac{\partial^2\Omega_\lambda}{\partial x_2\partial y_2}((\xi,0),(\eta,0)).$$

If now we substitute (6. 13) into (3. 11), we obtain a representation of type (3. 20). In order to formulate the result we need to introduce the appropriate integral concept. It is close to the definitions of §3. 3, Chapter VII.

Consider the matrix

$$T(\lambda)=\left\|\begin{matrix} t_{\xi,\eta}^{(0,0)}(\lambda) & t_{\xi,\eta}^{(0,1)}(\lambda) \\ t_{\xi,\eta}^{(1,0)}(\lambda) & t_{\xi,\eta}^{(1,1)}(\lambda)\end{matrix}\right\| \quad (-\infty<\lambda<\infty),$$

whose elements are functions $t_{\xi,\eta}^{(\alpha,\beta)}(\lambda)$, entire in ξ and η and of bounded variation in λ. We shall suppose that $T(\Delta)=T(b)-T(a)$ $(\Delta=[a,b))$ is p. d. in the sense that for any functionals $l_\xi^{(0)}$, $l_\xi^{(1)}$ over Z $\Sigma_{\alpha,\beta=0}^{1}(l_\xi^{(\alpha)}\otimes l_\eta^{(\beta)}, t_{\xi,\eta}^{(\alpha,\beta)}(\Delta))\geq 0$ We agree to call such a $T(\lambda)$ an analytic measure.

Suppose now that the functionals $l_\xi^{(\alpha)}$ are continuous (in the weak sense) in the parameter λ: $l_\xi^{(\alpha)}=l_\xi^{(\alpha)}(\lambda)$ $(\alpha=0,1;\ -\infty<\lambda<\infty)$. Then we may define an integral by the relation

$$\int_{-\infty}^{\infty}\sum_{\alpha,\beta=0}^{1}(l_\xi^{(\alpha)}(\lambda)\otimes l_\eta^{(\beta)}(\lambda), dt_{\xi,\eta}^{(\alpha,\beta)}(\lambda))=\lim\sum_{\nu=1}^{N}\sum_{\alpha,\beta=0}^{1}(l_\xi^{(\alpha)}(\lambda_\nu)$$

$$\otimes\, l_\eta^{(\beta)}(\lambda_\nu), t_{\xi,\eta}^{(\alpha,\beta)}(\Delta_\nu)),$$

where $\Delta_1,\cdots,\Delta_N$ is a decomposition of the $(-\infty,\infty)$ axis into intervals, $\lambda_\nu\in\Delta_\nu$, and the limit is taken over the extension of the decomposition. If the $l_\xi^{(\alpha)}$ are sufficiently small for large $|\lambda|$, then this limit exists and does not depend on the method of decomposition or the choice of the points $\lambda_\nu\in\Delta_\nu$. This concept of integral and the results obtained earlier make it possible to formulate the following theorem.

Theorem 6.2. *Suppose that* $K(x,y)\in C(E_2\times E_2)$ *is a p. d. kernel, and that the functionals* $\chi^{(0)}(x;\lambda)$ *and* $\chi^{(1)}(x;\lambda)$ *over* Z *are defined by relations* (6.11). *For each* $x,y\in E_2$ *the representation*

$$K(x,y)=\int_{-\infty}^{\infty}\sum_{\alpha,\beta=0}^{1}(\chi_\xi^{(\alpha)}(x;\lambda)\otimes\chi_\eta^{(\beta)}(y;\lambda), d\sigma_{\xi,\eta}^{(\alpha,\beta)}(\lambda)) \tag{6.14}$$

will hold, where $\Sigma(\lambda)=\|\sigma_{\xi,\eta}^{(\alpha,\beta)}(\lambda)\|_{\alpha,\beta=0}^{1}$ *is some analytic measure, if and only if* $K(x,y)$ *satisfies, in the sense of the distribution of L. Schwartz, the equation*

$$\Delta_x K=\Delta_y K. \tag{6.15}$$

The sufficiency is already almost proved: after substituting (6.13) into (3.11) we obtain (6.14) if we put

$$\sigma_{\xi,\eta}^{(\alpha,\beta)}(\Delta)=\int_\Delta \Omega_\lambda^{(\alpha,\beta)}((\xi,0),(\eta,0))\,d\varrho(\lambda).$$

The fact that the resulting matrix $\Sigma(\lambda)$ is an analytic measure is verified for example in the same way as the corresponding assertion on page 496. The necessity of condition (6. 15) when (6. 14) is valid is verified directly.

We may verify that $d\Sigma(\lambda)$ is uniquely defined if the closure in H_K of the operator $u \to \Delta u$ $(u \in C_0^\infty(E_2))$ is maximal. It follows from Theorem 3. 10 that *uniqueness will hold when for some* $N > 0$ *we have the estimate*

$$| K(x, y) | \leqslant Ce^{N(|x_1|^2+|x_2|^2+|y_1|^2+|y_2|^2)} (C > 0; x, y \in E_2).$$

It is clear that the construction presented above generalizes to strongly elliptic expressions L of the second order with analytic coefficients, in particular to the multidimensional Laplace expression.

3. **Expressions in partial differences.** For such expressions the problem of Cauchy is solved very nicely (see §4. 1, Chapter VII), and therefore for p. d. kernels *-commuting with them one may obtain representations of type (3. 20). We shall exhibit this on the simplest example of an expression in a halfplane. Thus, suppose that Π is the integer-valued right halfplane, i. e. the collection of points $j = (j_1, j_2)$, where $j_1 = 0, 1, \cdots$ and $j_2 = \cdots, -1, 0, 1, \cdots$). In Π we shall consider the p. d. kernel $K = K_{jk}$ $(j, k \in \Pi)$ (see §5. 3) and an expression L in partial differences analogous to the expression (4. 1) of Chapter VII, but, generally speaking, formally nonselfadjoint:

$$\begin{gathered}(Lu)_{j_1, j_2} = a_{j_1, j_2; (-1, 0)} u_{j_1-1, j_2} + a_{j_1, j_2; (+1, 0)} u_{j_1+1, j_2} \\ + a_{j_1, j_2; (0, -1)} u_{j_1, j_2-1} + a_{j_1, j_2; (0, +1)} u_{j_1, j_2+1} + a_{j_1, j_2; (0, 0)} u_{j_1, j_2} \\ ((j_1, j_2) = j \in \Pi).\end{gathered} \tag{6. 16}$$

Throughout what follows we shall suppose that u satisfies a zero boundary condition on the line $j_1 = -1$, i. e. in calculating $(Lu)_{0, j_2}$ we put $u_{-1, j_2} = 0$ $(j_2 = \cdots, -1, 0, 1, \cdots)$. The coefficients of (6. 16) are arbitrary complex numbers, about which we suppose only that $a_{j_1, j_2; (+1, 0)} \neq 0$ $((j_1, j_2) \in \Pi)$.

This last condition makes it possible to find the solution of the equation $(Lu)_j = zu_j$ $(j \in \Pi)$ by recurrence, if u_j is given on two successive vertical axes, for example $j_1 = -1$ and $j_1 = 0$. In particular, as on page 589 we may construct a solution $P_{\alpha; (j_1, j_2)}(z)$ of this equation satisfying the initial conditions $P_{\alpha; (-1, j_2)}(z) = 0$, $P_{\alpha; (0, j_2)}(z) = \delta_{\alpha j_2}$ $(\alpha, j_2 = \cdots, -1, 0, 1, \cdots)$. The form of these solutions will be the same as there. Any solution of the equation $(Lu)_j = zu_j$ $(j \in \Pi)$ may be expressed in terms of $P_{\alpha;(j_1,j_2)}(z)$ by means of the formula

$$u_{j_1, j_2} = \sum_{\alpha=-\infty}^{\infty} u_{0,\alpha} P_{\alpha;(j_1,j_2)}(z) \qquad ((j_1, j_2) \in \Pi). \tag{6.17}$$

Now we suppose that the kernel K_{jk} *-commutes with L:

$$(L_j K)_{jk} = (\overline{L}_k K)_{jk} \qquad (j, k \in \Pi). \tag{6.18}$$

Repeating the discussion of §5.1, we find that

$$K_{jk} = \int_{-\infty}^{\infty} \Omega_{\lambda;\, jk}\, d\varrho(\lambda) \qquad (j, k \in \Pi), \tag{6.19}$$

where the family of elementary p.d. kernels Ω_λ satisfies relations of the type (5.7). Taking into account formula (6.17), as in §4.1 of Chapter VII we express $\Omega_{\lambda;\, jk}\, d\rho(\lambda)$ in terms of $P_{\alpha;(j_1,j_2)}(z)$. As a result (6.19) goes into

$$K_{jk} = \sum_{\alpha,\beta=-\infty}^{\infty} \int_{-\infty}^{\infty} P_{\alpha;(j_1,j_2)}(\lambda)\, \overline{P_{\beta;(k_1,k_2)}(\lambda)}\, d\sigma_{\alpha\beta}(\lambda) \quad (j, k \in \Pi), \tag{6.20}$$

where $\|d\sigma_{\alpha\beta}(\lambda)\|_{-\infty}^{\infty}$ is a certain nonnegative operator measure (its values are operators in $l_2(-\infty, \infty)$), written in matrix form. It is clear that the converse also holds: every kernel of the form (6.20) will be p.d. and will satisfy equation (6.18).

In the case of kernels on the entire (j_1, j_2) plane $(j_1, j_2 = \cdots, -1, 0, 1, \cdots)$, the preceding schema is preserved. We need only to make use of the footnote to Theorem 4.1, Chapter VII. Now the role of the matrix $\|d\sigma_{\alpha\beta}(\lambda)\|_{-\infty}^{\infty}$ will be played by the matrix

$$\left\| \begin{matrix} d\sigma_{-1,-1;\,\alpha\beta}(\lambda) & d\sigma_{-1,0;\,\alpha\beta}(\lambda) \\ d\sigma_{0,-1;\,\alpha\beta}(\lambda) & d\sigma_{0,0;\,\alpha\beta}(\lambda) \end{matrix} \right\|_{\alpha,\beta=-\infty}^{\infty}$$

Consider a concrete example of the representation (6.20). Suppose that the p.d. kernel $K_{jk} = K_{j_1, j_2;\, k_1, k_2}$ $(j_1, j_2 = 0, 1, \cdots;\ k_1, k_2 = \cdots, -1, 0, 1, \cdots)$ satisfies the relation

$$\begin{gathered} K_{j_1-1, j_2;\, k_1, k_2} + K_{j_1+1, j_2;\, k_1, k_2} + K_{j_1, j_2-1;\, k_1, k_2} + K_{j_1, j_2+1;\, k_1, k_2} \\ = K_{j_1, j_2;\, k_1-1, k_2} + K_{j_1, j_2;\, k_1+1, k_2} + K_{j_1, j_2;\, k_1, k_2-1} + K_{j_1, j_2;\, k_1, k_2+1} \\ (j_1, j_2 = 0, 1, \ldots;\ k_1, k_2 = \ldots, -1, 0, 1, \ldots) \end{gathered} \tag{6.21}$$

(if one of the indices j_1, j_2, k_1, k_2 takes the value -1, we suppose that $K_{j_1, j_2; k_1, k_2} = 0$). Equation (6. 2) shows that K *-commutes with the expression $(Lu)_{j_1, j_2} = (1/2)u_{j_1-1, j_2} + (1/2)u_{j_1+1, j_2} + (1/2)u_{j_1, j_2-1} + (1/2)u_{j_1, j_2+1}$, considered in Π. The solutions are calculated according to formula (4. 38) of Chapter VII. If one substitutes these expressions in (6. 20), then one obtains the desired representation for the kernel K_{jk}.

NOTES ON THE LITERATURE

In the following remarks and references to the literature we shall consider only questions that are directly related to the exposition given in the book; for other questions we refer the reader to the various books in existence that give general surveys. In cases where there is no fear of misunderstanding, we shall refer to later and more complete works of the various authors, rather than to their preliminary publications.

Introduction

In order to read the present book it is necessary to be acquainted with the basic facts of the general theory of measure and integration as they are to be found, for example, in the book of Halmos [1]; for formula (3) see Saks [1], Chapter 4, §15. Also presupposed is a knowledge of the theory of operators in Hilbert space such as is to be found in Ahiezer and Glazman [1] or in Chapter 4 of Naĭmark [2]; see also the corresponding sections of Riesz and Sz.-Nagy [1] and Dunford and Schwartz [1,2]. For the facts about linear normed spaces see for example Kantorovič and Akilov [1], and for the elementary concepts of the theory of linear topological spaces see Chapter 11 of that book or Gel'fand and Šilov [2].

The theory of Sobolev spaces (subsections 5–6, 9–11) is given in Sobolev [3]; see also Kantorovič and Akilov [1], Chapters 9–10. For information about generalized functions see the first chapters of Gel'fand and Šilov [1]. The Ehrling-Nirenberg inequality is proved in the articles by Ehrling [1] and Nirenberg [1]; in its most general form it was obtained by V. P. Il'in [1], and by V. P. Gluško and S. G. Kreĭn [1,2].

Chapter I

Spaces with negative norms were introduced and studied by Leray [1] and in particular Lax [2] (however, these authors consider only positive spaces of the Sobolev type). Related problems were considered also in 1937 by M. G. Kreĭn (see [7]). Spaces with negative norms were originally applied to the study of boundary value problems for partial differential equations, but it later became apparent that these spaces could also be used in other problems, in spectral theory, in the theory of positive definite kernels, etc. We remark that this chapter is a repetition, almost without change, of an article of the author [16].

The introduction of positive and negative spaces, presented in §1, could be carried out by the general scheme of Lax. However, it has been more convenient to proceed by a different scheme, contained in the work of the author [7]. Another method of introducing essentially positive and negative norms is due to Kac [1,2]; the connection with this point of view is presented in §3.6. Theorem 1.1 is due to the author; Theorem 1.2 was obtained independently by M. G. Kreĭn [7] and Lax [1].

The abstract theory of generalized kernels, presented in §2, is similar to the theory of generalized kernels of L. Schwartz [2] and is constructed according to the scheme in the author's note [15]. Theorem 2.2 is a simple and natural variation of a theorem of Schwartz on kernels; for other results in this direction see Gel'fand and Vilenkin [1], Chapter 1, §3; see also Ehrenpreis [1]. The earliest theorem of the type of 2.2 was published by the author [3,6] in connection with expansions in generalized eigenfunctions; it is presented in §3 (Theorem 3.4). The concept of a quasi-nuclear inclusion, essentially, appears in G. I. Kac [1], and was inspired by a situation which occurs with respect to expansions in generalized eigenfunctions in Gel'fand and Kostjučenko [1] on the one hand, and the author [3] on the other. Here an essential role is played by the definition of nuclear in Grothendieck [1] and a work of Raĭkov [1].

In §3.1 we analyzed in detail the case of Lax, in which a Sobolev space in a bounded region is taken as the positive space. We point out results of other authors which are contained in this subsection: a theorem of the type 3.1 was published by L. and K. Maurin [1]: Theorem 3.6 is due to Hörmander [3]; and the construction in subsection 6, as already mentioned, is due to Kac. Further examples of positive and negative spaces are given in the following works. For negative spaces of the type $W_p^l(G)$ $(p \neq 2)$, see for example Lions and Magenes [1,2] or Schechter [10]. In connection with the results in §3 and the theory of Sobolev spaces see also the book of Hörmander [4] and the survey by Volevič and Panejah [1].

The purpose of §4 is to construct equipment for a Hilbert space by means of linear topological spaces. A detailed account of the corresponding results can be found in Gel'fand and Vilenkin [1], Chapter I (the term "equipment" is due to these authors).

Chapter II

In connection with the constructions of §1 see Petrovskiĭ [1], Chapter I.

The results of §2.2 (the concept of a solvable extension and Theorem 2.1 about its existence), and also of §2.4, are due to Višik [2]; see also Hörmander [1]. The facts mentioned in §2.3 and in §§3.1–3.4 (almost correct boundary conditions, conditional solvability, the existence of generalized solutions) were published by the author [12], [7], [9]. They appeared as a result of the above-mentioned works of Višik and Hörmander, and the works of Višik and Sobolev [1], Lax [2], Friedrichs [2], and Morawetz [1]. Similar results were obtained almost simultaneously by Schechter [6], [4], also [7]; similar facts are contained in the works of Lions [2] and Browder [9], and also in the earliest works of a similar nature due to Fichera [1], [2]. The approach used in §2.5 in the study of maximal operators is due to Hörmander [2].

The approach in §§3.6–3.8 leading to variational methods in the study of boundary value problems is developed by Višik [1] (see also Višik and Ladyženskaja [1]), and also by Gårding [1], Browder [2], Lax and Milgram [1], and Lions [1]. The works of Mosolov [1], [2] and Nikol'skiĭ [2] are connected with an application of the scheme of §3.8 to specific nonelliptic equations.

We note also that the surveys of Višik, Myškis, and Oleĭnik [1], Gårding [6], Višik and Šilov [1], and Dezin [1] are connected with problems in this and the following two chapters.

Chapter III

The concept of strong ellipticity is due to Višik, who proved part (the inequality (1.4)) of Theorem 1.1 (see Višik [1]). The remaining assertions of this theorem, which is basic for §§1–2, were proved by Gårding [1] and Browder [2]. The presentation of §2 follows Višik and Ladyženskaja [1].

Theorems 3.1 and 3.3, which are basic for the later energy inequality, were first proved for the Laplacian and null boundary conditions for $s = 0$ by Bernšteĭn [1,2]. For strongly elliptic expressions of the second order in the case of null boundary conditions a similar inequality was established by Ladyženskaja [1,2,3], Mihlin [1], and Cacciopoli [1]; for a bibliography on problems concerning expressions of the second order, see also Miranda [1]. This result was extended to arbitrary strongly elliptic systems (with null boundary conditions) by Guseva [1], and somewhat later a similar result was obtained by Browder [4]. For general boundary conditions, even nonhomogeneous conditions and general elliptic expressions, a similar inequality was proved by Slobodeckiĭ [1,3], Browder [8,10,11], Agmon, Douglis, and Nirenberg [1], and Schechter [2]; in some of these articles the estimate is proved not only with the L_2-norm, but also with L_p-norms and Schauder norms. We remark that the first estimate in L_p-norms in simpler cases was given by Košelev [1].

The localization idea for the proofs of Theorems 3.1 and 3.3 is due to Schauder [2] and was adopted by many of the above-mentioned authors. We carry out in the case $s = 0$ two proofs of Lemma 3.1, which is basic for the proof of Theorem 3.1. The first of these is based on integration by parts, developing a device of S. N. Bernšteĭn (see Ladyženskaja [1,2,3]), and is suitable for simple problems in the case of strongly elliptic expressions of second order (see also Lemma 3.7). The second uses techniques involving Fourier transforms and is suitable for the L_2-norm in the case of general elliptic expressions and general (even nonhomogeneous) boundary conditions (see the comments on §6 below); it is due to Schechter [1,2]. An important role is played in this proof by Lemma 3.3 of Aronszajn [2]. A general method, developed in the above-mentioned work of Agmon, Douglis, and Nirenberg and suitable for L_p-norms and Schauder norms, is not presented. It is mentioned in §3.3 and uses a theorem of Zygmund and Calderón on singular integral operators. The device which permits passage from the case $s=0$ to the case $s > 0$ (step 7) in the proof of Theorem 3.1 is due to Nirenberg [1] and Browder [4].

The method of extension by a parameter (§§3.4 and 3.5) has been long used in the theory of differential equations (Bernšteĭn [1], Schauder [1]). The account here is reproduced from Ladyženskaja [3].

Theorem 3.6 on homeomorphisms, which is important for problems concerning improved smoothness, in the case of the first pair of spaces follows from Theorem 3.1 and the method of extension by a parameter; in the case of the fourth pair it follows from the previous case by means of the well-known method of passage to adjoint operators (see Višik and Sobolev [1], Berezanskiĭ [9], or Schechter [7]). The intermediate cases (second and third pairs) are more complex. With the null conditions now under consideration, this part of the theorem was proved by Lions and Magenes [1]. We produce another proof, due to Ja. A. Roĭtberg and the author, which is partially based on an immediate conclusion from the energy inequality in negative norms (Theorem 3.2).

The existence proof for elliptic equations of classical fundamental solutions, the properties of which are mentioned in §4.1, is given by Lopatinskiĭ [1,2]; see also John [2]. The existence of fundamental solutions for minimal requirements of smoothness on coefficients (integral condition of Hölder) was recently proved by Matiĭčuk [1,2]. For the requirement of once continuous coefficients, fundamental solutions with the usual degree of singularity need not exist; see Gilbarg and Serrin [1], A. M. Il'in [1]. Concerning a connection, which is useful for a series of problems, between fundamental solutions of elliptic and parabolic equations, see Èĭdel'man [1]. Fundamental solutions over all of G were considered by Ljubič [3]. The first result concerning regularity inside a region of a generalized solution of an elliptic equation is due to Sobolev [1]; concerning other works in this direction for equations of the second order, see Miranda [1]. General assertions concerning interior regularity have been obtained by different methods by a series of mathematicians: Schwartz [1], Friedrichs [1], Browder [2], K. Maurin [1] and others. Theorems 4.1 and 4.3 are related to this family of results and are proved by a well-known method of application of fundamental solutions. Theorems 4.2 and 4.4 on smoothness of generalized kernels (in a somewhat more particular form) are due to Roĭtberg [1]. Theorem 4.6 on local improved smoothness of generalized solutions up to the boundary of the region (like the preceding Theorem 4.5) was proved by the author, S. G. Kreĭn, and Ja. A. Roĭtberg [1]. In earlier works dealing with smoothness up to the boundary, either smoothness was improved for local solutions appearing as ordinary functions (Nirenberg [1], Browder [4], Schechter [9]), or incomplete smoothness was obtained for generalized solutions considered over all of the region (Schechter [7], Peetre [1]). The second part of Theorem 4.8 (the other description of the maximal operator) was first proved by Birman [1,2]; the indicated simple proof is based on a device of Hörmander (Lemma 2.2, Chapter II).

We proceed to §5. Theorem 5.1, under somewhat more restrictive conditions, was established by the author [6]; the considerations in subsection 7 (products of resolvents) are due to the author [18]. Theorem 5.4 was proved by Browder [1,11]. The remaining results of this subsection are due to Ja. A. Roĭtberg and the author in their paper [1]. We remark that in the case of a Schrödinger equation in three-dimensional space and classical boundary conditions, the behavior of the kernel of the resolvent operator near the boundary of the region can be discovered from the work of Povzner [3]. In the general case, for expressions of high order, the realization of boundary conditions in a generalized sense for the resolvent kernel was proved by Gårding. In the case of equations of second order, considered in a bounded region with null boundary conditions, the behavior of the resolvent kernel up to the boundary of the region was studied by classical methods by V. A. Il'in and I. A. Šišmarev [1].

We consider §6. The first study of boundary value problems for general elliptic systems and general boundary conditions, defined by differential expressions, was carried out by Lopatinskiĭ [3]. In this work conditions were found for a similar problem to reduce to a regular integral equation (in simpler cases similar conditions were obtained by Šapiro [1]); the conditions were formulated in a form mentioned in §3.3. In the case of one equation it is equivalent to the covering condition stated in §6.1. In the mentioned work of Lopatinskiĭ, the concept of regular ellipticity is also introduced, and Lemma 3.2 is proved.

Much of the literature is devoted to boundary norms; see Hörmander and Lions [1], Slobodeckiĭ [2,3], Lions and Magenes [1,2], Nikol'skiĭ [1], and Volevič and Panejah [1]. However, to reconstruct the desired proofs in our cases, it is sufficient to have a knowledge of corresponding portions of the articles of Schechter [2,3] and Slobodeckiĭ [2].

Theorem 6.1 was proved by Slobodeckiĭ [1,3], Agmon, Douglis, and Nirenberg [1], Schechter [2], and Browder [10]. As was already mentioned, the proof of sufficiency of this theorem is similar to the presentation of the proof of Theorem 3.1; although Lemma 6.1 is formulated and proved as a generalization of Lemma 3.1, it is technically more complex. Its proof (as well as the proof of Lemma 3.1) is contained in Schechter [2]. The proof of necessity in Theorem 6.1 is already contained in this work (see also Agmon, Douglis and Nirenberg [1]).

The series of arguments in subsections 2, 4, 6 and 7 are well known; see for example Agmon, Douglis, Nirenberg [1], Schechter [3,4,5], Browder [8], or Peetre [1].

Lemma 6.4 is due to Browder; its proof in the case of null boundary conditions is contained in his article [8]; in the general case see also Šeftel' [2]. In connection with problems studied in subsection 3 see also Agranovič, Volevič and Dynin [1] (however, we emphasize that for the case of normal boundary conditions considered later Lemma 6.4 is not necessary, since finite dimensionality now follows from Lemma 6.2). Theorem 6.4 and its proof are due to Schechter [3]. The concept of a normal system of boundary conditions and the basic results of subsection 5 are due to Aronszajn and Milgram [1] and to Schechter [3].

The basic results in subsection 8 are due to Roĭtberg [3]. Those in subsection 10 are due to S. G. Kreĭn, Roĭtberg, and the author in their paper [1]. The spaces in the theorems on homeomorphisms, established in subsection 8 and 10, were constructed so that they could be applied to the problem of improved smoothness of generalized solutions; this is similar to what was done in the case of null boundary conditions in §4.6. Such an application of the results in subsection 8 is given in subsections 11–12; it is due to Roĭtberg [3]. The results in subsection 10 are less suitable in this respect, and the corresponding application, which is also due to Roĭtberg [2], is not presented. Homeomorphisms for other spaces (and with the use of L_p-norms) were established almost simultaneously and independently in the above-mentioned works of Lions and Magenes [1], and Schechter [10–12] (precisely, in these works Schechter proved a one-sided estimate of the type (6.78)). In the last work Schechter also proved theorems on local improved smoothness up to the boundary (even in the scheme of the L_p-theory) of the type presented in §§4 and 6. The elementary interpolation theorem 6.10, which was used to prove the theorems on homeomorphisms, was proved independently by Lions [3] and S. G. Kreĭn [1,2]. We remark that the survey of Magenes [1], dealing with further interpolation theorems and their applications to partial differential equations and the recent book of Hörmander [4] contain theorems on improved smoothness similar to those presented in §§4.6, 6.11 and 6.12. Concerning extensions of functions in the class $W_p^s(G)$ outside of G with preservation of the class and an inequality of the type (6.90), see Babič [1] or Slobodeckiĭ [2].

We comment on other works dealing with ideas of this chapter. Schechter [8] and independently, but later, Roĭtberg and Šeftel' [1,2,3] extended the L_2-theory for the solvability of boundary value problems of the type studied in §§3.1–3.6 and subsections 1–2 and 4–7 of §6 to elliptic equations with discontinuous coefficients, i.e. to diffraction type problems (the last two authors also extended the method of §§1–2). Then Šeftel' [1,2] developed an L_p-theory of solvability for such problems, and the remaining results in §§3–6 were carried over to these equations by Roĭtberg [4].

A series of basic results in Chapter III carry over to systems of elliptic equations with ordinary coefficients and with coefficients appearing as singular integral operators (Agranovič, Volevič and Dynin [1]). Moreover, Višik and Èskin [1] develop a similar theory for more general operators, containing a broad class of operators, and Agmon, Douglis, and Nirenberg [2] and Solonnikov [1] carry over the theory to more general systems ("systems elliptic in the sense of Douglis-Nirenberg"; a series of important problems reduce to such systems). We note some useful generalizations of the basic energy inequality in Theorem 3.1. In the case of strongly elliptic expressions L, M of the second order, it is possible to give a lower estimate not for $\|Lu\|_0^2 = (Lu, Lu)_0$, but $\operatorname{Re}(Lu, Mu)_0$; this is obtained by the method of proof using integration by parts (Sobolevskiĭ [1], Ladyženskaja [4]). Finally, the basic energy inequality can be proved in an unbounded region in spaces with weights (Browder [11], or Prokopenko [1]).

In conclusion we remark that a series of divisions in the theory of elliptic equations was not indicated above (equations of second order, L_p-theory, computation of index).

Chapter IV

We will not give an extensive list of literature relating to "nonclassical" boundary value problems but, aside from the works directly touching upon the presentation, will note only the works of a few authors who obtained the first results in this direction: Hadamard [1], Huber [1], Mangeron [1], Bourgin and Duffin [1], and John [1].

The results of §1 are due to Hörmander [1]. An exception is the more direct proof of Lemma 1.1, due to L. P. Nižnik and the author; a similar approach is suggested by Trèves [1]. The development of this method of proof of Lemma 1.1 is used in the constructions in §§2–3.

§2 contains essentially the work of the author [14]. The problem of Dirichlet type for the equation of the vibrating string is considered by a series of mathematicians: besides the above-mentioned works of Hadamard, Huber, Bourgin and Duffin, and John see Sobolev [4], Aleksandrjan [1], [2], Vahanija [1], Denčev [1], and Virabjan [1]. In contrast to these works we do not consider smooth solutions, but solutions in L_2. Therefore it is possible to construct examples of regions for which generalized solvability of the problem of Dirichlet type is stable with respect to small variations of the boundary. The arguments at the end of subsection 4 and in subsection 5 are of the type employed by Aleksandrjan [2].

We turn to §3. Functional methods of proof of the existence of weak solutions of boundary value problems were applied to equations of mixed type for the first time by Morawetz [1], who considered systems of the first order, equivalent to the Čaplygin equation; Friedrichs [2] studied very general systems. Morawetz' technique of obtaining energy inequalities is applied in the case of other equations and boundary conditions by Frankl′[1]; see also subsection 5 and the work of Lin′ Czjan′-bin [1] in connection with this. The results of subsections 1–4 are due to the author [13], [19]; they represent the other way of obtaining energy inequalities, giving estimates in different norms and for more general equations than the Čaplygin equation. As was already mentioned, the author arrived at this method in connection with the development of the proof of Lemma 1.1; on the other hand, it may be considered similar to the technique of Morawetz and as a development of the *abc*-method of Friedrichs of the proof of the uniqueness theorem for Čaplygin equations. The results of subsections 1–4 are closely connected with the paper of Protter [1] concerning similar uniqueness theorems. Concerning smoothness of weak solutions, obtained by means of Morawetz inequalities, see Lax and Phillips [1]. A detailed presentation of other approaches to equations of mixed type and a bibliography can be found in the books of Bers [1] and Bicadze [1].

In connection with the results of §§2–3 and Chapter II, we note their close relation to the ideas and techniques of the work of Fichera [3] concerning existence of weak solutions of boundary value problems for elliptic-parabolic equations of the second order. Sufficient smoothness of these solutions was recently established by Oleĭnik [1].

Chapter V

Historically, the path leading to the construction of expansions is generalized eigenfunctions and vectors was considerably more tortuous than the one given in this chapter. The construction of expansions in eigenfunctions in the case of a continuous spectrum led to significant difficulties, which were overcome in a long series of publications devoted, in particular, to the spectral theory of singular differential operators. Among all the publications in this field that have had an influence on the construction of the theory of this chapter, we shall mention the following.

M. G. Kreĭn [6, 8, 13] constructed the method of guiding functionals and used it to prove the theorem of expansion in eigenfunctions for ordinary selfadjoint differential operators of arbitrary order, and he also applied the theory to the integral representation of a positive definite kernel. Another proof of the expansion theorem is due to Kodaira [1]. The first article devoted to the spectral theory of a selfadjoint elliptic operator in an unbounded domain was the article of Carleman [1]. The theory of expansions in eigenfunctions of the Schroedinger operator in an unbounded domain was built up by Povzner [3,4], whose work was the starting point for a number of investigations in this field. For general selfadjoint elliptic operators similar results were obtained by Gårding [2,3] and Browder [1]. It was in the work of Mautner [1] that the idea was first clearly expressed of differentiating a resolution of the identity, and in the work of Hörmander [1] occur the first expansions in eigenfunctions of nonelliptic (namely hypoelliptic) operators. In the whole range of questions connected with the construction of the spectral theory, an important role was played by the books of Titchmarsh [1,2] and Levitan [1], which in particular aroused interest in the classical work of H. Weyl (1910) in this direction.

On the other hand, the construction of a theory of expansions in generalized eigenfunctions reactivated certain outstanding questions. Among them is the problem of the proof of the existence of eigenfunctions for a dynamic system and the problem of Sobolev on the investigation of eigenfunctions of the form $A\phi = \lambda B\phi$, where A and B are differential operators. It was in his study of the latter problem that Aleksandrjan [1,2] first formulated, as late as 1949, the particular concept of a generalized eigenfunction.

In 1955 appeared the fundamental work of Gel'fand and Kostjučenko [1] (see also Gel'fand and Šilov [3]), in which it was proved that every selfadjoint operator A, acting on a separable functional Hilbert space H, has a complete system of generalized eigenfunctions, which are functionals on a certain linear topological space of basic functions Φ. The authors examined special cases of Φ, but it was clear from their proof that it could be extended to an arbitrary countably-normed $\Phi = \bigcap_{n=1}^{\infty} \Phi_n$ which is "nuclear in the sense of Gel'fand": i.e. every weakly absolutely convergent sequence of functionals from Φ' is absolutely convergent in the norm of some Φ'_n.

In 1956 appeared the work of the author [3] (see also [6]), in which it was proved that for Φ we may take not a linear topological space but a certain Hilbert space. Then the generalized eigenfunctions become functionals of finite rank, depending only on the character of H. In this work $H = L_2(E_n)$, but the method of proof, as was stated, extends to a number of other functional spaces.

In 1956 Browder [3], on the basis of the above-mentioned article of Gel'fand and Kostjučenko, examined in detail the question of expansion in generalized eigenfunctions of the form $A\phi = \lambda B\phi$. In a review of an article of the author [3] Gårding [4] noted another refined approach to the basic result of the article, and this approach was later developed in abstract form by K. Maurin [2,3,4] for very general cases. He makes no use of a differentiation E but proceeds on the basis of von Neumann's theorem on the decomposition of a Hilbert space into a direct integral for a given A. It was proved by Raĭkov [1] that spaces which are nuclear in the sense of Grothendieck are also nuclear in the sense of Gel'fand, which provided a generalization of the theorem of Gel'fand and Kostjučenko to abstract Hilbert spaces H with imbedded Φ nuclear in the usual sense.

Also, as has already been emphasized, it became important to choose Φ as close as possible to H. On the question whether the clearance between Φ and H could not be very large, the results of the author on the possibility of choosing Hilbert spaces for Φ had something to say but they did not give the answer in an abstract and definitive form. Here the final role was played by the work of Kac [1,2,3] in which it was emphasized that the essential feature is not the intrinsic structure of Φ but the way in which it is imbedded in H. Namely, Kac showed that if $\Phi = H_+$ is a Hilbert space, then the quasinuclearity of the imbedding $H_+ \to H$ is necessary and sufficient in order that for an arbitrary selfadjoint operator A acting on H there should exist a complete system of generalized eigenvectors in H. Another approach to these results, which led to a development of the methods in his articles [3,6], was proposed by the author [10].

A further modification of these results and proofs is contained in the book of Gel'fand and Vilenkin [1] and in the works of Maurin [5] and Foiaş [1,2,3]. In particular, Foiaş investigated in detail the case when Φ is a Banach space. See also Nelson [1] and Gerlach [1]. The generalization of the theory to certain classes of nonselfadjoint operators is to be found in the work of Browder [6,7] and Ljance [1]. See also Daleckiĭ [1], where applications are given to continual integrals.

After this short survey we now proceed to give some information about facts mentioned in the present book. The construction in §§1–2 of expansions in generalized eigenvectors follows an article of the author [10] and the general ideas in his article [16]. Theorem 1.1 is also due to the author [10], and Theorem 1.2 to Dinculeanu [1]. Theorem 1.5 turns out to be due to Kac [1,3], although a shorter and simpler proof of it is implicit in the article of Foiaş [2]. In §4.2 a discussion is given of the above-mentioned method of proof due to Gårding and Maurin for the theorem on expansion. A useful remark concerning the fact that $\mathrm{Tr}\,(P(\lambda)) = 1$, and some refinements of this fact, are due to Oročko.

The results of §3 are due essentially to the author [3,6]. The spectral theory of Carleman operators was developed by Mautner [1] and Gårding [3], and in a more special case by Povzner [3]. The detailed study presented in §4 for the behavior of the spectral kernel $\Phi(x, y; \lambda)$ of such operators is due to the author [3,6,10]. The remark, important for §4, in subsection 1, is due to Kac [3] and the author [10], and Lemma 4.2 is also due to him. Theorems 5.1 and 5.2 are due to the author [3,6] and Theorems 5.3 and 5.4 to Oročko and the author in their article [1]. Theorem 5.5 is due to Kac, Kostjučenko and the author (the result was published in Berezanskiĭ [10]) and the Lemma 5.2 is due to M. G. Kreĭn [10].

Chapter VI

The theorems in subsections 1–3 of §1 seem to have been discovered independently by several mathematicians interested in spectral theory and boundary problems. Theorem 1.4 is essentially due to Carleman [1]. Theorems 1.5 and 1.6 are due to Nižnik [1,3], and Lemma 1.3 to Kato [1]. Concerning the questions discussed in §1.6, see Browder [11], Nižnik [3], Povzner [3], Ikebe [1], Kato [2] and Faddeev [4]. The first to point out the relationship between the selfadjointness of the Schroedinger operator and the uniqueness of the Cauchy boundary problem for the corresponding wave equation, and also the first to make use of this relationship for the proof of selfadjointness, was Povzner [3], and a similar method involving parabolic equations was later applied by Kostjučenko [1]. Theorem 1.7 is an abstract formulation of such a device. Theorem 1.8 for the Schroedinger expression is due to Povzner [3]. For the above question of the uniqueness of the solution of the Cauchy problem let us mention the publications of Ljubič [1,2], Prokopenko [2], and Agmon and Nirenberg [1]. For the selfadjointness of elliptic operators in a domain with corners see Birman and Skvorcov [1]. For the remarks at the end of subsection 7 see Levitan [5] on the selfadjointness of the Schroedinger operator.

Let us go on to §2. The spectral theory in a domain (subsection 1) for the Schroedinger operator was constructed by Povzner [3], and for the general case by Gårding [2] and Browder [1]; the refinements connected with the study of the growth of the spectral kernel $\Phi(x, y; \lambda)$ close to the boundary of the domain, with its expansion in a series and so forth, are due to the author [6,10,18], and Lemma 2.3 is due to M. G. Kreĭn [10]. The construction of the spectral theory up to and including the boundary (subsections 2–4) was constructed by the author [18]; the representation (2.21) essential for this construction is implied in a closely related transformation of Gårding [2], used by him for the construction of the theory in the interior of the domain. Let us note that some of the facts for the spectral theory, up to and including the boundary, for the Schroedinger equation are to be found in the work of Povzner [3]. For subsection 5 see the author's article [6]. The results of subsection 9 on hyperbolic equations are due to the author [1,8]; they were obtained by making use of the ideas of S. L. Sobolev [2] and the technique of M. Riesz [1]. The results of subsection 10, except for the assertion at the end, are due to the author; the latter assertion is due to G. I. Kac, A. G. Kostjučenko and the author (see Berezanskiĭ [10]). The estimate for the eigenfunctions of the type of Theorem 2.11, for the case $n = 1$ with semibounded $c(x)$, was obtained earlier by a different and more analytical method by Šnol' [2,3], for which it is not necessary to assume that $c(x)$ is uniformly continuous (see also Glazman [1]). The example discussed on p. 440 is due to Maslov [1]; concerning the results in subsection 10 see also the work of Kostjučenko [2] on estimation of the resolvent kernel of an elliptic operator. Recently Oročko [1] developed the method of subsection 10 and obtained estimates (2.96) for arbitrary n without any restrictions on the potential $c(x)$, except that it must be sufficiently smooth; here it is possible to eliminate ω from the estimates.

The results of subsections 1–3 of §3, are due to the author and were published in part in [6]; they are also the work of Nižnik [4]; for closely related facts see also Gel'fand and Šilov [1], Foiaş [4]. The construction of expansions in eigenfunctions of hypoelliptic operators was given by Hörmander [1], including the foundations of a general theory of expansions in eigenfunctions; the discussion given in subsection 4 for these results of Hörmander is presented from a different point of view. Let us note that essential progress has recently been made in the study of the asymptotic properties of the spectral function of a hypoelliptic operator; see Nilsson [1] and Gorčakov [1,2].

The construction of the theory of separation of variables (§4) basically follows the work of the author [6]. Among earlier publications in this direction let us note the articles of Cordes [1,2] and the "analytic" treatment of the question in the book of Titchmarsh [2]. §2 draws heavily on the work of L. and K. Maurin [2]. To these authors is due the essential formula (4.23).

The bibliography for §5 was given in the text.

Let us make a few supplementary remarks. For a study of the spectrum of differential operators see Glazman [1] and the survey by Glazman and Birman [1]. For the asymptotic properties (with respect to λ) of the spectral function, the eigenfunctions and so forth see the articles of Levitan [3,4] and Bergendal's dissertation [1]. A detailed study of the convergence of the expansions was carried out by V. A. Il'in [1]. Let us also refer here to the work of M. G. Kreĭn [12,16], which establishes profound analogies between the spectral theory for a Sturm-Liouville equation on the semiaxis (or more generally of the equation of the vibrating string), and the spectral theory for Jacobian matrices, and the classical problem of moments, and to the work of Marčenko [1] devoted to the construction of transform operators for the Sturm-Liouville equation and the study with its help of the harmonic analysis of expansions in eigenfunctions and the inverse problem.

Here we shall not touch upon the inverse problem of spectral analysis for the Sturm-Liouville equation on the semiaxis and the equation of the vibrating string, a problem which was solved in the well-known articles of Marčenko, Kreĭn, Gel'fand and Levitan. For part of the literature on this question see the survey of Faddeev [3] and the book of Agranovič and Marčenko [1]. Let us briefly refer to the inverse problem of spectral analysis for the simplest elliptic equation, namely the Schroedinger equation $\Delta u + c(x)u = \lambda u$ considered in a domain $G \subseteq E_n$ $(n = 2, 3)$ with a sufficiently smooth boundary Γ. The author [1,8] has shown that the coefficient $c(x)$ can be uniquely recovered from the spectral function $\Xi(x, y; \lambda)$ given on $(x, y; \lambda) \in I \times I \times (-\infty, \infty)$ where I is a (arbitrarily small) plane part of the boundary Γ. The analogous uniqueness theorem is also valid in the case $G = E_n$. The proofs of these statements depend essentially on certain results in subsections 9 and 10 of §2. The difference analogue for such a formulation of the problem is discussed in §4.5 of Chapter 7. Furthermore, the author has pointed out certain connections between this spectral statement of the inverse problem and a number of formulations with scattering data [2,8]. Let us note that these works essentially establish the energy dispersion relations for the Schroedinger equation with finite potential $c(x)$; more precisely, it has been shown that such relations, after certain estimates have been made, can be deduced from the work of Povzner [3]; for rapidly decreasing potentials see also Faddeev [2]. The same articles of the author also establish the asymptotic behavior of the amplitude of the scattering of plane waves, a result which enables us to justify the method of Šnol' [1] for the solution of the inverse problem with scattering data, and subsequently a similar result was obtained independently by Faddeev [1] for rapidly decreasing potentials. For the inverse problem for scattering data, let us also refer to Petrina [1], Nižnik [2], Mal'čenko [1], Lax and Phillips [2]. For the scattering problem for difference equations see Lifšic [1], Tarnopol'skiĭ [3], Èskin [1].

In conclusion let us note that the method of constructing expansions (and also the solution of the inverse problem) for ordinary differential equations with operator coefficients was given by Rofe-Beketov [1,2]. A number of eigenvalue problems for such equations in a finite interval have been studied in detail by S. G. Kreĭn and G. I. Laptev [1]. A characterization of all spectral measures was recently obtained by M. L. Gorbačuk.

Chapter VII

The classical theory of Jacobian matrices is presented in §1. The nature of the presentation is influenced by Ahiezer [1] and in particular by M. G. Kreĭn and M. A. Krasnosel'skiĭ [1]: subsections 4 and 6–8 consist basically of the difference interpretation of appropriate portions of the latter article. Theorem 1.3 is due to Carleman, Theorem 1.4 to Wouk [1], Theorem 1.5 to the author [5], Theorem 1.8 to M. G. Kreĭn [5], Theorem 1.10 to Naĭmark [1], Theorems 1.12–1.14 to Nevanlinna, and Theorem 1.16 is a modification of a theorem of Glazman and Naĭman [1]. For a proof of the Kreĭn-Mil'man theorem see for example Dunford and Schwartz [1]. Other approaches to the theory of Jacobian matrices, a series of related questions, an extensive bibliography, etc. can be found in Ahiezer [2]; in this book a complete proof of Theorem 1.14 is given. For a more classical approach see Shohat and Tamarkin [1]. §3 borders §1. The method of "duplication" presented here is due to the author [5].

We turn to §2. Pseudo-Hilbert spaces of the type l_2, composed of sequences of matrices of fixed finite order, were first considered by M. G. Kreĭn [11]. The author [5], and later V. G. Tarnopol'skiĭ [1], considered analogous spaces for matrices of infinite order and for operators. The general approach presented in subsections 1–4 is due to the author.

The spectral theory of formally selfadjoint ordinary difference expressions of second order, whose coefficients are matrices of fixed finite order, is constructed by M. G. Kreĭn [11]. Here he obtains best possible results such as in the case of the classical moment problem. The general theory of integral operators constructed by M. G. Kreĭn [2], [3], [9] is closely connected with this series of problems, allowing us to carry over the basic arguments of the moment problem to operators with finite deficiency numbers, having a determinate structure. We note for example that operators which appear in the theory of extensions of positive definite functions are related to integral operators. The spectral theory of formally selfadjoint partial difference expressions of the second order (§4) is due to the author [5]. It may be considered as a theory of the type of M. G. Kreĭn, but now infinite matrices of a special form serve as the coefficients. A generalization to the case of arbitrary coefficients, appearing only as bounded operators, is given by Tarnopol'skiĭ [1], [2]. The results of subsections 5–11 are essentially due to the author [5] and Tarnopol'skiĭ [1], [2]; in these works later results of the theory, which were mentioned at the end of subsection 11, are presented.

The results of §4 are partially generalized to the case of arbitrary even order by Bazanov [1], [2]. In connection with the problem of describing all spectral matrices see Štraus' work [1] concerning the general form of the resolvents of selfadjoint extensions of a Hermitian operator; his formula uses the above-mentioned works of Bazanov. For similar problems in the case of non-densely-defined operators see Loškarev [1].

Chapter VIII

The theorem on the integral representation of a bounded function, positive-definite in the generalized sense, in eigenfunctions of a Sturm-Liouville equation on the semiaxis was first obtained by the methods of the theory of normed rings by Povzner [1,2]. The general case of an ordinary differential equation without boundedness conditions on the function was completely studied by M. G. Kreĭn [6,8,10] by the method of guiding functionals discovered by him under the influence of a note by Livšic [1]. As a result of the basic idea of this method, the subsequent investigations were developed in the direction of obtaining integral representations of positive-definite kernels. Thus the author [4,11], by combining a device of M. G. Kreĭn for introducing a Hilbert space H_K with respect to the kernel K, with the theory of expansions in generalized eigenfunctions of the operator generated in H_K by the given differential expression, obtained results which extend to partial differential equations, where the method of guiding functionals is no longer applicable. Generalizations and refinements of these results were given by K. Maurin [2,3], who considered generalized positive-definite kernels, and by Browder [7]. The case of integral representations in eigenfunctions of more than one equation (multidimensional theorems) was studied independently, and almost simultaneously, with closely related methods by Kostjučenko and Mitjagin [1,2,3] and by the author [10,15]. The content of §§1–2 is essentially the theory developed in the latter article of the author. Let us note the results of other mathematicians contained in these sections. Theorem 2.2 is due to Kostjučenko and Mitjagin [3], Theorem 2.4 is essentially due to Gel'fand and Šilov [3], Theorem 2.6 was obtained in 1945 by Livšic and independently later by Èskin [1] (see also Ismagilov [1]). The proof given here is adapted to the description of all selfadjoint extensions. A result similar to Theorem 2.7 was published by Ismagilov [2]. Theorems 2.7 and 2.8 were published by the author [7]. For §§1–2 see also Foiaş [4].

Let us go on to §3. The results of subsections 1–2 are due to the author [4,11,15] and to F. E. Browder [7], the results of subsection 3 to M. G. Kreĭn [6,8] and Theorems 3.9 and 3.10 to the author [15]. The proof of these theorems makes use essentially of a modification of the theorem of Gel'fand and Šilov [3] on uniqueness classes for the Cauchy problem for general equations with positive coefficients. A similar method in the case $L = d^2/dx^2$ was applied earlier by Kostjučenko and Mitjagin [1,3], and still earlier by Povzner [3].

Let us discuss in greater detail the Theorem 3.9 for the expression $L = d^2/dx^2$ and the results of subsection 11. The representations given in subsection 11 are due to M. G. Kreĭn [6,8]. The uniqueness condition for the representation (3.87) is equivalent to the corollary to Theorem 3.18; the result formulated here was proved earlier, independently of the theory of positive-definite functions, by Levitan and Meĭman [1]. Theorems of the type 3.18 and 3.19 for $l = \infty$ in the case of generalized functions or the case of $k(t)$ were obtained by Gel'fand and Sja Do-Šin [1] (see also Gel'fand and Vilenkin [1] and Kostjučenko and Mitjagin [1,3]). The ordinary theorem of Bochner for generalized functions was proved by Schwartz [1]; for these questions see also his later work [3].

Let us note that the estimate (3.88) in Theorem 3.18 can be weakened; the function Ce^{Nt^2} can be replaced by $Ce^{Nt^2h(t)}$ where $h(t) > 0$ increases slowly to ∞, a result which is due to Vul [1]. A similar weakening of estimates can be obtained in the general case also for Theorems 3.9 and 3.10, as was done by Čaus [2]. He first proved a more precise theorem on uniqueness classes for the solution of the Cauchy problem for a general equation with positive coefficients than the theorem of Gel'fand and Šilov used in subsection 4, and then he applied the same method as in subsections 4–5.

Theorem 3.11 for $l = \infty$ is the ordinary theorem of Bochner [1], and for $l < \infty$ the theorem of M. G. Kreĭn [1] on the possibility of extension of a positive-definite function with preservation of its positive definiteness.

The basic results of subsections 8–9 on the determination of all extensions of positive-definite functions are also due to M. G. Kreĭn [1,2,3,9] and his later investigations. Its presentation here has been somewhat modified by the author with the idea of introducing the theory of spaces with positive and negative norms.

In subsections 8–9 only the first article of Kreĭn is presented on the determination of all extensions of positive-definite functions; we have not presented his further results, in which he essentially developed the continual "orthogonalization" δ_x, where x varies continuously in $[-l, l]$, and where by "orthogonalization" we mean that the Parseval equation is satisfied. These articles are all connected with the solution given by Kreĭn of the inverse problem of spectral analysis for the Sturm-Liouville equation and its more general analogues. We have not touched upon the interpretation of the theory of extension from the point of view of entire operators (Kreĭn [2,3,9]). Let us note that the first example of nonunique extension of a positive-definite function is due to Gnedenko [1].

Theorem 3.17 is due to Bernšteĭn [3], and the results of subsection 12 to Povzner [1,2] and M. G. Kreĭn [6,8]. Concerning the approach to the results of the type of subsection 12 through the theory of commutative rings (normed or topological) see Povzner [1,2], Levitan [2], Berezanskiĭ and S. G. Kreĭn [1], and Kostjučenko and Mitjagin [1,3].

For a number of interesting examples of integral representations of positive-definite kernels in eigenfunctions of ordinary differential expressions see the works of Schoenberg [1], M. G. Kreĭn [10], Devinatz [1,2], Kostjučenko and Mitjagin [3], and Ahiezer [2]. Certain of the constructions in §3 are also connected with the work of Aronszajn [1] on reproducing kernels (see also Nelson [1]).

Let us proceed to §4. The results of subsections 1–2 are due to the author [15]; for less general differential expressions (i.e., $L_t^{(j)} = i\ \partial/\partial t, \partial/\partial t, \partial^2/\partial t^2$) and kernels they were also obtained in part by Kostjučenko and Mitjagin [1,3]. Let us note that the latter authors also considered kernels constructed in terms of generalized functions $k(t)$ (for example, $K(x, y) = \frac{1}{2}(k(x+y) + k(x-y))$); multidimensional theorems of the Bochner type for generalized kernels of this sort were first set up by Vilenkin [1] (see also Gel′fand and Vilenkin [1]).

Theorems 4.4 and 4.5 are the classic multidimensional theorems of Bochner and Bernšteĭn (see for example Ahiezer [2]). Examples 3)–5), subsection 3 with larger $k(t)$ bounded in growth (for example, $e^{Nt^2 j}$ is replaced by $e^{Nt j}$), were already known; in the form just mentioned they were first obtained by Kostjučenko and Mitjagin [1,3]. "Mixed" positive-definite functions of the type of example 5) were first considered and given an integral representation by Devinatz [2]. As in the one-dimensional case, Čaus [2] obtained a weakening of the conditions (4.16) in the general Theorem 4.3.

Theorem 4.6 was established in 1945 by Livšic in his Ph.D. dissertation (Moscow, Steklov Institute), but was not published. Later it was established independently with some additional restrictions by Devinatz [4], and without the restrictions by Èskin [1]. The system mentioned in subsection 4 for the determination of extensions of positive-definite functions of two variables is due to the author. The theorem on integral representation of the form (4.33) for positive-definite operator functions is due to M. G. Kreĭn [8] and M. L. Gorbačuk [2]; in this article and its sequel [3] Gorbačuk extended to positive-definite operator functions basic facts of subsections 7–9 of §3, on the determination of extensions and thus made it possible in particular to complete the determination of extensions of positive-definite functions of two variables as described above in §4.4 (Berezanskiĭ and Gorbačuk [1]). Another approach to the determination of all extensions, based on obtaining for $k(t)$ $(t \in (-\infty, \infty) \times (-l_2, l_2))$, the formulas (4.32) with an integral, in general, instead of a sum, and on the further extension of the functions $k\alpha(t_2)$, is due to Ovčarenko [2] and Levin and Ovčarenko [1]. For general kernels, *-commuting with differential expressions, a similar determination was later obtained in another way by M. L. Gorbačuk [1]. These questions are also connected with the work of Ovčarenko [1].

An example of a positive-definite function in a rectangle that does not admit an extension to a positive-definite function on the whole plane was constructed by Calderón and Pepinsky [1], and independently later by Rudin [1]. An example of this sort for the two-dimensional moment problem, showing that this problem is not always solvable, was obtained by Zarhina [1], and a general treatment of this problem is given in Gel'fand and Vilenkin [1]. The same book also gives the construction by Hilbert of a positive polynomial in two variables which is not the sum of polynomial modules. This polynomial is utilized in all the examples just mentioned.

Let us proceed to §5. The results of subsections 2–3 are essentially due to Čaus [1]. The spaces $K_{p,q}$ used here are a generalization of the spaces applied earlier by Kostjučenko and Mitjagin [2,3] in closely related constructions for the moment problem. Recently Čan Čang [1] strengthened Theorems 5.3, 5.4 and 5.6. For example, in the estimate (5.19) the expression $|j|^{|j|/\rho}\,|k|^{|k|/\rho}$ can be replaced by $m_{|j|}\,m_{|k|}$ where the class $C(A^n_{n\rho}\,m_{n\rho})$ is quasi-analytic; here $A_n \geq 1$ $(n = 0, 1, \cdots)$ is a nondecreasing sequence such that $|a_{j\alpha}| \leq A_{|j|}$ ($a_{j\alpha}$ are the coefficients of the expression (5.1), which may be variables). Similarly, the estimate (5.29) may be weakened. This result was obtained by the method mentioned on p. 726.

In subsections 4–5 there is a discussion, partly from new points of view, of the classical questions of the problem of moments; for the literature see the books of Shohat and Tamarkin [1] and Ahiezer [2]. The multidimensional moment problem is discussed in the works of Haviland [1], Devinatz [2,3], Zarhina [1], Kostjučenko and Mitjagin [2,3]; the approach to this problem given in subsection 7 is due to Kostjučenko and Mitjagin. Theorem 5.11 in the two-dimensional case is due to Devinatz [3], and in the higher-dimensional case (in a somewhat weaker form) to Kostjučenko and Mitjagin [2,3]; Theorem 5.12 is due to Èskin [1].

The results of §6 are due to the author. For the device of passing from an elliptic equation to a hyperbolic, as discussed in subsection 2, see Vekua [1].

Let us make some further remarks. In connection with the difference expression with operator coefficients one may also consider the operator moment problem $S_n = \int_{-\infty}^{\infty} \lambda^n d\Sigma(\lambda)$ $(n = 0, 1, \cdots)$ (see §2.8 of Chapter VII). It was studied in detail by M. G. Kreĭn [11] (see also Kreĭn and Krasnosel'skiĭ [1]) for the case of matrices of finite rank depending on n.

The theory given in Chapter VIII may be constructed (admittedly with less completeness) for kernels $K(x, y)$ more general than positive-definite kernels. Namely, a kernel $K(x, y) \in C(E_n \times E_n)$ is said to be Hermite-indefinite with $\kappa (0 \leq \kappa < \infty)$ negative squares if the quadratic forms $\sum_{j,k=1}^{N} K(x_j, x_k)\xi_j\bar{\xi}_k$ $(x_1, \cdots, x_N \in E_n;\ N = 1, 2, \cdots)$ contained (after diagonalization) not more than κ negative squares, where at least one of these forms contains exactly κ such squares. For such kernels (*-commuting with the differential expression L) it is possible to construct the theory of integral representations in eigenfunctions of the equation $Lu = \lambda u$. Here also we have the multidimensional and the discrete analogies of the theory. The first results are due to M. G. Kreĭn (1948) and I. S. Iohvidov (1955) (see Iohvidov and Kreĭn [1], Iohvidov [1]). The integral representation for a continuous Hermite-indefinite function $k(t)$ defined on the whole axis (i.e., a function for which the kernel $K(x, y) = k(y - x)$ is Hermite-indefinite) was obtained by Kreĭn [19]. The general theory of integral representations of Hermite-indefinite kernels was developed by V. I. Gorbačuk [1–4]. In all these questions an essential role is played by the theorem of Pontrjagin [1] on invariant subspaces of a Hermitian operator acting in a space with indefinite metric.

A number of interesting approaches, not discussed in Chapter VIII, to positive-definite functions and their generalizations are to be found in the books of Gel'fand and Vilenkin [1] and Ahiezer [2].

BIBLIOGRAPHY

S. Agmon, A. Douglis and L. Nirenberg

1. *Estimates near the boundary for solutions of elliptic partial differential equations satisfying general boundary conditions.* I. Comm. Pure Appl. Math. 12 (1959), 623–727; Russian transl., IL, Moscow, 1962. MR 23 #A2610.
2. *Estimates near the boundary for solutions of elliptic partial differential equations.* II, Comm. Pure Appl. Math. 17 (1964), 35–92. MR 28 #5252.

S. Agmon and L. Nirenberg

1. *Properties of solutions of ordinary differential equations in Banach space,* Comm. Pure Appl. Math. 16 (1963), 121–239. MR 27 #5142.

Z. S. Agranovič and V. A. Marčenko

1. *The inverse problem of scattering theory,* Khar'kov State Univ. Press, Kharkov, 1960; English transl., Gordon & Breach, New York, 1963. MR 28 #5696.

M. S. Agranovič, L. R. Volevič and A. S. Dynin

1. *Solvability of general boundary problems for elliptic systems in multivariate domains,* Materials for the Joint Soviet-American Symposium on Partial Differential Equations, Novosibirsk, 1963. (Russian)

N. I. Ahiezer

1. *Infinite Jacobi matrices and the problem of moments,* Uspehi Mat. Nauk 9 (1941), 126–156. (Russian) MR 3, 110.
2. *The classicial moment problem and some related questions in analysis,* Fizmatgiz, Moscow, 1961; English transl., Hafner, New York, 1965. MR 27 #4028; MR 32 #1518.

N. I. Ahiezer and I. M. Glazman

1. *The theory of linear operators in Hilbert space,* GITTL, Moscow, 1950; English transl., Ungar, New York, 1961. MR 13, 358.

R. A. Aleksandrjan

1. *On Dirichlet's problem for the equation of a chord and on the completeness of a system of functions on the circle,* Dokl. Akad. Nauk SSSR 73 (1950), 869–872. (Russian) MR 12, 615.
2. *Spectral properties of operators arising from systems of differential equations of Sobolev type,* Trudy Moskov. Mat. Obšč. 9 (1960), 455–505. (Russian) MR 28 #1394.

N. Aronszajn

1. *The theory of reproducing kernels*, Trans. Amer. Math. Soc., 68 (1950), 337–404; Russian transl., Sborn. Per. Matematika 7 (1963), no. 2, 67–134. MR 14, 479.
2. *On coercive integro-differential quadratic forms*, Proc. Conf. Partial Differential Equations, Technical Report 14, Univ. of Kansas, 1954, 94–106.

N. Aronszajn and A. N. Milgram

1. *Differential operators on Riemannian manifolds*, Rend. Circ. Mat. Palermo Ser. (2) 2 (1953), 266–325. MR 16, 252.

V. M. Babič

1. *On the extension of functions*, Uspehi Mat. Nauk 8 (1953), no. 2 (54), 111–113. (Russian) MR 15, 110.

B. V. Bazanov

1. *Spectral functions of a symmetric partial difference operator*, Sibirsk. Mat. Ž. 2 (1961), 187–200. (Russian) MR 26 #2754.
2. *Some questions on the theory of symmetric finite-difference operators*, Volž. Mat. Sb. Teor. Ser. 1 (1963), 9–31. (Russian)

Ju. M. Berezanskiĭ

1. *On the uniqueness of the determination of Schrödinger's equation from its spectral function*, Dokl. Akad. Nauk SSSR 93 (1953), 591–594. (Russian) MR 15, 797.
2. *On the inverse problem of spectral analysis for the Schrödinger equation*, Dokl. Akad. Nauk SSSR 105 (1955), 197–200. (Russian) MR 17, 1210.
3. *On expansion according to eigenfunctions of general self-adjoint differential operators*, Dokl. Akad. Nauk SSSR 108 (1956), 379–382. (Russian) MR 18, 323.
4. *Generalization of Bochner's theorem to expansions according to eigenfunctions of partial differential equations*, Dokl. Akad. Nauk SSSR 110 (1956), 893–896. (Russian) MR 19, 1061.
5. *Expansion according to eigenfunctions of a partial difference equation of order two*, Trudy Moskov. Mat. Obšč. 5 (1956), 203–268. (Russian) MR 19, 288.
6. *Eigenfunction expansions for self-adjoint operators*, Mat. Sb. 43 (85) (1957), 75–126. (Russian) MR 21 #3646.
7. *On the boundary value problems for general partial differential operators*, Dokl. Akad. Nauk SSSR 122 (1958), 959–962. (Russian) MR 22 #896.
8. *The uniqueness theorem in the inverse problem of spectral analysis for the Schrödinger equation*, Trudy Moskov. Mat. Obšč. 7 (1958), 1–62; English transl., Amer. Math. Soc. Transl. (2) 35 (1964), 167–235. MR 21 #188.

9. *Generalized solutions of boundary value problems*, Dokl. Akad. Nauk SSSR 126 (1959), 1159–1162. (Russian) MR 23 #A1926.

10. *On an eigenfunction expansion for self-adjoint operators*, Ukrain. Mat. Ž. 11 (1959), 16–24. (Russian) MR 23 #A518.

11. *Representation of positive definite kernels by eigenfunctions of differential equations*, Mat. Sb. 47 (89) (1959), 145–176. (Russian) MR 21 #2774.

12. *Some examples of nonclassical boundary-value problems for partial differential equations*, Dokl. Akad. Nauk SSSR 131 (1960), 478–481 = Soviet Math. Dokl. 1 (1960), 259–262. MR 22 #9720.

13. *Energy inequalities for some classes of equations of mixed type*, Dokl. Akad. Nauk SSSR 132 (1960), 9–12 = Soviet Math. Dokl. 1 (1960), 447–451. MR 22 #11237.

14. *Über Randaufgabe von Dirichlet Typus für Schwingungsgleichung der Saite*, Ukrain. Mat. Ž. 12 (1960), 363–372. (Russian) MR 28 #2332.

15. *A generalization of a multidimensional theorem of Bochner*, Dokl. Akad. Nauk SSSR 136 (1961), 1011–1014 = Soviet Math. Dokl. 2 (1961), 143–147. MR 28 #489.

16. *Spaces with negative norm*, Uspehi Mat. Nauk 18 (1963), no. 1 (109), 63–96. (Russian) MR 29 #1553.

17. *Some questions on the spectral theory of selfconjugate differential operators in partial derivatives*, Materials for the Joint Soviet-American Symposium on Partial Differential Equations, Novosibirsk, 1963. (Russian)

18. *Smoothness of the spectral functions of a selfadjoint elliptic differential operator up to the boundary of the domain*, Dokl. Akad. Nauk SSSR 152 (1963), 511–514 = Soviet Math. Dokl. 4 (1963), 1319–1322. MR 27 #3936.

19. *Existence of weak solutions of certain boundary-value problems for equations of mixed type*, Ukrain. Mat. Ž. 15 (1963), 347–364. (Russian) MR 28 #370.

Ju. M. Berezanskiĭ and M. L. Gorbačuk

1. *Extension of positive definite functions of two variables*, Ukrain. Mat. Ž. 17 (1965), no. 5, 96–102. (Russian) MR 33 #499.

Ju. M. Berezanskiĭ and S. G. Kreĭn

1. *Hypercomplex systems with continuous basis*, Scientific Communications, Uspehi Mat. Nauk 12 (1957), no. 1 (73), 147–152; English transl., Amer. Math. Soc. Transl. (2) 16 (1960), 358–364. MR 19, 154.

Ju. M. Berezanskiĭ, S. G. Kreĭn and Ja. A. Roĭtberg

1. *A theorem on homeomorphisms and local increase of smoothness up to the boundary for solutions of elliptic equations*, Dokl. Akad. Nauk SSSR

148 (1963), 745–748 = Soviet Math. Dokl. 4 (1963), 164–167. MR 26 #4030.

Ju. M. Berezanskiĭ and Ju. B. Oročko

1. *A remark concerning the growth of eigenfunctions of self-adjoint operators,* Ukrain Mat. Ž. 14 (1962), 180–184. (Russian) MR 26 #2880.

Ju. M. Berezanskiĭ and Ja. A. Roĭtberg

1. *On the smoothness up to the boundary of the region of the kernel of the resolvent of an elliptic operator,* Ukrain. Mat. Ž. 15 (1963), 185–189. (Russian) MR 28 #2331.

G. Bergendal

1. *Convergence and summability of eigenfunction expansions connected with elliptic differential operators,* Medd. Lunds Univ. Mat. Sem. 15 (1959), 1–63. MR 21 #4287.

S. N. Bernšteĭn

1. *Study of the integration of differential equations with partial derivatives of second order elliptic type,* Soobšč. Khar'kov. Mat. Obšč (2) 11 (1908–1909), 1–164. (Russian)
2. *Some apriori estimates in Dirichlet's generalized problem,* Dokl. Akad. Nauk SSSR 124 (1959), 735–738. (Russian) MR 21 #196.
3. *Collected works.* Vol. I: *The constructive theory of functions* [1905–1930], Izdat. Akad. Nauk SSSR, Moscow, 1952. (Russian) MR 14, 2.

L. Bers

1. *Mathematical aspects of subsonic and transonic gas dynamics,* Surveys in Appl. Math., vol. 3, Wiley, New York and Chapman & Hall, London, 1958; Russian transl., IL, Moscow, 1961. MR 20 #2960; MR 23 #B134.

A. V. Bicadze

1. *Equations of the mixed type,* Izdat. Akad. Nauk SSSR, Moscow, 1959; English transl., Macmillan and Pergamon, New York, 1964. MR 29 #381.

M. Š. Birman

1. *On the theory of general boundary problems for elliptic differential equations,* Dokl. Akad. Nauk SSSR 92 (1953), 205–208. (Russian) MR 16, 42.
2. *Characteristics of elliptic differential operators with a maximal domain of definitions,* Vestnik Leningrad. Gos. Univ. Ser. Mat. Meh. Astronom. Fiz. Him. 19 (1957), 177–188. (Russian)

M. Š. Birman and I. M. Glazman

1. *Spectrum of singular differential operators,* Proc. Fourth All-Union Math. Congress, vol. II: Sectional Lectures, "Nauka", Leningrad, 1964, pp. 253–261. (Russian) MR 29 #4649.

M. Š. Birman and G. E. Skvorcov

1. *On square summability of highest derivatives of the solution of the Cauchy problem in a domain with piecewise smooth boundary*, Izv. Vysš. Učebn. Zaved. Matematika 1962, no. 5 (30), 11–21. (Russian) MR 26 #2731.

S. Bochner

1. *Vorlesungen über Fouriersche Integrale*, Leipzig, 1932.

N. Bourbaki

1. "Intégration vectorielle", *Intégration*, Chapter 6, Paris, 1959.
2. *Les structures fondamentales de l'analyse*, Livre V: *Espaces vectoriels topologiques*, Hermann, Paris, 1955; Russian transl., IL, Moscow, 1959. MR 14, 880; MR 17, 1109.

D. G. Bourgin and R. Duffin

1. *The Dirichlet problem for the vibrating string equation*, Bull. Amer. Math. Soc. 45 (1939), 851–859. MR 1, 120.

F. E. Browder

1. *The eigenfunction expansion theorem for the general self-adjoint singular elliptic partial differential operator*, I: *The analytical foundation*, Proc. Nat. Acad. Sci. U. S. A. 40 (1954), 454–467. MR 16, 134.
2. *Strongly elliptic system of differential equations*, Contributions to the Theory of Partial Differential Equations, Ann. of Math. Studies 33, Princeton Univ. Press, Princeton, N. J., 1954, pp. 15–51. MR 16 #705.
3. *Eigenfunction expansions for formally self-adjoint partial differential operators*. I, II, Proc. Nat. Acad. Sci. U. S. A. 42 (1956), 769–771; 870–872. MR 19, 1061.
4. *On the regularity properties of solutions of elliptic differential equations*, Comm. Pure Appl. Math. 9 (1956), 351–361. MR 19, 862.
5. *Eigenfunction expansions for non-symmetric partial differential operators*. I, Amer. J. Math. 80 (1958), 365–381. MR 20 #1064.
6. *Eigenfunction expansions for non-symmetric partial differential operators*. II, Amer. J. Math. 81 (1959), 1–22. MR 21 #5821.
7. *Eigenfunction expansions for non-symmetric partial differential operators*. III, Amer. J. Math. 81 (1959), 715–734. MR 22 #8230.
8. *Estimates and existence theorems for elliptic boundary value problems*, Proc. Nat. Acad. Sci. U. S. A. 45 (1959), 365–372. MR 24 #A2749.
9. *Functional analysis and partial differential equations*. I, Math. Ann. 138 (1959), 55–79. MR 21 #6540.
10. *A priori estimates for solutions of elliptic boundary-value problems*. I, II, Nederl. Akad. Wetensch. Proc. Ser. A 63 (1960) = Indag. Math. 22 (1960), 145–169. MR 23 #A1141.

11. *On the spectral theory of elliptic differential operators.* I, Math. Ann. 142 (1961), 22–130.

R. Cacciopoli

1. *Limitazioni integrali per le soluzioni di un'equazione lineare ellitica a derivate parziali,* Giorn. Mat. Battaglini (4) 4 (80) (1951), 186–212. MR 13, 749.

A. P. Calderón and R. Pepinsky

1. *On the phase of Fourier coefficients for positive real periodic functions,* Computing methods and the phase problem in x-ray crystal analysis, Department of Physics, Pennsylvania State College, State College, Pa., 1952, pp. 339–348.

Čan, Čang

1. *On the representation of positive definite matrices by eigenfunctions of difference operators,* Ukrain. Mat. Ž. 17 (1965), 124–129. (Russian)

T. Carleman

1. *Sur la théorie mathématique de l'equation de Schroedinger,* Ark. Mat. Astr. Fys. 24, 11, (1934), 1–7.

N. N. Čaus

1. *The uniqueness of the solutions of a Cauchy problem for systems of partial differential equations,* Ukrain. Mat. Ž. 17 (1965), 126–130. (Russian) MR 32 #7913.

2. *Uniqueness classes of solutions of the Cauchy problem and representations of positive definite kernels,* Dokl. Akad. Nauk SSSR 163 (1965), 36–39 = Soviet Math. Dokl. 6 (1965), 895–898.

H. O. Cordes

1. *Separation der Variablen in Hilbertschen Räumen,* Math. Ann. 125 (1953), 401–434. MR 14, 1096.

2. *Über die Spektralzerlegung von hypermaximalen Operatoren, die durch Separation der Variablen zerfallen.* I, II, Math. Ann. 128 (1954–1955), 257–289; 373–411. MR 16, 597.

Ju. L. Daleckiĭ

1. *Functional integrals associated with operator evolution equations,* Uspehi Mat. Nauk 17 (1962), no. 5 (107), 3–115. (Russian) MR 28 #4389.

R. T. Denčev

1. *The spectrum of an operator,* Dokl. Akad. Nauk SSSR 126 (1959), 259–262. (Russian) MR 23 #A2627.

A. Devinatz

1. *Integral representations of positive definite functions,* Trans. Amer. Math. Soc. 74 (1953), 56–77. MR 14, 659.

2. *Integral representations of positive definite functions.* II, Trans. Amer. Math. Soc. 77 (1954), 455–480. MR 16, 584.

3. *Two parameter moment problems*, Duke Math. J. 24 (1957), 481–498. MR 19, 1047.

4. *On the extensions of positive definite functions*, Acta Math. 102 (1959), 109–134. MR 22 #875.

A. A. Dezin

1. *Existence and uniqueness theorems for solutions of boundary problems for partial differential equations in function spaces*, Uspehi Mat. Nauk 14 (1959), no. 3 (87), 21–73; English transl., Amer. Math. Soc. Transl. (2) 42 (1964), 71–128. MR 22 #6922.

N. Dinculeanu

1. *Sur la représentation intégrale de certaines opérations linéaires.* III, Proc. Amer. Math. Soc. 10 (1959), 59–68. MR 21 #2909.

A. Douglis

1. See S. Agmon, A. Douglis and L. Nirenberg [1].

2. See S. Agmon, A. Douglis and L. Nirenberg [2].

R. Duffin

1. See D. G. Bourgin and R. Duffin [1].

N. Dunford and J. Schwartz

1. *Linear operators.* I: *General theory*, Pure and Appl. Math., vol. 7, Interscience, New York and London, 1958; Russian transl., IL, Moscow, 1962. MR 22 #8302.

A. S. Dynin

1. See M. S. Agranovič, L. R. Volevič and A. S. Dynin [1].

L. Ehrenpreis

1. *On the theory of kernels of Schwartz*, Proc. Amer. Math. Soc. 7 (1956), 713–718. MR 18, 584.

G. Ehrling

1. *On a type of eigenvalue problems for certain differential operators*, Math. Scand. 2 (1954), 267–285. MR 16, 706.

S. D. Èĭdel'man

1. *Parabolic systems*, "Nauka", Moscow, 1964. (Russian) MR 29 #4998.

G. I. Èskin

1. *A sufficient condition for the solvability of a multi-dimensional problem of moments*, Dokl. Akad. Nauk SSSR 133 (1960), 540–543 = Soviet Math. Dokl. 1 (1960), 895–898. MR 22 #12394.

2. See M. I. Višik and G. I. Èskin [1].

M. S. Èskina

1. *The direct and the inverse scattering problem for a partial differential equation,* Dokl. Akad. Nauk SSSR 166 (1966), 809–812 = Soviet Math. Dokl. 7 (1966), 193–197.

L. D. Faddeev

1. *Uniqueness of solution of the inverse scattering problem,* Vestnik Leningrad. Univ. 11 (1956), no. 7, 126–130. (Russian) MR 18, 259.
2. *Dispersion relations in non-relativistic scattering theory,* Ž. Èksper. Teoret. Fiz. 35 (1959), 433–439 = Soviet Physics JETP 35 (8) (1959), 299–303. MR 20 #7530.
3. *The inverse problem in the quantum theory of scattering,* Uspehi Mat. Nauk 14 (1959), no. 4 (88), 57–119; English transl., J. Math. Phys. 4 (1963), 72–104. MR 22 #1334; MR 26 #7328.
4. *Mathematical questions in the quantum theory of scattering for a system of three particles,* Trudy Mat. Inst. Steklov. 69 (1963). (Russian) MR 29 #995.

G. Fichera

1. *Alcuni recenti sviluppi della teoria dei problemi al contorno per le equazioni alle derivate parziali lineari,* Convegno Internaz. sulle Equazioni Lineari alle Deriviate Parziali, Trieste, 1954, pp. 174–227, Edizioni Cremonese, Roma, 1955. MR 17, 626.
2. *Premesse ad una teoria generale dei problemi al contorno per le equazioni differenziali,* Corsi Instituti Naz, Alta Matem., Libreria Veschi, Roma, 1958.
3. *On a unified theory of boundary value problems for elliptic-parabolic equations of second order. Boundary problems in differential equations,* Univ. Wisconsin Press, Madison, Wis., 1960, pp. 97–120; Russian transl., Sborn. Per. Matematika 7 (1963), no. 6, 99–121. MR 22 #2789.

C. Foiaş

1. *Décompositions intégrales des familles spectrales et semi-spectrales en opérateurs qui sortent de l'espace hilbertien,* Acta Sci. Math. Szeged 20 (1959), 117–155. MR 22 #5895.
2. *Sur la décomposition intégrale des mesures vectorielles et ses applications a la théorie spectrale.* I, II, Comm. Acad. R. P. Romîne 11 (1961), 301–307; 309–311. (Romanian) MR 23 #A4020.
3. *Décompositions en opérateurs et vecteurs propres. I. Etudes de ces décompositions et leurs rapports avec les prolongements des opérateurs,* Rev. Math. Pures Appl. 7 (1962), 241–282.
4. *Problèmes mixtes et décompositions en noyaux propres des opérateurs*

aux dérivées partielles, C. R. Acad. Sci. Paris 255 (1962), 247–248. MR 27 #1826.

F. I. Frankl′

1. *An existence theorem for a weak solution and first approximation of the direct problem in the theory of the plane-parallel Laval nozzle*, Izv. Vysš. Učebn. Zaved. Matematika 1959, no. 6 (13), 192–201. (Russian) MR 28 #805.

K. O. Friedrichs

1. *On the differentiability of the solutions of linear elliptic differential equations*, Comm. Pure Appl. Math. 6 (1953), 299–326. MR 15, 430.
2. *Symmetric positive linear differential equations*, Comm. Pure Appl. Math. 11 (1958), 333–418. MR 20 #7147.

L. Gårding

1. *Dirichlet's problem for linear elliptic partial differential equations*, Math. Scand. 1 (1953), 55–72. MR 16, 366.
2. *Eigenfunction expansions connected with elliptic differential operators*, Tolfte Skand. Mat., (May be ordered from Lunds Univ. Mat. Inst.) Lund, 1953 (1954), pp. 44–45. MR 17, 158.
3. *Applications of the theory of direct integrals of Hilbert spaces to some integral and differential operators*, Inst. Fluid Dynam. Appl. Math. Lect. Ser. no. 11, Univ. Maryland, College Park, 1954. MR 17, 159.
4. Ju. M. Berezanskiĭ's article, Math. Rev. vol. 18, 1957, p. 323.
5. *Eigenfunction expansions*, Partial differential equations, Proc. Seminar in Appl. Math., Boulder, Colorado, 1957, Interscience, New York, 1964, pp. 301–325. MR 29 #2525.
6. *Some trends and problems in linear partial differential equations*, Proc. Internat. Congress Math. 1958, Cambridge Univ. Press, New York, 1960, pp. 87–102; Russian transl., Uspehi Mat. Nauk 15 (1960), no. 1 (91), 137–152. MR 22 #8213; MR 22 #8214.

I. M. Gel′fand and A. G. Kostjučenko

1. *Expansion in eigenfunctions of differential and other operators*, Dokl. Akad. Nauk SSSR 103 (1955), 349–352. (Russian) MR 17, 388.

I. M. Gel′fand and G. E. Šilov

1. *Generalized functions.* Part I: *Generalized functions and operations on them*, Fizmatgiz, Moscow, 1958; 2nd ed., 1959; English transl. of 1st. ed., Academic Press, New York, 1964. MR 20 #4182; MR 29 #3869.
2. *Generalized functions.* Part II: *Spaces of fundamental and generalized functions*, Fizmatgiz, Moscow, 1958; German transl., Hochschulbücher für Mathematik, Bd. 48, VEB Deutscher Verlag, Berlin, 1962; English

transl., Academic Press, New York (In prep.). MR 21 #5142a; MR 26 #6765.

3. *Generalized functions.* Part III: *Some questions in the theory of differential equations*, Fizmatgiz, Moscow, 1958; German transl., Hochschulbücher für Mathematik, Bd. 49, VEB Deutscher Verlag, Berlin, 1964; English transl., Academic Press, New York (In prep.). MR 21 #5142b; MR 29 #2643.

I. M. Gel'fand and Sja, Do-Šin

1. *On positive definite distributions*, Uspehi Mat. Nauk 15 (1960), no. 1(91), 185–190. (Russian) MR 22 #2849.

I. M. Gel'fand and N. Ja. Vilenkin

1. *Generalized functions.* Part IV: *Some applications of harmonic analysis*, Fizmatgiz, Moscow, 1961; English transl., Academic Press, New York, 1964. MR 26 #4173; MR 30 #4152.

E. Gerlach

1. *On spectral representation for selfadjoint operators. Expansion in generalized eigenelements*, Technical Report 4, Univ. of Kansas, 1964; Ann. Inst. Fourier (Grenoble) 15 (1965), fasc. 2, 537–574. MR 32 #8172.

D. Gilbarg and J. Serrin

1. *On isolated singularities of second order elliptic differential equations*, J. Analyse Math. 4 (1955–1956), 309–340. MR 18, 399.

I. M. Glazman

1. *Direct methods of the qualitative spectral analysis of singular differential operators*, Fizmatgiz, Moscow, 1963; English transl., Israel Program for Scientific Translations, Jerusalem, 1965 and Davey, New York, 1966. MR 32 #2938; MR 32 #8210.
2. See N. I. Ahiezer and I. M. Glazman [1].
3. See M. Š. Birman and I. M. Glazman [1].

I. M. Glazman and P. B. Naĭman

1. *On the convex hull of orthogonal spectral functions*, Dokl. Akad. Nauk SSSR 102 (1955), 445–448. (Russian) MR 17, 618.

V. P. Gluško and S. G. Kreĭn

1. *Fractional powers of differential operators and imbedding theorems*, Dokl. Akad. Nauk SSSR 122 (1958), 963–966. (Russian) MR 20 #6578.
2. *Inequalities for norms of derivatives in weighted L_p spaces*, Sibirsk Mat. Ž. 1 (1960), 343–382. (Russian) MR 24 #A3507.

B. V. Gnedenko

1. *On characteristic functions*, Bull. Moskov. Gos. Univ. (A) 1 (1937), no. 5, 17–18. (Russian)

M. L. Gorbačuk

1. *A description of the continuation of positive definite kernels,* Dokl. Akad. Nauk SSSR 159 (1964), 710–722 = Soviet Math. Dokl. 5 (1964), 1566–1569. MR 30 #465.
2. *On the representation of positive-definite operator-functions,* Ukrain. Mat. Ž. 17 (1965), no. 2, 29–46. (Russian) MR 33 #1727.
3. *On describing the extensions of a positive definite operator function,* Ukrain. Mat. Ž. 17 (1965), no. 5, 102–110. (Russian) MR 33 #501.
4. See Ju. M. Berezanskiĭ and M. L. Gorbačuk [1].

V. I. Gorbačuk

1. *An integral representation of Hermitian indefinite kernels (the case of several variables),* Ukrain. Mat. Ž. 16 (1964), 232–236. (Russian) MR 29 #3849.
2. *The integral representation of hermitian-indefinite kernels,* Ukrain. Mat. Ž. 17 (1965), no. 3, 43–58. (Russian) MR 33 #521.
3. See V. I. Pljuščeva and V. I. Gorbačuk [1].
4. See V. I. Pljuščeva and V. I. Gorbačuk [2].

V. N. Gorčakov

1. *On the asymptotic behavior of the spectral function of a class of hypoelliptic operators,* Dokl. Akad. Nauk SSSR 152 (1963), 519–522 = Soviet Math. Dokl. 4 (1963), 1328–1331. MR 28 #494.
2. *Asymptotic properties of the spectral function of hypoelliptic operators,* Dokl. Akad. Nauk SSSR 160 (1965), 746–749 = Soviet Math. Dokl. 6 (1965), 170–173. MR 31 #4990.

E. A. Gorin

1. *Asymptotic properties of polynomials and algebraic functions of several variables,* Uspehi Mat. Nauk 16 (1961), no. 1 (97), 91–118. (Russian) MR 24 #A1269.

I. S. Gradšteĭn

1. See I. M. Ryžik and I. S. Gradštein [1].

A. Grothendieck

1. *Produits tensoriels topologiques et espaces nucléaires,* Mem. Amer. Mat. Soc. No. 16 (1955). MR 17, 763.

O. V. Guseva

1. *On boundary problems for strongly elliptic systems,* Dokl. Akad. Nauk SSSR 102 (1955), 1069–1072. (Russian) MR 17, 161.

J. Hadamard

1. *Équations aux dérivées partielles, le cas hyperbolique,* Enseignement Math. 35 (1936), 25–29.

P. R. Halmos

1. *Measure theory*, Van Nostrand, Princeton, N. J., 1950; Russian transl., IL, Moscow, 1953. MR 11, 504; MR 16, 22.

E. Haviland

1. *On the momentum problem for distribution functions in more than one dimension*. I, Amer. J. Math. 57 (1935), 562–568; II, 58 (1936), 164–168.

A. Ja. Hinčin

1. *Continued fractions*, 2nd ed., GITTL, Moscow, 1949; 1961; English transl., Noordhoff, Groningen, 1963 and Univ. of Chicago Press, Chicago, Ill., 1964. MR 13, 444; MR 28 #5037; MR 28 #5038.

L. Hörmander

1. *The theory of general differential operators in partial derivatives*, Russian transl., IL, Moscow, 1959.
2. *Definitions of maximal differential operators*, Ark. Mat. 3 (1958), 501–504. MR 21 #5067.
3. *Differential operators of principal type*, Math. Ann. 140 (1960), 124–146. MR 24 #A434.
4. *Linear partial differential operators*, Die Grundlehren der mathematischen Wissenschaften, Band 116, Academic Press, New York and Springer-Verlag, Berlin, 1963; Russian transl., Izdat. "Mir", Moscow, 1965. MR 28 #4221.

L. Hörmander and J. L. Lions

1. *Sur la completion par rapport à une intégrale de Dirichlet*, Math. Scand. 4 (1956), 259–270. MR 19, 420.

A. Huber

1. *Die erste Randwertaufgabe für geschlossene Bereiche bei der Gleichung* $\partial^2 z/\partial k \partial y = f(x, y)$, Monatschefte Math. und Phys. 39 (1932), 79–100.

T. Ikebe

1. *Eigenfunction expansions associated with the Schroedinger operators and their applications to scattering theory*, Arch. Rational Mech. Anal. 5 (1960), 1–34. MR 23 #B1398.

A. M. Il'in

1. *On the fundamental solution of a parabolic equation*, Dokl. Akad. Nauk SSSR 147 (1962), 768–771 = Soviet Math. Dokl. 3 (1962), 1697–1700. MR 29 #1453.

V. A. Il'in

1. *On convergence of expansions in eigenfunctions of the Laplace operator*, Uspehi Mat. Nauk 13 (1958), no. 1 (79), 87–180. (Russian) MR 20 #1828.

V. A. Il'in and I. A. Šišmarev

1. *On the equivalence of the systems of generalized and classical eigenfunctions,* Izv. Akad. Nauk SSSR Ser. Mat. 24 (1960), 757–774. (Russian) MR 23 #A1126.

V. P. Il'in

1. *Some functional inequalities of the type of theorems of imbedding,* Dokl. Akad. Nauk SSSR 123 (1958), 967–970. (Russian) MR 21 #103.

I. S. Iohvidov

1. *On the theory of indefinite Toeplitz forms,* Dokl. Akad. Nauk SSSR 101 (1955), 214–216. (Russian) MR 16, 1032.

I. S. Iohvidov and M. G. Kreĭn

1. *Spectral theory of operators with indefinite metric.* II, Trudy Moskov. Mat. Obšč. 8 (1959), 413–496; English transl., Amer. Math. Soc. Transl. (2) 34 (1963), 283–373. MR 21 #6543.

R. S. Ismagilov

1. *Self-adjoint extensions of a system of commuting symmetric operators,* Dokl. Akad. Nauk SSSR 133 (1960), 511–514 = Soviet Math. Dokl. 1 (1960), 867–870. MR 22 #12393.
2. *Self-adjoint extensions of commutative symmetric operators,* Uspehi Mat. Nauk 17 (1962), no. 1 (103), 177–181. (Russian) MR 24 #A1028.

F. John

1. *The Dirichlet problem for a hyperbolic equation,* Amer. J. Math. 63 (1941), 141–154. MR 2, 204.
2. *Plane waves and spherical means applied to partial differential equations,* Interscience, New York, 1955; Russian transl., IL, Moscow, 1958. MR 17, 746.

G. I. Kac

1. *Expansion in characteristic functions of self-adjoint operators,* Dokl. Akad. Nauk SSSR 119 (1958), 19–22. (Russian) MR 21 #3647.
2. *Generalized elements of a Hilbert space,* Ukrain. Mat. Ž. 12 (1960), 13–24. (Russian) MR 24 #A1029.
3. *Spectral decompositions of self-adjoint operators in terms of generalized elements of a Hilbert space,* Ukrain. Mat. Ž. 13 (1961), no. 4, 13–33. (Russian) MR 26 #1764.

A. V. Kantorovič and G. P. Akilov

1. *Functional analysis in normed spaces,* Fizmatgiz, Moscow, 1959; English transl., Pergamon Press and Macmillan, New York, 1964. MR 22 #9837; MR 31 #1536.

T. Kato

1. *Fundamental properties of Hamiltonian operators of Schrödinger type,* Trans. Amer. Math. Soc. 70 (1951), 195–211. MR 12, 781.
2. *Growth properties of solutions of the reduced equation with a variable coefficient,* Comm. Pure Appl. Math. 12 (1959), 402–425. MR 21 #7349.

K. Kodaira

1. *On ordinary differential equations of any even order and the corresponding eigenfunction expansions,* Amer. J. Math. 72 (1950), 502–544. MR 12, 103.

A. I. Košelev

1. *A priori estimates in L_p and generalized solutions of elliptic equations and systems,* Uspehi Mat. Nauk 13 (1958), no. 4 (82), 29–88; English transl., Amer. Math. Soc. Transl. (2) 20 (1962), 105–171. MR 23 #A2630.

A. G. Kostjučenko

1. *On the spectral properties of elliptical operators,* Dokl. Akad. Nauk SSSR 115 (1957), 34–37. (Russian) MR 20 #1068.
2. *An estimate of the resolvents of singular elliptic operators,* Dokl. Akad. Nauk SSSR 132 (1960), 32–35 = Soviet Math. Dokl. 1 (1960), 470–473. MR 24 #A3421.
3. See I. M. Gel'fand and A. G. Kostjučenko [1].

A. G. Kostjučenko and B. S. Mitjagin

1. *Positive definite functionals on nuclear spaces,* Dokl. Akad. Nauk SSSR 131 (1960), 13–16 = Soviet Math. Dokl. 1 (1960), 177–180. MR 22 #12391.
2. *The multi-dimensional problem of moments,* Dokl. Akad. Nauk SSSR 131 (1960), 1249–1252 = Soviet Math. Dokl. 1 (1960), 415–419. MR 22 #12392.
3. *Positive definite functionals on nuclear spaces,* Trudy Moskov. Mat. Obšč. 9 (1960), 283–316. (Russian) MR 23 #A2040.

M. A. Krasnosel'skiĭ

1. See M. G. Kreĭn and M. A. Krasnosel'skiĭ [1].

M. G. Kreĭn

1. *Sur le problème du prolongement des fonctions hermitiennes positives et continues,* Dokl. Akad. Nauk SSSR 26 (1940), 17–22. (Russian) MR 2, 361.
2. *On Hermitian operators whose deficiency indices are* 1, Dokl. Akad. Nauk SSSR 43 (1944), 323–326; *On Hermitian operators with deficiency indices equal to one.* II, Dokl. Akad. Nauk SSSR 44 (1944), 131–134. (Russian) MR 6, 131; MR 6, 179.
3. *On a remarkable class of Hermitian operators,* Dokl. Akad. Nauk SSSR 44 (1944), 175–179. (Russian) MR 6, 269.

4. *On the problem of continuation of helical arcs in Hilbert space*, Dokl. Akad. Nauk SSSR 45 (1944), 139–142. (Russian) MR 6, 269.

5. *On a problem of extrapolation of A. N. Kolmogoroff*, Dokl. Akad. Nauk SSSR 46 (1945), 306–309. (Russian) MR 7, 61.

6. *On a general method of decomposing Hermitian-positive nuclei into elementary products*, Dokl. Akad. Nauk SSSR 53 (1946), 3–6. (Russian) MR 8, 277.

7. *A continuous operator in functional spaces with two norms*, Akad. Nauk Ukrain. RSR Zbirnik Prac' Inst. Mat. 1947 (1947), no. 9, 104–129. (Russian)

8. *On Hermitian operators with directed functionals*, Akad. Nauk Ukrain. RSR Zbirnik Prac' Inst. Mat. 1948 (1948), no. 10, 83–106. (Russian) MR 14, 56.

9. *The fundamental propositions of the theory of representations of Hermitian operators with deficiency index* (m, m), Ukrain. Mat. Ž. 1 (1949), no. 2, 3–66. (Russian) MR 14, 56.

10. *Hermitian positive kernels on homogeneous spaces*. I, Ukrain. Mat. Ž. 1 (1949), 64–98; English transl., Amer. Math. Soc. Transl. (2) 34 (1963), 69–108. MR 14, 480.

11. *Infinite J-matrices and a matrix-moment problem*, Dokl. Akad. Nauk SSSR 69 (1949), 125–128. (Russian) MR 11, 670.

12. *On the Sturm-Liouville boundary problem in the interval* $(0, \infty)$ *and on a class of intergral equations*, Dokl. Akad. Nauk SSSR 73 (1950), 1125–1128. (Russian) MR 12, 339.

13. *On a one-dimensional singular boundary problem of even order in the interval* $(0, \infty)$, Dokl. Akad. Nauk SSSR 74 (1950), 9–12. (Russian) MR 12, 502.

14. *Solution of the inverse Sturm-Liouville boundary problem*, Dokl. Akad. Nauk SSSR 76 (1951), 21–24. (Russian) MR 12, 613.

15. *On a generalization of investigations of Stieltjes*, Dokl. Akad. Nauk SSSR 87 (1952), 881–884. (Russian) MR 14, 868.

16. *On the indeterminate case of the Sturm-Liouville boundary problem in the interval* $(0, \infty)$, Izv. Akad. Nauk SSSR Ser. Mat. 16 (1952), 293–324. (Russian) MR 14, 558.

17. *An analogue of the Čebyšev-Markov inequalities in a one-dimensional boundary problem*, Dokl. Akad. Nauk SSSR 89 (1953), 5–8. (Russian) MR 15, 316.

18. *On the transfer function of a one-dimensional boundary problem of second order*, Dokl. Akad. Nauk SSSR 88 (1953), 405–408. (Russian) MR 15, 316.

19. *Integral representation of a continuous Hermitian-indefinite function*

with a finite number of negative squares, Dokl. Akad. Nauk SSSR 125 (1959), 31–34. (Russian) MR 22 #877.

20. See I. S. Iohvidov and M. G. Kreĭn [1].

M. G. Kreĭn and M. A. Krasnosel'skiĭ

1. *Fundamental theorems on the extension of Hermitian operators and certain of their applications to the theory of orthogonal polynomials and the problem of moments*, Uspehi Mat. Nauk 2 (1947), no. 3 (19), 60–106. (Russian) MR 10, 198.

S. G. Kreĭn

1. Report given at the All-Union Conference on Functional Analysis and its Application, Baku, 1959. (Russian)
2. *On an interpolation theorem in operator theory*, Dokl. Akad. Nauk SSSR 130 (1960), 491–494 = Soviet Math. Dokl. 1 (1960), 61–64. MR 22 #9860.
3. See Ju. M. Berezanskiĭ and S. G. Kreĭn [1].
4. See Ju. M. Berezanskiĭ, Ja. A. Roĭtberg and S. G. Kreĭn [1].
5. See V. P. Glusko and S. G. Kreĭn [1].
6. See V. P. Glusko and S. G. Kreĭn [2].

S. G. Kreĭn and G. I. Laptev

1. *Boundary-value problems for an equation in Hilbert space*, Dokl. Akad. Nauk SSSR 146 (1962), 535–538 = Soviet Math. Dokl. 3 (1962), 1350–1353. MR 27 #6000.

O. A. Ladyženskaja

1. *On a method of Fourier for the wave equation*, Dokl. Akad. Nauk SSSR 75 (1950), 765–768. (Russian) MR 12, 615.
2. *On the closure of the elliptic operator*, Dokl. Akad. Nauk SSSR 79 (1951), 723–725. (Russian) MR 14, 280.
3. *A simple proof of the solvability of the fundamental boundary problems and of a problem in eigenvalues for linear elliptic equations*, Vestnik Leningrad. Univ. 10 (1955), no. 11, 23–29. (Russian) MR 17, 855.
4. *On integral estimates, convergence, approximate methods and solution in functionals for elliptic operators*, Vestnik Leningrad. Univ. 13 (1958), no. 7, 60–69. (Russian) MR 20 #5353.
5. See M. I. Višik and O. A. Ladyženskaja [1].

G. I. Laptev

1. See S. G. Kreĭn and G. I. Laptev [1].

P. D. Lax

1. *Symmetrizable linear transformations*, Comm. Pure Appl. Math. 7 (1954), 633–647. MR 16, 832.

2. *On Cauchy's problem for hyperbolic equations and the differentiability of solutions of elliptic equations,* Comm. Pure Appl. Math. 8 (1955), 615–633. MR 17, 1212.

P. D. Lax and A. N. Milgram

1. *Parabolic equations,* Contributions to the Theory of Partial Differential Equations, Ann. of Math. Studies 33, Princeton Univ. Press, Princeton, N. J., 1954, pp. 167–190. MR 16, 709.

2. *The wave equation in exterior domains,* Bull. Amer. Math. Soc. 68 (1962), 47–49.

J. Leray

1. *Lectures on hyperbolic equations with variable coefficients,* Institute for Advanced Study, Princeton, N. J., 1952.

B. Ja. Levin and I. E. Ovčarenko

1. *Description of the continuation of Hermitian positive functions,* Dokl. Akad. Nauk SSSR 159 (1964), 746–749 = Soviet Math. Dokl. 5 (1964), 1595–1598. MR 30, 466.

B. M. Levitan

1. *Expansion in characteristic functions of differential equations of the second order,* GITTL, Moscow, 1950. (Russian) MR 12, 183.

2. *The application of generalized displacement operators to linear differential equations of the second order,* Uspehi Mat. Nauk 4 (1949), no. 1(29), 3–112; English transl., Amer. Math. Soc. Transl. (1) 10 (1962), 408–541. MR 11, 116; MR 13, 463.

3. *Certain questions in the spectral theory of self-adjoint differential operators,* Uspehi Mat. Nauk 11 (1956), no. 6 (72) 117–144; English transl., Amer. Math. Soc. Transl. (2) 18 (1961), 49–79. MR 21, 2805; MR 23 #A1876.

4. Supplements VI and VII to the Russian transl. of the book of E. C. Titchmarsh [2], pp. 497–528.

5. *On a theorem of Titchmarsh and Sears,* Uspehi Mat. Nauk 16 (1961), no. 4 (100), 175–178. (Russian) MR 24 #A2133.

B. M. Levitan and N. N. Meĭman

1. *On a uniqueness theorem,* Dokl. Akad. Nauk SSSR 81 (1951), 729–731. (Russian) MR 13, 551.

I. M. Lifšic

1. *The scattering of short elastic waves in a crystal lattice,* Akad. Nauk SSSR Ž. Èksper. Teoret. Fiz. 18 (1948), 293–300. (Russian) MR 9, 548.

Lin', Czjan'-bin

1. *On some problems of Franckl,* Vestnik Leningrad. Univ. 16 (1961), no. 13,

28–39. (Russian) MR 25 #3285.

J. L. Lions

1. *Problèmes aux limites en théorie des distributions,* Acta Math. 94 (1955), 13–153. MR 17, 745.
2. *Conditions aux limites de Visik-Soboleff et problèmes mixtes,* C. R. Acad. Sci. Paris 244 (1957), 1126–1128. MR 20 #5352.
3. *Espaces intermédiaires entre espaces hilbertiens et applications,* Bull. Math. Soc. Sci. Math. Phys. R. P. Roumaine 2 (50) (1958), 419–432. MR 27 #1812.
4. *Équations différentielles opérationelles et problèmes aux limites,* Die Grundlehren der mathematischen Wissenschaften, Bd. 111, Springer-Verlag, Berlin, 1961. MR 27 #3935.
5. See L. Hörmander and J. L. Lions [1].

J. L. Lions and E. Magenes

1. *Problemi ai limiti non omogenei.* III, Ann. Scuola Norm. Sup. Pisa (3) 15 (1961), 41–103. MR 26 #4048.
2. *Problemi ai limiti non omogenei.* V, Ann. Scuola Norm. Sup. Pisa. (3) 16 (1962), 1–44. MR 26 #4049.

M. S. Livšic

1. *On an application of the theory of Hermitian operators to the generalized problem of moments,* Dokl. Akad. Nauk SSSR 44 (1944), 3–7. (Russian) MR 6, 131.

V. È. Ljance

1. *Unbounded operators commuting with the resolution of the identity,* Ukrain. Mat. Ž. 15 (1963), 376–384. (Russian) MR 28 #3327.

Ju. I. Ljubič

1. *Conditions for the uniqueness of the solution to Cauchy's abstract problem,* Dokl. Akad. Nauk SSSR 130 (1960), 969–972 = Soviet Math. Dokl. 1 (1960), 110–113.
2. *On the theorem of uniqueness of the solution of the abstract Cauchy problem,* Uspehi Mat. Nauk 16 (1961), no. 5 (101), 181–182. (Russian) MR 25 #1321.
3. *On the existence "in the large" of fundamental solutions of linear second-order elliptic equations,* Mat. Sb. 57 (99) (1962), 45–58. (Russian) MR 26 #B2724,

Ja. B. Lopatinskiĭ

1. *A fundamental system of solutions of an elliptic system of differential equations,* Ukrain. Mat. Ž. 3 (1951), 3–38. (Russian) MR 16, 928.

2. *Fundamental solutions of a system of differential equations of elliptic type*, Ukrain. Mat. Ž. 3 (1951), 290–316. (Russian) MR 16, 256.

3. *On a method of reducing boundary problems for a system of differential equations of elliptic type to regular integral equations*, Ukrain. Mat. Ž. 5 (1953), 123–151. (Russian) MR 17, 494.

B. I. Loškarev

1. *Spectral decomposition of an Hermitian finite difference operator of the second order*, Volž. Mat. Sb. Teor. Ser. 1 (1963), 138–144. (Russian) MR 33 #4681.

E. Magenes

1. *Spazi di interpolazione ed equazioni a derivate parziali*, Conferenza tenuta al VII Congress dell'UMI, Genova, 30 Settembre–5 Ottobre 1963.

2. See J. L. Lions and E. Magenes [1].

3. See J. L. Lions and E. Magenes [2].

4. *Eine Bemerkung zur allgemeinen Eigenfunktionsentwicklungen für vertauschbare Operatorensysteme beliebiger Machtigkeit*, Bull. Acad. Polon. Sci. Sér. Sci. Math. Astronom. Phys. 8 (1960), 381–384.

5. *Abbildungen vom Hilbert-Schmidtschen Typus und ihre Anwendungen*, Math. Scand. 9 (1961), 359–371.

V. I. Mal'čenko

1. *On the inverse problem for the equations of quantum mechanics*, Ukrain. Mat. Ž. 12 (1960), 93–96. (Russian) MR 24 #B2357.

S. Mandelbrojt

1. *Séries de Fourier et classes quasi-analytiques de fonctions*, Gauthier-Villars, Paris, 1935; Russian transl., GITTL, Moscow, 1937.

D. Mangeron

1. *Sopra un problema al contorno per un'equazione differenziale alle derivate parziali di quarto ordine con le caratteristiche reali doppie*, Rend. Accad. Sci. Fis. Mat. Napoli (4) 2 (1932), 29–40.

V. A. Marčenko

1. *Some questions of the theory of one-dimensional linear differential operators of the second order*. I, Trudy Moskov. Mat. Obšč. 1 (1952), 327–420; II, 2 (1953), 3–83. (Russian) MR 15, 315.

2. See Z. S. Agranovič and V. A. Marčenko [1].

V. P. Maslov

1. *On the asymptotics of generalized functions of the Schrödinger equation*, Uspehi Mat. Nauk 16 (1961), 253–254. (Russian)

M. I. Matiičuk

1. *Fundamental matrices of solutions of parabolic and elliptic systems whose*

coefficients satisfy an integral Hölder condition, Dokl. Akad. Nauk SSSR 150 (1963), 480–483 = Soviet Math. Dokl. 4 (1963), 697–700. MR 28 #4251.

2. *Fundamental matrices of the solutions of the general $2\vec{b}$-parabolic and $2\vec{b}$-elliptic systems whose coefficients satisfy an integral Hölder condition,* Dopovidi Akad. Nauk Ukraïn. RSR 1964, 1010–1014. (Ukrainian) MR 31 #6065.

K. Maurin

1. *Der Fundamentalsatz über schwache Lösungen der allgemeinen linearen Systeme der elliptischen Differentialgleichungen beliebiger Ordnung,* Bull. Acad. Polon. Sci. Cl. III 2 (1954), 457–461. MR 16, 705.
2. *Entwicklung positiv definiter Kerne nach Eigendistributionen. Differenzierbarkeit der Spektralfunktion eines hypoelliptischen Operators,* Bull. Acad. Polon. Sci Sér. Sci. Math. Astronom. Phys. 6 (1958), 149–155. MR 20 #4738.
3. *Allgemeine Eigenfunktionsentwicklungen. Spektraldarstellung abstrakter Kerne. Eine Verallgemeinerung der Distributionen auf Lie'schen Gruppen,* Bull. Acad. Polon. Sci. Sér. Sci. Math. Astronom. Phys. 7 (1959), 471–479. MR 22 #4960.

L. Maurin and K. Maurin

1. *Nuklearität gewisser Rellich-Sobolevschen Einbettung. Anwendung auf Spektraltheorie der Differentialoperatoren,* Bull. Acad. Polon. Sci. Sér. Sci. Math. Astronom. Phys. 8 (1960), 621–624. MR 28 #495.
2. *Spektraltheorie separierbarer Operatoren,* Studia Math. 23 (1963), 1–29. MR 27 #5123.

F. I. Mautner

1. *On eigenfunction expansions,* Proc. Nat. Acad. Sci. U.S.A. 39 (1953), 49–53. MR 14, 659.

N. N. Meĭman

1. See B. M. Levitan and N. N. Meĭman [1].

S. G. Mihlin

1. *On some estimates connected with Green's functions,* Dokl. Akad. Nauk SSSR 78 (1951), 443–446. (Russian) MR 13, 16.

A. N. Milgram

1. See N. Aronszajn and A. N. Milgram [1].
2. See P. D. Lax and A. N. Milgram [1].

C. Miranda

1. *Equazioni alle derivate parziali di tipo ellittico,* Ergebnisse der Mathematik und ihrer Grenzgebiete, Heft 2, Springer-Verlag, Berlin, 1955; Russian transl., IL, Moscow, 1957. MR 19, 421.

B. S. Mitjagin

1. See A. G. Kostjučenko and B. S. Mitjagin [1].
2. See A. G. Kostjučenko and B. S. Mitjagin [2].
3. See A. G. Kostjučenko and B. S. Mitjagin [3].

C. S. Morawetz

1. *A weak solution for a system of equations of elliptic-hyperbolic type*, Comm. Pure Appl. Math. 11 (1958), 315–331. MR 20 #3375.

P. P. Mosolov

1. *A boundary-value problem for hypo-elliptic operators*, Mat. Sb. 55 (97) (1961), 307–328. (Russian) MR 26 #451.
2. *A generalized first boundary-value problem for a certain class of differential operators*. I, Mat. Sb. 57 (99) (1962), 333–374; II, 59 (101) (1962), suppl., 165–188. (Russian) MR 25 #2318; MR 28 #1389.

A. D. Myškis

1. See M. I. Višik and A. D. Myškis [1].

P. B. Naĭman

1. See I. M. Glazman and P. B. Naĭman [1].

M. A. Naĭmark

1. *Extremal spectral functions of a symmetric operator*, Izv. Akad. Nauk SSSR Ser. Mat. 11 (1947), 327–344. (Russian) MR 9, 447.
2. *Linear differential operators*, GITTL, Moscow, 1954; German transl., Akademie-Verlag, Berlin, 1960. MR 16, 702.

E. Nelson

1. *Kernel functions and eigenfunction expansions*, Duke Math. J. 25 (1958), 15–27. MR 19, 969.

S. M. Nikol'skiĭ

1. *Imbedding, continuation and approximation theorems for differentiable functions of several variables*, Uspehi Mat. Nauk 16 (1961), no. 5 (101), 63–114. (Russian) MR 26, 6757.
2. *A variational problem*, Mat. Sb. 62 (104) (1963), 53–75; English transl., Amer. Math. Soc. Transl. (2) 51 (1966), 132–154. MR 28, 1391.

N. Nilsson

1. *Asymptotic estimates for spectral functions connected with hypoelliptic differential operators*, Ark. Mat.5 (1965), 527–540.

L. Nirenberg

1. *Remarks on strongly elliptic partial differential equations*, Comm. Pure Appl. Math. 8 (1955), 648–674. MR 17, 742.
2. See S. Agmon, A. Douglis and L. Nirenberg [2].

3. See S. Agmon and L. Nirenberg [1].

L. P. Nižnik

1. *On the spectrum of general differential operators,* Dokl. Akad. Nauk SSSR 124 (1959), 517–519. (Russian) MR 21, 5086.
2. *The scattering problem for non-stationary perturbations,* Dokl. Akad. Nauk SSSR 132 (1960), 40–43 = Soviet Math. Dokl. 1 (1960), 478–481. MR 23, A2621.
3. *Spectral structure and the self-adjointness of perturbations of differential operators with constant coefficients,* Ukrain. Mat. Ž. 15 (1963), 385–399. (Russian) MR 28, 1511.
4. *Spectral characteristics of selfadjoint differential operators in partial derivatives, similar to operators with constant coefficients,* Materials for the Joint Soviet-American Symposium on Partial Differential Equations, Novosibirsk, 1963. (Russian)

O. A. Oleĭnik

1. *On a problem of G. Fichera,* Dokl. Akad. Nauk SSSR 157 (1964), 1297–1300 = Soviet Math. Dokl. 5 (1964), 1129–1132. MR 30 #1293.
2. See M. I. Višik, A. D. Myškis and O. A. Oleĭnik [1].

Ju. B. Oročko

1. *The behavior of the eigenfunctions of Schrödinger's operator at infinity,* Dokl. Akad. Nauk SSSR 163 (1965), 1073–1076 = Soviet Math. Dokl. 6 (1965), 1075–1078. MR 32 #7938.
2. See Ju. M. Berezanskiĭ and Ju. B. Oročko [1].

I. E. Ovčarenko

1. *An application of the method of directional functionals in the theory of precommuting operators,* Dokl. Akad. Nauk SSSR 154 (1964), 1038–1041 = Soviet Math. Dokl. 5 (1964), 241–244. MR 28 #2440.
2. *On the continuation of Hermitian-positive functions,* Akad. Nauk Armjan. SSR Dokl. 38 (1964), 257–261. (Russian) MR 30 #409.
3. See B. Ja. Levin and I. E. Ovčarenko [1].

B. P. Panejah

1. See L. P. Volevič and B. P. Panejah [1].

J. Peetre

1. *Another approach to elliptic boundary problems,* Comm. Pure Appl. Math. 14 (1961), 711–731. MR 30 #1301.

R. Pepinsky

1. See A. P. Calderón and R. Pepinsky [1].

D. Ja. Petrina

1. *Solution of the inverse diffraction problem*, Ukrain. Mat. Ž. 12 (1960), 476–479. (Russian) MR 25 #1781.

I. G. Petrovskiĭ

1. *Lectures on partial differential equations*, 3rd ed, Fizmatgiz, Moscow, 1961; English transl. of 1st ed., Interscience, New York, 1954. MR 16, 478; MR 25 #2308.

R. S. Phillips

1. See P. D. Lax and R. S. Phillips [1].
2. See P. D. Lax and R. S. Phillips [2].

V. I. Pljuščeva

1. *An integral representation for Hermite indefinite matrices with κ-negative squares*, Ukrain. Mat. Ž. 14 (1962), 30–39. MR 25 #3946.
2. *An integral representation of continuous Hermite-indefinite kernels*, Dokl. Akad. Nauk SSSR 145 (1962), 534–537 = Soviet Math. Dokl. 3 (1962), 1061–1064. MR 25 #2414.

G. Pólya and G. Szegö

1. *Aufgaben und Lehrsätze aus der Analysis*, Die Grundlehren der mathematischen Wissenschaften, Bd. 1, 2nd ed., Springer-Verlag, Berlin, 1954; 3rd ed., 1964; Russian transl., IL, Moscow, 1956. MR 15, 512; MR 30 #1219a.

L. S. Pontrjagin

1. *Hermitian operators in spaces with indefinite metric*, Izv. Akad. Nauk SSSR Ser. Mat. 8 (1944), 243–280. (Russian) MR 6, 273.

A. Ja. Povzner

1. *Sur les équations du type de Sturm-Liouville et les fonctions "positives"*, Dokl. Akad. Nauk SSSR 43 (1944), 367–371. MR 6, 157.
2. *On differential equations of Sturm-Liouville type on a half axis*, Mat. Sb. 23 (65) (1948), 3–52; English transl., Amer. Math. Soc. Transl. (1) 4 (1962), 24–101. MR 10, 299.
3. *On the expansion of arbitrary functions in characteristic functions of the operator $-\Delta u + cu$*, Mat. Sb. 32 (74) (1953), 109–156; English transl, Amer. Math. Soc. Transl. (2) 60 (1966), 1–49. MR 14, 755.
4. *On expansions in functions which are solutions of a scattering problem*, Dokl. Akad. Nauk SSSR 104 (1955), 360–363. (Russian) MR 17, 1205.

I. I. Privalov

1. *Subharmonic functions*, Moscow, 1937.

L. N. Prokopenko

1. *The Cauchy problem for second-order parabolic equations with increasing coefficients,* Dokl. Akad. Nauk SSSR 144 (1962), 1221–1224 = Soviet Math. Dokl. 3 (1962), 884–888. MR 27 #1712.
2. *The uniqueness of the solution of the Cauchy problem for differential-operator equations,* Dokl. Akad. Nauk SSSR 148 (1963), 1030–1033 = Soviet Math. Dokl. 4 (1963), 227–230. MR 26 #6587.

M. H. Protter

1. *Uniqueness theorems for the Tricomi problem.* II, J. Rational Mech. Anal. 4 (1955), 721–732. MR 17, 270.

D. A. Raĭkov

1. *On a property of nuclear spaces,* Uspehi Mat. Nauk 12 (1957), no. 5 (77), 231–236. (Russian) MR 19, 967.

F. Riesz and B. Sz.-Nagy

1. *Leçons d'analyse fonctionnelle,* 3rd ed., Gauthier-Villars, Paris and Akad. Kiadó, Budapest, 1955; Russian transl., IL, Moscow, 1954; English transl. of 2nd ed., *Functional analysis,* Ungar, New York, 1955. MR 15, 132; MR 17, 175.

M. Riesz

1. *L'intégrale de Riemann-Liouville et le problème de Cauchy,* Acta Math. 81 (1949), 1–222. MR 10, 713.

F. S. Rofe-Beketov

1. "The expansion by eigenfunctions of infinite systems of differential equations" in *Functional analysis and its applications,* Proc. Fifth All-Union Conference on Functional Analysis and Its Applications, Izdat. Akad. Nauk Azerbaĭdžan. SSR, Baku, 1961. (Russian) MR 27 #560.
2. *Expansion in eigenfunctions of infinite systems of differential equations in a non-self-adjoint case,* Mat. Sb. 51 (93) (1960), 293–342. (Russian) MR 23 #A2603.

Ja. A. Roĭtberg

1. *The expansion by eigenfunctions of self-adjoint elliptical systems,* Dopovidi Akad. Nauk. Ukraïn. RSR 1960, 721–725. (Ukrainian) MR 26 #5287.
2. *Local increase of smoothness up to the boundary for solutions of elliptic equations,* Ukrain. Mat. Ž. 15 (1963), 444–448. (Russian) MR 28 #3239.
3. *Elliptic problems with non-homogeneous boundary conditions and local increase of smoothness of generalized solutions up to the boundary,* Dokl. Akad. Nauk SSSR 157 (1964), 798–801 = Soviet Math. Dokl. 5 (1964), 1034–1037. MR 29 #2511.

4. *On a theorem of homeomorphisms for elliptic problems*, Proc. Conference on Differential and Integral Equations, Dushambe, 1964.

5. See Ju. M. Berezanskiĭ and Ja. A. Roĭtberg [1].

6. See Ju. M. Berezanskiĭ, S. G. Kreĭn and Ja. A. Roĭtberg [1].

Ja. A. Roĭtberg and Z. G. Šeftel'

1. *On equations of elliptic type with discontinuous coefficients*, Dokl. Akad. Nauk SSSR 146 (1962), 1275–1278 = Soviet Math. Dokl. 3 (1962), 1491–1494. MR 26 #444.

2. *Energy inequalities for elliptic operators with discontinuous coefficients and for general boundary conditions and conjugacy conditions*, Dokl. Akad. Nauk SSSR 148 (1963), 531–533 = Soviet Math. Dokl. 4 (1963), 141–143. MR 26 #5441.

3. *General boundary-value problems for elliptic equations with discontinuous coefficients*, Dokl. Akad. Nauk SSSR 148 (1963), 1034–1037 = Soviet Math. Dokl. 4 (1963), 231–234. MR 26 #4029.

W. Rudin

1. *The extension problem for positive definite functions*, Illinois J. Math. 7 (1963), 532–539. MR 27 #1779.

I. M. Ryžik and I. S. Gradšteĭn

1. *Tables of integrals, sums, series and products*, 3rd ed., GITTL, Moscow, 1951; 4th ed., Fizmatgiz, Moscow, 1963; English transl., VEB Deutscher Verlag, Berlin, 1957. MR 14, 643; MR 22 #3120; MR 28 #5198.

S. Saks

1. *Théorie de l'intégrale*, Warsaw, 1933; English transl., G. E. Stechert, New York, 1937; Russian transl., IL, Moscow, 1949.

A. A. Samarskiĭ

1. See A. N. Tihonov and A. A. Samarskiĭ [1].

Z. Ja. Šapiro

1. *On general boundary problems for equations of elliptic type*, Izv. Akad. Nauk SSSR Ser. Mat. 17 (1953), 539–562. (Russian) MR 16, 42.

J. Schauder

1. *Über den Zusammenhang zwischen der Eindeutigkeit und Losbarkeit partieller Differentialgleichungen zweiter Ordnung von elliptischen Typus*, Math. Ann. 106 (1932), 661–721.

2. *Über lineare elliptische Differentialgleichungen*, Math. Z. 38 (1934), 257–282.

M. Schechter

1. *Coerciveness of linear partial differential operators for functions satisfying zero Dirichlet-type boundary data*, Comm. Pure Appl. Math. 11(1958),

153–174. MR 24 #A2747.

2. *Integral inequalities for partial differential operators and functions satisfying general boundary conditions*, Comm. Pure Appl. Math. 12 (1959), 37–66. MR 25 #5276.

3. *General boundary value problems for elliptic partial differential equations*, Comm. Pure Appl. Math. 12 (1959), 457–486; Russian transl., Sborn. Per. Matematika 4 (1960), no. 5, 93–122. MR 23 #A2626.

4. *Remarks on elliptic boundary value problems*, Comm. Pure Appl. Math. 12 (1959), 561–578. MR 23 #A2633.

5. *Mixed boundary problems for general elliptic equations*, Comm. Pure Appl. Math. 13 (1960), 183–201. MR 23 #A2634.

6. *A general approach to boundary problems*, Bull. Amer. Math. Soc. 66 (1960), 495–500. MR 24 #A2139.

7. *Negative norms and boundary problems*, Ann. of Math. (2) 72 (1960), 581–593. MR 23 #A2636.

8. *A generalization of the problem of transmission*, Ann. Scuola Norm. Sup. Pisa (3) 14 (1960), 207–236. MR 24 #A917.

9. *A local regularity theorem*, J. Math. Mech. 10 (1961), 279–288. MR 28 #1381.

10. *On the theory of differential boundary problems*, Illinois J. Math. 7 (1963), 232–245.

11. *Coerciveness in L^p*, Trans. Amer. Math. Soc. 107 (1963), 10–29. MR 26 #4210.

12. *On L^p estimates and regularity*. I, Amer. J. Math. 85 (1963), 1–13; II, Math. Scand. 13 (1963), 47–69. MR 32 #6051; MR 32 #6052.

I. J. Schoenberg

1. *Metric spaces and completely monotone functions*, Ann. of Math. 39 (1938), 811–841.

J. Schwartz

1. See N. Dunford and J. Schwartz [2].

L. Schwartz

1. *Théorie des distributions*, Tomes I, II, Actualités Sci. Ind. Nos. 1091, 1122, Hermann, Paris, 1950. MR 12, 31; MR 12, 833.

2. *Théorie des noyaux*, Proc. Internat. Congr. Math., Cambridge, Mass., 1950, vol. 1, Amer. Math. Soc., Providence, R.I., 1952, 220–230. MR 13, 562.

3. *Application of distributions to the study of elementary particles in relativistic quantum mechanics*, Notes and Lectures, University of California, 1961; Russian transl., Izdat. "Mir", Moscow, 1964. MR 32 #835.

Z. G. Šeftel′

1. *Estimates in L_p of solutions of elliptic equations with discontinuous coefficients and satisfying general boundary conditions and conjugacy conditions,* Dokl. Akad. Nauk SSSR 149 (1963), 48–51 = Soviet Math. Dokl. 4 (1963), 321–324. MR 33 #4459.
2. *The theory of elliptic equations with disconnected coefficients,* Voronež. Univ. Press, 1963. (Russian)
3. See Ja. A. Roĭtberg and Z. G. Šeftel′ [1].
4. See Ja. A. Roĭtberg and Z. G. Šeftel′ [2].
5. See Ja. A. Roĭtberg and Z. G. Šeftel′ [3].

J. Serrin

1. See D. Gilbarg and J. Serrin [1].

J. A. Shohat and J. D. Tamarkin

1. *The problem of moments,* Math. Surveys, no. 1, Amer. Math. Soc., Providence, R.I., 1943. MR 5, 5.

G. E. Šilov

1. *Local properties of solutions of partial differential equations with constant coefficients,* Uspehi Mat. Nauk 14 (1959), no. 5 (89), 3–44; English transl., Amer. Math. Soc. Transl. (2) 42 (1964), 129–173. MR 22 #9708.
2. See M. I. Višik and G. E. Šilov [1].
3. See I. M. Gel′fand and G. E. Šilov [1].
4. See I. M. Gel′fand and G. E. Šilov [2].
5. See I. M. Gel′fand and G. E. Šilov [3].

I. A. Šišmarev

1. See V. A. Il′in and I. A. Šišmarev [1].

Sja, Do-Šin

1. See I. M. Gel′fand and Do-Šin Sja [1].

G. E. Skvorcov

1. See M. Š. Birman and G. E. Skvorcov [1].

L. N. Slobodeckiĭ

1. *Estimates in L_p of solution of elliptic systems,* Dokl. Akad. Nauk SSSR 123 (1958), 616–619. (Russian) MR 21 #5061.
2. *Generalized Sobolev spaces and their applications to boundary problems for partial differential equations,* Leningrad. Gos. Ped. Inst. Učen. Zap. 197 (1958), 54–112; English transl., Amer. Math. Soc. Transl. (2) 57 (1966), 207–276.

3. *Estimates in L_2 for solutions of linear elliptic and parabolic systems.* I: *Estimates of solutions of an elliptic system*, Vestnik Leningrad. Univ. 15 (1960), no. 7, 28–47. (Russian) MR 22 #2794.

È. È. Šnol′

1. *On the conduct of eigenfunctions of the Schrödinger equations*, Author's review of his Candidate Dissertation, Moscow Univ. Press, Moscow, 1955. (Russian)
2. *On the behavior of eigenfunctions*, Dokl. Akad. Nauk SSSR 94 (1954), 389–392. (Russian) MR 16, 38.
3. *On the behavior of eigenfunctions of Schrödinger's equation*, Mat. Sb. 42 (84) (1957), 273–286; erratum, 46 (88) (1958), 259. (Russian) MR 23 #A2618.

S. L. Sobolev

1. *On a boundary value problem for polyharmonic equations*, Mat. Sb. 2 (44) (1937), 467–499; English transl., Amer. Math. Soc. Transl. (2) 33 (1963), 1–40.
2. *On a class of integral-differential equations with several independent variables.* I, Izv. Akad. Nauk SSSR Ser. Mat. 1937, 515–549; II, 1 (1938), 61–90. (Russian)
3. *Applications of functional analysis in mathematical physics*, Izdat. Leningrad. Gos. Univ., Leningrad, 1950; English transl., Transl. Math. Monographs, vol. 7, Amer. Math. Soc., Providence, R. I., 1963. MR 14, 565; MR 29 #2624.
4. *An instance of a correct boundary problem for the equations of string vibrations with the conditions given all over the boundary*, Dokl. Akad. Nauk SSSR 109 (1956), 707–709. (Russian) MR 18, 215.
5. See M. I. Višik and S. L. Sobolev [1].

P. E. Sobolevskiĭ

1. *On an inequality for elliptic operators*, Trudy Sem. Vektor. Tenzor. Anal. 6 (1958), 105–113. (Russian)

V. A. Solonnikov

1. *Bounds for the solutions of general boundary-value problems for elliptic systems*, Dokl. Akad. Nauk SSSR 5 (1963), 783–785 = Soviet Math. Dokl. 4 (1963), 1089–1091. MR 33 #1586.

A. V. Štraus

1. *Generalized resolvents of symmetric operators*, Izv. Akad. Nauk SSSR Ser. Mat. 18 (1954), 51–86. (Russian) MR 16, 48.

G. Szegö

1. See G. Pólya and G. Szegö [1].

B. Sz.-Nagy

1. See F. Riesz and B. Sz.-Nagy [1].

J. D. Tamarkin

1. See J. A. Shohat and J. D. Tamarkin [1].

V. G. Tarnopol'skiĭ

1. *On the self-adjointness of difference operators with operator coefficients,* Dopovidi Akad. Nauk Ukraïn. RSR 1959, 1189–1192. (Ukrainian) MR 22 #2901.
2. *The absolutely indefinite case for a difference operator with operator coefficients,* Dopovidi Akad. Nauk Ukraïn. RSR 1960, 305–308. (Ukrainian) MR 24 #A419.
3. *The dispersion problem for a difference equation,* Dokl. Akad. Nauk SSSR 136 (1961), 779–782 = Soviet Math. Dokl. 2 (1961), 135–138. MR 24 #A3435.

A. N. Tihonov and A. I. Samarskiĭ

1. *The equations of mathematical physics,* 2nd ed., GITTL, Moscow, 1953; English transl., Macmillan, New York, 1963. MR 16, 364; MR 29 #2498.

E. C. Titchmarsh

1. *Eigenfunction expansions associated with second-order differential equations.* Part I, Clarendon Press, Oxford, 1946; Russian transl., IL, Moscow, 1960. MR 8, 458; MR 22 #9662.
2. ibid., Part 2, Clarendon Press, Oxford, 1958; Russian transl., IL, Moscow, 1961. MR 20 #1065; MR 31 #426.

J. F. (François) Trèves

1. *Lectures on linear partial differential equations with constant coefficients,* Notas de Matématica, no. 27, Inst. de Mat. Pura e Apl., Rio de Janeiro, 1961; Russian transl., Izdat. "Mir", Moscow, 1965. MR 27 #5020.

N. N. Vahanija

1. *A boundary problem for a hyperbolic system equivalent to the string vibration equation,* Dokl. Akad. Nauk SSSR 116 (1957), 906–909. (Russian) MR 19, 965.

I. N. Vekua

1. *New methods for solving elliptic equations,* OGIZ, Moscow, 1948. (Russian) MR 11, 598.

N. Ja. Vilenkin

1. *On the theory of positive definite generalized kernels,* Uspehi Mat. Nauk 15 (1960), no. 3 (93), 139–146; English transl., Amer. Math. Soc. Transl. (2) 28 (1963), 197–210. MR 22 #9849.
2. See I. M. Gel'fand and N. Ja. Vilenkin [1].

G. V. Virabjan

1. *On the resolvent of an operator*, Dokl. Akad. Nauk SSSR 151 (1963), 258–261 = Soviet Math. Dokl. 4 (1963), 970–973. MR 27 #465.

M. I. Višik

1. *On strongly elliptic systems of differential equations*, Mat. Sb. 29 (71) (1951), 615–676. (Russian) MR 14, 174.
2. *On general boundary problems for elliptic differential equations*, Trudy Moskov. Mat. Obšč. 1 (1952), 187–246; English transl., Amer. Math. Soc. Transl. (2) 24 (1963), 107–172. MR 14, 473.

M. I. Višik and G. I. Èskin

1. *Boundary value problems for general singular equations in a bounded domain*, Dokl. Akad. Nauk SSSR 155 (1964), 24–27 = Soviet Math. Dokl. 5 (1964), 325–328. MR 28 #4319.

M. I. Višik and O. A. Ladyženskaja

1. *Boundary value problems for partial differential equations and certain classes of operator equations*, Uspehi Mat. Nauk 11 (1956), no. 6 (72), 41–97; English transl., Amer. Math. Soc. Transl. (2) 10 (1958), 223–281. MR 20 #1091.

M. I. Višik, A. D. Myškis and O. A. Oleĭnik

1. "Partial differential equations" in *Forty years of mathematics in the USSR*: 1917–1957. Vol. I; *Survey articles*, Fizmatgiz, Moscow, 1959, pp. 563–636. (Russian) MR 22 #6672.

M. I. Višik and G. E. Šilov

1. *The general theory of partial differential equations and certain problems in the theory of boundary-value problems*, Proc. Fourth All-Union Math. Congr., Leningrad, 1961, vol. I, Izdat. Akad. Nauk SSSR, Leningrad, 1963, pp. 55–85. (Russian) MR 28 #2349.

M. I. Višik and S. L. Sobolev

1. *General formulation of certain boundary problems for elliptic partial differential equations*, Dokl. Akad. Nauk SSSR 111 (1956), 521–523. (Russian) MR 20 #5351.

L. R. Volevič

1. See M. S. Agranovič, L. R. Volevič and A. S. Dynin [1].

L. R. Volevič and B. P. Panejah

1. *Some spaces of generalized functions and embedding theorems*, Uspehi Mat. Nauk 20 (1965), no. 1 (121), 3–74. (Russian) MR 30 #5160.

E. B. Vul

1. *Uniqueness theorems for a certain class of functions represented by integrals*, Dokl. Akad. Nauk SSSR 129 (1959), 722–725. (Russian) MR 22 #8093.

A. Wouk

1. *Difference equations and J-matrices,* Duke Math. J. 20 (1953), 141–159. MR 15, 323.

R. B. Zarhina

1. *On the two-dimensional problem of moments,* Dokl. Akad. Nauk SSSR 124 (1959), 473–476. (Russian) MR 21 #2161.

SUBJECT INDEX

NOTATION INDEX